# STATISTICS

# for PSYCHOLOGISTS

# WILLIAM L. HAYS

*University of Michigan*

# *STATISTICS*
# *for PSYCHOLOGISTS*

**HOLT, RINEHART
AND WINSTON**

NEW YORK · CHICAGO · SAN FRANCISCO
TORONTO · LONDON

# *PREFACE*

This book represents an attempt to give the elements of modern statistics in a relatively nonmathematical form, but in somewhat more detail than is customary in texts designed for psychologists, and with considerably more emphasis on the theoretical rather than the applied aspects of the subject. It is designed as a text of at least an intermediate level of difficulty. I have felt for some time that the serious student in experimental psychology both needs and wishes to know somewhat more of the language and concepts of theoretical statistics than is provided in the usual "cookbook" of statistical methods. Granted that a real understanding and appreciation of mathematical statistics requires a considerable degree of mathematical training and sophistication, a great deal of statistical theory can be got across to the serious student familiar only with elementary algebra, provided that a relatively detailed exposition of the concepts accompanies the mathematical treatment, and provided that the student is genuinely interested in acquiring a grasp of this subject.

I am not so naive as to suppose that all students will be mature enough or interested enough in learning about statistics to follow all of the exposition that this book contains; far from it! On the other hand, I think it is a mistake for us to teach for the lowest common denominator in our classes, and to leave the bright, mature student to fend for himself when he wants to go beyond the routine methods and gain more understanding of their underlying rationale. It is difficult to know where to send such a student for the information he wants; unless he has a better background in mathematics than we ordinarily assume, texts and the published literature in mathematical statistics are largely closed to him.

Furthermore, I feel that a research psychologist must be able to consult with a statistician, and that one of the objectives of a course in statistics for psychologists should be that of imparting the basic concepts and vocabulary used in mathematical statistics. All too often consultation between statisticians and psychologists is less than satisfactory, both because the psychologist fails to communicate his problem in terms familiar to the statistician and because the statistician employs a language and a set of concepts only vaguely apprehended by the psychologist. For good or ill, statistical methods are now very much a part of psychological research, and, if these methods are to be used at all, they ought to be used correctly. The modern researcher has an enormous variety of statistical methods from which to choose, and the choice and correct use of a method are not easy for the relatively inexperienced person. The well-trained research psychologist should know more about statistics than the mechanics of the *t* test, the analysis of variance, and correlation; at least he should understand enough of theoretical statistics to profit from the availability of a statistician for consultation.

This text grew out of a series of notes for an undergraduate honors section in elementary statistics. It should, however, find considerable use with advanced undergraduate or with graduate classes. Although enough material is included for a two-semester course, the chapters are divided rather closely into sections, so that a certain amount of flexibility in the choice of topics is afforded.

I have assumed the student using this text to have some background in college mathematics, and so have not provided tutorial or remedial material in college algebra. The calculus is not, however, assumed, and on the rare occasions when concepts from the calculus appear their meaning is immediately obvious from the context.

An unusual feature is the large amount of space devoted to elementary set theory, to the basic theory of relations and functions, and to formal probability theory. My own experience is that students with a fair background in college algebra often have little or no acquaintance with these fundamental ideas, and that much of the difficulty experienced with statistical concepts by such students comes from this lack. Even a superficial introduction to these foundation concepts in mathematics (which, hopefully, the current generation of elementary school children are learning, but which were so sadly neglected in the traditional curriculum) can do a great deal toward clarifying mathematical reasoning for the student in psychology.

Finally, I have tried not to "sugar-coat" a number of more or less controversial issues connected with statistics. I have tried to give a fair picture of the role of statistical decision theory as related to the purposes of the experimenter, and not pretend that the conventions of statistics and statistical tests are somehow dictated by scientific method. Furthermore, I have attempted to suggest that available statistical methods do not dictate the kinds of data one *ought* to collect, but rather that statistical methods are useful only so long as they clarify and exhibit the meaning in the experiment. Above all, I have tried to impart the attitude that the proper application of statistical methods involves *thought* on the experimenter's part, and that conventions in data analysis must be distinguished clearly from some necessary mode of procedure. Statistics has, unfortunately, achieved almost the status of a superstition in some quarters in psychology, and I hope, in all humility, that this text sets a slightly more liberal and rational tone.

I am deeply grateful to all of the people who provided help and encouragement in bringing this work to completion. In particular, I am indebted to Professor R. Duncan Luce, whose wise, patient, and sympathetic reactions to an early (and woefully inadequate) draft of this book did much to impart whatever value it may now have. Among the other readers, Professor William McGill especially gave much needed advice and encouragement. Dr. Albert Madansky made many valuable comments, particularly on Chapter 9. Among my own colleagues Professors John Milholland, Warren Norman, Ward Edwards, Robert Hefner, Wilbert McKeachie, and Clyde Coombs contributed to my own thinking and to the actual structure of this book, often in ways of which they were unaware. Thanks are due to Mr. G. Croft Henry and to Mrs. Lois Portman for help with the galleys and with the index. I also wish to express my thanks to Professor E. S. Pearson and the trustees of *Biometrika*, for their kind permission to reproduce portions of tables from the *Biometrika Tables for Statisticians*, Vol. I.

My wife Palma deserves my greatest thanks. Her help and devotion never failed during a task that often seemed interminable to us both.

W. L. H.

Ann Arbor, Michigan
*July 1963*

# CONTENTS

PREFACE v

INTRODUCTION 1

0.1 To the Student
0.2 The Motivation behind This Book
0.3 The Organization of This Book
0.4 Mathematical Expressions and Notation
0.5 The Nature of Statistics
0.6 Abstract Mathematical Systems
0.7 Mathematical Models of Real Objects and Events
0.8 The Problem of Inductive Inference

1. SETS AND FUNCTIONS 13

1.1 Sets
1.2 Ways of Specifying Sets
1.3 Universal Sets
1 4 Subsets
1.5 Finite and Infinite Sets
1.6 Venn Diagrams
1.7 The Empty Set
1.8 New Sets from Old: Operations with Sets
1.9 The Intersection of Sets
1.10 The Complement of a Set
1.11 The Difference between Two Sets
1.12 The Algebra of Sets
1.13 Postulates and Theorems about Sets
1.14 Set Products and Relations
1.15 Specifying Relations
1.16 The "All" and the "Empty" Relations
1.17 The Importance of Mathematical Relations
1.18 The Domain and Range of a Relation
1.19 Functional Relations
1.20 Variables and Functional Notation
1.21 Independent and Dependent Variables
1.22 Continuous Variables and Functions
1.23 Functions with Several Independent Variables
1.24 Functions and Precise Prediction
1.25 Statistics in the Search for Relations

2. ELEMENTARY PROBABILITY THEORY 47

2.1 Simple Experiments
2.2 Events
2.3 Events as Sets
2.4 Families of Events

**2.5** Probability Functions

**2.6** A Special Case: Equally Probable Elementary Events

**2.7** "In the Long Run"

**2.8** Bernoulli's Theorem

**2.9** An Example of Simple Statistical Inference

**2.10** Other Interpretations of Probability

**2.11** Random Sampling

**2.12** Random Number Tables

### 3. FREQUENCY AND PROBABILITY DISTRIBUTIONS 68

**3.1** Measurement Scales

**3.2** Measurement Levels and Statistical Methods

**3.3** Frequency Distributions

**3.4** Frequency Distributions with a Small Number of Measurement Classes

**3.5** Grouped Distributions

**3.6** Class Interval Size and Class Limits

**3.7** Interval Size and the Number of Class Intervals

**3.8** Midpoints of Class Intervals

**3.9** Another Example of a Grouped Frequency Distribution

**3.10** Frequency Distributions with Open or Unequal Class Intervals

**3.11** Graphs of Distributions: Histograms

**3.12** Frequency Polygons

**3.13** Cumulative Frequency Distributions

**3.14** Probability Distributions

**3.15** Random Variables

**3.16** Discrete Random Variables

**3.17** Graphs of Probability Distributions

**3.18** Continuous Random Variables

**3.19** Cumulative Distribution Functions

**3.20** Continuous Random Variables as an Idealization

**3.21** Graphic Representations of Continuous Distributions

**3.22** Frequency and Probability Distributions in Use

### 4. JOINT EVENTS AND INDEPENDENCE 108

**4.1** Joint Events

**4.2** Combining Probabilities of Joint Events

**4.3** Conditional Probability

**4.4** Relations among Conditional Probabilities

**4.5** Bayes' Theorem

**4.6** Independence

**4.7** Representing Joint Events in Tables

**4.8** Independence of Random Variables

**4.9** Independence of Functions of Random Variables

**4.10** Representation of Joint Random Variables

**4.11** Joint Frequency Distributions and Inferences about Association

**4.12** Statistical Relations and Association

### 5. A THEORETICAL DISTRIBUTION: THE BINOMIAL 131

**5.1** Computing Probabilities

**5.2** Sequences of Events

**5.3** Number of Possible Sequences for $N$ Trials: Counting Rule 1

**5.4** Counting Rule 2

**5.5** Counting Rule 3: Permutations

**5.6** Counting Rule 4: Ordered Combinations

**5.7** Counting Rule 5: Combinations

**5.8** Some Examples: Poker Hands

**5.9** Bernoulli Trials and Distributions

**5.10** Sampling from a Bernoulli Distribution

**5.11** Number of Successes as a Random Variable: The Binomial Distribution

**5.12** The Binomial Distribution and the Binomial Expansion

**5.13** Probabilities of Intervals in the Binomial Distribution

**5.14** The Binomial Distribution of Proportions

**5.15** The Form of a Binomial Distribution

**5.16** The Binomial as a Sampling Distribution

**5.17** A Preview of a Use of the Binomial Distribution

**5.18** The Multinomial Distribution

**5.19** The Hypergeometric Distribution

### 6. CENTRAL TENDENCY AND VARIABILITY 157

**6.1** The Summation Notation

**6.2** Measures of Central Tendency

6.3 The Mode
6.4 The Median
6.5 The Arithmetic Mean
6.6 The Mean as the "Center of Gravity" of a Distribution
6.7 "Best Guess" Interpretations of the Mode and Median
6.8 Central Tendency in Discrete Probability Distributions
6.9 The Mean of a Random Variable as the Expectation
6.10 A Theoretical Expectation: The Mean of the Binomial Distribution
6.11 The Algebra of Expectations: Appendix B
6.12 The Expectation of a Continuous Random Variable
6.13 The Mean as a Parameter of a Probability Distribution
6.14 The Mode and Median of a Continuous Distribution
6.15 Relations between Central Tendency Measures and the "Shapes" of Distributions

6.16 Measures of Dispersion in Frequency Distributions
6.17 The Standard Deviation
6.18 The Computation of the Variance and Standard Deviation
6.19 Some Meanings of the Variance and Standard Deviation
6.20 The Mean as the "Origin" for the Variance
6.21 The Variance of a Discrete Random Variable
6.22 An Example of the Variance of a Discrete Random Variable: The Binomial Distribution Once Again
6.23 The Variance of a Continuous Random Variable
6.24 Moments of Distribution
6.25 The Relative Location of a Score in a Frequency Distribution: Standardized Scores
6.26 Standardized Scores in Probability Distributions
6.27 Tchebycheff's Inequality

## 7. SAMPLING DISTRIBUTIONS AND POINT ESTIMATION 192

7.1 Populations, Parameters, and Statistics
7.2 Sampling Distributions
7.3 Characteristics of Single-Variate Sampling Distributions
7.4 The Mean and Variance of a Sampling Distribution
7.5 Sample Statistics as Estimators
7.6 Unbiased Estimators
7.7 Consistency
7.8 Relative Efficiency
7.9 Sufficiency
7.10 The Sample Mean as an Estimator
7.11 The Variance and Standard Error of the Mean
7.12 Standardized Scores Corresponding to Sample Means
7.13 Finding the Largest Sample Size Required for a Given Accuracy of Estimation

7.14 Correcting the Bias in the Sample Variance as an Estimator
7.15 Estimating the Standard Deviation of the Population and the Standard Error of the Mean
7.16 Parameter Estimates Based on Pooled Samples
7.17 Sampling from Finite Populations
7.18 The Sample Proportion as an Unbiased Estimator
7.19 The Sampling Distribution of the Sample Variance
7.20 The Uses of Sampling Distributions
7.21 The Principle of Maximum Likelihood
7.22 Other Kinds of Sampling
7.23 To What Populations Do Our Inferences Refer?

## 8. NORMAL POPULATION AND SAMPLING DISTRIBUTIONS 218

8.1 The Normal Distribution
8.2 Cumulative Probabilities and Areas for the Normal Distribution
8.3 The Use of Tables of the Normal Distribution

8.4 The Importance of the Normal Distribution
8.5 The Normal Approximation to the Binomial

**8.6** The Theory of the Normal Distribution of Error

**8.7** Statistical Properties of Normal Population Distributions

**8.8** Independence of Sample Mean and Variance

**8.9** Distributions of Linear Combinations of Scores

**8.10** Means and Variances of Linear Combinations

**8.11** The Central Limit Theorem

**8.12** The Central Limit Theorem and Linear Combinations of Means

**8.13** Using the Normal Distribution in Inferences about Means

## 9. HYPOTHESIS TESTING AND INTERVAL ESTIMATION 245

**9.1** Statistical Tests

**9.2** Statistical Hypotheses

**9.3** Assumptions in Hypothesis Testing

**9.4** Testing a Hypothesis in the Light of Sample Evidence

**9.5** Choosing a Way to Decide between Two Exact Hypotheses

**9.6** Errors and Losses

**9.7** Expected Loss as a Criterion for Choosing a Decision-Rule

**9.8** Subjective Expected Loss as a Criterion for Choosing among Decision-Rules

**9.9** The Failure of the Decision-Theory Approach in Psychological Research

**9.10** The Option of Suspending Judgment

**9.11** Deciding between Two Hypotheses about a Mean

**9.12** Conventional Decision-Rules

**9.13** The Power of a Statistical Test

**9.14** Power of Tests against Various True Alternatives

**9.15** Power and the Size of $\alpha$

**9.16** The Effect of Sample Size on Power

**9.17** Power and "Error Variance"

**9.18** Testing Inexact Hypotheses

**9.19** Type I and Type II Errors

**9.20** The Basis for the Conventions about Type I Errors

**9.21** One-Tailed Rejection Regions

**9.22** Two-Tailed Tests of Hypotheses

**9.23** Relative Merits of One- and Two-Tailed Tests

**9.24** Some Remarks on the General Theory Underlying Tests of Hypotheses

**9.25** Confidence Intervals

**9.26** Approximate Confidence Intervals for Proportions

**9.27** Sample Size and the Accuracy of Estimation of the Mean

**9.28** An Example of Sample Size Determined by Desired Accuracy of Estimation

**9.29** Evidence and Change in Personal Probability

**9.30** Significance Tests and Common Sense

## 10. INFERENCES ABOUT POPULATION MEANS 301

**10.1** Large Sample Problems with Unknown Population $\sigma^2$

**10.2** Confidence Intervals for Large Samples with Unknown $\sigma^2$

**10.3** The Problem of Unknown $\sigma^2$ When Sample Size Is Small

**10.4** The Distribution of $t$

**10.5** The $t$ and the Standardized Normal Distribution

**10.6** The Application of the $t$ Distribution When the Population Is Not Normal

**10.7** Tables of the $t$ Distribution

**10.8** The Concept of Degrees of Freedom

**10.9** Significance Tests for Single Means Using the $t$ Distribution

**10.10** Confidence Limits for the Mean Using $t$ Distributions

**10.11** Questions about Differences between Population Means

**10.12** The Sampling Distribution of Differences between Means

**10.13** An Example of a Large-Sample Significance Test for a Difference between Means

**10.14** Large-Sample Confidence Limits for a Difference

**10.15** Using the $t$ Distribution to Test Hypotheses about Differences

**10.16** An Example of Inferences about a Difference for Small Samples

10.17 The Importance of the Assumptions in a *t* Test of a Difference
10.18 The Power of *t* Tests
10.19 Testmanship, or How Big Is a Difference?
10.20 Estimating the Strength of a Statistical Association from Data

10.21 Strength of Association and Sample Size
10.22 Can a Sample Size Be Too Large?
10.23 Paired Observations
10.24 Significance Testing in More Complicated Experiments

## 11. THE CHI-SQUARE AND THE *F* DISTRIBUTIONS     336

11.1 The Chi-square Distribution
11.2 The Function Rule and the Mean and Variance for a Chi-square Distribution
11.3 Tables of the Chi-square Distribution
11.4 The Addition of Chi-square Variables
11.5 The Distribution of a Sample Variance from a Normal Population
11.6 Testing Exact Hypotheses about a Single Variance
11.7 Confidence Intervals for the Variance and Standard Deviation

11.8 The Importance of the Normality Assumption in Inferences about $\sigma^2$
11.9 The Normal Approximation to the Chi-square Distribution
11.10 The *F* Distribution
11.11 The Use of *F* Tables
11.12 Using the *F* Distribution to Test Hypotheses about Two Variances
11.13 The Assumption of the Normal Distribution in Testing Hypotheses about Two Variances
11.14 Relationships among the Theoretical Distributions

## 12. THE ANALYSIS OF VARIANCE: MODEL I, FIXED EFFECTS     356

12.1 Model I: Fixed Effects
12.2 The Idea of an Effect
12.3 The Linear Model in the Fixed Effects Situation
12.4 The Partition of the Sum of Squares for Any Set of *J* Distinct Samples
12.5 Assumptions Underlying Inferences about Treatment Effects
12.6 The Mean Square between Groups
12.7 The Mean Square within Groups
12.8 The Sampling Distribution of MS within
12.9 The *F* Test in the Analysis of Variance
12.10 Computational Forms for the Simple Analysis of Variance
12.11 A Computational Outline for the One-way Analysis of Variance
12.12 The Analysis of Variance Summary Table
12.13 An Example
12.14 The *F* Test and the *t* Test
12.15 Another Example of a Simple, One-way Analysis of Variance
12.16 The Importance of the Assumptions in the Fixed Effects Model
12.17 The Problem of Testing for Homogeneity of Variance

12.18 Estimating the Strength of a Statistical Relation from the One-way Analysis of Variance
12.19 The Power of the *F* Test in the Analysis of Variance
12.20 The Two-way Analysis of Variance with Replication
12.21 Crossing and Nesting in Experiments
12.22 The Fixed Effects Model in the Two-way Analysis
12.23 The Importance of Interaction Effects
12.24 The Idea of Replication
12.25 Orthogonal Designs for Experiments
12.26 Sums of Effects in the Fixed Model
12.27 The Partition of the Sums of Squares for the Two-way Analysis of Variance
12.28 Assumptions in the Two-way Fixed Effects Model
12.29 The Mean Squares and Their Expectations
12.30 Computing Forms for the Two-way Analysis with Replications
12.31 A Computational Outline for the Two-way Analysis under the Fixed Effects Model
12.32 The Summary Table for a Two-way Fixed Effects Analysis of Variance with Replications

12.33 An Example
12.34 Estimating Strength of Association from a Two-way Analysis of Variance
12.35 The Importance of the Assumptions in the Two-way (or Higher) Analysis of Variance with Fixed Effects

12.36 The Analysis of Variance as a Summarization of Data
12.37 Analyzing Experiments with More than Two Experimental Factors

## 13. THE ANALYSIS OF VARIANCE: MODELS II AND III, RANDOM EFFECTS AND MIXED MODELS 413

13.1 Model II: Random Effects
13.2 Assumptions Made in the Random Effects Model
13.3 The Mean Squares for Model II
13.4 The Null Hypothesis for Model II
13.5 An Example
13.6 Estimation of Variance Components in a One-way Analysis
13.7 The Intraclass Correlation Coefficient
13.8 Interval Estimation for Proportion of Variance Accounted for
13.9 Other Hypotheses Testable Using Model II
13.10 Importance of the Assumptions in Model II
13.11 Two-factor Experiments with Sampling of Levels
13.12 Model II for Two-factor Experiments
13.13 The Mean Squares
13.14 Hypothesis Testing in the Two-way Analysis under Model II

13.15 An Example
13.16 Point Estimation of Variance Components
13.17 Model III: A Mixed Model
13.18 A Mixed Model for a Two-factor Experiment
13.19 The Expected Mean Squares in a Mixed Model
13.20 An Example Fitting Model III
13.21 Variance Estimation in Model III
13.22 Some Connections among the Three Models
13.23 Randomization in Experiments
13.24 Simple Matched-Groups Experiments under the Mixed Model: Randomized Blocks
13.25 Repeated Observation of the Same Subjects
13.26 The General Problem of Experimental Design

## 14. INDIVIDUAL COMPARISONS AMONG MEANS 459

14.1 Asking Specific Questions of Data
14.2 Planned Comparisons
14.3 Estimates of Population Comparison Values
14.4 The Sampling Variance of Planned Comparisons
14.5 Interval Estimates and Tests for Planned Comparisons
14.6 Independence of Planned Comparisons
14.7 An Illustration of Independent and Nonindependent Planned Comparisons
14.8 Multiple *t* Tests on a Set of Data
14.9 The Independence of Sample Comparisons and the Grand Mean

14.10 The Number of Possible Independent Comparisons
14.11 Planned Comparisons and the Analysis of Variance
14.12 Pooling the Sums of Squares for "Other Comparisons"
14.13 An Example Using Planned Comparisons
14.14 The Choice of the Planned Comparisons
14.15 Incidental or Post-hoc Comparisons in Data
14.16 An Example of Post-hoc Comparisons Following a One-way Analysis of Variance
14.17 Planned versus Post-hoc Comparisons

## 15. PROBLEMS IN LINEAR REGRESSION AND CORRELATION 490

15.1 Regression and Correlation Problems

15.2 The Descriptive Statistics of Regression and Correlation

**15.3** The Regression Equation for Predicting $z_Y$ from $z_X$

**15.4** The Standard Error of Estimate for Standard Scores

**15.5** Interpretations of the Correlation Coefficient in a Sample

**15.6** The Idea of Regression toward the Mean

**15.7** The Proportion of Variance Accounted for by Linear Regression

**15.8** The Regression of $z_X$ on $z_Y$

**15.9** The Regression Equations for Raw Scores

**15.10** The Errors of Estimate for Raw Scores

**15.11** Computational Forms for $r_{XY}$ and $b_{Y \cdot X}$

**15.12** An Example of Regression and Correlation Computations for a Sample

**15.13** Assumptions Made in Computing Correlation and Regression Coefficients for Sample Data

**15.14** Population Correlation and Regression

**15.15** Estimates of the Parameters of the Population Regression Equation, and Standard Errors

**15.16** The Model for Simple Linear Regression

**15.17** The Sums of Squares for Regression Problems

**15.18** The Expectation of the SS for Linear Regression

**15.19** The Expectation of the Other Sums of Squares

**15.20** Assumptions Underlying a Test Using This Regression Model

**15.21** Tests for Zero Linear Regression

**15.22** Interval Estimation in Regression Problems

**15.23** Estimating the Strength of Linear Association in a Regression Problem

**15.24** An Example of a Regression Problem

**15.25** Problems in Correlation in Bivariate Normal Populations

**15.26** Tests and Interval Estimates in Correlation Problems

**15.27** Confidence Intervals for $\rho_{XY}$

**15.28** An Example of a Correlation Problem

**15.29** Retrospect: Regression and Correlation Problems

## 16. OTHER TOPICS IN REGRESSION AND CORRELATION    539

**16.1** Curvilinear Regression

**16.2** The Model for Linear and Curvilinear Regression

**16.3** Another Look at the Partition of the Sum of Squares for Regression Problems

**16.4** Testing for Linear and Nonlinear Regression

**16.5** Estimation of the Strength of Linear and Curvilinear Relationship from Data

**16.6** The Correlation Ratios $\eta^2_{Y \cdot X}$ and $\eta^2_{X \cdot Y}$

**16.7** An Example of Tests for Linear and Curvilinear Regression

**16.8** Planned Comparisons for Trend: Orthogonal Polynomials

**16.9** Computations for Trend Analysis Using Orthogonal Polynomials

**16.10** An Example of Planned Comparisons for Trend

**16.11** Estimation of a Curvilinear Prediction Function

**16.12** Trend Analysis in Post-hoc Comparisons

**16.13** Other Uses of Regression Theory

**16.14** Linear versus Curvilinear Regression

**16.15** Some Rudiments of Multiple Regression Theory

**16.16** The Coefficient of Multiple Correlation

**16.17** The Standard Error of Estimate and the Interpretation of $R^2$

**16.18** Multiple Regression Equation for Raw Scores

**16.19** Inferences about Multiple Regression and Correlation

**16.20** Partial Correlation

**16.21** Testing Significance for Intercorrelations

## 17. COMPARING ENTIRE DISTRIBUTIONS: CHI-SQUARE TESTS    578

**17.1** Comparing Sample and Population Distributions: Goodness of Fit

**17.2** The Relation to Large-Sample Tests of a Single Proportion

**17.3** A Special Problem: A Goodness-of-Fit Test for a Normal Distribution

**17.4** Pearson $\chi^2$ Tests of Association

**17.5** An Example of a Test for Independence in a Larger Table

**17.6** The Special Case of a Fourfold Table

**17.7** The Assumptions in $\chi^2$ Tests for Association

**17.8** Likelihood Ratio Tests for Categorical Data

**17.9** The Possibility of Exact Tests for Goodness of Fit and for Association

**17.10** A Test for Correlated Proportions in a Two-by-Two Table

**17.11** Measures of Association in Contingency Tables

**17.12** The Phi-Coefficient and Indices of Contingency

**17.13** A Measure of Predictive Association for Categorical Data

**17.14** Information Theory and the Analysis of Contingency Tables

**17.15** Retrospect: The $\chi^2$ Tests and Measures of Association

## 18. SOME ORDER STATISTICS                                      615

**18.1** Order Techniques as Substitutes for the Classical Methods

**18.2** Comparing Two or More Independent Groups: The Median Tests

**18.3** The Median Test for Matched Groups

**18.4** The Sign Test for Matched Pairs

**18.5** Cochran's Test

**18.6** The Wald-Wolfowitz "Runs" Test for Two Samples

**18.7** The Mann-Whitney Test for Two Independent Samples

**18.8** The Wilcoxen Test for Two Matched Samples

**18.9** The Kruskal-Wallis "Analysis of Variance" by Ranks

**18.10** The Friedman Test for $J$ Matched Groups

**18.11** Rank-Order Correlation Methods

**18.12** The Spearman Rank Correlation Coefficient

**18.13** The Kendall Tau Coefficient

**18.14** Kendall's Tau versus the Spearman Rank Correlation

**18.15** Kendall's Tau with Ties

**18.16** A Measure of Association in Ordered Classes

**18.17** Kendall's Coefficient of Concordance

## APPENDIX A. RULES OF SUMMATION                                659

Subscripts

Rules of Summation

Summation Rules for Two or More Variables

## APPENDIX B. THE ALGEBRA OF EXPECTATIONS                       667

## APPENDIX C. TABLES                                            672

Table I: Cumulative Normal Probabilities

Table II: Upper Percentage Points of the $t$ Distribution

Table III: Upper Percentage Points of the $\chi^2$ Distribution

Table IV: Percentage Points of the $F$ Distribution

Table V: The Transformation of $r$ to $Z$

Table VI: Coefficients of Orthogonal Polynomials

Table VII: Factorials of Integers

Table VIII: Binomial Coefficients, $\binom{N}{r}$

Table IX: Powers and Roots

## REFERENCES                                                    697

## GLOSSARY OF SYMBOLS                                           700

## INDEX                                                         710

# *INTRODUCTION*

## 0.1 To the student

It is almost impossible to write a textbook of this sort without using the pronouns "you" and "we." Many textbooks give the impression that the author actually has someone in mind to whom he is explaining the materials, just as a teacher talks to his students. This author is no exception, and perhaps it will be informative to explain precisely who the "you" in this book is supposed to be.

This book is addressed to an advanced undergraduate or beginning graduate student in psychology who is interested in experimentation. This student has had a number of courses in psychology, and has some idea both of the character of psychological experiments and of the problems in which experimental methods are used. In fact, the student has begun to do some simple experimentation as part of his course work. He is interested in a career in scientific psychology, and is preparing for an eventual graduate degree in this field. Hence, he takes his course work in psychology, and especially in experimental psychology, as serious technical preparation for this career.

This person has a background of genuine interest in science and in its methods. He is quite capable of dealing with abstractions, and he feels satisfied only when he apprehends the connections among concepts. He took some physical and biological science courses in high school and college, enjoyed these subjects, and looks forward to taking more such courses. In mathematics, his high-school preparation was relatively good, and this background in mathematics was reinforced by one or more courses in college. Certainly, he is not dismayed by simple algebraic manipulations, nor by the prospect of learning more mathematics. This student finds it interesting, and often exciting, to follow a logical argument and to try to anticipate what the next step will be. The reason that he chose research psychology as a career rather than mathematics or one of the other sciences is that he is sincerely interested in the scientific study of behavior; he wants to do his share in pushing forward our understanding of the bases of human behavior, and he sees the importance of experimental method in reaching this goal.

This, in brief, is the "you" in this book. The picture may sound idealized, but the author has been fortunate enough to know a number of such students, and this book is for them and others like them. The author is not seriously concerned about the student who is just "passing through" or who is looking for an elective. He is most *unconcerned* about the student who either does not care to, or does not know how to, *think.* But he is very concerned about the serious student who needs to understand something about statistics at the very beginning of his career in experimental psychology (that is, research psychology involving experiments).

## 0.2 THE MOTIVATION BEHIND THIS BOOK

Anyone who has had any exposure at all to experimental psychology does not need to be told that statistics is an important tool in the experimenter's work. Statistics serves in at least two capacities. First, it gives methods for organizing, summarizing, and communicating data. Second, it provides methods for making inferences beyond the observations actually made to statements about large classes of *potential* observations. The set of methods serving the first of these functions is generally called **descriptive statistics,** the body of techniques for effective organization and communication of data. When the man on the street speaks of "statistics" he usually means data organized by these methods. However, the major emphasis in this book is on **inferential statistics,** the body of methods for arriving at conclusions extending beyond the immediate data. A large part of the mathematical theory of statistics is concerned with the problem of inference, and with the development of inferential methods. Furthermore, most of the interesting and important applications of mathematical statistics to psychology concern problems of inference. This book attempts to lay some of the groundwork for the experimental psychologist's understanding of the origins of inferential methods and their applications to data.

You will soon discover that the main concern in this book is with the mathematical theory underlying inferential methods, rather than with a detailed exposition of all the different methods psychologists find useful. The author had no intention of writing a "cookbook" that would equip the student to meet every possible situation he might encounter in his work. Many methods will be introduced, it is true, and we will, in fact, discuss most of the elementary techniques for statistical inference currently used in psychology. However, in the past few years psychological experiments have begun to grow increasingly complicated. Psychological theory is growing, psychologists are turning their attention to new problems, and techniques for experimentation are becoming much more sophisticated than in the past. The statistical analyses required in many such experiments are simply not in the "cookbooks." From all indications, this trend will continue, and by the time that you, the student, are in the midst of your professional career it may well be the case that entirely new statistical methods will be required for psychological experiments, replacing many of the methods that psychologists currently find useful.

As psychological research becomes more sophisticated and mathematical statistics produces more and more methods appropriate to particular experimental situations, a point is rapidly being reached where the experimental psychologist simply cannot be familiar with all the statistical methods appropriate to his work. It seems unfair to demand that each competent experimental psychologist must also be a competent mathematical statistician as well, although a few gifted individuals (*not* including the author) have somehow found time and brain-power to be both. Furthermore, the advent of electronic computers has opened up new avenues of data-analysis for the psychologist, making it possible for him to answer questions that were formerly unanswerable because of the sheer arithmetical complexity of the analysis involved. In short, the days when each experimental psychologist was his own "do it yourself" statistician, relying on his handy cookbook, are about over.

What, then, is the experimental psychologist to do? He wants the answers that statistical analysis can give him, but he may not know the range of methods open to him within theoretical statistics itself. The answer is very simple: when in doubt, ask a statistician, a man whose principal training and commitment is in mathematical statistics and the development of such methods. A large part of the work of most applied statisticians consists of consultation on problems of design and analysis of experiments, and many are available for such consultation on a professional basis. The statistician can usually provide answers to the psychologist's questions, *provided that the statistician is asked about the problem before the data are collected, and can participate in the efficient and logical planning of the experiment*. It is most unreasonable to expect the statistician to reach in his hat and pull out a method that will extract meaning from a poorly designed or executed experiment.

In order to use the resources of mathematical statistics and statisticians the psychologist must know something about the nature of mathematical statistics. He should be able at least to talk to the statistician in terms they both understand. The statistician does not expect the psychologist to know all about theoretical statistics, nor does the psychologist expect the statistician to know all about his particular experimental problem. But to work together effectively, each must have some idea of the basic concepts the other uses. This is the reason for the theoretical emphasis in this book. At the very outset, the student needs to know something about the nature of theoretical statistics if he is to appreciate the resources of statistics and not become lost in the complexities of using statistical methods effectively.

*This book is not, nor does it pretend to be, a first course in mathematical statistics.* Ideally, the serious student in experimental psychology should take at least one such course. However, there are two practical difficulties: The content and the organization of courses in mathematical statistics are framed for the training of statisticians, not experimental psychologists, and the peculiar problems of psychology are not emphasized in such courses. This is as it should be. In the second place, to become a really good experimental psychologist is a full-time job, and the student may not have the time to devote to the mathematical statistics courses and their prerequisites in order to gain the essential background he needs.

Thus, this book contains some of the concepts, results, and theoretical arguments that come from mathematical statistics, but these results and arguments are given at a far more intuitive and informal level than would be the case for a student in mathematics. Only very seldom will the level of mathematics used rise above the high school level, although the mathematical concepts used will occasionally be unfamiliar to most students. In particular we will use some results coming from the application of the calculus, especially results having to do with the idea of a "limit"; these ideas really cannot be treated adequately at an elementary level. From a mathematician's technical point of view, many of our statements are incomplete, poorly framed, or imprecise. On the other hand, many of these ideas can be grasped intuitively by the serious student, and the author feels that this intuitive understanding is better than no understanding at all, *provided* that the student understands the limitations of a presentation such as this.

A number of topics have been included that have little or no direct application to psychology at this time, because the author feels that these topics do help to clarify some theoretical point. On the other hand, a few topics ordinarily included in statistics books for psychologists have been omitted, largely because they have rather minor importance and the author preferred to devote space to other matters. Finally, some techniques are included simply because the author feels that you, as an experimenting psychologist, might want to know these methods. These are techniques that are useful even in elementary experimentation, although they are usually given extensive coverage only in more advanced texts.

The student also should understand that the examples in this book are hypothetical. This, admittedly, goes against current practice in such texts. On the other hand, the author feels that it is more important to have a fairly simple and plausible problem that the beginner in experimentation can understand and that illustrates the method clearly, than to try to provoke the student into exclaiming, "Gee, they really *do* use statistics in psychology!" Presumably, a student who has had an adequate introductory course in psychology knows this already.

## 0.3 THE ORGANIZATION OF THIS BOOK

A glance at the table of contents reveals the topics covered, and there is little point in a detailed listing here. However, it should be pointed out that the chapters in this book fall roughly into two sections: Chapters 1 through 8 deal very largely with the essential ideas of probability and of distributions, the two central notions of theoretical statistics. The first chapter lays a foundation for these topics by introducing three very fundamental mathematical concepts: set, relation, and function. A clear idea of these concepts can do a great deal to clarify the remainder of the book. Chapters 2 through 8 are very closely related in the topics covered, and each succeeding chapter builds on the concepts introduced in the preceding ones.

Chapter 9 develops some of the issues connected with the actual use of results from theoretical statistics, particularly the problem of making up one's mind from data. Chapters 10 through 18 discuss particular methods for various kinds of inferences to be made in simple experimental situations.

A theme that runs throughout this book is the search for relationships through experimentation. A statistical relation will be said to exist when knowledge of one property of an object or event *reduces our uncertainty* about another property that object or event will show. A statistical relation occurs when things tend to "go together" in a systematic way. This theme will recur *ad nauseam* in the chapters to follow, but it is an important one.

Furthermore, there is another source of unity among the chapters: by and large, the only techniques to be discussed are those appropriate to the elementary experiments that beginners in psychology are likely to do. The pattern of such an experiment is: the experimenter or nature causes subjects to be different in one or more respects—are subjects treated differently also different in some other respect? A main problem of the experimenter is to answer the question, "Although different experimental treatments appear to have different effects in the data I actually observed, is this due to what I did, or is there only some chance influence operating on what I see?" The most widely used methods of inferential statistics help the experimenter answer this question. If the experimenter is satisfied that there is actually some statistical relation between what he did and the effects he observes, then he may want to go on to estimate the strength, or predictive power, inherent in this relation. Furthermore, he may want to try to estimate the *rule* that actually permits one best to predict the one thing from knowledge of the other. The methods of Chapters 10 through 18 are devoted to ways of answering these questions in very simple experiments. However, the basic ideas underlying these methods extend to quite complicated situations as well.

## 0.4 MATHEMATICAL EXPRESSIONS AND NOTATION

Very many mathematical expressions occur throughout this text. These are of three kinds: algebraic equivalences serving as steps in some derivation, actual definitions or principles stated mathematically, and computational formulas useful in some method. Some of the mathematical expressions are numbered; this occurs when some reference will be made to that expression at a later point. If the number for any expression is followed by an asterisk (*), then this is an important definition or relationship that is worthy of your special attention. If an expression is primarily a computing formula, then this will be given a dagger (†) following the number.

A few words must also be said about the symbols we will use. Ordinarily, when a new symbol is introduced, it will be given an "on the spot" definition. However, there are a few symbols in such widespread use that the author may omit their definition; or you may have forgotten what the symbol meant on its first introduction. In either case you will find the glossary of symbols in the back of the book helpful. Furthermore, Appendixes A and B, rules for the manipulation of summations and of expectations, are very important, since we will use these rules to considerable extent in our simple derivations of results.

## 0.5 THE NATURE OF STATISTICS

So far we have talked at length about the author's expectations about the student and the reasons underlying this book, but we have failed to say much about the topic itself. Next we will take an overview of what inferential statistics is about. In addition, some ideas about formal systems and mathematical models will be given, which may help the student understand how "statistics" can mean both a body of applied methods and a mathematical theory.

Applications of statistics occur in virtually all fields of research endeavor—the physical sciences, the biological sciences, the social sciences, engineering, market and consumer research, quality control in industry, and so on, almost without end. Although the actual methods differ somewhat in the different fields, the applications all rest on the same general theory of statistics. By examining what the fields have in common in their applications of statistics we can gain a picture of the basic problem studied in mathematical statistics. *The major applications of statistics in any field all rest on the possibility of repeated observations or experiments made under essentially the same conditions.* That is, either the researcher actually can observe the same process repeated many times, as in industrial quality control, or there is the *conceptual* possibility of repeated observation, as in a scientific experiment that might, in principle, be repeated under identical conditions. However, in any circumstance where repeated observations are made, even though every precaution is taken to make conditions exactly the same the results of observations will vary, or tend to be different, from trial to trial. The researcher has control over some, but not all, of the factors that make outcomes of observations tend to differ from each other.

In some areas of research, objects or phenomena viewed under the same conditions will vary only to a small extent. This is certainly true in some branches of physical science, where observations made under carefully controlled conditions give virtually identical results. On the other hand, in the biological, and especially the social, sciences, even though the experimenter exerts almost superhuman efforts to observe repeatedly under precisely the same conditions, some differences among his observations will occur, and these differences are ordinarily *not* negligible.

When observations are made under the same conditions in one or more respects, but they give outcomes differing in other ways, then there is some *uncertainty* connected with observation of any given object or phenomenon. Even though some things are known to be true about that object in advance of the observation, the experimenter cannot predict with complete certainty what its other characteristics will be. Given enough repeated observations of the same object or kind of object the experimenter may be able to formulate a good bet about what the other characteristics are likely to be, but he cannot be completely sure of the status of any given object.

This fact leads us to the central problem of theoretical statistics: *in one sense, mathematical statistics is a theory about uncertainty, the tendency of outcomes to vary when repeated observations are made under identical conditions.* Granted that certain conditions are fulfilled, theoretical statistics permits deductions about the *likelihood* of the various possible outcomes of observation. The essential concepts in statistics derive from the theory of probability, and the deductions made within the theory of statistics are, by and large, statements about the probability of particular kinds of outcomes, given that initial, mathematical, conditions are met.

Mathematical statistics is a formal mathematical system. Perhaps the nature of this system as a branch of mathematics will be clarified by a brief look at mathematical systems in general.

## 0.6   ABSTRACT MATHEMATICAL SYSTEMS

Any mathematical system consists of these basic parts:

1. A collection of undefined **"things"** or **"elements,"** considered only as abstract entities;
2. A set of undefined **operations,** or possible relations among the abstract elements;
3. A set of **postulates** and **definitions,** each asserting that some specific relation holds among the various elements, the various operations, or both.

For example, each of us is familiar with at least one mathematical system: ordinary arithmetic. This system deals with the *basically* undefined "number" symbols such as "0," "1," "2," and so on. There are *operations* that are also undefined, such as "$+$," "$-$," etc. Finally, there are some statements asserted to be true, which are the postulates of this system. For example, two postulates of arithmetic might be

$$X + 0 = X$$

where $X$ is any number whatsoever, and

$$\frac{(X)}{(X)} = 1, \text{ when } X \text{ is not equal to } 0.$$

From a collection of such postulates, all the mathematical "truths" that we call arithmetic can be derived by the application of logic. The same is true of any mathematical system: the application of logic to combinations of the postulates and definitions leads to *new* statements, or theorems, about the undefined elements of the system. *Given* that the original postulates and definitions are true, then the new statements *must* be true. Mathematical systems are purely abstract, and essentially undefined, **deductive** structures. In the first chapter, the theory of sets will be used as an example of an abstract system of this sort, and the theory of probability also has this character, as we shall see.

Mathematical systems are not really "about" anything in particular. They are systems of statements about "things" having the formal properties given by the postulates. The mathematician does not, in fact, have to commit himself about what he really has in mind to call these abstract elements; indeed, he may have absolutely nothing in mind that exists in the real world of experience, and his sole concern may be in what he can derive about the other necessary relations among abstract elements given particular sets of postulates. It is perfectly true, of course, that many mathematical systems originated from attempts to describe real objects or phenomena and their interrelationships: historically, the abstract systems of geometry, school algebra, and the calculus grew out of problems where something very concrete was in the back of the mathematician's mind. However, as *mathematics* these systems deal with completely abstract entities.

## 0.7 MATHEMATICAL MODELS OF REAL OBJECTS AND EVENTS

The employment of mathematical systems, apart from their study as formal logical systems, comes about when the elements of the system are actually identified with real "things." We say that the system is "interpreted" in terms of the real world. For example, the abstract symbols "1" and "2" may be identified with one pound and two pounds of very real butter. Now within the mathematical system of arithmetic itself, the following *formal* statement is true:

$$1 + 2 = 3.$$

We use this formal, abstract, result to assert that,

> "one pound of butter added to two pounds of butter is
> equivalent to the object 'three pounds of butter.'"

Provided that the postulates about the abstract objects are true when interpreted as statements about real objects, then any deduction we make about abstract objects in the system is *also* true about real objects.

On the other hand, it is quite possible to find situations where the mathematical system does *not* necessarily yield true statements about objects, because the objects in question do not satisfy one or more properties of the system. For example, if we added one lighted match to two gallons of gasoline, we would have at best only one very loud *bang*, simply because these objects do not happen to combine in the way dictated by the abstract symbol "+."

When a mathematical system is interpreted in terms of real objects or events, then the system is said to be a **mathematical model** for those objects or events. Somewhat more precisely, the undefined terms in the mathematical system are identified with particular, relevant, **properties** of objects or events;

thus, in applications of arithmetic, the number symbols are identified with magnitudes or amounts of some particular property that objects possess, such as weight, or extent, or numerosity. The system of arithmetic need not apply to other characteristics of the same objects, as, for example, their colors. Once this identification can be made between the mathematical system and the relevant properties of objects, then anything that is a logical consequence in the system is a true statement about objects in the model, *provided*, of course, *that the formal characteristics of the system actually parallel the real characteristics of objects in terms of the particular properties considered.* In short, in order to be useful as a mathematical model, a mathematical system must have a formal structure that "fits" at least one aspect of a real situation.

Probability theory and statistics are each both mathematical systems *and* mathematical models. Probability theory deals with elements called "events," which are completely abstract. Furthermore, these abstract things are paired with numbers called "probabilities." The theory itself is the system of logical relations among these essentially undefined things. The experimenter uses this abstract system as a mathematical model: his experiment produces a real outcome, which he calls an event, and he uses the model to find a probability, which he interprets as the relative frequency of occurrence for that outcome. However, if his experiment really does not fit the requirements of probability theory as a system, then the statement he makes about his actual result need not be true.

There are really a number of mathematical systems that we group together under the general heading, "mathematical statistics." Each "little" mathematical system is based upon certain postulated relations among the mathematical entities. When the experimenter takes the statistical system as a mathematical model, he must *assume* that the requirements of the system are met. His conclusions are always of the form *"If* my data fit this model, then . . . " The statistical method he uses was developed as a *mathematical* consequence of certain postulated relations; this method is *right*, in the sense that *if* particular conditions are met, the answer will be a true statement. On the other hand, a statistical method is incorrectly applied when the underlying mathematical conditions are not truly met, and the truth of the answer the experimenter obtains by this method will be in doubt. This is why the mathematical requirements or assumptions that go into the formal derivation of statistical methods are very important, as we shall see. There is no guarantee that a statistical method will give the answer the experimenter is seeking unless the mathematical conditions used to derive that method are truly met.

## 0.8   THE PROBLEM OF INDUCTIVE INFERENCE

Mathematical systems such as probability theory and the theory of statistics are, by their very nature, **deductive.** That is, formal assertions are postulated as true, and then by logical argument true conclusions are reached. All well-developed theories have this formal, logico-deductive character.

On the other hand, the problem of the empirical scientist is essentially different from that of the logician or mathematician. Scientists search for general relations among events; these general relations are those which can be expected to hold whenever the appropriate set of circumstances exists. The very name "empirical science" asserts that these laws shall be discovered and verified by the actual observation of what happens in the real world of experience. However, no mortal scientist ever observes all the phenomena about which he would like to make a generalization. He must always draw his conclusions about what would happen for *all* of a certain class of phenomena by observing a very few particular cases of that phenomenon. For example, Torricelli, the inventor of the barometer, arrived at the relation that holds between the air pressure and the height of a column of mercury in a glass tube. He was not at all interested, per se, in what happened to a particular glass tube filled with mercury on a particular day in two particular spots in Italy in the year 1643. Rather, he wished to find some general statement he could make about the relation between the height of the column of mercury and the altitude at which it was placed that would be true for any tube, any experimenter, any place, any year, under the right conditions. Or consider the observations of Charles Darwin: the principles of natural selection he formulated were supposed to hold for any form of animal life in any locale, but his actual observations of this natural selection in action were of its manifestations in a relatively limited number of animal species, such as the finches of the Galapagos Islands. Freud theorized about basic processes inherent in all human life from his own experience with a few patients in Vienna at the turn of the century. Of course, these are examples of generalizations by men of real genius. Nevertheless, any empirical scientist must eventually face this problem: how does one generalize from observing a limited number of cases?

The student acquainted with logic will recognize that this is a problem of **induction**. The rules of logical *deduction* are rules for arriving at true consequences from true premises. Scientific theories are, for the most part, systems of deductions from basic principles held to be true. If the basic principles are true, then the deductions must be true. However, how does one go about arriving at and checking the truth of the initial propositions? The answer is, for an empirical science, observation and inductive generalization—going from what is true of some observations to a statement that this is true for *all possible* observations made under the same conditions. Any empirical science begins with observation and generalization.

Furthermore, even after deductive theories exist in a science, experimentation is used to check on the truth of these theories. Observations that contradict deductions made within the theory are prima-facie evidence against the truth of the theory itself. Yet, how does the scientist know that his results are not an accident, the product of some chance variation in procedure or conditions over which he has no control? Would his result be the same in the long run if the experiment could be repeated many times?

It takes only a little imagination to see that this process of going from the specific to the general is a very risky one. Each observation the scientist makes is different in some way from the next. Innumerable influences are at work altering—sometimes minutely, sometimes radically—the similarities and differences the scientist observes among events. Controlled experimentation in any science is an attempt to minimize at least part of the accidental variation or "error" in observation. Precise techniques of measurement are aids to the scientist in sharpening his own rather dull powers of observation and comparison among events. So-called "exact sciences," such as physics and chemistry, have thus been able to remove a substantial amount of the unwanted variation among observations from time to time, place to place, observer to observer, and hence are often able to make general statements about physical phenomena with great assurance from the observation of quite limited numbers of events. Observations in these sciences can often be made in such a way that the generality of conclusions is not a major point at issue.

In the biological and social sciences, however, the situation is radically different. In these sciences the variations between observations are not subject to the precise experimental controls that are possible in the physical sciences. Refined measurement techniques have not reached the stage of development that they have attained in physics and chemistry. Consequently, the drawing of general conclusions is a much more dangerous business in these fields, where the sources of variability among living things are extremely difficult to identify, measure, and control. And yet the aim of the social or biological scientist is precisely the same as that of the physical scientist—arriving at general statements about the phenomena under study.

Faced as he is with only a limited number of observations or with an experiment that he can conduct only once, the scientist can reach general conclusions only in the form of a "bet" about what the true, long run, situation actually is like. Given only sample evidence, the scientist is always unsure of the "goodness" of any assertion he makes about the true state of affairs. The theory of statistics provides ways to assess this uncertainty and to calculate the probability that he will be wrong if he decides in a particular way. *Provided that the experimenter can make some assumptions about what is true, then the deductive theory of statistics tells him how likely he is to observe particular results.* Armed with this information, the experimenter is in better position to decide, if he must, what he will say about the true situation. Regardless of what he decides from his evidence, he *could* be wrong; but using deductive statistical theory he can at least determine the probabilities of error in a particular decision.

In recent years, a branch of mathematics has been developed around this problem of decision-making under uncertain conditions. This is sometimes called "statistical decision theory." One of the main problems treated in decision theory is the choice of a decision rule, or "deciding how to decide" from evidence. Decision theory evaluates rules for deciding from evidence in the light of what the decision-maker wants to accomplish. As we shall see in later chapters, mathematics can tell us wise ways to decide how to decide under some circumstances, but it can never tell the experimenter how he *must* decide in any particular situation. The theory of statistics supplies one very important piece of information to the experimenter: the probability of sample results *given* certain conditions. Decision theory supplies another: optimal ways of using this and other information to accomplish certain ends. Nevertheless, neither theory tells the experimenter *exactly* how to decide—how to make the inductive leap from what he observes to what is true in general. This is the experimenter's problem, and he must seek the answer outside of deductive mathematics, and in the light of what he is trying to do.

This point will occur a number of times in our discussion. Now, we turn to the problem of laying a foundation for the study of statistics itself.

# SETS AND FUNCTIONS

*1*

It may seem surprising that a book about statistics starts off with a discussion of sets. Although the study of sets and functions is not usually a part of a course in statistics, these topics actually provide the most fundamental concepts we will use. Set theory will be the basis for our discussion of probability theory, to be introduced in the next chapter. The idea of a function pervades virtually all mathematics and is a key concept in modern scientific work as well. Even at the high-school level most of us are exposed to the notion of a mathematical function, and we know that saying that "$Y$ is a function of $X$" expresses something about a relation between two things. However, unless the student has a very good background in mathematics, he is usually somewhat vague about the precise meaning of the word "function" used in mathematical or scientific writing. One of the primary purposes of this chapter is to give a very concrete and restricted meaning to this term. It will be shown that the idea of a function is a very simple one, which grows out of the notion of a set.

## 1.1 SETS

The concept of a set is the starting point for all of modern mathematics, and yet this idea could hardly be more simple:

**Any well-defined collection of objects is a set.**

The individual objects making up the set are known as the "elements" or "members" of the set. The set itself is the aggregate or totality of its members. If a given object is in the set, then one says that the object is an **element** of, or a **member** of, or **belongs** to, the set.

For example, all students enrolled at a given university in a given year is a set, and any particular student is an element of that set. All living men whose last name is "Jones" is another set. All of the whole numbers between 10 and 10,000 is a set, all animals of the species *Rattus norvegicus* living at this particular moment make up a set, all possible neural pathways in John Doe's brain form a set, and so on, ad infinitum.

It is important to note that in the definition of a set the qualification "well-defined" occurs. This means that *it must be possible, at least in principle, to specify the set so that one can decide whether any given object does or does not belong.* This does not mean that sets can be discussed only if their members actually exist: it is perfectly possible to speak of the set of all women presidents of the United States, for example, even though there are not any such objects at this writing. What *is* required is some procedure or rule for deciding whether or not an object is or is not in the set; given an object, one can decide if it meets the qualifications of a female president of the United States, and thus the set is well-defined.

The word "object" in the definition can also be interpreted quite liberally. Often, sets are discussed having members that are not objects in the usual sense but rather are "phenomena," or "happenings," or possible outcomes of observation. We will have occasion to use sets of "logical possibilities," all the different ways something might happen, where each distinct possibility is thought of as one member of the set. Very often the members of a set will be sets themselves, or the names of sets. For example, a set of numbers can be thought of as a set of sets, each number ultimately signifying a set of objects each showing the same property of "magnitude." A set of nouns can also be regarded as a set of sets, where each noun designates some set of objects.

## 1.2 WAYS OF SPECIFYING SETS

In discussing sets, we will follow the practice of letting a capital letter, such as $A$, symbolize the set itself, with a small letter, such as $a$, used to indicate a particular member of the set. The symbol "$\epsilon$" (small Greek epsilon) is often used to indicate "is a member of"; thus,

$$a \in A$$

is read "*a* is a member of *A*."

There are two different ways of specifying a set. The first way is by *listing* all of the members. For example,

$$A = \{1,2,3,4,5\}$$

is a complete specification of the set $A$, saying that it consists of the numbers 1, 2, 3, 4, and 5. The braces around the listing are used to indicate that the list makes up a set. Another set specified in a similar way is

$$B = \{\text{orange, grapefruit, lemon, lime, tangerine, kumquat, citron}\}$$

and another is

$$C = \{\text{Roosevelt, Truman, Eisenhower, Kennedy}\}.$$

ffigure, Venn diagrams actually represent infinite sets, but they are useful for representing any set. For example, a Venn diagram picturing the universal set $W$ and the subset $A$ would look like Figure 1.6.1. Since $A$ is a subset of $W$, the area of the circle $A$ is completely included in the area of the rectangle $W$.

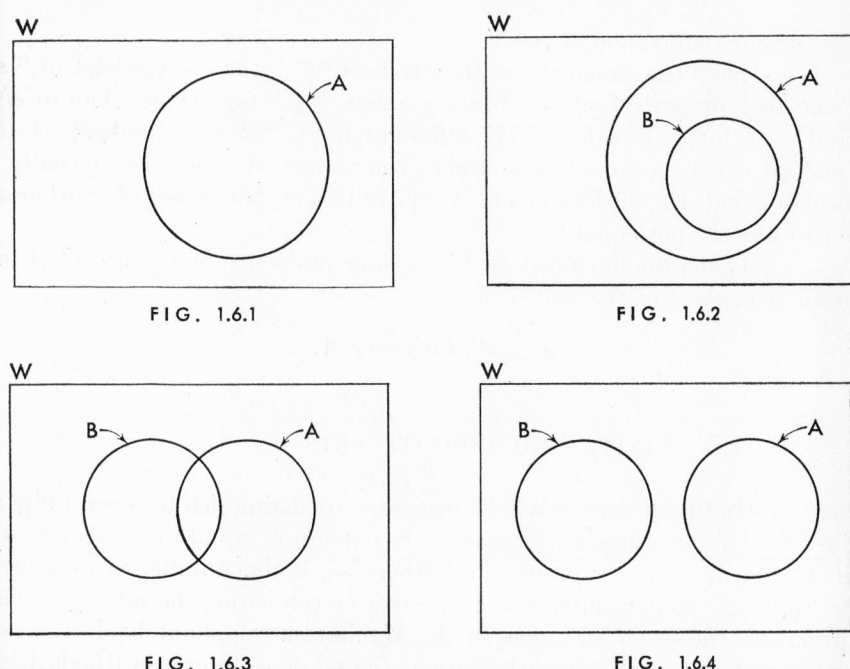

FIG. 1.6.1

FIG. 1.6.2

FIG. 1.6.3

FIG. 1.6.4

Now consider another set $B \subseteq W$. If $B \subset A$, the Venn diagram would be as shown by Figure 1.6.2. On the other hand, if $B$ were not a subset of $A$, then Figure 1.6.3 would be the Venn diagram if $A$ and $B$ shared members in common. Or perhaps Figure 1.6.4, if the two sets had no members in common.

## 1.7 THE EMPTY SET

Just as the number "zero" is important in ordinary arithmetic, so the theory of sets requires the notion of the "empty set." **Any set that contains no members is called the empty set.** The empty set is usually identified by the symbol Ø, a zero with a diagonal slash. We have already had one example of the empty set, the set of all women presidents of the United States. It is not hard to dream up other examples: the set of all months containing 38 days, the set of all people with 3 legs, the set of all numbers not divisible by 1, and so on.

This set has a very special property: **the empty set is a subset of every set.** Notice that the definition of a subset as given in Section 1.4 does not rule out the empty set; since the empty set has no members, the definition of subset is not contradicted, and so $\emptyset \subseteq A$ for every $A$.

In each instance the respective elements of the set are simply listed. These sets are thought of as unordered, since the order of the listing is completely irrelevant so long as each member is included once and only once in the list.

The other way of specifying a set is to give a *rule* that lets one decide whether or not an object is a member of the set in question. Thus, set $A$ may be specified by

$$A = \{a \mid a \text{ is an integer and } 1 \leq a \leq 5\}.$$

(The symbol | is read as "such that," so that the expression above is, in words, "the set of all elements $a$ such that $a$ is an integer between 1 and 5 inclusive.") Given this rule, and any potential element of the set $A$, we can decide immediately whether or not the object actually does belong to the set.

The rule for set $B$ would be

$$B = \{b \mid b \text{ is the name of a kind of citrus fruit}\}$$

and for set $C$

$$C = \{c \mid c \text{ is a United States President elected between 1932 and 1960 inclusive}\}.$$

It is quite possible to specify sets in terms of other sets. For example, we might specify a set $D$ by

$$D = \{d \mid d = a + 15, \text{ for all } a \, \epsilon \, A\}.$$

When listed, the elements of $D$ would be

$$D = \{16,17,18,19,20\}.$$

It is usually far more convenient to specify a set by its rule than by listing the elements. For example, sets such as the following would be awkward or impossible to list:

$$G = \{g \mid g \text{ is a human born in 1955}\}$$
$$X = \{x \mid x \text{ is a positive number}\}$$
$$Y = \{y \mid y \, \epsilon \, X \text{ and } y \text{ is an integer}\}.$$

## 1.3 UNIVERSAL SETS

There are many instances in set theory when it becomes convenient to consider only objects belonging to some "large" set. Then, given that all objects to be discussed belong to this "universal" set, we proceed to talk of particular groupings of elements. The introduction of a universal set acts to set the stage for the kinds of sets that will be introduced. For example, we may wish to deal only with U.S. students enrolled in college in the year 1961, and so we begin by specifying a universal set:

$$W = \{w \mid w \text{ was a U.S. student enrolled in college in 1961}\}.$$

Then particular subsets of $W$ are introduced:

$$A = \{a|a \, \epsilon \, W \text{ and } a \text{ was a student at Harvard}\}$$
$$B = \{b|b \, \epsilon \, W \text{ and } b \text{ was classified as a sophomore}\}$$

and so on. Or perhaps the universal set is

$$W = \{w|w \text{ is a symbol for a sound}\}$$
$$A = \{a|a \, \epsilon \, W \text{ and } a \text{ is a letter in the Cyrillic alphabet}\}$$
$$B = \{b|b \, \epsilon \, W \text{ and } b \text{ is a letter in the Greek alphabet}\}$$

and so on.

Up until this point, the individual member of a set has been denoted by a small letter, $a$, $b$, $w$, and so on, depending on the capital letter used for the set itself. This is not strictly necessary, however, as any symbol that serves as a "place holder" in the rule specifying the set would do as well. In future sections it will sometimes prove convenient to use the same symbol for a member of several sets, so that the neutral symbol $x$ will be used, indicating any member of the universal set under discussion. Furthermore, it is redundant to state that $x \, \epsilon \, W$ after the universal set $W$ has been specified, and so this statement will be omitted from the rule for particular subsets of the universal set. Nevertheless, it is always understood that any member of a set is automatically a member of some universe $W$. In the example just given, the sets are adequately specified by

$$W = \{x|x \text{ is a symbol for a sound}\}$$
$$A = \{x|x \text{ is a letter in the Cyrillic alphabet}\}$$
$$B = \{x|x \text{ is a letter in the Greek alphabet}\}.$$

## 1.4  SUBSETS

Suppose that there were some set $A$ and another set $B$, so that any element which is in $B$ is also in $A$. Then $B$ *is a subset of* $A$. This is symbolized by

$$B \subseteq A,$$

read as "$B$ is a subset of $A$." More formally,

**The set $B$ is a subset of the set $A$ if and only if for each $x \, \epsilon \, B$ then $x \, \epsilon \, A$.**

For example, consider the set $A$ of all male citizens of the United States at this moment. Now let set $B$ be the set of all living U.S. Army generals; the set $B$ is a subset of the set $A$. Or, let $A$ be the set of all numbers, and let $B$ indicate the set of all whole numbers. Once again, $B$ is a subset of $A$.

If there is at least one element of $A$ not in $B$, then $B$ is a **proper subset** of $A$, symbolized by

$$B \subset A.$$

In both the examples just given the set $B$ is a proper subset of $A$, since some U.S.

men are not generals, and some numbers are not whole. ( every single element in $B$ is in $A$, *and* every single element $B \subseteq A$ and $A \subseteq B$, then

$$A = B,$$

the two sets are equivalent or equal.

Note the similarity of the symbols "$\subseteq$," for "$\subset$," for "is a proper subset of," to the symbols "$\leq$," for to," and "$<$," for "is less than." The difference in "$\subseteq$" and that one set can be a subset of another even though the identical or equal element by element; a set can be a proper if the two sets are not equal.

Given the universal set $W$ for some problem, discussed is a subset of the universal set,

$$A \subseteq W, \text{ for every } A.$$

## 1.5  FINITE AND INFINITE SETS

In future work it will be necessary to distingu infinite sets. For our purposes, a finite set has members eq specifiable positive integer or to zero. Otherwise, if the greater than any positive integer you conceivably can nam infinite. Thus, the set of all names in the Manhattan tele all books printed in the nineteenth century, the set of all h the set of all living mammals, are all finite sets, even thoug bers each includes is very large. On the other hand, the set circle, the set of all real numbers (including all rational and negative numbers), the set of all intervals into which a divided, are examples of infinite sets.

In our discussion in the next few sections, all though they were finite. The general ideas apply to infinite qualifications have to be made in some of the definition overlook these.

## 1.6  VENN DIAGRAMS

A scheme that is very useful for illustratin relations among them is the Venn diagram (named afte 1834–1923). These are sometimes referred to as Euler diag matician L. Euler, 1707–1783; both men made importar theory of sets). A Venn diagram pictures a set as all poi circle, square, or other closed geometrical figure.

Since there is an infinite number of possible

## 1.8   NEW SETS FROM OLD: OPERATIONS WITH SETS

Given some universal set $W$, and a set of its subsets, $A$, $B$, $C$, and so on, it is possible to "operate" on sets to form new sets, each of which is also a subset of $W$.

The first of these operations is the **union** of two or more sets. Given $W$ and the two subsets $A$ and $B$, then the union of $A$ and $B$ is written $A \cup B$ (a useful mnemonic device for the symbol $\cup$ is the $u$ in $u$nion). By definition,

$A \cup B$ **is the set of all elements that are members of** $A$, **or of** $B$, **or of both:**

$$A \cup B = \{x | x \,\epsilon\, A \text{ or } x \,\epsilon\, B, \text{ or both}\}.$$

For example, let

$$W = \{x | x \text{ is a living American war veteran}\}$$
$$A = \{x | x \text{ is a veteran of World War II}\}$$
$$B = \{x | x \text{ is a veteran of the Korean War}\}.$$

Then

$$A \cup B = \{x | x \text{ is a veteran of World War II, or}$$
$$x \text{ is a veteran of the Korean War, or}$$
$$x \text{ is a veteran of both}\}.$$

In the Venn diagram (Fig. 1.8.1), the shaded portion shows the union of $A$ and $B$. Notice that we include the possibility that an element of the union could be a

FIG. 1.8.1

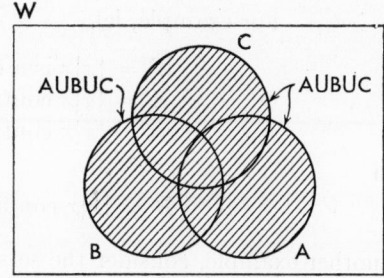

FIG. 1.8.2

member of *both* $A$ and $B$. Note further that in this example, $A \cup B \subset W$, the union is a *proper* subset of the universal set, since there are some living American war veterans who belong neither to $A$ nor $B$.

The idea of the union may be extended to more than two sets. For instance, given $W$ and three sets $A$, $B$, and $C$, then

$$A \cup B \cup C = \{x | x \,\epsilon\, A, \text{ or } x \,\epsilon\, B, \text{ or } x \,\epsilon\, C\},$$

as shown in Figure 1.8.2.

As an example of the union of three sets, let

$$W = \{x|x \text{ is a positive integer, } 1 \leq x \leq 10\}$$
$$A = \{x|x \text{ is a perfect square}\} = \{1,4,9\}$$
$$B = \{x|x \text{ is divisible by 3}\} = \{3,6,9\}$$
$$C = \{x|x \text{ is divisible by 7}\} = \{7\}.$$

Then

$$A \cup B \cup C = \{1,3,4,6,7,9\}.$$

The union of any set with a subset of itself is simply the larger set: given $B \subseteq A$, then $A \cup B = B \cup A = A$. It follows that

$$A \cup \emptyset = A$$

and

$$W \cup A = W.$$

## 1.9  THE INTERSECTION OF SETS

The verbal rule for the union of two sets always involves the word "or"; the union $A \cup B$ is the set made by finding the elements that are members of $A$ *or* of $B$ *or* of both. However, what of the set of elements in *both* $A$ and $B$? This set is included in the union, but we are most often interested in this set by itself as the **intersection** of $A$ and $B$:

The intersection of sets $A$ and $B$, written $A \cap B$, is the set of all members belonging to both $A$ and $B$: $A \cap B = \{x|x \in A \text{ and } x \in B\}$.

For example, let

$$W = \{x|x \text{ is a chemical compound}\}$$
$$A = \{x|x \text{ contains chlorine}\}$$
$$B = \{x|x \text{ contains oxygen}\}.$$

Then

$$A \cap B = \{x|x \text{ contains chlorine and oxygen}\}.$$

As another example, consider the sets of numbers

$$W = \{x|x \text{ is a positive integer}\}$$
$$A = \{1,2,3,4,5,6,7,8,9,10\}$$
$$B = \{8,9,10,11,12,13\}.$$

Then

$$A \cap B = \{8,9,10\}$$

since only these elements appear in both $A$ and $B$.

The intersection of two sets $A$ and $B$ is always a subset of their union:

$$A \cap B \subseteq A \cup B.$$

If the intersection of two sets is empty, $A \cap B = \emptyset$, then the sets are said to be **disjoint** or **mutually exclusive**.

The intersection of two sets presented in a Venn diagram appears as Figure 1.9.1.

Whenever $B$ is a subset of $A$, then the intersection $A \cap B$ or $B \cap A$ is equal to the *smaller* of the two sets, or $B$. Thus,

$$A \cap \emptyset = \emptyset,$$

and

$$A \cap W = A,$$

since $\emptyset$ is a subset of $A$, and $A$ is a subset of $W$.

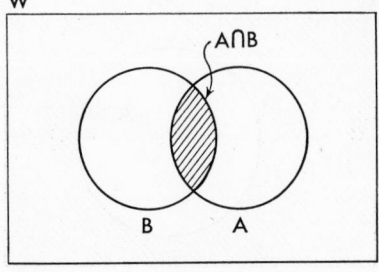

FIG. 1.9.1

The intersection may be defined for any number of sets taken together. For example, the intersection of three sets $A$, $B$, and $C$ is

$$A \cap B \cap C = \{x | x \in A \text{ and } x \in B \text{ and } x \in C\}.$$

Thus, if $A$ were all women, $B$ were all librarians, and $C$ were all persons with blue eyes, then $A \cap B \cap C$ would be the set of all women librarians having blue eyes.

## 1.10   THE COMPLEMENT OF A SET

Another operation on sets is called taking the **complement** of a set. Given $W$ and a subset $A$, then the complement of $A$ is made up of all members of $W$ that are *not* in $A$. In symbols,

the complement of $A = \bar{A} = \{x | x \notin A\}$

where the symbol $\notin$ is read as "not a member of" the set following. For example, if

$W = \{x | x$ is a name in the 1962 Detroit, Michigan, telephone directory$\}$

and

$A = \{x | x$ begins with the letter "S"$\}$,

then

$\bar{A} = \{x | x$ does not begin with the letter "S"$\}$.

The intersection of any set and its complement is always empty,

$$A \cap \bar{A} = \emptyset$$

since no element could be simultaneously a member of both $A$ and $\bar{A}$. The union of $A$ and $\bar{A}$, however, always equals the universal set $W$

$$A \cup \bar{A} = W.$$

Notice that the complement of any set is always relative to the universal set; this is why specifying the universal set is so important, since one cannot determine the complement of a set without doing so. For example, suppose that we specified the following set:

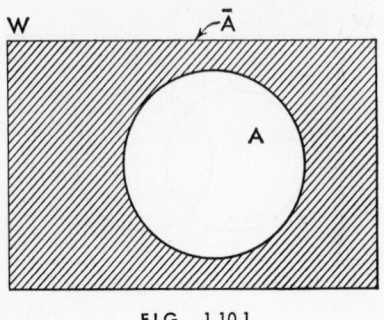

FIG. 1.10.1

$$A = \{x | x \text{ has blue eyes}\}.$$

What is $\bar{A}$? That depends on what we assumed $W$ to be. If

$$W = \{x | x \text{ is a woman living in the United States}\},$$

then $\bar{A}$ consists of all non-blue-eyed women living in the U.S. However, if

$$W = \{x | x \text{ is a person living in the U.S.}\},$$

the $\bar{A}$ is quite a different set, including non-blue-eyed men and children as well. If

$$W = \{x | x \text{ is an organism}\},$$

then $\bar{A}$ would include all non-blue-eyed organisms, among them some that have no eyes at all. The complement of a set simply has no meaning without a universal set for reference.

The complement of a set is shown in Figure 1.10.1 as the shaded area in the Venn diagram.

## 1.11  THE DIFFERENCE BETWEEN TWO SETS

The difference between two sets is closely allied to the idea of a complement. Given the universal set, the **difference** between sets $A$ and $B$ is

$$A - B = A \cap \bar{B} = \{x | x \, \epsilon \, A \text{ and } x \, \epsilon \, \bar{B}\}.$$

In other words, the difference contains all elements that are members of $A$ *but not* members of $B$.

Although it makes no difference which set we write first in the symbols for union and intersection,

$$A \cup B = B \cup A$$

and

$$A \cap B = B \cap A,$$

the order is very important for the difference between two sets. The difference $A - B$ is *not* the same as the difference $B - A$.

As an example of the two differences, $A - B$ and $B - A$, let

$$W = \{x | x \text{ was an elected official of the U.S. government in 1960}\}$$
$$A = \{x | x \text{ was a member of the U.S. Congress}\}$$
$$B = \{x | x \text{ was a lawyer}\}.$$

Then

$$A - B = \{x | x \text{ was a member of the U.S. Congress who was not a lawyer}\}$$

and

$$B - A = \{x | x \text{ was a lawyer who was not a member of the U.S. Congress}\}.$$

It is easy to see that these two differences are quite different sets: A congressman who is not a lawyer is not the same as a lawyer who is not a congressman.

The Venn diagram for a difference $A - B$ is the shaded area in Figure 1.11.1.

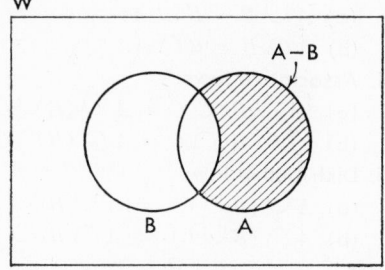

FIG. 1.11.1

### 1.12   THE ALGEBRA OF SETS

In the algebra that everyone studies in high school, there are certain rules which the operations symbolized by "$+$," "$\cdot$," and so on must obey. The study of algebra is largely the study of these basic rules and of the mathematical consequences of the application of these operations to numbers. In the same way, an algebra of sets exists, consisting of a system for forming and manipulating sets by operations of union, intersection, complement, and so on, according to a specific set of rules or postulates. An algebra of sets has a great many similarities to, as well as some important differences from, ordinary school algebra. In a course in modern mathematics one learns to use set algebra (often called a Boolean algebra, after the nineteenth-century British mathematician, G. Boole, who first developed it). Although there is little point in dwelling upon set algebra at length in a course in statistics, it may be instructive to list the basic "rules" for an algebra of sets and to give examples of how simple theorems about sets may be proved using those rules. Just as in any formal mathematical system, the basic postulates are used to derive new conclusions by logical argument. Since we are going to be discussing a closely related system in the next chapter, a view of the foundations of this simplest of all mathematical systems may give the reader a somewhat better idea of how postulates are used.

These postulates refer to **abstract sets,** any collections of undefined elements. These statements about abstract sets are assumed true without question; they are simply "postulated." In order for set theory to be a model of sets of *real* objects, it must be true that the conditions specified by the postulates are met by the real sets. For most practical purposes these postulates *are* true of real sets. Every statement that one can make about new sets formed from old by the operations "$\cup$," "$\cap$," and complement can be deduced from these postulates.

### 1.13 POSTULATES AND THEOREMS ABOUT SETS

The postulates of set-theory can be stated as follows:

1. (a) if $A$ and $B$ are sets, then $A \cup B$ is a set;
   (b) if $A$ and $B$ are sets, then $A \cap B$ is a set.
2. (a) there is one and only one set $\emptyset$, such that $A \cup \emptyset = A$ for any $A$;
   (b) there is one and only one set $W$, such that $A \cap W = A$ for any set $A$.
3. Commutative laws:
   (a) $A \cup B = B \cup A$;
   (b) $A \cap B = B \cap A$.
4. Associative laws:
   (a) $(A \cup B) \cup C = A \cup (B \cup C)$;
   (b) $(A \cap B) \cap C = A \cap (B \cap C)$.
5. Distributive laws:
   (a) $A \cup (B \cap C) = (A \cup B) \cap (A \cup C)$;
   (b) $A \cap (B \cup C) = (A \cap B) \cup (A \cap C)$.
6. For every set $A$ there is one and only one set $\bar{A}$ such that

$$A \cup \bar{A} = W \text{ and } A \cap \bar{A} = \emptyset.$$

7. (a) $A = B$ and $C = D$ implies that $A \cup C = B \cup D$;
   (b) $A = B$ and $C = D$ implies that $A \cap C = B \cap D$;
   (c) $A = B$ implies that $\bar{A} = \bar{B}$.
8. There are at least two distinct sets.

Upon these statements about sets and the operations "$\cup$," "$\cap$," and complement, an elaborate mathematical structure can be erected. It is very important to note that nowhere in these postulates is there an explicit definition of what is meant by a "set," by "$\cup$," and by "$\cap$." The postulates deal with equivalences among *undefined operations* carried out on *undefined things*. In this sense, the set of postulates is said to be "formal."

It is interesting to note that some of these postulates are true if we happen to be talking about the ordinary algebra of numbers rather than sets, and if "$\cup$" is replaced by "$+$" and "$\cap$" is replaced by "$\cdot$." For instance, postulate 1(a) corresponds to a similar postulate about numbers: if $x$ and $y$ are numbers, then $x + y$ is a number. Similarly, postulates 3, 4, and 5(b) have equivalent statements in ordinary algebra:

Commutative laws:     $x + y = y + x$ and $x \cdot y = y \cdot x$.

Associative laws:

$$(x \cdot y) \cdot z = x \cdot (y \cdot z) \text{ and } x + (y + z) = (x + y) + z.$$

Distributive law:     $x \cdot (y + z) = x \cdot y + x \cdot z.$

Notice, however, that a statement corresponding to postulate 5(a) is *not*, in general, true of numbers:

$$x + (y \cdot z) \text{ is not equal to } (x + y) \cdot (x + z).$$

Thus the algebra of sets, though similar to ordinary school algebra, does differ from it in important respects.

Now an example will be given of how these postulates are used to arrive at new statements, or theorems, not specifically among these original statements. As with any mathematical system, a logical argument is used to arrive at true conclusions *given* that the postulates are true. First of all, a simple but very important theorem will be proved:

**THEOREM I:**  For any set $A$, $A \cap A = A$.

| | |
|---|---|
| $A \cap A = (A \cap A) \cup \emptyset$ | by Postulate 2(a) |
| $= (A \cap A) \cup (A \cap \bar{A})$ | Postulate 6 |
| $= A \cap (A \cup \bar{A})$ | Postulate 5(b) |
| $= A \cap W$ | Postulate 6 |
| $= A$ | Postulate 2(b). |

By a series of equivalent statements (the "substitutions" familiar from school algebra), each justified by a postulate, we have arrived at a new statement, $A \cap A = A$, which we know must be true whenever the postulates are true.

As a slightly more complicated example of how these postulates are used, together with theorems already proved, consider the following:

**THEOREM II:**  If $A \cup B = B$, then $A \cap B = A$.

| | |
|---|---|
| $B = A \cup B$ | Given. |
| $A \cap B = A \cap (A \cup B)$ | Postulate 7(b) |
| $= (A \cap A) \cup (A \cap B)$ | Postulate 5(b) |
| $= A \cup (A \cap B)$ | Theorem I |
| $= (A \cap W) \cup (A \cap B)$ | Postulate 2(b) |
| $= A \cap (W \cup B)$ | Postulate 5(b). |

However,

| | |
|---|---|
| $(B \cup W) = (B \cup W) \cap (B \cup \bar{B})$ | Postulates 2(b), and 6 |
| $= B \cup (W \cap \bar{B})$ | Postulate 5(a) |
| $= B \cup \bar{B}$ | Postulate 2(b) |
| $= W$ | Postulate 6 |

so that

| | |
|---|---|
| $A \cap B = A \cap W$ | Substitution |
| $A \cap B = A$ | Postulate 2(b). |

Here we have proved a much less obvious statement to be true. Anyone who has studied high-school geometry will appreciate the fact that with an accumulation of such theorems, plus the original postulates, there is virtually no end to the numbers of new theorems that can be proved in this way. The interesting thing is that each of these theorems will ordinarily be true if one takes sets of real objects and combines and recombines them in the ways represented by ∪ and ∩. Remember that the algebra of sets is not about any particular set of sets, but about "sets" defined abstractly. Propositions about abstract sets will be true of real sets satisfying the postulates exactly as an expression in school algebra will be true when the symbols are turned into numbers. Just as school algebra is a mathematical model for solving problems about real quantities, and one can find characteristics of real figures using the model of Euclidean geometry, so does the algebra of sets become a useful mathematical model in some real situations. One striking example is the theory underlying the large electronic computers, although very many other instances could be given. Set theory is providing a useful model for areas in psychology as well, especially in problems of learning, perception, and cognition.

Although this very hurried sketch of set theory cannot possibly give you any real facility with the set-language, perhaps it will help when the essential ideas about sets recur in later chapters. However, the real motive that underlies the discussion of sets is that it permits us to go on to a topic of great importance, both in statistics and in scientific enterprise in general: the study of mathematical relations.

### 1.14 SET PRODUCTS AND RELATIONS

The business of science or of any other field of knowledge is to discover and describe relationships among things. Everybody knows what is meant by a relationship or connection among objects or phenomena; in order to use language itself we must group our experiences into classes or sets (using the nouns and adjectives) and then state relationships linking one kind of thing with another (using the verbs). However, it is very important that we settle on a formal definition of what makes a **mathematical relation** before turning to other matters. It will be seen that the idea of a mathematical relation is nothing more than an extension of the ideas of set and subset.

Just as a set is defined as a collection of objects, it is also possible to define a special kind of set made up of *pairs of objects.* Let a pair of objects be symbolized by (*a,b*), where *a* is a member of some set *A*, and *b* is a member of some set *B*. Each pair of objects is thought of as **ordered,** meaning that the way the objects are listed in a pair is important. Every day we encounter such ordered pairs of objects, where the two members are distinguished from each other by the role they play: husband-wife pairs, right and left hands, first and second movie in a double-feature, and so on. For an ordered pair (*a,b*), the order of listing is significant for the role played by each element of the pair, so that the pair (*a,b*) is not necessarily the same as the pair (*b,a*).

Now suppose that we have two sets, *A* and *B*. *All possible* pairs (*a,b*) are found, each pair associating a member of *A* with a member *B*. This set of all possible pairings of an *a* ∈ *A* with a *b* ∈ *B* is called the **Cartesian product,** or the **set product,** of *A* and *B*:

$$A \times B = \{(a,b) | a \in A, b \in B\}.$$

The product $A \times B$ is only a set, but this time the elements are the possible pairs, as symbolized by $(a,b)$. The product $B \times A$ would be different set, with members $(b,a)$.

This idea of a set of ordered pairs originated with the mathematician and philosopher Descartes (1596–1650; Latin: Cartesius), who used it as the foundation of analytic geometry; hence the name *Cartesian* product. The "product" part of the name is attributable to the fact that the total number of possible pairs is always the number of members of $A$ *times* the number of members of $B$.

As a simple example of a set product, consider these two sets:

$$A = \{\text{Mary, Susan, Tom, Bill}\}$$
$$B = \{\text{Smith, Jones, Brown, Adams}\}.$$

The product of the two sets, $A \times B$, is nothing more than the set of all possible pairings of one of the first names with one of the last names:

$A \times B = \{$(Mary, Smith) (Mary, Jones) (Mary, Brown) (Mary, Adams)
(Susan, Smith) (Susan, Jones) (Susan, Brown) (Susan, Adams)
(Tom, Smith) (Tom, Jones) (Tom, Brown) (Tom, Adams)
(Bill, Smith) (Bill, Jones) (Bill, Brown) (Bill, Adams)$\}$.

Notice that a pair $(b,a)$ such as (Jones, Mary) is not a member of the product, since the first element must be a member of $A$ (first names) and the second a member of $B$ (last names). This illustrates that the ordering of a pair is important in determining which pairs are included.

The pairs making up $A \times B$ can also be shown graphically, as in Figure 1.14.1. In this graph, each point formed by the intersection of a vertical line with one of the horizontal lines symbolizes one pair in the set $A \times B$.

It is also possible to talk about the product of a set with itself. That is, if we have the set $A$, then $A \times A$ consists

FIG. 1.14.1

of all possible pairings of a member of $A$ with a member of $A$. For the example just given,

$A \times A = \{$(Mary, Mary) (Mary, Susan) (Mary, Tom) (Mary, Bill)
(Susan, Mary) (Susan, Susan) (Susan, Tom) (Susan, Bill)
(Tom, Mary) (Tom, Susan) (Tom, Tom) (Tom, Bill)
(Bill, Mary) (Bill, Susan) (Bill, Tom) (Bill, Bill)$\}$.

Again, it *does* make a difference which member comes first in a pair; thus the pair (Mary, Susan) is not considered the same as (Susan, Mary).

One of the most important examples of a Cartesian product is known to anyone who has taken high-school algebra. Suppose that we have the set $R$, which is the set of all possible **real numbers** (that is, the set of all numbers that can be put into exact one-to-one correspondence with points on a straight line). We take the product $R \times R$, which is the set of all pairings of *two* real numbers. Any given pair might be symbolized $(x,y)$, where $x$ is a number called the value on the $X$-coordinate or "abscissa," and $y$ is a number standing for value on the $Y$-coordinate, or "ordinate." This should be a familiar idea, since the product $R \times R$ is used any time one plots points on a graph or a curve. The first set $R$ is the "$X$-axis," and the second set $R$ is the "$Y$-axis" of the "Cartesian coordinates."

FIG. 1.14.2

When a pair such as $(5,1)$ is used to locate a point on a graph, it means that the number 5 is the element from the first set of numbers, and 1 from the second set. The entire set $R \times R$ consists of all points that one *could* locate in the plane where the two axes of the graph lie. Pictorially, the product $R \times R$ and the pair $(5,1)$ might be shown as in Figure 1.14.2. Regardless of whether you are dealing with pairs of objects, as in the first example, or pairs of numbers, as in the second, the idea of a Cartesian product is the same: the set of all ordered pairs, the first being a member of one specified set, and the second a member of another.

The sets in a Cartesian product need not contain the same kinds of elements. To illustrate a product of a set of objects with a set of numbers, let

$$A = \{a|a \text{ is a man living in the United States}\}$$
$$G = \{g|g \text{ is a weight in pounds}\}.$$

Then

$$A \times G = \{(a,g)|a \, \epsilon \, A, \, g \, \epsilon \, G\},$$

the set of all possible pairings of a man with a weight. If each man were represented by a point along a horizontal axis, and each weight by a point along a vertical axis, then each intersection of a vertical with a horizontal line stands for a possible man-weight pair, such as (John Jones, 165 pounds).

Given the idea of a product of two sets, then it is finally possible to state what we mean by a **mathematical relation**:

**A mathematical relation on two sets $A$ and $B$ is a subset of $A \times B$.**

In other words, any mathematical relation is a subset of a Cartesian product, *some specific set of pairs out of all possible pairs*. At first blush, this seems to be an extremely trivial idea, but it actually is a remarkably subtle and elegant way to approach a difficult problem.

We often speak loosely of the husband-wife relation, the hand-fits-glove relation, the pitcher-catcher relation, the height-weight relation, the relation of the side of a square to its area, and so on. In each case, the fact of the relation implies that *some* pairs out of all possible pairs make a statement "$a$ plays such and such a role relative to $b$" a true one. For any "husband" some, but not all, women qualify as "wife"; for any hand, only certain gloves fit; for any side-length of a square, only a certain number can be the area.

On the other hand, a few words of warning are in order before this topic is pushed further. It is important not to confuse the idea of a mathematical relation with the idea of a *true relationship* among objects. All relationships that are true in our experience can be represented as mathematical relations, but it is *not necessarily true* that every mathematical relation we might invent must correspond to a real relationship among things. Furthermore, several different relationships, meaning quite different things in our ordinary experience, may show up as the *same* mathematical relation, in that exactly the same pairs qualify for the relation. For example, it *might* happen that for some set of men and some set of women, the relationship "*a* is married to *b*" would involve exactly the same pairs as "*a* files a joint income tax return with *b*." The two *relations* would be identical, but the *relationship* represented means something quite different in each instance.

## 1.15  SPECIFYING RELATIONS

Being a set, a mathematical relation can be specified in either of the two ways used for any set. In the first place, a relation may be specified by a listing of all pairs that qualify for the relation. In the example of Section 1.14, the set $A$ was four first names, and the set $B$ was four last names. In this circumstance the relation $L$ *might* be

$$L = \{(\text{Mary, Jones}) \ (\text{Susan, Brown}) \ (\text{Tom, Adams}) \ (\text{Bill, Smith})\}.$$

This relation could also be displayed graphically (Fig. 1.15.1), the filled dots in the diagram showing the pairs in the relation $L$; all the remaining pairs in $A \times B$ but not in $L$ are shown unfilled.

FIG. 1.15.1          FIG. 1.15.2

Quite often, the graph itself serves as a kind of symbolic listing when the pairs are too numerous to list explicitly. For example, for the product $R \times R$, the curve in Figure 1.15.2 stands in place of a listing of $(x,y)$ pairs. In this instance, the number-pair represented by any point falling *on* the curve is *in* the relation.

The point's two coordinates denote the particular pair of numbers. This specifies the relation unambiguously, and really serves the purpose of a list. The test of membership for any pair of numbers is whether or not the corresponding point falls exactly on the curve.

Plots of other relations may show up as areas or sectors rather than curves, as for example, in Figure 1.15.3. Here, any pair of numbers $(x,y)$, such as $(7,5)$, qualifies for the relation if the corresponding point falls into the shaded sector of the graph.

FIG. 1.15.3

The more usual way of specifying a relation is by a statement of the **rule** by which a pair qualifies. For example, if $A$ is the set of all women, and $B$ is the set of all men, the relation $S$ might be specified by

$$S = \{(a,b) \ \epsilon \ (A \times B) | a \text{ is married to } b\}.$$

If $A$ is the set of all men in the United States, and $G$ is the set of all weights in

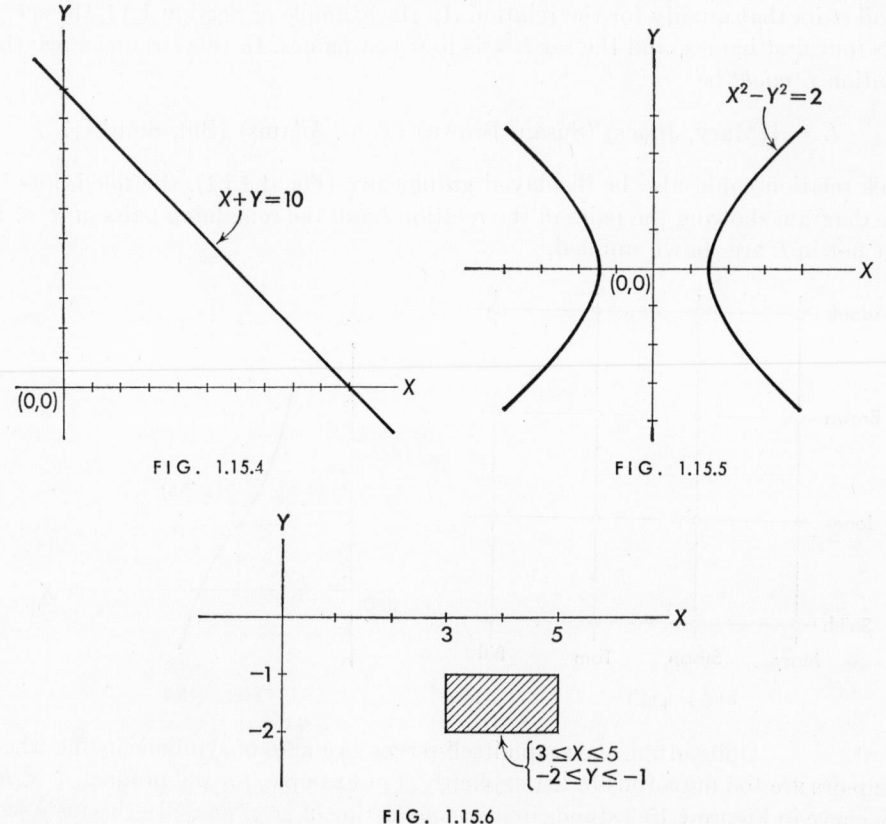

FIG. 1.15.4

FIG. 1.15.5

FIG. 1.15.6

pounds, a relation $T$ might be specified by

$$T = \{(a,g) \; \epsilon \; A \times G | \text{the weight of } a \text{ is } g\}.$$

If the Cartesian product is $R \times R$, then the most common way to specify a relation is by a mathematical expression giving the qualifications a number-pair must meet: As examples, consider

$$F = \{(x,y) | x + y = 10\}$$
$$V = \{(x,y) | x^2 - y^2 = 2\}$$
$$Z = \{(x,y) | 3 \leq x \leq 5, \; -2 \leq y \leq -1\}$$

which are but a few of the countless ways of specifying a relation by a mathematical rule. For these numerical relations, the corresponding graphs are shown in Figures 1.15.4–6.

## 1.16   THE "ALL" AND THE "EMPTY" RELATIONS

Any discussion of sets includes a definition of a universal set and the empty set, and the same is true for relations. The universal relation is called the "all-relation." The all-relation is simply $A \times B$,

$$\text{the all-relation} = \{(a,b) \; \epsilon \; A \times B\} = A \times B.$$

In the all-relation, every single member of $a$ is paired with every single member of $b$.

On the other hand, the empty relation includes *no* pairs $(a,b)$:

$$\emptyset = \{(a,b) \; \epsilon \; A \times B | (a,b) \notin A \times B\}.$$

## 1.17   THE IMPORTANCE OF MATHEMATICAL RELATIONS

Scientific knowledge is a body of statements about true relationships. Putting the matter very crudely, you might say that science is concerned with questions of "what goes with what." Given a particular set of phenomena, some, but not all, of another set of phenomena may occur, and there exists a relationship that can be described as a mathematical relation. For example, given a set of varieties of animals, each variety can breed with some, but not all, of the others; this relation in part gives rise to notions of species and evolutionary connections. The fact that some chemical elements will displace other elements in a compound can be stated as a relation, giving rise to many important ideas in chemistry. In any text in elementary psychology there are many examples of well-established relations, such as that between the spacing of trials in a given learning task and the rate of forgetting of materials once learned, to give only one example.

Any relation that corresponds to a true relationship among things is, quite literally, a statement of "what goes with what." If there is some set of phenomena $A$, and another set of phenomena $B$, and if the *all* relation is true for $A$

and *B*, *anything can go with anything;* specifying an element of *A* does not narrow down the possibilities for elements of *B* at all. On the other hand, suppose that a true relation exists between these two sets of phenomena, so that only a certain *proper subset* of *B* can be paired with any given element of *A*. Now if you give me the element *a*, I will be able to narrow down the possibilities for *b* more than if I knew nothing at all about the element *a*. One might say that when there is a true relation *A* provides *information* about *B*, and that knowledge of an element *a* increases my ability to *predict* the element of *B*. The goal of scientific knowledge is the ability to predict one thing *exactly* from knowledge of another, and the discovery of a true relation is the first step in this direction.

Given the discovery of some true relation, scientific enterprise does not stop, however. Ideally, the scientist hopes to study and understand the relation well enough so that finally he may be able to state a rule, or principle, that summarizes and generalizes the original finding. He also tries to account for the existence of the relation by appealing to other known or theoretical relations; this is one role of a scientific theory, which is a relatively small set of postulated relations from which it is possible to deduce and account for a great many other relations observable among things.

When a relation among sets of phenomena has been found and studied enough that the scientist knows *exactly* the conditions under which the relation may be observed, he can sometimes give the relation a *rule* completely specifying it. True relations that can be given mathematical rules are sometimes called **laws.** The laws of physical science are mathematical specifications of relations that will always be true under the appropriate circumstances. For example, Ohm's law for direct current can be stated as follows: for a given voltage *v* and a given resistance *r*, then the current *c* is $c = v/r$. Notice how this is a way of specifying a relation: let the voltage, for example, be fixed at some number. Then given the resistance *r*, what is the current *c* that is paired with *r* in this relation? The only number pairs that qualify are those for which $c = v/r$, or $cr = v$, so that this physical law is a mathematical specification of a relation. This law specifies that given *v*, not only are some *possible* $(r,c)$ pairs disqualified, but also that *only one c* can be paired with each *r*.

We might also interpret Ohm's law as a relation in another way. Think of the set of all $(r,c)$ pairs as itself a set with elements *a*. Then the law says that the only elements *v* that can be associated with a given pair *a* are those for which $cr = v$. Thus $(a,v) = ((10,5),2)$ does not qualify for the relation, although $(a,v) = ((2,5),10)$ does so.

Laws in the physical and other sciences are, obviously, often more complicated than the simple relation just given. Fortunately, the mathematical idea of a relation is extremely general and can be extended to more than just two sets. For three sets, one may define the Cartesian product $A \times B \times C$ as the set of all ordered triples, $(a,b,c)$. A relation on the three sets is *some subset* of $A \times B \times C$. If there are some *N* sets, *A*, *B*, $\cdots$, *T*, the product is $A \times B \times \cdots \times T$, consisting of all *n-tuples* of ordered elements $(a, b, \cdots, t)$. The more complicated scientific relations are described in terms of these "larger" set-products. However, the principle is the same: a mathematical relation is some subset of a Cartesian product, and is specified by a listing procedure or by a statement of the rule that qualifies the *n*-tuple for the relation.

## 1.18   THE DOMAIN AND RANGE OF A RELATION

In discussing relations, we need some way to distinguish between the different sets of elements that play different roles. In a relation that is a subset of $A \times B$, it may be true that only *some* elements *a* enter into one or more $(a,b)$ pairs; what we want is a way to discuss those elements of $A$ that actually *are* paired with *b* elements in the relation itself. This subset of elements of $A$ actually figuring in the relation is called the **domain,** and it is defined as follows:

**Given some relation** $S$, **which is a subset of** $A \times B$, **then**

$$\text{domain of } S = \{a \in A \,|\, (a,b) \in S, \text{ for at least one } b \in B\}.$$

Notice that **the domain of the relation** $S$ **is always a subset of** $A$. The domain includes each element in $A$ that actually plays a role in the relation, vis-à-vis some *b*.

For example, let $A$ be the set of all men, and $B$ the set of all women. Let the relation $S \subseteq A \times B$ be "*a* is married to *b*." Then the domain of $S$ is "all married men," since only the subset of married men in $A$ can figure in at least one pair $(a,b)$ in the relation.

As another example, suppose that the product is $R \times R$, and the relation is given by the rule

$$C = \{(x,y)\,|\,x^2 + y^2 = 4\}.$$

What is the domain of $C$? The very largest number that $x$ could be is 2 for any $(x,y)$ pair in $C$, and the very smallest number is $-2$. Thus, $x$ can be any number between $-2$ and 2 inclusive, but all other numbers in $R$ are excluded. Hence,

$$\text{domain of } C = \{x \in R\,|\,-2 \leq x \leq 2\}.$$

The idea of the **range** of a relation is very similar to that of the domain, except that it applies to members of the set $B$, the second members of pairs $(a,b)$.

**The set of all elements** *b* **in** $B$ **paired with at least one** *a* **in** $A$ **in the relation** $S$ **is called the range of** $S$:

$$\text{range of } S = \{b \in B\,|\,(a,b) \in S, \text{ for at least one } a \in A\}.$$

In the example of the relation "*a* is married to *b*," the range is the set of all married women, a subset of $B$. In the example of the relation $C$, for $y$ to be a real number the value of $y$ must lie between $-2$ and 2, and so the range is

$$\text{range of } C = \{y \in R\,|\,-2 \leq y \leq 2\}.$$

It is entirely possible for the domain to be equal to $A$, and for the range to be equal to $B$, in some examples. In others, both the range and the domain will be proper subsets of $A$ and $B$, respectively. On the other hand, neither the range nor the domain may be empty unless the relation itself is empty.

## 1.19 FUNCTIONAL RELATIONS

We come now to one of the most important mathematical concepts, from the points of view both of mathematics itself and of its applications in science. This is the idea of a **functional relation,** or **function.** The definition we will use is:

**A relation is said to be a *functional relation* or a *function* if each member of the domain is paired with *one and only one* member of the range.**

That is, in a functional relation each $a$ entering into the relation has *exactly one pair-mate b*. Thus a function is just a special kind of relation. In some mathematical writing this is called a "single-valued function," and a relation is a "multiple-valued function." However, the author feels that it is useful to call only the former a "function."

This idea will become clearer if we inspect some relations that are, and that are not, functions:

Given $A$ as the set of all men and $B$ the set of all women in some society, the relation

$$\{(a,b) \epsilon A \times B | \text{``a is married to b"}\}$$

is a function *if the society is monogamous*, so that each man may have only one wife. Here, each member of the domain, a married man, has one and only one wife, a member of the range. If, on the other hand, the society is polygamous so that a man may have two or more wives, then the relation is not necessarily a function.

Consider the relation defined on pairs of real numbers:

$$\{(x,y)|x^2 = y\}.$$

This relation is a function; corresponding to each $x$, there is one and only one $y$, which is the same as the square of $x$. Thus, $x = 2$ can be paired only with $y = 4$, $x = 5$ only with $y = 25$, and so on. Contrast this with the relation

$$\{(x,y)|x^2 = y^2\}.$$

In this case, the pair $(2,2)$ qualifies, but so does the pair $(2,-2)$. Each value of $x$ can be associated with *two* values of $y$ by this rule, and so the relation is not a function. Figures 1.19.1–2 show how these two relations can be plotted. Notice how in the first example a vertical line drawn from any point on the $X$ axis will intercept the curve in at most *one* place, while in the second example *two* interceptions are possible. The same criterion may be applied to the plot of any relation between two numbers in order to determine if it is a function.

There is nothing in the definition of a function that limits the number of times an element *b in the range* may appear in a pair. Thus, in the marriage example, the relation is still a function even though the same woman is married to several men, and in the relation with rule $x^2 = y$, the same $y$ value is associated with two $x$ values (for example, $y = 4$ is paired both with $x = 2$ and $x = -2$). It follows that a given rule relating $x$ and $y$ may specify a function for $(x,y)$ pairs, but may specify a nonfunctional relation for $(y,x)$ pairs.

Functions are relations, and hence are **sets of pairs,** and the set itself should be distinguished from the rule specifying the set. The distinction is

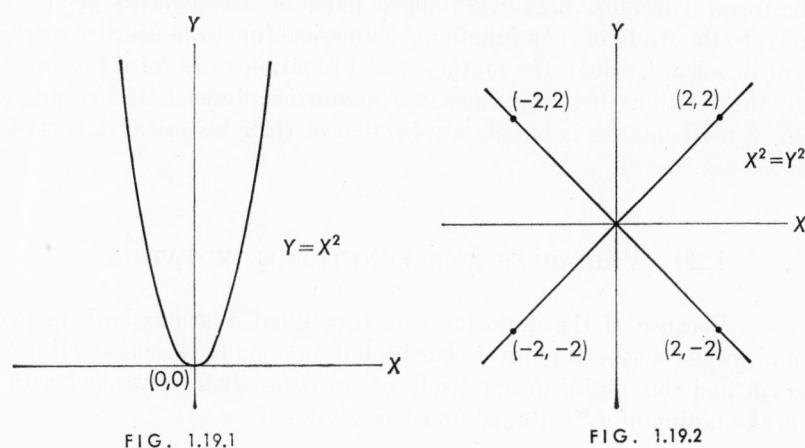

FIG. 1.19.1                    FIG. 1.19.2

not always clear in mathematical writing, where commonly both the set and the rule are called functions. However, if you remember that the function itself is the set of pairs, you should have little difficulty in deciding which is meant in a discussion using this word.

A very large part of mathematics deals with functions and the properties of their rules as specifications of what the set itself, or certain subsets, must be like. When a mathematician describes the "curve" or plot of a numerical function on the basis of its mathematical rule, he is really saying something about how the set is delimited by the rule. Any curve that can be plotted for a function can be regarded as a symbolic listing of pairs of numbers.

The function idea, of course, applies to products of *any* sets. As we have seen, it is quite possible to describe a function where the elements are pairs of people. Other examples can be given where a variety of other things are paired. However, for mathematicians the most interesting functions involve numbers, either as the range of the function, or as both range and domain.

An important kind of function is one having numbers as the range and a **set of sets** as the domain. This is called a **set function.** For example, suppose that the name of a state in the United States is given to a set of all persons residing in that state on January 1, 1960. Then the whole collection of the fifty state-sets is a set of sets; let us call this set of sets $A$. For the moment, let the symbol $P$ stand for the set of all *positive* numbers. Then the product $A \times P$ is the set of all pairings of a *set* with a positive number. Consider the relation:

$$\{(a,p) \, \epsilon \, A \times P | \text{``the total population of } a \text{ was } p \text{ on January 1, 1960''}\}.$$

This relation is a set function, since associated with each and every set of state-residents there is one and only one population number $p$ for the date January 1, 1960. One of the most important applications of the idea of a set function is a probability function, to be introduced in the next chapter.

Nevertheless, most of the interesting and useful functions relate numbers to numbers, since their rules can be given quite precise algebraic or symbolic form. The most highly developed parts of mathematics are devoted, essentially, to the study of such functions. Numerical functions are also extremely important in science, where the mathematical function rules form precise statements of the relations between measured quantities. Indeed, the emphasis on functions in mathematics is largely a reflection of their historical importance in physical science.

## 1.20   VARIABLES AND FUNCTIONAL NOTATION

Because of the importance of functional relations both in mathematics and science a special notation has been developed for discussing functions, and we will find this useful in our study of statistics. Before we deal with this notation, the notion of a "variable" must be clarified:

**A variable is a symbol that can be replaced by any one of the elements of some specified set. The particular set is called the range of the variable.**

Note carefully that the variable is only a stand-in or placeholder, which can *always* be replaced by a particular element from some set of possibilities. Thus, if $x$ is a variable, wherever $x$ appears in a mathematical expression it can be replaced by *one* element from some specified set. This idea should be a familiar one, since school algebra deals largely with variables ranging over the real numbers. Throughout our discussion of set theory, a variable such as $X$ symbolized a set, which could be any member of some *set of sets;* the variable $x$ stood for *some particular member* of the set $X$.

Variables may range over any well-defined set. For example, the variable $C$ might symbolize any of a set of colors; the variable $g$ might range over the 365 different dates in the year; the variable $y$ might be any one of the infinite set of possible temperatures in Farenheit degrees. When someone says, "You are a no-good blankety-blank!" he is using "blankety-blank" much like a variable, standing for any one of a set of expressions; the range is left to your imagination.

Despite its name, a variable is not something that varies, or wiggles, or scurries around while you work with it. If a variable is used as a symbol in a given mathematical discussion, then replacing the variable by some specific element of its range at one place requires you to replace it with the same element *wherever* the variable appears. The same variable may appear many times in the same discussion, and it retains its identity throughout; if $x$ is replaced by some number in one place, it is replaced by the same number in all other appearances. The name "variable" actually comes from the fact that a symbol represents "various" values. This distinguishes such symbols from mathematical *constants*. Unlike a variable, which can stand for a variety of things, a symbol that can be replaced by *one and only one* number in a given expression is a constant for the expression. For example, consider the well-known mathematical expression

$$c = 2\pi r.$$

The symbols $c$ and $r$ here are variables; each stands for any one of an infinite set of *positive numbers*. However, the symbol $\pi$ is a constant, which can be replaced only with a *particular* number. Regardless of the values assumed by $r$ and $c$, $\pi$ is the same. Note also, in this instance, that $c$ and $r$ are *functionally related* variables: the value that $c$ can assume is dictated by the value of $r$ (and vice versa).

Most of the variables that will concern us here represent sets of numbers, so that given some range of numbers, $x$ stands for any specific member of the range. For instance, the statement, "let $X$ be a variable ranging over the real numbers" means that $X$ is a stand-in for any one of the numbers that can be represented as points on a line. The $X$-axis in a graph is a representation of the range of this variable. When one number, say 10, is selected to replace $X$, then we say "$X$ assumes the value 10." Quite often we want to discuss several variables $X$, $Y$, $Z$, and so on, simultaneously. Each of these symbolizes one of a range of numbers, but *not necessarily the same number, or even the same range of numbers*. For example, the $X$-axis and the $Y$-axis in a graph each symbolize ranges of possible numbers; when $X$ assumes the particular value $x$, and $Y$ the particular value $y$, we have the pair of numbers $(x,y)$.

Sometimes the range of a numerical variable is specified as other than all real numbers. For example, one might have the variable $X$, followed by the statement $3 \leq X \leq 5$, meaning that the only values that $X$ symbolizes are those lying between 3 and 5 inclusive ($X$ *ranges* between 3 and 5 inclusive). Or perhaps $X$ is a variable that is integral, meaning that the only numbers that can replace the symbol $X$ are whole numbers.

The mathematical use of the term "variable" here is slightly different from its use in some scientific writing. A "variable" in science is often a name for a *factor* or *influence* that enters into our observation or measurement of a phenomenon; it is something that makes a difference in something else. However, as you can see, the mathematical use of the term "variable" is much more restricted than this; it is simply a symbol, usually for any one of some set of numerical values. There is no connotation that the variable means something or does something. Nevertheless, mathematical variables are useful devices for science, since they enter into the mathematical rules for true relations. Here they are stand-ins for the measured values of real "variables," which do mean something.

Variables are the basis for the notation most commonly used for functions. Given the variables $x$ and $y$, each with specified range, a relation between the variables is a subset of all possible $(x,y)$ pairs. If this relation is a function, then this fact is symbolized by any of the statements such as

$$y = f(x)$$
$$y = G(x)$$
$$y = \varphi(x)$$

and so on. In words, these expressions all say:

"There is a rule that pairs each possible value
of $x$ with at most one value of $y$."

The different Roman and Greek letters that precede the symbol $(x)$ simply indicate different rules, giving different functions or subsets of all $(x,y)$ pairs. *This notation does nothing more than assert that the function rule exists.* It says "Give me the rule, and the value of $x$, and I'll give you $y$."

Notice that a symbol $f(x)$ actually stands for a value of $y$: this is the value of $y$ that is paired with $x$ by the function rule. The symbol $f(x)$ is *not* the function, but an indicator that the function rule exists, turning a value $x$ into some value $f(x)$, or $y$.

Sometimes the function rule itself is stated:

$$y = f(x) = x^3 - 2x^2 + 4$$
$$y = G(x) = k \log (x), \qquad x > 0$$
$$y = \varphi(x) = \frac{1}{\sqrt{2\pi}\sigma} \exp \left[ - \frac{(x - \mu)^2}{2\sigma^2} \right]$$

are but a few of the countless function rules that might be stated for the variables $x$ and $y$, both ranging over the real numbers. The terms such as $k$, $e$, $\sigma$, and $\mu$ in these rules are simply constants having the same value in a given function rule regardless of the value that $x$ symbolizes. In each example, the function rule stated permits the association of some $y$ value with a given value of $x$. *Be sure to notice that these expressions are the rules, not the functions.*

Functional notation has been shown here only for the case where both $x$ and $y$ range over numbers, primarily because this is the most common situation in mathematics. However, the same general form can be used for other functions. Suppose that the variable $a$ stands for any one of a set of men, and the variable $y$ stands for any one of the set of positive numbers that are possible scores on an intelligence test. Granted that each man must have one and only one score, then a function exists relating $a$ and $y$. This could be symbolized by

$$y = f(a)$$

where $a$ designates a particular man. We would be hard put, however, to state the rule for this function, and so we cannot go beyond the simple assertion that a function exists, unless we undertook to list each man paired with his score. In general, such functions are a pain in the neck to specify, and this accounts for some of the elaborate attempts made in science to describe relationships as numerical functions which *can* be given mathematical rules.

Once again, you are warned that the word "function" is often used to refer *both* to the set of pairs, which is actually the function, and the function rule, which specifies the set. In particular, when one says, "$Y$ is a function of $X$," he is making the assertion symbolized by $Y = f(X)$, that some rule exists pairing no more than one $Y$ with each $X$. Then he may go ahead to specify the function rule. On the other hand, when he talks about *the* function relating $X$ and $Y$, he is usually referring to the set of pairings of an $X$ with a $Y$ given by that rule.

## 1.21   INDEPENDENT AND DEPENDENT VARIABLES

It is customary to talk about the symbol for values in the **domain** of the function, values that come first in $(x,y)$ pairs, as the **independent variable,** or the **argument** of the function rule. In practice, this is the $X$ value known first, or given, if one is to find the $f(X)$ or $Y$ value. The variable $X$ is "independent" because its value can be anything in the domain of the function. However, given the value of $X$, and the rule, the value of $Y$ is completely determined, making $Y$ the **dependent variable.**

These terms have carried over into experimental practice: the feature in the experiment that one manipulates at will is often called the independent variable. Then the measured value standing for some other aspect of the phenomena, presumably determined by the initial manipulation, is called the dependent variable.

## 1.22   CONTINUOUS VARIABLES AND FUNCTIONS

In statistics it is often necessary to specify that a variable or a function is continuous. Unfortunately, an accurate definition of "continuous" requires more mathematics than many students can command at this point. However, the following way of thinking about continuous variables and functions, though not really adequate as a definition, will serve our purposes.

Consider a variable $x$. If there are two numbers $u$ and $v$ such that the range of $x$ is $u \leq x \leq v$, *all real numbers lying between u and v*, then $x$ is said to be continuous in the interval $\langle u,v \rangle$. If the variable $x$ is continuous over all possible intervals defined by pairs of real numbers $u$ and $v$, then $x$ is said to be continuous over the real numbers.

The idea of a **continuous function** is best conveyed by a picture of a curve without "gaps" or "breaks" in terms of values of $y$; that is, a function $y = f(x)$ is continuous in the interval of numbers $u \leq x \leq v$ if each and every number between $f(u)$ and $f(v)$ also occurs in the range of $y$ values. For each $x$ in the interval, some particular number $y$ can be found by the function rule, if the function is continuous in the interval. A function that is continuous over all possible intervals of real numbers, so that the domain includes all real numbers, is called simply "continuous." Thus, for example, the function given by $y = 3x^2 - 5$ is continuous over all real numbers, since for every possible $x$ there exists a determinable $y$, and hence all real values of $x$ are in the domain. On the other hand, a function with the rule $y = 1/(x + 1)$ is **discontinuous,** since for $x = -1$ there is no exactly determinable value of $y$ that can be associated with $x$, and hence the domain does not include $x = -1$.

The study of discontinuous functions is an important part of mathematics, but most of the functions that concern us here will either have a specified number of possible values that $x$ can assume, or will be continuous over the real numbers.

### 1.23 FUNCTIONS WITH SEVERAL INDEPENDENT VARIABLES

The idea of a numerical function can be extended without difficulty to the case with two or more independent variables. Here the domain of the function is a set of *pairs* of numbers. Given variables $x$, $y$, and $z$, each ranging over the real numbers, the statement

$$y = f(x,z)$$

means that a rule exists such that given any pair of numbers $x$ and $z$ in the domain, then the value of $y$ is known. For example, it may be that

$$y = f(x,z) = 3x^2 - 2z^2 + 4,$$

so that given this rule, and letting $x$ and $z$ assume some pair of values $(x,z)$, we have completely determined the value of $y$. Or, it may be that a different rule applies, such as

$$y = g(x,z) = 2(x)^z,$$

making this second function a very different subset from among all $(x,z,y)$ triples.

In general, if there is some function with two or more independent variables, and we fix one or more variables at a constant value but leave the other variables free to take on different values, then this also results in a function. For example, consider the function having the following rule:

$$y = xz.$$

Suppose that $x$ were fixed at the value 3, while $z$ can take on any value. Then we have the function

$$y = 3z,$$

which has only one independent variable. The particular mathematical rule for $y = f(z)$ in this case depends upon the value chosen for $x$. The same idea applies to functions with any number of independent variables: fixing the value of one or more variables results in a new function, where the fixed values appear as constants in the mathematical rule.

### 1.24 FUNCTIONS AND PRECISE PREDICTION

In the scientist's use of mathematics, numerical variables symbolize real quantities or magnitudes that can be found (potentially) from measurements of phenomena. Real relationships are summarized as mathematical relations, having some mathematical expression as the specifying rule. When the scientific fact is a true functional relation between quantities, then this fact is communicated in its most concise and elegant form by a statement of the function rule.

One of the goals of any science is prediction: given some set of known circumstances, what else can we expect to be true? If the scientific relation is functional in form, then *precise* prediction is possible; given the true value of $X$ in the domain, precisely one value of $Y$ will be observed, all other things being constant. However, in this qualification, "all other things being constant," lies one of the central problems of any science.

Each of us, scientist or layman, has learned from infancy that there are relationships in the world about us; things go together, and some things lead to other things. On the other hand, everyone knows that precise prediction of the world about him is virtually impossible. Even given some information about an object or event, we never know *exactly* what its other properties will be. True enough, providing us with information may let us restrict the *range* of things we *expect* to observe, but the possibility of exact prediction is almost unknown in the everyday world. Nevertheless, the more advanced sciences are very successful in describing relationships *as though* they were mathematical functions. How has this come about? What does the scientist do that makes it possible for him to make precise predictions from known situations, when the world of the man on the street is such a disorderly and unpredictable affair?

It seems safe to say that the world is full of marvelously complicated relationships and that any event we experience must have its character determined by a vast number of influences. Some of these may exert major forces on what we observe, and others may be quite minor in shaping a given event. Most scientists would subscribe to the idea that, ultimately, if we knew the values of all of the independent variables, all of the influences that go into the determination of an event, and the rule that relates these variables to the event itself, then precise prediction would always be possible. It may be that given the complete information about the circumstances, all true relations are functional. Even if this is true, however, it does the scientist little good because he is never given all of the information. On the other hand, *if $Y$ is, ultimately, a function of many independent variables, $X$, $Z$, $W$, · · · , and if it really were possible to hold everything constant except $X$ and $Y$, then we should observe a functional relation between $X$ and $Y$.* The scientist, who searches for precise functional relations among all of this real-world confusion, *must* restrict the kinds of things he studies, and the situations in which he studies them. Only through controlled experimentation is one able to observe something like precise, functional relations. Ideally, a controlled experiment is a device for observing the consequences of the variation of some things on the measured value of another thing, with all other factors held constant. The ability to make precise predictions is bought by paying the price of careful experimental controls.

Even so, the experiment has never been done where all the "other" things that might make a difference in the result have been controlled. Even though the experiment is a marvel of ingenuity, it is never possible to make several observations under truly identical conditions. Even the act of observation itself may influence the outcome. Fortunately, however, the ideal of a controlled experiment can at least be approximated. In the first place, some features attending different observations of the same phenomena are more or less irrelevant: the relation emerging from the data is more or less the same whether or not these features are controlled.

Nonetheless, the discovery of the irrelevances attending any relation, the things that safely can be ignored, is not the smallest problem of a science. It took a man of Galileo's intellectual stature to realize that some of the really obvious differences between a feather and a stone are quite irrelevant if we want to know how quickly each will fall from a given height. How many centuries it must have taken man to learn what to ignore before even the simplest physical relationships were determined!

Of course, other variables are quite relevant and do obscure the presence of functional relations unless they are controlled (taken at constant value) or otherwise represented systematically in the experiment. For example, we might, as Torricelli did, observe a relation between altitude and the height of a column of mercury in a glass tube (a simple barometer). We might also infer that this relation gives an indication of the air pressure at any given point. Suppose, however, that in discovering the relation we took the readings of our barometer for various places *and* times; once on a mountain top in a period of clear sunny weather, and again at sea-level just before a storm. A relation of sorts would still emerge between altitude and the barometer reading, but we would probably not find the true functional relation. Things beside altitude influence the barometer reading; in particular, the weather conditions. Only when various altitudes are studied under exactly the same weather conditions will the true functional relation begin to show up. Then, once the function relating altitude and barometric reading is known for a *given* weather condition, the *change* in this function for different weather conditions can be studied. Finally, we might find the function showing how *both* altitude and atmospheric conditions determine the mercury barometer's height, other things being equal. The two methods suggested here, control and systematic variation, are the time-honored strategies for finding relations and refining them into functional relations.

Even primitive man must have noticed some of the connections that eventually became physical laws, although he had neither the accumulated experience nor the symbols to let him express and refine his observations. Nevertheless, the irrelevancies were gradually weeded away and the factors that affected the observed relation were discovered. In the centuries that led up to modern physics the point was finally reached where mathematical expressions relating $X$ and $Y$ could be stated, giving at least a good estimate of the $Y$ value that goes with any $X$, under the appropriate conditions. The first triumphs of modern physics were the laws that gave precise, functional form to these relations.

However, are the functions specified by physical laws really true? The answer is both yes and no, depending on what you mean by "really." If you mean, "Is the prediction of the actual value of an observation as precise as the mathematical rule suggests?" then the answer is no. As we have already noted, such laws are modified by the phrases "other things being equal" or "holding other relevant variables constant." To observe phenomena in the relations that the laws embody, you must arrange things in a particular way. If it is possible to achieve this ideal condition for observation, then the phenomena should behave in *exactly* the predicted way. But this is a very large "if." It is well-nigh impossible to hold all the relevant variables constant in a real situation, and the best that the scientist can do is to restrict the range of these "nuisance" variables to the point where the relations that *are* observed are *almost* functions. This means that given $x$ only a very small range of $y$ values can occur. The value of $y$ observed is seldom exactly the value given by the function rule, but the discrepancy can be made so slight as to be negligible. Physics and related sciences are precise in this sense: function rules exist that permit predictions from known $x$ values to exact $y$ values which differ only negligibly from actual observation.

There is another important aspect to the fact that much of physical science deals with functional relations: the ability to describe relations mathematically gives great power and elegance to the scientists' results. The meaningless or misleading "gimcracks and gingerbread" that ornament ordinary verbal communication are stripped away, so that the scientist not only knows something exact, he can say it exactly, with a minimum of effort. Imagine what a precise scientific statement would be like without mathematical language! For example, consider Ohm's law once again. Without the ability to embody this function mathematically, the scientist could communicate only by giving all pairings of values, something like this: "Under fixed conditions, and with voltage equal to 3, then if resistance is equal to 1, current is equal to 3; resistance equal to 2, current equal to 1.5; resistance equal to 3, current equal to 1; . . . " and so on ad infinitum. Historians of science tell us that this way of transmitting scientific knowledge occurred in ancient times: for example, the Egyptians had observed a relationship among the sides of right triangles, but this was part of the lore of builders and surveyors and was known only for certain proportions among the sides, such as $3:4:5$. It remained for the Greeks to specify the relation mathematically in the famous Pythagorean theorem (the square of the hypotenuse is equal to the sum of the squares of the remaining sides), summarizing a fact applicable to every idealized right triangle in a plane.

Once the relations among a number of interdependent variables are put into precise mathematical form, then mathematical logic comes into play. Well-established principles serve as axioms for deducing new mathematical relations that should be true. In modern physics, for example, mathematics ranks alongside actual experimentation as a device for seeking knowledge about the physical world. Experimentation is, of course, the proof of the pudding, but the basic relationships among the things studied are so well known, and can be specified so exactly in mathematical form, that the physicist has great confidence that deductions from these basic principles will also be found true.

In summary, the laws of a quantitative science are usually function rules, giving the mathematical expressions that real measurements will satisfy. These laws are idealizations, of course, and always specify that the function specified will be observed *if* certain conditions are true. Nevertheless, within these limitations they are exact, and the ability to specify the relation by a mathematical function rule reflects this exactitude. Furthermore, once the interrelations among many kinds of measurements are put into mathematical form, then mathematical logic alone can take over the job of seeking out new relations for study.

## 1.25 Statistics in the Search for Relations

The other sciences, and notably the behavioral sciences, are not so far along in this use of mathematics to specify real relations. This does not mean that these scientists do not rejoice in known mathematical functions describing behavioral phenomena when these are found. And found they sometimes are; a large body of established relations, many of known mathematical forms, already exists in psychology. In order to appreciate this one has only to consider the 1362 pages of relations, many of them quite solidly established, outlined in the *Handbook of Experimental Psychology* (Stevens, 1951). Psychologists already know a great deal on which to base a full-fledged quantitative science of behavior, and it is not too much to expect that psychology will continue to evolve in this direction.

Nevertheless, the precision and control in experimentation often possible in the physical sciences is not attainable in most psychological experiments at this time, largely because the psychologist cannot specify exactly how variables relevant to his experimental result influence the things he actually observes. Among the foremost of the missing ingredients are numerical measurements for many important features we believe to underlie behavior. Measurement procedures exist for some things, it is true, but many of the really key concepts in behavioral science are captured only crudely, if at all, in numerical measurements at this time. We should not, of course, discount the possibility of establishing empirical relations using only qualitative or nonnumerical features of behavior; there is certainly nothing in the nature of scientific investigation that limits the interesting and important relations to those based on numerical measurements. We have just seen that it is perfectly possible to discuss a mathematical relation or even a function purely in terms of qualitatively defined sets, and there are unlimited possibilities for development of nonnumerical mathematical models appropriate for analyzing and describing certain kinds of behavior.

However, if we hope ever to develop powerful and general psychological theories following the example of the physical sciences, theories that permit far-reaching deductions from a few central concepts, then the problem of precise numerical measurement becomes an important one. A satisfactory scientific theory must permit deductions to be made that can then be subjected to empirical test, and for this to be possible the constructs entering into the theory must have *specified* relations with each other and with observable phenomena. The scientist's ability to make deductions within a theory actually depends on the fact that constructs are related to each other in known ways. Furthermore, his ability to check the deductions arrived at from the theory depends on known relations between what he observes and the various constructs entering into the theory. If either the relations among the constructs or, most important, the relation between the constructs and observables, cannot be made precise, then the problem of inferring the truth of the theory from obtained data is a most difficult one.

In short, the development of *powerful* and *testable* scientific theories depends on our ability to frame known relations in precise terms, and the greatest economy and exactitude of statement in mathematical form is possible when the variables involved represent numerical measurements. On the other hand, for a developing science like psychology, we cannot be sure of the relations of our constructs to each other, or of the relation of behavior to construct, which makes the experimental test of almost any theoretical proposition ambiguous. Do the data fail to agree with theoretical prediction because the theory is wrong, or because of a nonfunctional relation between measurements and one or more constructs in the theory? If we knew how to measure the relevant factors more precisely, and especially if we knew how to measure, represent, and control other factors which we wish to rule out of the experiment, would the result show more or less agreement with some theoretical prediction? The use of statistics can handle some, though not all, of the problems arising from our imperfect knowledge of how to measure important psychological factors. The psychologist often uses statistical methods on his experimental data to help him judge agreement with some theoretical prediction in spite of his inability to measure or to specify relations among factors he believes to be relevant to his result.

A second barrier to functional principles in a behavioral science is the lack of knowledge about the features in an observed relationship which *are* relevant. The psychologist is still trying to find the variables that are irrelevant and those that must either be manipulated or controlled if functional relations or their close approximations are to emerge from his data. He does this by studying the factors that seem to make a difference in (that is, are related to) behavior. However, in a real experiment, only a very few factors can be studied at one time. If behavior is, ultimately, the consequence of a vast number of influences, how does he know that what he observes in an experiment is the result of what he did, rather than of something completely out of his control? How does he know that his failure to find a certain kind of relation is not due to extraneous circumstances masking the true relationship?

In a field such as psychology, where the full range of relevant factors is quite unknown, statistics becomes a most useful tool. The theory of inferential statistics deals with the problem of "error," the failure of an observation to agree with a true situation. Error is the product of "chance," the influence of the innumerable uncontrolled factors determining an experimental result. The concept of "probability" is introduced to evaluate the likelihood that a given observation will disagree to a certain extent with a true value. Instead of being certain or nearly certain about the conclusions reached from observations, as the physical scientist often is, the scientist using statistics draws his conclusion much like a bet.

The gambler placing a bet is faced with a situation he knows very little about; heaven alone knows the real reasons why a coin comes up heads on a given toss or a particular card comes up on the third draw of a poker game. However, given that some things are true, it can be deduced that some things are more or less *likely* to occur, and still other things *unlikely*, regardless of the reasons why.

The gambler knows only that he has a given probability of being right, and also of being wrong, in a given decision, and the wise gambler places his bets accordingly. In the same general way, the scientist faced with data containing error uses deductions from the theory of probability in deciding how to interpret his results. However, his decisions usually deal with relationships among things, and he "wins" if he infers the true relation, and loses otherwise.

In succeeding sections we will continue to compare the task of the scientist to that of the gambler, and to show how statistical theory aids the scientist in making his own sorts of bets. In order to do this, we need some of the ideas of probability theory, to be introduced in the next chapter.

In summary, the discovery of fundamental relations that can be put into mathematical form, with formal mathematical rules like those of physics, depends upon our ability to observe the *right things* in the *right ways* under the *right circumstances*. Presumably, as we learn more and more about the relation of behavior to a variety of factors, we will begin to construct formal, deductively powerful theories based on a number of fundamental constructs and their relations. However, we are still limited by our ignorance of the factors that are relevant in accounting for particular kinds of behavior, and particularly by our lack of knowledge of the relations of those factors to each other and to the behavior we observe. Given these limitations, statistical methods are particularly useful in drawing conclusions from psychological data, and undoubtedly will continue to be so for many years to come. Experimental evidence is accumulating at a rapid rate in psychology, and efforts at constructing psychological theories with mathematical deductive power are constantly being made. However, it seems safe to say that it will be some time before there are psychological laws and theories on a par with those of physics. The absence of a general theory does *not* imply that known relations are missing or unimportant in psychology; the discovery and specification of relations is the process by which theories are built. Conversely, our present inability to give exact mathematical expression to many known relations does not mean that we have no theories or that they are irrelevant to our experimental work. Our theories, however, do not yet have the powerful, formal, deductive character we hope they eventually will have. We do not yet know how to measure and control most of the factors responsible for variability in our data. Until psychological knowledge reaches this level, the theory of statistics will continue to be useful to the psychologist both in his task of hunting for fundamental relations and in testing his current theories against evidence.

# ELEMENTARY PROBABILITY THEORY

2

Statistical inference involves statements about probability. Everyone has the words "probable" or "likely" in his vocabulary, and most of us have some notion of the meaning of statements such as "The probability is one-half that the coin will come up heads." However, in order to understand the methods of statistical inference and use them correctly, one must have some grasp of probability theory. This is a mathematical system, closely related to the algebra of sets described in the last chapter. Like many mathematical systems, probability theory becomes a useful model when its elements are identified with particular things, in this case the *outcomes of real or conceptual experiments*. Then the theory lets us deduce propositions about the likelihood of various outcomes, if certain conditions are true.

Originally, of course, the theory of probability was developed to serve as a model of games of chance—in this case the "experiment" in question was rolling a die, or spinning a roulette wheel, or dealing a hand from a deck of playing cards. As this theory developed, it became apparent that it could also serve as a model for many other kinds of things having little obvious connection with games, such as results in the sciences. One feature is common to most applications of this theory, however: the observer is uncertain about what the outcome of some observation will be, and he must eventually infer or guess what will happen. In particular, he needs to know what will happen *in the long run* if observations could be made indefinitely.

In this respect the scientist is like the gambler keeping track of the numbers coming up on a roulette wheel. At any given opportunity he can observe only the tiniest part of the total set of things he would like to know about. Given his human frailty as an observer, he must fall back on logic; *given* that certain things are true, he can make deductions about what *should* be true in the long run. The logical machinery of "in the long run" is formalized in the theory of proba-

bility. The scientist's statements about *all* observations of such and such phenomena are on a par with the gambler's; both are deductions about what should be
true, if the initial conditions are met. Furthermore, the gambler, the business man,
the engineer, the scientist, and, indeed, the man on the street must make decisions
based on incomplete evidence. Each does so in the face of risk about how good
those decisions will turn out to be. Probability theory alone does not tell any of
these people how they should decide, but it does give ways of evaluating the degree
of risk one takes for some decisions.

The theory of probability is very closely tied to the theory of sets.
Indeed, the main undefined terms in the theory, the "events," are simply sets of
possibilities. Before we develop this idea further, we need to talk about the ways
that events are made to happen: simple experiments.

## 2.1 Simple experiments

We shall mean nothing very fancy by the term "simple experiment,"
and there is no implication that a simple experiment need be anything even
remotely resembling a laboratory experiment. **A simple experiment is some well-
defined act or process that leads to a single well-defined outcome.** Some simple
experiments are tossing a coin to see whether heads or tails comes up, cutting a
deck of cards and noting the particular card that appears on the bottom of the cut,
opening a book at random and noting the first word on the right-hand page,
running a rat through a **T** maze and noting whether he turns to the right or the
left, lifting a telephone receiver and recording the time until the dial-tone is heard,
asking a person his political preference, giving a person an intelligence test and
computing his score, counting the number of colonies of bacteria seen through a
microscope, and so on, literally without end. The simple experiment may be real
(actually carried out) or conceptual (completely idealized), but it must be capable
of being described and be repeatable (at least in principle). We also require that
each performance of the simple experiment have one and only one outcome, that
we can know when it occurs, and that the set of all possible outcomes can be specified. Any single performance, or trial, of the experiment must eventuate in one of
these possibilities.

Obviously, this concept of a simple experiment is a very broad one,
and almost any describable act or process can be called a simple experiment. There
is no implication that the act or process even be initiated by the experimenter; he
need function only in the role of an observer. On the other hand, it is essential that
the outcome, whatever it is, be unambiguous and capable of being categorized
among all possibilities.

## 2.2 Events

The basic elements of probability theory are the possible distinct
outcomes of some idealized simple experiment. The set of all possible distinct out-

comes for a simple experiment will be called the **sample space** for that experiment. Any member of the sample space is called a **sample point,** or an **elementary event.** Every separate and "thinkable" result of an experiment is represented by *one and only one* sample point or elementary event. Any elementary event is *one possible result* of a single trial of the experiment.

For example, we have a standard deck of playing cards. The simple experiment is drawing out one card, haphazardly, from the shuffled deck. The sample space consists of the fifty-two separate and distinct cards that we might draw. If the experiment is stopping people on the street, then the sample space consists of all the different individuals we might possibly stop. If the experiment is reading a thermometer under particular conditions, then the sample space is all the different numerical readings that the thermometer might show.

Seldom, however, is the *particular* elementary event that occurs on a trial of any special interest. Rather the actual outcome takes on importance only in relation to all possible outcomes. Ordinarily we are interested in the kind or class of outcome an observation represents. The outcome of an experiment is *measured*, at least by allotting it to some qualitative class. For this reason, the main concern of probability theory is with *sets* of elementary events. **Any set of elementary events is known simply as an event, or an event-class.**

Imagine, once again, that the experiment is carried out by drawing playing cards from a standard pack. The fifty-two sample points (the distinct cards) can be grouped into sets in a variety of ways. The suits of the cards make up four sets of thirteen cards each. The event "spades" is the set of all card possibilities showing this suit, the event "hearts" is another set, and so on. The event "ace" consists of four different elementary events, as does the event "king," and so on.

If the experiment involves stopping people on the street and noting their eye color, the experimenter may designate seven or eight different eye-color classes. Each such set is an event. The event "blue eyes" is said to "occur" when we run into a person who is a member of the class "blue eyes." If, on the other hand, we find the weight of each person we stop, then there may be a vast number of "weight events," different weight numbers standing for classes into which people may fall. If a person is stopped and weighs exactly 168 pounds, then the event "168 pounds" is said to occur.

In short, **events are sets, or classes, having the elementary events as members.** The elementary events are the raw materials that make up event-classes. The occurrence of any member of event-class *A* makes us say that event *A* has occurred. Since *any* subset of the sample space is an event, then some event *must* occur on each and every trial of the experiment.


## 2.3   EVENTS AS SETS

The symbol $S$ will be used to stand for the *sample space*, the set of all elementary events that are possible outcomes of some simple experiment. Then capital letters *A, B,* and so on will represent events, each of which is some subset of §. Notice how the sample space § is used like a universal set; for a given simple experiment, *every event discussed must be some subset of* §.

The set § may contain either a finite or an infinite number of elements. In this elementary discussion the number of elements assumed in § will always be finite. Nevertheless, in many of the most important instances in the theory the sample space is infinitely large.

Since any event $A$ is a subset of §, the operations and postulates of set theory carry over directly to operations on events to define other events.

First of all, the set § is an event: § is the "sure event," since it is *bound* to occur (one of its members must turn up on every trial). The event $\emptyset$ is called the "impossible event," since it cannot occur, having no members. It is important to remember that the empty or impossible event $\emptyset$ is, nevertheless, an *event* according to our definition, since the empty set is a subset of every set, and thus $\emptyset \subset$ §.

By our definition of an event as a subset of §, then if $A$ and $B$ are both events, the union $A \cup B$ is also an event. The event $A \cup B$ occurs if we observe a member of $A$, or a member of $B$, or a member of both.

In the same way, $A \cap B$ is an event. The event $A \cap B$ requires an outcome that is *both* an $A$ and a $B$ in order to occur. Notice that any occurrence of $A \cap B$ is automatically an occurrence of $A \cup B$, but that the reverse is not true.

If $A$ is an event, then so is its complement $\bar{A}$, and both $A$ and $\bar{A}$ cannot occur since $A \cap \bar{A} = \emptyset$. On the other hand, either $A$ or $\bar{A}$ must occur, since $A \cup \bar{A} =$ §. The difference between two events, $A - B$, is likewise an event. **In short, each and every subset formed from the elementary events in § is an event.**

Two events $A$ and $B$, neither equal to $\emptyset$, are said to be **mutually exclusive** if $A \cap B$ cannot occur—that is, if $A \cap B = \emptyset$. Two or more events are said to be **exhaustive** if their union *must* occur; thus $A$ and $\bar{A}$ are exhaustive events, since $A \cup \bar{A} =$ §.

Let us take a concrete example of some events. Suppose that we had a list containing the name of every living person in the United States. We close our eyes, point a finger at some spot on the list, and choose one person to observe. The elementary event is the actual person we see as the result of that choice, and the set § is the total set of possible persons. Suppose that the event $A$ is the set "female," and $B$ is the set "red headed," among this total set of persons. If our chosen person turns out to be female, then event $A$ occurs; if not, event $\bar{A}$. If he turns out to be red headed, this is an occurrence of event $B$; if not, event $\bar{B}$. If the observation shows up as both female and red headed, $A \cap B$ occurs; if either female or red headed, then event $A \cup B$ occurs. If the person is female but not red headed, this is an occurrence of the event $A - B$. Only one thing is sure; we will observe a person living in the United States, and the event § must occur.

## 2.4 FAMILIES OF EVENTS

In the example just given, the choice of the two events $A$ and $B$ was completely arbitrary, and the example could have been given just as well with any other scheme for arranging elementary events into event classes. Ordinarily, there is some restricted set of events of interest, but any scheme for arranging elementary events into event classes can be used.

In the next section we are going to define probability in terms of events. However, we want to do this in some way so that probability can be discussed regardless of how the sample space is broken into subsets. This is accomplished by considering all possible subsets of sample space $S$. Given $N$ elementary events in $S$, there are exactly $2^N$ event classes that can be formed, including $\emptyset$ and $S$. *The set $\mathcal{A}$ consisting of all possible subsets of the sample space $S$ will be called the family of events in $S$.* This set of subsets $\mathcal{A}$ will be the basis for the definition of probability to follow.

## 2.5   PROBABILITY FUNCTIONS

We are now ready for a formal definition of what is meant by probability. This definition will be given in terms of a probability function, a pairing of each event with a positive real number (or zero), its probability. The question of how this probability is to be interpreted will be discussed a little later.

**DEFINITION:**   Given the sample space $S$, and the family $\mathcal{A}$ of events in $S$, a probability function associates with each event $A$ in $\mathcal{A}$ a real number $p(A)$, the *probability* of event $A$, such that the following axioms are true:
1. $p(A) \geqq 0$ for every event $A$.
2. $p(S) = 1$.
3. If there exists some countable set of events, $\{A_1, A_2, \cdots, A_N\}$, and if these events are all mutually exclusive, then $p(A_1 \cup A_2 \cup \cdots \cup A_N) = p(A_1) + p(A_2) + \cdots + p(A_N)$ (the probability of the union of mutually exclusive events is the sum of their separate probabilities).

In essence, this definition states that paired with each event $A$ is a nonnegative number, probability $p(A)$, and that the probability of the sure event $S$, or $p(S)$, is always 1.00. Furthermore, if $A$ and $B$ are any two *mutually exclusive* events in the sample space, the probability of their union, $p(A \cup B)$, is simply the sum of their two probabilities, $p(A) + p(B)$.

It is important to remember at this stage that this is a purely formal definition of probability in terms of a function assigning numbers to sets. *Events* have probabilities, and in order to discuss probability we must always discuss the events to which these probabilities belong. When we speak of the probability that a person in the United States has red hair, we are speaking of the probability number assigned to the event "red hair" in the sample space "all persons in the United States." Similarly, when we say that the probability that a coin will come up heads is .50, we are saying that the number .50 is assigned in the probability function to the event "heads" in the sample space "all possible results of tossing a particular coin."

This may seem to be an extremely unmotivated and arbitrary way to discuss probability. We all know that the word "probability" means more than a mere number assigned to a set, and we shall certainly give these probability numbers meaning in the sections to follow. For the nonce, however, let us simply accept this purely formal definition at face value.

Given our definition of a probability function, we can begin to deduce other features that probabilities of events must have. Now we shall proceed to derive some consequences of the formal axioms included in our definition above; not only will this demonstrate that deductions do, in fact, follow directly from the axioms of this formal mathematical system, but also we will find the elementary rules of probability to be derived extremely useful when we begin to calculate probabilities.

First of all, we will give an informal proof of the following statement:

$$p(\bar{A}) = 1 - p(A), \qquad\qquad [2.5.1^*]$$

**for any event** $A$, **the probability of the complementary event "not-**$A$**" is 1 minus the probability of** $A$. We proceed as follows: we know from the algebra of sets that $A$ and $\bar{A}$ are mutually exclusive $(A \cap \bar{A} = \emptyset)$, and that $A \cup \bar{A} = \mathcal{S}$. Then, by axiom 2 above

$$p(A \cup \bar{A}) = p(\mathcal{S}) = 1.$$

Furthermore, by axiom 3, since $A$ and $\bar{A}$ are mutually exclusive,

$$p(A \cup \bar{A}) = p(A) + p(\bar{A}).$$

Then it follows that

$$p(A) + p(\bar{A}) = 1$$

so that

$$p(\bar{A}) = 1 - p(A)$$

and

$$p(A) = 1 - p(\bar{A}).$$

In this simple way we have proved an elementary theorem in the formal theory of probability.

Next, we will show that

$$0 \leq p(A) \leq 1, \qquad\qquad [2.5.2^*]$$

for any event $A$ in the family of events $\mathcal{S}$. That is, **the probability of any event must lie between zero and one inclusive.** Suppose that some event $A$ could be found where $p(A) > 1$; would this lead to a contradiction of one or more of our axioms? If so, then under these axioms no event can have a probability greater than 1. From the theorem just proved above,

$$p(A) + p(\bar{A}) = 1$$

If $p(A)$ should be greater than 1, then it must be true that $p(\bar{A})$ is less than zero; however, axiom 1 dictates that *any* event must have a probability greater than or equal to zero. Thus, if $p(A)$ were greater than 1 a contradiction is generated, and this means than any event must have a probability lying between zero and 1 inclusive.

The third theorem we shall prove states that

$$p(\emptyset) = 0, \qquad\qquad [2.5.3^*]$$

**the probability of the empty or "impossible" event is zero.** To show this we recall that

$$\bar{S} = \emptyset,$$

the set of all elementary events not in $S$ is empty. Also, we know that

$$S \cup \bar{S} = S \cup \emptyset = S.$$

Then, by **2.5.1,**

$$\begin{aligned} p(\emptyset) &= 1 - p(S) \\ &= 0, \end{aligned}$$

proving the theorem.

Still another important elementary theorem of probability goes as follows:

If $A \subseteq B$, where $A$ and $B$ are two events in $S$, then

$$p(A) \leq p(B). \qquad\qquad [2.5.4^*]$$

In other words, **if the occurrence of an event $A$ implies that an event $B$ occurs, so that the event-class $A$ is a subset of the event-class $B$, then the probability of $A$ is less than or equal to the probability of $B$.** Here, we start by using a set-theoretic result: if $A \subseteq B$, then

$$\begin{aligned} A \cap B &= A \\ A \cup B &= B. \end{aligned}$$

Now the set $B$ can be thought of as the union of *two* mutually exclusive sets:

$$B = (A \cap B) \cup (\bar{A} \cap B)$$

or, since $A$ is a subset of $B$,

$$B = A \cup (\bar{A} \cap B).$$

Then, by axiom 3,

$$p(B) = p(A) + p(\bar{A} \cap B)$$

and

$$p(B) - p(A) = p(\bar{A} \cap B).$$

Since $p(\bar{A} \cap B)$ cannot be negative, $p(B)$ must be greater than or equal to $p(A)$.

Two immediate and useful consequences of the theorem just proved are the following statements:

For any pair of events, $A$ and $B$, $p(A \cap B) \leq p(A \cup B)$.   $[2.5.5^*]$

If $A \subseteq B$, then $p(B - A) = p(B) - p(A)$.   $[2.5.6^*]$

The last theorem to be proved here is actually a most important one for all sorts of probability calculations:

Given two events $A$ and $B$, then

$$p(A \cup B) = p(A) + p(B) - p(A \cap B). \qquad\qquad [2.5.7^*]$$

In order to see why this is true, recall that

$$A = (A \cap B) \cup (A \cap \bar{B})$$

so that

$$p(A) = p(A \cap B) + p(A \cap \bar{B}).$$

In the same way,

$$p(B) = p(A \cap B) + p(\bar{A} \cap B).$$

On the other hand, if we break the *union* of $A$ and $B$ into the union of mutually exclusive sets, we find that

$$(A \cup B) = (A \cap \bar{B}) \cup (A \cap B) \cup (\bar{A} \cap B)$$

so that, by axiom 3,

$$p(A \cup B) = p(A \cap \bar{B}) + p(A \cap B) + p(\bar{A} \cap B).$$

If we added $p(A \cap B)$ to both sides of this equation, we would have

$$p(A \cup B) + p(A \cap B) = p(A \cap \bar{B}) + p(A \cap B) + p(\bar{A} \cap B) + p(A \cap B)$$

so that on substituting $p(A)$ and $p(B)$ for their equivalents found above, we have

$$p(A \cup B) + p(A \cap B) = p(A) + p(B)$$

or.

$$p(A \cup B) = p(A) + p(B) - p(A \cap B).$$

In other words, **to find the probability that $A$ or $B$ (or both) occurs, we must know the probability of $A$, the probability of $B$, and also the probability that $A$ and $B$ both occur.** Be sure to notice, however, that if $A$ and $B$ are *mutually exclusive* events, so that $p(A \cap B) = 0$, then

$$p(A \cup B) = p(A) + p(B),$$

just as provided by axiom 3.

It should be obvious that there is no end to the number of new deductions we could make using the original three axioms and the accumulated theorems such as those just proved. Enormous volumes have been filled with such probability theorems, all deduced in essentially the same way from the same axioms we have been using. Naturally, only some of the most elementary results have been shown here, and these particular results have been chosen because of their simple proofs and because they will be useful for us to have in future sections. The idea to be conveyed, however, is that one can deduce all sorts of consequences which *must* be true of these numbers we call probabilities, if these numbers obey the *formal* definition set forth at the beginning of this section. Not once has it been necessary for us to say what probability "really" means in order to deduce all sorts of rules that probabilities must obey. In short, probability theory can perfectly well be studied strictly as an abstract mathematical system without any interpretation at all.

The simple rules we have deduced and the three basic axioms will all be useful to us in learning to calculate probabilities. For the while, however, we must turn to the interpretation of these numbers called probabilities. What do we usually mean by this number when we assign it to a possible outcome of an experiment we actually carry out?

## 2.6 A SPECIAL CASE: EQUALLY PROBABLE ELEMENTARY EVENTS

Most simple probability calculations actually rest on the "addition" principle embodied in axiom 3 of Section 2.5. The elementary events making up the sample space $S$ are conceived as the set of all possible *distinctly different* outcomes of the particular simple experiment. Each such elementary event is an event in its own right, since each constitutes a one-element subset of $S$. Furthermore, the elementary events are mutually exclusive; if one distinct elementary outcome occurs, no other elementary event may occur. Now under this view, if we somehow knew the probability for each and every elementary event making up the sample space $S$, then we would also be able to compute the probability of any event in $S$. Since the elementary events can be regarded as themselves mutually exclusive events, **the probability of any event in $S$ is simply the sum of the probabilities of the elementary events qualifying for that event class;** this is an immediate consequence of axiom 3. Thus, the probability of any event corresponding to a subset of $S$ can be found provided that the probability associated with each and every elementary event is known.

However, the practical difficulty in actually computing probabilities is in knowing the probabilities of the elementary events themselves. Fortunately, a great many of the simple experiments for which we need to calculate probabilities, and particularly games of chance, have a feature that does away with this problem. A great many simple experiments are conducted in such a way that it is reasonable to assume that each and every distinct elementary event has the *same* probability. When tickets are drawn in a lottery, for example, great pains are taken to have the tickets well shaken-up in a tumbler before each one is drawn; this mixing operation makes it reasonable to believe that any particular ticket has the same chance of being drawn as any other. Cards are thoroughly shuffled and cut, perfectly balanced dice are thrown in a dice-cage, and, in fact, almost all gambling situations have some feature which makes this equal-chances assumption reasonable. As we shall see presently, even experiments that are not games of chance also are carried in such a way that each and every elementary event should have the same probability.

When it can be assumed that each and every one of a finite number of possible elementary events has exactly the same probability, then the probability of any event is particularly easy to compute. That is, imagine a sample space $S$ containing $N$ distinct elementary events. Then, for any event $A$, let the number of elementary events that are members of $A$ be denoted by $n(A)$. The following principle applies:

**If all elementary events in the sample space $S$ have exactly the same probability, then the probability of any event $A$ is given by**

$$p(A) = \frac{\text{number of elementary events in } A}{\text{total number of elementary events in } S}$$

$$= \frac{n(A)}{N}. \qquad\qquad\qquad [2.6.1*]$$

It is easy to see that this rule must hold for the probability of any event provided that the various elementary events are equally probable. Suppose that there were $N$ elements in $S$. Now consider a subset $A$ consisting of exactly two elementary events, $A = \{a_1, a_2\}$. What is the probability of $A$? Since all such events are equally likely, $p(a_1) = 1/N$ and $p(a_2) = 1/N$. The set $A$ is the union $a_1 \cup a_2$ of two mutually exclusive sets; thus, by axiom 3, Section 2.5, $p(A) = 1/N + 1/N$ or $2/N$. Proceeding in this way, suppose the set $A$ contained $n$ events. Here $p(A) = 1/N + 1/N + \cdots + 1/N$, or $1/N$ summed $n$ times, so that for any $n$, $0 \leq n \leq N$,

$$p(A) = \frac{\text{number of elements in } A}{\text{total number of elements}} = \frac{n(A)}{N}.$$

**For equally likely elementary events, the probability of an event $A$ is its relative frequency in the sample space.**

As an illustration, suppose that a box contains ten marbles. Five of these marbles are white, three are red, and two are black. We perform the simple experiment of drawing a marble out of the box (without looking) in such a way that the marbles are well mixed up, and that there is no reason for any given marble to be favored in our drawing. Now we can identify our experiment with the model of probability we have been discussing. An outcome is the result of our drawing a marble and looking at it. An elementary event is a particular marble, in this instance, and there are exactly ten distinct marbles; hence there are ten elementary events making up the sample space $S$. The marble-events are mutually exclusive, and each has probability $1/10$.

We are concerned with the three events: "white," "red," and "black." Notice that these three events are subsets of $S$, containing five, three, and two elementary events (marbles), respectively. What is the probability of our drawing a red marble? The answer is given by

$$p(\text{red}) = \frac{\text{number of red marbles}}{\text{total number of marbles}}$$

$$= \frac{3}{10}$$

so that we may say correctly that the probability of the event "red" in this experiment is .30. In the same way, one can find

$$p(\text{white}) = .50, \text{ and } p(\text{black}) = .20.$$

Furthermore, it is easy to see, by applying the rules of Section 2.5, that

$p$(no color) $= .00$
$p$(red or white) $= .30 + .50 = .80$
$p$(red and white) $= .00$
$p$(red or black) $= .30 + .20 = .50$
$p$(red or white or black) $= .30 + .20 + .50 = 1.00$

and so on, for any other event.

Consider another example. A teacher has thirty children in a classroom. In some completely "random" and unsystematic way, the teacher chooses a child to tell his father's occupation. The children are each equally likely to be chosen by the teacher. In this example the elementary events are the different children who might be chosen: there are thirty such elementary events possible, making up the sample space $S$. Now suppose that there are only four classes of occupation represented in the room: professional, white-collar, skilled labor, and unskilled labor. These four classes will be labeled events $A$, $B$, $C$, and $D$. If three children represent group $A$, fifteen, group $B$, ten, group $C$, and two, group $D$, what is the probability that a child chosen will fall into a given group? In other words, what are the probabilities of the four different events? Once again, these probabilities are given by the relative frequencies:

$$p(A) = \frac{\text{number of elementary events in } A}{\text{total number of elementary events}}$$
$$= \frac{3}{30} = .10.$$

In the same way we find:

$$p(B) = \frac{15}{30} = .50$$

$$p(C) = \frac{10}{30} = .33$$

$$p(D) = \frac{2}{30} = .07.$$

Finally, suppose that the experiment in question were that of throwing a fair (that is, unloaded) die, marked with spots from 1 to 6 on its sides. The die is constructed and thrown so that each of the sides is equally likely to appear. There are six distinct outcomes, so that there are six elementary events making up $S$. The probability of the event "1" is thus 1/6, the event "2" has probability 1/6, and so on. What is the probability of the event "odd number"? An odd number occurs when the die comes up with one, three, or five spots. That is, the desired probability is

$p$(one or three or five spots) $= p$(odd number).

Since these events are mutually exclusive, the desired probability is found from axiom 3 to be

$$p(\text{one or three or five spots}) = \frac{1}{6} + \frac{1}{6} + \frac{1}{6} = .50.$$

## 2.7 "In the long run"

Each of these examples illustrates how the outcomes of an experiment are identified with the elementary events in a sample space, and how probabilities may be computed as relative frequencies. However, we have still not really answered the question of what these probabilities mean. How are probabilities reflected in what we observe?

In the first example, if one were to keep drawing marbles out of the box, and after each draw were to replace the marble in the box before drawing again, then in the *long run*, after very many observations, *what proportion of the marbles drawn should be red?* It should take only a very little thought to arrive at the conclusion that one should *expect* about 3 in 10 such observations to be red. In the same way, in the second example, suppose that the teacher keeps choosing children in this unsystematic way, and any given child can be chosen over and over again. If each child is equally likely to be chosen at any time, then it seems reasonable that in the long run, over a large number of such observations, about .10 or one in ten of the children chosen should be of occupation group $A$.

Finally, in the die example, about half the time in the long run one should expect an odd number to turn up on the die if it were thrown repeatedly. In each example, **the probability of an event denotes the relative frequency of occurrence of that event to be expected in the long run.**

Simple examples of this sort all involve equally likely elementary events, and in many applications of probability theory, especially to games of chance, this assumption is made. On the other hand, the same idea applies even when elementary events are *not* equally likely: *in the long run, the relative frequency of occurrence approaches the probability for any event.*

Thus, the idea of relative frequency is connected with probability in two ways:

1. If elementary events are equally probable, the probability of an event is its relative frequency in the sample space.
2. The *long-run* relative frequency of occurrences of event $A$ over trials of the experiment *should approach* $p(A)$. This is true regardless of whether elementary events are equally probable or not, provided that observations are made "independently" and "at random."

## 2.8 Bernoulli's theorem

The connection between probability and long-run relative frequency is a simple and appealing one, and it does form a tie between that basically undefined notion, "the probability of an event," and something we can actually observe, a relative frequency of occurrence. A statement of probability tells us what to *expect* about the relative frequency of occurrence of an event given that enough sample observations are made at random: In the long run, the relative frequency of occurrence of event $X$ should approach the probability of this event, if independent trials are made at random over an indefinitely long sequence. As it stands, this idea is a familiar and reasonable one, but it will be useful to have a more exact statement of this principle for use in future work. The principle was first formulated and proved by James Bernoulli in the early eighteenth century, and it often goes by the name "Bernoulli's theorem." A more or less precise statement of Bernoulli's theorem goes as follows:

If the probability of occurrence of the event $X$ is $p(X)$, and if $N$ trials are made, independently and under exactly the same conditions, then the probability that the relative frequency of occurrence of $X$ differs from $p(X)$ by any amount, however small, approaches zero as the number of trials grows indefinitely large.

The theorem may also be represented by the following mathematical expression:

$$\text{prob}\left(\left|\frac{f}{N} - p\right| \geq \epsilon\right) \to 0, \text{ as } N \to \infty,$$

where $f$ stands for the frequency of occurrence of event $X$ among the $N$ trials, $p$ is the probability of $X$, $\epsilon$ is some arbitrarily small positive number, and $N \to \infty$ indicates that the number of trials increases until it approaches an infinite number. The mathematical statistician says that the proportion $f/N$ approaches the value $p$ "in probability" as $N$ becomes indefinitely large.

In effect, the theorem says this: Imagine some $N$ trials made at random and in such a way that the outcome on any one trial cannot possibly influence the probability of outcomes on any other trial; that is, $N$ independent trials are made. This act of taking $N$ independent trials of the same simple experiment may itself be regarded as another experiment in which the possible outcomes are the numbers of times event $X$ occurs out of $N$ trials. Each possible such outcome has a probability. Then the most probable result of carrying out $N$ trials is a proportion of occurrences of $X$ that is very nearly the value of $p(X)$ for one trial (equal to $p(X)$ when that proportion can occur; see Section 5.15). Although this is the most probable outcome of $N$ trials of the same experiment, this does not mean, however, that the proportion of $X$ occurrences among any $N$ trials *must* be $p(X)$; the proportion actually observed might be any number between 0 and 1. Nevertheless, given more and more trials, the relative frequency of $X$ occurrences may be expected to come closer and closer to $p(X)$.

In one way, this principle is what people have in mind when they refer to "the law of averages." Most of us have the intuition that the relative number of times an event occurs over repeated opportunities reflects its probability. Given enough experimental trials or sample observations from the sample space, we expect the relative frequency of occurrence to balance out to equal the probability.

However, *do not fall into the error of thinking that an event is ever due to occur on any given trial.* If you toss a coin 100 times, you expect about 50 percent of the tosses to show the event "heads," since the theoretical probability of that event for a fair coin is .50. This does not mean, however, that for any given one-hundred trials (or one-thousand, or million, or billion trials) the coin must show 50 percent heads. This need not be true at all. Every one of your 100 tosses *could* result in the event heads, or none of them might result in this event—the coin does not ever have to come up heads in any finite number of tosses. Only in an infinite number of tosses must the relative frequency equal .50. The only thing which we can say with assurance is that .50 is the relative frequency of heads we should expect to observe in any given number $N$ of tosses, and that it is increasingly probable that we observe close to 50 percent heads as the $N$ grows larger. But on any finite number of tosses of the coin, the relative frequency of heads observed can be anything. This same is true for the occurrence of any event in any simple experiment in which observations are made at random and in which the probability $p(X)$ of the event $X$ is other than 1 or 0.

Although it is true that the relative frequency of occurrence of any event must exactly equal the probability only for an infinite number of independent trials, this point must not be overstressed. Even with relatively small numbers of trials we have very good reason to expect the observed relative frequency to be quite close to the probability. The rate of convergence of the relative frequency to the probability is very rapid, even at the lower levels of sample size, although the probability of a small discrepancy between relative frequency and probability is much smaller for extremely large than for extremely small samples. A probability is not a curiosity requiring unattainable conditions, but rather a value that can be estimated with considerable accuracy from a sample. Our best bet about the probability of an event is the actual relative frequency we have observed from some $N$ trials, and the larger $N$ is, the better the bet.

In a later section we will actually prove the main features of Bernoulli's theorem, but this must wait until Chapter 6. As yet, we lack the vocabulary to give a precise meaning to terms, such as "at random" and "independent events," that figure in this theorem. Nevertheless, accepting this principle at face value for the moment, we can show a simple example of its use.

## 2.9 AN EXAMPLE OF SIMPLE STATISTICAL INFERENCE

Imagine that we were faced with the following problem: We are given a coin and asked to decide if the coin is fair (that is, if the probability of heads is .50). This is to be decided through the repeated simple experiment of tossing the coin. If the coin actually is fair, then in an infinite number of tosses the relative frequency of the event heads must occur with probability of exactly .50. However, on any given number of tosses, we should only expect a relative frequency of .50 to occur. The larger the number of tosses, the more nearly should we expect the relative frequency to approach .50.

Now we toss the coin four times; suppose that four heads occur. This would cast no special doubt upon the fairness of the coin, since it is relatively likely that the relative frequency of heads will depart widely from .50 on such a small number of trials. However, if after 500 tosses, the number of heads were 500, we would begin to have very serious doubts about the fairness of the coin; although this *could* happen, it is far from what one *expects*. Nevertheless, we still could not be sure. If we tossed the coin 500 million times, still with 100 percent heads, we could be practically certain that the probability of a head for this coin is not .50— *practically* certain, that is, but still not *completely* certain. Only if we tossed the coin an infinite number of times would we be absolutely certain that the coin was not fair, given that the long-run relative frequency differed from .50 in any way.

This hypothetical example exhibits one of the basic features of statistical inference as applied to many real problems. One starts out with a theoretical state of affairs that can be represented by a statement of the probability for one or more events. He wishes to use empirical evidence to check the truth of that theoretical situation. Therefore he conducts an experiment in which the event or events in question are possible outcomes, and he takes some $N$ observations at random. The theoretical probabilities tell him what to expect with regard to the relative frequencies of the events in question, and he compares the obtained relative frequencies against those expected. To the extent that the obtained relative frequencies of events depart widely from the expected, he has some evidence that the theory is not true. Moreover, given any degree of departure of observed from the expected relative frequency, he is more certain that the theory is not true the larger the sample $N$. However, *he can never be completely sure in his judgment that the theory is false unless he has made an infinite number of observations.*

By the same token, he can never be completely sure that the theory is true. An extremely biased coin (short of a coin which must come up heads with probability 1 or tails with probability 1) *can* give exactly 50 percent heads on any set of $N$ trials. Even though the evidence appears to agree well with the theory, this in no way implies that the theory must be true. Only after an infinite number of trials, when the relative frequency of occurrence of events matches the theoretical probability exactly, can one assert with complete confidence that the theory is true. Increased numbers of trials lend confidence to our judgments about the true state of affairs, but we can always be wrong, short of an infinite number of observations.

The principle embodied in Bernoulli's theorem can be used not only to compare empirical results with theoretical probabilities, but also to let us *estimate* true probabilities of events by observing their relative frequencies over some limited number of trials. For example, suppose that once again we had a box containing marbles of different solid colors. We do not know how many marbles there are in the box, and we do not know how many different colors, but our task is to find out the probability of each color. We conduct the simple experiment of mixing up the marbles well, drawing one out, observing its color, and putting it back (random sampling with replacement). Now suppose that the first marble is white. The observed relative frequencies of colors are white 1.00, other .00. We wish to decide about the probabilities in such a way that our estimate would, if correct, have made the occurrence of this particular sample result have the greatest prior probability. What probability of the event "white" would make drawing a white marble most likely? The answer is $p$(white) = 1.00, and $p$(other) = .00, so that this is our first estimate of the probabilities of the colors of the marbles.

However, we now draw a second marble at random with replacement. This marble turns out to be red, and our best guess about the probabilities is now white .50, red .50, other .00, as these probabilities would make the occurrence of the actual sample of two marbles most likely. If we kept on drawing, observing, and replacing marbles for 100 trials, shaking the box so that the marbles (elementary events) are equally likely to be chosen on a trial, we might begin to get a reasonably clear picture of the probabilities of the colors:

| Color | Relative frequency |
|-------|--------------------|
| white | .24 |
| red   | .50 |
| blue  | .26 |

By the time we had made 10,000 observations, we could be even more confident that the probabilities are close to:

| Color | Relative frequency |
|-------|--------------------|
| white | .24 |
| red   | .50 |
| blue  | .24 |
| green | .02 |

and so on. Given an infinite number of trials, we could specify the relative frequencies (that is, the probabilities) of the marbles in the box precisely. The larger the number of observations, the less do we expect to "miss" in our estimates of what the box contains. However, for fewer than an infinite number of observations, the observed relative frequencies *need not* reflect the probabilities of the colors exactly, though they may.

It is important to note that since we are drawing samples *with replacement* in this situation the fact that there may be only some finite numbers of distinct elementary events (marbles in this case) in no way prevents us from taking a very large or even an infinite number of sample observations with replacement after each trial. Thus Bernoulli's theorem applies perfectly well to situations in which there may be a very small number of distinct elementary events possible, so long as one can draw an unlimited number of samples or make an unlimited number of trials of the experiment (as in coin tossing or die rolling).

The scientist making observations is doing something quite similar to drawing marbles from a box. He cannot see "into the box" and observe all such phenomena about which he wishes to generalize, but he can observe samples drawn from among all such elementary events, and generalize from what he actually observes. His generalization is much like a bet, and how good the bet is depends to great extent on how many sample observations he makes. He can never be completely sure that his generalization is the correct one, but he can make the risk of being wrong very small by making a sufficient number of observations.

## 2.10  OTHER INTERPRETATIONS OF PROBABILITY

Long-run relative frequency is but one interpretation that can be given to the formal notion of probability. It is important to remember that this is an *interpretation* of the abstract model. The model per se is a system of relations among and rules for calculating with numbers that happen to be called probabilities. There is no "true meaning" of probability, any more than there is a true meaning of the symbol "*x*" as used in school algebra. Probability is an abstract mathematical concept that takes on meaning in the ordinary sense only when it is identified with something in our experience, such as relative frequency of real events.

The probability concept acquired its interpretation as relative frequency because it was originally developed to describe certain games of chance where plays (such as spinning a roulette wheel or tossing dice or dealing cards) are indeed repeated for very many trials. Similarly, there are situations in which the scientist makes many observations under the same conditions, and so the mathematical theory of probability is given a relative frequency interpretation here as well.

On the other hand, there are some students of the matter who object to this as the exclusive interpretation of probability, and who have shown that quite different interpretations can be advanced that do not identify formal probability exclusively with relative frequency. Indeed, an everyday use of the probability concept does not have this relative frequency connotation at all. We say "It will probably rain tomorrow," or "The Yankees will probably win the pennant," or "I am unlikely to pass this test"; our hearers have no difficulty in understanding what we mean in each instance, but it is very difficult to see how these statements describe long-run relative frequencies of outcomes of simple experiments repeated over and over again. Each such statement describes the speaker's *certainty* or *degree of belief* about an event that will occur once and once only. Our inclination to use naive notions of probability in this way is one of the reasons theorists have sought other interpretations.

Nevertheless, probability, as we will use the term, will usually correspond to a long-run relative frequency. Most applications of statistics deal with situations where sampling can be repeated many times, and here this interpretation does make sense. However, in one place (Chapter 9) we will have occasion to discuss "personal probabilities" that reflect the experimenter's degree of belief.

## 2.11 RANDOM SAMPLING

Given some simple experiment and the sample space of elementary events, the set of outcomes of $N$ separate trials is a **sample.** When the sample is drawn *with replacement*, the same elementary event can occur more than once. When the sample is drawn *without replacement*, the same elementary event can occur no more than once in a given sample. Ordinarily, probability and statistics deal with **random samples.** The word "random" has been used rather loosely in the foregoing discussion, and now the time has come to give it a more restricted meaning in connection with random samples.

It has already been suggested that probability calculations can be made quite simple when the elementary events in a sample space have equal probabilities. The theory of statistics deals with samples of size $N$ from a specified sample space, and here, too, great simplification is introduced if each distinct sample of a particular size can be assumed to have equal probability of selection. For this reason, the elementary theory of statistics is based on the idea of simple random sampling:

**A method of drawing samples such that each and every distinct sample of the same size $N$ has exactly the same probability of being selected is called simple random sampling.**

In other words, our discussion will be confined to the situation where all possible samples of the same size have exactly the same probability. For us, sampling "at random" will always mean simple random sampling, as defined above. This does not mean, however, that the theory of statistics does not apply to situations where samples have unequal probabilities of occurrence; in more advanced work the theory and methods can be extended to any sampling scheme where the probabilities of the various samples are *known*, even though they are unequal.

An alternative definition of simple random sampling in terms of elementary events can also be given: "Simple random sampling is a process of selecting elementary events for observation in such a way that each and every elementary event has precisely the same probability of being included in any sample of $N$ observations." In *random sampling with replacement*, each elementary event has exactly the same probability of occurring on each trial. In random sampling *without replacement*, the composition of sample space $S$ changes with each trial since an elementary event can occur only once in $N$ trials. However, we shall assume that among the elementary events available for selection on a given trial, the probabilities are equal.

We shall also have many occasions to require **independent random sampling.** You may recall that independence was specified in Bernoulli's theorem. Although an adequate definition of independence of events cannot be given until later (Chapter 4), we can, for the moment, use the term as follows: elementary events are sampled independently when the occurrence of one elementary event has *absolutely no connection* with the probability of occurrence of the same or another elementary event on a subsequent trial. A series of tosses of a coin can be thought of as a random and independent sampling of events: what happens on one toss has no conceivable connection with what happens on any other. Each trial of a simple experiment is a sampling of elementary events, and the trials are independent when no connection exists between the particular outcomes of different trials.

Take care to notice that our assuming samples of size $N$ thus to be equally probable does not imply that *events* must be equally probable. Thus, in the marble example above, samples of $N$ marbles were assumed equally probable, but the probabilities of the colors of the marbles were not equal. The assumption of equal probabilities is simply a way of saying that any elementary event has just as good an opportunity as any other to serve as a sample on any given experimental trial.

## 2.12  RANDOM NUMBER TABLES

In practical situations, there are a number of schemes for sampling the elementary events randomly and independently. One of the most common is by use of a table of random numbers. Random number tables consist of many pages filled with digits, from 0 through 9. These tables have been composed in such a way that each digit is approximately equally likely to occur in any spot in the table and there is no systematic connection between the occurrence of any digit in the sequence and any other. Most books on the design of experiments contain pages of random numbers, and very extensive tables of random numbers may be found in a book prepared by the RAND Corporation (1955).

In order to use these tables for random sampling, one must list the possible elementary events (distinct units that might be observed). Each unit is then given a different number. The table of random numbers is entered by choosing some starting point at random and reading to the right or left, up or down. If the sample space contains only ten or fewer individual points, then the digits 0 through 9 themselves are used; if there are one-hundred or fewer members of the sample space, digits are grouped by pairs, 00 through 99, and so on. Then the first $N$ nonrepeated random numbers or groups of numbers are chosen, where $N$ is the required sample size. The individual units corresponding to these numbers comprise the sample, which can be regarded as chosen at random.

This method is subject to two drawbacks. In the first place, unless one has an infinitely large table of random numbers, the one he uses must contain either some differences in probability or some dependence among the digits. This makes a sample chosen with any given table only approximately random. Second, and much more important, is the fact that a *listing* of the members of the sample space (all potential observation-units) must be possible. Except in some very restricted situations this is exceedingly difficult, or even impossible, to do. What usually happens in psychology is that selection is made from some sample space much smaller than the one the experimenter would really like to use. For example, he might like to make statements about all people of a certain age, but the only group he can really sample randomly is college sophomores in a certain locale. Then one of two things must occur; either the experimenter assumes that the sample space actually used is itself a random sample from the larger space, or he restricts his inferences to the group that he can sample randomly. Regardless of which course he takes, if he is going to make probability statements the sample must be drawn at random from *some* specific sample space of potential observations.

Tables of random numbers are used in the same way to achieve randomization in experiments. For example, an experimenter is going to administer three different treatments to a sample of rats, with one third of the rats getting each treatment. He lists the members of his total sample, and then assigns them to the different groups by selecting random numbers. This randomization is an extremely important part of experimental procedure, as we shall see, even though the sample itself is a random selection from some sample space.

Quite apart from their utility for drawing random samples, random number tables are interesting as another instance of the notion of "randomness" that is idealized in the theory of probability. A random process is one in which only chance factors determine the particular outcome of any single trial of the experimental operation. The possible outcomes are known in advance, but not the exact outcome to be realized on any given trial. Nevertheless, built into the process is some regularity, so that each class of outcome (or event) can reasonably be assigned a probability, representing its long-run relative frequency. Perhaps the simplest example of a random phenomenon is the result of tossing a coin. Only chance factors determine whether heads or tails will come up on a particular toss, but a fair coin is so constructed that there is just as much physical reason for heads to appear as for tails, and so we have the justification we need in order to say that, in the long run, heads will appear just as often as tails. This property of the coin is idealized when we say that the probability of heads is .50. A fair die is constructed in such a way that each of the six sides should have the same physical opportunity to appear on a given throw, although unknown factors dictate which side actually does appear on that throw; we idealize this property of the die when we say that the probability of, say, three spots is 1/6. One can construct a random number table by use of a ten-sided die, each side labeled with a number from 0 through 9. Then any sequence of tosses gives a sequence of random numbers. In practice, of course, random numbers are generated electronically, but the general idea is the same: the physical process is such that no single number is favored for any particular outcome, and chance alone actually dictates the number that does occur in any place in a sequence. When we use random numbers to select samples, we are using this property of randomness, which was inherent in the process by which the numbers themselves were generated. The point is that the ideas of randomness and of probability are not just misty abstractions; we know how to create processes and devise operations that are approximately "random" and we *do* know how to manufacture events with particular probabilities, at least with probabilities that are approximately known.

In summary, the calculation of probabilities requires that the basic outcomes of observation, or elementary events, occur with probabilities that are known. Random sampling methods are ways of observing sequences or sets of $N$

such elementary events so that the probabilities associated with the various possible sample results actually *are* known. In simple random sampling, each potential observation-unit or elementary event has the same probability of appearing in a sample of $N$ observations.

The student may be a bit puzzled as we proceed by the insistence on random sampling with *replacement*, when it is perfectly obvious that in most sampling $N$ different subjects or observation units are chosen, and each unit is *not* replaced before the next is sampled. This is done in experimental psychology and related fields because the number of potential observations in the sample space is extremely large. The selection and nonreplacement of a unit does virtually nothing to the probabilities of events. In such situations, sampling without replacement can be treated exactly like sampling with replacement. On the other hand, as we shall see in Section 7.16, when the number of elementary events in the sample space is relatively small, sampling without replacement requires special procedures, since the probabilities of events are altered appreciably with each new observation made. This does no real violence to the notion of simple random sampling, however; instead of requiring that each elementary event be equally likely to occur on each trial, we require that *all samples of N possible outcomes be equally likely to occur*. This will be illustrated in Chapter 5 when we deal with sequences of events. However, in virtually all elementary applications in experimental psychology sampling is thought of as being with replacement.

# FREQUENCY AND PROBABILITY DISTRIBUTIONS

## 3

Given the definitions of "event" and of "probability" in the last chapter, we are now ready to take up the first major set of concepts in statistics. First of all, the idea of a frequency distribution for sets of observations will be introduced, together with some of the mechanics for constructing distributions of data. Then this idea of a frequency distribution will be paralleled by that of a probability distribution. The important special case of numerical events will be introduced under the heading "random variables."

Prior to any concerns he may have with summarizing his data, or comparing it with some theoretical state of affairs, the experimenter must first measure the phenomena he studies. It therefore seems appropriate to mention the process of measurement at this point, and to indicate the role measurement considerations will play in the remainder of this text. The author will not even attempt to undertake a thorough discussion of this topic, but he will try to suggest its relevance to statistics.

## 3.1 MEASUREMENT SCALES

Whenever the scientist makes observations of any kind, he employs some scheme for classifying and recording what he observes. Any phenomenon or "thing" will have many distinguishable characteristics or attributes, but *the scientist must first single out those properties relevant to the question being studied.* For example, a scientist tries out a new serum on laboratory rats infected with a disease. Any single rat differs from any other rat in innumerable ways: his coat markings, his heart rate, the length of his tail, his exact age, and so on. The scientist is interested, however, in only one thing: did the rat recover or did he die of the disease? Or, perhaps, the intelligence level of a group of boys is being compared

68

with that of a group of girls. Individual boys and girls differ and same-sex groups differ among themselves in ways as diverse as body temperature, size of head, weight, color of hair, father's income, name, and so on ad infinitum. All these properties are ignored by the experimenter as immaterial to his immediate purpose, which is giving each child a number representing his intelligence.

The classifying scheme the scientist uses is based upon differences in some *particular* property or attribute that objects of observation exhibit. The scientist simply cannot pay attention to all the ways that things differ from each other. Many of these differences obviously are irrelevant to his purpose, and other potential differences are controlled by the scientist in making his observations: only rats (not all kinds of animals) are given the serum, and each child is given the same intelligence test in the same way. Still other differences that are germane to his conclusions, but not specifically controlled, are treated as statistical "error."

When the scientist has singled out the property or properties he wants to study, he applies his classifying scheme to each observation. Such a scheme is essential if he wants to record, summarize, and communicate what he observes. At its very simplest, *this scheme is a rule for arranging observations into equivalence classes, so that observations falling into the same set are thought of as qualitatively the same and those in different classes as qualitatively different in some respect.* In general, *each observation is placed in one and only one class, making the classes mutually exclusive and exhaustive.*

The process of grouping individual observations into qualitative classes is measurement at its most primitive level. Sometimes this is called **categorical or nominal scaling.** The set of equivalence classes itself is called a **nominal scale.** There are many areas in science where the best one can do is to group observations into classes, each given a distinguishing symbol or name. For example, taxonomy in biology consists of grouping living things into phyla, genera, species, and so on, which are simply sets or classes. Psychiatric nosology contains classes such as schizophrenic, manic-depressive, paretic, and so on; individual patients are classified on the basis of symptoms and the history of their disease.

Notice that even this kind of measurement can be thought of in terms of a function: the domain of this function is a set of individual observations, and the range is the set of equivalence classes (the nominal scale). The measurement procedure is like a function rule that permits the assignment of each individual observation to one and only one qualitative class. The class paired with an individual informs us of some qualitative property that he exhibits.

The word "measurement" is usually reserved, however, for the situation where each individual is assigned a *number;* this number reflects a magnitude of some *quantitative* property. A function exists associating one and only one number with each individual, and the measurement procedure fills the role of a rule for this function.

There are at least three kinds of numerical measurement that can be distinguished: these are often called ordinal scaling interval scaling, and ratio scaling. A really accurate description of each kind of measurement is beyond the scope of this book, but we can gain some idea of these distinctions by using the function terminology once again.

Imagine a set of objects $\mathcal{O}$, and any pair of objects in that set, say $o_1$ and $o_2$. Now suppose that there is some property that all objects in the set show, such as temperature, or weight, or length, or intelligence, or motivation. Furthermore, let us suppose that each object $o$ has a certain amount or degree of that property. In principle we could assign a number, $t(o)$, to any object standing for the amount that $o$ actually "has" of that characteristic.

Ideally, in order to measure an object $o$, we would like to determine this number $t(o)$ directly. However, this is not always (or even usually) possible, and so what we do is to devise a procedure for pairing each object with another number $m(o)$, that can be called its *numerical measurement*. The measurement procedure we use constitutes a function rule, telling how to give an object $o$ its $m(o)$ value. But just any measurement procedure will not do; *we want the various $m(o)$ values at least to reflect the different $t(o)$ values for different degrees of the property*. A measurement rule would be nonsense if it gave numbers having no connection at all with the amounts of some property different objects possess. Even though we may never be able to determine the $t(o)$ values exactly, we would like to find $m(o)$ numbers that will at least be related to them in a systematic way. The measurement numbers must be good reflections of the true quantities, so that information about magnitudes actually is contained in our numerical measurements.

*Measurement operations or procedures differ in the information that the numerical measurements themselves provide about the true magnitudes*. Some ways of measuring permit us to make very strong statements about what the differences or ratios among the true magnitudes must be, and thus about the actual differences in, or proportional amounts of, some property that different objects possess. On the other hand, some measurement operations permit only the roughest inferences to be made about true magnitudes from the measurement numbers themselves.

Suppose that we had a measurement procedure or rule for assigning a number $m(o)$ to each object $o$, and suppose that the following statements were true:

1. For any pair of objects $o_1$ and $o_2$,
    $m(o_1) \neq m(o_2)$ only if $t(o_1) \neq t(o_2)$.
2. $m(o_1) > m(o_2)$ only if $t(o_1) > t(o_2)$.

In other words, by this rule we can at least say that if two measurements are unequal the true magnitudes are unequal, and if one measurement is larger than another one magnitude exceeds another. Any measurement procedure for which both statements 1 and 2 are true is an example of **ordinal scaling,** or measurement at the **ordinal level.**

For example, suppose that the objects in question were minerals of various kinds. Each mineral has a certain degree of *hardness*, represented by the quantity $t(o)$. We have no way to know these quantities directly, and so we devise the following measurement rule: take each pair of minerals and find if one *scratches* the other. Presumably, the harder mineral will scratch the softer in each case. When this has been done for each pair of minerals, give the mineral scratched by everything some number, the mineral scratched by all but the first a higher number, and so on, until the mineral scratching all others but scratched by nothing else gets the highest number of all. In each pair the "scratcher" gets a higher number than the "scratchee." (Here we are assuming tacitly that "*a* scratches *b*" and "*b* scratches *c*" implies that "*a* scratches *c*," and that we will get a *simple ordering* of "what scratches what.")

This measurement procedure gives an example of *ordinal* scaling. The possible numerical measurements themselves might be some set of numbers, such as $(1, 2, 3, 4, \cdots )$ or $(10, 17, 24, \cdots )$ or even other symbols having some conventional order, as $(A, B, C, \cdots )$. In any case, the assignment of numbers or symbols to objects is a form of ranking, showing which is "more" something. In the example, if one mineral gets a higher number than another then we can say that the first mineral is harder than the second. Notice, however, that this is really all we can say about the degree or amount of hardness each possesses. If we find two objects where $m(o_1) = 3$ and $m(o_2) = 2$ by this procedure, then it is perfectly true that the difference between the *numbers* is $3 - 2 = 1$, but we have no basis at all for saying that $t(o_1) - t(o_2) = 1$. The difference in hardness between the two minerals could be any positive number. In short, *although the numbers standing for ordinal measurements may be manipulated by arithmetic, the answer cannot necessarily be interpreted as a statement about the true magnitudes of objects, nor about the true amounts of some property.*

However, other measurement procedures give functions pairing objects with numbers where much stronger statements can be made about the true magnitudes from the numerical measurements. Suppose that the following statement, in addition to statements 1 and 2, were true:

3. $t(o) = x$ if and only if $m(o) = ax + b$, where $a > 0$.

That is, the measurement number $m(o)$ is some *linear function* of the true magnitude $x$ (the rule for a linear function is $x$ multiplied by some constant $a$ and added to some constant $b$). When the statements 1, 2, and 3 are all true, the measurement operation is called **interval scaling,** or measurement at the **interval-scale level.**

Much stronger inferences about magnitudes can be made from interval-scale measurements than from ordinal measurements. In particular, we can say something precise about *differences* in objects in terms of magnitude. Consider two objects, $o_1$ and $o_2$, once again. Then if we find

$$m(o_1) - m(o_2) = 4,$$

we can conclude that

$$t(o_1) - t(o_2) = 4a,$$

the difference between the magnitudes of the two objects is 4 units, where $a$ is simply some constant changing measurement units into "real" units, whatever they may be.

For example, finding temperature in Fahrenheit units is measurement on an interval scale. If object $o_1$ has a reading of 180° and $o_2$ has 140°, the difference $(180 - 160)$ times a constant actually *is* the difference in "temperature-magnitude" between the objects. It is perfectly meaningful to say that the first object has twenty units more temperature than the second. However, even stronger statements can be made. If $m(o_3) = 140°$, so that

$$m(o_1) - m(o_3) = 40°$$
$$m(o_1) - m(o_2) = 20°$$

then

$$\frac{40°}{20°} = \frac{t(o_1) - t(o_3)}{t(o_1) - t(o_2)} = 2.$$

One can say that in true amount of "temperature," object $o_3$ is twice as different from $o_1$ as $o_2$ is from $o_1$.

Given some measurement operation yielding an interval scale of some property, then *any other measurement operation for the same property also gives an interval scale, provided that the second way of measuring yields numbers that are a linear function of the first:* thus, let some second measurement operation give numbers $g(o)$ to each object $o$, and let it be true that

$$g(o) = c[m(o)] + d, \qquad c > 0,$$

where $c$ and $d$ are constants. However, by statement 3,

$$m(o) = ax + b$$

so that

$$g(o) = c[ax + b] + d = cax + bc + d.$$

The number $ca$ and the number $bc + d$ are constants, and so the $g(o)$ values satisfy statement 3 as well, showing that this second measurement procedure gives an interval scale. A familiar example of this principle is temperature measurement in Fahrenheit and in Centigrade degrees; each is an interval-scale measurement procedure, and the reading on one scale is a function of the reading on the other. If the $m(o)$ are Fahrenheit readings, and the $g(o)$ are Centigrade, then it will always be true that for any three objects

$$\frac{m(o_1) - m(o_3)}{m(o_1) - m(o_2)} = \frac{g(o_1) - g(o_3)}{g(o_1) - g(o_2)}.$$

Hence, if we conclude from a Fahrenheit thermometer that $o_3$ is twice as different from $o_1$ as $o_2$ is from $o_1$, we would reach exactly the same conclusion from a Centigrade thermometer.

*When measurement is at the interval-scale level, any of the ordinary operations of arithmetic may be applied to the differences between numerical measurements, and the result interpreted as a statement about magnitudes of the underlying property. The important part is this interpretation of a numerical result as a quantitative statement about the property shown by the objects.* This is not generally possible for ordinal-scale measurement numbers, but it *can* be done for differences between interval-scale numbers. In very simple language: one can do arithmetic to his heart's content on any set of numbers, but his results are not necessarily true statements about amounts of some property objects possess unless interval-scale requirements are met by the procedure for obtaining those numbers.

Interval scaling is about the best one can do in most scientific work, and even this level of measurement is all too rare in psychology. However, especially in physical science, it is sometimes possible to find measurement operations making the following statement true:

4. $t(o) = x$ if and only if $m(o) = ax$, where $a > 0$.

When the measurement operation defines a function such that statements 1 through 4 are all true, then measurement is said to be at the **ratio-scale level.** For such scales, *ratios* of numerical measurements can be interpreted directly as ratios of magnitudes of objects:

$$\frac{m(o_1)}{m(o_2)} = \frac{t(o_1)}{t(o_2)}.$$

For example, the usual procedure for finding the length of objects provides a ratio scale. If one object has a measurement value of 10 feet, and another a value of 20 feet, then it is quite legitimate to say that the second object has twice as much length as the first. Notice that this is not a statement one ordinarily makes about the *temperatures* of objects (on an interval scale): if the first object has a temperature reading of 10° and the second 20°, we do not ordinarily say that the second has twice the temperature of the first. Only when scaling is at the ratio level can the full force of ordinary arithmetic be applied directly to the measurements themselves, and the results reinterpreted as statements about magnitudes of objects.

There are any number of examples that could be adduced to illustrate the differences among these levels of measurement, and other possible intermediate levels as well. The student who is interested in this topic enough to explore it further is urged to look into the initial chapters of the books by Stevens (1951), by Thrall, Coombs, and Davis (1954), and by Torgerson (1958); each gives a slightly different perspective on psychological measurement. Our immediate concern, however, is to see the implications of different levels of measurement for probability and statistics.

## 3.2   MEASUREMENT LEVELS AND STATISTICAL METHODS

Any scientific investigation uses measurement, if only at the nominal-scale level, and certainly it behooves the investigator to think very carefully about the level of measurement he is using. Can he take the numbers he assigns to objects and deduce true statements about the property measured? Do mathematical manipulations of those numbers *necessarily* yield answers that are themselves interpretable as statements about magnitudes of some characteristic? It is quite easy to show a situation in psychology where it is not possible to go from numerical scores to statements about quantities. For example, in intelligence testing, a score called a "mental age" is sometimes the end product of giving a person a test. It is reasonable that the more intelligence a person really has the greater this mental age should be, other things being equal. *As numbers*, mental ages can be subjected to any arithmetic operation we choose, but the rub comes in translating the resultant numbers back into statements about amounts of intelligence. Thus, suppose that one five-year-old child has a mental age of 4 years, and another a mental age of 8 years. As numbers, it is quite true that 4 goes into 8 exactly 2 times; but can we assert that the second child is twice as intelligent as the first? Not without considerably more justification than we have at present. There is no solid theoretical or empirical reason for thinking that intelligence scores must relate to "real" amounts of intelligence in the way specified by the definitions of ratio, or even interval, scaling. On the other hand, we do feel justified in thinking of intelligence tests as giving at least ordinal scales, if not more. The point is that one cannot simply assume that a certain level of scaling is or is not reached without some theoretical or empirical basis, showing how the quantities we hope to measure actually are reflected in the numbers we get.

The problem of measurement, and especially of attaining interval scales, is an extremely serious one for psychology. It is unfortunate but true that in their search for quantitative methods psychologists sometimes overlook the question of level of measurement and tend to read quite unjustified meanings into their results. This has brought about a reaction in some quarters, where people insist that psychologists are not justified in using most of the machinery of mathematics on their generally low-level measurements. Others have argued that psychologists are too concerned with level of measurement, and that ordinary mathematical techniques apply to virtually any numerical measurements. There has been considerable controversy about the applicability of statistical methods according to the scale requirements met by the data. Indeed, some statistics texts have even been organized on the basis of the different levels of measurement.

It seems to this author that statistics qua statistics is quite neutral on this issue. In developing procedures, mathematical statisticians have assumed that techniques involving numerical scores, orderings, or categorization are to be applied where these numbers or classes are appropriate and meaningful within the experimenter's problem. If the statistical method involves the procedures of arithmetic used on numerical scores, then the numerical answer is formally correct. Even if the numbers are the purest nonsense, having no relation to real magnitudes or the properties of real things, the answers are still right *as numbers*. The difficulty comes with the interpretation of these numbers back into statements about the real world. If nonsense is put into the mathematical system, nonsense is sure to come out.

On the other hand, there are many instances where the experimenter is interested in numerical scores *as scores*. For example, he may want to compare one group of five-year-old children with another on the basis of mental age scores, and so he averages the numerical scores for each group. The fact that he cannot say that one group has an average of 65 units of intelligence and the other 60 units does not alter the practical advantage he may gain by finding average scores. There are very many instances where the level of measurement may not reach the level supposed by the statistical technique, and yet the method itself may be quite adequate for showing what the experimenter wants to know. Any statistical method designed for numerical scores can be used, provided that the purely mathematical-statistical requirements of the method are met, and provided that the experimenter wants to reach a conclusion about such measurements. However, he is not necessarily entitled to translate the statistical result back into a direct numerical statement about quantities or magnitudes of some property, unless measurement is at the interval- or ratio-scale level. Even so, although the statistical result does not translate into a conclusion about the properties of objects, it is nonetheless a true conclusion about *measurement numbers of this sort*. In some instances, this may be enough for the experimenter's immediate purpose.

The problem of level of measurement really lies outside the province of mathematics and statistics. Statistics deals with numbers, and statistical methods yield conclusions based on numbers, but there is absolutely nothing in the mathematical machinery that whistles and waves a flag to show that the numbers supplied are not really interval-scale measurements of some property of objects or human beings. The machinery works the same way and gives the same result regardless of whether the numbers are made up from the whole cloth or are the product of the most refined measurement procedures imaginable. Only the users of the statistical result, the experimenter and his readers, can judge the reinterpretability of the numerical result into a valid statement about properties of things. Sometimes the psychologist regards the numerical conclusion as a statement about *scores*, and does not go beyond this statement to a conclusion about the real magnitudes of some property. In other instances the whole investigation makes no sense at all unless the numerical conclusion can refer directly to magnitudes of some property. Surely the individual psychologist knows his problem and his measurement procedures better than a stranger dogmatizing about hypothetical situations in a textbook! The experimenting psychologist must face the problem of the interpretation of statistical results *within psychology* and on *extramathematical* grounds.

For this reason, very little more will be said about scales of measurement in this book. Everything depends upon what the psychologist is measuring, how he goes about it, what he is trying to find out, and, most of all, what he wants to say about the "real properties" underlying his numerical measurements.

Most of the statistical techniques introduced in this book are designed for numerical scores, presumably arising from application of measurement techniques at the interval-scale level. This does not mean that these techniques cannot be applied to numerical data where the interval-scale level of measurement is not met; these techniques can be applied to *any* numerical data where the purely *statistical* assumptions are met. It does mean, however, that caution must be exercised in the interpretation of these statistical results in terms of some property the experimenter intended to measure. The statistical conclusion may be quite valid for these scores *as scores*, but the experimenter must think quite seriously about the further interpretations he gives to the result.

Of course, it is completely obvious that interval scales simply cannot be attained for some things. It may be that an ordering of objects on some basis is the very best the experimenter can do. In this case, ordinal methods like those in Chapter 18 are helpful; each of these techniques is designed specifically for ordinal data. Even when measurement is only nominal, statistical methods can be applied; some of these are discussed in Chapter 17. The most common situation is, however, one where numerical measurements are made, but where the interval-scale assumptions are hard to justify. In these cases, the user of the statistical techniques should understand the limitations imposed by his measurement device (not by statistics): the road from objects to numbers may be easy, but the return trip from numbers to properties of objects is not.

### 3.3 FREQUENCY DISTRIBUTIONS

As we have just seen, even in the simplest instances of measurement the experimenter makes some $N$ observations and classifies them into a set of qualitative measurement classes. These qualitative classes are mutually exclusive and exhaustive, so that each observation falls into one and only one class.

As a summarization of his observations, the experimenter often reports the various possible classes, together with the number of observations falling into each. This may be done by a simple listing of classes, each paired with its frequency number, the number of cases observed in that category. The same information may be displayed as a graph, perhaps with the different classes represented by points or segments of a horizontal axis, the frequency shown by a point or a vertical bar above each class. Regardless of how this information is displayed, such a listing of classes and their frequencies is called a *frequency distribution. Any representation of the relation between a set of mutually exclusive and exhaustive measurement classes and the frequency of each is a frequency distribution.*

Notice that a frequency distribution is a function: each of a set of classes is paired with a number, its frequency. Thus, in principle, a frequency distribution of real or theoretical data can be shown by any of the three ways one specifies any function: an explicit listing of class and frequency pairs, graphically, or by the statement of a rule for pairing a class of observations with its frequency. In describing actual data, the first two methods are almost always used alone, but there are circumstances where the experimenter wants to describe some theoretical frequency distribution, and in this case the mathematical rule for the function sometimes is stated.

The set of measurement classes may correspond to a nominal, an ordinal, an interval, or a ratio scale. Although the various possible classes will be qualitative in some instances and number classes in others, a frequency distribution can always be constructed, provided that each and every observation goes into one and only one class. Thus, for example, suppose that some $N$ native United States citizens are observed, and the state in which each was born noted. This is like nominal measurement, where the measurement classes consist of the fifty states (and the District of Columbia) into which subjects could be categorized. On the other hand, the subjects might be students in a course and graded according to $A$, $B$, $C$, and so on. Here the frequency distribution would show how many got $A$, $B$, and so on. Notice that in this case the measurement actually is ordinal: $A$ is better than $B$, $B$ better than $C$. Nevertheless, the frequency distribution is constructed in the same way, except that the various classes are displayed in their proper order.

Even when measurement is at the interval- or ratio-scale level, one actually reports frequency distributions in this general way. Suppose that $N$ college students were each weighed, and the weights noted to the nearest pound. The set of weight classes into which students are placed would perhaps consist of

fifty or sixty different numbers; a weight class is the set of students getting the
same weight number. There may be only one, or even no students, in a particular
weight class. Nevertheless, the frequency distribution would show the pairing of
each possible class with some number from zero to $N$, its frequency.

As we shall see, when the number of possible classes is very large,
or even potentially infinite, the task of constructing a frequency distribution is
made easier by a process of combining classes. The principle is, however, always
the same: a display of the function relating classes and their frequencies.

### 3.4  FREQUENCY DISTRIBUTIONS WITH A SMALL NUMBER OF MEASUREMENT CLASSES

The reasons for dealing with frequency distributions rather than
raw data are not hard to see. Raw data almost always take the form of some sort
of listing of pairs, each consisting of an object and its measurement class or number. Thus, if we were noting the hair color of eleven persons, our raw data might
be something like this:

|              |        |
|--------------|--------|
| John Jones   | black  |
| Mary Smith   | blonde |
| Jim Hardy    | brown  |
| Horace Goodman | brown |
| Alice Adams  | blonde |
| Ann Wilk     | red    |
| William Thomas | brown |
| Bert Fox     | red    |
| Homer Giddens | black |
| Shirley Snider | brown |
| Richard Rowan | blonde |

This set of pairs does contain all the relevant information, but if there are a great
many objects being measured such a listing is not only laborious but also very
confusing to anyone who is trying to get a picture of the set of observations as a
whole. If we are interested only in the "pattern" of hair color in the group the
names of the persons are irrelevant, and all that is necessary is the number of
individuals having each hair color.

There are only four measurement classes in this example that show
one or more cases, and so the frequency distribution can be displayed in this way:

| Hair color | Frequency |
|------------|-----------|
| black      | 2         |
| red        | 2         |
| blonde     | 3         |
| brown      | 4         |
|            | 11 = $N$  |

It is possible to illustrate this idea of a frequency distribution in any number of ways: consider a study done on a group of twenty-five males, in order to determine their blood types. The subjects were classified variously as having blood types "A," "B," "AB," or "O." Table 3.4.1 lists the measurements of these

**Table 3.4.1**

| Man number | Blood type |
|:---:|:---:|
| 1 | A |
| 2 | B |
| 3 | A |
| 4 | A |
| 5 | A |
| 6 | AB |
| 7 | O |
| 8 | A |
| 9 | A |
| 10 | A |
| 11 | O |
| 12 | B |
| 13 | O |
| 14 | B |
| 15 | A |
| 16 | B |
| 17 | O |
| 18 | B |
| 19 | O |
| 20 | A |
| 21 | B |
| 22 | B |
| 23 | A |
| 24 | A |
| 25 | O |

twenty-five men. These data condense into the following frequency distribution:

| Class | $f$ |
|:---:|:---:|
| A | 11 |
| B | 7 |
| AB | 1 |
| O | 6 |
| | $25 = N$ |

In another study, 2000 families in some city were interviewed about their preferences in art, music, literature, recreation, and so forth. After each interview, the family was characterized as having "highbrow," "middlebrow," or "lowbrow" tastes. This we can consider as a case of ordinal-scale measurement, since these three "taste" categories do seem to be ordered: "highbrow" and "lowbrow" should be more different from each other than "middlebrow" is from either. A listing of families in terms of these classes would be confusing, if not grounds for libel suits. However, just as before, we can construct a frequency distribution summarizing these data:

| Class | $f$ |
|---|---|
| highbrow | 50 |
| middlebrow | 990 |
| lowbrow | 960 |
|  | $2000 = N$ |

Notice how much more clearly the characteristics of the group as a whole emerge from a frequency distribution such as this than they possibly could from a listing of 2000 names each paired with a rating.

It is appropriate to point out that a frequency distribution provides clarity at the expense of some information in the data. It is not possible to know from the frequency distribution alone whether the family of John Jones at 2193 Spring Street is high-, middle-, or low-browed. Such information about *particular* objects is sacrificed in a frequency distribution to gain a picture of the group of measurements *as a whole*. This is true of all descriptive statistics; we want clear pictures of large numbers of measurements, and we can do this only by losing detail about particular objects. The process of weeding out particular qualities of the object that happen to be irrelevant to our purpose, begun whenever we measure, is continued when we summarize a set of measurements.

## 3.5  GROUPED DISTRIBUTIONS

In the distributions shown above, there were a few "natural" categories into which all the data fit. It often happens, however, that data are measured in some way giving a great many categories into which a given observation might fall. Indeed, the number of potential categories of description often vastly exceeds the number of cases observed, so that little or no economy of description would be gained by constructing a distribution showing each *possible* class. The most usual such situation occurs when the data are measured in numerical terms. For instance, in the measurement of height or weight, there are, in principle, an infinite number of numerical classes into which an observation might fall: all the positive real numbers. Even when the measurements result in fewer than an infinite number of possibilities, it is still quite common for the number of available categories to be very large.

For this reason, it is necessary to form **grouped** frequency distributions. Here the domain of the frequency function is not each possible measurement category, but rather intervals or groupings of categories.

For example, consider a number of people who have been given an intelligence test. The data of interest are the numerical IQ scores. Immediately, we run into a problem of procedure. It could very well turn out that for, say 150 individuals, the IQ score would be different for each case, and thus a frequency distribution using each different IQ number as a measurement class would not condense our data any more than a simple listing.

The solution to this problem lies in grouping the possible measurement classes into new classes, called **class intervals,** each including a range of score possibilities. Proceeding in this way, if the IQs 105, 104, 100, 101, and 102 should turn up in our data, instead of listing each in a different class, we might put them all into a single class, 100–105, along with any other IQ measurements that fall between these limits. Similarly, we group other sets of numbers into class intervals. On our doing this, one way that the frequency distribution might look for a group of 150 persons is shown in Table 3.5.1.

**Table 3.5.1**

| Class interval | Midpoint | f |
|---|---|---|
| 124–129 | 126.5 | 8 |
| 118–123 | 120.5 | 0 |
| 112–117 | 114.5 | 10 |
| 106–111 | 108.5 | 20 |
| 100–105 | 102.5 | 65 |
| 94– 99 | 96.5 | 22 |
| 88– 93 | 90.5 | 23 |
| 82– 87 | 84.5 | 2 |
| | | 150 = N |

Forming class intervals has enabled us to condense the data so that a simple statement of the frequency distribution can be made in terms of only a few classes. In this distribution, the various class intervals are shown in order in the first column on the left. The extreme right column lists the frequencies, each paired with the class in that row of the table. The sum of the frequencies must be *N*, the total number of observations. The middle column contains the midpoint of each class interval; these will be discussed in Section 3.8.

## 3.6 CLASS INTERVAL SIZE AND CLASS LIMITS

The first problem in constructing a grouped frequency distribution is deciding upon a class interval size. Just how large shall the range of numbers included in a class be? The class interval size for a grouped distribution is the difference between the largest and the smallest number that may go into any class interval. We will let the symbol $i$ denote this interval size.

In the example above, as in most examples to follow, the size $i$ is the same for each class interval. This is the accepted convention for most work in psychology. (Some exceptions will be mentioned in Section 3.10, however.) For the example, $i = 6$, which means that the largest and the smallest score going into a class interval differ by six units. Take the class interval labelled 100–105. It may seem that the smallest number going into this interval is 100, and the largest 105; this is not, however, true. Actually, the numbers 99.5, 99.6, 99.7 would also go in this interval, should they occur in the data. Also, the numbers 105.1, 105.2 are included. On the other hand, 99.2 or 105.8 would be excluded. The interval actually includes any number *greater than or equal to* 99.5 *and less than* 105.5. These are called the **real limits** of the interval, in contrast to those actually listed, which are the **apparent limits**. Thus, the real limits of the interval 100–105 are

$$99.5 \text{ to } 105.5$$

and

$$i = 105.5 - 99.5 = 6.$$

In general,

real lower limit = apparent lower limit minus .5(unit difference)
real upper limit = apparent upper limit plus .5(unit difference).

The term "unit difference" demands some explanation. In measuring something we usually find some limitation on the accuracy of the measurement, and seldom can one measure with *any* desired degree of accuracy. For this reason, measurement in numerical terms is always rounded, either during the measurement operation itself, or after the measurement has taken place. In measuring weight, for example, we obtain accuracy only within the nearest pound, or the nearest one tenth of a pound, or one hundredth of a pound, and so on. If one were constructing a frequency distribution where weight had been rounded to the nearest pound, then a unit difference is one pound, and the real limits of an interval such as 150–190 would be 149.5–190.5. The $i$ here would be 41 pounds.

On the other hand, suppose that weights were accurate to the nearest one tenth of a pound; then the unit difference would be .1 pound, and the real class interval limits would be

$$149.05\text{–}190.05.$$

The way that rounding has been carried out will have a real bearing on how the successive class intervals will be constructed. Suppose that we wanted to construct the distribution of annual income for a group of American men, where the income figures have been rounded to the nearest thousand dollars. We have decided that the apparent upper limit of the top interval shall be 25,000 dollars, and that $i$ should equal 5,000. Then the classes would have the following limits:

| Real | Apparent |
|------|----------|
| 20,500–25,500 | 21,000–25,000 |
| 15,500–20,500 | 16,000–20,000 |
| 10,500–15,500 | 11,000–15,000 |
| 5,500–10,500 | 6,000–10,000 |
| 500– 5,500 | 1,000– 5,000 |

Here, one half of a unit difference is 500 dollars.

Now suppose that each man's income has been rounded to the nearest one hundred dollars. Once again, with $i$ = \$5,000 and with the top apparent limit \$25,000, we form class intervals, but this time the class limits are:

| Real | Apparent |
|------|----------|
| 20,050–25,050 | 20,100–25,000 |
| 15,050–20,050 | 15,100–20,000 |
| 10,050–15,050 | 10,100–15,000 |
| 5,050–10,050 | 5,100–10,000 |
| 50– 5,050 | 100– 5,000 |

This difference in unit for the two distributions could make a difference in the "picture" we get of the data. For example, a man making exactly \$20,100 would fall into the top interval in the second distribution, but into the second from top interval in the first. It is important to decide upon the accuracy represented in the data before the real limits for the class intervals are chosen. Is every digit recorded in the raw data regarded as significant, or will the data be rounded to the "nearest" unit?

## 3.7 INTERVAL SIZE AND THE NUMBER OF CLASS INTERVALS

One can use any number for $i$ in setting up a distribution. However, it should be obvious that there is very little point in choosing $i$ smaller than the unit difference (for example, letting $i$ = .1 pound when the data are in nearest whole pounds), or in choosing $i$ so large that all observations fall into the same class interval. Furthermore, $i$ is usually chosen to be a *whole number* of units, whatever the unit may be. Even within these restrictions, there is considerable flexibility of choice. For example, the data of Section 3.5 could have been put into a distribution with $i$ = 3, as shown in Table 3.7.1. Notice that this distribution with $i$ = 3 is somewhat different from the distribution with $i$ = 6, even though they are based on the same set of data. For one thing, here there are sixteen class intervals, whereas there were eight before. This second distribution also gives somewhat more detail than the first about the original set of data. We now know, for example, that there was no one in the group of persons who got an IQ score between the real limits of 83.5 and 86.5, whereas we could not have told this from the first distribution. We can also tell that more cases showed IQs between 101.5 and 104.5 than between 98.5 and 101.5; conceivably this could be a fact of some importance. On the other hand, the first distribution gives a simpler and, in a sense, a neater picture of the group than does the second.

**Table 3.7.1**

| Class interval | Midpoint | f |
|:---:|:---:|:---:|
| 126–128 | 127 | 5 |
| 123–125 | 124 | 3 |
| 120–122 | 121 | 0 |
| 117–119 | 118 | 0 |
| 114–116 | 115 | 7 |
| 111–113 | 112 | 3 |
| 108–110 | 109 | 8 |
| 105–107 | 106 | 13 |
| 102–104 | 103 | 44 |
| 99–101 | 100 | 20 |
| 96– 98 | 97 | 10 |
| 93– 95 | 94 | 12 |
| 90– 92 | 91 | 14 |
| 87– 89 | 88 | 9 |
| 84– 86 | 85 | 0 |
| 81– 83 | 82 | 2 |
| | | 150 = N |

The decision facing the maker of frequency distributions is, "Shall I use a small class-interval size and thus get more detail, or shall I use a large class-interval size and get more condensation of the data?" There is no fixed answer to this question; it depends on the kind of data and the uses to which they will be put. However, a convention does exist which says that for most purposes *ten to twenty class intervals* give a good balance between condensation and necessary detail, and in practice one usually chooses his class-interval size to make about that number of intervals.

A handy rule of thumb for deciding about the size of class intervals is given by

$$i = \frac{\text{highest score in data} - \text{lowest score}}{\text{number of class intervals}}.$$

After deciding on some convenient number of class intervals, you divide this number into the difference between the highest and lowest scores, or the **range** of scores, and find the size that $i$ will have to be. In practice, this may give an $i$ that is not a whole number, in which case you simply use the nearest whole number for *i.* In the example just given, the data showed 128 as the highest and 82 as the lowest scores, with a range of 46. To find *i* giving about 16 class intervals we would divide the range by 16:

$$\frac{128 - 82}{16} = 2.87.$$

Since this is a decimal number, we choose the nearest whole number, or 3.

Note that in the last distribution some intervals show a frequency of 0; it is not absolutely necessary that such intervals be listed. However, intervals with zero frequency are usually listed when they fall between other intervals that do not have a zero frequency. We could have had an interval 129–131 having a zero frequency in the last distribution; however, we did not list this interval because, unlike the interval 120–122, it did not fall between other nonzero intervals.

Two other conventions are useful in making distributions from data. The first is that the class intervals are usually listed starting with low numbers at the bottom of the list and with the high numbers at the top, as shown in the example. Another convention followed here is to start figuring the class intervals by listing the *highest score* in the data as the *apparent upper limit of the top interval;* then it is a simple matter to find the other apparent upper limits by subtracting the class-interval size successively from this number. The apparent *lower* limit of each interval is then *one unit more* than the *upper* apparent limit of the interval below it. For example, suppose 128 were the top score in the data, and that *i* were 3. Taking 128 as the highest apparent limit, the upper limit of the next interval would be 128 − 3, or 125, next would be 125 − 3 or 122, and so on, until all upper limits were found. Then, given an interval with apparent upper limit of 122, the lower limit of the next interval up would be 123, and given the interval with upper limit 125, the lower limit of the next interval up would be 126, and so on.

## 3.8 MIDPOINTS OF CLASS INTERVALS

There is one more feature of frequency distributions that has not yet been discussed. When one puts a set of measurements into a frequency distribution, he loses the power to say exactly what the original numbers were. For the example of Section 3.7, if a person in the group of 150 cases has an IQ of 102, he is simply counted as one of the 44 individuals who make up the frequency for the interval 102–104. You cannot tell from the distribution exactly what the IQs of those 44 individuals were, but only that they fell within the limits 102–104. What do we call the IQs of these 44 individuals? We call them all 103, the midpoint of the interval. **The midpoint of any class interval is that number which would fall exactly halfway among the possible numbers included in the interval.** A moment's thought will convince you that 103 falls halfway between the real limits of 101.5 and 104.5. In a like fashion, all 5 cases falling into the class interval 126–128 will be called by the midpoint 127; all 3 cases in the interval 123–125 will be called 124, and so on for each of the other class intervals.

The real limits can also be defined in terms of the midpoint:

$$\text{real limits} = \text{midpoint} \pm .5i.$$

Thus, given only the midpoints of the distribution, one can find the class limits.

In computations using grouped distributions the midpoint is used to substitute for each raw score in the interval. For this reason, it is convenient to choose an odd number for $i$ whenever possible; this makes the midpoint a whole number of units and simplifies computations.

## 3.9 ANOTHER EXAMPLE OF A GROUPED FREQUENCY DISTRIBUTION

Suppose that seventy-five students in high school had been used as subjects in an experiment on verbal memory. Each student was given a list containing forty-eight pairs of words and allowed to study the list as a whole for ten

### Table 3.9.1
SCORES OF SEVENTY-FIVE STUDENTS IN ONE TRIAL OF PAIRED-ASSOCIATE LEARNING

| Student | Score | Student | Score | Student | Score |
|---------|-------|---------|-------|---------|-------|
| 1 | 19 | 26 | 18 | 51 | 15 |
| 2 | 16 | 27 | 14 | 52 | 15 |
| 3 | 11 | 28 | 26 | 53 | 14 |
| 4 | 13 | 29 | 16 | 54 | 11 |
| 5 | 12 | 30 | 19 | 55 | 23 |
| 6 | 20 | 31 | 21 | 56 | 13 |
| 7 | 11 | 32 | 17 | 57 | 19 |
| 8 | 24 | 33 | 20 | 58 | 17 |
| 9 | 19 | 34 | 12 | 59 | 21 |
| 10 | 16 | 35 | 22 | 60 | 15 |
| 11 | 12 | 36 | 11 | 61 | 20 |
| 12 | 24 | 37 | 13 | 62 | 16 |
| 13 | 19 | 38 | 16 | 63 | 12 |
| 14 | 17 | 39 | 10 | 64 | 10 |
| 15 | 18 | 40 | 17 | 65 | 10 |
| 16 | 25 | 41 | 17 | 66 | 15 |
| 17 | 16 | 42 | 19 | 67 | 18 |
| 18 | 20 | 43 | 11 | 68 | 10 |
| 19 | 17 | 44 | 10 | 69 | 19 |
| 20 | 19 | 45 | 15 | 70 | 14 |
| 21 | 15 | 46 | 10 | 71 | 12 |
| 22 | 35 | 47 | 13 | 72 | 18 |
| 23 | 16 | 48 | 13 | 73 | 14 |
| 24 | 11 | 49 | 14 | 74 | 15 |
| 25 | 26 | 50 | 10 | 75 | 20 |

minutes. The first member of each pair was then shown in order to the individual student, and his task was to recall the second word. The raw data are shown in Table 3.9.1. The largest number of words recalled by any student was thirty-five, and the smallest number was ten. The range was thus $35 - 10$ or 25.

Now we want to make a frequency distribution having about ten class intervals. According to our rule of thumb, given above:

$$i = \frac{\text{range}}{\text{number of intervals}} = \frac{25}{10} = 2.5.$$

Thus $i = 3$ should provide us with a convenient class-interval size.

We start with the largest number, 35, and make it the upper apparent limit of the highest class interval. That interval must then have real limits of 32.5 and 35.5 with apparent limits of 33–35. The real limits of the second from highest interval must be 29.5–32.5, and so on. Each time, the difference between the real limits to an interval must be $i$, or 3, and the differences between the successive lower apparent limits (and also successive upper limits) must also be 3. Proceeding in this way, we find the class intervals shown in Table 3.9.2.

### Table 3.9.2

NUMBER OF PAIRED ASSOCIATES
RECALLED ON THE FIRST TRIAL
BY A SAMPLE OF SEVENTY-FIVE
HIGH SCHOOL STUDENTS

| Class interval | Midpoint | $f$ |
|---|---|---|
| 33–35 | 34 | 1 |
| 30–32 | 31 | 0 |
| 27–29 | 28 | 0 |
| 24–26 | 25 | 5 |
| 21–23 | 22 | 4 |
| 18–20 | 19 | 17 |
| 15–17 | 16 | 20 |
| 12–14 | 13 | 15 |
| 9–11 | 10 | 13 |
| | | 75 = N |

Table 3.9.2 is completed by inspecting the raw data to find the number of cases that fall into each class interval. Only one case falls between the real limits 32.5–35.5, and so the frequency for the highest interval is 1. The frequency for the lowest interval is 13, since exactly thirteen individuals showed scores between the real limits 8.5 and 11.5. Just as in the preceding examples, the midpoint for each interval stands exactly midway between the two real limits.

What can the experimenter tell from looking at this distribution that would not have been obvious from the raw data? First of all the "typical" range of performance is really a fairly short interval of scores; the large majority of students scored in the range of 11 points from 9 through 20. The most "popular" score interval is 15–17. Note that this concentration of cases lies at the low end of the *conceivable range* of scores 0 through 48. If the experimenter thinks of a score as reflecting the student's ability to memorize paired associates, then the task is, by and large, a hard one for the students. The single individual scoring in the interval 33–35 is really most atypical. His score falls very far from the bulk of the cases in the distribution.

Naturally, there are other, more precise statements that the experimenter can make about what this distribution shows. We will discuss these summary indices in Chapter 6. For the moment, however, it should be clear that a distribution does communicate information about a set of observations *as a whole* even without further analysis of the data.

### 3.10   FREQUENCY DISTRIBUTIONS WITH OPEN OR UNEQUAL CLASS INTERVALS

Quite often the data are such that it is not possible to make a frequency distribution with intervals of a constant size. This most commonly occurs in psychology when exact scores are not known for some of the cases. For example, in a study of the trials that it takes an animal to learn a discrimination problem the experimenter found that out of 100 animals, 5 could not learn the problem in sixty trials. He felt that some of the animals would never learn the problem at all, and he ceased running these animals at the sixtieth trial. This means, however, that the 5 animals could not be given an exact score, and could only be put in the top class of the score distribution, in an interval called "sixty or more." This interval is **open,** since there is no way to determine its upper real limit. Furthermore, there is no way to give such an open interval a midpoint.

It is perfectly correct to show open intervals at either end of a frequency distribution. However, no computations involving the midpoints can be carried out from this distribution, unless the cases in the open intervals are dropped from the sample.

In other instances, it may be that there are extreme scores in a distribution that are widely separated from the bulk of the cases. When this is true, a class-interval size that is small enough to show "detail" in the more concentrated part of the distribution will eventuate in very many classes with zero frequency before the extreme scores are included. Enlarging the class-interval size will reduce the number of unnecessary intervals, but will also sacrifice detail. When this situation arises, it is often wise to have a varying class-interval size, so that the class intervals are narrow where the detail is desired, but rather broad toward the extreme or extremes of the distribution. In this case, class-interval limits and midpoints can be found in the usual way, provided that one takes care to notice where the interval size changes. Furthermore, midpoints of these intervals can be used for further computations using the methods given in Chapter 6.

### 3.11 GRAPHS OF DISTRIBUTIONS: HISTOGRAMS

Now we direct our attention for a time to the problem of putting a frequency distribution into graphic form. Often a graph shows that the old bromide, "a picture is worth a thousand words," is really true. If the purpose is to provide an easily grasped summary of data, nothing is so effective as a graph of a distribution.

FIG. 3.11.1 (*left*). Blood types of twenty-five American males. FIG. 3.11.2 (*right*). Taste ratings for two thousand American families.

FIG. 3.11.3. Intelligence quotients of a sample of one hundred and fifty subjects.

There are undoubtedly all sorts of ways any frequency distribution might be graphed. A glance at any national news magazine will show many examples of graphs which have been made striking by some ingenious artist. However, we shall deal with only three "garden varieties": the histogram, the frequency polygon, and the cumulative frequency polygon.

The histogram is really a version of the familiar "bar graph." In a histogram, each class or class interval is represented by a portion of the horizontal axis. Then over each class interval is erected a bar or rectangle equal in height to

FIG. 3.11.4

the frequency for that particular class or class interval. The histograms representing the frequency distributions in Sections 3.4 and 3.7 are shown in Figures 3.11.1–3. It is customary to label both the horizontal and the vertical axes as shown in these figures, and to give a label to the graph as a whole. In the case where class intervals are employed to group numerical measurements, a saving of time and space may

be accomplished by labeling the class intervals by their midpoints (as in Figure 3.11.3) rather than by their apparent or real limits. With categorical measurements, this problem does not arise, of course, since each class can only be given its name or symbol.

If you will look at the two histograms shown in Figures 3.11.4 and 3.11.5, you will get very different first impressions, even though they represent the same frequency distribution. These two figures illustrate the effect that proportion can have on the viewer's first impressions of graphed distributions. Various conventions about graphs of distributions exist in different fields, of course. In fact, those who make a business of using statistics for persuasion often choose a proportion designed to give a certain impression. However, in psychology, it is most usual to find graphs arranged so

FIG. 3.11.5

that the vertical axis is about three fourths as long as the horizontal. This usually will give a clear and esthetically pleasing picture of the distribution.

### 3.12 FREQUENCY POLYGONS

The histogram is a useful way to picture any sort of frequency distribution, regardless of the scale of measurement of the data. However, a second kind of graph is often used to show frequency distributions, particularly those that are based upon numerical data: this is the frequency polygon. In order to construct the frequency polygon from a frequency distribution one proceeds exactly as though one were making a histogram; that is, the horizontal axis is marked off

FIG. 3.12.1. Intelligence quotients of a sample of one hundred and fifty subjects.

into class intervals and the vertical into numbers representing frequencies. However, instead of using a bar to show the frequency for each class, a point on the graph corresponding to the midpoint of the interval and the frequency of the interval is found. These points are then joined by straight lines, each being connected to the point immediately succeeding and the point immediately following, as in Figure 3.12.1.

The frequency polygon is especially useful when there are a great many potential class intervals, and it thus finds its chief use with numerical data that could, in principle, represent a continuous variable. For a distribution based on a very large number of numerical measurements on a potentially continuous scale, if we maintained the same proportions in our graph, but employed a much greater number of class intervals, the frequency polygon would provide a picture more like a smooth curve, as shown in Figures 3.12.2–4, based on several thousand cases. Although the function rule describing the frequency polygon may be extremely complicated to state, the function rule for a smooth curve approximately the same as that of the distribution may be relatively easy to find. For this reason, a frequency polygon based upon interval-or ratio-scale measurement with a relatively large number of classes is sometimes "smoothed" by creating a curve that approximates the shape of the frequency polygon. This new curve may have a rule that is simple to state and that may serve as an approximation of the rule describing the frequency distribution itself. While the procedures for smoothing such a frequency polygon and finding a function rule that comes close to describing the distribution are outside the scope of this book, they may be found in many advanced texts on the analysis of experimental data. Suffice it to say, for the moment, that when we come to a discussion of the "shapes" of distributions, we shall often refer to smooth curves as examples of types of distributions, when actually the frequency distributions themselves could only be represented by "jagged" polygons composed of straight lines. Nevertheless we may use the smooth curves as good approximations to the picture that the frequency polygon presents of the distribution.

FIG.  3.12.2                    FIG.  3.12.3

FIG.  3.12.4

## 3.13   CUMULATIVE FREQUENCY DISTRIBUTIONS

For some purposes it is convenient to make a different arrangement of data into a distribution, called a cumulative frequency distribution. Instead of showing the relation that exists between a class interval and its frequency, **a cumulative distribution shows the relation between a class interval and the frequency at or below its real upper limit.** In other words, the cumulative frequency shows how many cases fall into *this interval or below.* Thus, in the distribution in Section 3.5, the lowest interval shows two cases, and its cumulative frequency is 2. Now the next class interval has a frequency of 23, so that its cumulative frequency is 23 + 2, or 25. The third interval has a frequency of 22, and its cumulative frequency is 22 + 23 + 2, or 47, and so on. The cumulative frequency of the very top interval must always be $N$, since all cases must lie either in the top interval or below. The cumulative frequency distribution for the example of Section 3.5 is given below.

| Class interval | Cumulative frequency |
|----------------|----------------------|
| 124–129 | 150 |
| 118–123 | 142 |
| 112–117 | 142 |
| 106–111 | 132 |
| 100–105 | 112 |
| 94– 99 | 47 |
| 88– 93 | 25 |
| 82– 87 | 2 |

Cumulative frequency distributions are often graphed as polygons. The axes of the graph are laid out just as for a frequency polygon, except that the class intervals are labeled by their *real upper limits* rather than by their midpoints. The numbers on the vertical axis are now cumulative frequencies, of course. The

FIG. 3.13.1

graph of the example from Section 3.5 is shown in Figure 3.13.1. Cumulative frequency distributions always have more or less this characteristic S shape, although the slope and the size of the "tails" on the S will vary greatly from distribution to distribution. Like a frequency polygon, a cumulative frequency polygon is sometimes smoothed into a curve as similar as possible to the polygon. You sometimes encounter a reference to such a smoothed cumulative distribution curve under the term **ogive**.

## 3.14 PROBABILITY DISTRIBUTIONS

Suppose that there were some finite set of objects, and that we sampled these objects at random with replacement. Each object sampled is measured in some way. The measurement may be at the nominal-, ordinal-, interval-, or ratio-scale level, so long as each object is measured by the same procedure. *Now notice that each object is an elementary event, and that the actual measurement class or number assigned each object is an event.* Since many different elementary events can be allotted the same number or classification, each measurement class is an event class. These measurement events are mutually exclusive and exhaustive, each object being given one and only one number or category.

Furthermore, since the different possible measurement classes are events, there is a probability that can be assigned to each; there is, for example, some probability that the score of an object will be 10, or that the object will be assigned to the class "high need for achievement." In short, given the sample space $S$ and a set of measurement events, we can think of a probability function pairing some probability with each possible measurement class.

**Any statement of a probability function having a set of mutually exclusive and exhaustive events for its domain is a probability distribution.**

Notice how the idea of probability distribution exactly parallels that of frequency distribution: each is a function on a set of mutually exclusive and exhaustive measurement classes. In a frequency distribution, each measurement class is paired with a frequency, and in a probability distribution each is paired with its probability. Just as the sum of the frequencies must be $N$ in a distribution, so must the sum of the probabilities be 1.00.

As a simple example of a probability distribution, imagine a sample space of all boys of high-school age. A boy is selected at random and classified as "right-handed," "left-handed," or "ambidextrous." The probability distribution might be:

| Class | $p$ |
|---|---|
| right | .60 |
| left | .30 |
| ambidextrous | .10 |
| | 1.00 |

Or, perhaps, the height of a boy drawn at random is measured. Some seven class intervals are used to record the height of any boy, and the probability distribution might be

| Height in inches | $p$ |
|---|---|
| 78–82 | .002 |
| 73–77 | .021 |
| 68–72 | .136 |
| 63–67 | .682 |
| 58–62 | .136 |
| 53–57 | .021 |
| 48–52 | .002 |
| | 1.000 |

Here, each class interval is an event.

*Corresponding to any frequency distribution of N cases there is a probability distribution, if single cases are selected from the total group of N cases at random with replacement.* Thus, imagine a set of 50 persons, whose scores on some test formed the following distribution:

| Scores | f |
|--------|-----|
| 90–99 | 3 |
| 80–89 | 8 |
| 70–79 | 15 |
| 60–69 | 14 |
| 50–59 | 10 |
| | 50 |

One person is drawn at random from among this set. What are the probabilities associated with the various intervals he might fall into? If the individuals are all assumed equally likely to be observed, then for any class interval $A$,

$$p(A) = \frac{\text{frequency of } A}{\text{total frequency}}.$$

Thus, the class interval 90–99 has a probability of 3/50, or .06, and the other probabilities can be found in the same way, giving

| Scores | p |
|--------|-----|
| 90–99 | .06 |
| 80–89 | .16 |
| 70–79 | .30 |
| 60–69 | .28 |
| 50–59 | .20 |
| | 1.00 |

In short, any group of cases summarized in a frequency distribution can also be regarded as a sample space of *potential* observations. If a single case is sampled at random, then the probabilities of the various classes are the same as the relative frequencies of those classes.

Furthermore, given some theoretical probability distribution, and $N$ observations made independently and at random with replacement, then there is a *theoretical frequency distribution* as well, where for any event class $A$

$$\text{theoretical frequency} = Np(A).$$

This is the frequency distribution we *expect* to observe, given the theoretical probability distribution. For example, suppose that the probability distribution of heights of boys given above were true. What is the theoretical frequency distribution of heights for 1000 boys sampled independently and at random? The answer is

| Height in inches | $f = Np(A)$ |
|---|---|
| 78–82 | 2 |
| 73–77 | 21 |
| 68–72 | 136 |
| 63–67 | 682 |
| 58–62 | 136 |
| 53–57 | 21 |
| 48–52 | 2 |
| | 1000 |

Given that the probability distribution is correct, then for a sample of 1000 boys we should expect our obtained frequency distribution to show 682 boys in the interval 63–67 inches, only 2 boys in the interval 78–82, and so on. This distribution might never actually occur in practice, but it is our best guess about what will occur if the probability distribution is a correct statement. Whereas the frequencies in real distributions must always be whole numbers, in theoretical distributions it is possible to have fractional frequencies; if only 100 boys were observed in this example, then the frequencies for the top and bottom intervals would be, in theory, .2 each.

Like frequency distributions, a probability distribution may be specified either by a listing such as we have shown here, or in graphic form. However, unlike actual obtained distributions of data, the most important probability distributions are theoretical ones that can be given a mathematical rule. In order to discuss such distributions we need the concept of a "random variable."

## 3.15   RANDOM VARIABLES

A special terminology is useful for discussing probability distributions of numerical scores. Imagine that a single number could be assigned to each and every possible elementary event in some $S$. Various elementary events are paired with various values of a variable. Thus, an elementary event may be a person, with some height in inches; or the elementary event may be the result of tossing a pair of dice, with the assigned number being the total of the spots that come up; or the elementary event may be a rat, with the number standing for the trials taken to learn a maze. Each and every elementary event is thought of as getting one and only one such number.

The symbol $X$ will be used to stand for any particular number assigned to any given elementary event. Thus, $X$ is a variable, and any value of $X$ is also an event, since there will be some set of elementary events assigned this value.

Furthermore, since a value of $X$ is an event, this event will have a probability $p(X)$ for the sample space $\mathcal{S}$. **A symbol $X$ standing for any of a range of number events, each having a probability $p(X)$, is called a random variable.**

Although the term "random variable" is rather awkward, it will be used here because of its popularity in statistical writing. The terms "chance variable" or "stochastic variable" are sometimes used. These all mean precisely the same thing, however; a symbol for number events each having a probability.

Given the random variable $X$, other events may be defined. Thus, given two numbers $a$ and $b$,

$$(a \leq X \leq b)$$

is the event of some number $X$ lying between the numbers $a$ and $b$ (inclusive). This event has some probability $p(a \leq X \leq b)$. Furthermore, there is the event

$$(a \leq X),$$

a number greater than or equal to the number $a$; this has probability $p(a \leq X)$.

This leads us to an alternate, and somewhat more modern, definition of a random variable:

**A quantity symbolized by $X$ is said to be a random variable if for every real number $a$ there exists a probability $p(X \leq a)$ that $X$ is less than or equal to $a$.**

As we shall see, this definition has its advantages when the variable $X$ is continuous, ranging over all the real numbers, although there is nothing in this definition that says that the random variable *must* be continuous.

As an example of a random variable, suppose that $X$ symbolizes the height of an American man, measured to the nearest inch. Here, there is some probability that $X \leq 60$, or $p(X \leq 60)$, since there is presumably some set of American men with heights less than or equal to 60 inches. Furthermore, there is some probability $p(70 \leq X \leq 72)$, since there is a set of American men having heights between five feet ten inches and six feet, inclusive. Here, $X$ symbolizes the numerical value (height in inches) assigned to an American man (an elementary event). This symbol $X$ represents any one of many different such values, and for any arbitrary number $a$ there is some probability that the value of $X$ is less than or equal to the value of $a$.

## 3.16  DISCRETE RANDOM VARIABLES

There are very many situations where the random variable $X$ can assume only a particular *finite* set of values. In other words, some of the real numbers or intervals of real numbers cannot occur as events in such a situation. For example, suppose that the simple experiment consists of selecting one United States family for observation and noting the number of children in that family; here, an elementary event is one particular United States family, and associated with each family is a number $X$. Here, $X$ can assume only certain values between, say, 0 and 30, and these values must be integers. The numbers 3.68, or $-17$, or $\pi$ simply cannot be associated appropriately with any elementary event in the sample space. In this instance, the random variable is said to be **discrete**. Or, take a roulette wheel marked off into numbers in the standard way. Only a small set of numbers can possibly be the outcomes of spinning the wheel, and each is a value of a discrete random variable $X$.

In general, a discrete random variable can be defined as follows:

**A random variable is discrete if for every pair of values $a$ and $b$ such that $0 < p(X \leq a) < p(X \leq b)$, there exists another value $d$ between $a$ and $b$ such that $p(a < X \leq d) = 0$ or $p(d \leq X < b) = 0$, or both.**

In other words, for a discrete random variable, given any pair of values $a$ and $b$ having nonzero cumulative probabilities of occurrence there will always be an interval of values somewhere between $a$ and $b$ having a zero probability of occurrence. Thus, in our example of American families, there is some probability that a family has 2 or fewer children, and a higher probability that a family has 3 or fewer children, but the probability is zero that a family has more than 2 but fewer than 3, since this would mean a fractional number of children. It suffices to remember that a random variable that can take on only whole-number values, or a finite number of values, is discrete.

Given a discrete random variable taking on only the $K$ different values $\{a_1, a_2, \cdots, a_K\}$, then the following statement is true:

$$p(X = a_1) + p(X = a_2) + \cdots + p(X = a_K) = 1.00,$$

the sum of the probabilities over all of the different values $X$ can assume must be 1.00.

Quite often one is interested in finding the probability that the obtained value of $X$ will fall *between* two particular values, or in some interval. For example, the number of spots coming up on a pair of dice is a discrete random variable taking on only the whole number values 2 through 12 (the probabilities of 0 and of 1 are both zero, of course). What is the probability that $X$, the number of spots, is between 3 and 5 inclusive?

In order to find such probabilities, we rely once again on rule 3 of Section 2.5. The various possible values of $X$ are mutually exclusive events, and so

$$p(3 \leq X \leq 5) = p(3 \cup 4 \cup 5) = p(3) + p(4) + p(5).$$

If $X$ is the number of spots on a pair of dice, then the random variable can be shown to have the distribution of Table 3.16.1.

Table 3.16.1

| $X$ | $p(X)$ |
|---|---|
| 12 | 1/36 |
| 11 | 2/36 |
| 10 | 3/36 |
| 9 | 4/36 |
| 8 | 5/36 |
| 7 | 6/36 |
| 6 | 5/36 |
| 5 | 4/36 |
| 4 | 3/36 |
| 3 | 2/36 |
| 2 | 1/36 |
| | 36/36 |

Using these probabilities, we find

$$p(3 \leq X \leq 5) = p(X = 3) + p(X = 4) + p(X = 5)$$
$$= \frac{2 + 3 + 4}{36} = \frac{1}{4}.$$

Similarly,

$$p(9 \leq X \leq 10) = p(X = 9) + p(X = 10) = \frac{7}{36}.$$

In general, the probability that $X$ falls in the interval between any two numbers $a$ and $b$, inclusive, is found by the sum of probabilities for $X$ over *all possible* values between $a$ and $b$, inclusive:

$$p(a \leq X \leq b) = \text{sum of } p(X = c) \text{ for all } c \text{ such that } a \leq c \leq b.$$

By the same argument,

$$p(a \leq X) = \text{sum of } p(X = c) \text{ for all } c \text{ such that } a \leq c.$$

Furthermore,

$$p(X < a) = 1 - p(a \leq X).$$

For this example,

$$p(5 \leq X) = p(X = 5) + \cdots + p(X = 12) = \frac{4}{36} + \cdots + \frac{1}{36}$$
$$= \frac{30}{36} = \frac{5}{6},$$
$$p(X < 5) = p(X = 4) + p(X = 3) + p(X = 2)$$
$$= \frac{3}{36} + \frac{2}{36} + \frac{1}{36} = \frac{1}{6}.$$

If cases are sampled from any frequency distribution that has been grouped into class intervals, then the random variable $X$ is usually regarded as symbolizing the midpoints of the intervals. For a finite number of class intervals, such an $X$ is a discrete random variable. Also, when measurements have been rounded to the *nearest* unit, as in height to the nearest inch, this is like forming class intervals, and the random variable standing for such a rounded measurement is often thought of as discrete.

## 3.17  GRAPHS OF PROBABILITY DISTRIBUTIONS

The same general procedure is used for graphing either a frequency or probability distribution. The two most common forms are histograms and smooth curves, for discrete and continuous variables respectively.

FIG. 3.17.1

FIG. 3.17.2

When the random variable is discrete and can take on only a few values, it is customary to show each value as an interval on the $X$ axis, with the height of the bar above that interval indicating the probability. For example, the distribution in Section 3.16 gives the histogram of Figure 3.17.1. Notice that each of the blocks making up the column above a value of $X$ has exactly the same area, and the number of blocks divided by the total number gives the probability. In other words, if each block had area of $1/36$, the total area would be $1.00$, and the area of any column would be the probability of that value of $X$.

This idea extends to the histogram of any probability distribution: the total area covered by all columns is regarded as $1.00$, and the area of any single column representing an interval or class is thought of as a probability for that interval or class.

As another example of a probability distribution graphed as a histogram, consider the example of heights from Section 3.14. This being a grouped distribution, each interval is shown as a corresponding interval on the $X$ axis (Fig. 3.17.2). If total area of the histogram is 1.00, then the area of any column is the probability of the corresponding interval.

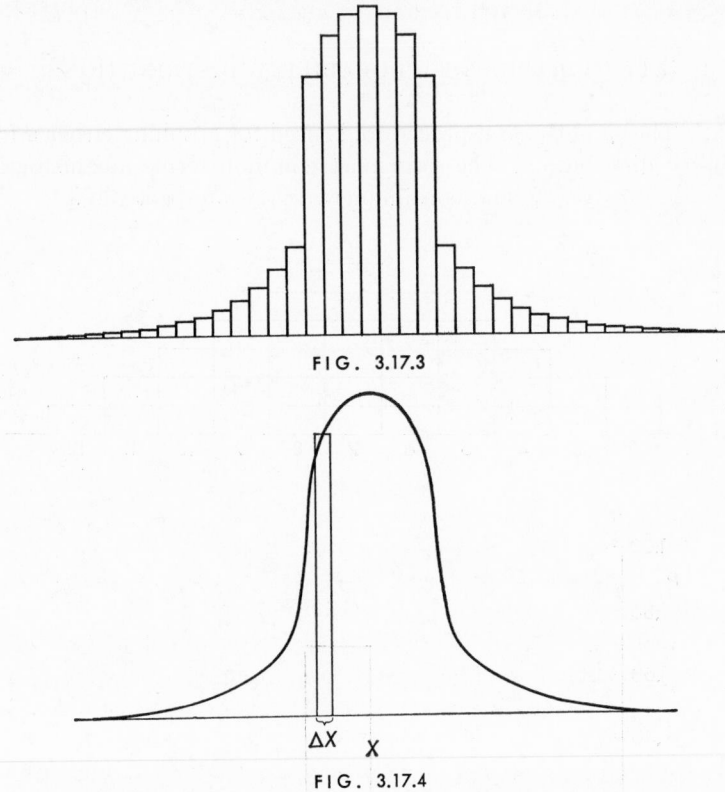

FIG. 3.17.3

FIG. 3.17.4

Suppose that the random variable $X$ were such that we could choose *any* class-interval size $i$, greater than zero, and still have a nonzero probability for that interval, so long as the interval lay between two extreme values of $X$, say $u$ and $v$. For example, suppose that in the measurement of height we could arrange observations according to any class interval, however small, and still have a chance of observing a case in that interval. For an interval size smaller than the $i = 5$ used above, say $i = 1$, our histogram might look like that shown in Figure 3.17.3. Here, the number of intervals is larger and the histogram area for each is smaller. Suppose that the class interval size were made *extremely* small, $i = \Delta X$, still under the assumption that any class interval within the limits $u$ and $v$ will have a probability greater than zero. In this circumstance each class interval will have an extremely small corresponding area, and the area for the histogram as a whole would be very nearly the same as enclosed in a smooth curve (Fig. 3.17.4).

The width of the bar shown on the graph is a representative class interval. Notice that the area cut off by the interval with width $\Delta X$ under the curve is almost the same as the area of the histogram bar itself; that is, the area under the curve for that interval is almost the same as the probability.

Finally, imagine that the class-interval size is made *very nearly zero*. As the class-interval size $\Delta X$ approaches zero, the probability associated with any class interval and the area cut off by the interval under the curve should agree increasingly well. A random variable that can be represented in terms of arbitrarily small class intervals of size $\Delta X$, with the probability of any interval corresponding *exactly* to the area cut off by the interval under a smooth curve, is called **continuous**. Notice, however, that as the class-interval size $\Delta X$ approaches zero, the probability associated with any class interval must also approach zero, since the corresponding area under the curve is steadily reduced. Next we will discuss some of the ramifications of this property of a continuous random variable.

### 3.18  CONTINUOUS RANDOM VARIABLES

For our purposes, a continuous random variable may be defined as follows:

**A random variable $X$ is said to be continuous if for every pair of values $u$ and $v$ such that $p(X \leq u) < p(X \leq v)$, it is true that $p(u < X < v) > 0$.**

Notice that for a random variable to be continuous in an interval limited by the values $u$ and $v$, it is necessary that every nonzero interval in this range have a nonzero probability.

It is very difficult to find real examples of continuous random variables; this concept is really an idealization that is never quite true, but has enormous mathematical utility. The closest one might come to a simple example is to imagine an infinitely large set of men, each of whom is weighed on a fantastically accurate spring balance, giving his weight to any number of decimal places. Obviously, no man will weigh as little as zero pounds, and it is hardly possible to find a man weighing many tons. However, between *some* limits any class interval of nonzero size should have nonzero probability. The weights would then be a continuous random variable between the specified limits.

In Section 3.16 it was possible for us to discuss discrete random variables in terms of probabilities $p(X)$, the probability that the random variable takes on exactly some value. However, the fact we have just illustrated in Section 3.17, that the area in any interval under a smooth curve approaches zero when interval size goes toward zero, makes it necessary to discuss continuous random variables in a special way.

Consider the example of an infinite set of men weighed with any degree of accuracy. What is the probability that a man will be observed at random weighing *exactly* 160 pounds? This event is an interval of values smaller than 159.5–160.5, or 159.95–160.05, or any other interval $160 \pm .5i$, where $i$ is not exactly zero. Since the smaller the interval, the smaller the probability, the probability of exactly 160 pounds is, in effect, zero. **In general, for continuous random variables, the occurrence of any exact value of $X$ may be regarded as having zero probability.**

For this reason, one does not usually discuss the probability *per se* for a value of a continuous random variable; probabilities are discussed only for *intervals* of $X$ values in a continuous distribution. Instead of the probability that $X$ takes on some value $a$, we deal with the so-called **probability density** of $X$ at $a$, symbolized by

$$f(a) = \text{probability density of } X \text{ at } a.$$

A fairly "rough" definition of a probability density can be given as follows: for any distribution it is proper to speak of the probability associated with an interval. Imagine an interval with limits $a$ and $b$. Then the probability of that interval is

$$p(a \leq X \leq b) = p(X \leq b) - p(X < a).$$

Now suppose that we let the size of the interval be denoted by

$$\Delta X = b - a$$

so that

$$b = a + \Delta X.$$

Then the probability of the interval *relative* to $\Delta X$ is just

$$\frac{p(a \leq X \leq b)}{\Delta X} = \frac{p(X \leq a + \Delta X) - p(X < a)}{\Delta X}.$$

Now suppose that we fix $a$, but allow $\Delta X$ to vary; in fact, let $\Delta X$ approach zero in size. What happens to the probability of this interval relative to the interval size? Both numbers will change, and the ratio will change, but this ratio will approach some **limiting value** as $\Delta X$ comes close to zero. That is, we can speak of the limit of $p(a \leq X \leq b)/\Delta X$ as $\Delta X$ approaches zero. *This limit gives the probability density of the variable $X$ at value $a$.* Loosely speaking, one can say that the probability density at $a$ is the *rate of change* in the probability of an interval with lower limit $a$, for minute changes in the size of the interval. This rate of change will depend on two things: the function rule assigning probabilities to intervals such as $(X \leq a)$ and the particular "region" of $X$ values we happen to be talking about. Rather than talk about probabilities of $X$ values per se, for continuous random variables it is mathematically far more convenient to discuss the probability density and reserve the idea of probability only for the discussion of *intervals* of $X$ values. This need not trouble us especially, as we will be interested only in intervals of values in the first place. We will even continue to speak loosely of the probabilities for different $X$ values. However, distribution functions plotted as smooth curves are really plots of probability *densities,* and the only probabilities represented are the areas cut off by nonzero intervals under these curves. Furthermore, when we come to look at a function rule for a continuous random variable, we will actually be looking at the rule for a density function.

If the random variable is discrete, then we can say that

$$p(X = a) = f(a) = \text{the probability density of } X \text{ at value } a.$$

Intervals can always be given probabilities, regardless of whether the random variable is discrete or continuous. For continuous random variables, the probability of any interval depends on the probability density associated with each value in the interval. The probability of any continuous interval is given by

$$p(a \leq X \leq b) = \int_a^b f(x)\ dx.$$

The mathematically unsophisticated reader need not worry over the symbolism used here; **it suffices to say that the probability of an interval is the same as the area cut off by that interval under the curve for the probability densities, when the random variable is continuous, and the total area is equal to 1.00.** The expression $f(x)\ dx$ can be thought of as the area of a minute interval with midpoint $X = x$, somewhere between $a$ and $b$. When the number of such intervals approaches an infinite number and their size approaches zero, the sum of all these areas is the *entire* area cut off by the limits $a$ and $b$. Since there is an infinite number of such intervals, this sum is expressed by the definite integral sign $\int_a^b$.

Note that this agrees with the definition of the probability of an interval for a discrete variable. In Section 3.16 it was stated that the probability that $X$ lies between two numbers, $a$ and $b$ inclusive, is a sum of probabilities. Since each probability can be thought of as an area in a histogram of the distribution, the probability of an interval is a sum of areas, if the total area is 1.00.

## 3.19 CUMULATIVE DISTRIBUTION FUNCTIONS

In Section 3.13 a cumulative distribution of frequencies was defined as the relation between class intervals and the frequency at or below the real upper limit of any interval: how many cases fall *into or below* a given class interval.

A similar conception is very important for both discrete and continuous probability distributions. The probability that a random variable $X$ takes on a value at or below a given number $a$ is written as

$$F(a) = p(X \leq a).$$

The symbol $F(a)$ denotes the particular probability for the interval $X \leq a$; the general symbol $F(X)$ is sometimes used to represent the existence of the function relating the various values of $X$ to the corresponding *cumulative* probabilities.

The probability that a continuous random variable takes on any value between limits $a$ and $b$ can be found from

$$p(a \leq X \leq b) = F(b) - F(a).$$

This is seen easily if it is recalled that $F(b)$ is the probability that $X$ takes on value $b$ or below, $F(a)$ is the probability that $X$ takes on value $a$ or below; their difference must be the probability of a value between $a$ and $b$.

In the inequalities such as $a \leq X \leq b$, the "less than or equal to" sign is used. These could just as well be written with "less than" signs alone, however, and the statements would still be true for a *continuous* distribution. The reason is that for a continuous random variable the probability that $X$ equals any exact number is regarded as zero, and thus the probabilities remain the same whether or not $a$ or $b$ or both are considered inside or outside of the interval. However, for discrete variables, $<$ and $\leq$ signs may lead to different probabilities.

The symbol $F(a)$ can be used to represent the cumulative probability that $X$ is less than or equal to $a$ either for a continuous or a discrete random variable. All random variables have cumulative distribution functions. However, remember that symbols such as $f(a)$ are read differently for continuous and discrete variables. For a continuous variable, $f(a)$ means the *probability density* for $X$ at the exact value $a$; this is not a probability. On the other hand, if the symbol $f(a)$ is applied to a discrete random variable, this *can* be read as the probability for $X = a$. To avoid possible confusion the density notation $f(a)$ will be reserved for *continuous* variables in all of the following, and $p(a)$ will be used both for discrete variables and for *intervals* of continuous variables, as in $p(a \leq X \leq b)$. Occasionally in mathematical statistics the terms "distribution function" or "probability function" are used to refer only to the *cumulative* distribution of a random variable, and "density function" is used where we have used "probability distribution." However, the author believes the terms used here are simpler for the beginning student to learn and use.

Tables of theoretical probability distributions are most often given in terms of the cumulative distribution, or $F(X)$, for a random variable. Given these cumulative probabilities for various values of $X$ it is easy to find the probability for any interval by subtraction. When we come to use the table of the so-called "normal" distribution, we will find that cumulative probabilities are shown.

## 3.20 CONTINUOUS RANDOM VARIABLES AS AN IDEALIZATION

A continuous distribution of a random variable is a theoretical state of affairs. Continuous distributions can never be observed, but are only idealizations. In the first place, no set of potential observations is actually infinite in number; the mortal scientist can deal only with finite numbers of real things, and so obtained data distributions are always discrete. Regardless of the size of his sample, it will never be large enough to permit each of the possible real numbers in any interval to be observed as values of the random variable. In the second place, measurements are imprecise. Not even in the most precise work known can accuracy be obtained to *any* number of decimals. This puts a limit to the actual possibility of encountering a continuous distribution in practice.

Why, then, do statisticians so often deal with these idealizations? The answer is that, mathematically, continuous distributions are far more tractable than discrete distributions. The function rules for continuous distributions are relatively easy to state and to study using the full power of mathematical analysis. This is not usually true for discrete distributions. On the other hand, continuous distributions are very good approximations to many truly discrete distributions. This fact makes it possible to organize statistical theory about a few such idealized distributions and find methods that are good approximations to results for the more complicated discrete situations. Nevertheless, the student should realize that these continuous distributions are mathematical abstractions that happen to be quite useful; they do not necessarily describe "real" situations.

## 3.21   GRAPHIC REPRESENTATIONS OF CONTINUOUS DISTRIBUTIONS

A continuous probability distribution is always represented as a smooth curve erected over the horizontal axis, which itself represents the possible values of the random variable $X$. A curve for some hypothetical distribution is

FIG. 3.21.1

shown in Figure 3.21.1. The two points $a$ and $b$ marked off on the horizontal axis represent limits to some interval. The shaded portion between $a$ and $b$ shows

$$p(a \leq X \leq b),$$

the probability that $X$ takes on a value between the limits $a$ and $b$. Remember that this probability corresponds to an *area* under the curve: in any continuous distribution, the probability of an interval can be represented by an area under the distribution curve. The total area under the curve represents 1.00, the probability that $X$ takes on *some* value.

In Figure 3.21.1, the shaded portion of the curve to the right of the point $c$ is the probability $p(c < X)$. This is found by first taking

$$F(c) = p(X \leq c).$$

Since the total probability is 1.00, and since $(X \leq c)$ and $(c < X)$ are mutually exclusive events, then

$$p(c < X) = 1.00 - F(c).$$

Cumulative distribution curves always have more or less the characteristic S shape shown in Figure 3.21.2. Here, the horizontal axis shows possible

FIG. 3.21.2

values of $X$; for any point on the axis, $a$, the *height* of the curve, $F(a)$, is the probability that $X$ is less than or equal to $a$.

## 3.22 FREQUENCY AND PROBABILITY DISTRIBUTIONS IN USE

Both frequency and probability distributions exhibit the same basic features: each is a statement of a relation between the various possible measurement classes into which observations may fall and a number attached to each class. In the case of frequency distributions, this number is the frequency of cases actually observed in a particular class or class interval. For probability distributions, each class or interval is accompanied by its probability. In future chapters we will see that the same language is applied in the further summarization of either kind of distribution.

However, there is an important difference between frequency distributions of data and probability distributions. The latter almost invariably represent *hypothetical* or *theoretical* distributions. A probability distribution is some idealization of the way things might be, could we but have all of the information. The frequency distribution represents what we have actually seen to be true from some limited number of observations.

The connection between frequency and probability distributions should be obvious by now: the probability distribution dictates what we should expect to observe in a frequency distribution, if the given state of affairs is true. Thus, if theoretically the random variable $X$ has probability of .30 of taking on a value in the interval between 100 and 102, then given a frequency distribution of 500 sample observations we should expect the class interval 100–102 to contain $(500)(.30)$ or 150 cases. This does not mean that this will be true for any given sample; we *might* observe any frequency between 0 and 500. Nevertheless, in the long run, if we sample indefinitely, 30 percent of all cases sampled should show scores in that interval, provided that our hypothetical probability distribution is right.

This is the reason for the parallel development of frequency and probability distributions carried on here. Each form of distribution plays a role in inference: the probability distribution specifies what to expect when the data are put into distribution form, and the obtained frequency distribution supplies us with our best evidence about the probability distribution (the *relative* frequencies of occurrence being estimates of the true probabilities). This parallel discussion will be continued in other chapters. However, the immediate goal is to show how theoretical probability distributions can be constructed. In order to do this we must pick up a few more rudiments of probability theory. These will be presented in the next chapter.

# JOINT EVENTS AND INDEPENDENCE

## 4

The idea of independent events has already figured in our discussion, and we have dealt only with events sampled independently. Now this concept of independence will be elaborated, both for qualitative events and for random variables. However, the idea of joint events must first be introduced.

### 4.1 JOINT EVENTS

As we have seen, the elementary events making up the sample space may be grouped into events in variety of ways. For example, if the sample space is a set of outcomes of drawing one card from a deck of playing cards, we might find the probability of the event "red suit," or the event "picture card," or the event "ten." However, notice that there is nothing to keep any given card from qualifying for two or more events, provided those events are not mutually exclusive. For example, an observed card might be both a red card and a picture card. When we draw such a card, the joint event "red *and* picture card" occurs.

The same idea applies to any sample space: **any event that is the intersection of two or more events is a joint event.** Thus, given the event $A$ and the event $B$, the joint event is $A \cap B$. The event $A \cap B$ occurs when any elementary event belonging to this set is actually observed.

Since a member of $A \cap B$ must be a member of set $A$, and also of set $B$, both $A$ and $B$ events occur when $A \cap B$ occurs. Furthermore, a member of $A \cap B$ is a member of $A \cup B$, and so whenever the joint event occurs, $A \cup B$ occurs as well.

Provided that the elements of $S$ are all equally likely to occur, the probability of the joint event is found in the usual way:

*108*

$$p(A \cap B) = \frac{\text{number of elementary events in } A \cap B}{\text{total number of elementary events}}. \qquad \text{[4.1.1]}$$

With playing cards, the joint event "red and three" is the set of all cards having a red suit and three spots. There are exactly two cards, the three of diamonds and the three of hearts, meeting this qualification, and so

$$p(\text{red and three}) = \frac{2}{52} = \frac{1}{26}.$$

As another example, imagine a simple experiment consisting of rolling a die *and* tossing a penny. Each elementary event consists of the number that comes up on the die and the side that comes up on the penny. The sample space is shown below:

SIDE OF PENNY

H  •  •  •  •  •  •

T  •  •  •  •  •  •

1  2  3  4  5  6

NUMBER ON DIE

Each point in the diagram is one elementary event, a possible outcome of this experiment, and there are exactly $(2)(6) = 12$ such outcomes.

Consider the joint event "coin comes up heads, and die comes up with an odd number." There are exactly three elementary events that qualify: (heads, 1) (heads, 3), and (heads, 5). Since there are twelve elementary events in all,

$$p(\text{H and odd}) = \frac{3}{12} = \frac{1}{4}.$$

This simple experiment illustrates that an elementary event can also be a joint event: the event (head, 1) is the intersection of the event "heads" and the event "1," and so on. This is very often the case in experiments where all events of interest are not mutually exclusive; each elementary event is the intersection of two or more events. Referring to the example of cards once again, we see that each distinct card represents the intersection of some suit-event with some number or picture-event.

Many situations give simple examples of joint events: imagine that someone samples students on a college campus at random and asks each his age, his sex (if necessary), and his field of concentration. Let the event $A$ be that the student is 21 years or older, the event $B$ that he is male, and $C$ that he is an English major. The set of all students on the campus who are 21 or over and male English majors is $A \cap B \cap C$. The probability that a student sampled at random represents this joint event is

$$p(A \cap B \cap C) = \frac{\text{number of students in } A \cap B \cap C}{\text{total number of students}}. \qquad \text{[4.1.2]}$$

### 4.2 COMBINING PROBABILITIES OF JOINT EVENTS

For any event $A$ there is also an event $\bar{A}$, consisting of all of the elementary events not in the set $A$. In preceding chapter it was pointed out that

$$p(A) + P(\bar{A}) = 1.$$

Furthermore, along with $A \cap B$ we can discuss the other joint events:

$A \cap \bar{B}$, consisting of all elementary events in $A$ and not in $B$;
$\bar{A} \cap B$, consisting of all elementary events not in $A$ but in $B$;
$\bar{A} \cap \bar{B}$, consisting of all elementary events neither in $A$ nor in $B$.

These four events are all mutually exclusive, so that

$$\begin{aligned}
p(A \cap B) + p(A \cap \bar{B}) &= p(A) \\
p(A \cap B) + p(\bar{A} \cap B) &= p(B) \\
p(\bar{A} \cap B) + p(\bar{A} \cap \bar{B}) &= p(\bar{A}) \\
p(A \cap \bar{B}) + p(\bar{A} \cap \bar{B}) &= p(\bar{B}).
\end{aligned}$$

[4.2.1]

Another principle for combining the probabilities of joint events also comes from rule **2.5.7** given in Section 2.5. Suppose that there are two events $A$ and $B$, and that we wish to determine the probability of the occurrence of the event $A$ or $B$ or both. That is, we wish to determine the probability of the event-class $A \cup B$. As we saw in Section 2.5, this probability is given by

$$p(A \cup B) = p(A) + p(B) - p(A \cap B).$$

[4.2.2]

In other words, the probability of the occurrence of an $A$ event or a $B$ event or an elementary event falling into *both* classes is given by the probability of $A$ plus the probability of $B$ *minus* the probability of the compound event $A$ and $B$. Recall that this is true because

$$p(A) + p(B) = p(A \cap \bar{B}) + p(\bar{A} \cap B) + 2p(A \cap B),$$

and

$$p(A \cup B) = p(A \cap \bar{B}) + p(\bar{A} \cap B) + p(A \cap B).$$

Thus, $p(A \cap B)$ must be subtracted from $p(A) + p(B)$ to find the probability of the union $A \cup B$. This rule for finding the probability of the union of two event classes is sometimes called the "or" rule, because $p(A \cup B)$ can be read as the probability of $A$ *or* $B$ *or* both.

The most important case of the *or* rule is that in which the two events $A$ and $B$ are *mutually exclusive*, so that the probability of the joint event $A \cap B$ is zero. Here, axiom 3 of Section 2.5 applies directly. In this case, for mutually exclusive events

$$p(A \cup B) = p(A) + p(B).$$

[4.2.3]

As an illustration of the use of the *or* rule for combining probabilities, think of a city school system, where we are going to sample one pupil at random. In this school system, we know that 35 percent of the pupils are left-handed, so that we know also that the probability is .35 for the event "left-handed." In the same way we know that the probability is .51 of our observing a girl, and that the probability is .10 of observing a girl who is left-handed. What is the probability of observing *either* a left-handed student *or* a girl (or both)? The answer according to the *or* rule is

$$p(\text{left-handed or girl}) = .35 + 51 - .10 = .76.$$

Now suppose that .25 is the probability of observing a left-handed boy, and .10 is the probability of observing a left-handed girl. What is the probability of observing either a left-handed boy or a left-handed girl? It is not possible for an elementary event to fall both into the set of left-handed boys and the set of left-handed girls: these two events are mutually exclusive. Thus the desired probability is

$$p(\text{left-handed boy or left-handed girl}) = .25 + .10 = .35,$$

which is just the probability of "left-handed" alone.

The *or* rule for events may be generalized to more than two events. Consider three events $A$, $B$, and $C$. Then

$$p(A \cup B \cup C) = p(A) + p(B) + p(C) - p(A \cap B) - p(A \cap C) \\ - p(B \cap C) + p(A \cap B \cap C). \quad \textbf{[4.2.4]}$$

Similar expressions exist for the union of more than three events, but we will not have occasion to use them in our elementary work. If three or more events are mutually exclusive, then the union is just the sum of the separate probabilities:

$$p(A \cup B \cup C) = p(A) + p(B) + p(C), \qquad \textbf{[4.2.5]}$$

as given in axiom 3, Section 2.5.

## 4.3   CONDITIONAL PROBABILITY

Suppose that in sampling children in a school system, we restrict our observations only to girls. Here, there is a new sample space including only part of the elementary events in the original set. In this new sample space, consisting only of girls, what is the probability of observing a left-handed person? If all girls in the school system are equally likely to be observed, it is obvious that

$$p(\text{left-handed, among the girls}) = \frac{\text{number left-handed girls}}{\text{total number of girls}}.$$

This probability can be found from the *original* probabilities for the total sample space: first of all we know that

$$p(\text{left-handed and girl}) = \frac{\text{number left-handed girls}}{\text{total number of pupils}} = .10$$

and that

$$p(\text{girl}) = \frac{\text{total number of girls}}{\text{total number of pupils}} = .51.$$

It follows that

$$p(\text{left-handed, among the girls}) = \frac{p(\text{left-handed and girl})}{p(\text{girl})} = \frac{.10}{.51} = .196$$

since the two probabilities put into ratio each have the same denominator.

The probability just found, based on only a part of the total sample space, is called a conditional probability. A more formal definition follows:

Let $A$ and $B$ be events in a sample space made up of a finite number of elementary events. Then the conditional probability of $B$ given $A$, denoted by $p(B|A)$, is

$$p(B|A) = \frac{p(A \cap B)}{p(A)}, \qquad \text{[4.3.1*]}$$

provided that $p(A)$ is not zero.

Notice that the conditional probability symbol, $p(B|A)$, is read as "the probability of $B$ *given* $A$." In the example it was given that the observation would be a girl; the value desired was the probability of "left-handed," given that a girl were observed.

For any two events $A$ and $B$, there are two conditional probabilities that may be calculated:

$$p(B|A) = \frac{p(A \cap B)}{p(A)}$$

and

$$p(A|B) = \frac{p(A \cap B)}{p(B)}.$$

We might find the probability of left-handed, given girl $(.10/.51 = .19)$ or the conditional probability of girl, given left-handed $(.10/.35 = .29)$. In general, these two conditional probabilities will not be equal, since they represent quite different sets of elementary events.

As another example, take the probabilities found in the example for a coin and a die in Section 4.1. Here, the probability of a tail coming up on the coin is .50, and the probability of an odd number on the die *and* a tail on the coin is .25. The probability that the die comes up with an odd number, *given* that the coin comes up tails is

$$p(\text{odd}|\text{tails}) = \frac{.25}{.50} = .50.$$

The probability that the coin comes up tails and the die comes up with a 1 or a 2 can be found from the example to be 1/6 or .167. If we wish to know the probability that the die comes up with a 1 or a 2 given that the coin comes up tails, the probability is

$$p(1 \text{ or } 2|\text{tails}) = \frac{.167}{.50} = .33.$$

## 4.4  RELATIONS AMONG CONDITIONAL PROBABILITIES

The conditional probability $p(B|A)$ can either be larger or smaller than $p(B)$; there is no necessary relation between the size of $p(B)$ and the size of $p(B|A)$, other than that they both must lie between zero and one.

For any event and its complement,

$$p(B|A) + p(\bar{B}|A) = 1. \qquad [4.4.1*]$$

This is easily seen to be true if one remembers that

$$p(A \cap B) + p(A \cap \bar{B}) = p(A),$$

so that

$$\frac{p(A \cap B)}{p(A)} + \frac{p(A \cap \bar{B})}{p(A)} = 1.$$

If there are three events, $A$, $B$, and $C$, then

$$p(B|A) + p(C|A) - p(B \cap C|A) = p(B \cup C|A), \qquad [4.4.2]$$

since *within the set A* it is also true that

$$p(A \cap B) + p(A \cap C) - p(A \cap B \cap C) = p[(A \cap B) \cup (A \cap C)]$$

so that

$$\frac{p(A \cap B)}{p(A)} + \frac{p(A \cap C)}{p(A)} - \frac{p(A \cap B \cap C)}{p(A)} = \frac{p[A \cap (B \cup C)]}{p(A)}.$$

If we know the conditional probability $p(B|A)$ and also $p(A)$, then we can also find the joint probability $p(A \cap B)$:

$$p(A)p(B|A) = p(A \cap B) \qquad [4.4.3*]$$

and

$$p(B)p(A|B) = p(A \cap B),$$

since, by definition,

$$p(B|A) = \frac{p(A \cap B)}{p(A)}$$

and

$$p(A|B) = \frac{p(A \cap B)}{p(B)}.$$

It follows that

$$p(A)p(B|A) = p(B)p(A|B) \qquad [4.4.4]$$

and that

$$\frac{p(B|A)}{p(A|B)} = \frac{p(B)}{p(A)}.$$

## 4.5  BAYES' THEOREM

The relation among various conditional probabilities are embodied in the theorem named for Bayes, an English clergyman who did early work in probability and decision theory. The simplest version of this theorem follows: for two events $A$ and $B$, the following relation must hold:

$$p(A|B) = \frac{p(A \cap B)}{p(B)}$$

$$= \frac{p(B|A)p(A)}{p(B|A)p(A) + p(B|\bar{A})p(\bar{A})}. \qquad [4.5.1^*]$$

For example, suppose you were given

$$p(A) = .40 \text{ and } p(\bar{A}) = .60$$
$$p(B|A) = .80$$
$$p(B|\bar{A}) = .30.$$

You want to find the conditional probability of $A$ given $B$, or $p(A|B)$. This must be

$$p(A|B) = \frac{(.80)(.40)}{(.80)(.40) + (.30)(.60)}$$

$$= \frac{.32}{.50} = .64.$$

To illustrate Bayes' theorem, suppose you awake in the middle of the night with a headache and stumble into the bathroom without turning on the light. In the dark you grab one of three bottles containing pills and take one. An hour later you become very ill, and the thought strikes you that one of the three bottles contains a poison, the other two, aspirin. With a few assumptions this can be made into a problem in conditional probability. (Before you jump to any unflattering conclusions about a professor's thoughts as he lies dying, be assured that a doctor most certainly would be called. If you will, this is an exercise to fill the time until the doctor comes.)

Let's assume that you have a medical text handy, and that it shows that 80 percent of normal individuals show your symptoms after taking the poison, and that only 5 percent have these symptoms from taking aspirin. Let $B$ stand for the event "symptoms," and let $A$ stand for the event "took poison," with $\bar{A}$ for the event "took aspirin." In effect, the sample space is restricted to those individuals who took *either* aspirin or poison. According to your information, you assume that

$$p(B|A) = .80$$
$$p(B|\bar{A}) = .05.$$

If each bottle had equal probability of being chosen in the dark, then

$$p(A) = 1/3$$
$$p(\bar{A}) = 2/3.$$

Given these figures, what is the probability that someone in this situation has taken poison, given that he has the symptoms? This is

$$p(A|B) = \frac{(.80)(.33)}{(.80)(.33) + (.05)(.67)} = .89.$$

If you consider yourself a random sample from among all normal persons who might be subjected to this "simple experiment," then it is a very good thing that the doctor *was* called! The conditional probability of "took poison, given the symptoms" is high.

Although this example is dramatic, it hardly illuminates the real uses to which this idea can be put, provided that one knows the necessary initial probabilities. Consider this example: at a university it is decided to try out a new placement test for admitting students to a special mathematics class. Experience has shown that in general only 60 percent of students applying for admission actually can pass this course. Heretofore, each student applying for the course was admitted. Of the students who passed the course, some 80 percent passed the placement test beforehand, whereas only 40 percent of those who failed the course could pass the placement test initially. If this test is to be used for placement, and only students who pass the test are to be admitted to the course, what is the probability that such a student will pass the course?

First of all, event $A$ is defined to be "passes the course," and it is assumed that $p(A) = .60$. The event $B$ is "passes the test." The conditional probabilities are taken to be

$$p(B|A) = .80 \qquad p(\bar{B}|A) = .20$$
$$p(B|\bar{A}) = .40 \qquad p(\bar{B}|\bar{A}) = .60.$$

However, we want to know the conditional probability, $p(A|B)$, that a student will pass the course, *given* that he has passed the test. Bayes' theorem shows

$$p(A|B) = \frac{(.80)(.60)}{(.80)(.60) + (.40)(.40)}$$
$$= \frac{.48}{.48 + .16} = .75.$$

Thus, the probability is .75 for a student's passing the course *given* that he passed the test. If we wanted to find other conditional probabilities, we could also apply the theorem. For example,

$$p(\bar{A}|\bar{B}) = \frac{(.60)(.40)}{(.60)(.40) + (.20)(.60)}$$
$$= \frac{.24}{.24 + .12} = .67.$$

Notice that the probability of a student's passing the course given that he passes the test is greater than the probability in general of passing the course. Any student is a better bet to pass the course if he has passed the placement test.

What is the probability of being *right* if students are admitted or refused the course strictly on the basis of this test? The probability of a correct decision can be found by

$$p(A \cap B) + p(\bar{A} \cap \bar{B}) = p(\text{correct}).$$

By equation **4.4.1** this is

$$p(\text{correct}) = p(B|A)p(A) + p(\bar{B}|\bar{A})p(\bar{A})$$

$$= (.80)(.60) + (.60)(.40) = .72.$$

In other words, the administrator will have a probability of .72 of being right about a student's proper placement if he uses the test. If he does not use the test and simply admits all students to the course, the probability of being right (of the student passing the course) is only .60. Thus, the test does something for the administrator; its use allows him to increase the probability of being right about a given student selected at random.

Bayes' theorem and other calculations with conditional probability are often used in this way, especially in questions of selection or diagnosis of subjects where initial probabilities are known. Good selection or diagnostic procedures are those permitting an increase in the probability of being right about an individual given some prior information, and such *conditional* probabilities can often be calculated by Bayes' theorem.

On the other hand, Bayes' theorem can be misapplied, especially when the probabilities do not all have a simple relative-frequency interpretation. In earlier uses of probability theory this misapplication sometimes went to ridiculous lengths, and the employment of this principle itself fell into disrepute. However, when all of the probabilities do in fact have a simple relative frequency interpretation and one knows all the relevant information, it can be applied effectively to many problems.

Bayes' theorem can be put into much more general form: If $\{A_1, A_2, \cdots, A_J\}$ represents a set of $J$ mutually exclusive events, and if $B \subset A_1 \cup A_2 \cup \cdots \cup A_J$, so that $p(B) < p(A_1) + p(A_2) + \cdots + p(A_J)$, then

$$p(A_j|B) = \frac{p(B|A_j)p(A_j)}{p(B|A_1)p(A_1) + \cdots + p(B|A_j)p(A_j) + \cdots + p(B|A_J)p(A_J)}$$

$$[4.5.2*]$$

for any event $A_j$ in the set. (Notice that $A_j$ and $A_J$ do not necessarily symbolize the same event.)

## 4.6 INDEPENDENCE

Now we are ready to take up the topic of independence. The general idea used heretofore is that independent events are those having nothing to do with each other: the occurrence of one event in no wise affects the probability of the other event. But how does one know if two events $A$ and $B$ are independent? If the occurrence of the event $A$ has nothing whatever to do with the occurrence of event $B$, then we should expect the conditional probability of $B$ given $A$ to be exactly the same as the probability of $B$, $p(B|A) = p(B)$. Likewise, the conditional probability of $A$ given $B$ should be equal to the probability of $A$, or

$p(A|B) = p(A)$. The information that one event has occurred does not affect the probability of the other event, when the events are independent.

The condition of independence of two events may also be stated in another form: if $p(B|A) = p(B)$, then

$$\frac{p(A \cap B)}{p(A)} = p(B) \qquad\qquad [4.6.1*]$$

so that

$$p(A \cap B) = p(A)p(B).$$

In the same way,

$$p(A|B) = p(A) \qquad\qquad [4.6.2*]$$

leads to the statement that

$$p(A \cap B) = p(A)p(B).$$

This fact leads to the usual definition of independence:

**If events $A$ and $B$ are independent, then the joint probability $p(A \cap B)$ is equal to the probability of $A$ times the probability of $B$,**

$$p(A \cap B) = p(A)p(B). \qquad\qquad [4.6.3*]$$

For example, suppose that you go into a library and at random select one book (each book having an equal likelihood of being drawn). The sample space consists of all distinct books that a person might select. Suppose that the proportion of books then on the shelves and classified as "fiction" is exactly .15, so that the probability of selecting such a book is also .15. Furthermore, suppose that the proportion of books having red covers is exactly .30. If the event "fiction" is independent of the event "red cover," the probability of the joint event is found very easily:

$$p(\text{fiction and red cover}) = p(\text{fiction})p(\text{red cover}) = (.15)(.30) = .045.$$

You should come up with a red-covered piece of fiction in about forty-five out of one thousand random selections.

The example in which a coin is tossed and a die rolled also illustrates independent events. In this example, the probability that the coin comes up heads is .50, and the probability that the die comes up with an odd number is also .50. If we assume that the two events are independent, then the probability of the event "heads and odd number" is given by

$$p(\text{heads and odd number}) = p(\text{heads})p(\text{odd number}) = (.50)(.50) = .25.$$

If you look at the sample space for this experiment, pictured in Section 4.1, you will find that this number .25 agrees with the probability for the joint event "heads and odd number" calculated directly. When all the elementary events in this sample space are equally likely, these two events actually are independent.

It is certainly not true that all events must be independent. It is very easy to give examples where the joint probability of two events is not equal to the product of their separate probabilities. For example, suppose that children were selected at random. A child is observed and his hair color noted, and also whether or not he is freckled. For our purposes, the event $A$ consists of the set of all children having red hair, and the event $B$ is the set of all children who are freckled. Is it reasonable that the event $A$ will be independent of the event $B$? The answer is no; everyone knows that among red-heads freckles are much more common than among children in general. One would expect in this case $p(B|A)$ to be *greater* than $p(B)$, so that it should *not* be true that $p(A \cap B) = p(A)p(B)$. The events "red hair" and "freckled" *do* tend to occur together and are not ordinarily regarded as independent.

This example suggests one of the uses of the concept of independent events. The definition of independence permits us to decide whether or not events *are associated* or *dependent* in some way:

**If, for two events $A$ and $B$, $p(A \cap B)$ is not equal to $p(A)p(B)$, then $A$ and $B$ are said to be associated or dependent.**

For example, consider a sample space with elementary events consisting of all the adult male persons in the United States. We wish to answer the question, "Is making over twenty-thousand dollars a year independent of having a college education?" Let us call event $A$ "makes over twenty-thousand dollars a year," and $B$ "has a college education." Now suppose that the proportion of adult males in the United States who make more than twenty-thousand a year is .06; if each adult male is equally likely to be selected, the probability of event $A$ is thus .06. Suppose also that the proportion of adult males with a college education is .30, so that $p(B) = .30$. Finally, the probability of an event $A \cap B$, our observing an adult male making over twenty-thousand a year and who has a college education is .04. If the events were independent, this probability $p(A \cap B)$ *should* be $(.06)(.30) = .018$; the actual probability is .04. This leads immediately to the conclusion that these two events are *not* independent (or *are* associated). The probability that event $B$ will occur given event $A$ is much greater than it should be if the events were independent: $p(B|A) = .04/.06 = .67$, whereas if the events were independent, it should be true that

$$p(B|A) = p(B) = .30.$$

This idea of independence is very important to many of the statistical techniques to be discussed in later chapters. The question of association or dependence of events is central to the scientific question of the relationships among the phenomena we observe (literally, the question of "what goes with what"). The techniques for studying the presence and degree of relatedness among observations, particularly those of Chapter 17, will depend directly upon this idea of comparing probabilities for joint events with the probabilities when events are independent.

However, the concept of association of events must not be confused with the idea of causation. Association, as used in statistics, means simply that the events are not independent, and that a certain correspondence between their joint and separate probabilities does not hold. When events $A$ and $B$ are associated, it need not mean that $A$ causes $B$ or that $B$ causes $A$, but only that the events occur together with probability different from the product of their separate probabilities. This warning carries force whenever we talk of the association of events; association may be a consequence of causation, but this need not be true.

## 4.7   REPRESENTING JOINT EVENTS IN TABLES

Sometimes it is convenient to list joint events by means of a table, with each cell representing one joint possibility. For example, consider a sample space consisting of all individual students at a particular college campus. Each student is either male or female, of course, and when asked his opinion on some question, a student will respond either "yes" or "no." The possible joint events are as follows:

| | | |
|---|---|---|
| Male | (male and yes) | (male and no) |
| Female | (female and yes) | (female and no) |
| | Yes | No |

It might be that on this particular campus, the probability of our observing a male student is .55 and of observing a female .45. Furthermore, suppose that the probability of obtaining a "yes" answer is .40, and .60 for obtaining a "no." Then the table of probabilities follows this general pattern:

| | | |
|---|---|---|
| $p$(Male) $= .55$ | $p$(Male and Yes) | $p$(Male and No) |
| $p$(Female) $= .45$ | $p$(Female and Yes) | $p$(Female and No) |
| | $p$(Yes) $= .40$ | $p$(No) $= .60$ |

The values of $p$(Male), $p$(Female), $p$(Yes), and $p$(No) are called the **marginal probabilities** (they get the name from the obvious circumstance of appearing in the *margin* of the table). Each marginal probability is a sum of all the joint probabilities in some particular row or column of the table:

$$p(\text{Male}) = p(\text{Male and Yes}) + p(\text{Male and No});$$
$$p(\text{Female}) = p(\text{Female and Yes}) + p(\text{Female and No});$$
$$p(\text{Yes}) = p(\text{Male and Yes}) + p(\text{Female and Yes});$$
$$p(\text{No}) = p(\text{Male and No}) + p(\text{Female and No}).$$

Ordinarily the event classes that appear together along any margin of the table are *mutually exclusive and exhaustive.* Thus, the events "Yes" and "No" are mutually exclusive and exhaustive and so are the events "Male" and "Female." Any set of mutually exclusive and exhaustive event classes that make up one margin of the table can be called an **attribute** or a **dimension.** This table embodies two attributes, "the sex of the student" and "the response of the student," respectively.

Suppose that the two attributes of the table were independent: this means that any event along one margin must be independent of every event along the other margin. Here, this is tantamount to saying that the sex of the student has absolutely nothing to do with how he answers the question. **If independence exists, the probability of each joint event** (as given in a cell of the table) **must be equal to the product of the probabilities of the corresponding marginal events.**

For example, if the two attributes are independent, then the probability $p$(Male and Yes) must be equal to the product of the two marginal probabilities,

$$p(\text{Male and Yes}) = p(\text{Male})p(\text{Yes}) = (.55)(.40) = .22.$$

In the same way the joint probabilities for each of the other cells may be found from products of marginal probabilities, and the following table should be correct:

| $p$(Male) = .55 | $p$(Male)$p$(Yes) = (.55)(.40) = .22 | $p$(Male)$p$(No) = (.55)(.60) = .33 |
|---|---|---|
| $p$(Female) = (.45) | $p$(Female)$p$(Yes) = (.45)(.40) = .18 | $p$(Female)$p$(No) = (.45)(.60) = .27 |
| | $p$(Yes) = .40 | $p$(No) = .60 |

It is important to remember, however, that these will be the correct joint probabilities only if the attributes *are* independent. It might be that the following table is the true one:

| $p$(Male) = .55 | $p$(Male and Yes) = .10 | $p$(Male and No) = .45 |
|---|---|---|
| $p$(Female) = .45 | $p$(Female and Yes) = .30 | $p$(Female and No) = .15 |
| | $p$(Yes) = .40 | $p$(No) = .60 |

When this is true it is safe to assert that for this sample space the sex of the student *is* associated with how he will answer the question. Look at the conditional probabilities: here, the probability of the student's answering "yes" if he is a male is

$$p(\text{Yes}|\text{Male}) = \frac{.10}{.55} = .18$$

and the probability of a "yes" answer if the student is a female is

$$p(\text{Yes}|\text{Female}) = \frac{.30}{.45} = .67.$$

Thus, a female is much more likely to answer "yes" to this question than is a male. On the other hand, had the two attributes been independent, these two conditional probabilities *should* have been the same:

$$p(\text{Yes}|\text{Male}) = \frac{.22}{.55} = .40$$

$$p(\text{Yes}|\text{Female}) = \frac{.18}{.45} = .40,$$

indicating that sex gives no information about how a person tends to respond to the question.

This idea of representing probabilities in tabular form can be extended to any number of attributes, each consisting of any number of event classes. For example, consider four mutually exclusive and exhaustive classes labeled $\{A_1, A_2, A_3, A_4\}$, which we may call the attribute $A$, and another set of classes $\{B_1, B_2, B_3\}$, which is the attribute $B$. Then the joint events consisting of the intersection of an event class from $A$ with an event class from $B$ may be represented by the table

| | | | |
|---|---|---|---|
| $B_1$   $(A_1 \cap B_1)$ | $(A_2 \cap B_1)$ | $(A_3 \cap B_1)$ | $(A_4 \cap B_1)$ |
| $B_2$   $(A_1 \cap B_2)$ | $(A_2 \cap B_2)$ | $(A_3 \cap B_2)$ | $(A_4 \cap B_2)$ |
| $B_3$   $(A_1 \cap B_3)$ | $(A_2 \cap B_3)$ | $(A_3 \cap B_3)$ | $(A_4 \cap B_3)$ |
| $A_1$ | $A_2$ | $A_3$ | $A_4$ |

(Notice the similarity of this formulation of joint events to the idea of a Cartesian product introduced in Section 1.14; the set of all joint-event pairs is nothing more than the Cartesian product $A \times B$.)

Associated with any joint-event class there is a probability, such as $p(A_1 \cap B_1)$ or $p(A_1 \cap B_2)$. Each of the marginal probabilities is a sum of the probabilities in a row or a column of the table: thus,

$$p(B_1) = p(A_1 \cap B_1) + p(A_2 \cap B_1) + p(A_3 \cap B_1) + p(A_4 \cap B_1),$$

and so on for the other marginal probabilities.

Given that the attributes are independent, then the joint probabilities are the products of the marginal probabilities, and the table becomes:

| | | | |
|---|---|---|---|
| $p(B_1)$   $p(A_1)p(B_1)$ | $p(A_2)p(B_1)$ | $p(A_3)p(B_1)$ | $p(A_4)p(B_1)$ |
| $p(B_2)$   $p(A_1)p(B_2)$ | $p(A_2)p(B_2)$ | $p(A_3)p(B_2)$ | $p(A_4)p(B_2)$ |
| $p(B_3)$   $p(A_1)p(B_3)$ | $p(A_2)p(B_3)$ | $p(A_3)p(B_3)$ | $p(A_4)p(B_3)$ |
| $p(A_1)$ | $p(A_2)$ | $p(A_3)$ | $p(A_4)$ |

Again it must be emphasized, however, that the joint probabilities are equal to the products of the marginals *only* when the attributes represented by the margins are independent.

### 4.8 INDEPENDENCE OF RANDOM VARIABLES

Suppose that we have two discrete random variables:

$X$, ranging over the values $\{a_1, a_2, \cdots, a_J\}$

and

$Y$, ranging over the values $\{b_1, b_2, \cdots, b_K\}$.

We can discuss the joint event that $X$ takes on some value $a$ *and* that $Y$ takes on some value $b$: this is the event $(X = a, Y = b)$, with probability $p(X = a, Y = b)$.

Furthermore, the conditional probability that $X = a$, given that $Y = b$ is

$$p(X = a|Y = b) = \frac{p(X = a, Y = b)}{p(Y = b)}. \qquad [4.8.1]$$

In the same way, the conditional probability of $Y = b$ given $X = a$ is found from

$$p(Y = b|X = a) = \frac{p(X = a, Y = b)}{p(X = a)}. \qquad [4.8.2]$$

For example, consider a sample space of American men, once again. Let the random variable $X$ be the hat size of a man, and let $Y$ be his shoe size. Imagine that we know

$$p(X = 7) = .30$$
$$p(Y = 9) = .20.$$

Furthermore,

$$p(X = 7, Y = 9) = .10.$$

Then the probability that a man wears hat size 7 given that his shoe size is 9 is found to be

$$p(X = 7|Y = 9) = \frac{.10}{.20} = .50.$$

**Two discrete random variables are independent if and only if**

$$p(X = a, Y = b) = p(X = a)p(Y = b) \qquad [4.8.3*]$$

**for all pairs of values $a$ and $b$.**

Thus, in the example just given, if shoe size were independent of hat size, then it would be true that

$$p(X = 7, Y = 9) = p(X = 7)p(Y = 9) = (.30)(.20) = .06.$$

If the joint probability .10 is the true one, then $X$ and $Y$ are *not* independent.

The same idea applies to continuous random variables as well, except that the definition is stated in terms of probability densities:

A random variable $X$ with density $g(a)$ at value $a$, and a random variable $Y$ with density $h(b)$ at value $b$ are independent if and only if for all $(a,b)$

$$f(a,b) = g(a)h(b) \qquad\qquad [4.8.4*]$$

where $f(a,b)$ is the *joint* density for the event $(a,b)$.

Just as for conditional probability, it is also possible to define **conditional density:**

$$w(b|a) = \frac{f(a,b)}{g(a)} \qquad\qquad [4.8.5]$$

where $w(b|a)$ symbolizes the density for $Y = b$ given some value $a$ of $X$. *The conditional distribution of $Y$ given $X$ will be exactly the same as the distribution of $Y$ with $X$ left unspecified when $X$ and $Y$ are independent:* for all $(a,b)$,

$$w(b|a) = h(b), \qquad X \text{ and } Y \text{ independent.}$$

In the same way,

$$w(a|b) = g(a)$$

when the variables are independent.

For any random variables, one often has occasion to consider **joint intervals,** the event

$$[(a \leq X \leq b) \text{ and } (c \leq Y \leq d)],$$

some value of $X$ lying between $a$ and $b$, and some value of $Y$ between $c$ and $d$. For independent random variables:

$$p(a \leq X \leq b \text{ and } c \leq Y \leq d) = p(a \leq X \leq b)p(c \leq Y \leq d) \quad [4.8.5*]$$

just as for any independent events.

The idea of independent random variables permeates all statistical theory. In some instances, $X$ and $Y$ are different kinds of measurements, and one is interested in the association between the attributes they represent. However, equally important is the situation where a series of observations are made, each observation producing one value of the *same* random variable $X$. The series of outcomes can be regarded as a set of random variables $X_1$, $X_2$, $X_3$ and so on, each having exactly the same distribution. The subscripts refer only to the order of sampling in the sequence, the value observed first, second, and so on. For example, we might be measuring the same individual over time, or drawing several cases from the same group of people measured in the same way. If these observations are independent, then for, say, $X_1$ and $X_2$,

$$f(X_2|X_1) = f(X_2)$$

and

$$f(X_1|X_2) = f(X_1),$$

the distribution of $X$ is the same regardless of which observation in the sequence or in the total sample we are considering. This amounts to saying that the chances for different intervals of values of $X$ to occur stay the same regardless of where we are in the sampling process.

## 4.9 INDEPENDENCE OF FUNCTIONS OF RANDOM VARIABLES

The idea of independence of random variables can be extended to functions of random variables as well. That is, suppose we have a random variable $X$ with a density $g(X)$, and an *independent* random variable $Y$ with density $h(Y)$, as before.

Now imagine some function of $X$: associated with each possible $X$ value is a new number $V = t(X)$. For example, it might be that

$$V = aX + b$$

so that $V$ is some linear function of $X$. Or perhaps,

$$V = 3X^2 + 2X,$$

and so on for any other function rule. Furthermore, let there be some function of $Y$:

$$W = s(Y),$$

so that a new number $W$ is associated with each possible value of $Y$. *Then V and W are independent random variables, provided that X and Y are independent.* This principle applies both to continuous and to discrete random variables, and to all the ordinary functions studied in elementary mathematical analysis. We will make extensive use of this principle in later sections on sampling random variables.

It is especially interesting to apply this principle to measurements as functions of underlying magnitudes of properties. Imagine that the true magnitudes on two properties for some sample space of objects are represented by the random variables $X$ and $Y$, and that the numerical measurements assigned to these objects are represented by $V$ and $W$. Furthermore, suppose that $V$ is some function of $X$, and $W$ is some function of $Y$. Then if the underlying variables $X$ and $Y$ are independent, the measurements $V$ and $W$ must be independent as well. Conversely, if $V$ and $W$ are not independent, $X$ and $Y$ are not independent.

## 4.10 REPRESENTATION OF JOINT RANDOM VARIABLES

The joint distribution of two discrete random variables may also be displayed in a table. This shows the possible pairs of values $X$ and $Y$, each pair associated with a joint probability. The different $X$ values are assigned to the columns of the table, with $Y$ values to the rows, so that any cell is an $(X,Y)$ pair.

For example, the joint distribution of two random variables is shown in Table 4.10.1.

### Table 4.10.1

| Y | p(Y) | | | | |
|---|------|------|------|------|------|
| 10 | .0950 | .0875 | .0075 | .0000 | .0000 |
| 9 | .1300 | .0975 | .0300 | .0025 | .0000 |
| 8 | .1150 | .0475 | .0575 | .0100 | .0000 |
| 7 | .1150 | .0150 | .0675 | .0300 | .0025 |
| 6 | .1250 | .0025 | .0500 | .0525 | .0200 |
| 5 | .1275 | .0000 | .0275 | .0625 | .0375 |
| 4 | .1225 | .0000 | .0100 | .0525 | .0600 |
| 3 | .0825 | .0000 | .0000 | .0300 | .0525 |
| 2 | .0600 | .0000 | .0000 | .0100 | .0500 |
| 1 | .0200 | .0000 | .0000 | .0000 | .0200 |
| 0 | .0075 | .0000 | .0000 | .0000 | .0075 |
| | 1.0000 | .2500 | .2500 | .2500 | .2500 | p(X) |
| | | 8 | 16 | 24 | 36 | X |

The sample space for this joint distribution might be conceived in this way: some specific group of human subjects is sampled at random and independently with replacement. Each subject sampled is also allotted *at random* to one of four experimental treatments. In one treatment he is deprived of sleep for eight hours, in the second he goes for sixteen hours without sleep, with twenty-four, and thirty-six hours sleep-deprivation being given as the other treatments. The elements in the sample space in this example can be thought of as the possible outcomes of giving each of a set of persons each of this set of treatments.

Since each and every person sampled is assigned some particular treatment on a trial, any treatment-class is an event, and the number of hours of sleep-deprivation are values of a discrete random variable $X$. By the nature of the assignment of observations to treatments, the probability of each possible value of $X$ is .25, as shown in the marginal distribution for columns.

In the experiment proper, each person is given a motor-skills performance test after losing the specified amount of sleep. The scores on this performance are values of a discrete random variable $Y$, with probabilities given by the marginal distribution of the rows. Then the joint probability of any value of $X$ paired with any value of $Y$ is shown in the body of the table.

If one knew these probabilities, could he say that motor performance scores are independent of hours of sleep deprivation? Look at any cell of the table, say, for ($X = 24$, $Y = 5$). If the two random variables are independent, then it must be true that

$$p(24,5) = p(24)p(5) = (.25)(.1275) = .0319.$$

This is different from the probability for the event ($X = 24$, $Y = 5$) in the joint distribution, which is .0625. Since these are the actual probabilities of occurrence, this discrepancy alone is sufficient to let us say that the variables $X$ and $Y$ are not independent, and *are* associated. For $X$ and $Y$ to be independent, the probability of every event ($X,Y$) must be the product of the two marginal probabilities, $p(X)p(Y)$.

The association between $X$ and $Y$ can also be seen from a conditional distribution, showing $p(Y|X)$ for some fixed $X$ and over the different $Y$ values. Consider the column $X = 8$. The conditional distribution is shown in Table 4.10.2.

**Table 4.10.2**

| $Y$ | $p(Y|X = 8) = \dfrac{p[(X = 8) \cap Y]}{p(X = 8)}$ | | |
|---|---|---|---|
| 10 | .35 | = | .0875/.25 |
| 9 | .39 | = | .0975/.25 |
| 8 | .19 | = | .0475/.25 |
| 7 | .06 | = | .0150/.25 |
| 6 | .01 | = | .0025/.25 |
| 5 | .00 | = | .0000/.25 |
| 4 | .00 | = | .0000/.25 |
| 3 | .00 | = | .0000/.25 |
| 2 | .00 | = | .0000/.25 |
| 1 | .00 | = | .0000/.25 |
| 0 | .00 | = | .0000/.25 |
| | 1.00 | | |

This is rather different from the *marginal* distribution of $Y$. For instance, a $Y$ score of 10 has a probability of .35 for $X = 8$, but only .095 if $X$ is not specified. This also demonstrates that $X$ and $Y$ are not independent, since any conditional distribution must be identical to the corresponding marginal distribution when variables are independent. We *can* say that performance scores on this test are associated with hours of sleep-deprivation.

This same idea can be employed for either discrete random variables or continuous random variables grouped into class intervals. After such grouping, any variable can be treated as discrete, and independence or association can be judged from the joint probabilities of *intervals* of $X$ and $Y$ relative to the product of the marginal probabilities of those intervals.

As another example, consider observations of rats in a laboratory situation. Each rat has an age in months (the variable $X$) at the time of the experiment. In the experiment proper, an animal is confined alone in a cage containing an activity wheel, which records how active the given animal is in any period of time. Let the variable $Y$ be the number of revolutions in the first twenty-four hours. This set of elementary events can be thought of as the collection of all rats actually given this treatment in some laboratory, so that the probabilities are relative frequencies of actual rats. It is also possible to think of this set of rats as hypothetical, or as all rats of a specified kind who *might* be given this treatment; in this case the probabilities are purely hypothetical. Nevertheless, in either case, we are discussing probabilities in a specified sample space.

In principle, these two variables $X$ and $Y$ might either be continuous or discrete. However, in either circumstance, if the marginal distributions are arranged into class intervals, then the various *joint intervals* might be represented as cells in a table:

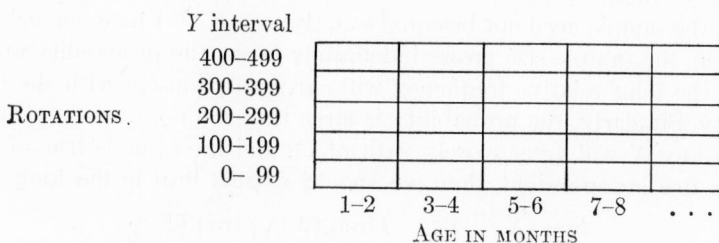

Each column or row will give a conditional distribution, based on the joint probabilities. If $X$ and $Y$ are independent, so that age is unrelated to activity in this experimental situation, each conditional probability distribution must be identical to the corresponding marginal distribution. *If we but knew these probability distributions, we could say without hesitation that there is or is not an association between these two variables in the specified sample space.*

## 4.11 JOINT FREQUENCY DISTRIBUTIONS AND INFERENCES ABOUT ASSOCIATION

It should be apparent that actual data can be put into the form of a *joint frequency distribution* in exactly the same way that events are shown in a joint probability distribution. The only difference is that the observed frequency is shown for each joint event or joint interval. When the events of both attributes are qualitative, then the joint distribution is often called a **contingency table.** For numerical scores, it is often convenient to show occurrence of a joint event by a point on a graph, where the $X$ and $Y$ axes symbolize the two variables. However, for the same reason that numerical distributions are grouped into class intervals, it may be more convenient to break each axis into class intervals and show the frequency of occurrence of the joint intervals in the data. Such bivariate frequency distributions are often called **scatter plots** or **scatter diagrams.**

The principle embodied in Bernoulli's theorem holds for such bivariate (or even multivariate) frequency distributions: g'ven random samples from a specific joint or bivariate distribution of events, the obtained relative frequencies of the various joint events must, in the long run, equal the probabilities for such joint events. Thus, any sample's joint distribution provides an estimate of the joint probability distribution, just as for single variate distributions.

Can the independence of events be judged from a sample joint distribution? Suppose that in one of the experiments of the section above some $N$ cases were sampled in all. A joint frequency distribution similar to the joint distributions above could be constructed. In any cell the obtained relative frequency of a joint event $X \cap Y$, or

$$\text{relative frequency } (X \cap Y) = \frac{\text{freq.}(X \cap Y)}{N}, \qquad [4.11.1]$$

is our best estimate of $p(X \cap Y)$. Because of sampling error, this relative frequency in the sample need not be equal exactly to $p(X \cap Y)$. Nevertheless, in the long run, as the sample size grows indefinitely large, the probability approaches 1.00 that the joint relative frequency will agree very closely with the true joint probability. Similarly, the probability is large that the relative frequency associated with any $X$ will agree closely with $p(X)$, and the same is true of $Y$. **If the variables are independent, then we should expect that in the long run**

$$\frac{\text{freq.}(X \cap Y)}{N} = \left(\frac{\text{freq.}(X)}{N}\right)\left(\frac{\text{freq.}(Y)}{N}\right),$$

**the relative frequency of any joint event** $(X \cap Y)$ **should equal the relative frequency of** $X$ **times the relative frequency of** $Y$ **for those particular values of** $X$ **and** $Y$.

Provided that $X$ and $Y$ are independent, the best estimate we can make of what to *expect* in a cell, given only the marginal frequencies, is

$$\text{expected frequency } (X \cap Y) = \frac{\text{freq.}(X) \text{ times freq.}(Y)}{N}. \qquad [4.11.2]$$

Now suppose that the experimenter draws a sample and actually constructs the table of joint frequencies. By the rule just given, he can estimate what the expected frequency of each cell should be, provided that $X$ and $Y$ were independent. Any departure of any cell's frequency from this expected number is a small piece of evidence that $X$ and $Y$ are not independent, and he may even say that $X$ and $Y$ are *apparently associated*. However, for any sample, it is quite possible for $X$ and $Y$ apparently to be associated, even though the variables are really independent. Conversely, finding relative frequencies that *exactly* conform to expectation about independent variables does not necessarily mean that $X$ and $Y$ are independent. Unequivocal statements about independence or association can never be made from sample results alone; these statements can be made with complete confidence only if the probabilities are known. The experimenter *never* has enough evidence to say for sure, unless his set of observations includes the entire sample space.

On the other hand, the more the joint frequencies depart from the frequencies to be expected for independent $X$ and $Y$, the better is the bet that $X$ and $Y$ are associated. Big departures from expectation should be unusual for relatively large sample size and for truly independent random variables. However, we still cannot say for sure, even for very large departures, that $X$ and $Y$ are associated.

## 4.12  STATISTICAL RELATIONS AND ASSOCIATION

Most applications of statistics to experimental data are concerned with association among two or more variables. Regardless of what the scientist studies, he can be sure that *for any observation showing a given value on one variable, there will be a whole distribution of values that might occur on some other variable.* That is, given the value of $X$, there is some conditional distribution of $Y$. Almost never will it be possible for one and only one $Y$ value to occur for each possible $X$; instead there will be any number of different $Y$ values that one might observe, each with some probability.

This is what we mean when we say that any set of data shows *variability.* No matter how we restrict the sample space, making it true that all observations represent the same event when looked at in one way, the individuals sampled will "scatter" over many events when regarded in some other way. As we said in Chapter 1, in some physical sciences this variability can be made so small as to be negligible; given $X$, different possibilities for $Y$ still exist, but different observations give $Y$ values so nearly alike as to be practically identical.

This is seldom the case with observations of living things. Human monozygotic twins, who are nearly identical in every physical respect, and who have been reared in virtually the same environment, still differ in important psychological characteristics. Even observations of the same individual taken over time show variability, and most of all on measures reflecting psychological processes.

For this reason, it is useful to think of each value of $X$ as paired with some distribution of $Y$ values, and to discuss this pairing of $X$ values with $Y$ distributions as a *statistical relation.* When each and every $X$ value possible is paired with exactly the same $Y$ distribution, then the variables $X$ and $Y$ are statistically independent, and one says that there is *no* statistical relationship. On the other hand, when different conditional distributions of $Y$ are paired with different values of $X$, then one says that a statistical relationship *does* exist. For example, in Section 4.10 each event corresponding to a number of hours of sleep deprivation, or a value of $X$, is paired with a whole conditional distribution of $Y$, or values representing performance on a motor task. In this example, the conditional distributions were different, and so we could say that a statistical relationship exists, or that $X$ and $Y$ are *associated.* On the other hand, had every conditional distribution of $Y$ given $X$ been the same, the variables would have been independent.

Psychologists using statistics are very interested in comparing distributions to see if they are identical or different in some way; the reason for this interest becomes clear when differences among distributions are viewed as suggesting a statistical relationship or association between variables. Perhaps the psychologist arranges an experiment, and both samples subjects at random and allots them at random to experimental groups. The assignment of a particular subject at random to a particular experimental group is an occurrence of an event $X$; this may actually be a number, such as the amount of some drug administered, or a qualitative class, such as a particular kind of visual stimulation given the subject. In either instance, the experimenter actually *makes* some experimental events occur in his sample. Then he looks at the distribution of $Y$ for each different $X$ possibility. Are these distributions different? If so, he has some evidence for association between $X$ and $Y$. The more that specifying the value of $X$ reduces the uncertainty about $Y$, the stronger is the evidence for association.

In other problems, nature or society has already defined the $X$ events that may occur. Such events as "male," "15 years old," "college sopho-more," "rat," "brain-injured," "Democrat," are well-defined classes of observations that may occur in samples. The experimenter actually samples members of several of these classes, and then looks at the distribution of $Y$ within each sample. Or he may sample individuals at random, and look at the distribution of $(X, Y)$ pairs. Once again, association is inferred from differences among conditional distributions.

In short, the comparison of obtained $Y$ distributions, conditional to specific $X$ values, or different qualitative categories, gives clues to association between variables. Nevertheless, even though differences among frequency distributions may suggest association, the goodness of this evidence must be evaluated in terms of probability. In particular, the experimenter knows that sample distributions need not be like the true probability distributions, and, unfortunately, association is defined in terms of the true state of affairs for all such observations. The theory of statistical inference gives the ingredients for this judgment about association from samples.

Several things must be considered before we can discuss how this is done. In the first place, more must be said about probability distributions and random variables, and especially about how a purely theoretical distribution can be constructed. Second, it is awkward to compare entire distributions. In most instances distributions can be contrasted much more efficiently in terms of some single number, such as an average. We need to take up the summary characteristics of distributions, ways of compressing the information they contain into much more compact form. Finally, we need to know the rules for statistical inference; how do you decide *how to decide* on the basis of probability?

The first of these issues will be developed in the next chapter. Chapter 6 will introduce the common summary measures, both for frequency and probability distributions. The succeeding chapters build toward an answer to the last question.

# A THEORETICAL DISTRIBUTION: THE BINOMIAL

## 5

The main burden of this chapter is to show how a theoretical distribution of a discrete random variable can be constructed. The particular distribution to be introduced is the binomial, which will play a very important role in much that follows in other chapters. First of all, it will be necessary to show some elementary probability calculations and to introduce some "counting rules" for these computations.

### 5.1 COMPUTING PROBABILITIES

Almost any simple problem in probability can be reduced to a problem in counting. Especially for a sample space containing equally probable elementary events, the computation of probability involves two quantities, both of which are *counts of possibilities:* the total number of elementary events, and the number qualifying for a particular event class. The key to solving probability problems is to learn to ask: "How many distinctly different ways can this event happen?" It may be possible simply to list the number of different elementary events that make up the event-class in question, but it is often much more convenient to use a rule for finding this number. Once the probabilities of events are found, the rules of Chapters 2 and 4 permit one to deduce other probabilities.

There is really no way to become expert in probability computations except by practice in the application of these various counting procedures. Naturally, problems differ widely in the particular principles they involve, but most problems should be approached by these steps:

1. Determine exactly the sample space of elementary events with which this problem deals.

2. Find out how many elementary events make up the sample

space. What are all the distinct outcomes that might conceivably occur? If the elementary events are equally probable, then the probability of any single elementary event is one over the total number of elementary events.

3. Decide on the particular events for which probabilities are to be found. How many elementary events qualify for each event class? If no other counting method is available, *list* the elements of these different events and count them. Be sure to remember that if event $A$ can occur in $n(A)$ ways and event $B$ in $n(B)$ ways, then event $(A \cap B)$ might occur in $n(A)n(B)$ ways.

4. For equally probable elementary events the probability of any event $A$ is simply the ratio of the number of members of $A$ to the total number of elementary events. Even though elementary events are not equally probable, we can still use the fact that elementary events are mutually exclusive to find the probability of any event $A$ by taking the *sum* of the probabilities of all members of that set.

A game of chance such as roulette shows how probabilities may be computed simply by listing elementary events. A standard roulette wheel has 37 equally spaced slots into which a ball may come to rest after the wheel is spun. These slots are numbered from 0 through 36. One half the numbers 1 through 36 are red, the others are black, and the zero is generally green.

In playing roulette, you may bet on any single number, on certain groups of numbers, on colors, etc. One such bet might be on the odd numbers (excluding zero of course). The only elementary events in the sample space are the numbers 0 through 36 with their respective colors. Which numbers qualify for the event "odd"? It is easy to count these numbers: they form the set

$$\{1,3,5,7,9,11,13,15,17,19,21,23,25,27,29,31,33,35\}.$$

Since there are exactly 18 elementary events qualifying as odd numbers, if each slot on the roulette wheel is equally likely to receive the ball, the probability of "odd" is 18/37, slightly less than 1/2.

As a more complicated example that can be solved by listing, let us find the probability that the number contains a "3" as one of the digits. The elementary events qualifying are:

$$\{3,13,23,30,31,32,33,34,35,36\}.$$

Here the probability is 10/37, if the 37 different elementary events are equally likely.

As a final example, consider the probability of a number that is "even and red" on the roulette wheel. These are

$$\{12,14,16,18,30,32,34,36\}$$

and the probability is 8/37.

There is no end to the examples that might be brought in at this point to show this counting principle in operation, but there is little point in spending more time with it. Just remember that almost all simple problems in probability can be solved in this same way. The important thing to understand is,

"When in doubt, make a list." This will usually work, although, as we shall see, other counting methods are often more efficient.

## 5.2 SEQUENCES OF EVENTS

In many problems, an elementary event may be *the set of outcomes of a series or sequence of observations*. Such sequences can also be considered joint events, but it is convenient to regard an entire sequence as an elementary event. Suppose that any trial of some simple experiment must result in one of $K$ mutually exclusive and exhaustive events, $\{A_1, \cdots, A_K\}$. Now the experiment is *repeated* $N$ times. This leads to a sequence of events: the outcome of the first trial, the outcome of the second, and so on in order through the outcome of the $N$th trial. The outcome of the whole series of trials might be the sequence $(A_3, A_1, A_2, \cdots, A_3)$. This denotes that the event $A_3$ occurred on the first trial, $A_1$ on the second trial, $A_2$ on the third, and so on. The place in order gives the trial on which the event occurred, and the symbol occupying that place shows the event occurring for that trial. For example, it might be that the simple experiment is drawing one marble at a time from a box, with replacement after each drawing. The marbles observed may be red, white, or black. For four drawings a sequence of outcomes might be (R,W,B,W), or perhaps (W,W,B,B).

The idea of a sequence also extends to a series of *different* simple experiments. Here the place in the sequence corresponds to the particular experiment being performed. For example, suppose that on the first trial, the experimenter draws a marble from a box, on the second he flips a coin, and on the third he tosses a die. Then the sequence of events observed might be (R,Heads,6) for example, where the position describes the particular simple experiment, and the symbol in that position tells the observed event.

Remember that each possible sequence can be thought of in two ways: it is a joint event from the standpoint of a series of simple experiments, but it is also an elementary event if one thinks of the *experiment itself* as the series of trials. Each *whole* or *compound experiment* has as its outcome one and only one sequence. Such experiments producing sequences as outcomes are very important to statistics, and so we will begin our study of counting rules by finding how many different sequences a given series of trials could produce.

## 5.3 NUMBER OF POSSIBLE SEQUENCES FOR $N$ TRIALS: COUNTING RULE 1

Suppose that a series of $N$ trials were carried out, and that on each trial any of $K$ events might occur. Then the following rule holds:

Counting rule 1: If any one of $K$ mutually exclusive and exhaustive events can occur on each of $N$ trials, then there are $K^N$ different sequences that may result from a set of trials.

As an example of this rule, consider a coin's being tossed. Each toss can result only in a $H$ or a $T$ event ($K = 2$). Now the coin is tossed five times, so that $N = 5$. The total number of *possible* results of tossing the coin five times is $K^N = 2^5 = 32$ sequences. Exactly the same number is obtained for the possible outcomes of tossing five coins simultaneously, if the coins are thought of as numbered and a sequence describes what happens to coin 1, to coin 2, and so on.

As another example, the outcome of tossing two dice is a sequence: what number comes up on the first die, and what number comes up on the second. Here $K = 6$ (six different numbers per die), and $N = 2$. There are exactly $6^2 = 36$ different sequences possible as results of this experiment.

## 5.4  COUNTING RULE 2

Sometimes the number of possible events in the first trial of a series is different from the number possible in the second, the second different from the third, and so on. It is obvious that if there are different numbers $K_1, K_2, \cdots, K_N$ of events possible on the respective trials, then the total number of sequences will not be given by rule 1. Instead, the following rule holds:

**Counting rule 2:**  If $K_1, \cdots, K_N$ are the numbers of distinct events that can occur on trials 1, $\cdots$, $N$ in a series, then the number of different sequences of $N$ events that can occur is $(K_1)(K_2) \cdots (K_N)$.

For example, suppose that for the first trial you toss a coin (two possible outcomes) and for the second you roll a die (six possible outcomes). Then the total number of different sequences would be $(2)(6) = 12$.

Notice that counting rule 1 is actually a special case of rule 2. If the same number $K$ of events can occur on any trial, then the total number of sequences is $K$ multiplied by itself $N$ times, or $K^N$.

## 5.5  COUNTING RULE 3: PERMUTATIONS

A rule of extreme importance in probability computations concerns the number of ways that objects may be arranged in order. The rule will be given for arrangements of objects, but it is equally applicable to sequences of events:

**Counting rule 3:**  The number of different ways that $N$ distinct things may be arranged in order is $N! = (1)(2)(3) \cdots (N - 1)(N)$, (where $0! = 1$). An arrangement in order is called a permutation, so that the total number of permutations of $N$ objects is $N!$ The symbol $N!$ is called "$N$ factorial."

As an illustration of this rule, suppose that a classroom contained exactly 10 seats for 10 students. How many ways could the students be assigned to the chairs? Any of the students could be put into the first chair, making 10 possibilities for chair 1. But, given the occupancy of chair 1, there are only 9 students for chair 2; the total number of ways chair 1 and chair 2 could be filled is $(10)(9) = 90$ ways. Now consider chair 3. With chairs 1 and 2 occupied, 8 students remain, so that there are $(10)(9)(8) = 720$ ways to fill chairs 1, 2, and 3. Finally, when 9 chairs have been filled there remains only 1 student to fill the remaining place, so that there are

$$(10)(9)(8)(7)(6)(5)(4)(3)(2)(1) = (10)! = 3628800$$

ways of arranging the 10 students into the 10 chairs.

Now suppose that there are only $N$ different events that can be observed in $N$ trials. Imagine that the occurrence of any given event "uses up" that event for the sequence, so that each event may occur *once and only once* in the sequence. In this case there must be $N!$ different orders in which these events might occur in sequence. Each sequence is a permutation of the $N$ possible events.

To take a homely example, suppose that a man is observed dressing. At each point in our observation there are three articles of clothing he might put on: his shoes, his pants, or his shirt. However each article can be put on only once. We might observe the following sequences:

(shoes, pants, shirt)
(shoes, shirt, pants)
(shirt, shoes, pants)
(shirt, pants, shoes)
(pants, shoes, shirt)
(pants, shirt, shoes)

The man's putting on any one of these articles of clothing literally uses up that outcome for any sequence of observations, so that there are $N! = (1)(2)(3) = 6$ possible permutation sequences.

The procedure of counting sequences as permutations in order is especially important for sampling without replacement. For example, suppose that a teacher has the names of five students in a hat. She draws the names out at random one at a time, *without* replacement. Then there are exactly $5!$ or 120 different sequences of names that she might observe. If all sequences of names are equally likely to be drawn, then the probability for any one sequence is $1/120$.

What is the probability that the name of any given child will be drawn first? Given that a certain child is drawn first, the order of the remainder of the sequence is still unspecified. There are $(N - 1)! = 4! = 24$ different orders in which the other children can appear. Thus the probability of any given child being first in sequence is $24/120 = .20$ or $1/5$.

Suppose that exactly *two* of the names in the hat are girls'. What is the probability that the first two names drawn belong to the girls? Given the first two names are girls', there are still $3! = 6$ ways three boys may be arranged. The girls' names may themselves be ordered in two ways. Thus, the probability of the girls' names being drawn first and second is $(2)(6)/120 = 1/10$.

## 5.6 Counting Rule 4: ordered combinations

Sometimes it is necessary to count the number of ways that $r$ objects might be selected from among some $N$ objects in all, $(r \leqq N)$. Furthermore, each different *arrangement* of the $r$ objects is considered separately. Then the following rule applies:

**Counting rule 4:** The number of ways of selecting and arranging $r$ objects from among $N$ distinct objects is $\dfrac{N!}{(N-r)!}$.

The reasoning underlying this rule becomes clear if a simple example is taken: Consider a classroom teacher, once again, who has 10 students to be assigned to seats. This time, however, imagine that there are only 5 seats. How many different ways could the teacher select 5 students and arrange them into the available seats? Notice that there are 10 ways that the first seat might be filled, 9 ways for the second, and so on, until seat 5 could be filled in 6 ways. Thus there are

$$(10)(9)(8)(7)(6)$$

ways to select students to fill the 5 seats. This number is equivalent to

$$\frac{10!}{5!} = \frac{N!}{(N-r)!},$$

the number of ways that 10 students out of 10 may be selected and arranged, but divided by the number of arrangements of the 5 *unselected* students in the 5 *missing* seats.

As an example of the use of this principle in probability calculations, consider the following: In lotteries it is usual for the first person whose name is drawn to receive a large amount, the second some smaller amount, and so, until some $r$ prizes are awarded. This means that some $r$ names are drawn in all, and the *order* in which those names are drawn determines the size of the prizes awarded to individuals. Suppose that in a rather small lottery 40 tickets had been sold, each to a different person, and only 3 were to be drawn for first, second, and third prizes. Here $N = 40$ and $r = 3$. How many different assignments of prizes to persons could there be? The answer, by counting principle 4, is

$$\frac{40!}{(40-3)!} = \frac{40!}{37!} = (38)(39)(40) = 59,280.$$

On how many of these possible sequences of winners would a given person, John Doe, appear as first, second, *or* third prize winner? If he were drawn first, the number of possible selections for second and third prize would be $39!/37! = 1482$. Similarly, there would be 1482 sequences in which he could appear second, and a like number where he could appear third. Thus, the probability that he appears in a sequence of three drawings, winning first, second, or third prize is (by axiom 3, Section 2.5)

$$p(\text{first, second, or third}) = \frac{3(1482)}{59{,}280} = \frac{3}{40}.$$

## 5.7 COUNTING RULE 5: COMBINATIONS

In a very large class of probability problems, we are not interested in the *order* of events, but only in the number of ways that $r$ things could be selected from among $N$ things, *irrespective of order*. We have just seen that the total number of ways of selecting $r$ things from $N$ and ordering them is $\dfrac{N!}{(N-r)!}$, by rule 4. Each set of $r$ objects has $r!$ possible orderings, by rule 3. A combination of these two facts gives us

**Counting rule 5:** The total number of ways of selecting $r$ distinct combinations of $N$ objects, irrespective of order, is

$$\frac{N!}{r!\,(N-r)!} = \binom{N}{r}.$$

The symbol $\binom{N}{r}$ is *not* a symbol for a fraction, but instead denotes the number of combinations of $N$ things, taken $r$ at a time. Sometimes the number of combinations is known as a "binomial coefficient," and occasionally $\binom{N}{r}$ is replaced by the symbols $^{N}C_r$ or $_NC_r$. However, the name and symbol introduced in rule 5 will be used here.

It is helpful to note that

$$\binom{N}{r} = \binom{N}{N-r}.$$

Thus, $\binom{10}{3} = \binom{10}{7}$, $\binom{50}{49} = \binom{50}{1}$, and so on.

As an example of the use of this rule, suppose that a total of 33 men were candidates for the board of supervisors in some community. Three supervisors are to be elected at large; how many ways could 3 men be selected from among these 33 candidates? Here, $r = 3$, $N = 33$, so that

$$\binom{N}{r} = \frac{(33)!}{3!\,(30)!} = \frac{(1 \cdot 2 \cdot \,\cdots\, \cdot 32 \cdot 33)}{(1 \cdot 2 \cdot 3)(1 \cdot 2 \cdot \,\cdots\, \cdot 29 \cdot 30)}.$$

Cancelling in numerator and denominator, we get

$$\binom{33}{3} = \frac{(31)(32)(33)}{6} = (31)(16)(11) = 5456.$$

If all sets of three men are equally likely to be chosen, the probability for any given set is 1/5456.

Because of their utility in probability calculations, a table of $\binom{N}{r}$ values for various values of $N$ and $r$ is included in Appendix C. Although this table shows values of $N$ only up to 20, and values of $r$ up to 10, other values can be found by the relation given above, and also by the relation known as Pascal's Rule:

$$\binom{N}{r} = \binom{N-1}{r-1} + \binom{N-1}{r}.$$

Still other values may be worked out from the table of factorials also included in the Appendix C, in terms of rule 5.

## 5.8   SOME EXAMPLES: POKER HANDS

These five rules provide the basis for many calculations of probability when the number of elementary events is finite, especially when sampling is without replacement. One of the easiest examples of their application is the calculation of probabilities for poker hands.

The game of poker as discussed here will be highly simplified and not very exciting to play: the player simply deals five cards to himself from a well-shuffled standard deck of fifty-two cards. Nevertheless, the probabilities of the various hands are interesting, and can be computed quite easily.

The particular hands we will examine are the following:

    a. one pair, with three different remaining cards
    b. full house (three of a kind, and one pair)
    c. flush (all cards of the same suit).

First of all we need to know how many different *hands* may be drawn. A given hand of five cards will be thought of as an elementary event; notice that the order in which the cards appear in a hand is immaterial. By rule 5, since there are 52 different cards in all and only 5 are selected, then there are

$$\binom{52}{5} = \frac{52!}{5!\,47!}$$

different hands that might be drawn. If all hands are equally likely, then the probability of any given one is $1 \Big/ \binom{52}{5}$.

There are 13 numbers that a pair of cards may show (counting the picture cards), and each member of a pair must have a suit. Thus by rule 5 there are $13\binom{4}{2}$ different pairs that might be observed. The remaining cards must show three of the twelve remaining numbers and each of the three cards may be of any suit. By rules 1 and 5 there are $\binom{12}{3}(4)(4)(4)$ ways of filling out the hand in this way. Finally, we find that there are

$$13 \binom{4}{2} \binom{12}{3} 4^3$$

different ways for this event to occur. Thus,

$$p(\text{one pair}) = \frac{13 \binom{4}{2} \binom{12}{3} 4^3}{\binom{52}{5}}.$$

This number can be worked out by writing out the factorials, cancelling in numerator and denominator, and dividing. It is approximately equal to .42. The chances are roughly four in ten of drawing a single pair in five cards, if all possible hands are equally likely to be drawn.

This same scheme can be followed to find the probability of a full house. There are thirteen numbers that the three of a kind may have, and then twelve numbers possible for the pair. The three of a kind must represent three of four suits, and the pair two of four suits. This gives

$$13 \binom{4}{3} 12 \binom{4}{2}$$

different ways to get a full house. The probability is

$$p(\text{full house}) = \frac{13 \binom{4}{3} 12 \binom{4}{2}}{\binom{52}{5}}$$

which is about .0014.

Finally, a flush is a hand of five cards all of which are in the same suit. There are exactly four suit possibilities, and a selection of five out of thirteen numbers that the cards may show. Hence, the number of different flushes is $4 \binom{13}{5}$, and

$$p(\text{flush of five cards}) = \frac{4 \binom{13}{5}}{\binom{52}{5}}$$

or about .002.

The probabilities of the various other hands can be worked out in a similar way. The point of this illustration is that it typifies the use of these counting rules for actually figuring probabilities of complicated events, such as particular poker hands. Naturally, a great deal of practice is usually necessary before one can visualize and carry out probability calculations from "scratch" with any facility. Nevertheless, such probability calculations usually depend upon counting how many ways events of a certain kind can occur, if the elementary events are finite in number.

Now we will turn to a special use of these counting rules in finding the distribution of a discrete random variable.

## 5.9 BERNOULLI TRIALS AND DISTRIBUTIONS

The very simplest probability distribution is one with only two event classes. For example, a coin is tossed and one of two events, heads or tails must occur, each with some probability. Or a normal human being is selected at random and his sex noted: the outcome can be only Male or Female. Such experiments that can eventuate in only one of two outcomes are usually called Bernoulli trials, and we will call the two event classes and their associated probabilities a Bernoulli distribution.

In general, one of the two events is called a "success" and the other a "failure" or "nonsuccess." These names serve only to tell the events apart, and are not meant to bear any connotation of "goodness" of the event. In the discussion to follow, the symbol $p$ will stand for the probability of a success, and $q = 1 - p$ for the probability of a failure. Thus, in tossing a fair coin, let a head be a success. Then $p = 1/2$, $q = 1 - p = 1/2$. If the coin is biased, so that heads are twice as likely to come up as tails, then $p = 2/3$, $q = 1/3$. In the following, take care to distinguish between $p$, standing for the probability of a success, and $p(X)$, standing for the probability of some value of a random variable.

## 5.10 SAMPLING FROM A BERNOULLI DISTRIBUTION

Suppose that some sample space exists fitting a Bernoulli distribution. Furthermore, suppose that either we sample independently with replacement, or that an infinite number of elementary events exist, so that for each sample observation out of $N$ trials, $p$ and $q$ are unchanged.

Now we proceed to make $N$ independent observations. Let $N$ be, say, 5. How many different sequences of five outcomes could be observed? The answer by rule 1, is $2^5 = 32$. *However, here it is not necessarily true that all sequences will be equally probable.* The probability of a given sequence depends upon $p$ and $q$, the probabilities of the two events. Fortunately, since trials are independent one can compute the probability of any sequence by the application of rule **4.6.3**.

We want to find the probability of the particular sequence of events:

$$(S, S, F, F, S)$$

where $S$ stands for a success and $F$ for failure. The probability of first observing an $S$ is $p$. If the second observation is independent of the first, then by rule **4.6.3,**

$$\text{probability of } (S, S) = p \cdot p = p^2.$$

The probability of an $F$ on the third trial is $q$, so that the probability of $(S, S)$ followed by $F$ is $p^2q$. In the same way the probability of $(S, S, F, F) = p^2q^2$, and that of the entire sequence is $p^2q^2p = p^3q^2$.

The same argument shows that the probability of the sequence $(S, F, F, F, F)$ is $pq^4$, that of $(S, S, S, S, S)$ is $p^5$, of $(F, S, S, S, F)$ is $p^3q^2$, and so on.

Now if we write out all of the possible sequences and their probabilities, an interesting fact emerges: **the probability of any given sequence of** $N$ **independent Bernoulli trials depends only on the number of successes and** $p$, **the probability of a success.** That is, regardless of the *order* in which successes and failures occur in a sequence, the probability is

$$p^r q^{N-r} \qquad\qquad\qquad \text{[5.10.1]}$$

where $r$ is the number of successes, and $N - r$ is the number of failures. Suppose that in a sequence of 10 trials, exactly 4 successes occur. Then the probability of that particular sequence is

$$p^4 q^6.$$

If $p = 2/3$, then the probability can be worked out from

$$\left(\frac{2}{3}\right)^4 \left(\frac{1}{3}\right)^6.$$

The same procedure would be followed for any $r$ successes out of $N$ trials for any $p$.

For example, if we toss a fair coin $(p = 1/2)$ six times, what is the probability of observing three heads followed in order by three tails? The answer is

$$p^3 q^3 = \left(\frac{1}{2}\right)^3 \left(\frac{1}{2}\right)^3 = \frac{1}{64}.$$

This is also the probability of the sequence $(H, T, H, T, H, T)$, of the sequence $(H, T, T, T, H, H)$, and of any other sequence containing exactly three successes or heads.

The probabilities just found are for *particular sequences*, arrangements of $r$ successes and $N - r$ failures in a certain order. What we have found is that if we want to know the probability of a particular sequence of outcomes of independent Bernoulli trials, that sequence will have the same probability as any other sequence with exactly the same number of successes, given $N$ and $p$.

In most instances, however, one is not especially interested in particular sequences *in order*. We would like to know probabilities of given numbers of successes *regardless* of order in which they occur. For example, when a coin is tossed five times, there are several sequences of outcomes where exactly two heads occur:

$$(H, H, T, T, T)$$
$$(H, T, H, T, T)$$
$$(H, T, T, H, T)$$
$$(H, T, T, T, H)$$
$$(T, H, T, T, H)$$
$$(T, H, H, T, T)$$
$$(T, H, T, H, T)$$
$$(T, T, H, H, T)$$
$$(T, T, H, T, H)$$
$$(T, T, T, H, H).$$

Each and every one of these different sequences must have the same probability, $p^2q^3$, since each shows exactly two successes and three failures. Notice that there are $\binom{N}{r} = \binom{5}{2} = 10$ different such sequences, exactly as counting rule 5 gives for the number of ways 5 things can be taken 2 at a time.

What we want now is the probability that $r = 2$ successes will occur *regardless* of order. This could be paraphrased as "the probability of the sequence $(H, H, T, T, T)$ or the sequence $(H, T, H, T, T)$ or any other sequence showing exactly 2 successes in 5 trials." Such "or" statements about mutually exclusive events recall axiom 3 in Section 2.5: if $A$ and $B$ are mutually exclusive events, then $p(A \cup B) = p(A) + p(B)$. Thus, the probability of 2 successes in any sequence of 5 trials is $p(2 \text{ successes in 5 trials}) = p^2q^3 + p^2q^3 + \cdots + p^2q^3 = \binom{5}{2} p^2q^3$ since each of these sequences has the same probability and there are $\binom{5}{2}$ of them.

Generalizing this idea for any $r$, $N$, and $p$, we have the following principle: **in sampling from a Bernoulli distribution, with the probability of a success equal to** $p$, **the probability of observing exactly** $r$ **successes in** $N$ **independent trials is**

$$p(r \text{ successes}|N,p) = \binom{N}{r} p^r q^{N-r}. \qquad [5.10.1*]$$

For example, imagine that in some very large population of animals 80 percent of the individuals have normal coloration, and only 20 percent are albino (no skin and hair pigmentation). This may be regarded as a Bernoulli distribution with "albino" being a success and "normal" a failure. Suppose that the probabilities are $.20 = p$ and $.80 = q$. A biologist manages to sample this population at random, catching three animals. What is the probability that he will catch one albino? Here, $N = 3$, $r = 1$, so that

$$p(1 \text{ albino in 3 animals}) = \binom{3}{1} (.20)^1 (.80)^2$$
$$= .384.$$

If the sampling is random, and if the population is so large that sampling without replacement still permits one to regard the results of the successive trials as independent, then the biologist has about 38 chances in 100 of observing exactly 1 albino in his sample of 3 animals.

As a more complex example, consider a psychological experiment in which an animal has the task of running through a maze. The maze has eight choice points, where the animal has to go either to the right or to the left. If the animal is equally likely to choose the right or the wrong path on any choice point, and if successive choices are independent, what is the probability that he will make exactly four errors in traversing the maze? Here the sample space is the set of all possible behaviors for the animal at choice points: these are grouped into only two classes, "right" or "wrong." The eight points in the maze are regarded as a random sample of such choice behaviors, and each occurrence of a choice behavior is assumed to be independent of every other. Then,

$$p(4 \text{ errors in } 8 \text{ trials}) = \binom{8}{4} (.5)^4 (.5)^4$$

$$= \frac{(8)(7)(6)(5)}{(1)(2)(3)(4)} (.5)^8 = .27.$$

This event of 4 errors in 8 trials should occur with relative frequency of about 27 in 100 independent repetitions of the experiment.

## 5.11   NUMBER OF SUCCESSES AS A RANDOM VARIABLE: THE BINOMIAL DISTRIBUTION

When samples of $N$ trials are taken from a Bernoulli distribution, the number of successes is a discrete random variable. Since the various values are counts of successes out of $N$ observations the random variable can take on only the whole values from 0 through $N$. We have just seen how the probability for any given number of successes can be found. Now we will discuss the distribution pairing each possible number of successes with its probability. This distribution of number of successes in $N$ trials is called the **binomial distribution.** This is the first distribution we have studied that can easily be described not only by listing or graphic methods but also by its mathematical rule.

A binomial distribution can be illustrated most simply as follows: Consider a simple experiment repeated independently five times. Each trial must result in only one of two outcomes and the result of five trials is a sequence of outcomes like those in the preceding sections. However, we are not at all interested in the order of the outcomes, but only in the number of successes in the set of trials.

In order to find the probability for each value of the discrete random variable, given $N$ and $p$, let us begin with the largest value, $X = 5$. By counting rule 5, there must be $\binom{5}{5} = 1$ possible sequence where all of the outcomes are successes. The probability of this sequence is $p^5 q^0 = p^5$, so that we have

$$p(X = 5 | N = 5, p) = \binom{5}{5} p^5 = p^5.$$

For four successes, we find that by counting rule 5,

$$\binom{5}{4} = \frac{5!}{4! \, 1!} = \frac{(1)(2)(3)(4)(5)}{(1)(2)(3)(4)(1)} = 5,$$

so that four successes can appear in five different sequences. Each sequence has probability $p^4 q^1$. Thus,

$$p(X = 4 | N = 5, p) = \binom{5}{4} p^4 q^1 = 5 p^4 q^1.$$

Going on in this way, we find

$$p(X = 3|N = 5, p) = \binom{5}{3} p^3 q^2 = 10p^3 q^2$$

$$p(X = 2|N = 5, p) = \binom{5}{2} p^2 q^3 = 10p^2 q^3$$

$$p(X = 1|N = 5, p) = \binom{5}{1} pq^4 = 5pq^4$$

$$p(X = 0|N = 5, p) = \binom{5}{0} q^5 = q^5.$$

(Note that $\binom{5}{0} = \dfrac{5!}{0! \, 5!} = 1$, since 0! is 1 by definition.)

To take a concrete instance of this binomial distribution, let the experiment be that of tossing a fair coin five times. Then $p = 1/2$, and the binomial distribution for the number of heads is

| $X$ | $p(X)$ | |
|---|---|---|
| 5 | $(1/2)^5$ | $= 1/32$ |
| 4 | $5(1/2)^4(1/2)$ | $= 5/32$ |
| 3 | $10(1/2)^3(1/2)^2$ | $= 10/32$ |
| 2 | $10(1/2)^2(1/2)^3$ | $= 10/32$ |
| 1 | $5(1/2)(1/2)^4$ | $= 5/32$ |
| 0 | $(1/2)^5$ | $= 1/32$ |
| | | $32/32$ |

Notice that the probabilities over all values of $X$ sum to 1.00, just as they must for any probability distribution.

Now consider another example that is formally identical to this last one, but provides different probability values. Suppose that among American male college students who are undergraduates, only one in ten is married. A sample of five male students is drawn at random. Let $X$ be the number of married students observed. (We will assume the total set of students to be large enough that sampling can be without replacement without affecting the probabilities and that observations are independent.) Here, $p = .10$ and the distribution is

| $X$ | $p(X)$ | |
|---|---|---|
| 5 | $(1/10)^5$ | $= 1/100,000$ |
| 4 | $5(1/10)^4(9/10)$ | $= 45/100,000$ |
| 3 | $10(1/10)^3(9/10)^2$ | $= 810/100,000$ |
| 2 | $10(1/10)^2(9/10)^3$ | $= 7,290/100,000$ |
| 1 | $5(1/10)(9/10)^4$ | $= 32,805/100,000$ |
| 0 | $(9/10)^5$ | $= 59,049/100,000$ |
| | | $100,000/100,000$ |

Contrast this distribution with the preceding one: When $p$ was 1/2 the distribution showed the greatest probability for $X = 2$ and $X = 3$, with the probabilities diminishing gradually both toward $X = 0$ and toward $X = 5$. On the other hand, in the second distribution, the most probable value of $X$ is 0, with a steady decrease in probability for the values 1 through 5. The distribution over such values of $X$ is very different in these two situations, even though the probabilities are found by exactly the same *formal* rule. This illustrates that **the binomial is actually a family of theoretical distributions, each following the same mathematical rule for associating probabilities with values of the random variable, but differing in particular probabilities depending upon $N$ and $p$.**

The general definition of the binomial distribution can be stated as follows:

**Any random variable $X$ with probability function given by**

$$p(X = r) = \binom{N}{r} p^r q^{N-r}, \qquad 0 \leq X \leq N,$$

**is said to have a binomial distribution with parameters $N$ and $p$.**

The unspecified mathematical constants such as $N$ and $p$ that enter into the rules for probability or density functions indicate **parameters.** Families of distributions share the same mathematical rule for assigning probabilities or probability densities to values of $X$; in these rules the parameters are simply symbolized as constants. Actually assigning values to the parameters, such as we did for $p$ and $N$ in the distributions above, gives some particular distribution belonging to the family. Thus, *the* binomial distribution usually refers to the family of distributions having the same rule, and *a* binomial distribution is a particular one of this family found by fixing $N$ and $p$.

Almost all theoretical distributions of interest in statistics can be specified by stating the function rule. The way this simplifies the discussion of distributions will be obvious as we go along; indeed, continuous distributions cannot really be discussed at all except in terms of their function rule.

## 5.12   THE BINOMIAL DISTRIBUTION AND THE BINOMIAL EXPANSION

In school algebra you were very likely taught how to expand an expression such as $(a + b)^n$ by the following rule:

$$(a + b)^n = a^n + \frac{n!}{(n-1)!\,1!}\, a^{n-1}b + \frac{n!}{(n-2)!\,2!}\, a^{n-2}b^2 + \cdots$$
$$+ \frac{n!}{1!\,(n-1)!}\, ab^{n-1} + b^n.$$

For example, $(a + b)^3 = a^3 + 3a^2b + 3ab^2 + b^3$ according to this rule. This is the familiar "binomial theorem" for expanding a sum of two terms raised to a power.

Notice that the various probabilities in the binomial distribution are simply terms in such a binomial expansion. Thus, if we take $a = p$, $b = q$, and $n = N$,

$$(p + q)^N = p^N + \binom{N}{N-1} p^{N-1}q + \binom{N}{N-2} p^{N-2}q^2 + \cdots + q^N.$$

Since $p + q$ must equal 1.00, then $(p + q)^N = 1.00$, and the sum of all of the probabilities in a binomial distribution is 1.00.

### 5.13   PROBABILITIES OF INTERVALS IN THE BINOMIAL DISTRIBUTION

In Chapter 3 we saw how to find a probability that a value of a random variable lies in an interval, such as $p(2 \leq X \leq 8)$, the probability that the random variable $X$ takes on some value between 2 and 8 inclusive. This idea is easy to extend to a binomial variable.

Consider the binomial distribution shown in Table 5.13.1, where $p = .3$ and $N = 10$.

#### Table 5.13.1

| $X$ | $\binom{N}{r} p^r q^{N-r} = p(X = r)$ |
|:---:|:---:|
| 10 | .00001 |
| 9 | .00014 |
| 8 | .00145 |
| 7 | .00900 |
| 6 | .03676 |
| 5 | .10292 |
| 4 | .20012 |
| 3 | .26683 |
| 2 | .23347 |
| 1 | .12106 |
| 0 | .02824 |
| | 1.00000 |

First of all we will find the probability $p(1 \leq X \leq 7)$, that $X$ lies between the values 1 and 7 inclusive. This is given by the sum

| | |
|:---|:---:|
| $p(X = 1)$ | .12106 |
| $+p(X = 2)$ | .23347 |
| $+p(X = 3)$ | .26683 |
| $+p(X = 4)$ | .20012 |
| $+p(X = 5)$ | .10292 |
| $+p(X = 6)$ | .03676 |
| $+p(X = 7)$ | .00900 |

$$.97016 = p(1 \leq X \leq 7).$$

The probability is about .97 that an observed value of $X$ will lie between 1 and 7 inclusive. Thus, if we were drawing random samples of 10 observations with replacement from a Bernoulli distribution where the probability of a success were .3, we should be very likely to observe a number of successes between 1 and 7 inclusive.

By the same token, we can find

$$p(8 \leq X) = p(X = 8) + p(X = 9) + p(X = 10) = .00160.$$

The chances are less than two in a thousand of observing eight or more successes, *if $p$ = .30.*

Notice that

$$p(X = 0, \text{ or } 8 \leq X) = .02824 + .00160 = .02984,$$

which is the same as

$$1 - p(1 \leq X \leq 7) = 1 - .97016 = .02984,$$

so that this is also that probability that $X$ falls *outside* the interval bounded by 1 and 7.

Binomial distributions can also be put into cumulative form. Thus, the probability that $X$ falls at or below a certain value $a$ is the probability of the interval $X \leq a$. For this particular distribution, the corresponding cumulative distribution is

| $X$ | $p(X \leq r)$ |
|---|---|
| 10 | 1.00000 |
| 9 | .99999 |
| 8 | .99985 |
| 7 | .99840 |
| 6 | .98940 |
| 5 | .95264 |
| 4 | .84972 |
| 3 | .64960 |
| 2 | .38277 |
| 1 | .14930 |
| 0 | .02824 |

In this distribution, we see that about 65 percent of samples of 10 should show 3 or fewer successes, about 85 percent should have 4 or fewer, 99.8 percent should have 7 or fewer. Every sample (100 percent) must have ten or fewer successes, of course, since $N = 10$.

It must be re-emphasized that the binomial distribution is *theoretical*. It shows the probabilities for various numbers of successes out of $N$ trials *if* independent random samplings are carried out from a Bernoulli distribution and *if $p$* is the probability of a success. Given a different value of $p$ or of $N$ (or of both) the probabilities will be different. Nevertheless, regardless of $N$ or $p$, the probabilities are found by the same, binomial, rule.

### 5.14 THE BINOMIAL DISTRIBUTION OF PROPORTIONS

Quite often researchers are interested not in the number of successes that occur for some $N$ trial observations, but rather in the *proportion* of successes, $X/N$. The proportion of successes is also a random variable, taking on fractional (or decimal) values between 0 and 1.00. Such sample proportions will be designated by the capital letter $P$, to distinguish them from $p$, the probability of a success.

The probability of any given proportion $P$ of successes among $N$ cases sampled from a given Bernoulli distribution is exactly the same as the probability of the number of successes; that is

$$p\left(P = \frac{r}{N}\right) = p(X = r).$$ [5.14.1]

For instance, if $N = 6$ and $r = 4$

$$p(X = 4) = p\left(P = \frac{4}{6}\right) = \binom{6}{4} p^4 q^2.$$

The distribution of sample proportions is therefore given by the binomial distribution, the only difference being that each possible value of $X$ becomes a value of $P = X/N$, so that prob.$(P = a)$ = prob.$(X = Na)$ for any particular value $a$. In the further discussion of the binomial distribution in Chapter 8, care will be taken to specify whether the random variable is regarded as $X$ or $P$, since the arithmetic is slightly different in the two situations. Nevertheless, the probability of any given $P$ is the same as for the corresponding $X$, given the sample size $N$.

### 5.15 THE FORM OF A BINOMIAL DISTRIBUTION

Although the mathematical rule for a binomial distribution is the same regardless of the particular values of $N$ and $p$ entering into the expression, the "shape" of a histogram or other representation of a binomial distribution will depend upon $N$ and $p$. In general, the probabilities increase for increasing values of $X$ until some maximum point is reached, and then for $X$ values beyond this point the probabilities decrease once again. This makes the picture given by the distribution show a single "hump" somewhere between $X = 0$ and $X = N$, with probabilities gradually decreasing to either side of this maximum point. The exact location of this highest probability relative to $X$ depends, of course, on $N$ and $p$.

One device for locating where this maximum point must occur in any binomial distribution is to find the ratio of probabilities for successive values of $X$. That is, we take $X = r'$ and $X = r$, where $r' = r - 1$, and put these probabilities in ratio:

$$\frac{p(X = r|N,p)}{p(X = r'|N,p)} = \frac{\binom{N}{r} p^r q^{N-r}}{\binom{N}{r'} p^{r'} q^{N-r'}} = 1 + \frac{(N + 1)p - r}{qr}.$$ [5.15.1]

When this ratio is greater than 1.00, the probabilities are successively increasing; when the ratio is less than 1.00, the probabilities are decreasing; when the ratio is exactly equal to 1.00, the successive probabilities are exactly the same.

Now consider the situation where $X$ can assume the exact value $Np$ (that is, $Np$ is an integer). If we take $r = Np$, we find that the ratio **5.15.1** is a number greater than 1.00, indicating that the probability for $X = Np$ is greater than the probability for $X = Np - 1$. On the other hand, if we take $r = Np + 1$ we find this ratio is less than 1, meaning that the probability for $Np + 1$ is less than that for $Np$. In this way it can be shown that when $Np$ is an integer, the probability associated with $X = Np$ is greater than that for any other value of $X$; in this situation, the maximum point in a graph of the binomial distribution occurs at $X = Np$. Therefore, one finds that in this special situation the value $P = p$ is the most probable relative frequency of occurrence of an event with probability $p$.

On the other hand, it may be that $X$ cannot attain the exact value $Np$, since $Np$ need not be an integer. However, by exploring the changes in the ratio of probabilities, we would find that in this situation the value $X = r$ with the highest probability is *no more* than $p$ or $q$ away from the value of $Np$; that is

$$-q \leq r - Np \leq p,$$

where $r$ is the value of $X$ having highest probability in the binomial distribution. Actually, the statement interpreting Bernoulli's theorem in Section 2.8 should be read as meaning "the most probable proportion of the event's occurrences to the total number of trials is also $p$, whenever that value of $X/N$ can actually occur." Nevertheless, the most probable relative frequency is always a number *close* to the true value of $p$, even though this exact value may not occur for some values of $N$.


## 5.16   THE BINOMIAL AS A SAMPLING DISTRIBUTION

A binomial distribution is one example of a very important kind of theoretical distribution encountered again and again in statistics. These are sampling distributions, where a random variable $X$ denotes a possible value of some measure *summarizing* the outcomes of $N$ distinct observations. In the binomial case, this random variable is either the number of successes out of $N$ trials, or, perhaps, $P$, the proportion of successes out of the $N$ trials. In other contexts the random variable may be some other number summarizing a sample result, such as an average, or some index of variability. There are many different kinds of sampling distributions, depending on the basic sample space and the way that samples are summarized. Nevertheless, the essential idea is the same: a sample of $N$ observations is drawn at random, so that each and every distinct sample possible has an equal probability of occurrence. A number is attached to the sample, in some way summarizing the $N$ outcomes observed. In principle, different values will be found for different samples, and each sample-value may be regarded as a value of a random variable. The sampling distribution is a theoretical statement of the probability of observing various intervals of values of such a random variable over all possible samples of the same size $N$ drawn at random.

For example, imagine that all United States adults could be classified into two categories:

success = prefers foreign movies
failure = prefers U.S. movies.

We will assume that each person has one of these two preferences, and that there is an almost infinite number of such persons. This population could be arranged in a Bernoulli distribution, pairing each of the two classes with its proportion, $p$ or $q$.

We sample United States adults at random, asking each his preference. Suppose that our random sample consists of exactly 10 adults. The number of successes observed could be any number from 0 through 10, and there is some probability that can be associated each possible number, given the true $p$. The pairing of different sample values one might get and the probability of each is the sampling distribution. Note well, however, that the sampling distribution depends upon how the sampling was done, how we attached the value to a sample, and most of all, what the *true* situation is. If only .30 of the population of adults prefer foreign movies, then the sampling distribution for number of successes is given by Table 5.13.1. This tells us that if we observe 10 successes out of 10 cases, then we have encountered an event that should occur only once in 100,000 samples of 10 people, *if p is .30*. On the other hand, for $p = .30$, we should expect 3 out of 10 to occur relatively often; about 26 in 100 samples should give us this exact value. About 70 in 100 samples should give us 3, 4, or 5 people preferring foreign movies, and so on. In short, a sampling distribution allows one to judge the probability of a particular kind of sample result, given that something is true in general about the population being sampled. Before one can find the sampling distribution, however, he must postulate something true about the general situation: in this case, we postulated that exactly 30 percent of United States adults prefer foreign movies. Given that this is true, the sampling distribution specifies the probabilities of various sample numbers who show this preference.

In the next section a little preview of statistical inference will be given, in which the binomial rule provides a sampling distribution. This example cannot be complete at this time simply because all the necessary ingredients have not been introduced. On the other hand, the author feels it important that the student get some feel for the use of theoretical distributions as early as possible, to provide a basis for the more technical development to follow.

## 5.17 A PREVIEW OF A USE OF THE BINOMIAL DISTRIBUTION

It is now possible to point ahead to an important use of the binomial distribution. This example will deal with an experiment in psychology where we must use the data to decide whether or not a particular hypothesis actually seems to fit the data we obtain.

The context of the experiment is this: a psychophysical threshold or limen is that value on some physical measurement of a stimulus object at which a human subject is just capable of responding—in somewhat inexact terms, if the stimulus is a point of light in a darkened room, the threshold might be the physical intensity the light would have to have so that the subject would just be able to "see" the stimulus. It has, however, been suspected for some time that subjects may be able to respond in certain ways to stimuli which are actually below their known threshold of awareness. Such stimuli are said to be subliminal; the subject may not really be conscious that he "sees" the light—nevertheless, he may be able to respond *as though* he were capable of seeing the light.

Think of a hypothetical study of this question: "If a human is subjected to a stimulus below his threshold of conscious awareness, can his behavior somehow still be influenced by the presence of the stimulus?" The experimental task is as follows: the subject is seated in a room in front of a square screen divided into four equal parts. He is instructed that his task is to guess in which part of the screen a small, very faint, spot of light is thrown. He is to do this for many trials, and is told the light will be projected on the screen in a completely "haphazard," "random" manner over the trials. The light projected is made to be so faint that the subject cannot in any sense actually "see" the light. However, unknown to the subject, the spot is always projected into the same one of the four parts of the screen over the various trials. For our computational convenience, suppose that only 10 trials are taken for this one subject.

Our hypothesis goes like this: if the subject really is in no way being influenced by the small "invisible" spot of light, then his guesses should be random, haphazard affairs themselves, so that he should be right in his guess only 1/4 of the time by accident. Thus, under this hypothesis of "only guessing," the sample space of the subject's response to this situation should be distributed in this way:

| Class | $p$ |
|-------|-----|
| right | 1/4 |
| wrong | 3/4 |
| | 4/4 = 1.00 |

The explicit assumption made is that the various trials for the subject are independent of each other. Now what sampling distribution holds for 10 trials for this subject if this hypothesis is true? His number of correct guesses *could* range from 10 right to 0 right, and the distribution would be a binomial distribution with $p$(right) $= 1/4$, $N = 10$. If we apply the rule for the binomial, we find the distribution that appears in Table 5.17.1. This binomial distribution gives all the possible numbers of correct guesses that this subject *could* make in the ten trials, and the probability for each, *if* he truly were guessing in a haphazard manner.

Given this theoretical distribution of possible outcomes, we turn to the actual result of the experiment. It is found that the subject guessed correctly on 7 out of the 10 trials. What then is the probability that exactly this result *should* have come up by chance? The binomial probability for 7 correct is 3,240 out of 1,048,576, or about .0031. Thus the probability of his getting exactly this number correct by random guessing alone is about 31 chances in 10,000. In other words, if we repeated the experiment, giving the subject 10,000 independent sets of ten trials, about 31 of these repetitions should give us exactly 7 correct guesses. The exact sample result obtained is *not* a very likely thing to occur if the hypothesis is correct.

Table 5.17.1

| $X$ | $p(X)$ |
|---|---|
| 10 right | $\binom{10}{10} (1/4)^{10}(3/4)^{0} = .0000(+)$ |
| 9 | $\binom{10}{9} (1/4)^{9}(3/4)^{1} = .0000(+)$ |
| 8 | $\binom{10}{8} (1/4)^{8}(3/4)^{2} = .0004$ |
| 7 | $\binom{10}{7} (1/4)^{7}(3/4)^{3} = .0031$ |
| 6 | $\binom{10}{6} (1/4)^{6}(3/4)^{4} = .0162$ |
| 5 | $\binom{10}{5} (1/4)^{5}(3/4)^{5} = .0584$ |
| 4 | $\binom{10}{4} (1/4)^{4}(3/4)^{6} = .1460$ |
| 3 | $\binom{10}{3} (1/4)^{3}(3/4)^{7} = .2503$ |
| 2 | $\binom{10}{2} (1/4)^{2}(3/4)^{8} = .2816$ |
| 1 | $\binom{10}{1} (1/4)^{1}(3/4)^{9} = .1877$ |
| 0 | $\binom{10}{2} (1/4)^{0}(3/4)^{10} = .0563$ |

However, we should be interested in the probability not only of his getting exactly 7 correct, but rather the probability of getting *this many or more* correct, since we are really interested in this result as evidence of whether or not he is guessing, or doing something which will make him be more often correct than should simple, haphazard guessing. What is the probability that he should get *7 or more* correct trials? The answer is readily seen if we remember that this is asking for the probability of an interval:

$$p(7 \leq X) = p(7) + p(8) + p(9) + p(10) = .0035(+).$$

Seven or more correct guesses should occur only about 35 times in 10,000 independent replications of this experiment, if guessing alone is responsible for the subject's behavior. Does this unlikely result cast any doubt on the theory that the stimulus has no effect on guessing behavior? The answer is yes. For a theory to be "good," it should forecast results that agree with what we actually obtain. If the subject had come up with 2, 3, or 4 correct responses, then we would have little reason to doubt the "guessing" hypothesis, since these results fall among those that are quite probable according to the sampling distribution. However, the results obtained are quite unlikely to occur if the hypothesis is true, and so the evidence does not seem to favor this hypothesis.

On the other hand, are we completely safe in inferring that the subject was not just guessing? The answer is, of course, no. Even though this many or more correct responses obtained is improbable if the hypothesis is true, it is still not impossible that the subject might have been only guessing. We need some way to state just how much of a chance we are taking in saying that the hypothesis is not true, and that the subject is in some way being influenced by the stimulus. *The best measure of the amount of risk we run by abandoning this hypothesis on the evidence is given by the probability of sample results as extreme or more extreme than those actually obtained, if the hypothesis were true.* The evidence apparently diverges considerably from what we should expect (about 1/4 correct) if the subject were guessing, and the probability of such a divergent sample is only about 35 in 10,000. The probability of our being *wrong* in rejecting the guessing-hypothesis equals the probability of the divergent result, or .0035. We *could* be wrong in rejecting the hypothesis that the subject is guessing, but the probability of our being wrong is not very great. The more our sample result departs from what we expect given a hypothetical situation, and the more improbable that departure is, the less credence is given the hypothesis. In a later chapter we shall discuss in detail the rules for (and precautions in) evaluating hypotheses in the light of obtained results. However, this illustration exhibits the general logic underlying all "tests" of hypotheses: from the hypothetical population distribution one obtains a theoretical sampling distribution. Then the obtained results are compared with the sampling distribution probabilities. If the probability of samples such as the one obtained is high, the hypothesis is regarded as tenable. On the other hand, if the probability of such a sample (or one in more extreme disagreement with what is expected) is quite small, then doubt is cast on the hypothesis.

Although this little example should not be taken as a model of sophisticated scientific practice, it does suggest the use of a theoretical distribution of sample results as an aid in making inferences about a hypothetical situation. The binomial distribution is only one of a number of such sampling distributions we shall employ in this general way.

Before we continue further into the problem of statistical inference, we must develop more vocabulary for discussing distributions. In particular, it is not always convenient or to the point to compare sample and population distribution directly, and we need to introduce certain features of distributions such as their "central tendency" and their measures of "spread" or variability. These indices will give us the ability to make more succinct statements about real or theoretical sets of data than does a display of the entire function. These topics will be the subject of the next chapter.

However, in theory the problem of comparing theoretical and sample results *might* be solved in terms of the whole distribution of observations. To illustrate this remark, two more theoretical distributions will be mentioned.

## 5.18   THE MULTINOMIAL DISTRIBUTION

The basic rationale underlying the binomial distribution can be generalized to situations with more than two event classes. This generalization is known as the "multinomial distribution," having the following rule:

Consider $K$ classes, mutually exclusive and exhaustive, and with probabilities $p_1, p_2, \cdots, p_K$. If $N$ observations are made independently and at random, then the probability that exactly $n_1$ will be of kind 1, $n_2$ of kind 2, $\cdots$, and $n_K$ of kind $K$, where $n_1 + n_2 + \cdots + n_K = N$, is given by

$$\frac{N!}{n_1!\, n_2! \, \cdots \, n_K!} (p_1)^{n_1}(p_2)^{n_2} \cdots (p_K)^{n_K}.$$

Think once again of colored marbles mixed together in a box, where the following probability distribution holds:

| Color | $p$ |
|-------|------|
| Black | .40 |
| Red | .30 |
| White | .20 |
| Blue | .10 |
| | 1.00 |

Now suppose that 10 balls were drawn at random and with replacement. The sample shows 2 black, 3 red, 5 white, and 0 blue. What is the probability of a sample distribution such as this? On substituting into the multinomial rule, we have

$$\frac{10!}{(2!)(3!)(5!)(0!)} (.4)^2(.3)^3(.2)^5(.10)^0$$

$$= \frac{1 \cdot 2 \cdot 3 \cdot 4 \cdot 5 \cdot 6 \cdot 7 \cdot 8 \cdot 9 \cdot 10}{(1 \cdot 2)(1 \cdot 2 \cdot 3)(1 \cdot 2 \cdot 3 \cdot 4 \cdot 5)(1)} (.4)^2(.3)^3(.2)^5$$

since 0! and $(.1)^0$ are both equal to 1. Working out this number, we find that .087 is the probability of the *sample* distribution

| | |
|-------|------|
| Black | 2 |
| Red | 3 |
| White | 5 |
| Blue | 0 |
| | 10 |

if the probability distribution given above is the true one. Using this multinomial rule, one could work out a probability for each *possible sample distribution*.

Although the multinomial rule is relatively easy to state, a tabulation or graph of this distribution is very complicated: here a sample result is not a single number, as for the binomial, but rather *an entire frequency distribution*.

This raises an interesting possibility. Given any discrete probability distribution, one might work out the probability of all possible sample distributions for $N$ observations. Then, in terms of these probabilities, the disagreement of sample and theoretical distributions could be evaluated. Although this is possible in principle, the drawbacks should be obvious. For any but small numbers of possible events and small $N$, the sheer number of different sample distributions is fantastically large. Ordinarily we are not interested in the probability of our sample alone, but rather in that of samples *as deviant or more so* than ours. This makes for too much computation to be practical in most instances. Furthermore, we run into trouble in trying to formulate a similar scheme for *continuous* theoretical distributions. For these reasons, the multinomial distribution plays a rather small role in theoretical statistics. The probability of obtaining an entire sample distribution is not usually of interest; instead, we will be finding probabilities for various indices summarizing a sample distribution.

## 5.19   THE HYPERGEOMETRIC DISTRIBUTION

Another theoretical probability distribution deserves passing mention for the same reason. The multinomial rule (and the binomial, of course) assumes either that the sampling is done with replacement, or that the sample space is infinite, so that the basic probabilities do not change over the trials made. However, suppose that one were sampling from a finite space *without* replacement; then the probabilities would change for each observation made. By a series of arguments very similar to those used for finding probabilities of poker hands in Section 5.8, we could arrive at a new rule for finding the probabilities of sample results.

This rule describes the hypergeometric distribution, and can be stated as follows:

Given a sample space containing a finite number $T$ of elements, suppose that the elements are divided into $K$ mutually exclusive and exhaustive classes, with $T_1$ in class 1, $T_2$ in class 2, $\cdots$ , $T_K$ in class $K$. A sample of $N$ observations is drawn at random without replacement, and is found to contain $n_1$ of class 1, $n_2$ of class 2, $\cdots$ , $n_K$ of class $K$. Then the probability of occurrence of such a sample is given by

$$\frac{\binom{T_1}{n_1}\binom{T_2}{n_2}\cdots\binom{T_K}{n_K}}{\binom{T}{N}}$$

where $n_1 + n_2 + \cdots + n_K = N$ and $T_1 + T_2 + \cdots + T_K = T$.

For an illustration of the use of the hypergeometric rule, let us return to the problem of drawing marbles at random from a box (Section 5.17), but this time *without* replacement. Suppose there had been 30 balls in the box originally, with the following distribution of colors:

| Color | f |
|-------|-----|
| Black | 12 |
| Red | 9 |
| White | 6 |
| Blue | 3 |
| | 30 |

Notice that the relative frequencies are the same as the probabilities in the previous example. Now ten balls are drawn at random without replacement. We want the probability that the *sample* distribution is

| Color | f |
|-------|-----|
| Black | 2 |
| Red | 3 |
| White | 5 |
| Blue | 0 |
| | 10 |

Using the hypergeometric rule, we get

$$\frac{\binom{12}{2}\binom{9}{3}\binom{6}{5}\binom{3}{0}}{\binom{30}{10}}$$

which works out to be about .0011. This is not, of course, the same probability as we found for this sample result using the multinomial rule, since the entire sampling scheme is assumed different in this second example. This illustrates that *the sampling scheme adopted makes a real difference in the probability of a given result.*

However, this is a practical consideration only when the basic sample space contains a finite and small number of elementary events. When there is a very large number of elementary events in the sample space, the selection and nonreplacement of a particular unit for observation has negligible effect on the probabilities of events for successive samplings. For this reason, the hypergeometric probabilities are very closely approximated by the binomial or multinomial probabilities when $T$, the total number of elements in the sample space, is extremely large. The distinction between these different distributions becomes practically important only when samples are taken from relatively small sets of potential units for observation.

# CENTRAL TENDENCY
# AND VARIABILITY

6

Any frequency distribution is a summarization of data, but for many purposes it is necessary to summarize still further. Rather than compare entire distributions of data with each other or with hypothetical distributions, it is generally more efficient to compare only certain characteristics of distributions. Two such general characteristics of any distribution, whether frequency or probability, obtained or theoretical, are its measures of central tendency and variability. Indices of central tendency are ways of describing the "typical" or the "average" value in the distribution. Indices of variability, on the other hand, describe the "spread" or the extent of difference among the observations making up the distribution.

The more basic of these two concerns is the description of central tendency. This will be treated first for obtained frequency distributions, and then the ideas will be extended to probability distributions as well. Next, the measurement of the dispersion or spread of a frequency distribution will be taken up, and a parallel treatment will once again be given probability distributions. Finally, an attempt will be made to show how two indices, the mean and standard deviation, form the cornerstone of most statistical inference.

## 6.1 THE SUMMATION NOTATION

In this chapter it will be necessary to introduce the summation symbol $\Sigma$ (capital Greek sigma). This is read as "the sum of," and tells us to take the sum of the values represented by the expressions following the symbol. Thus, for example, $\Sigma X$ stands for the sum over all the different values that the variable $X$ can assume. Most simple statistical derivations involve various sums, and the use of this symbol introduces considerable economy of statement into these formulations.

There are a number of simple rules for the algebraic manipulation of the summation sign. These rules are given and illustrated in Appendix A. The student who has not already encountered summation notation in school algebra or elsewhere is urged to study these rules until he is thoroughly familiar with them. Actually, the rules themselves are easy, and a little practice at writing out the sums symbolized can familiarize one very quickly with the various ways sums can be manipulated. A little time spent in this way will greatly increase your ability to follow the simple mathematical arguments used in later sections.

## 6.2   MEASURES OF CENTRAL TENDENCY

Imagine an obtained distribution of numerical scores. If you were asked to state *one value* that would best "capture" and communicate the distribution as a whole, which value should you choose? One way to answer this question is to find that score-value which is a good "bet" about any randomly selected case from this distribution. Such a score may not be exactly correct for any given case, but it should be a fairly good guess about the obtained score for that case. However, there are at least three different ways to specify what we mean by a "good bet" about any case: (1) the most frequent (most probable) measurement class, (2) the point exactly midway between the top and bottom halves of the distribution, and (3) the arithmetic average of the distribution. The first of these ways of defining the central tendency leads to the measure known as the **mode;** the second leads to the **median** of the distribution; the third is merely the familiar average, or **mean.**

## 6.3   THE MODE

The mode is certainly the most easily computed and the simplest to interpret of all the measures of central tendency. It is merely the midpoint or class name of the most frequent measurement class. If a case were drawn at random from the distribution, then that case is more likely to fall in the **modal class** than any other. So it is that in the graph of any distribution, the modal class shows the highest "peak" or "hump" in the graph. The mode may be used to describe any distribution, regardless of whether the events are categorized or numerical.

On the other hand, there are some disadvantages to the mode. One is that there may be more than one modal class: it is perfectly possible for two or more measurement classes to show frequencies that are equal to each other and higher than the frequency shown by any other class. In this case, there is ambiguity about which class gives *the* mode of the distribution, as two or more values are "most popular." Fortunately, this does not happen very often; even though there are two or more "humps" in the graph of a distribution, the class having the highest frequency or probability is still taken as *the* mode. Nevertheless, in such a distribution, where one measurement class is not clearly most popular, the mode loses its effectiveness as a characterization of the distribution as a whole.

Another disadvantage is that the mode is very sensitive to the size and number of class intervals employed when events are numerical; the value of the mode may be made to "jump around" considerably by changing the class intervals for a distribution.

Finally, the mode of a sample distribution forms a very undependable source of information about the mode of the basic probability distribution. For these reasons, our use of the mode will be restricted to situations where: (1) the data are truly nominal scale in nature; (2) only the simplest, most easily computed, measure of central tendency is needed.

## 6.4   THE MEDIAN

The median score in any set of observations or in a distribution is also, in a sense, a good bet about any case in the total set represented. Just as its name implies, the median is the score corresponding to the middle individual when all individual cases are arranged in order by scores, or to a score that divides the cases into two intervals having equal frequency. Thus, if you drew a case at random from any set of $N$ observations, and guessed that this case showed the median score, you are just as likely to be guessing too high as too low.

The median for a set of observed data is ordinarily defined in slightly different ways depending upon whether $N$ is odd or even, and upon whether raw data or a grouped frequency distribution is to be described. For a set of raw scores, **when $N$ is odd the median corresponds to the score of individual number** $(N + 1)/2,$ **when all individuals are arranged in order by scores; when** $N$ **is even, the median is defined as the score-value midway between the scores for individual** $(N/2)$ **and individual** $(N/2) + 1$ **in order.** Then either for odd or even $N$ it will be true that exactly as many cases fall above as fall below the median score.

On the other hand, this way of computing a median is not usually applicable if the data have been arranged into a grouped frequency distribution. **For any such grouped distribution, the median is defined as the point at or below which exactly 50 percent of the cases fall.** Consequently the first step in finding the median of a grouped distribution is to construct the *cumulative* frequency distribution. This is illustrated in the table shown on page 160.

The last column given shows the cumulative frequencies for the class intervals. Since, by definition, the median will be that point in the distribution at or below which 50 percent of the cases fall, the cumulative frequency *at* the median score should be $.50N$. Thus, the cumulative frequency is $.50(200) = 100$ at the median for this example. Where would such a score fall? It can be seen that it could not fall in any interval below the real limit of 43.5, since only 85 cases fall at or below that point. However, it does fall below the real limit 48.5, since 102 cases fall at or below that point. Hence, we have located the median as being in the class interval with real limits 43.5 and 48.5.

We must still ascertain the *score* that corresponds to the median, and this is where the process of interpolation comes in. The median score is somewhere in the interval 44–48. We assume that the 17 cases in that interval are evenly scattered over the interval width of 5 units, as in Figure 6.4.1.

The median score, which is greater than or equal to exactly 100 cases, must then exceed not only the 85 cases below 43.5, but also equal or exceed 15 cases above 43.5. In other words, the median is 15/17 of the way *up* the interval

| Class | f | cf |
|-------|-----|-----|
| 74–78 | 10 | 200 |
| 69–73 | 18 | 190 |
| 64–68 | 16 | 172 |
| 59–63 | 16 | 156 |
| 54–58 | 11 | 140 |
| 49–53 | 27 | 129 |
| 44–48 | 17 | 102 |
| 39–43 | 49 | 85 |
| 34–38 | 22 | 36 |
| 29–33 | 6 | 14 |
| 24–28 | 8 | 8 |
| | 200 | |

from the lower limit. Next, what score is exactly 15/17 of the way between 43.5 and 48.5? Since the difference between these two limits is 5, the class interval size, we take (15/17)5, or 4.4 as the amount that must be added to the lower real limit to find the median score, so that the median must be 43.5 + 4.4 or 47.9.

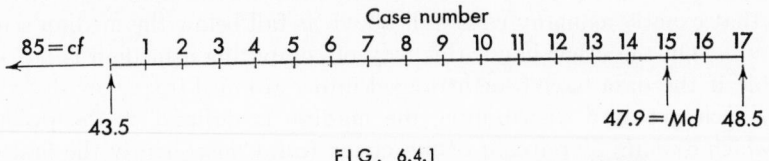

FIG. 6.4.1

A little computational formula that summarizes the steps just described is given by:

$$\text{median} = \text{lower real limit} + i \frac{(.50N - cf \text{ below lower limit})}{f \text{ in interval}} \qquad [6.4.1\dagger]$$

where the lower real limit used belongs to the interval containing the median, and the *cf* refers to the cumulative frequency *up to* the lower limit of the interval. For the example, we find

$$\text{median} = 43.5 + 5 \frac{[.50(200) - 85]}{17} = 47.9.$$

If the median can fall only in some class interval with nonzero frequency, this method of interpolation gives a unique value. However, if the interval frequency happens to be zero, then actually any point in the interval serves equally well as the distribution median; here one usually takes the midpoint as the median.

Even when the raw data are available, it is often worthwhile to define and compute the median as for a grouped frequency distribution. In the first place, for a sizable $N$, ordering all of the cases by their score magnitudes can be a considerable chore, and it may be simpler to construct a grouped distribution. Secondly, a troublesome problem arises when two or more cases in the raw data are tied in order at the median position, and here it often makes sense to calculate the median by interpolation as for a grouped distribution.

In principle, a median may be found for any distribution in which the variable represents an interval or even an ordinal scale; it is not, in general, applied to a distribution in which the measurement classes are purely categorical, since such classes are unordered.

The median is considerably less sensitive to the distribution's grouping into class intervals than is the mode. Furthermore, when one is making inferences about a large "population" of potential observations from a sample, the median is generally more useful and informative than the mode, although the median itself is not ordinarily so useful as the mean, to be discussed next. We will have more to say about characteristics of the median in future sections. For the moment, we need to consider the third, and most used, of the indices of central tendency: the mean.

## 6.5   THE ARITHMETIC MEAN

By far the most used and familiar index of central tendency for a set of raw data or a distribution is the mean, or simple arithmetic average. Surely everyone knows that to take the average of a set of raw scores you simply add them all up and divide by the total number, $N$:

$$M = \frac{\sum_i X_i}{N}.$$ [6.5.1*]

(Here, $X_i$ stands for the score of the observation labeled $i$, and the sum is taken over all of the $N$ different observations $i$.) Thus, equation **6.5.1** actually defines the mean for any set of raw data in the form of numerical scores.

Since expressions representing means will occur so frequently in all of the later sections, it is well to point out that we might also represent the arithmetic mean by

$$M = \sum_i \frac{X_i}{N},$$

standing for each value $X_i$ first divided by $N$ and then summed over the individual observations $i$. The value $M$ represented by either of these expressions is precisely the same; this accords with rule 1 of Appendix A, that the sum of $N$ observations each multiplied by a constant number is the same as the sum itself multiplied by that number. Therefore, in succeeding sections sometimes one and sometimes the other way of expressing the mean will be used, depending on the algebraic and typographical requirements of the particular discussion in which these expressions occur.

The definition and computation of the arithmetic mean for raw data is simple enough, but the situation is slightly more complicated when one wishes to find the mean of a grouped distribution of scores. You will recall (Section 3.8) that when a distribution is grouped into class intervals the midpoint $x$ of each class interval was taken to represent the score of each of the cases in the interval. Thus, in an interval 59–73 with midpoint 66 and frequency 16, the sum of the scores of the 16 cases falling into this interval is taken to be 66 summed 16 times, or $(66)(16) = xf$. Similarly, when all of the scores in any interval are assumed the same, their sum is the midpoint of that particular interval times the frequency for that interval, or $xf$. Then the sum of *all* of the scores in the distribution is taken to be the sum of the values of $x$ times $f$ over all of the respective intervals, and thus the mean is found from

$$M = \frac{\Sigma xf}{N}.$$  [6.5.2*]

(Note that here $x$ is *any* midpoint, $f$ is the frequency corresponding to that interval, and the sum is taken over *all intervals*.)

For example, consider once again the distribution shown in Section 6.5 (Table 6.5.1). The frequency of each class interval is multiplied by its midpoint, and these are then summed and divided by $N$ to given the distribution mean.

**Table 6.5.1**

| Class | $x$ | $f$ | $xf$ |
|-------|-----|-----|------|
| 74–78 | 76 | 10 | 760 |
| 69–73 | 71 | 18 | 1278 |
| 64–68 | 66 | 16 | 1056 |
| 59–63 | 61 | 16 | 976 |
| 54–58 | 56 | 11 | 616 |
| 49–53 | 51 | 27 | 1377 |
| 44–48 | 46 | 17 | 782 |
| 39–43 | 41 | 49 | 2009 |
| 34–38 | 36 | 22 | 792 |
| 29–33 | 31 | 6 | 186 |
| 24–28 | 26 | 8 | 208 |
| | | 200 | 10,040 = $\Sigma xf$ |

$$M = \frac{\Sigma xf}{N} = \frac{10040}{200} = 50.2$$

The mean calculated from a distribution with grouped class intervals need not agree exactly with that calculated from raw scores. Information is lost and a certain amount of inaccuracy introduced when scores are grouped and treated as though each corresponded to the midpoint of some interval. The coarser the grouping, in general, the more likely is the distribution mean to differ from the raw-score mean. For most practical work the rule of ten to twenty class intervals gives relatively good agreement, however. Nevertheless, it is useful to think of the mean calculated from any given distribution as the mean of that *particular* distribution, a particular set of groupings with their associated frequencies.

## 6.6   THE MEAN AS THE "CENTER OF GRAVITY" OF A DISTRIBUTION

The mean of a distribution parallels the physical idea of a center of gravity, or balance point, of ideal objects arranged in a straight line. For example, imagine an ideal board having zero weight. Along this board are arranged stacks of objects at various positions. The objects have uniform weight and differ from each other only in their positions on the board. The board is marked off in equal units of some kind, and each object is assigned a number according to its position.

FIG. 6.6.1

This is shown in Figure 6.6.1. Now given this idealized situation, at what point would a fulcrum placed under the board create a state of balance? That is, what is the point at which the "push" of objects on one side of the board is exactly equal to the push exerted by objects on the other side? This is found from the mean of the positions of the various objects:

$$M = \frac{2 + 2 + 8 + 10 + 10 + 10 + 15 + 15 + 18 + 20}{10} = 11.$$

Here, the board would exactly balance if a fulcrum were placed at the position marked 11. Note that since there were piles of uniform objects at various positions on the board, this center of gravity was found in exactly the same way as for the mean of a distribution, since the position (midpoint of an interval) was in effect multiplied by the number of objects at that position (the class frequency), and then these values were summed and divided by the number of objects (the total frequency).

In short, the position of any object on the board is analogous to the score of a case, and each case is treated as having equal "weight" in our computations. The arithmetic mean is then like the center of gravity, or balance point. The mean is that score about which deviations in one direction exactly equal deviations in the other. The tendency for cases in a distribution to differ from the mean in one way is exactly balanced by the tendency to differ in the opposite way.

This property of the mean is bound up in the statement that **the sum of the deviations about the mean is zero in any distribution.** A deviation from the mean is simply the signed difference between the score for any case and the mean score:

$$d_i = (X_i - M). \qquad [6.6.1]$$

In order to show that the sum of these deviations must be zero, suppose that we had a frequency distribution consisting of the scores for $N$ observed cases. For each observation's score $X_i$ we find the deviation $d_i$ from the mean and then find the sum over these $N$ deviations:

$$\sum_i d_i = \sum_i (X_i - M).$$

By rule 4 in Appendix A this is the same as

$$\sum_i d_i = \sum_i X_i - \sum_i M,$$

or, since $M$ is a constant number for each in every case, by rule 1, Appendix A,

$$\sum_i d_i = \sum_i X_i - NM.$$

However, since by definition $M = \dfrac{\sum_i X_i}{N}$,

then

$$NM = \sum_i X_i.$$

Thus,

$$\sum_i d_i = NM - NM = 0,$$

the sum of the signed deviations about the mean is always zero.

A simple consequence of this fact is that *the mean signed deviation from the mean is zero:*

$$\frac{\sum_i d_i}{N} = \frac{0}{N} = 0. \qquad [6.6.2*]$$

Suppose once again that you were told to *guess* the score of some case picked at random from a distribution. If you guessed the mean for each case you might be in error to some extent on each trial, since it need not be true that the mean is exactly the same as any obtained score. The *extent* of error for a given case is $d$, the departure of the true score from the mean. Over all possible cases that might be drawn from the distribution the average error would be $\sum_i d_i/N$, the mean deviation. But we have just seen that the mean deviation is always zero. Hence, the following statement is true: **if the mean is guessed as the score for any case drawn at random from the distribution, on the average the amount of signed error will be zero.** This is a most important interpretation of the mean: the mean is the best guess about the score of any case in the distribution, if one wishes his *average* signed error to be zero.

## 6.7 "BEST GUESS" INTERPRETATIONS OF THE MODE AND MEDIAN

We have just seen that for any distribution of cases the mean provides a best guess about any randomly selected case, provided that one is interested in making the signed error zero on the average.

However, both the mode and the median can also be given the same kind of interpretation as best guesses if, instead of wishing to make average signed error zero, we want something else to be true about errors.

First of all, suppose there were some distribution where you had to guess the score of a case picked at random, and you wanted to be *absolutely right* with the highest possible probability. Then you should guess the mode rather than the mean; since it is the most frequent score, guessing the mode guarantees the greatest likelihood of hitting the score "on the nose" for a case drawn at random.

On the other hand, it might be that in guessing the score drawn at random you are not interested in being exactly right most often, nor in making signed error zero on the average, but rather wanted to make the *smallest absolute error* on the average. Here the *sign* of the error is unimportant, but the *size* of the error in absolute terms is what matters. Then the best guess is the median, which makes average absolute error as small as possible. The median is the typical score in this sense: it is closest on the average to all of the scores in the distribution.

There is really no way to say which is the best measure of central tendency in general terms. This depends very much on what one is trying to do and what one wants to communicate in summary form about the distribution. Each of the measures of central tendency is, in its way, a best guess about any score, but the sense of "best" differs with the way error is regarded. If both the size of the errors and their signs are considered, and we want zero error in the long run, then the mean serves as a best guess. If a miss is as good as a mile, and one wants to be exactly right as often as possible, then the mode is indicated. If one wants to come as close as possible on the average, irrespective of sign of error, then the median is a best guess.

From the point of view of purely descriptive statistics, as apart from inferential work, the median is a most servicable measure. Its property of representing the typical (most nearly like) score makes it fit the requirements of simple and effective communication better than the mean in many contexts.

On the other hand, the median is usually inferior to the mean when our purpose is to make inferences beyond the sample. The median has mathematical properties making it difficult to work with, whereas the mean is mathematically tractable. For this and other reasons, mathematical statistics has taken the mean as the focus of most of its inferential methods, and the median is relatively unimportant in inferential statistics. Nevertheless, as a description of a given set of data, the median is extremely useful in communicating the typical score.

### 6.8  CENTRAL TENDENCY IN DISCRETE PROBABILITY DISTRIBUTIONS

The ideas of mean, median, and mode apply to distributions of discrete random variables just as they do to frequency distributions. However, as we shall see, in probability distributions measures of central tendency such as the mean often play a much more important role: not only do such measures summarize the distribution, but also they may serve as parameters entering into the mathematical rule for the probability associated with a value or interval of values of the random variable.

For a discrete random variable, the mode is simply the *most probable* value. For example, in the discrete distribution shown in Table 6.8.1, the mode is 41, since this is the midpoint of the most probable class (recall that each case in any interval of a grouped distribution is ordinarily treated as though it had the value of the midpoint).

A median value for a discrete random variable need not be unique. Any value qualifies if the probability for $X$ less than or equal to that value equals .50, $p(X \leq Md) = .5$. The median is any value that evenly divides the distribution. The median of a grouped probability distribution is found in exactly the same way as for a frequency distribution, except that probabilities take the place of frequencies in the computations:

$$Md = \text{lower real limit} + i \left[ \frac{.50 - p(X \leq \text{lower real limit})}{p(\text{lower limit} \leq X \leq \text{upper limit})} \right] \quad \text{[6.8.1]}$$

where "lower limit" and "upper limit" refer to the interval containing the median. The example below shows the computation of the median in such a distribution.

Finally, the mean of a discrete distribution is found much as for a grouped frequency distribution: each distinct value of $X$, or midpoint of an interval, is multiplied by the *probability* that $X$ takes on that value (or that $X$ lies in the interval). Then the sum of these products is found:

$$\text{mean} = \Sigma X p(X) \quad \text{[6.8.2*]}$$

summed over all possible values of $X$, or

$$\text{mean} = \Sigma x p(X \text{ in interval}) \quad \text{[6.8.3*]}$$

where $x$ is the midpoint of the interval, and the sum is over all intervals.

In general, **the mean of a discrete random variable is the sum of
the products of the different values of** $X$ **each times the probability that** $X$ **takes
on that value.**

All three central tendency indices are found in Table 6.8.1, an example of a probability distribution grouped into class intervals.

Table 6.8.1

| Class interval | $x$ | $p(X \ in\ interval)$ | $xp(X \ in\ interval)$ |
|---|---|---|---|
| 74–78 | 76 | .050 | 3.80 |
| 69–73 | 71 | .090 | 6.39 |
| 64–68 | 66 | .080 | 5.28 |
| 59–63 | 61 | .080 | 4.88 |
| 54–58 | 56 | .055 | 3.08 |
| 49–53 | 51 | .135 | 6.89 |
| 44–48 | 46 | .085 | 3.91 |
| 39–43 | 41 | .245 | 10.05 |
| 34–38 | 36 | .110 | 3.96 |
| 29–33 | 31 | .030 | .93 |
| 24–28 | 26 | .040 | 1.04 |
| | | | 50.21 |

Mode = 41 = (midpoint of interval with probability = .245)

$$\text{Median} = 43.5 + \frac{5(.50 - .465)}{.085}$$

(where .465 is $p(X \leq 43.5)$)

Mean = $\Sigma xp(X \ in\ interval) = 50.21$

## 6.9   THE MEAN OF A RANDOM VARIABLE AS THE EXPECTATION

A special term is often used to denote the mean of a probability distribution. This is the "expectation" or the "expected value" of a random variable $X$. The symbol $E(X)$ simply represents the mean of the probability distribution of $X$, and if $X$ is discrete,

$$E(X) = \Sigma X p(X) = \text{mean of } X, \qquad [6.9.1*]$$

the sum being taken over all values that $X$ can assume.

The idea of expectation of a random variable is closely connected with the origin of statistics in games of chance. Gamblers were interested in how much they could "expect" to win in the long run in a game, and in how much they should wager in certain games if the game was to be "fair." Thus, expected value originally meant the expected long-run winnings (or losings) over repeated play;

this term has been retained in mathematical statistics to mean the long-run average for any random variable over an indefinite number of samplings.

The use of expectation in a game of chance is easy to illustrate. For example, suppose that someone were setting up a lottery, selling 1000 tickets at $1 per ticket. He is going to give a prize of $750 to the winner of the first draw. Suppose now that you buy a ticket. How *good* is this ticket in the sense of *how much you should expect to gain?* Should you have bought it in the first place? You can think of your chances of winning and losing as represented in a probability distribution where the outcome of any drawing falls into one of two event categories:

| *Class* | *Prob.* |
|---------|---------|
| win | 1/1000 |
| don't win | 999/1000 |

Translated into the amount of money gained (the random variable $X$), and with a loss regarded as a negative gain, this distribution becomes

| $X$ | $p(X)$ |
|-----|--------|
| $749 | 1/1000 |
| $-\$\ 1$ | 999/1000 |

Since this is the distribution of a discrete random variable, the mean of the distribution can be found by the methods of Section 6.8; that is,

$$E(X) = \Sigma X p(X) = 749(1/1000) + (-1)(999/1000)$$
$$= .749 - .999 = -.25.$$

This amount, a *minus* 25 cents, is the amount which you can expect to gain by buying the ticket, meaning that if you played the game over and over indefinitely, in the long run you would be poorer by a quarter. Should you buy the lottery ticket? Probably not, if you are going to be strictly rational about it; the mean winnings (the expected value) is certainly not in your favor.

On the other hand, suppose that the prize offered were $1000, so that the gain in winning is $999. Now the expected value is

$$E(X) = 999(1/1000) + (-1)(999/1000) = .00.$$

Here the game is more worth your while, as there is at least no amount of money to be lost *or* gained in the long run. Such a game is often called "fair." Obviously, truly fair lotteries and other games of chance are hard to find, since their purpose is to make money for the proprietors, not to break even or lose money. If the prize were $2000, you would likely jump at the opportunity, as in this case the expected value would be exactly the *gain* of one dollar.

In figuring odds in gambling situations one uses the expected value to find what constitutes a fair bet; that is, a bet where the mean of the probability distribution of gains and losses is zero. For instance, it is known that in a particular game the odds are 4 to 1 *against* winning. This means that the probability of winning is 1/5 and that of losing is 4/5. It costs the player exactly $1 to play the game once. How much should the amount he gains by winning be in order to make this a fair game with expectation of zero? The expectation is

$$E(X) = \text{(gain value)}p(\text{win}) + \text{(loss value)}p(\text{lose})$$
$$= \text{(gain value)}(1/5) - \$1(4/5).$$

Setting $E(X)$ equal to zero and solving gives

$$\text{(gain value)}(1/5) - \$1(4/5) = 0$$

or

$$\text{gain value} = \$4.$$

In short, one should stand to gain $4 for $1 put up if the game is to be fair. In general, if odds are $A$ to $B$ against winning, the game or bet is fair when $B$ dollars put up gains $A$ dollars.

In betting situations, the random variable is, of course, gains or losses of amounts of money, or of other things having utility value for the person. Nevertheless, the same general idea applies to any random variable; the expectation is the long-run average value that one should observe.

### 6.10  A THEORETICAL EXPECTATION: THE MEAN OF THE BINOMIAL DISTRIBUTION

As an example of how the mean of a theoretical probability distribution may be deduced mathematically, we will consider the binomial distribution once again. Here we will see that the distribution rule alone dictates what the expectation of a binomial variable must be. What we will show is that if $X$ is a binomial variable, then

$$E(X) = Np,  \qquad\qquad [6.10.1^*]$$

the expectation is the number of observations times the probability of a success.

We start off with the definition of expectation for any discrete random variable

$$E(X) = \Sigma X p(X).$$

For the binomial distribution, the probability that the number of successes $X$ takes on any value $r$ is $\binom{N}{r} p^r q^{N-r}$ for $0 \leq X \leq N$. Thus, any value $r$ multiplied by the probability $p(X = r)$ is

$$r\left[\frac{N!}{r!\,(N-r)!}\, p^r q^{N-r}\right].  \qquad\qquad [6.10.2]$$

Now notice that we could factor this expression somewhat, cancelling $r$ in the numerator and denominator and bringing an $N$ and a $p$ outside the brackets:

$$Np\left[\frac{(N-1)!}{(r-1)!\,(N-r)!}\, p^{r-1}q^{N-r}\right].  \qquad\qquad [6.10.3]$$

For $r = 0$, expression **6.10.2** is equal to zero, and so there is no equivalent expression **6.10.3**. On substituting expression **6.10.3** into the expression for $E(X)$ we have

$$E(X) = \sum_{r=1}^{N} Np \left[ \frac{(N-1)!}{(r-1)!\,(N-r)!}\, p^{r-1}q^{N-r} \right] \qquad \text{[6.10.4]}$$

with the sum going from $r = 1$ to $r = N$, since the term is zero for $r = 0$. By rule 1 in Appendix A, this is the same as

$$E(X) = Np \sum_{r=1}^{N} \frac{(N-1)!}{(r-1)!\,(N-r)!}\, p^{r-1}q^{N-r}. \qquad \text{[6.10.5]}$$

However, if we wrote out the various terms represented in expression **6.10.5** beyond the summation sign, we would find that each is a binomial probability for a distribution with parameters $N-1$ and $p$, and thus their sum must be 1.00. Thus

$$E(X) = Np.$$

We have just proved that the mean of a binomial distribution depends only on the two parameters, $N$ and $p$. If $N = 10$ and $p$ is 1/2, then the expectation or mean of the distribution is $(10)(1/2) = 5$. If $N = 25$ and $p = .3$, the mean is $(25)(.3) = 7.5$, and so on. Notice that the mean *can* be some value that $X$ cannot take on, as in this last example. Nevertheless, the mean or expectation is a perfectly good statement about the "best guess" for any set of $N$ observations, provided that we want our long-run error to be zero in guessing.

This is the best illustration we have had of the use of the distribution's function rule to derive characteristics that the distribution must have. In particular, this was our first use of the expectation idea to derive a *formal* result in statistics. We will have many occasions in what follows to use the mathematical expectation in some derivation, and we will find it a most handy tool for deducing consequences about random variables.

## 6.11 The algebra of expectations, appendix B

Since the idea of expectation is so pervasive in theoretical statistics, it is very convenient to have available some list of the formal rules for dealing with expectations mathematically. These rules are summarized in Appendix B and should clarify the ways that expectations will be treated algebraically in other sections. The student is advised to become familiar with these rules, as with the rules of summation, which they greatly resemble. If he does so he should have very little trouble in following simple derivations in mathematical statistics such as this book contains.

## 6.12   THE EXPECTATION OF A CONTINUOUS RANDOM VARIABLE

The mean or expectation of a continuous random variable is defined in a way very similar to that for a discrete variable. However, since $X$ may assume any of an infinite set of particular values, and because, for the reasons outlined in Section 3.18, it is necessary to discuss the *probability density* associated with any particular value of $X$, the actual definition of the mean is somewhat different. If we let $f(X)$ symbolize the probability density associated with any particular value of $X$, then

$$E(X) = \int_{-\infty}^{\infty} Xf(X)\, dX. \qquad [6.12.1*]$$

Here, the integral sign indicates the infinite sum of $X$ times a factor $f(X)\, dX$ for all real number values between the ultimate limits of $-\infty$ and $+\infty$. Notice that, much as in the discrete case, the expectation of the continuous random variable $X$ is actually a sum of products. In the former the products were of values of $X$ each times the probability of that value, but for the continuous case each value of $X$ is weighted by a factor depending on the probability density at that value.

The rules for expectations and their manipulations given in Appendix B are valid either for continuous or for discrete random variables, with a few minor exceptions that need not bother us in an elementary discussion. This is extremely convenient, since it makes it possible to demonstrate certain general features of statistics without having to qualify the result as pertaining to discrete or continuous variables.

## 6.13   THE MEAN AS A PARAMETER OF A PROBABILITY DISTRIBUTION

In many important instances of probability distributions, the mean or expectation is a parameter. That is to say, the mean enters into the function rule assigning a probability or probability-density to each possible value of $X$. A simple example is the binomial distribution of sample proportions (or, more properly, the distribution of sample proportions $P$, which can be found from the binomial distribution). Here, it is easy to show that $E(P) = p$, one of the two parameters figuring in the function rule for the binomial distribution.

In the preceding section we showed that, for a binomial distribution with parameters $p$ and $N$,

$$E(X) = Np.$$

Now suppose the random variable were

$$P = \frac{X}{N}.$$

By rule 1 for expectations (Appendix B),

$$E(P) = E\left(\frac{X}{N}\right) = \frac{E(X)}{N} = \frac{Np}{N} = p. \qquad [6.13.1^*]$$

For the binomial distribution of proportions $P$, the expectation is the parameter $p$.

It will sometimes be convenient to use still another symbol when we are dealing with the mean of a random variable, especially in its role as a parameter. The small Greek letter mu, $\mu$, will stand for the mean of a probability distribution of a random variable $X$. That is

$$E(X) = \mu = \text{mean of the distribution of } X. \qquad [6.13.2^*]$$

In much of what follows, small Greek letters will be used to indicate parameters of probability distributions, while Roman letters will stand for sample values. The word "parameter" will always indicate a characteristic of a probability distribution, and the word "statistic" will denote a summary value calculated from a sample. Thus, given some sample space and the random variable $X$, the mean of the distribution of $X$ is a parameter, $\mu$, and the mean of any given sample, $M$, is a statistic.

### 6.14 THE MODE AND MEDIAN OF A CONTINUOUS DISTRIBUTION

When the random variable $X$ is continuous, the mode and median can be defined much as in the discrete case. The mode of a continuous variable, provided that there is a single mode, is the value of $X$ for which the probability density is greatest. In the smooth curve representing the distribution, the mode is the $X$ value corresponding to the very top of the largest "hump" in the curve. There may be several values of $X$ each associated with the same density, which is greater than any density elsewhere in the range of values, and in this instance there are two or more values that qualify as "the" mode.

The median is that value $a$ such that the probability that $X$ is less than or equal to $a$ is exactly .50. That is, $a$ is the median value if and only if

$$F(a) = \text{prob.}(X \leq a) = \int_{-\infty}^{a} f(X)\, dX = .5.$$

### 6.15 RELATIONS BETWEEN CENTRAL TENDENCY MEASURES AND THE "SHAPES" OF DISTRIBUTIONS

In discussions either of obtained frequency or of theoretical probability distributions, it is often expedient to describe the general "shape" of the distribution curve. Although the terms used here can be applied to any distribution, it will be convenient to illustrate them by referring to graphs of continuous distributions.

First of all, a distribution may be described by the number of relative maximum points it exhibits, its "modality." This usually refers to the number of "humps" apparent in the graph of the distribution. Strictly speaking, if the density (or probability or frequency) is greatest at one point, then that value is *the* mode, regardless of whether other relative maxima occur in the distribution or not. Nevertheless, it is common to find a distribution described as **bi-modal** or **multimodal** whenever there are two or more pronounced humps in the curve, even though there is only one distinct mode. Thus, a distribution may have no modes (Fig. 6.15.1), may be unimodal (Fig. 6.15.2), or may be multimodal (Fig. 6.15.3).

FIG. 6.15.1

FIG. 6.15.2

FIG. 6.15.3

FIG. 6.15.4

Once again, notice that the possibility of multimodal distributions lowers the effectiveness of the mode as a description of central tendency.

Another characteristic of a distribution is its symmetry, or conversely, its skewness. A distribution is **symmetric** only if it is possible to divide its graph into two "mirror-image halves," as illustrated in Figure 6.15.4. Note that in the graph of Figure 6.15.2 there is no point at which the distribution may be divided into two similar parts, as in the first example. When a distribution is symmetric, it will be true that the mean and the median are equal in value. It is not necessarily true, however, that the mode(s) will equal either the mean or the median; witness the example of Figure 6.15.5. On the other hand, a nonsymmetric distribution is sometimes described as **skewed,** which means that the length of one of the **tails** of the distribution, relative to the central section, is disproportionate to the other. For example, the distribution in Figure 6.15.6 is skewed to the right, or **skewed positively.** In a positively skewed distribution, the bulk of the cases fall into the lower part of the range of scores, and relatively few show extremely high values. This is reflected by the relation

Mean > Median

usually found in a positively skewed distribution.

On the other hand, it is possible to find distributions skewed to the left, or **negatively skewed.** In such a distribution, the long tail of the distribution occurs among the low values of the variable. That is, the bulk of the distribution shows relatively high scores, although there are a few quite low scores (Fig. 6.15.7).

FIG. 6.15.5

FIG. 6.15.6

FIG. 6.15.7

Generally in a negatively skewed distribution, Median > Mean. Thus, a rough and ready way to describe the skewness of a distribution is to find the mean and median; if Mean > Median, then you can conclude that the distribution is skewed to the right (positively). If Median > Mean, then you should conclude that negative skewness exists. If a more accurate determination is needed, other indices reflecting skewness are available; however, this is seldom an important problem in psychological research. A word of warning: if a distribution is symmetric, then Mean = Median, but the fact that Mean = Median does not necessarily imply that the distribution is symmetric.

Describing the skewness of a distribution in terms of measures of central tendency again points up the contrast between the mean and the median as measures of central tendency. The mean is much more affected by the extreme cases in the distribution than is the median. Any alteration of the scores of cases at the extreme ends of a distribution will have no effect at all on the median so long as the rank order of the scores is roughly preserved; only when scores near the center of the distribution are altered is there likelihood of altering the median.

This is not true of the mean, which is very sensitive to score changes at the extremes of the distribution. The alteration of the score for a single extreme case in a distribution may have a profound effect on the mean. It is evident that the mean follows the skewed tail in the distribution, while the median does so to less extent. *The occurrence of even a few very high or very low cases can seriously distort the impression of the distribution given by the mean, provided that one mistakenly interprets the mean as the typical value.* If you are dealing with a nonsymmetric distribution, and you want to communicate the typical value, you must report the median. On the other hand, in spite of the distribution's shape, the mean always communicates the same thing: the point about which the sum of deviations is zero.

FIG. 6.15.8          FIG. 6.15.9

*The choice of an index must depend on what the user is trying to get across about the distribution.*

Symmetry and skewness in theoretical distributions may be illustrated by the two binominal distributions shown in Section 5.11. The graphs of these two distributions are shown in Figures 6.15.8 and 6.15.9.

In Figure 6.15.8, a binomial distribution with $p = .5$, the distribution is symmetric since the two halves of the histogram are exact mirror images when the division of the graph is made at the mean, $Np = 2.5$. The median of this distribution is also 2.5. Therefore, in the example, the mean equals the median, just as it must for any symmetric distribution.

On the other hand, in the second example with $p = .10$ and $N = 5$, the mode of the distribution occurs at $X = 0$, and the long tail of the distribution extends toward the high values of $X$. The mean, $Np$, is .5, and the median is .36 (by interpolation). The fact that the mean is larger than the median reflects the positive skewness of the distribution.

Differences in shape are only rough, qualitative ways of distinguishing among distributions. The only adequate description of a theoretical distribution is its **function rule.** Distributions that look similar in their graphic form may be very different functions. Conversely, distributions that appear quite different when graphed actually may belong to the same family; witness the two binomial distributions in the example. A description in terms of modality and skewness is sometimes useful for giving a general impression of what a distribution is like, but it does not communicate its essential character. Similarly, for obtained frequency distributions, an actual statement of the distribution contains far more information than is ever given by any report of central tendency or shape alone.

## 6.16 MEASURES OF DISPERSION IN FREQUENCY DISTRIBUTIONS

An index of central tendency summarizes only one special aspect of a distribution, be it mode, median, or mean. Any distribution has at least one more feature that must be summarized in some way. Distributions exhibit **spread** or **dispersion,** the tendency for observations to depart from central tendency. If central tendency measures are thought of as good bets about observations in a distribution, then measures of spread represent the other side of the question: dispersion reflects the "poorness" of central tendency as a description of a randomly selected case, the tendency of observations *not* to be like the average.

The mean is a good bet about the score of any observation sampled at random from a distribution, but *no observed case need be exactly like the mean.* A **deviation** from the mean expresses how "off" the mean is as a bet about a particular case, or how much *in error* is the mean as a description of this case:

$$d_i = (X_i - M)$$

where $X_i$ is the value of a particular observation.

In the same way, we could talk about a deviation from the median, if we wished,

$$d_i' = (X_i - Md)$$

or even perhaps from the mode. It is quite obvious that the larger such deviations are, on the whole, from a measure of central tendency, the more do cases differ from each other and the more spread does the distribution show. What we need is an index (or set of indices) to reflect this spread or variability.

First of all, why not simply take the average of the deviations about the mean as our measure of variability:

$$\frac{\sum_i (X_i - M)}{N}$$

or

$$\frac{\Sigma(x - M)\ \text{freq.}(x)}{N} ?$$

This will not work, however, because in Section 6.6 it was shown that in any frequency distribution the mean deviation from the mean must be zero.

The device used to get around this difficulty is to take the *square* of each deviation from the mean, and then to find the average of these squared deviations:

$$s^2 = \frac{\sum_i (X_i - M)^2}{N} = \frac{\sum_i d_i^2}{N}.$$

[6.16.1*]

For any distribution, the index $s^2$, equal to the average of the squared deviations from the mean, is called the **variance** of the distribution. *The variance reflects the degree of spread, since $s^2$ will be zero if and only if each and every case in the distribution shows exactly the same score, the mean. The more that the cases tend to differ from each other and the mean, the larger will the variance be.*

The variance is defined in equation **6.16.1** *as though* the raw score of each of $N$ cases were known, and can be computed by this formula when the raw data have not been grouped into a distribution. However, when data are in a grouped distribution, an equivalent definition of the variance is given by

$$s^2 = \frac{\Sigma(x - M)^2 \text{ freq.}(x)}{N}$$

[6.16.2*]

where $x$ is, as usual, the midpoint of an interval. Here, for each interval, the deviation of the midpoint from the mean is squared, and multiplied by the frequency for that interval. When this has been done for each interval, the average of these products is the variance, $s^2$. Just as with the mean, the value of $s^2$ calculated for a grouped distribution need not agree exactly with that based on the raw scores; nevertheless, if a relatively large number of class intervals is used these two values should agree very closely.

## 6.17   THE STANDARD DEVIATION

Although the variance is an adequate way of describing the degree of variability in a distribution, it does have one important drawback. The variance is a quantity in squared units of measurement. For instance, if measurements of height are made in inches, then the mean is some number of inches, and a deviation from the mean is a difference in inches. However, the square of a deviation is in *square-inch units*, and thus the variance, being a mean squared deviation, must also be in square inches. Naturally, this is not an insurmountable problem: taking the positive square root of the variance gives an index of variability in the original units. **The square root of the variance for a distribution is called the standard deviation, and is an index of variability in the original measurement units.**

The small letter $s$ will be used to denote the standard deviation for a frequency distribution:

$$s = \sqrt{s^2} = \sqrt{\frac{\sum_i (X_i - M)^2}{N}}$$

[6.17.1*]

or

$$s = \sqrt{\frac{\Sigma(x - M)^2 \text{ freq.}(x)}{N}}.$$

[6.17.2*]

### 6.18 THE COMPUTATION OF THE VARIANCE AND STANDARD DEVIATION

The variance and standard deviation can be computed from a list of raw scores by formulas **6.16.1** and **6.17.1**. This entails finding the mean, subtracting it successively from each score, squaring each result, adding the squared deviations together, and dividing by $N$ to find the variance. Obviously, this is relatively laborious for a sizable number of cases. However, it is possible to simplify the computations by a few algebraic manipulations of the original formulas. This may be shown as follows: For any single deviation, expanding the square gives

$$(X_i - M)^2 = X_i^2 - 2X_iM + M^2,$$

so that, on averaging these squares, we have

$$\sum_i \frac{(X - M)^2}{N} = \sum_i \frac{(X_i^2 - 2X_iM + M^2)}{N}.$$

By rule 4 in Appendix A, the summation may be distributed, so that

$$\sum_i \frac{(X_i - M)^2}{N} = \sum_i \frac{X_i^2}{N} - 2 \sum_i \frac{X_iM}{N} + \sum_i \frac{M^2}{N}.$$

However, wherever $M$ appears it is a constant over the sum, and so, by rules 1 and 2 in Appendix A,

$$\sum_i \frac{(X_i - M)^2}{N} = \sum_i \frac{X_i^2}{N} - 2M \sum_i \frac{X_i}{N} + \frac{NM^2}{N}$$

or

$$s^2 = \sum_i \frac{X_i^2}{N} - 2M^2 + M^2 = \frac{\sum_i X_i^2}{N} - M^2. \qquad [6.18.1\dagger]$$

Finally,

$$s = \sqrt{\frac{\sum_i X_i^2}{N} - M^2}. \qquad [6.18.2\dagger]$$

These last formulas, **6.18.1** and **6.18.2**, give a way to calculate the indices $s^2$ and $s$ with some saving in steps. These formulas will be referred to as the "raw-score computing forms" for the variance and standard deviation. For an example of the use of these forms, study the example shown in Table 6.18.1, based on seven cases. These two methods must always agree exactly, as in the example.

It is also possible to find similar computing forms for grouped distributions. Starting with the definition of the variance of a grouped distribution,

$$s^2 = \frac{\Sigma(x - M)^2 \, \text{freq.}(x)}{N}$$

## Table 6.18.1

| Scores $X_i$ | Deviation method | | Raw-score method $X_i^2$ |
|---|---|---|---|
| | $d_i = (X_i - M)$ | $d_i^2$ | |
| 11 | 6 | 36 | 121 |
| 10 | 5 | 25 | 100 |
| 9 | 4 | 16 | 81 |
| 8 | 3 | 9 | 64 |
| 6 | 1 | 1 | 36 |
| $-4$ | $-9$ | 81 | 16 |
| $-5$ | $-10$ | 100 | 25 |
| $35 = \sum_i X_i$ | 0 | $268 = \sum_i d_i^2$ | $443 = \sum_i X_i^2$ |

$$M = 5 \qquad s^2 = \frac{\sum_i d_i^2}{N} = \frac{268}{7} = 38.28 \qquad s^2 = \frac{\sum_i X_i^2}{N} - M^2$$

$$= \frac{443}{7} - 25 = 38.28$$

$$s = \sqrt{38.28} = 6.19$$

## Table 6.18.2

| Class | $x$ | $f$ | $xf$ | $x^2$ | $x^2 f$ |
|---|---|---|---|---|---|
| 46–50 | 48 | 6 | 286 | 2304 | 13814 |
| 41–45 | 43 | 8 | 338 | 1849 | 14792 |
| 36–40 | 38 | 10 | 380 | 1444 | 14440 |
| 31–35 | 33 | 5 | 165 | 1089 | 5445 |
| 26–30 | 28 | 3 | 84 | 784 | 2252 |
| 21–25 | 23 | 1 | 23 | 529 | 529 |
| | | 33 | $1276 = \Sigma xf$ | | $51282 = \Sigma x^2 f$ |

$$M = \frac{\Sigma xf}{N} = \frac{1276}{33} = 38.67$$

$$s^2 = \frac{51282}{33} - 1495.36 \qquad s = \sqrt{58.64} = 7.66$$

$$= 58.64$$

we could develop the following computing forms:

$$s^2 = \frac{\Sigma x^2 \text{ freq.}(x)}{N} - M^2 \qquad \textbf{[6.18.3†]}$$

$$= \frac{\Sigma x^2 \text{ freq.}(x)}{N} - \left[\frac{\Sigma x \text{ freq.}(x)}{N}\right]^2. \qquad \textbf{[6.18.4†]}$$

Then, as usual,

$$s = \sqrt{s^2}. \qquad \textbf{[6.18.5†]}$$

This little derivation is left to you as an exercise.

An example of the computation of the mean and standard deviation from a frequency distribution is given in Table 6.18.2.

### 6.19 SOME MEANINGS OF THE VARIANCE AND STANDARD DEVIATION

Since the variance and standard deviation will figure very largely in our subsequent work, it is well to gain some intuition about what they represent. One interpretation is provided by the fact that **the variance is directly proportional to the average squared difference between all pairs of observations:**

$$\sum_{(i,j)} \frac{(X_i - X_j)^2}{\binom{N}{2}} = \frac{2N}{N-1} s^2. \qquad \textbf{[6.19.1]}$$

(Here $(i,j)$ indicates summation over all possible *pairs* of scores.) The variance summarizes *how different the various cases are from each other,* just as it reflects how different each case is from the mean. Given some $N$ cases, the more that pairs of cases tend to be unlike in their scores, the larger the variance and standard deviation.

Still another way to think of the variance and standard deviation is by a physical analogy. A deviation from the mean can be identified with a certain amount of *force* exerted by a variety of factors making this case different from others in its group. Think of any score as composed of the mean, plus a deviation from the mean,

$$X_i = M + d_i,$$

where the deviation is the resultant force of these "influences." Picturing a deviation from the mean as we would show a physical force away from a point, we have:

$$M \underbrace{\longrightarrow}_{d_i} X_i.$$

Now suppose that we think of two cases from the larger group, each of which has a deviation from the mean, or $d_1$ and $d_2$ respectively. These two cases are independent, so that we can represent their deviations as forces acting at right angles (Fig. 6.19.1). How would you find the *net force* away from the mean for these two cases? The rule of the parallelogram of forces shows the resultant force to be the *diagonal length* in Figure 6.19.1. This diagonal has length

$$\sqrt{\Sigma d^2} = \sqrt{(X_1 - M)^2 + (X_2 - M)^2}$$

by the Pythagorean theorem. If we divide by $N$ before taking the square root, this looks much like the standard deviation.

Suppose that there were three independent cases. When their deviations are interpreted as forces away from the mean, the diagram shown in Figure 6.19.2 holds, and the resultant force is $\sqrt{d_1^2 + d_2^2 + d_3^2}$. The resultant force away from the mean per observation would again be calculated much like a standard deviation. In short, a physical analogy to the standard deviation is a resultant

FIG. 6.19.1

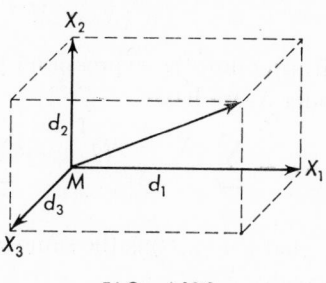

FIG. 6.19.2

force away from the mean per unit observation. A large standard deviation is analogous to a large "push" away from the mean per observation, due to all the factors making observations heterogeneous. In statistics, "error" is often viewed as such a resultant force away from homogeneity, and in terms of this physical analogy the standard deviation should reflect the net effect of such forces per observation.

The reader acquainted with elementary physics may recognize not only that the mean is the center of gravity of a physical distribution of objects, but also that the variance is the **moment of inertia** of a distribution of mass. Furthermore, the standard deviation corresponds to the radius of gyration of a mass distribution; this is the real basis for regarding the standard deviation as analogous to a resultant force away from the mean. These physical conceptions and their associated mathematical formulations have influenced the course of theoretical statistics very strongly, and have helped to shape the form of statistical inference as we will encounter it.

## 6.20   The mean as the "origin" for the variance

This question may already have occurred to the reader: "Why is the variance, and hence the standard deviation, always calculated in terms of deviations from the *mean?* Why couldn't one of the other measures of central tendency be used as well?" The answer lies in the fact that **the average squared deviation (i.e., the variance) is smallest when calculated from the mean.** That is, if the disagreement of any score with the mean is indicated by the square of its difference from the mean, then on the average the mean agrees better with the scores than any other single value one might choose.

This may be demonstrated as follows: Suppose that we chose some arbitrary value $C$, and calculated a "pseudo-variance" $s_C^2$ by subtracting $C$ from each score, squaring, and averaging:

$$s_C^2 = \sum_i \frac{(X_i - C)^2}{N}.$$

Adding and subtracting $M$ for each score would not change the value of $s_C^2$ at all. However, if we did so, we could expand each squared deviation as follows:

$$(X_i - C)^2 = (X_i - M + M - C)^2$$
$$= (X_i - M)^2 + 2(X_i - M)(M - C) + (M - C)^2.$$

Substituting into the expression for $s_C^2$, and distributing the summation by rule 4, Appendix A, we have

$$s_C^2 = \sum_i \frac{(X_i - M)^2}{N} + 2 \sum_i \frac{(X_i - M)(M - C)}{N} + \sum_i \frac{(M - C)^2}{N}.$$

Notice that $(M - C)$ is the same for every score summed, so that by rules 1 and 2 in Appendix A

$$s_C^2 = \sum_i \frac{(X_i - M)^2}{N} + 2(M - C) \sum_i \frac{(X_i - M)}{N} + (M - C)^2.$$

However, the first term on the right above is simply $s^2$, the variance about the mean, and the second term is zero, since the average deviation from $M$ is zero. On making these substitutions, we find

$$s_C^2 = s^2 + (M - C)^2.$$

Since $(M - C)^2$ is a squared number it can be only positive or zero, and so $s_C^2$ must be greater than or equal to $s^2$. The value of $s_C^2$ can be equal to $s^2$ only when $M$ and $C$ are the same. In short, we have shown that the variance calculated about the mean will always be smaller than about any other point.

If we are going to use the mean to express the central tendency of a distribution, and if we let the standard deviation indicate the extent of error we stand to make in guessing the mean for any score, then this error-quantity is at its minimum when we guess the mean in place of any other single value for all scores. However, it is a curious fact that if we appraise error by taking the absolute difference (disregarding sign) between a score and a measure of central tendency, then **the average absolute deviation is smallest when the median is used.** This is one of the reasons that squared deviations rather than absolute deviations figure in the indices of variability when the mean is used to express central tendency. When the median is used to express central tendency it is often accompanied by the average absolute deviation from the median to indicate dispersion, rather than by the standard deviation which is more appropriate to the use of the mean. The average absolute deviation is simply

$$A.D. = \sum_i \frac{|X_i - Md|}{N} \tag{6.20.1}$$

where the vertical bars indicate a disregarding of sign. Analogically speaking this measure is to the median as the standard deviation is to the mean.

### 6.21  THE VARIANCE OF A DISCRETE RANDOM VARIABLE

The small Greek letter sigma, $\sigma$, is generally used to denote the standard deviation of a random variable, and $\sigma^2$ its variance. When the random variable is discrete, the variance is defined by

$$\sigma^2 = \Sigma[X - E(X)]^2 p(X) \tag{6.21.1*}$$

which is equivalent to

$$\sigma^2 = E(X^2) - [E(X)]^2, \tag{6.21.2*}$$

the expectation of the square of $X$ minus the square of the expectation of $X$. Then the standard deviation $\sigma$ of the random variable $X$ is just the square root of the variance, exactly as in a frequency distribution.

The variance and standard deviation of a probability distribution have exactly the same interpretations as do the corresponding indices for a frequency distribution: each is a measure of the variability or spread, the former in squared units and the latter in the original units of the random variable. However, like the mean of a probability distribution, the variance (or standard deviation) often figures as a parameter entering into the function rule for the distribution.

### 6.22  AN EXAMPLE OF THE VARIANCE OF A DISCRETE RANDOM VARIABLE: THE BINOMIAL DISTRIBUTION ONCE AGAIN

As an example of the computation of the variance for a discrete random variable, let us take the binomial distribution with $p = 2/3$, and with $N = 6$:

| $X$ | $\binom{N}{r} p^r q^{N-r} = p(X = r)$ |
|---|---|
| 6 | 64/729 |
| 5 | 192/729 |
| 4 | 240/729 |
| 3 | 160/729 |
| 2 | 60/729 |
| 1 | 12/729 |
| 0 | 1/729 |
| | 729/729 |

(Notice that the distribution is negatively skewed, since the long tail of the distribution extends toward low values of $X$.)

In calculating the variance of this distribution, we will make use of the fact gained in Section 6.10, that the expectation of a binomial variable of number of successes is $Np$; thus,

$$E(X) = Np = (6)(2/3) = 4.$$

To find the variance, we take first the square of each value of $X$ multiplied by its probability, and sum:

$$\Sigma X^2 p(X) = (6)^2(64/729) + (5)^2(192/729) + (4)^2(240/729) + (3)^2(160/729)$$
$$+ (2)^2(60/729) + (1)^2(12/729) + 0$$

$$= \frac{12636}{729} = 17.33.$$

Finally,
$$\sigma^2 = \Sigma X^2 p(X) - [E(X)]^2 = 17.33 - 16 = 1.33$$

and the standard deviation is

$$\sigma = \sqrt{1.33}.$$

This same result could have been found from a general expression for the variance of a binomial distribution. By algebraic manipulation of binomial probabilities substituted into the formula defining the variance of a discrete random variable (**6.21.1**), much as we did in Section 6.10, it can be shown that for any binomial distribution,

$$\sigma^2 = Npq \qquad\qquad [6.22.1^*]$$

and that
$$\sigma = \sqrt{Npq}. \qquad\qquad [6.22.2^*]$$

Therefore, for the example the variance must be

$$\sigma^2 = (6)(2/3)(1/3)$$
$$= 1.33.$$

Observe that, just as for the mean of a binomial distribution, the two parameters $p$ and $N$ determine the value of $\sigma^2$.

When the random variable is $P$, the proportion of successes in the sample of $N$ observations, then

$$\sigma_P^2 = \frac{pq}{N}. \qquad\qquad [6.22.3^*]$$

This can be shown rather easily: From **6.21.2**,

$$\sigma_P^2 = E(P^2) - [E(P)]^2$$
$$= \frac{E(X^2)}{N^2} - \frac{[E(X)]^2}{N^2},$$

by the definition of $P$ and by rule 1, Appendix B.

Then,

$$\frac{E(X^2) - [E(X)]^2}{N^2} = \sigma_P^2$$

so that from **6.22.1,**

$$\sigma_P^2 = \frac{Npq}{N^2} = \frac{pq}{N}.$$

### 6.23   THE VARIANCE OF A CONTINUOUS RANDOM VARIABLE

For a distribution of a continuous random variable the variance is defined in the same general way. As always for a continuous variable, the place of probability is taken by the probability density for each value that $X$ can assume. The simplest definition of the variance for such a variable in simply **6.21.2** once again:

$$\sigma^2 = E(X^2) - [E(X)]^2,$$

the expectation of the square of the variable, minus the square of the expectation.

### 6.24   MOMENTS OF DISTRIBUTION

A truly mathematical treatment of distributions would introduce not only the mean and the variance, but also a number of other summary characteristics. These are the so-called "moments" of a distribution, which are simply **the expectations of different powers of the random variable.** Thus, the first moment about the origin of a random variable $X$ is

$$E(X) = \text{the mean.}$$

The second moment about the origin is

$$E(X^2),$$

the third

$$E(X^3),$$

and so on. When the mean is subtracted from $X$ before the power is taken, then the moment is said to be **about the mean;** the variance

$$E[X - E(X)]^2$$

is the second moment about the mean;

$$E[X - E(X)]^3$$

is the third moment about the mean, and so on.

Just as the mean describes the "location" of the distribution on the $X$ axis, and the variance describes its dispersion, so do the higher moments reflect other features of the distribution. For example, the third moment about the mean is used in certain measures of degree of **skewness**: the third moment will be zero for a symmetric distribution, negative for skewness to the left, positive for skewness to the right. The fourth moment indicates the degree of "peakedness" or **kurtosis** of the distribution, and so on. These higher moments have relatively little use in elementary applications of statistics, but they are important for mathematical statisticians in the study of the properties of distributions and in arriving at theoretical distributions fitting observed data. The entire set of moments for a distribution will ordinarily determine the distribution exactly, and distributions are sometimes specified in this way when their general function rules are unknown or difficult to state.

### 6.25 THE RELATIVE LOCATION OF A SCORE IN A FREQUENCY DISTRIBUTION: STANDARDIZED SCORES

A major use of the mean and standard deviation is in transforming a raw score into a **standardized score,** showing *the relative status* of that score in a distribution. If you are given the information, "John Doe has a score of 60," you really know very little about what this score means. Is this score high, low, middling, or what? However, if you know something about the distribution of scores for the group including John Doe, you can judge the location of the score in the distribution. The score of 60 gives quite a different picture when the mean is 30 and the standard deviation 10, than when the mean is 65 and the standard deviation is 20.

Each value in any distribution can be converted into a standardized score, or $z$ **score,** expressing the deviation from the mean in standard deviation units:

$$z = \frac{X - M}{s}. \qquad [6.25.1*]$$

The $z$ score tells how many standard deviations away from the mean is $X$. The two distributions mentioned above give quite different $z$ scores to the score of 60:

$$z_1 = \frac{60 - 30}{10} = 3$$

$$z_2 = \frac{60 - 65}{20} = -.25.$$

The conversion of raw scores to $z$ scores is handy when one wishes to emphasize the *location* or *status* of a score in the distribution, and in future sections we will deal with standardized scores when this aspect of any score is to be discussed.

Changing each of the scores in a distribution to a standardized score creates a distribution having a "standard" mean and standard deviation: **the mean of a distribution of standardized scores is always 0, and the standard**

**deviation is always 1.** This is easily shown as follows:

$$\text{mean of } z \text{ scores} = M_z = \sum_i \frac{z_i}{N} = \sum_i \frac{(X_i - M)}{Ns}. \qquad [6.25.2]$$

Since $N$ and $s$ are constant over the summation, this becomes

$$M_z = \frac{1}{Ns} \sum_i (X_i - M) = 0 \qquad [6.25.3^*]$$

since the sum of deviations about the mean is always zero.

In a similar fashion,

$$\text{variance of } z \text{ scores} = s_z^2 = \sum_i \frac{z_i^2}{N} = \sum_i \frac{(X_i - M)^2}{Ns^2}$$

$$= \frac{s^2}{s^2} = 1, \qquad [6.25.4^*]$$

$$\text{standard deviation of } z \text{ scores} = s_z = 1.$$

Although it is true that the mean and standard deviation of a distribution of $z$ scores will always be 0 and 1 respectively, *changing the scores in any distribution to $z$ scores does not alter the shape (or mathematical form) for the distribution. The frequency of any given $z$ score is exactly that of the $X$ score corresponding to it in the distribution.*

## 6.26  STANDARDIZED SCORES IN PROBABILITY DISTRIBUTIONS

Standardized scores have exactly the same use in probability distributions as in frequency distributions. If $X$ is a value of a random variable, then the corresponding standardized score, relative to the probability distribution, is

$$z = \frac{X - E(X)}{\sigma} = \frac{X - \mu}{\sigma}. \qquad [6.26.1^*]$$

The standardized score is a deviation from expectation, relative to the standard deviation. The standardized score corresponding to any value of $X$ is found in precisely the same way whether the distribution is discrete or continuous.

Furthermore, the mean of the standardized scores is zero for any probability distribution:

$$E(z) = E\left[\frac{X - E(X)}{\sigma}\right] = \frac{E(X) - E(X)}{\sigma} = 0 \qquad [6.26.2^*]$$

since $E(X)$ and $\sigma$ are constants over the various possible values of $X$. The standard deviation of standardized scores is always 1 in a probability distribution:

$$\sigma_z^2 = E(z^2) - [E(z)]^2 = E\left[\frac{X - E(X)}{\sigma}\right]^2 = E\frac{[X - E(X)]^2}{\sigma^2}$$

$$= \frac{\sigma^2}{\sigma^2} = 1 \qquad\qquad [6.26.3^*]$$

and $\qquad\qquad \sigma_z = 1.$

The form of the probability distribution is not changed at all by the transformation to $z$ scores, in the sense that the probability (or probability density) of any value of $z$ is simply the probability (or probability density) of the corresponding value of $X$.

### 6.27 TCHEBYCHEFF'S INEQUALITY

There is a very close connection between the size of deviations from the mean and probability, holding for distributions having finite expectation and variance. The following relation is called Tchebycheff's inequality, after the Russian mathematician who first proved this very general principle:

$$\text{prob.}(|X - \mu| \geqq b) \leqq \frac{\sigma^2}{b^2}, \qquad\qquad [6.27.1^*]$$

the probability that a random variable $X$ will differ absolutely from expectation by $b$ or more units ($b > 0$) is *always* less than or equal to the ratio of $\sigma^2$ to $b^2$. Any deviation from expectation of $b$ or more units can be *no more probable* than $\sigma^2/b^2$.

This relation can be clarified somewhat by dealing with the deviation in $\sigma$ units, making the random variable a standardized score. If we let $b = k\sigma$, then the following version of the Tchebycheff inequality is true:

$$\text{prob.}\left(\frac{|X - \mu|}{\sigma} \geqq k\right) \leqq \frac{1}{k^2}, \qquad\qquad [6.27.2^*]$$

the probability that a standardized score drawn at random from the distribution has *absolute* magnitude greater than or equal to some positive number $k$ is *always* less than or equal to $1/k^2$. Thus, given a distribution with some mean and variance, the probability of drawing a case having a standardized score of 2 or more (disregarding sign) must be *at most* 1/4. The probability of a standardized score of 3 or more must be no more than 1/9, the probability of 10 or more can be no more than 1/100, and so on.

This last form of the Tchebycheff inequality (**6.27.2**) is quite simple to prove for a discrete random variable. Let

$$z = \frac{X - \mu}{\sigma}.$$

Then $p(z) = p(X)$, $E(z) = 0$, and $\sigma_z^2 = 1$. Now the probability of a $z$ value equaling or exceeding any arbitrary positive number in absolute value is, for a discrete variable,

$$\text{prob.}(|z| \geqq k) = \sum_{(z \geqq k)} p(z) + \sum_{(z \leqq -k)} p(z)$$

so that, multiplying both sides of this equation by $k^2$ we have

$$k^2 \text{ prob.}(|z| \geqq k) = \sum_{(z \geqq k)} k^2 p(z) + \sum_{(z \leqq -k)} k^2 p(z).$$

However, each and every value of $z$ represented in the sum on the right of the equation above is greater than or equal to $k$ in absolute value. Thus,

$$\sum_{(z \geqq k)} k^2 p(z) + \sum_{(z \leqq -k)} k^2 p(z) \leqq \sum_{(z \geqq k)} z^2 p(z) + \sum_{(z \leqq -k)} z^2 p(z).$$

Furthermore,

$$\sum_{(z \geqq k)} z^2 p(z) + \sum_{(z \leqq -k)} z^2 p(z) \leqq \sigma_z^2,$$

by the definition of $\sigma_z^2$ for a discrete random variable (**6.26.3**). Then

$$k^2 \text{ prob.}(|z| \geqq k) \leqq \sigma_z^2$$

and

$$\text{prob.}(|z| \geqq k) \leqq \frac{1}{k^2}.$$

Once the Tchebycheff inequality has been proved for a discrete variable, it is very easy to show that Bernoulli's theorem must be true. It has just been shown that the mean of the distribution of values of $P$ is $p$, the probability of a "success" on a single trial. Furthermore, in Section 6.22 the variance of the distribution of the random variable $P$ was found to be $\frac{pq}{N}$. Now substituting these values into the Tchebycheff inequality, we find

$$\text{prob.}(|P - p| \geqq k) \leqq \frac{pq}{Nk^2}.$$

Now suppose that $k$ is some arbitrarily small positive number, and that $N$ is allowed to become indefinitely large. The larger the value of $N$, the smaller the ratio to the right of the expression becomes; as $N$ approaches an infinite value, then the probability represented on the left of the inequality must grow closer and closer to zero. This is equivalent to the statement that

$$\text{prob.}(|P - p| < k) \rightarrow 1.00, \text{ as } N \rightarrow \infty,$$

which is actually Bernoulli's theorem.

This way of proving Bernoulli's theorem rests ultimately on the fact that as $N$ becomes larger, the value of the variance of the distribution of $P$ must become smaller, other things being equal. For this reason, no matter how small $k$ may be, as $N$ increases the probability that the absolute difference between $P$ and $p$ is greater than $k$ must approach zero.

When the value of $k^2$ is less than or equal to 1.00, the Tchebycheff inequality itself is quite trivial. Here, the value of 1 divided by $k^2$ must be a number no less than 1.00, and we have a statement that we know *must* be true for any probability:

$$\text{prob.}(|z| \geqq k) \leqq v, \text{ for any } v \geqq 1.00.$$

On the other hand, for any value of $k$ greater than 1.00, the Tchebycheff inequality is not trivial, and it does set broad limits to the probability associated with extreme intervals of $z$ values, or of deviations of $X$ values from the mean in terms of standard deviation units.

As a fairly concrete example of how this principle might be applied, imagine a personality test that has been constructed to have a mean of 100 and a standard deviation of 25 in the population of American adults. Unfortunately, we know nothing more of the score distribution over this set of people. We give the test to a person sampled at random, and find that he has a score of 175. What can we say about the probability of observing a score this much or more deviant (in either direction) from the mean? The standardized score relative to mean of 100 and $\sigma$ of 25 is

$$z = \frac{175 - 100}{25} = 3.$$

Now by setting $k = 3$ in the Tchebycheff inequality, we find

$$\text{prob.}(|z| \geqq 3) \leqq \frac{1}{9}.$$

The probability of observing a score 3 or more standard deviations from the mean is *no more* than 1/9, regardless of the distribution of scores.

Within how many standard deviations from the mean must *at least one half* the population of American adults fall on this test? That is, we want the absolute value $k$ of $z$ for which

$$p(|z| \geqq k) \leqq \frac{1}{2}.$$

By **6.27.2** the value is $\sqrt{2}$, or about 1.4. Regardless of how the scores are actually distributed, we can state that one half or more of the population must lie within the approximate limits $100 - (1.4)(25)$ and $(100) + (1.4)(25)$, or 65 to 135.

Although this principle is very important theoretically, it is not extremely powerful as a tool in applied problems. The Tchebycheff inequality can be strengthened somewhat if we are willing to make assumptions about the general form of the distribution, however. For example, if we assume that the distribution of the random variable is both *symmetric* and *unimodal*, then the relation becomes

$$p(|z| \geqq k) \leqq \frac{4}{9}\left(\frac{1}{k^2}\right). \qquad \text{[6.27.3*]}$$

For such distributions, we can make somewhat "tighter" statements about how large the probability of a given amount of deviation may be. For the example of the personality test, if the distribution were unimodal-symmetric a score differing by three or more standard deviations from the mean should be observed with probability *no greater than* $(4/9)(1/9)$, or about .05. Similarly, we could find that at least $1 - 4/9$ or $5/9$ of American adults fall within one standard deviation to either side of the mean. Furthermore, $1 - (4/9)(1/4)$ or $8/9$ must fall within two standard deviations, and so on.

Thus, by adding assumptions about the form of the distribution to the general principle relating standardized values to probabilities we are able to make stronger and stronger probability statements about a sample result's departures from the mean. In order to make very precise statements one has to make even stronger assumptions about the distribution of the random variable, unless he is dealing with very large samples of cases, as we shall see. This chapter has concluded with the introduction of the Tchebycheff inequality to suggest that the mean and the standard deviation play a key role in the theory of statistical inference. The mean and standard deviation are, of course, useful devices for summarizing data if that is our purpose, although there are situations where other measures of central tendency and variability may do equally well or better. The really paramount importance of mean and standard deviation does not emerge until one is interested in making *inferences*, involving the estimation of parameters, or assigning probabilities to sample results. Here, we shall find that most "classical" statistical theory is erected around these two indices, together with their combination in standardized scores.

# SAMPLING DISTRIBUTIONS AND POINT ESTIMATION

# 7

## 7.1 POPULATIONS, PARAMETERS, AND STATISTICS

Formerly we have called the entire set of elementary events the *sample space*, since this term is useful and current in probability theory. However, in psychology and other fields using statistics it is more common to find the word **population** used to mean the totality of potential units for observation; these potential units for observation are very often real or hypothetical sets of people or animals, and *population* provides a very appropriate alternative to *sample space* in such instances. Nevertheless, whenever the term "population" is used in the following, we shall mean only the sample space of elementary events from which samples are drawn.

Given a population of potential observations, we shall think of the particular numerical score assigned to any particular unit observation as a value of a random variable; the distribution of this random variable is the **population distribution**. This distribution will have some mathematical form, with a mean $\mu$, a variance $\sigma^2$, and all the other characteristic features of any distribution. If you like, you can usually think of the population distribution as a frequency distribution based upon some large but finite number of cases. However, population distributions are almost always discussed as though they were theoretical probability distributions; the process of random sampling of single units with replacement insures that the long-run relative frequency of any value of the random variable is the same as the probability of that value. Later we shall have occasion to idealize the population distribution and treat it as though the random variable were continuous. This is virtually impossible to be true of real-world observations, but we shall assume that it is "true enough" as an approximation to the population state of affairs.

Population values such as $\mu$ and $\sigma^2$ will be called **parameters of the**

*192*

**population** (or sometimes, **true values**). Strictly speaking, a parameter is a value entering as an arbitrary constant in the particular function rule for a probability distribution, although the term is used more loosely to mean any value summarizing the population distribution. Just as parameters are characteristics of populations, so are **statistics** summary properties of samples. The sample mean $M$, the sample variance $s^2$, and so on, are examples of statistics. The main business of this chapter is to show the relation of statistics, particularly the sample mean and variance, to their parameter counterparts, the population mean and variance.

## 7.2  SAMPLING DISTRIBUTIONS

In actual practice, random samples seldom consist of single observations. Almost always some $N$ observations are drawn at random from the same population. Since this is true, we must designate another kind of theoretical distribution, called a *sampling distribution*.

A sampling distribution is a theoretical probability distribution that shows the functional relation between the possible values of some summary characteristic of $N$ cases drawn at random and the probability (density) associated with each value over all possible samples of size $N$ from a particular population.

In general, the sampling distribution of values for a sample statistic will not be the same as the population distribution. We shall see, however, that *the sampling distribution always depends in some specifiable way upon the population distribution.*

We have already used sampling distributions in the preceding chapters. For example, a binomial distribution is a sampling distribution. Recall that a binomial distribution is based on a two-category population distribution, or Bernoulli distribution. A sample of $N$ cases is drawn at random with replacement from such a distribution, and the number (or proportion) of successes is calculated for each sample. Then the binomial distribution is the sampling distribution showing the relation between each possible sample result and the theoretical probability of occurrence. The binomial distribution is *not* the same as the Bernoulli distribution unless $N$ is 1; however, given the Bernoulli distribution and the size of the sample, $N$, the binomial distribution may be worked out.

Another example of a sampling distribution already introduced is the multinomial distribution. Here, the population distribution has several event categories. A sample of size $N$ is drawn at random with replacement and summarized according to how many of each measurement class occurred. The multinomial distribution gives the probability of each possible sample distribution.

Other examples of sampling distributions will now be given. A most important distribution we shall employ is the sampling distribution of the mean. Here, samples of $N$ cases are drawn at random from some population and each observation is measured numerically. The population distribution has some mean $\mu$, and for each sample drawn the sample mean $M$ is calculated. **The theoretical distribution that relates the possible values of the sample mean to the probability (density) of each over all possible samples of size $N$ is called the sampling distribution of the mean.** Furthermore, there is a population variance, $\sigma^2$. For each sample of size $N$ drawn, the sample variance $s^2$ is found. The theoretical distribution of sample variances in relation to the probability of each is the sampling distribution of the variance. By the same token, *the sampling distribution of any summary characteristic* (mode, median, range, etc.) *of samples of N cases may be found, given the population distribution and the sample size N. This fact is all-important for the theory of statistics, as it provides ways to make inferences about population parameters on the basis of random samples, in terms of the probability of a sample's value arising by chance from a certain population.* The bulk of the material in the remainder of this book will deal with various ways of using theoretical sampling distributions to make such inferences.

## 7.3 CHARACTERISTICS OF SINGLE-VARIATE SAMPLING DISTRIBUTIONS

A sampling distribution is a theoretical probability distribution, and like any such distribution, is a statement of the functional relation between the values or intervals of values of some random variable and probabilities. Sampling distributions differ from population distributions in that *the random variable is always the value of some statistic based on a sample of N cases*, such as the sample mean, or the sample variance, the sample median, etc. Thus, a plot of a sampling distribution, such as that in Figure 7.3.1, always has for the abscissa (or horizontal axis) the different sample statistic values that might occur. Figure 7.3.1, for example, shows a theoretical distribution for sample variances for all possible samples of size 7 drawn from a particular population. Any point on the horizontal axis is a possible value of a sample variance, and the height of the curve on the vertical axis gives the probability density $f(s^2)$, for that particular value.

FIG. 7.3.1. A theoretical sampling distribution of $s^2$ for $N = 7$.

Like population distributions, sampling distributions may be either continuous or discrete. The binomial distribution is discrete, although in applied problems it is sometimes treated as though it were continuous. Most of the commonly encountered sampling distributions based on a continuous population distribution will be continuous.

It should be clear that for any given population sampled at random there will be any number of different sampling distributions, depending upon the particular statistic used to describe the sample. Thus there will be a theoretical sampling distribution of means, a different distribution that is the theoretical sampling distribution of variances, still another distribution that is the sampling distribution of medians, and so on, for as many ways as a statistic can be computed for a sample of $N$ cases. Obviously, we should seldom choose to describe a sample in *some* ways, such as describing the entire sample by the square root of the score of the third case observed; even so, the theoretical distributions of even such esoteric statistics can be worked out.

It is a good idea to reiterate at this point: so far three distinct kinds of distributions have been introduced. The first was *the sample distribution*, which is a frequency distribution summarizing a given set of data, based on a randomly selected subset of a population. The second kind of distribution with which we dealt was the *population distribution*. This is a theoretical distribution, which describes the relative frequency associated with each of the various measurement classes, or intervals of values of a numerical variable, into which an entire set of possible observations may be mapped. Finally there was the *sampling distribution*. This is a theoretical probability distribution which relates various values or intervals of values of some sample statistic to their probabilities of occurrence over all possible samples of size $N$ given a specific population distribution. In order to know any sampling distribution exactly, we must specify the population distribution, but the population distribution will, in general, be unlike the sampling distribution. Only when the sample size is 1, and the statistic is simply the score-value, will the sampling distribution be exactly like the population distribution. The sampling distribution, in turn, must be known before the probability of the occurrence of a particular sample statistic value or interval of values can be calculated. It is very important to bear these distinctions in mind, since all three kinds of distributions will be considered in the sections to follow.

## 7.4  THE MEAN AND VARIANCE OF A SAMPLING DISTRIBUTION

Except for a few statistical curiosities that need not concern us here, any random variable will have a determinable mean and variance. Since a sample statistic is a random variable, the mean and variance of any sampling distribution are defined in the usual way. That is, let $G$ be any sample statistic; then if the sampling distribution of $G$ is discrete, its expectation or mean is

$$E(G) = \mu_G = \Sigma G p(G) \qquad\qquad [7.4.1*]$$

(see Section 6.8). If the variable $G$ is continuous, then

$$E(G) = \mu_G = \int_{-\infty}^{\infty} G f(G) \, dG, \qquad\qquad [7.4.2*]$$

just as for any other continuous random variable (Section 6.12).

In the same way, the variance of a sampling distribution for some statistic $G$ can be defined:

$$\sigma_G^2 = E(G - \mu_G)^2 \qquad\qquad [7.4.3^*]$$

or

$$\sigma_G^2 = E(G^2) - [E(G)]^2. \qquad\qquad [7.4.4^*]$$

**The variance of the statistic $G$ gives a measure of the dispersion of particular sample values about the average value of $G$ over all possible samples of size $N$.** The standard deviation $\sigma_G$ of the sampling distribution reflects the extent to which sample $G$ values tend to be *unlike* the expectation, or are *in error*. To aid in distinguishing the standard deviation of a sampling distribution from the standard deviation of a population distribution, a standard deviation such as $\sigma_G$ is usually called the "standard error" of the statistic $G$. When one speaks of the standard error of the mean, he is referring to the standard deviation of the distribution of possible sample means, for all possible samples of size $N$ drawn from a specified population. Similar meanings hold for the standard error of the median, the standard error of the standard deviation, the standard error of the range, and so on.

## 7.5 SAMPLE STATISTICS AS ESTIMATORS

Each population parameter has its parallel in some sample statistic: the population mean $\mu$ has its sample counterpart in $M$, the variance $\sigma^2$ in the sample variance $s^2$, the population proportion $p$ in the sample proportion $P$, and so on. The value of a sample statistic must contain evidence about the value of the corresponding population value, and a central problem in inferential statistics is the use of sample statistics as *estimators* of population values. The use of a sample value to infer the population value is called **point estimation,** since a single value (or point in the "space" of all possible values) is taken as the estimate.

How does one go from the sample value to an inference about the population parameter? The fact that the sample represents only a small subset of observations drawn from a much larger set of potential observations makes it risky to say that any estimate is exactly like the population value. As a matter of fact they very probably will not be the same, as all sorts of different factors of which we are in ignorance may make the sample a poor representation of the population. Such factors we lump together under the general rubrics *chance* or *random effects*. Nevertheless, in the long run such samples drawn at random should reflect the population characteristics. This is the reason that we insist on random samples, so that "in-the-long-run" statements may be made in terms of principles such as Bernoulli's theorem and the Tchebycheff inequality. However, practical action can seldom wait for "in the long run"; things must be decided here and now in the face of limited evidence. We need to know how to use the available evidence in the best possible ways to infer the characteristics of the population. Therefore general principles for estimation have been formulated.

There are a number of properties that a statistic should have in order to be a good estimator of a population parameter. Some of these follow.

1. The estimate should be *unbiased*.
2. The estimate should be *consistent*.
3. The method of estimation should be relatively *efficient*.
4. The estimate should be *sufficient*.

Although few statistics satisfy all of these desirable properties as estimators, each criterion is an important property for an estimator to possess if possible. These four criteria for good estimators will now be discussed in turn.

## 7.6  UNBIASED ESTIMATORS

Suppose that one is interested in estimating the value of population parameter $\theta$ (Greek theta), and he is considering the use of some sample statistic $G$ as an estimate of the value of $\theta$. Then an estimate of the parameter $\theta$ made from the sample statistic $G$ is said to be an unbiased estimate if

$$E(G) = \theta. \qquad [7.6.1*]$$

That is, the sample quantity $G$ is unbiased as an estimate of $\theta$ if the expectation of $G$ is $\theta$; in the long run, $G$ averaged over all possible random samples is exactly $\theta$.

For example, consider the mean of a sample as an estimator of the mean of the population. Here

$$G = M = \frac{\sum\limits_{i} X_i}{N}$$

and

$$\theta = \mu.$$

Is the sample mean an unbiased estimate of the population mean $\mu$? *Yes*, since it is quite easy to show that

$$E(M) = \mu. \qquad [7.6.2*]$$

This may be shown as follows:

$$E(M) = E\,\frac{(X_1 + X_2 + \cdots + X_N)}{N}.$$

Using rules 5 and 2 for expectations, we have

$$E(M) = \frac{E(X_1) + E(X_2) + \cdots + E(X_N)}{N}.$$

But any $E(X)$ is $\mu$ by definition, for observations taken at random from the same population. Hence,

$$E(M) = \frac{NE(X)}{N} = \mu.$$

**The mean of a random sample is an unbiased estimate of the population mean $\mu$.**

In exactly the same way, for samples from a Bernoulli population where each observation is put into one of two categories, it can be shown that the **sample proportion $P$ of cases in a given category is an unbiased estimate of the population proportion $p$:**

$$E(P) = p. \qquad [7.6.3]$$

(As a matter of fact, this was shown in Section 6.13.)

What would an example of a *biased* estimate be like? An example is provided by a sample variance. The sample variance $s^2$ is a biased estimate of the population variance $\sigma^2$, since

$$E(s^2) \neq \sigma^2. \qquad [7.6.4*]$$

This can be demonstrated as follows: the expectation of a sample variance is

$$E(s^2) = E\left(\frac{\sum_i X_i^2}{N} - M^2\right) = E\left(\frac{\sum_i X_i^2}{N}\right) - E(M^2).$$

Let us consider the two terms on the extreme right separately. By rules 5 and 2 for expectations,

$$E\left(\frac{\sum_i X_i^2}{N}\right) = \frac{\sum_i E(X_i^2)}{N}.$$

From the definition of the variance of the population,

$$\sigma^2 = E(X_i^2) - \mu^2$$

so that

$$E(X_i^2) = \sigma^2 + \mu^2$$

for any observation $i$. Thus

$$E\left(\frac{\sum_i X_i^2}{N}\right) = \frac{\sum_i (\sigma^2 + \mu^2)}{N} = \sigma^2 + \mu^2. \qquad [7.6.5]$$

Now the variance of the sampling distribution of means is, from **7.4.4,**

$$\sigma_M^2 = E(M^2) - \mu^2$$

so that

$$E(M^2) = \sigma_M^2 + \mu^2. \qquad [7.6.6]$$

Putting these two results (**7.6.5** and **7.6.6**) together, we have

$$E(s^2) = \sigma^2 - \sigma_M^2, \qquad [7.6.7*]$$

the expectation of the sample variance is the *difference* between the population variance $\sigma^2$ and the variance of the sampling distribution of means $\sigma_M^2$. In general this difference will not be the same as $\sigma^2$, since ordinarily the variance $\sigma_M^2$ will not be zero, and so the sample variance is biased as an estimator of the population variance. In particular, the sample variance is, on the average, smaller than the population variance $\sigma^2$. A way of correcting the sample variance for this bias will be given in Section 7.13.

## 7.7   CONSISTENCY

For an estimate to be a good one, **the sample estimate should have a higher probability of being close to the population value** $\theta$ **the larger the sample size** $N$. Statistics that have this property are called consistent estimators. More formally: the statistic $G$ is a consistent estimator of $\theta$ if for any arbitrary positive number $\epsilon$,

$$\text{prob.}(|G - \theta| \leq \epsilon) \to 1, \text{ as } N \to \infty. \qquad [\textbf{7.7.1*}]$$

The probability that $G$ is within a certain distance $\epsilon$ of the parameter $\theta$ approaches 1 as the sample size $N$ approaches infinity, however small the size of the positive number $\epsilon$.

The sample mean, the sample variance, and many other statistics are consistent estimators, as they tend in likelihood to get closer to the true population value the larger the sample. It is, however, possible to create sample statistics that are not consistent estimators. For example, suppose that one wished to estimate the population mean, and he decided to take the score of the second observation made in any sample as the estimate. Would this be a consistent estimate? No, since the second observation's score would not tend in likelihood to get any closer to the mean value of the population the larger the sample. According to the criterion of consistency, this would not be a good way to estimate the mean. (Would this be an unbiased estimate of the mean, however?)

## 7.8   RELATIVE EFFICIENCY

A third criterion for evaluating a statistic $G$ as an estimator of a parameter $\theta$ is that $G$ be efficient relative to other statistics that might be used to estimate $\theta$. You will recall that the standard deviation (or standard error as it is called when the distribution it describes is a sampling distribution) represents the extent of the difference that chance factors tend to create between a sample estimate and a true parameter value. Good estimators should have sampling distributions with small standard errors, given the $N$ of the sample.

Suppose that there were two different sample statistics $G$ and $H$ calculated from the same data, and that these two statistics were each unbiased estimators of the same population parameter $\theta$. The theoretical sampling distribution of $G$ figured from samples of size $N$ has a standard error $\sigma_G$. There is also a theoretical sampling distribution of $H$, having a standard error $\sigma_H$. Each of these two standard errors reflects the tendency of the sample statistic to deviate by chance from the population value. Then, for any $N$, the efficiency of the statistic $G$

relative to the statistic $H$, both as estimators of $\theta$, is given by

$$\frac{\sigma_H^2}{\sigma_G^2} = \text{efficiency of } G \text{ relative to } H. \qquad [7.8.1*]$$

The more efficient estimator has the smaller standard error, so that the ratio is greater than 1.00 when the variance of the more efficient estimator appears in the denominator. Other things, such as sample size, being equal, relatively inefficient statistics have relatively larger standard errors than other estimators of the same parameter value.

For example, in a unimodal symmetric distribution the population mean and the population median both have the same value, $Md = \mu$. We wish to estimate this value $\mu$ by drawing a random sample of $N$ cases. We could use either the sample mean (statistic $G$, let us say) or we could use the sample median (statistic $H$). In any given sample, these values will very likely not be the same. Which should we use to estimate $\mu$? The answer involves efficiency. If the standard error of the mean is represented by $\sigma_M$ and the standard error of the distribution of sample medians is represented by $\sigma_{Md}$, then it is true that for unimodal symmetric population distributions $\sigma_{Md}$ is greater than $\sigma_M$ for a given sample size, $N > 2$. For such populations, and for a reasonably large $N$, the magnitude of error in any given estimate of the population mean from the sample mean is likely to be less than in an estimate of $\mu$ from the sample median. This says that for such situations

$$\frac{\sigma_{Md}^2}{\sigma_M^2} > 1.00,$$

the relative efficiency of the mean will be greater than 1.00, indicating that the mean is a more efficient estimator than the median for symmetric unimodal populations. This is one reason that so much of statistical inference deals with the mean rather than the median; the median is less efficient than the mean as an estimator of $\mu$ for a symmetric unimodal population distribution, and such distributions are very often assumed in statistical work.

## 7.9 SUFFICIENCY

A concept of great importance in the theory of estimation is that of a sufficient estimator. A statistic $G$ is said to be a sufficient estimator of the parameter $\theta$ if $G$ contains *all* the information available in the data about the value of $\theta$. A sufficient statistic $G$ is a "best" estimator of $\theta$ in the sense that $G$ cannot be improved by considering any other aspects of the sample data not already included in the statistic $G$ itself.

A slightly more formal definition of sufficiency may be given as follows: Consider the estimator $G$ of $\theta$ once again, and then let $H$ be any other sample statistic. We can consider the *conditional* distribution of $H$ given the value of $G$. Then if the conditional distribution of $H$ given $G$ does not depend in any way on the value of $\theta$, $G$ is a sufficient statistic.

An example of a sufficient estimator is the sample proportion $P$ when samples are drawn at random from a Bernoulli distribution. The sampling distribution of $P$ can be found from the binomial rule in this situation, of course. If we are estimating the population value $p$, then $P$ is a sufficient statistic, since there is no information we could add to $P$ to make it a better estimator of $p$. For a particularly important kind of continuous population distribution (the normal distribution), the sample mean $M$ is a sufficient estimator of $\mu$, the population mean; for this situation the sample mean "wraps up" all of the available information about $\mu$ in the sample.

Sufficient estimators do not always exist, and hypothetical situations can be constructed where no way to find a sufficient estimator of a given parameter can be found. Nevertheless, sufficient estimators, when they do exist, are very important, since if one can find a sufficient estimator it is ordinarily possible to find an unbiased and efficient estimator based on the sufficient statistic.

In most of the work to follow, the estimators will be the sample mean and the corrected sample variance, both of which will fulfill these criteria for good estimators in the particular situations where they will be used. This does not imply, however, that other estimators failing to meet one or more of these criteria are useless. In particular, special situations exist where other methods of estimating central tendency may be better than either mean or median, and variance estimates other than $s^2$ are called for. Other statistics are useful on occasion, but we will focus most attention on the mean and the corrected variance, since they occupy a central place in the "classical" statistical methods we will be treating.

## 7.10   THE SAMPLE MEAN AS AN ESTIMATOR

We have just seen that the sample mean comes off very well by the criteria for a good estimator. In general, the sample mean is unbiased, is consistent, and in an important set of circumstances is both efficient relative to other statistics and sufficient.

For our immediate purposes, the most important of these properties is that of being unbiased: the expectation of the sample mean is the population mean,

$$E(M) = E(X) = \mu.$$

For random sampling from any population, you can be sure that the long-run average of sample means will be identical to the population mean.

This same statement can be interpreted in another way: **the mean of the sampling distribution of means is the same as the population mean.** However, it is not true that the sampling distribution of the mean will be the same as the population distribution; in fact, these distributions will ordinarily be quite different, depending particularly on sample size. In the first place, the variance of the sampling distribution of means will not be the same as $\sigma^2$, but instead will be smaller than $\sigma^2$ for samples of size 2 or larger. This will be shown in the next section.

## 7.11   THE VARIANCE AND STANDARD ERROR OF THE MEAN

Intuitively it seems quite reasonable that the larger the sample size the more confident we may be that the sample mean is a close estimate of $\mu$. When it was asserted that the mean is a consistent estimator (Section 7.7) this was another way of saying that the mean is a better estimator for large than for small samples. Now we can put that intuition on a firm basis by looking into the effect of sample size on the variance and standard deviation of the distribution of sample means.

By definition, the variance of the distribution of means, from samples drawn at random from a population with mean $\mu$ and variance $\sigma^2$, is

$$\begin{aligned} \sigma_M^2 &= E(M^2) - [E(M)]^2 \\ &= E(M^2) - \mu^2. \end{aligned} \qquad [7.11.1^*]$$

Bear in mind that we are assuming that the sample mean is based on $N$ *independent* observations. Let us call any pair of these observations $i$ and $j$, with scores $X_i$ and $X_j$. The square of the sample mean is

$$\begin{aligned} M^2 &= \frac{(X_1 + X_2 + \cdots + X_N)^2}{N^2} \\ &= \frac{1}{N^2}\left(X_1^2 + \cdots + X_N^2 + 2\sum_{(i,j)} X_i X_j\right), \end{aligned} \qquad [7.11.2]$$

the sum of the squared scores, plus twice the sum of the products of all pairs of scores, all divided by $N^2$. For any single observation $i$,

$$E(X_i^2) = \sigma^2 + \mu^2 \qquad [7.11.3]$$

since, from Section 6.21,

$$\sigma^2 = E(X_i^2) - \mu^2.$$

For a pair of *independent* observations, $i$ and $j$, rule 6 in Appendix B gives

$$E(X_i X_j) = E(X_i)E(X_j) = \mu^2. \qquad [7.11.4]$$

Thus, putting these two facts (**7.11.3** and **7.11.4**) together, we have

$$\begin{aligned} E(M^2) &= \frac{1}{N^2}\left[E(X_1^2) + E(X_2^2) + \cdots + 2\sum_{(i,j)} E(X_i X_j)\right] \\ &= \frac{N\sigma^2 + N\mu^2 + (N)(N-1)\mu^2}{N^2} \\ &= \frac{\sigma^2}{N} + \mu^2. \end{aligned} \qquad [7.11.5]$$

Making this substitution in expression **7.11.1** we find

$$\sigma_M^2 = E(M^2) - \mu^2 = \frac{\sigma^2}{N}. \qquad [7.11.6^*]$$

**The variance of the sampling distribution of means for independent samples of size $N$ is always the population variance divided by the sample size, $\sigma^2/N$.**

This is a most important fact, and gives direct support to our feeling that large samples produce better estimators of the population mean than do small. When the sample size is only 1, then the variance of the sampling distribution is exactly the same as the population variance. If however, the sample mean is based on two cases, $N = 2$, then the sampling variance is only 1/2 as large as $\sigma^2$. Ten cases give a sampling distribution with variance only 1/10 of $\sigma^2$, $N = 500$ gives a sampling distribution with variance 1/500 of $\sigma^2$, and so on. If the sample size approaches infinity, then $\sigma^2$ approaches zero. **If the sample is large enough to embrace the entire population, there is no difference between the sample mean and $\mu$.**

**In general, the larger the sample size, the more probable it is that the sample mean comes arbitrarily close to the population mean.** This fact is often called **the law of large numbers,** and is closely allied both to Bernoulli's theorem and the Tchebycheff inequality.

Given the Tchebycheff inequality and the variance of the mean, it is easy to see that the law of large numbers must be true. From the Tchebycheff inequality (**6.27.1**), it is true that for any random variable,

$$\text{prob.}(|X - \mu| < k) \geqq 1 - \frac{\sigma^2}{k^2}, \qquad k > 0. \qquad [\textbf{7.11.7}]$$

Let the random variable be $M$, and the variance be $\sigma_M^2$. Then

$$\text{prob.}(|M - \mu| < k) \geqq 1 - \frac{\sigma_M^2}{k^2}. \qquad [\textbf{7.11.8*}]$$

When $N$ becomes very large, $\sigma_M^2$ approaches zero. Thus, regardless of how small $k$ is, the probability approaches 1 that the value of $M$ will be within $k$ units of $\mu$ when sample size grows large.

### 7.12   STANDARDIZED SCORES CORRESPONDING TO SAMPLE MEANS

The standard error of the mean is

$$\sigma_M = \sqrt{\sigma_M^2} = \frac{\sigma}{\sqrt{N}}. \qquad [\textbf{7.12.1*}]$$

so that when a sample mean is put into standardized form, we have

$$z_M = \frac{M - \mu}{\sigma_M} = \frac{M - \mu}{\sigma/\sqrt{N}}. \qquad [\textbf{7.12.2*}]$$

The larger the standard score of a mean, relative to $\mu$ and the standard error, the *less likely* is one to observe a mean this much or more deviant from $\mu$. Any given degree of departure of $M$ from $\mu$ corresponds to a larger absolute standard score value, and hence a less probable class of result, the larger the sample size $N$.

For example, suppose that in sampling from some population a sample mean was found differing by 10 points from the population mean. Suppose that $\sigma$ were 5 and the sample size were 2. Then the standard score $z_M$ would be

$$z_M = \frac{10}{5/\sqrt{2}} = 2.8,$$

disregarding sign. The Tchebycheff inequality tells us that means this deviant or more so from expectation can occur with probability no greater than about $1/(2.8)^2$ or .13.

Suppose, however, that the sample size had been 200. Here

$$z_M = \frac{10}{5/\sqrt{200}} = 28.28$$

so that a sample $M$ deviating this much or more from expectation could occur only with probability no greater than about $1/(28.28)^2$ or .0013. An extent of deviation of $M$ from the true mean that could occur relatively often for small samples is rare when the sample size is large. Notice that knowing the standard error of the mean is essential if we are going to judge the agreement between a sample and a population mean in terms of the probability of occurrence for a given extent of deviation. For the moment we are assuming that this information is simply given to us.

### 7.13 FINDING THE LARGEST SAMPLE SIZE REQUIRED FOR A GIVEN ACCURACY OF ESTIMATION

The law of large numbers, as embodied in the Tchebycheff inequality, can be put to practical use in deciding the largest number of observations required to achieve a given accuracy of estimation. Even if nothing at all is known about the population distribution or the sampling distribution of the mean, but the experimenter has an idea about what makes a sufficiently good estimate of $\mu$, then an upper limit to size of sample actually required can be found. That is, given a degree of deviation of $M$ from $\mu$ which the experimenter wants to be sure will occur only with very low probability, the experimenter can find a sample size which is sufficiently large to give the required insurance. This is best illustrated concretely.

Suppose that in some psychological experiment it is desired to estimate the mean to within one tenth of a standard deviation. The experimenter wants to be very sure of doing this, so he decides that he would like the probability to be .95 or more that his estimate is within $.1\sigma$ of the true value. If he knows nothing at all about the sampling distribution of the mean, what is the size of the sample that would meet his qualifications?

The answer can be found from the Tchebycheff inequality, as given by **7.11.8,** with the value of $k$ set equal to $.1\sigma$: we want

$$\text{prob.}(|M - \mu| < .1\sigma) \geqq 1 - \frac{\sigma^2}{N(.1\sigma)^2}$$

when the right hand side of the inequality is replaced by .95. Actually setting the right hand of the inequality equal to .95, and solving for $N$, we have

$$1 - \frac{1}{N(.01)} = .95$$

$$\frac{1}{N} = .0005$$

$$N = 2000.$$

The largest number of cases that the experimenter is required to observe in order to meet these qualifications is 2000. If he actually takes 2000 observations then he can be sure that the probability is at least 95 in 100 that the sample value is within .1 standard deviation of the true mean.

However, the number arrived at, 2000, is actually the *largest* number of cases that he need take to be this confident that the obtained mean is within $.1\sigma$ of $\mu$. Naturally, if he chooses to take more than 2000 cases in his sample, then he can be even more confident, as the more cases he takes in the sample the closer to 1.00 is the probability that $M$ is within any desired limits of $\mu$. On the other hand, it might be that given more information about the sampling distribution of $M$ he could satisfy the same conditions with *fewer* cases in the sample. As one consequence of the Tchebycheff inequality in Section 6.27, we find that for a unimodal symmetric distribution

$$\text{prob.}(|X - \mu| < k) \geqq 1 - \frac{4\sigma^2}{9k^2}.$$

Applying this information, and assuming that a sampling distribution for means is unimodal-symmetric, the experimenter would find that no more than 889 cases are required in the sample to make the probability at least .95 that the value of $M$ comes within $.1\sigma$ of $\mu$. As usual in matters of statistical inference, the more one can assume true about the population or about the sampling distribution of a particular statistic, the "tighter" are the statements one can deduce from general statistical principles.

These values for $N$ arrived at from the Tchebycheff inequality are useful only in setting *maximum* sample size requirements. In most instances the sample sizes given by the Tchebycheff inequality are much too large, and they are employed only when the experimenter cannot commit himself at all about the basic form of the population distribution.

Now we can look ahead to a principle that makes it unimportant in most instances whether or not the form of the population distribution is known. In the next chapter the **central limit theorem** will be introduced, which is an extremely general principle letting us know the approximate form of the sampling distribution of the mean regardless of the form of the population distribution, provided that the sample size is relatively large. We shall find that as sample size becomes relatively large, the sampling distribution of the mean approaches a unimodal, symmetric form known as the **normal distribution.** Although the sampling distribution of means from a given population need never be exactly like the normal distribution, nevertheless with a sufficiently large $N$ per sample, the normal distribution provides an excellent approximation to the exact sampling distribution of the mean. This makes it possible to solve problems such as those of required sample size much more accurately and efficiently than does the Tchebycheff inequality. For example, by use of the normal distribution it can be shown that for large samples

$$\text{prob.} \left( \left| \frac{M - \mu}{\sigma_M} \right| < 1.96 \right) = .95.$$

Now if we wish the probability to be .95 that the difference between $M$ and $\mu$ falls within $.1\sigma$, and if we know by the central limit theorem that the sampling distribution of $M$ is approximately normal, we can solve for the required $N$ as follows:

$$\frac{M - \mu}{\sigma_M} = 1.96$$

$$\frac{.1\sigma}{\sigma/\sqrt{N}} = 1.96$$

$$N = (19.6)^2 = 384.$$

If the experimenter takes a sample of 384 cases, then he can state that the probability is approximately .95 that $M$ falls within $.1\sigma$ of $\mu$. This statement is only approximate, because the sampling distribution of $M$ is only approximately like the normal distribution. Nevertheless, if he takes as many as 384 cases the approximation is extremely good, and the experimenter can feel confident that $M$ estimates $\mu$ within the desired limits. Contrast this estimated sample size, a required 384 cases, with the values 2000 and 889 cases set by use of the Tchebycheff inequality! This is but one instance of the enormous practical utility of the central limit theorem in statistics. We will have a great deal more to say about this principle, but this must wait until Chapter 8.

## 7.14 CORRECTING THE BIAS IN THE SAMPLE VARIANCE AS AN ESTIMATOR

As shown in Section 7.6, the sample variance is a biased estimator of the population variance $\sigma^2$. At first this may seem a serious drawback, since our only knowledge of the population variance, and hence of the standard error of the mean, must come from samples. However, now that the variance of the sampling distribution of the mean has been found, we can work out a simple way to correct the sample variance as an estimator of $\sigma^2$.

It will be shown first that the expectation of the variance from samples of size $N$ is

$$E(s^2) = \frac{N-1}{N} \sigma^2. \qquad [7.14.1^*]$$

We found in Section 7.6 that the expectation of the sample variance is actually a difference between two variances:

$$E(s^2) = \sigma^2 - \sigma_M^2.$$

However, we have just found that

$$\sigma_M^2 = \frac{\sigma^2}{N}.$$

On making this substitution, we have

$$E(s^2) = \sigma^2 - \frac{\sigma^2}{N} = \left(\frac{N-1}{N}\right)\sigma^2,$$

so that on the average the sample variance is *too small* by a factor of $\dfrac{N-1}{N}$.

Since this is true, a way emerges for correcting the variance of a sample to make it an unbiased estimator. **The unbiased estimate of the variance based on any sample of $N$ independent cases is**

$$\hat{s}^2 = \frac{N}{N-1} s^2. \qquad [7.14.2^*]$$

The carat or "hat" ($\wedge$) will always be placed over the symbol for a sample variance when it is an unbiased estimate, to distinguish it from the ordinary sample variance. It is simple to show that $\hat{s}^2$ is indeed unbiased:

$$E(\hat{s}^2) = \frac{N}{N-1} E(s^2) = \frac{N}{(N-1)} \frac{(N-1)}{N} \sigma^2 = \sigma^2. \qquad [7.14.3^*]$$

Quite often it is convenient to calculate the unbiased variance estimate $\hat{s}^2$ directly, without the intermediate step of calculating $s^2$. This is done either by the formula

$$\hat{s}^2 = \frac{\sum_i X_i^2 - NM^2}{N-1} \qquad [7.14.4\dagger]$$

or by

$$\hat{s}^2 = \frac{\sum_i X_i^2}{N-1} - \frac{\left(\sum_i X_i\right)^2}{N(N-1)}. \qquad [7.14.5\dagger]$$

Even though we will be using the square root of $\hat{s}^2$, or $\hat{s}$, to estimate the population $\sigma$, it should be noted that $\hat{s}$ is not *itself* an unbiased estimate of $\sigma$, and that

$$E(\hat{s}) \neq \sigma$$

in general. The correction factor used to make $\hat{s}$ an unbiased estimate of $\sigma$ depends upon the form of the population distribution; thus, for the unimodal symmetric distribution known as the "normal" distribution (Chapter 8) an unbiased estimate for large $N$ is provided by

$$\text{unbiased estimate of } \sigma = \left[ 1 + \frac{1}{4(N-1)} \right] \hat{s}. \qquad [7.14.6]$$

Furthermore, special tables exist for correcting the estimate of $\sigma$ for relatively small samples from such populations (Dixon and Massey, 1957). However, the problem of estimating $\sigma$ from $\hat{s}$ is bypassed, in part, by the methods we will use in Chapter 11 and elsewhere, and, if the sample size is reasonably large, the amount of bias in $\hat{s}$ as an estimator of $\sigma$ ordinarily is rather small. For these reasons, we will not trouble to correct for the bias in $\hat{s}$ found from the *unbiased* estimate $\hat{s}^2$ of $\sigma^2$.

Some modern statistics texts completely abandon the idea of the sample variance $s^2$ as used here, and introduce only the unbiased estimate $\hat{s}^2$ as *the* variance of a sample. However, this is apt to be confusing in some work, and so we will follow the older practice of distinguishing between the sample variance $s^2$ as a descriptive statistic, and $\hat{s}^2$ as the unbiased estimate of $\sigma^2$.

### 7.15 ESTIMATING THE STANDARD DEVIATION OF THE POPULATION AND THE STANDARD ERROR OF THE MEAN

In most elementary work the standard deviation of the population, $\sigma$, is estimated simply by taking the square root of the unbiased estimate $\hat{s}^2$,

$$\text{estimated } \sigma = \sqrt{\hat{s}^2}. \qquad [7.15.1]$$

In the same way, one estimates the standard error of the mean by using the unbiased estimate $\hat{s}^2$:

$$\text{estimated } \sigma_M = \frac{\text{estimated } \sigma}{\sqrt{N}} = \sqrt{\frac{\hat{s}^2}{N}}. \qquad [7.15.2\dagger]$$

On the other hand, if the sample variance (not the unbiased estimate) is used, then the estimate may be arrived at as follows:

$$\text{estimated } \sigma_M = \sqrt{\frac{\hat{s}^2}{N}} = \sqrt{\frac{N}{(N-1)} \frac{s^2}{N}} = \frac{s}{\sqrt{N-1}}. \qquad [7.15.3\dagger]$$

This last is the version of the estimated standard error of the mean usually encountered in psychology: the ordinary sample standard deviation divided by the square root of $N - 1$. This form will be followed here.

## 7.16  PARAMETER ESTIMATES BASED ON POOLED SAMPLES

Sometimes it happens that one has several independent samples, and that each provides an estimate of the same parameter or set of parameters. The most usual situation occurs when one is estimating $\mu$ or $\sigma^2$, or both. When this happens there is a real advantage in pooling the sample values to get an unbiased estimate. These pooled estimates are actually weighted averages of the estimates from the different samples. The big advantage lies in the fact that the sampling error will tend to be smaller for the pooled estimate than that for any single sample's value taken alone.

Suppose that there were two independent samples, based on $N_1$ and $N_2$ observations respectively. From each sample a mean $M$ is calculated, each of which estimates the same value $\mu$. Then the pooled estimate of the mean is

$$\text{pooled } M = \text{est. } \mu = \frac{N_1 M_1 + N_2 M_2}{N_1 + N_2}. \qquad [7.16.1\dagger]$$

It is easy to see that this must give an unbiased estimate of $\mu$:

$$E\left[\frac{N_1 M_1 + N_2 M_2}{N_1 + N_2}\right] = \frac{N_1 E(M_1) + N_2 E(M_2)}{N_1 + N_2}$$

$$= \frac{\mu(N_1 + N_2)}{N_1 + N_2} = \mu.$$

For some $J$ different and independent samples, where any given sample $j$ gives an estimate $M_j$ of $\mu$, the pooled estimate is

$$\text{est. } \mu = \frac{\sum_j N_j M_j}{\sum_j N_j}. \qquad [7.16.2\dagger]$$

The fact that the pooled estimate is likely to be better than the single sample estimates taken alone is shown by the standard error of the pooled mean. For two independent samples, each composed of independent observations drawn from the same population,

$$\sigma_M = \frac{\sigma}{\sqrt{N_1 + N_2}}, \qquad [7.16.3]$$

which *must* be smaller than the standard error either of $M_1$ or of $M_2$. Similarly, for any number $J$ of independent samples, with $N_1, N_2, \cdots, N_J$ as the respective sample sizes,

$$\sigma_M = \frac{\sigma}{\sqrt{\sum_j N_j}}.$$

[7.16.4*]

Naturally, these standard errors refer to the situation where the respective samples all come from the *same* population with mean $\mu$ and variance $\sigma^2$.

In the same general way it is possible to find pooled estimates of $\sigma^2$. For two independent samples,

$$\text{est. } \sigma^2 = \frac{N_1 s_1^2 + N_2 s_2^2}{N_1 + N_2 - 2},$$

[7.16.5†]

which is an unbiased estimate of $\sigma^2$, the variance estimated from either sample alone by $\hat{s}^2$.

For any number $J$ of independent samples, then the corresponding unbiased estimate of $\sigma^2$ is

$$\text{est. } \sigma^2 = \frac{\sum\limits_j N_j s_j^2}{\left(\sum\limits_j N_j\right) - J}.$$

[7.16.6†]

We are going to make a great deal of use of this pooling principle in Chapters 10 and 12.

## 7.17 SAMPLING FROM FINITE POPULATIONS

It has been mentioned repeatedly that most sampling problems deal with populations so large that the fact that samples are taken without replacement of single cases can safely be ignored. However, it may happen that the population under study is not only finite, but relatively small, so that the process of sampling without replacement has a real effect on the sampling distribution.

Even in this situation the sample mean is still an unbiased estimate regardless of the size of the population sampled. Hence no change in procedure for mean estimation is needed.

However, for finite populations the sample variance is biased as an estimator of $\sigma^2$ in a way somewhat different from the former, infinite-population, situation. When samples are drawn without replacement of individuals, the unbiased estimate of $\sigma^2$ is

$$\hat{s}^2 = \text{est. of } \sigma^2 = \frac{(N)(T-1)}{(N-1)(T)} s^2$$

[7.17.1†]

where $T$ is the *total number* of elements in the population.

Another difference from the infinite-population situation comes with the variance of the sampling distribution of means. For a population with $T$ cases in all, from which samples of size $N$ are drawn, the sampling variance of the mean is

$$\sigma_M^2 = \left(\frac{T - N}{T - 1}\right)\frac{\sigma^2}{N}. \tag{7.17.2\dagger}$$

The variance of the mean tends to be *somewhat smaller* for a fixed value of $N$ when sampling is from a finite population than when it is from an infinite population. Note that here the size of $\sigma_M^2$ depends both upon $T$, the total number in the population, and upon $N$, the sample size. An unbiased estimate of the variance of the mean is thus given by

$$\text{est. } \sigma_M^2 = \left(\frac{T - N}{T - 1}\right)\frac{\hat{s}^2}{N}. \tag{7.17.3\dagger}$$

The square root of this value gives the estimate of $\sigma_M$, for sampling from a finite population.

Sometimes the number $C = N/T$ is called the "sampling fraction," and when $T$ is at least moderately large, the variance of the mean, $\sigma_M^2$, is approximately

$$\frac{\sigma^2}{N}(1 - C).$$

When $T$ is so large that $C$ is virtually zero, the sampling variance is the same as for the infinite-population situation.

## 7.18   THE SAMPLE PROPORTION AS AN UNBIASED ESTIMATOR

When the observations made in an experiment fall into qualitative classes, then the sample proportion $P$ in each class is the usual summary statement of the sample result. This is an unbiased estimate of the population proportion $p$ in that class:

$$E(P) = p. \tag{7.18.1}$$

This is true for any number of classes.

When there are exactly two classes, the sampling distribution of the proportion $P$ is found from the binomial, with variance

$$\sigma_P^2 = \frac{pq}{N} \tag{7.18.2}$$

and standard error

$$\sigma_P = \sqrt{\frac{pq}{N}}. \tag{7.18.3*}$$

Notice that unlike the situation for the mean, once the population $p$ is specified, and given $N$, the standard error of $P$ is known completely. There is ordinarily no reason to estimate the standard error separately from sample data, as one must when using the mean.

### 7.19  THE SAMPLING DISTRIBUTION OF THE SAMPLE VARIANCE

We have already seen that the mean of the distribution of the sample variances is $((N-1)/N)\sigma^2$. It is also possible to specify the standard error of the sample variance. However, there are some special problems connected with the sampling distribution of the variance that cannot be discussed properly until after the sample mean is explored more fully. The question of the distribution of the variance will be taken up once again in Chapter 11.

### 7.20  THE USES OF SAMPLING DISTRIBUTIONS

The remainder of this text will be devoted to problems in using sampling distributions for statistical inference. Parameter estimation is but the starting place for inference. The really essential features of sampling distributions, the standard errors and the probabilities associated with intervals of sample values, have not yet been brought into systematic use. It has been suggested in the preceding chapter that a sampling distribution, such as the binomial, may be used to assess the probability of a certain kind of sample result, given some hypothetical population situation. However, a set of formal procedures still must be given that will permit a similar kind of inference to be made about *any* population or population characteristic. This set of procedures using specific sampling distributions is known as **hypothesis-testing** and will be introduced in Chapter 9.

Specific sampling distributions also give a way to carry on the second important part of estimation, the so-called **interval estimation.** It is not enough to estimate population values from sample statistics; the statistician must provide some estimate of the sampling error involved. Moreover, he uses his knowledge of the sampling distribution to set up a *range of values* which, over all possible samples, has a high probability of covering the true population value—these are called **confidence intervals** for the population value. A much stronger inference may be made using confidence intervals than using the point estimate alone, since a very positive statement can be made about a *range* of values very likely to contain the true value. This method of interval estimation will also be considered in Chapter 9.

Before leaving the problem of point estimation, let us consider a point of view underlying much of the work to follow. This is the principle of maximum likelihood, a statement of statistical "strategy" in inference from samples to populations.

### 7.21  THE PRINCIPLE OF MAXIMUM LIKELIHOOD

Even though a formal presentation of the maximum-likelihood principle is far beyond our scope, some intuitive feel for this idea may help you understand the methods that follow.

Basically, the problem of the person using statistics is, "Given several possible population situations, any one of which might be true, how shall I bet on the basis of the evidence so as to be as confident as possible of being right?" Everyone who uses statistical inference is faced with this question. He knows that any number of things might be true of the population. Fortunately, he can "snoop" on the population to a certain extent by taking a sample, but he knows that the evidence he gains will be faulty. Since this evidence is all there is, the person must use it nevertheless to form an opinion or make up his mind. How does one decide on the basis of evidence that is probably erroneous? The principle of maximum likelihood gives a general strategy for such decisions, and may be paraphrased as follows.

Suppose that a random variable $X$ has a distribution that depends only upon some population parameter $\theta$. The form of the density function will be assumed known, but not the value of $\theta$. A sample of $N$ independent observations is drawn, producing the set of values $(X_1, X_2, \cdots, X_N)$. Let

$$L(X_1, \cdots, X_N|\theta)$$

represent the likelihood, or probability (density), of this particular sample result *given* $\theta$. For each possible value of $\theta$, the likelihood of the sample result will be different, perhaps. Then, **the principle of maximum likelihood requires us to choose as our estimate that possible value of** $\theta$ **making** $L(X_1, \cdots, X_N|\theta)$ **take on its largest value.**

In effect this principle says that when faced with several parameter values, any of which might be the true one for a population, the best "bet" is that parameter value which would have made the sample actually obtained have the highest prior probability. When in doubt, place your bet on that parameter value which would have made the obtained result most likely.

This principle may be illustrated very simply for the binomial distribution. Suppose that a sample is drawn at random from a population of college graduates. Each graduate is classified either as a "literary-college major" or as a graduate from some other university college. Now three possibilities or hypotheses are entertained about the proportion of college graduates from literary colleges. Hypothesis 1 states that .5 of all graduates are from such colleges, hypothesis 2 states that .4 of the graduates are from such schools, and hypothesis 3 states that .6 are literary-college graduates.

Now suppose that some 15 college graduates are drawn at random and classified according to "literary-college degree" versus "nonliterary degree." The result is that 9 out of the 15 hold a literary-college degree (we are supposing that no one in the population holds more than one degree). What decision about the three available hypotheses should we reach? This is a simple binomial sampling problem, so that the probability of each sample result may be calculated for each of the three hypothetical values of the parameter $p$: $p = .5$, $p = .4$, or $p = .6$.

If $p = .5$ the prior probability of a sample result such as that obtained would be

$$\binom{15}{9} (.5)^9 (.5)^6 = .153.$$

For $p = .4$ the prior probability becomes

$$\binom{15}{9} (.4)^9 (.6)^6 = .061.$$

Finally, if $p$ were .6 the prior probability of 9 successes out of 15 would be

$$\binom{15}{9} (.6)^9 (.4)^6 = .207.$$

The use of the principle of maximum likelihood to decide among these three possibilities leads to the choice of hypothesis 3, that .6 is the population proportion, since this is the parameter value among the possibilities considered that would have made the obtained sample result most likely, a priori.

This principle has a great deal of use in theoretical statistics, since general methods exist for finding the value of $\theta$ that maximizes the likelihood of a sample result. Statistics chosen as estimators because their values substituted for the parameter maximize the likelihood of the sample result are called **maximum-likelihood estimators.** For example, if there were no prior information at all about the number of literary-college graduates, so that any number between 0 and 1.00 might be entertained as a hypothesis about the value of $p$, the maximum likelihood estimate of $p$ would be the sample $P$, or 9/15, since among all possible values of $p$ this value makes the occurrence of the actual result have greatest a priori likelihood (the student may check a few values of $p$ for himself to see that this is true). For populations having a normal distribution, the sample mean $M$ is a maximum-likelihood estimator of $\mu$, since if $M = \mu$, the obtained sample is made more likely than for any other possible value of $\mu$, other things being equal. The principle of maximum likelihood gains its greatest importance from the fact that if a *sufficient* estimator of a parameter exists, the maximum-likelihood estimate is based on this sufficient statistic. Thus, the principle of maximum likelihood provides a fairly routine way of finding estimators having "good" properties.

However, the principle of maximum likelihood is introduced here not only because of its importance in estimation, but also because of the general point of view it represents about inference. This point of view is that *true population situations should be those making our empirical results likely; if a theoretical situation makes our obtained data have very low prior likelihood of occurrence, then doubt is cast on the truth of the theoretical situation.* Theoretical propositions are believable to the extent that they accord with actual observation. If a particular result should be very unlikely given a certain theoretical state of affairs, and we do get this result nevertheless, then we are led back to examine our theory. Good theoretical statements accord with observation by giving predictions having high probability of being observed.

Naturally, the results of a single experiment, or even of any number of experiments, cannot prove or disprove a theory. Replications, variants, different ways of measuring the phenomena, must all be brought into play. Even then, proof or disproof is never absolute. Nevertheless, the principle of maximum likelihood is in the spirit of empirical science, and it runs throughout the methods of statistical inference.

## 7.22   OTHER KINDS OF SAMPLING

The model of simple random sampling is the basis of almost all the discussion to follow. The classical procedures of statistical inference rest upon the sampling scheme in which each and every population element sampled is independent of every other, and is equally likely to be included in any sample. However, it is well to know that other sampling methods are employed in special kinds of problems.

In some instances, it is not true that each and every member of the population has equal probability of appearing in a sample. However, each potential observation has some probability of showing up in a sample, and it may be that these probabilities are known. The sample is then drawn by some method consistent with these probabilities, and the probabilities are taken into account in estimates made from any sample. This is sometimes known as **probability sampling.** Many methods exist for dealing with such samples, and often these methods differ from those we will discuss. Simple random sampling is but one special version of this scheme.

Another common scheme is called **stratified sampling.** Here, the population is divided into a number of parts, called "strata." A sample is drawn independently and at random in each part. Given the sizes of the various strata, one can make inferences about the total population represented. Such a scheme is very good for insuring a representative sample, and it may reduce the error in estimation, although it does require special methods over and above those given here.

## 7.23   TO WHAT POPULATIONS DO OUR INFERENCES REFER?

Most psychologists who use inferential statistics in research rely on the model of simple random sampling. Yet how does one go about getting such a "truly" random sample? It is not easy to do, unless, as in all probability sampling, each and every potential member of the population may somehow be listed. Then, by means of a device such as random number tables, individuals may be assigned to the sample with approximately equal probabilities.

However, in behavioral sciences such as psychology, interest often lies in experimental effects that, presumably, should apply to very large populations of men or other living organisms. Such a listing procedure is simply not possible. Still other experiments may refer to all possible measurements that *might* be made of some phenomenon under various experimental conditions, where estimated true values may be sought from the experimental observation of a few instances. Here, the population is not only infinite, it is hypothetical, since it includes all *future* or *potential* observations of that phenomenon under the different conditions. In sampling from such experimental populations, where there is no possibility of listing the elements for random assignment to the sample, the only recourse of the experimenter is to draw his basic experimental units in some more or less random, "haphazard," way, and then *make sure that in his experiment only random factors determine which unit gets which experimental treatment*. In other words, there are two ways in which randomness is important in an experiment: the first is in the selection of the sample as a whole, and the second is in the allotment of individuals to experimental treatments. Each kind of randomness is important for the "generalizability" of the experimental results, so that when one does an experiment he usually takes pains to see that both kinds of randomness are present. However, even given that individual cases are assigned to experimental manipulations at random, the possible inferences are still limited by the fundamental population from which the total sample is drawn.

How does one know the population to which the statistical inferences drawn from a sample apply? If random sampling is to be assumed, *the population is defined by the sample and the manner in which it is drawn. The only population to which the inferences strictly apply is that in which individuals have equal likelihood of appearing in the sample*. It should be obvious that simple random samples from one population may not be random samples of another population. For example, suppose that some one wishes to sample American college students. He obtains a directory of college students from a Midwestern university and, using a random number table, takes a sample of these students. He is not, however, justified in calling this a random sample of the population of American college students, although he may be justified in calling this a random sample of students at *that* university. *The population is defined not by what he said, but rather by what he did to get the sample.* For any sample, one should always ask the question, "What is the set of potential cases that could have appeared in my sample with equal probability?" If there is some well-defined set of cases which fits this qualification, then inferences may be made to that population. However, if there is some population whose members could not have been represented in the sample with equal probability, then inferences do not *necessarily* apply to that population when methods based on simple random sampling are used. Any generalization beyond the population actually sampled at random must rest on extrastatistical, scientific, considerations.

From a mathematical-statistical point of view the assumption of random sampling makes it possible to determine the sampling distribution of a particular statistic given some particular population distribution. If the various values of the statistic can arise from samples having undetermined or unknown probabilities of occurrence, then the statistician has no way to determine the sampling distribution of that statistic. On the other hand, if each and every distinct sample of $N$ observations has equal probability of occurrence, as in simple random sampling, then the sampling distribution of any given statistic is relatively easy to study, given, of course, the population situation. It is a sad fact that if one knows nothing about the probability of occurrence for particular samples of units for observation, he can use very little of the machinery of statistical inference. This is why the assumption of random sampling is not to be taken lightly. All the techniques and theory that we will discuss apply to random samples, and do not necessarily hold for any data collected in any way. In practical situations, the experimenter may be hard put to show that a given sample is "truly" random, but he must realize that he is acting *as if* this were a random sample from some well-defined population when he applies methods of statistical inference. Unless this assumption is at least reasonable, the results of inferential methods mean very little, and these methods might as well be omitted. Data that are not the product of random sampling may yield extremely valuable conclusions in their own right, but there is usually little to be gained from the application of inferential methods to such data. Certainly, the application of some statistical method does not somehow magically make a sample random, and the conclusions therefore valid. Inferential methods apply to random samples, and there is no guarantee of their validity in other circumstances.

# NORMAL POPULATION AND SAMPLING DISTRIBUTIONS

8

## 8.1 THE NORMAL DISTRIBUTION

Heretofore, the discrete binomial distribution has been used as our prime example of a sampling distribution. Now we consider a type of distribution having a domain which is *all* of the real numbers. This is the so-called "normal" or "Gaussian" distribution. The normal distribution is but one of a vast number of mathematical functions one might invent for a distribution; it is purely theoretical. At the very outset let it be clear that, like binomial or other probability functions, the normal distribution is not a fact of nature that one actually observes to be exactly true. Rather, the normal distribution is a theory about what might be true of the relation between intervals of values and probabilities for some variable. There is nothing magical about the normal distribution; it happens to be only one of a number of theoretical distributions that have been studied and found useful as an idealized mathematical concept. Normal distributions do not really exist, however, and in applied situations the closest we can come to finding a normal distribution will never quite correspond to the requirements of the mathematical rule. Many concepts in mathematics and science that are never quite true give good practical results nevertheless, and so does the normal distribution.

Like most theoretical functions, a normal distribution is completely specified only by its mathematical rule. Quite often, the distribution is symbolized by a graph of the functional relation generated by that rule, and the general picture that a normal distribution presents is the familiar bell-shaped curve of Figure 8.1.1. The horizontal axis represents all the different values of $X$, and the vertical axis $f(X)$ their densities. The normal distribution is continuous for all values of $X$ between $-\infty$ and $\infty$, so that each conceivable nonzero *interval* of real numbers has a probability other than zero. For this reason, the curve is shown as never quite touching the horizontal axis; the tails of the curve show decreasing probability densities as values grow extreme in either direction from the mode, but any interval representing *any* degree of deviation from central tendency is possible in this theoretical distribution. The distribution is absolutely symmetric and uni-modal, and mean, median, and mode all have the same value of $X$. Bear in mind that since the normal distribution is continuous, the height of the curve shows the probability *density* for each $X$ value. However, as for any continuous distribution, **the area cut off beneath the curve by any interval is a probability,** and the entire area under the curve is 1.00.

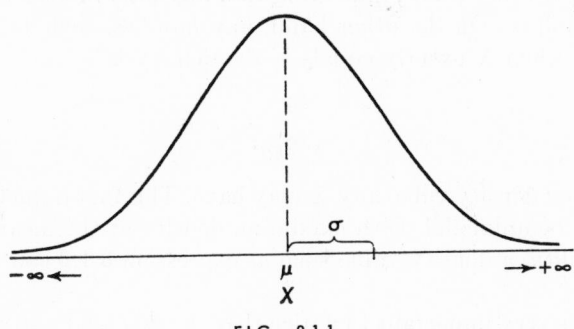

FIG.  8.1.1

The student is warned not to let the graph of any distribution lead him into jumping to conclusions about the kind of distribution represented. Although the normal distribution graphs as a bell-shaped curve, just any bell-shaped curve is not necessarily a normal distribution. The kind of distribution, the family to which it belongs, depends absolutely on the function rule, and on nothing else. Only if each possible value of $X$ is paired with a density in the way provided by the normal function rule can one say that the distribution is normal. Other rules may give similar pictures or probabilities that are close to their normal counterparts but, by definition, these distributions are not exactly normal.

The mathematical rule for a normal density function is as follows:

$$f(X) = \frac{1}{\sqrt{2\pi\sigma^2}}\, e^{-(X-\mu)^2/2\sigma^2}. \qquad\qquad [8.1.1^*]$$

This rule pairs a probability density $f(X)$ with each and every possible value $X$. This rule looks somewhat forbidding to the mathematically uninitiated, but actually it is not. The $\pi$, the $e$, and the 2, of course, are simply positive numbers acting as mathematical constants. The "working" part of the rule is the exponent

$$-\frac{(X-\mu)^2}{2\sigma^2} \qquad\qquad [8.1.2]$$

where the particular value of the variable $X$ appears, along with the two parameters $\mu$ and $\sigma^2$.

The more that the value of $X$ differs from $\mu$, the larger will the quantity in the numerator of this exponent be. However, this deviation of $X$ from $\mu$ enters as a squared quantity, so that *two* different $X$ values showing the same absolute deviation from $\mu$ have the same probability density according to this rule. This dictates the symmetry of the normal distribution. Furthermore, the exponent as a whole has a negative sign, meaning that the larger the absolute deviation of $X$ from $\mu$, the smaller will the density assigned to $X$ be by this rule. This dictates that either tail of the distribution shows decreasing density, since the wider the departure of $X$ values from $\mu$ the lower will be the height of this function's curve. However, a little thought will convince you that no real and finite value of $X$ can possibly make the density itself negative or exactly zero: the normal function curve never touches the $X$ axis, indicating that any interval of numbers will have a nonzero probability. On the other hand, any number, such as $e$, raised to the zero power is 1; when $X$ exactly equals $\mu$, the density is

$$\frac{1}{\sqrt{2\pi\sigma^2}} \qquad\qquad [8.1.3]$$

which is the *largest* density value any $X$ may have. This fact implies that the function curve must be unimodal, with maximum density at the mean, $\mu$. Note that, unlike a probability, a density value such as expression **8.1.3** can be greater than 1.00.

It is very important to notice that the precise density value assigned to any $X$ by this rule cannot be found unless the two parameters $\mu$ and $\sigma$ are specified. The parameter $\mu$ can be any finite number, and $\sigma$ can be any finite *positive* number. Thus, like the binomial, the normal distribution rule actually specifies a family of distributions. Although each distribution in the family has a density value paired with each $X$ by this same general rule, the *particular* density that is paired with a given $X$ value differs with different assignments of $\mu$ and $\sigma$. Thus, normal distributions may differ in their means (Fig. 8.1.2); in their standard deviations (Fig. 8.1.3); or in both means and standard deviations (Fig. 8.1.4). Never-

$\mu_1=10 \quad \mu_2=20$

FIG. 8.1.2

$\sigma=1.6$

$\sigma=10$

$\mu=0$

FIG. 8.1.3

$\sigma_1=4$

$\sigma_2=10$

$\mu_1=-3 \qquad \mu_2=9.5$

FIG. 8.1.4

theless, given the mean and standard deviation of the distribution, the rule for finding the probability density of any value of the variable is the same.

Since the normal distribution is really a family of distributions, statisticians constructing tables of probabilities found by the normal rule find it convenient to think of the variable in terms of standardized or $z$ scores. That is to say, if the random variable is a standardized score, $z$, so that $\mu = 0$ and $\sigma = 1.00$, then the rule becomes simpler:

$$f(z) = \frac{1}{\sqrt{2\pi}} \, e^{-z^2/2}. \qquad\qquad [8.1.4*]$$

For standardized normal variables, the density depends only on the *absolute* value of $z$; since both $z$ and $-z$ give the same value $z^2$, they both have the same density. The higher the $z$ in absolute value, the less the associated density. The standard-ized-score form of the distribution makes it possible to use one table of densities for any normal distribution, regardless of its particular parameters. Thus, if we want to know the density of a score $x$ in a normal distribution, with mean equal to 80 and standard deviation equal to 5, we can look up the density associated with a standardized score $(x - 80)/5$, and this gives the desired number.

## 8.2  CUMULATIVE PROBABILITIES AND AREAS FOR THE NORMAL DISTRIBUTION

In Section 3.18 it was pointed out that when a distribution is con-tinuous the probability that $X$ takes on some exact value $x$ is, in effect, zero. For this reason, *all probability statements we will make using a normal distribution will be in terms either of cumulative probabilities or the probabilities of intervals.*

The cumulative probability

$$F(a) = p(X \leqq a)$$

can be thought of as the area under the normal curve in the interval bounded by $-\infty$ and the value $a$ (Fig. 8.2.1).

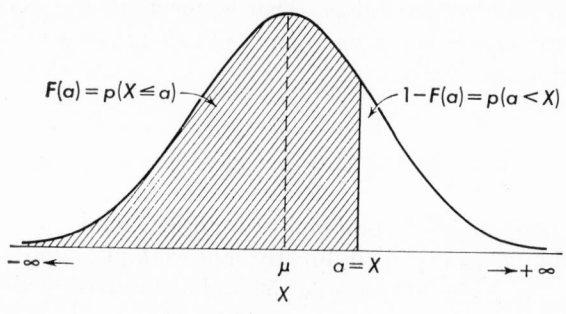

FIG. 3.2.1

In terms of the density function, this area is given by

$$F(a) = \int_{-\infty}^{a} f(X) \, dX$$

where $f(X)$ is the normal density of any value in the interval from $-\infty$ to $a$.

These cumulative probabilities can be used to find the probability of any interval. For example, suppose that in some normal distribution we want to find the probability that $X$ lies between 5 and 10, given some exact values for $\mu$ and $\sigma$. This is the probability represented by the area shown in Figure 8.2.2. The

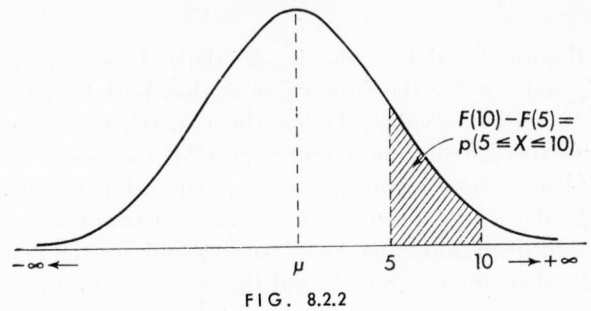

FIG. 8.2.2

cumulative probability *up to and including* 10, or $F(10)$, minus the cumulative probability up to and including 5, or $F(5)$, gives the probability in the interval:

$$p(5 \leq X \leq 10) = F(10) - F(5).$$

In the same way, the probability of any other interval with limits $a$ and $b$ can be found from cumulative probabilities:

$$P(a \leq X \leq b) = F(b) - F(a).$$

### 8.3 THE USE OF TABLES OF THE NORMAL DISTRIBUTION

Most tables of the normal distribution give the cumulative probabilities for various *standardized* values. That is, for a given $z$ score the table provides the cumulative probability *up to and including that standardized score* in a normal distribution: for example:

$$F(2) = p(z \leq 2)$$
$$F(-1) = p(z \leq -1)$$

and so on.

If the cumulative probability is to be found for a positive $z$, then Table I in Appendix C can be used directly. For example, suppose that a normal distribution is known to have a mean of 50 and a standard deviation of 5. What is the cumulative probability of a score of 57.5? The corresponding standardized score is

$$z = \frac{57.5 - 50}{5} = 1.5.$$

A look at Table I shows that for 1.5 in the first column, the corresponding cumulative probability in the column labeled $F(z)$ is .933, approximately. This is the probability of observing a score *less than or equal to* 57.5 in this particular distribution. The cumulative probability for any other positive $z$ score can be found in the same way.

If the $z$ score is negative, this procedure is changed somewhat. Since the normal distribution is symmetric, the density associated with any $z$ is the same as for the corresponding value with a negative sign, or $-z$. However, the cumulative probability for a negative standardized score is 1 minus the cumulative probability for the $z$ value with a positive sign:

$$F(-z) = 1 - F(z)$$

where $z$ is the positive standardized score of the same magnitude. Figure 8.3.1 will

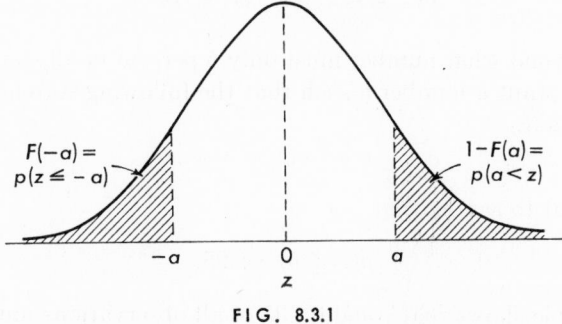

FIG.  8.3.1

clarify this point. The shaded area on the left is the cumulative probability for a value $z = -a$. The table gives only the area falling below the point $z = a$, the positive number of the same absolute value as $-a$. However, the shaded area on the *right*, which is $1 - F(a)$, is the same as the shaded area on the *left*, $F(-a)$.

For example, suppose that in a distribution with mean equal to 107 and standard deviation of 70, we want the cumulative probability of the score 100. In standardized form,

$$z = \frac{100 - 107}{70} = -.1.$$

We look in the table for $z$ equal to *positive* .1, which has a cumulative probability of approximately .5389. The cumulative probability of a $z$ equal to $-.1$ must be approximately

$$F(-.1) = 1 - .5389 = .4611.$$

We may also answer questions about the probabilities of various intervals from the table. For example, what proportion of cases in a normal distribution must lie within one standard deviation of the mean? This is the same as the probability of the interval $(-1 \leq z \leq 1)$. The table shows that $F(1) = .8413$, and we know that $F(-1)$ must be equal to $1 - .8413$ or $.1587$.

Thus,

$$p(-1 \leq z \leq 1) = F(1) - F(-1) = .8413 - .1587 = .6826.$$

**About 68 percent of all cases in a normal distribution must lie within one standard deviation of the mean.**

To find the proportion lying between 1 and 2 standard deviations *above* the mean, we take

$$p(1 \leq z \leq 2) = F(2) - F(1).$$

From the table, these numbers are $.9772$ and $.8413$, so that

$$p(1 \leq z \leq 2) = .9772 - .8413 = .1359.$$

**About 13.6 percent of cases in a normal distribution lie in the interval between $1\sigma$ and $2\sigma$ above the mean.** By the symmetry of the distribution we know immediately that

$$p(-2 \leq z \leq -1) = .1359$$

as well.

Beyond what number must only 5 percent of all standardized scores fall? That is, we want a number $b$ such that the following statement is true for a normal distribution:

$$p(b < z) = .05.$$

This is equivalent to saying that

$$p(z \leq b) = .95.$$

A look at the table shows that roughly $.95$ of all observations must have $z$ scores at or below $1.65$. Thus,

$$p(1.65 < z) = .05, \text{ approximately.}$$

If intervals are mutually exclusive, their probabilities can be added by the "or" rule to find the probability that $X$ falls into either interval. For example, we want to know

$$p(z < -2.58 \text{ or } 2.58 < z),$$

which is the same as

$$p(2.58 < |z|).$$

For the first of these intervals, we find

$$F(2.58) = .995$$

so that

$$F(-2.58) = 1 - .995 = .005.$$

For the other interval, the probability is also

$$p(2.58 < z) = 1 - F(2.58) = .005.$$

The two intervals are mutually exclusive events, and so

$$p(z < -2.58 \text{ or } 2.58 < z) = .005 + .005 = .01.$$

Put in the other way,

$$p(2.58 < |z|) = .01,$$

the probability that $z$ exceeds 2.58 in absolute value is about one in one hundred. This probability is given by the extreme tails of the distribution in the graph of Figure 8.3.2.

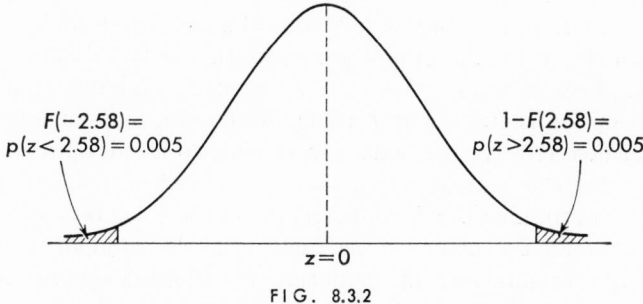

$$F(-2.58) = \\ p(z < 2.58) = 0.005$$

$$1 - F(2.58) = \\ p(z > 2.58) = 0.005$$

$$z = 0$$

FIG. 8.3.2

It is interesting to compare the probability just found with that given by the Tchebycheff inequality for *any* symmetric, unimodal distribution (Section 6.27):

$$p(2.58 \leqq |z|) \leqq \frac{4}{9} \left[ \frac{1}{(2.58)^2} \right].$$

On working out the number on the right, we find about .067. That is, for *any* unimodal symmetric distribution the probability of a score deviating 2.58 or more standard deviations from expectation is less than about seven in one hundred. By specifying that the distribution is *normal*, we pin this probability down to the exact value .01. The more one assumes or knows about the population distribution, the stronger is the statement he can make about the probability of any degree of deviation from expectation.

## 8.4   THE IMPORTANCE OF THE NORMAL DISTRIBUTION

The normal is by far the most used distribution in inferential statistics. There are at least four very good reasons why this is true.

**A population may be assumed to follow a normal law because of what is known or presumed to be true of the measurements themselves.** There are two rather broad instances in which the random variable is a measurement of some kind, and the distribution is conceived as normal. The first is when one is considering a hypothetical distribution of "errors," such as errors in reading a dial, in discriminating between stimuli, or in test performance. Any observation can be assumed to represent a "true" component plus an error. Each error has a magnitude, and this number is thought of as a reflection of "pure chance," the resultant of a vast constellation of circumstances operative at the moment. Any factor influencing performance at the moment contributes a tiny amount to the size of the error and to its direction. Furthermore, such errors are appropriately considered to push the observed measurement up or down with equal likelihood, to be independent of each other over samplings, and to "cancel out" in the long run. Thus, in theory, it makes sense that errors of measurement or errors of discrimination follow something like the normal rule.

In other instances, the distribution of *true magnitudes* of some trait may be thought of as normal. For example, human heights form approximately a normal distribution, and so, we believe, does human intelligence. Indeed, there are many examples, especially in biology, where the distribution of measurements of a natural trait seems to follow something closely resembling a normal rule. No obtained distribution is ever exactly normal, of course, but some distributions of measurements have relative frequencies very close to normal probabilities. However, the view that the distribution of almost any trait of living things should be normal, although prominent in the nineteenth century, has been discredited. The normal distribution is not, in any sense, "nature's rule," and all sorts of distributions having little resemblance to the normal distribution occur in all fields.

**It may be convenient, on mathematical grounds alone, to assume a normally distributed population.** Mathematical statisticians do not devote so much attention to normal distributions just because they think bell-shaped curves are pretty! The truth of the matter is that the normal function has important mathematical properties shared by no other theoretical distribution. Assuming a normal distribution gives the statistician an extremely rich set of mathematical consequences that he can use in developing methods. Very many problems in mathematical statistics either are solved, or can be solved, *only* in terms of a normal population distribution. We will find this true especially when we come to methods for making inferences about a population variance. The normal distribution is the "parent" of several other important theoretical distributions that figure in statistics. In some practical applications the methods developed using normal theory work quite well even when this assumption is not met, despite the fact that the problem can be given a *formal* solution only when a normal population distribution is assumed. In other instances, there just is not any simple way to solve the problem when the normal rule does not hold for the population, at least approximately.

**The normal distribution may serve as a good approximation to a number of other theoretical distributions, having probabilities that are either laborious or impossible to work out exactly.** For example, in the following section it will be shown that the normal distribution can be used to approximate binomial probabilities under some circumstances, even though the normal distribution is continuous, and the binomial discrete. For very large $N$, binomial probabilities are troublesome to work out exactly; on the other hand, intervals based on the normal function give probabilities that can be used as though they were binomial probabilities.

There is a very intimate connection between the size of sample $N$ and the extent to which a sampling distribution approaches the normal form. Many sampling distributions based on large $N$ can be approximated by the normal distribution even though the population distribution itself is definitely not normal. This is the extremely important principle that we will call the **central limit theorem.** The normal distribution is the *limiting form* for large $N$ for a very large variety of sampling distributions. This is one of the most remarkable and useful principles to come out of theoretical statistics.

Thus, you see, it is no accident that the normal distribution is the workhorse of inferential statistics. The assumption of normal population distributions or the use of the normal distribution as an approximation device is not as arbitrary as it sometimes appears; this distribution is part of the very fabric of inferential statistics. These features of the normal distribution will be illustrated in the succeeding sections.

## 8.5   THE NORMAL APPROXIMATION TO THE BINOMIAL

One of the interpretations given to the normal distribution is that it is the limiting form of a binomial distribution as $N \to \infty$ for a fixed $p$. If one drew samples of $N$ from a Bernoulli distribution with the probabilities of the two categories being $p$ and $q$, respectively, he should expect a binomial distribution of number of successes. Suppose that first he does this for all possible samples of size 10. Next he draws all possible samples with $N = 10,000$, then repeats the sampling with an $N$ of 10,000,000, and so on. For each sample size, there will be a different binomial distribution he should observe when *all possible* samples of that size have been drawn.

How does the binomial distribution change with increasing sample size? In the first place, the actual range of the possible number of successes grows larger, since the whole numbers 0 through $N$ form a larger set with each increase in $N$. Second, the expectation, $Np$, is larger for each increase in $N$ for a fixed $p$, and the standard deviation $\sqrt{Npq}$ also increases with $N$. Finally, the probability associated with any given exact value of $X$ tends to *decrease* with *increase* in $N$.

However, suppose that for any value of $N$ the number of successes $X$ were put into standardized form:

$$z = \frac{X - Np}{\sqrt{Npq}} = \frac{X - E(X)}{\sigma}.$$

Then regardless of the size of $N$, the mean of the $z$ scores for a binomial distribution will be 0, and the standard deviation 1. The probability of any $z$ score is the same as for the corresponding $X$. Any $z$ score interval can be given a probability in the particular binomial distribution, and the same interval can also be given a probability for a normal distribution. We can compare these two probabilities for any interval; if the two probabilities are quite close over all intervals, the normal distribution gives a good approximation to the binomial probabilities. On making this comparison of binomial and normal interval probabilities, we should find that the larger the sample size $N$ the better is the fit between the two kinds of probabilities. **As $N$ grows infinitely large, the normal and binomial probabilities become identical for any interval.**

For example, imagine that $p = .5$, and $N = 5$. Here the expectation is $(5)(.5)$, or $2.5$, and the standard deviation is $\sqrt{5(.5)(.5)} = \sqrt{1.25}$ or about $1.12$. The binomial distribution for these values of $p$ and $N$ is given below:

| $X$ | $p(X)$ |
|-----|--------|
| 5 | .0312 |
| 4 | .1563 |
| 3 | .3125 |
| 2 | .3125 |
| 1 | .1563 |
| 0 | .0312 |

For the moment, let us pretend that this is actually a continuous distribution, and that the possible numbers of successes are midpoints of class intervals. Furthermore, let us turn each $X$ into its standardized value $z$, by taking

$$z = \frac{X - E(X)}{\sigma} = \frac{X - 2.5}{1.12}.$$

Then the distribution is

| $z$ real limits | $z$ midpoint | $p(X)$ | Normal |
|-----------------|--------------|--------|--------|
| (1.79 to 2.68) | 2.23 | .0312 | .0367 |
| (.89 to 1.79) | 1.34 | .1563 | .1500 |
| (.00 to .89) | .45 | .3125 | .3132 |
| (−.89 to .00) | −.45 | .3125 | .3132 |
| (−1.79 to −.89) | −1.34 | .1563 | .1500 |
| (−2.68 to −1.79) | −2.23 | .0312 | .0367 |

Here, the $z$ intervals were found by converting each real limit for the distribution of successes (regarded as continuous) into its equivalent $z$ score: thus, $1.79 = (4.5 - 2.5)/1.12$, and so on. Note that the probabilities are the same for these intervals as for the original $X$ values.

The last column gives the probabilities that these same intervals would have in a normal distribution, found by using Table I in Appendix C. Thus, the interval .89 to 1.79 has probability

$$F(1.79) - F(.89) = .96327 - .81327 = .1500$$

and the other probabilities are found in the same way. The top and bottom intervals are given the probabilities

$$1 - F(1.79) = .0367$$

and

$$F(-1.79) = .0367$$

in order to make the probabilities over all intervals sum to 1.00.

Observe how closely the normal probabilities approximate their binomial counterparts: each normal probability is correct to two decimal places as an approximation to a binomial probability. The difference in the two probabilities is smallest for the middle intervals, and is larger for the extremes. Thus, even when $N$ is only 5, the normal distribution gives a respectable approximation to binomial probabilities for $p = .5$.

Now suppose that for this same example, $N$ had been 15. Here the expectation is 7.5, and the standard deviation is $\sqrt{(15)(.25)} = 1.94$. The distribution, with $z$ score intervals and both binomial and normal probabilities, is shown in Table 8.5.1.

**Table 8.5.1**

| $X$ | $z$ intervals | | $p(X)$ | Normal probabilities |
|---|---|---|---|---|
| 15 | 3.608 to | 4.124 | .00003 | .0002 |
| 14 | 3.092 to | 3.608 | .0005 | .0012 |
| 13 | 2.577 to | 3.092 | .0032 | .0036 |
| 12 | 2.061 to | 2.577 | .0139 | .0147 |
| 11 | 1.546 to | 2.061 | .0416 | .0409 |
| 10 | 1.030 to | 1.546 | .0916 | .0909 |
| 9 | .515 to | 1.030 | .1527 | .1501 |
| 8 | .000 to | .515 | .1964 | .1984 |
| 7 | − .515 to | .000 | .1964 | .1984 |
| 6 | −1.030 to − | .515 | .1527 | .1501 |
| 5 | −1.546 to | −1.030 | .0916 | .0909 |
| 4 | −2.061 to | −1.546 | .0416 | .0409 |
| 3 | −2.577 to | −2.061 | .0139 | .0147 |
| 2 | −3.092 to | −2.577 | .0032 | .0036 |
| 1 | −3.608 to | −3.092 | .0005 | .0012 |
| 0 | −4.124 to | −3.608 | .00003 | .0002 |

For this distribution the normal approximation gives an even better fit to the exact binomial probabilities; the average absolute difference in probability over the intervals is about .001, whereas when $N$ was only 5, the average absolute difference was about .004. In general, as $N$ is made larger, the fit between normal and binomial probabilities grows increasingly good. In the limit, when $N$ approaches infinite size, the binomial probabilities are exactly the same as the normal probabilities for any interval, and thus one can say that the normal distribution is the limit to the binomial. This is true regardless of the value of $p$.

On the other hand, for any finite $N$, the more $p$ departs from .5, the less well does the normal distribution approximate the binomial. When $p$ is not exactly equal to .5, the binomial distribution is somewhat skewed for any finite sample size $N$, and for this reason the normal probabilities will tend to fit less well than for $p = .5$, which always gives a symmetric distribution. For example, notice that for $N = 5$ and $p = .3$, illustrated below, the correspondence is not so good as before:

| $X$ | $p(X)$ | *Normal probabilities* |
|---|---|---|
| 5 | .00243 | .0017 |
| 4 | .02835 | .0239 |
| 3 | .13230 | .1379 |
| 2 | .30870 | .3365 |
| 1 | .36015 | .3365 |
| 0 | .16807 | .1635 |

Here the normal probabilities are still reasonably close to the binomial, but the fit is not as good as for $p = .5$.

Given a sufficiently large $N$, normal probabilities may always be used to approximate binomial probabilities irrespective of the value of $p$, the true probability of a success. The more that $p$ departs in either direction from .5, the less accurate is this approximation for any given $N$. In practical situations where the sampling distribution is binomial, the normal approximation may ordinarily be used safely if the *smaller* of $Np$, the number of successes expected, or $Nq$, the expected number of failures, is 10 or more. Otherwise, binomial probabilities can either be calculated directly or found from tables that are readily available. Obviously, this rule requires a larger sample size the smaller the value of either $p$ or $q$, and if one must use the normal approximation to make an inference about the value of $p$, he is wise to plan on a relatively large sample.

In a more advanced study of the normal distribution we would show that as $N$ becomes infinite with fixed $p$ the mathematical rule for a binomial distribution becomes identical with the rule for a normal density function, with $\mu = Np$ and $\sigma = \sqrt{Npq}$. Unfortunately, this sort of demonstration is far beyond our managing at this point.

In any practical use of the normal approximation to binomial probabilities, it is important to remember that here we regard the binomial distribution as though it were continuous, and actually find the normal probability associated with an interval with real lower limit of $(X - .5)$ and real upper limit of $(X + .5)$, where $X$ is any given number of successes. Thus, in order to find the normal approximation to the binomial probability of $X$, we take

$$\text{prob.} \left( \frac{X - Np - .5}{\sqrt{Npq}} \leq z \leq \frac{X - Np + .5}{\sqrt{Npq}} \right)$$

by use of the standardized normal tables.

As noted above, the normal distribution need not be particularly good as an approximation to the binomial if either $p$ or $q$ is quite small, and if either $p$ or $q$ is extremely small the normal approximation may not be satisfactory even when $N$ is quite large. In these circumstances another theoretical distribution, the Poisson, provides a better approximation to binomial probabilities. This distribution, though important theoretically and extremely useful, lies somewhat out of our immediate scope.

## 8.6  THE THEORY OF THE NORMAL DISTRIBUTION OF ERROR

The fact that the limiting form of the binomial is the normal distribution actually provides a rationale for thinking of random error as distributed in this normal way. Consider an object measured over and over again independently and in exactly the same way. Imagine that the value $S$ obtained on any occasion is a sum of two independent parts:

$$S = T + e.$$

That is, the obtained score $S$ is a sum of a constant *true* part $T$ plus a random and independent *error* component. However, the error portion can also be thought of as a sum:

$$e = g[e_1 + e_2 + e_3 + \cdots + e_N]$$

Here, $e_1$ is a random variable that can take on only two values

$e_1 = 1$, when factor 1 is operating
$e_1 = -1$, when factor 1 is not operating.

The $g$ is merely a constant, reflecting the "weight" of the error in $S$. Similarly, the other random errors are attributable to different factors, and take on only the values 1 and $-1$. Now imagine a vast number of influences at work at the moment of any measurement. Each of these factors operates independently of each of the others, and whether any factor exerts an influence at any given moment is purely a chance matter. If you want to be a little anthropomorphic in your thinking about this, visualize old Dame Fortune tossing a vast number of coins on any occasion, and from the result of each deciding on the pattern of factors that will operate. When coin one comes up heads, $e_1$ gets value 1, and if tails, value $-1$, and the same principle determines the value for every other error portion of the observed score.

Now under this conception, the number of factors operating at the moment one observes $S$ is a number of successes in $N$ independent trials of a Bernoulli experiment. If this number of successes is $X$, then

$$e = gX - g[N - X] = g[2X - N].$$

The value of $e$ is exactly determined by $X$, the number of "influences" in operation at the moment, and the probability associated with any value of $e$ must be the same as for the corresponding value of $X$. If $N$ is very large, then the distribution of $e$ must approach a normal distribution. Furthermore, if any factor is equally likely to operate or not operate at a given moment, so that $p = 1/2$, then

$$E(e) = g[2E(X) - N],$$

so that, since $E(X) = Np = 1/2$,

$$E(e) = 0.$$

In the long run, over all possible measurement occasions the errors all "cancel out." This makes it true that

$$E(S) = E(T) + E(e) = T,$$

the long-run expectation of a measurement $S$ is the true value $T$, provided that error really behaves in this random way as an additive component of any score.

This is a highly simplified version of the argument for the normal distribution of errors in measurement. Much more sophisticated rationales can be invented, but they all partake of this general idea. Moreover, the same kind of reasoning is sometimes used to explain why distributions of natural traits, such as height, weight, and size of head, follow a more or less normal rule. Here, the mean of some population is thought of as the "true" value, or the "norm." However, associated with each individual is some departure from the norm, or error, representing the culmination of all the billions of chance factors that operate on him, quite independently of other individuals. Then by regarding these factors as generating a binomial distribution, we can deduce that the whole population should take on a form like the hypothetical normal distribution. However, this is only a theory about how errors might operate and there is no reason at all why errors must behave in the simple additive way assumed here. If they do not, then the distribution need not be normal in form at all.

## 8.7 STATISTICAL PROPERTIES OF NORMAL POPULATION DISTRIBUTIONS

As suggested earlier in this chapter, the normal distribution has mathematical properties that are most important for theoretical statistics. For the moment, we are going to discuss only two of these general properties, both of which will be useful to know in later sections. The first has to do with the independence of the sample mean and variance, and the second concerns the distribution of combinations of random variables.

## 8.8 INDEPENDENCE OF SAMPLE MEAN AND VARIANCE

Any sample consisting of $N$ independent observations of the same random variable provides both a sample mean $M$ and a sample variance. The sample mean estimates $\mu$ and the unbiased sample variance, $\hat{s}^2$, estimates $\sigma^2$. These two values $(M, \hat{s}^2)$ obtained from any sample can be thought of as a joint event. But are these two estimates independent? That is, is the conditional distribution of

$\hat{s}^2$ given $M$ the same as the marginal distribution of $\hat{s}^2$, and is the distribution of $M$ given $\hat{s}^2$ like the marginal distribution of $M$?

The answer to these questions is provided by the following important principle:

**Given random and independent observations, the sample mean $M$ and the sample variance (either $\hat{s}^2$ or $s^2$) are independent if and only if the population distribution is normal.**

The information contained in the sample mean in no way dictates the value of the sample variance, and vice-versa, when a normal population is sampled. Furthermore, **unless the population actually is normal, these two sample statistics are not independent across samples.**

This is a most important principle, since a great many problems concerned with a population mean can be solved only if one knows something about the value of the population variance. At least an estimate of the population variance is required before particular sorts of inferences about the value of $\mu$ can be made. Unless the estimate of the population variance is statistically independent of the estimate of $\mu$ made from the sample, no simple way to make these inferences may exist. This question will be considered in more detail in Chapters 10 and 11. For the moment, suffice it to say that this principle is one of the main reasons for statisticians' assuming normal population distributions.

## 8.9   DISTRIBUTIONS OF LINEAR COMBINATIONS OF SCORES

So far we have emphasized the sample mean as a description of a particular set of data, and as an estimator of the corresponding population mean. However, in many situations the sample mean and the mean of the population do not really tell the experimenter what he wishes to find out from the data. It well may be that other ways of weighting and summing the scores or means obtained in one or more samples will answer particular questions about the phenomena under study. Therefore, we need to know something about the sampling distributions of weighted combinations of sample data.

Such weighted sums of sample scores are thought of as values of **linear combinations of random variables.** As a very simple case of a linear combination, imagine two distinct random variables, labeled $X_1$ and $X_2$ to show that their values need not be the same. We draw samples of two observations at a time, obtaining one value of $X_1$ and one of $X_2$. Then we combine these two numbers into a new value $Y$ in some way such as

$$Y = 3X_1 - 2X_2.$$

We continue to sample $X_1$, $X_2$ pairs of values, and each time we combine the results in the same way, turning each pair of values into a single combined value.

This gives a new random variable $Y$. The range of possible values of $Y$ depends, as you can see, on the ranges of $X_1$ and $X_2$. Furthermore, over all possible such samples the probabilities of the various $Y$ values must depend on the *joint* probabilities of $(X_1, X_2)$ pairs. Over all possible samples of $(X_1, X_2)$ pairs drawn at random there is some probability distribution of $Y$.

In general, given any $n$ random variables, $(X_1, \cdots, X_n)$, a *linear combination* of values of those variables is a weighted sum,

$$Y = c_1 X_1 + c_2 X_2 + \cdots + c_n X_n, \qquad [8.9.1^*]$$

where $(c_1, \cdots, c_n)$ is any set of $n$ real numbers (not all zero) used as weights.

In short, each sample produces a value for each of $n$ random variables. These are weighted and summed in the same way for each sample to produce a new random variable $Y$, the linear combination.

The weights in a linear combination can be any set of $n$ real numbers, provided that at least one weight is not zero. For example, for two random variables, a linear combination might be

$$Y = X_1 + X_2$$

where $c_1 = 1$ and $c_2 = 1$; or

$$Y = 7X_1 - 10X_2$$

where $c_1 = 7$ and $c_2 = -10$; or

$$Y = -4/5 X_1 + 7/8 X_2,$$

with $c_1 = -4/5$, $c_2 = 7/8$, and so on.

Perhaps values for six random variables are represented in a sample, and the linear combination chosen is

$$Y = 5X_1 - 3X_2 + 7X_3 + 3/4 X_4 - .8X_5 + 0X_6.$$

Here, $(c_1, \cdots, c_6) = (5, -3, 7, 3/4, -.8, 0)$.

One very familiar linear combination of random variables is the mean of a random sample: given that $X_1$ is the score of the first case, $X_2$ that of the second, and so on, then

$$M = \frac{1}{N} X_1 + \frac{1}{N} X_2 + \cdots + \frac{1}{N} X_N,$$

where each value obtained is weighted by $1/N$ and the sum taken. This linear combination is also a random variable, and its distribution is the sampling distribution of the mean.

Now for the important principle involving the normal distribution:

**Given some $n$ independent random variables $X_1, \cdots, X_n$, each normally distributed, then any linear combination of these variables is also a normally distributed random variable.**

In other words, if one takes samples, obtaining $n$ independent values in each, and if the random variable represented by each value has a normal distribution, then any weighted sum of those values gives another normally distributed random variable. Thus, if $X_1$ and $X_2$ are independent and have normal distributions, then so does the variable $Y$, whose values are

$$Y = 3X_1 - 2X_2,$$

or any other variable obtained by weighting and summing $X_1$ and $X_2$ values in some constant way over all samples.

An immediate and useful consequence of this principle is this:

**Given random samples of $N$ independent observations each drawn from a normal population, then the distribution of the sample means is normal, irrespective of the size of $N$.**

We have just seen that the sample mean of $N$ cases is a linear combination, where the score of case 1, representing random variable 1, is given the weight $1/N$, and so on for all other scores. Hence, if the scores of the $N$ individuals are independent of each other and are drawn from a normal population, the sampling distribution of the mean is exactly normal, regardless of how large or small $N$ may be. As we saw in the last chapter, the standard error of this distribution, $\sigma_M$, will be smaller the larger the $N$, and so the particular probabilities of various sample values will differ with $N$. On the other hand, the distribution *rule*, given $\mu$ and $\sigma_M$, will be that for the normal function.

We are going to make a great deal of use of this principle. When we can assume that a population with known $\mu$ and $\sigma$ has a normal distribution a major problem in statistical inference is solved, since we can then give a probability to a sample mean's falling into any interval also in terms of a normal distribution. This will be illustrated both at the end of this chapter, and in the next.

## 8.10   MEANS AND VARIANCES OF LINEAR COMBINATIONS

While on the subject of linear combinations, we should look into the question of the mean and variance of the sampling distribution of a linear combination of random variables. These two principles do not depend upon the normal distribution, however. **Given $n$ independent random variables, and some linear combination,**

$$Y = c_1X_1 + \cdots + c_nX_n,$$

**the expected value of $Y$ over all random samples is**

$$E(Y) = c_1E(X_1) + c_2E(X_2) + \cdots + c_nE(X_n). \qquad [8.10.1*]$$

The expectation of any linear combination is the same linear combination of the expectations.

This really follows quite simply from rules 5 and 2 in Appendix B, since the expectations of a sum is always a sum of expectations, and the expectation of a constant times a variable is the constant times the expectation.

A special case of this principle gives us the following:

**Given $n$ independent sample values from the same distribution with mean $\mu$, then the expectation of any linear combination of those sample values is**

$$E(Y) = \mu(c_1 + c_2 + \cdots + c_n).\qquad [8.10.2^*]$$

This principle accords with our earlier result that the expectation of the sample mean is the population mean:

$$E(M) = E\left(\frac{1}{N}X_1 + \cdots + \frac{1}{N}X_N\right) = \mu\left(\frac{1}{N} + \frac{1}{N} + \cdots + \frac{1}{N}\right) = \mu.$$

However, suppose that samples of two cases were drawn, and the linear combination were

$$Y = X_1 - X_2.$$

In this instance it would not be true that the expectation of this combination equals $\mu$; instead we would have $E(Y) = \mu(1 - 1) = 0$.

As a concrete example, suppose that samples of two cases were observed, one case being a male drawn from the population of all males, with $\mu = 25$, and the other a female drawn from the female population, with $\mu = 27$. The score of the male is represented by $X_1$ and that of the female by $X_2$. For each sample, the difference between the male's and the female's scores is taken:

$$Y = X_1 - X_2.$$

Then, over all such samples, the expectation is

$$E(Y) = E(X_1) - E(X_2) = \mu_1 - \mu_2 = -2.$$

Furthermore, if the scores of the two cases are independent, and if both populations have a normal distribution, the sample difference $Y$ is normally distributed as well.

The variance of the sampling distribution of any linear combination can also be found by the following rule:

**Given $n$ independent random variables, with variances $\sigma_1^2, \sigma_2^2, \cdots, \sigma_n^2$ respectively, and the linear combination**

$$Y = c_1 X_1 + c_2 X_2 + \cdots + c_n X_n,$$

**then the distribution of $Y$ has variance given by**

$$\sigma_Y^2 = c_1^2 \sigma_1^2 + c_2^2 \sigma_2^2 + \cdots + c_n^2 \sigma_n^2.\qquad [8.10.3^*]$$

The variance of a linear combination of independent random variables is a weighted sum of their separate variances, each weight being the *square* of the original weight given the variable.

Thus, in the preceding example, if the population of males has a variance of 10, and that of females a variance of 12, the variance of the difference, $X_1 - X_2$, is

$$\sigma_Y^2 = (1)^2\sigma_1^2 + (-1)^2\sigma_2^2 = 10 + 12 = 22.$$

As a more complicated example, suppose that three independent observations at a time are made, drawn respectively from populations represented by the three random variables

$$X_1, \text{ with } \mu_1 = 20, \sigma_1^2 = 5$$
$$X_2, \text{ with } \mu_2 = 16, \sigma_2^2 = 9$$
$$X_3, \text{ with } \mu_3 = 25, \sigma_3^2 = 7.$$

If all three random variables are normally distributed, what will the distribution of the linear combination

$$Y = \frac{X_1}{2} + \frac{X_2}{2} - X_3$$

be like? In the first place, we know from the principle of Section 8.9 that $Y$ will be normally distributed. Second, the mean of the distribution of $Y$ will be

$$E(Y) = \frac{\mu_1}{2} + \frac{\mu_2}{2} - \mu_3 = 10 + 8 - 25 = -7.$$

The variance of $Y$ must be

$$\sigma_Y^2 = \left(\frac{1}{2}\right)^2 \sigma_1^2 + \left(\frac{1}{2}\right)^2 \sigma_2^2 + (-1)^2\sigma_3^2$$
$$= \frac{5 + 9}{4} + 7 = 10.5.$$

Under these conditions, the three principles of Sections 8.9 and 8.10 allow us to specify the distribution of $Y$ completely, and we could proceed to evaluate the probability that an obtained value of $Y$ falls into any given interval.

The variance of the sampling distribution of the mean, found in Section 7.10 to be $\sigma^2/N$, can also be found by using principle **8.10.3.** Here, samples of $N$ independent observations are made from the same distribution, with some true mean $\mu$ and with some true variance $\sigma^2$. The sample mean itself is, as we have seen, a linear combination of the scores, each weighted by $1/N$. Then, by the application of the principle,

$$\sigma_M^2 = \left(\frac{1}{N}\right)^2\sigma^2 + \left(\frac{1}{N}\right)^2\sigma^2 + \cdots + \left(\frac{1}{N}\right)^2\sigma^2$$
$$= \frac{N}{N^2}\sigma^2 = \frac{\sigma^2}{N}.$$

You are probably wondering why anyone would be interested in linear combinations other than the sample mean. Actually, as we shall see in Chapter 14, forming linear combinations of the data is one way of answering particular questions about what goes on in an experiment based on two or more samples. Each item of information about different experimental treatments that the experimenter gains from his data usually corresponds to one way of weighting and summing means of the various samples. The linear combination applied to the set of sample means gives an estimate of the same combination applied to the corresponding set of population means. Thus, the study of the sampling distribution of linear combinations forms an important part of the theory of sampling.

The most important point that should emerge from this discussion of linear combinations is that, given normal population distributions, the sampling distribution of the mean or of any other linear combination of scores or of sample means must be normal. Thus, the assumption of a normal distribution for the population settles the question of the exact form of the sampling distribution for any linear combination of scores in the sample data, including the mean. This is true quite irrespective of the sample size. Do not lose sight of the fact that the size of the sample does, however, determine how small the variance of the sampling distribution will be.

## 8.11  THE CENTRAL LIMIT THEOREM

It is quite common for the psychologist to be concerned with populations where the distribution should *definitely not be normal*. We may know this either from empirical evidence about the distribution, or because some theoretical issue makes it impossible for scores to be this kind of random variable. Illustrations are distributions of intelligence scores among graduate engineers, and of measures of socially nonconforming behavior among normal adults. In principle both these distributions should be extremely skewed, though for quite different reasons: in the first, there is a selection in the education process making it rather unlikely for anyone in the middle or low intelligence ranges to qualify as an engineer; in the second, social nonconformity is something that most people must show in very small degree. The assumption of a normal distribution does not make sense in such instances.

Nonetheless, very often an inference must be made about the mean of such a population. To do this effectively the experimenter needs to know the sampling distribution of the mean, and to know this exactly, he has to be able to specify the particular form of the population distribution. However, if we had enough evidence to permit this, we would likely have an extremely good estimate of the population mean in the first place, and would not need any other statistical methods!

The way out of this apparent impasse is provided by the **central limit theorem,** which can be given an approximate statement as follows:

**If a population has a finite variance $\sigma^2$ and mean $\mu$, then the distribution of sample means from samples of $N$ independent observations approaches a normal distribution with variance $\sigma^2/N$ and mean $\mu$ as sample $N$ increases. When $N$ is very large, the sampling distribution of $M$ is approximately normal.**

*Absolutely nothing is said in this theorem about the form of the popula-tion distribution.* Regardless of the population distribution, if sample size $N$ is large enough, the normal distribution is a good approximation to the sampling distribu-tion of the mean. This is the heart of the theorem, since, as we have already seen, the sampling distribution will have a variance $\sigma^2/N$ and mean $\mu$ for any $N$.

The sense of the central limit theorem is illustrated by Figures 8.11.1–4. The solid curve in Figure 8.11.1 is a very skewed population distribution in $z$-score form, and the dotted curve is a standardized normal distribution. The

A negatively skewed population distribution (Fig. 8.11.1, left) and a sampling distribution of M for N = 2 (Fig. 8.11.2, right), with comparable normal distributions

other figures show the standardized form of the sampling distribution of means for samples of size 2, 4, and 10 respectively from this population, together with the corresponding standardized normal distributions.

Even with these relatively small sample sizes it is obvious that each increase in sample size gives a sampling distribution more nearly symmetric and tending more toward the normal distribution with the same mean and variance. This symmetry increases with increasing sample size until, in the limit, the normal distribution is reached.

Sampling distributions of M for N = 4 (Fig. 8.11.3, left) and N = 10 (Fig. 8.11.4, right), with comparable normal distributions

It must be emphasized that in most instances the tendency for the sampling distribution of $M$ to be like the normal distribution is very strong, even for samples of moderate size. Naturally, the more similar to a normal distribution the original population distribution, the more nearly will the sampling distribution of $M$ be like the normal distribution for any given sample size. However, even extremely skewed or other nonnormal distributions may yield sampling distribu-tions of $M$ that can be approximated quite well by the normal distribution, for samples of at least moderate size. In the examples shown in Figures 8.11.1–4 the correspondence between the exact probabilities of intervals in the sampling distri-bution and intervals in the normal distribution is fairly good even for samples of only 10 observations; for a rough approximation, the normal distribution proba-bilities might be useful even here in some statistical work. In a great many instances in psychological research, a sample size of 30 or more is considered large enough to permit a satisfactory use of normal probabilities to approximate the unknown exact probabilities associated with the sampling distribution of $M$. Thus, even though the central limit theorem is actually a statement about what happens *in the limit* as $N$ approaches an infinite value, the principle at work is so strong that in many instances the theorem is practically useful even for moderately large samples.

The mathematical proof of this theorem is extremely advanced, and many eminent mathematicians over the centuries contributed to its development before it was finally proved in full generality. However, some intuitive feel for why it should be true can be gained from the following example. Here we will actually work out the sampling distribution of the mean for a special and very simple population distribution.

Imagine a random variable with the following distribution:

| $X$ | $p(X)$ |
|---|---|
| 5 | 1/3 |
| 4 | 1/3 |
| 3 | 1/3 |

The $\mu$ of this little distribution is 4. However, instead of dealing directly with this random variable, let us consider the deviation $d$ from $\mu$, or

$$d = (X - \mu).$$

The distribution of $d$ has a form identical to the distribution of $X$ itself, although the mean $d$ is zero. Since $X$ can assume only three values, each equally probable, there are three possible deviation values of $d$, also equally probable.

Suppose that sample observations were taken two at a time, independently and at random. The deviation value of the first observation made is $d_1$ and that of the second $d_2$. Corresponding to each joint event $(d_1, d_2)$ there is a mean deviation, $(d_1 + d_2)/2$, which is equal to $M - \mu$. The following table shows the mean deviation value that is produced by each possible joint event:

| $d_2$ | $-1$ | $0$ | $1$ |
|---|---|---|---|
| 1 | 0 | .5 | 1 |
| 0 | $-.5$ | 0 | 5 |
| $-1$ | $-1$ | $-.5$ | 0 |
|  | $-1$ | $0$ | $1$ $\quad d_1$ |

Since $X_1$ and $X_2$ are independent, then $d_1$ and $d_2$ are also independent, according to Section 4.9. The probability associated with each cell in the table is thus $p(d_1)p(d_2)$ or 1/9.

Now let us find the probabilities of the various values of mean $d$. The value $-1$ can occur in only one way, and so its probability is 1/9. On the other hand, −.5 can occur in two mutually exclusive ways, giving a probability of 2/9. In this same way we can find the other probabilities, and form the distribution of the mean $d$ and the mean $X$ values, as follows:

| $M$ | *Mean d* | $p(M) = p(mean\ d)$ |
|---|---|---|
| 5.0 | 1.0 | 1/9 |
| 4.5 | 0.5 | 2/9 |
| 4.0 | 0 | 3/9 |
| 3.5 | −0.5 | 2/9 |
| 3.0 | −1.0 | 1/9 |

where $M$ = mean $d + \mu$. Now notice that whereas in the original distribution there was no distinct mode, in this sampling distribution there *is* a distinct mode at 4, with exact symmetry about this point. What causes the sampling distribution to differ from the population distribution in this way? Look at the table of mean deviations corresponding to joint events once again: there are simply more possible ways for a sample to show a small than an extreme deviation from $\mu$. There are more ways for a sample joint event to occur where the deviations tend to "cancel out" than where deviations tend to cumulate in the same direction.

Exactly the same idea could be illustrated for any discrete population distribution, whatever its form. The small and "middling" deviations of $M$ from $\mu$ always have a numerical advantage over the more extreme deviations. This superiority in number of possibilities for a small mean deviation increases as $N$ is made larger. Regardless of how skewed or otherwise irregular a population distribution is, by increasing sample size one can make the advantage given to small deviations so big that it will overcome any initial advantage given to extreme deviations by the original population distribution. The numerical advantage given to relatively small deviations from $\mu$ effectively swamps any initial advantage given to other deviations by the form of the population distribution, as $N$ becomes large.

Perhaps this simple example gives you some feel for why it is that the sampling distribution of the mean approaches a unimodal, symmetric form. Of course, this is a far cry from showing that the sampling distribution must approach a *normal* distribution, which is the heart of the central limit theorem. Nevertheless, the basic operation of chance embodied in this theorem is of this general nature: for large $N$ it is relatively much easier to get a small deviation of $M$ from $\mu$ than a large one.

## 8.12  THE CENTRAL LIMIT THEOREM AND LINEAR COMBINATIONS OF MEANS

As suggested above, it is very common for an experimenter to be interested in the means of several samples put into some kind of weighted sum, or linear combination. The central limit theorem applies to such weighted combinations as well:

**Given** $K$ independent samples, containing $N_1$, $N_2$, $\cdots$, $N_K$ independent observations respectively, then the sampling distribution of any linear combination of means of those samples approaches a normal distribution as the size of each sample grows large.

It is easy to see that the central limit theorem applies to the sampling distribution of each mean separately as the sample size increases. In the limit, each mean has a normal sampling distribution. Then by the principle described in Section 8.9, any linear combination of normal random variables is normal so that the sampling distribution of the linear combination of means approaches a normal distribution as the sample sizes all grow large.

This is but one of the most elementary extensions of the central limit theorem. It can be shown that a great many of the sampling distributions of all sorts of sample characteristics also approach a normal distribution with increasing sample size. However, in elementary work we will have most occasions to use the principle as it applies to means.

### 8:13 USING THE NORMAL DISTRIBUTION IN INFERENCES ABOUT MEANS

We have seen that there are two circumstances in which the sampling distribution of the mean can be considered normal: when the population distribution itself is normal, and when the population is not normally distributed but the sample size is large. In either case, the normal tables can be used to find the probability that the sample mean will fall into any interval, given $\mu$ and $\sigma_M$.

For an example of the first situation, suppose that samples of size 25 were drawn independently and at random from a normal population, so that the sampling distribution of the mean is *exactly* normal. Given that $\mu = 138$ and $\sigma = 20$ for the population, what is the probability of observing a sample mean in the interval 136–140? To find this probability, one needs, first of all, $\sigma_M$, given by

$$\sigma_M = \frac{\sigma}{\sqrt{N}} = \frac{20}{5} = 4.$$

The standardized score corresponding to the *lower limit* of the interval is

$$z = \frac{136 - 138}{4} = -.5$$

and for the *upper limit*,

$$z = \frac{140 - 138}{4} = .5.$$

The probability of the interval is, from Table I,

$$p(136 \nleq M \nleq 140) = F(.5) - F(-.5) = .6915 - .3085$$
$$= .3830.$$

Only about thirty-eight times in one hundred random samples should one expect to observe a sample mean in this particular interval if $\mu = 138$, $\sigma = 20$, and $N = 25$.

On the other hand, we might have the situation where the population distribution is not normal, but the same size is relatively quite large, say 900. Here we could be sure that the normal approximation to the exact probabilities is very good. In this instance, suppose that we have a hunch or hypothesis that the value of $\mu$ is 35.7 with $\sigma = 1.3$. If these parameter values are true, what is the probability that an observed sample mean should exceed 35.8? Since $N$ is so large, $\sigma_M$ is quite small,

$$\sigma_M = \frac{1.3}{30} = .043.$$

The value 35.8 thus corresponds to

$$z = \frac{35.8 - 35.7}{.043} = \frac{.1}{.043} = 2.33.$$

What we want is the area on the upper tail of the normal curve cut off by a $z$ of 2.33. This area or probability is

$$p(2.33 < z) = 1 - F(2.33) = 1 - .9901 = .0099$$

or about .01. Thus, only about one time in one hundred samples with $N = 900$ should we expect to observe a sample $M$ value this deviant from expectation, if the expected value is 35.7 and $\sigma = 1.3$. Granted that our hypothetical expectation and standard error are both correct and we do, nevertheless, observe the value exceeding 35.8, then we have encountered a value qualifying for a "rare" interval of events. On the other hand, if $\mu$ were, say, 35.78, a sample mean exceeding 35.80 could hardly be classed as unusual. In this instance,

$$z = \frac{35.80 - 35.78}{.043} = .465, \text{ or about } .47.$$

From the table we find that

$$F(.47) = .6808$$

and so

$$p(35.80 \nleq M) = 1 - F(.47) = .32, \text{ approximately.}$$

Deviations of $M$ from expectation this big or bigger should occur in about 32 percent of all such samples.

At this point it should be reiterated that a large sample, in the sense of the central limit theorem, does not necessarily mean a *vast* sample. The theorem deals with the limit when $N$ is infinite, but the normal approximation is usually good long before that point is reached. When the population distribution is unimodal and symmetric, then even quite small samples (10 cases or so) afford a fairly good fit between the exact sampling distribution and the normal approximation. Obviously, the more skewed or otherwise irregular the population distribution, the poorer the fit will be, and the relatively larger the sample size must be to permit use of the normal approximation. On the other hand, unless the population distribution is quite skewed, a sample size of some thirty or more cases is almost always adequate to permit the use of normal probabilities in the work we will be doing. Be sure to notice that even the normal probabilities cannot be found unless one specifies both $\mu$ and $\sigma$ for the population.

Very often one wishes to evaluate some theoretical assertion or hypothesis about $\mu$ or $\sigma$, or both, in the light of sample evidence. When true, does this hypothesis assign our sample result to a category of *improbable* events? If so, either the hypothesis is true and we have hit upon a rarity, or the hypothesis is not true. This idea of hypothesis testing always involves a theoretical sampling distribution that *would* be the true one (or a good approximation to it) *were* the situation stated in the hypothesis true of the population sampled.

In the next chapter some of the reasoning behind and procedures for testing hypotheses will be introduced. Each example will use one of the two sampling distributions we have studied in detail: the normal and the binomial. Once several issues about the purposes and limitations of hypothesis testing have been aired, we can turn in Chapter 10 to the uses of this technique in real situations.

# HYPOTHESIS TESTING
# AND INTERVAL ESTIMATION

# 9

## 9.1 Statistical tests

Let us assume that the general motivation for inferential statistics is clear to you by now, and you are ready for some concrete procedures. In each of the preceding chapters the author has referred repeatedly to the theme underlying our whole discussion: how do you say something about the population given only the sample evidence? We have seen that certain sample statistics are capable of giving good estimates of particular population parameters; ordinarily, these point estimates are the first and foremost statistical inferences one makes from his data. On the other hand, there is almost always a dark side to the picture: virtually any estimate will be in error to some extent due to fluctuations of sampling, and so we discussed the concept of a sampling distribution of a particular statistic based on a sample of size $N$. In particular we focused on the mean of the sampling distribution as the expected value of the statistic, and the standard deviation of the sampling distribution as the standard error. Finally, in the last chapter we found that sampling distributions of statistics such as $M$ can often be regarded as normal, particularly when $N$ is large. Given the form of the population distribution together with the appropriate parameter values such as $\mu$ and $\sigma$, then we can find the probability that the sample value for a statistic such as $M$ will fall into any given interval of values in the sampling distribution. In short, the point has now been reached where most of the basic pieces that fit into the theory of significance tests and interval estimation have been introduced.

The title of this chapter might well be "How to decide how to decide," or "How much evidence is enough?" A psychologist or anyone else who samples from a population is trying to decide, or at least form an opinion on, something about the population. Quite often he wants to decide if some hypothetical population situation appears reasonable in the light of the sample evidence. Sometimes the problem is to judge which of several possible population situations is best supported by the evidence at hand. In either instance, one is trying to make up his mind from evidence. However, as we shall see, there are many possible ways of making this kind of decision, depending on what information in the sample is actually used, the various possibly true population situations being compared, and especially the risk one is willing to take of being wrong in his decision.

The first problem to be faced in making a decision from data is that of choosing the relevant and appropriate statistic for the particular purpose. Obviously, different combinations of the sample data give different kinds and amounts of information about the population. Reaching a conclusion about some population characteristic requires effective use of the right information in the sample, and various statistics differ in their relevance to different questions about the population. Sometimes the best statistic to permit us to form a judgment about the population also happens to be the best estimate of the particular population parameter under study, but in other instances statistics may be used which are not estimates of any population parameter at all. Such "test statistics" will be introduced in Chapter 10. In this chapter we will use only the simple statistics $M$ or $P$, since they happen to be best for illustrative purposes, but elsewhere quite different statistics will provide the information we require from the sample.

Granting for the moment that we know the information we need from the sample and how to extract it, how do we judge the tenability of a particular hypothesis about the population? It seems reasonable that a tenable or "good" hypothesis about the population should provide us with a "good" expectation about the sample result in terms of the relevant statistic. That is, the hypothesis gives a good fit to the data if, as a consequence of that hypothesis' being true, we can deduce an expected value of the statistic that agrees quite well with the value actually observed; if the hypothesis is true, there is some value that we should expect the appropriate sample statistic to show. Naturally, in any given sample the obtained value of the statistic will not exactly equal the expectation dictated by the hypothesis, and there is a theoretical sampling distribution of values for the statistic that can be worked out once the hypothetical population situation is specified. Nevertheless, if the hypothesis is a good one, our obtained sample result should fall into a region of values relatively close to the expected value the truth of the hypothesis dictates for our statistic.

A deviation between the obtained value of the statistic and its expected value under the hypothesis implies one of two things: either the hypothesis is right, and the difference in value between the statistic and its expectation is the product of chance, or the hypothesis is wrong and we were not led to expect the right thing of our sample statistic. In particular, if the sample value falls so far from expectation that it lies in an interval of values very improbable given the hypothesis, but this sort of sample result would be made probable if some alternative hypothesis were true, then doubt is cast on the original hypothesis and we reject it in favor of the alternative. Obviously, however, these notions of "disagree with expectation," "improbable," and "probable" are relative matters; when do we say that a sample result disagrees "enough" with expectation under some hypothesis to warrant rejection of the hypothesis itself?

One of the stickiest problems in comparing sample results with expectation given by some hypothesis is deciding what we mean by a sufficient kind and degree of disagreement. How and by how much must the sample statistic's value disagree with expectation before we decide that one hypothesis should be abandoned in favor of another? What we need is a decision-rule, a guide giving the conclusion we will reach depending on how the data turn out, and which can be formulated even before the data themselves are seen. However, there is literally no end to the number of decision-rules that one might formulate for a particular problem. Some of these ways of deciding might be very good in a particular circumstance, but not so good in others, and so we need to decide how to decide on the basis of what we wish to accomplish in a specific situation. The branch of mathematics known as "decision theory" treats of this problem of choosing a decision-rule, and we are going to apply some of its elementary principles here. We will find that there is no rigid formula supplying the right way to decide in all situations, and, indeed, we often lack the information necessary for choosing an optimal decision-rule. For this reason psychologists and others using statistical inference most often fall back on accepted conventions for evaluating evidence, and these conventions may have very little to do with the principles of decision theory. Nevertheless, the application of principles from decision theory to the problem of statistical inference does shed some light on the theory underlying tests of statistical hypotheses.

The process of comparing two hypotheses in the light of sample evidence is usually called a "statistical test" or a "significance test." The competing hypotheses are stated in terms of the form, or of one or more parameters, of the distribution for the population. Then the statistic containing the relevant information is chosen, having a sampling distribution dictated by the population distribution specified in the particular hypotheses. The hypothesis that dictates the particular sampling distribution against which the obtained sample value is compared is said to be "tested." The significance test is based on the sampling distribution of the statistic given that the particular hypothesis is true. If the observed value of the statistic falls into an interval representing a kind and degree of deviation from expectation which is improbable given the hypothesis, but which would be relatively probable given the other, alternative, hypothesis, then the first hypothesis is said to be rejected. The actual decision to entertain or to reject any hypothesis is thus based on whether or not the sample statistic falls into a particular region of values in the sampling distribution dictated by that hypothesis. However, the immediate statistical outcome of any significance test can be thought of as a *conditional probability*, the probability of a result this much or more deviant from expectation in a particular way given that the hypothesis tested is really true. The interpretation and use of this conditional probability depends on the purposes of the experimenter, and the particular decision-rule he may have adopted.

A few words of warning before we go further: In the first place, although we will speak of testing some single hypothesis, in practice the experimenter always acts as though he is deciding between *two* hypotheses. A great many issues connected with the use of significance tests can be understood only if this decision-making task is presupposed. Second, even though the form of significance testing is based on decision making, this does not mean that the experimenter must actually make such a decision, particularly in a situation where he himself is not able to apply principles for actually choosing the best decision-rule. When, in following sections, we speak of the necessity for the experimenter to decide between two hypotheses, we will mean only that the particular conclusions follow if we act as if this were the experimenter's concern; the standard practices can be justified only if we suppose this to be the experimenter's task. Thus, in the following sections significance testing will be treated in this decision-making setting, since the problem is most easily discussed in these terms, and most psychologists and others using inferential statistics have come to think in this way. In addition, presenting hypothesis testing in a decision context will also make it possible to point out some of the inadequacies and misuses of this approach from the psychologist's point of view.

Now we are ready to look into this problem of the choice of a decision-rule, using the mean $M$ and the proportion $P$ as examples of statistics on which decisions are based. However, before we can consider these ideas more closely, some standard terminology must be given.

## 9.2 STATISTICAL HYPOTHESES

A statistical hypothesis is usually a statement about one or more population distributions, and specifically about one or more parameters of such population distributions. It is always a statement about the population, not about the sample. The statement is called a hypothesis because it refers to a situation that *might* be true. Statistical hypotheses are almost never equivalent to the hypotheses of science, which are usually statements about phenomena or their underlying bases. Quite commonly, statistical hypotheses grow out of or are implied by scientific hypotheses, but the two are seldom identical. The statistical hypothesis is usually a concrete description of one or more summary aspects of one or more populations; there is no implication of *why* populations have these characteristics.

We shall use the following scheme to indicate a statistical hypothesis: a letter $H$ followed by a statement about parameters, the form of the distribution, or both, for one or more specific populations. For example, one hypothesis about a population could be written

$H$: the population in question is normally distributed with $\mu = 48$ and $\sigma = 13$,

and another

$H$: the population in question has a Bernoulli (two-class) distribution with $p = .5$.

Hypotheses that completely specify a population distribution are known as **simple hypotheses.** In general, the sampling distribution of any statistic also is completely specified given a simple hypothesis and $N$, the sample size.

We will also encounter hypotheses such as:

$H$: the population is normal with $\mu = 48$.

Here, the exact population distribution is not specified, since no requirement was put on $\sigma$, the population standard deviation. When the population distribution is not determined completely, the hypothesis is known as **composite.**

Hypotheses may also be classified by whether they specify *exact* parameter values, or merely *a range* or *interval* of such values. For example, the hypothesis

$$H: \mu = 100$$

would be an exact hypothesis, although

$$H: \mu \geq 100$$

would not be exact.

## 9.3 ASSUMPTIONS IN HYPOTHESIS TESTING

In applied situations very seldom will a hypothesis specify the sampling distribution completely. Simple hypotheses are just not of interest or are not available in most practical situations. On the other hand, it *is* necessary that the sampling distribution be completely specified before any precise probability statement can be made about the sample results. For this reason assumptions usually are made, which, taken together with the hypothesis itself, determine the relevant statistic and its sampling distribution and justify a test of the hypothesis. These assumptions differ from hypotheses in that they are rarely or never tested against the sample data. They are assertions that are simply assumed true, or the evidence is collected in such a way that they must be true.

First and foremost among such assumptions is that the sample is random. In all discussion of significance tests and confidence methods to follow, we shall assume simple random sampling unless it is specifically indicated otherwise. Independence of two or more random variables is another assumption frequently made. At other points we shall assume that the population distribution is normal, that the variances of different populations are equal, and so on. Wherever such assumptions underlying a test are important they will be pointed out.

These assumptions are necessary for the formal justification of many of the methods to be discussed. It is not true, however, that these assumptions are always or even ever realized in practice. The results of any data analysis leading to statistical inference can always be prefaced by "If such and such assumptions are true, then . . . ." The effects of the violation of these assumptions on the conclusions reached can be very serious in some circumstances, and only minor in others. In later sections the importance of the most common assumptions will be discussed. Nevertheless, these assumptions should always be kept in mind, along with the conditional character of any result subject to the assumptions being true.

## 9.4 TESTING A HYPOTHESIS IN THE LIGHT OF SAMPLE EVIDENCE

Every test of a hypothesis involves the following features:

1. The hypothesis to be tested is stated, together with an alternative hypothesis.
2. Additional assumptions are made, permitting one to specify the sample statistic that is most relevant and appropriate to the test, as well as the sampling distribution of that statistic.
3. Given the sampling distribution of the test statistic when the hypothesis to be tested is true, a **region of rejection** is decided upon. This is an interval of possible values deviant from expectation if the hypothesis were true, but which more or less accord with expectation if the alternative were true. This region of rejection contains values relatively improbable of occurrence if the first hypothesis were true, but relatively probable given the alternative. The risk one is willing to take in rejecting the tested hypothesis *falsely* determines the size of the region of rejection, and the alternative hypothesis determines its location.
4. The sample itself is obtained. If the computed value of the test statistic falls into the region of rejection, then doubt is cast on the hypothesis, and it is said to be rejected in favor of the alternative. If the result falls out of the region of rejection, then the hypothesis is not rejected, and the experimenter may choose either to accept the hypothesis or to suspend judgment, depending on the circumstances. A sample result falling into the region of rejection is said to be **significant** or **to depart significantly from expectation** under the hypothesis.

As an example, suppose that an experimenter entertains the hypothesis that the mean of some population is 75:

$$H_0: \mu = 75.$$

This is actually a composite hypothesis, since nothing whatever is said about the form of the population distribution nor about other parameters such as the standard deviation. The experimenter is, however, prepared to assume that whatever is true about the mean the population has a normal distribution, and that the standard deviation for the population is 10; for the moment, let us imagine that both of these assumptions are reasonable in the light of what the experimenter already knows about his problem. In effect, the addition of these two assumptions to the original hypothesis makes this hypothesis simple:

$$H_0: \mu = 75, \sigma = 10, \text{ normal distribution.}$$

Now, what of the alternative hypothesis? It might be that the alternate hypothesis is

$$H_1: \mu \neq 75.$$

Note that this alternative happens to be inexact, and really asserts that some (unspecified) value of $\mu$ other than 75 is true. However, even if $H_1$ is true and $H_0$

false, the experimenter will still assume that the distribution is normal with a standard deviation of 10.

It has already been decided that 25 independent observations will be made. Given this sample size $N$, the information in the hypothesis $H_0$, and the assumptions, the sampling distribution of the mean is known completely: this must be a normal distribution with a mean of 75, and a standard error of $10/\sqrt{25}$ or 2, if the hypothesis $H_0$ is true.

Now in accordance with $H_1$, the experimenter decides that he will reject this hypothesis $H_0$ only if his sample mean falls among the extremely deviant ones in either direction from the value 75; in fact, he will reject $H_0$ only if the probability is .05 or less for the occurrence a sample mean as deviant or more so from 75. Thus, the region of rejection for this hypothesis contains only 5 percent of all possible sample results when the hypothesis $H_0$ is actually true. Such sample

FIG. 9.4.1

values depart widely from expectation and are relatively improbable given that $H_0$ is true; on the other hand, samples falling into these regions are relatively more probable if a situation covered by $H_1$ is true. These regions of rejection in the sampling distribution are shown in Figure 9.4.1.

From tables of the normal distribution, he finds that a $z$ score of 1.96 shows a cumulative probability $F(1.96)$ of about .975. Hence only .025 of all sample means should lie *above* 1.96 standard errors from $\mu$. Similarly, it must be true that about .025 of all sample means will lie below $-1.96$ standard errors from $\mu$. In short, the region of rejection includes all sample means such that, in this sampling distribution,

$$1.96 \leq z_M$$
or
$$z_M \leq -1.96$$

giving a total probability of .025 + .025 or .05 for the combined intervals. A value of the sample mean that lies exactly on the boundary of a region of rejection is called a **critical value** of $M$; the critical $z_M$ values here are $-1.96$ and 1.96, so that the critical values of $M$ are

$$-1.96\sigma_M + \mu = -1.96(2) + 75 = 71.08$$
and
$$1.96\sigma_M + \mu = \phantom{-}1.96(2) + 75 = 78.92.$$

Now the sample is drawn and turns out to have a mean of 79. The corresponding $z_M$ score is

$$z_M = \frac{79 - \mu}{\sigma_M} = \frac{79 - 75}{2} = 2.$$

Notice that this $z_M$ score *does* fall into the region of rejection, since it is greater than a critical value of 1.96. Then the experimenter says that the sample result is **significant beyond the 5 percent level.** Less than 5 percent of all samples should show results this deviant (or more so) from expectation under $H_0$, if $H_0$ is actually true. If the experimenter has decided in advance that samples falling into this region show sufficient departure from expectation to be called *improbable* results, then doubt is cast on the truth of the hypothesis, and $H_0$ is said to be rejected.

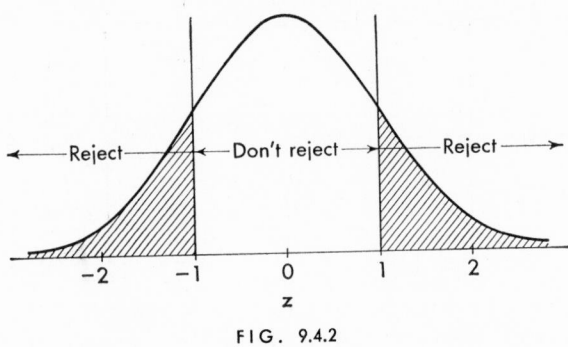

FIG. 9.4.2

In its essentials this simple problem exemplifies all significance tests. Naturally, the details vary with the particular problem. Hypotheses may be about variances, or any other characteristic feature of one or more populations. Other statistics may be appropriate to a test of the particular hypothesis. Other assumptions may be made to permit the specification of the sampling distribution of the relevant statistic. Other regions of rejection may be chosen in the sampling distribution. *But once these specifications are made, the experimenter knows, even before he sees the sample, how he will make up his mind, if he must, in the light of what the sample shows.*

Here the region of rejection was simply specified without any particular explanation. In this step, however, lies a key problem of significance tests. In the choice of the region of rejection the experimenter is deciding how to decide from the data. It is perfectly obvious that there are very many ways that the experimenter could have chosen a rejection region. He could have decided to reject the hypothesis if the sample result fell beyond one standard error of the mean specified by the hypothesis, as in Figure 9.4.2, or if the sample result fell between 3 and 4 standard errors below the hypothetical mean, as in Figure 9.4.3, and so on ad infinitum, for any interval or set of intervals. There is no law against using any decision-rule for rejection, although on intuitive grounds alone the one actually used here seems somehow more sensible than the others suggested.

In the next section we are going to address ourselves to this problem of choosing a rejection region. This can be discussed most simply if we consider a choice between *two exact hypotheses*. Admittedly, this is an extremely artificial situation, and almost never does one actually have this kind of choice to make. Nevertheless, the terminology and procedures of hypothesis testing can best be understood by acting as if this were the experimenter's problem.

FIG. 9.4.3

## 9.5 CHOOSING A WAY TO DECIDE BETWEEN TWO EXACT HYPOTHESES

An experimenter has two alternative theories about some behavior. According to Theory I, exactly .80 of all human subjects should exhibit this behavior in his experimental situation, whereas in Theory II, .40 should be the proportion doing this. The task of the experimenter is to form a judgment about the two theories. Imagine, if you can, that the two theories exhaust the logical possibilities accounting for what he observes: either one or the other must be true.

These two theories suggest the two competing hypotheses:

$$H_0: p = .80$$
$$H_1: p = .40.$$

The subscripts 0 and 1 have no particular meaning here; they are merely indices to let us tell the hypotheses apart.

Some $N$ subjects are to be drawn at random and independently for introduction into the experimental situation. The occurrence of the behavior for any subject is a "success," and for either hypothesis there is a binomial sampling distribution giving probabilities for various possible values of $P$, the sample *proportion* of successes. Of course, the probabilities of different sample $P$ values differ under the two hypotheses, since $p = .8$ in one and only .4 in the other.

For the sake of simplicity, let us suppose that there are to be only ten cases in the sample. Then the sampling distributions of $P$ found from the binomial distribution under the two hypotheses are as shown in Table 9.5.1.

The experimenter knows the probability of each possible sample $P$ result given the possible truth of either of the two hypotheses.

Table 9.5.1

| | $p(P)$ | |
|---|---|---|
| $P$ | *if* $p = .8$ | *if* $p = .4$ |
| 1.0 | .107 | .0001(+) |
| .9 | .268 | .002 |
| .8 | .302 | .011 |
| .7 | .201 | .042 |
| .6 | .088 | .111 |
| .5 | .026 | .200 |
| .4 | .006 | .251 |
| .3 | .001 | .215 |
| .2 | .000(+) | .121 |
| .1 | .0000(+) | .040 |
| .0 | .0000(+) | .006 |

How shall the experimenter decide upon seeing the evidence? What he needs is a decision-rule, some way that lets him judge which of the two hypotheses is actually favored by the sample result. There are any number of decision-rules that could be formulated, but for the moment we will consider only the following three possibilities:

**Decision-rule 1:**  If $P$ is greater than or equal to .8, choose $H_0$; otherwise $H_1$.
**Decision-rule 2:**  If $P$ is greater than or equal to .6, choose $H_0$; otherwise $H_1$.
**Decision-rule 3:**  If $P$ falls between .2 and .8 inclusive, choose $H_0$; otherwise $H_1$.

Regardless of which decision-rule is selected there are two ways that the experimenter *could* be right, and two ways of his making an *error*. This is diagrammed below:

TRUE SITUATION

$H_0$          $H_1$

|  | $H_0$ | correct | error |
|---|---|---|---|
| DECISION | | | |
|  | $H_1$ | error | correct |

If he decides $H_0$, and $H_1$ is actually true, an error is made. Furthermore, he can make an error if he decides on $H_1$ and $H_0$ is actually true. The other possibilities lead, of course, to correct decisions.

Given the sampling distributions under each of the two hypotheses, and any decision-rule, we can find the *probabilities* of these two kinds of error. The experimenter has no idea which hypothesis is true, and all he can go by is the occurrence of a $P$ value leading him to reject one or the other of the hypotheses. Suppose that decision rule 1 were adopted. This rule requires that the occurrence of any $P$ of .8 or more lead automatically to a decision that $H_0$ is true. What is the probability of observing such a sample result *if $H_1$ is true?* Notice that whenever this happens, there will be a wrong decision and so this probability is that of *one kind* of error. The binomial distribution for $p = .4$ shows a probability of about .013 for $P$ greater than or equal to .8, and so the probability is .013 of *wrongly* deciding that $H_0$ is true.

In the same way, we can find the probability of the error made in choosing $H_1$ when $H_0$ is true. By decision-rule 1, $H_1$ is chosen whenever $P$ is less than or equal to .7; in the distribution under $H_0$, this interval of values has a probability of about .323. Thus, the probabilities of error and correct decisions are, under decision-rule 1,

TRUE SITUATION

|  | $H_0$ | $H_1$ |
|---|---|---|
| $H_0$ | .677 | *.013* |
| $H_1$ | *.323* | .987 |

DECISION

The probability of a correct decision is $1 - p(\text{error})$ for either of the possibly true situations (the two error probabilities appear in italics). Notice that the experimenter is far more likely to make an erroneous judgment by using this rule when $H_0$ is true than for a true $H_1$.

Exactly the same procedure gives the erroneous and correct decision probabilities under rule 2:

|  | $H_0$ | $H_1$ |
|---|---|---|
| $H_0$ | .966 | *.166* |
| $H_1$ | *.034* | .834 |

By this second rule, the probability of error is relatively smaller when $H_0$ is true than it is for rule 1. However, look what happens to the probability of the other error! This illustrates a general principle in the choice of decision-rules: *any change in a decision-rule that makes the probability of one kind of error smaller will ordinarily make the other error probability larger* (other things, such as sample size, being equal).

Before trying to choose between rules 1 and 2, let us write down the probabilities for decision-rule 3.

|  | $H_0$ | $H_1$ |
|---|---|---|
| $H_0$ | .625 | *.952* |
| $H_1$ | *.375* | .048 |

Even on the face of it this decision-rule does not look sensible. The probability of error is large when $H_0$ is true, and the experimenter is almost sure to make an error if $H_1$ is the true situation! This illustrates that not all decision-rules are reasonable if the experimenter has any concern at all with making an error; here regardless of what is true the experimenter has a larger chance of making an error using this rule than in using either rules 1 or 2. Rules such as this are called **inadmissible** by decision theorists. We need confine our attention only to the two relatively "good" rules 1 and 2.

There is a real problem in deciding between the rules 1 and 2; rule 1 is good for making error probability small when $H_1$ is true, but risky when $H_0$ represents the true state of affairs. On the other hand, rule 2 makes for small chance of error when $H_0$ is true, but gives relatively large probability of error when $H_1$ holds. Obviously, any choice between these two rules must have something to do with the relative importance of the two kinds of errors. It might be that making an error is a minor matter when $H_0$ is true, but very serious given $H_1$. In this case rule 1 is preferable. On the other hand, were error very serious given $H_0$, rule 1 could be disastrous. In short, any rational way of choosing among rules must involve some notion of the loss involved in making an error.

## 9.6 ERRORS AND LOSSES

Decision theory, which grew out of problems of economic decision-making, is concerned with the possible outcomes of an action. Any decision-maker has several courses of action open to him, and once he has chosen a course of action some event or chain of events is going to occur. However, the decision-maker does not necessarily know what this outcome will be. Instead, there are various "states of the world" that might be true, and the outcome of any decision to take action depends both on what is decided and what is really true.

As a simple example, imagine a man interested in buying a sweater. His interest at the moment is in finding a sweater that will wash without shrinking. He locates a sweater that he likes, but he does not know if it is washable. For this particular sweater, two courses of action are open to him: "buy" or "don't buy." However, there are also two possibilities for the "real" nature of the sweater: either it won't shrink, or it will. The courses of action, the states of the world, and the different action-outcome possibilities are shown in the following table:

|  |  | STATE OF THE WORLD | |
|---|---|---|---|
|  |  | *sweater won't shrink* | *sweater will shrink* |
| POSSIBLE | *buy* | (buy, good sweater) | (buy, sweater shrinks) |
| ACTIONS | *don't buy* | (don't buy, miss a good sweater) | (don't buy, miss a shrunken sweater) |

In two of these action-outcome possibilities there is possibly a real economic gain to the buyer; the man does well if either the combination (buy, good sweater) or the combination (don't buy, miss a shrunken sweater) occurs. On the other hand, two possibilities for error exist as well: (buy, sweater shrinks), and (don't buy, miss a good sweater). In principle, each of these action-outcome possibilities has some value or utility for the buyer, and his choice to buy or not to buy should depend upon these relative values.

With only this to go on the buyer still has the problem of making up his mind. However, just as the experimenter gathers data in order to "snoop" on the possible states of the world, the buyer decides that he will do a little snooping on his own, and he looks for the cleaning instructions tag on the sweater. He happens to know that only once in about one hundred times does a sweater factory label a garment "washable" when it is not. On the other hand, he knows that among washable sweaters, only nine in ten bear instructions that definitely say so. Thus, if he decides solely on the basis of what the tag says, he has the following probabilities of error and right decisions (assuming that this is a random sample from among one of the two sorts of sweaters):

|  | *will not shrink* | *will shrink* |
|---|---|---|
| *tag says washable (buy)* | .90 | .01 |
| *tag does not say washable (don't buy)* | .10 | .99 |

Here, the chances are much smaller of making the mistake of buying a sweater that will shrink, than of failing to buy a sweater that will not shrink. Is this a good way to decide? That depends upon the value to him of the various outcomes. If the sweater is very expensive and buying a sweater that shrinks means a big loss, then he probably should use this rule. On the other hand, if the man needs a sweater very badly and the price is low, so that much would be lost if this opportunity were mistakenly passed up, the rule is not so good. Here the various outcomes of the actions have a very real, and perhaps even a dollar-and-cents, value to the buyer. Not only the probabilities, but also the possible losses attached to the different outcomes, should figure in the buyer's choice of a way to decide.

In business situations, it is frequently true that a given action must be followed by one of a fairly small and specifiable set of outcomes. The decision-maker does not know what the particular outcome of his action will be, but at least he is able to state the possible outcomes. The one that occurs may depend upon economic conditions in general, quality of product, competition, and so on. Furthermore, each of these possible outcomes to any action can be assigned a profit or loss value, at least in principle.

On the other hand, the possible outcomes of actions taken by the scientist are far more difficult to specify. It is clear that some definite courses of action are usually open to the experimenter: he may decide to publish or withhold his findings, to collect or not to collect more data, to pursue or abandon the line of investigation, to ask for funds for further research or to forget the whole matter. By stretching a point, we might say that finding out what the true situation is constitutes an outcome following any action. However, this outcome may not apply to the experimenter at all, but rather may serve as an outcome for the science he represents. It is important to recognize that the scientist, human being that he is, may be capable of foreseeing only the short-term monetary, prestige or other outcome possibilities of his actions, which are insignificant compared to the long-range impact of his action on knowledge and human welfare.

At any rate, let us assume that all actions available to the scientist are contingent upon a few basic actions he may take: he may decide that any one of the set of hypotheses entertained is true, or he may suspend judgment pending further evidence. Parenthetically, we note that this last possibility distinguishes much of the scientist's decision-making from that of the businessman: few people could stay in business by suspending judgment almost indefinitely, and yet this is almost an ideal in science. Unfortunately, even the modern scientist cannot suspend judgment forever, and sooner or later he must take a course of action equivalent to the decision that "such and such is true."

Whatever the set of actions open to the scientist, each is accompanied by some set of potential outcomes and it is reasonable that some outcomes are good and others bad from his point of view. Each possible outcome has some "weight" for him and his science. Experimentation costs time and money, not to speak of the mental exertion involved. A person living in the twentieth century does not need to be reminded that scientific actions can lead directly to miraculous advances in social welfare, as well as genuine catastrophes. Fortunately, these are the exceptions; but even pursuing dead ends on the basis of faulty evidence or failing to reap the benefits of potential knowledge are costly matters for the scientist.

### 9.7 EXPECTED LOSS AS A CRITERION FOR CHOOSING A DECISION-RULE

Let us imagine each action-outcome combination as having some numerical value for the experimenter. The exact nature of the value need not concern us here: it may reflect dollars, time, prestige, pleasure, or any of a variety of other things. Let us assume only that some function exists assigning one number to each action-outcome combination for a particular problem. Thus, the combination "decide $H_0$ and $H_1$ turns out to be true" is accompanied by the numerical value

$$u(H_0;H_1).$$

For our purposes we need consider these values only as *losses*. Each loss value is some positive number or zero given to an action-outcome combination. If the combination represents the best available action under the true circumstances, then the decision is *right* and the loss-value is zero. On the other hand, if the action is less desirable than the best available action, then this is an *error* and the loss-value is positive. (A more technical term for such a value is *opportunity loss*.)

Now let us return to the poor experimenter who is faced with two hypotheses, and who was left in the lurch in Section 9.5. Suppose that the potential losses connected with the two erroneous decision-possibilities were

$$\text{T\scriptsize RUE \normalsize SITUATION}$$
$$H_0 \qquad H_1$$

|  |  | $H_0$ | $H_1$ |
|---|---|---|---|
| | $H_0$ | 0 | 5 |
| P\scriptsize OSSIBLE \normalsize  *decide* | | | |
| A\scriptsize CTIONS | | | |
| | $H_1$ | 10 | 0 |

so that

$$u(H_0;H_1) = 5$$
$$u(H_1;H_0) = 10.$$

Each possible decision rule $D$ can be given an *expected loss value*

$$E(u;D,H_0) = (\text{expected loss given } D \text{ and true } H_0)$$

for any specified true situation such as $H_0$. Here

$$E(u;D,H_0) = u(H_1;H_0)p(\text{decide } H_1 \text{ by rule } D \text{ given } H_0 \text{ actually true})$$
$$+ u(H_0;H_0)p(\text{decide } H_0 \text{ true given } H_0 \text{ true}).$$

Furthermore,

$$E(u;D,H_1) = u(H_0;H_1)p(\text{decide } H_0 \text{ true given } H_1 \text{ actually true})$$
$$+ u(H_1;H_1)p(\text{decide } H_1 \text{ true given } H_1 \text{ true}).$$

For example, consider our decision-rule 1 once again. Here

$$E(u;D_1,H_0) = 10(.323) = 3.23$$

which is just the loss associated with an error multiplied by its probability under $D_1$. When $H_1$ is true, then

$$E(u;D_1,H_1) = 5(.013) = .065.$$

The two expected losses for $D_1$ can be written together as the first row in Table 9.7.1.

**Table 9.7.1**

|  |  | T\scriptsize RUE | |
|---|---|---|---|
| | | $H_0$ | $H_1$ |
| | $D_1$ | 3.23 | .065 |
| D\scriptsize ECISION-RULE \normalsize $D_2$ | | .34 | .83 |
| | $D_3$ | 3.75 | 4.76 |

Notice that the expected loss using this rule is rather high when $H_0$ is true, but low when $H_1$ is true. The other rows of the table can be filled out using decision-rules 2 and 3:

$$E(u;D_2,H_0) = 10(.034) = .34$$
$$E(u;D_2,H_1) = 5(.166) = .83$$

and

$$E(u;D_3,H_0) = 10(.375) = 3.75$$
$$E(u;D_3,H_1) = 5(.952) = 4.76.$$

*A good decision-rule is one giving low expected loss regardless of what the true situation turns out to be.* Let us apply this criterion.

An inspection of this table shows, once again, the absurdity of rule 3. Given either true situation (a column of .Table 9.7.1) the expected loss for rule 3 is greater than that for either rule 1 or rule 2, and hence this rule is far less desirable than either of the others. In general, any rule that gives a higher expected loss than another *regardless* of the true situation is disqualified (or is inadmissable).

Can we choose between rules 1 and 2, however, on the basis of expected loss? A device within decision theory for choosing between rules is known as the "minimax" principle. Applying this principle leads us to choose that rule showing the *minimum maximum-expected-loss* over all possible true situations. For expected-loss tables such as 9.7.1, a minimax decision-rule is one having a largest entry in its row that is smaller than the largest entry in any other row of the table. Notice that in this situation, rule 2 has .83 as the largest value in its row; this is smaller than the largest value for rule 1, or 3.23. Thus, applying the minimax principle, we find that rule 2 is the one to use. Using rule 2, the largest that we expect long-run loss to be is smaller than for either rule 1 or rule 3.

This minimax criterion for choosing among decision-rules is very important in the theory of games and in decision theory, and it does give a way to compare decision-rules on the basis of their expected losses. However, this criterion is often criticized for being unduly conservative, and actually this way of choosing a decision-rule can produce results that go against our intuition in some problems. The minimax criterion seems especially to be out of the spirit of scientific research, since it focusses only on the extreme potential loss in making errors, and not on the very large gains one can make through increased knowledge *despite* the risk of being wrong on occasion. An alternative to the minimax criterion is given below.

## 9.8 SUBJECTIVE EXPECTED LOSS AS A CRITERION FOR CHOOSING AMONG DECISION-RULES

One of the considerations left completely out of our discussion so far is the fact that the experimenter usually knows something (or at least believes something) about the hypotheses before the experiment takes place. The scientist does not operate in a vacuum; for any experimental problem many sources of prior information are open to him. There are related experiments (or even repetitions of the same experiment) done by others, there are theories that differ in their logical tightness and plausability, there are the scientist's own informal observations of the world about him, and so on. The net result is that the experimenter has some initial ideas about how credible each of the hypotheses is in the light of what he already knows. He is not certain about which one of the available hypotheses is true or otherwise he would not trouble to do the experiment. However, if asked to bet about which is true, he may be able to give odds he considers fair for this bet. In short, there are prior beliefs, or opinions, or objective knowledge that make some of the possibilities for a true situation a better bet than others for the experimenter.

There is a school of thought among statisticians holding that these prior considerations must be brought into the choice of a decision-rule. It is possible to speak of the "personal probability" of the experimenter, reflecting the degree of prior confidence he has that any hypothesis is true *before* seeing the evidence. That is, imagine that we could assign numbers between 0 and 1 to hypotheses such as $H_0$ and $H_1$, standing for the experimenter's personal probability for each. If you will, these numbers index his degree of belief in the respective hypotheses. To distinguish these personal probabilities from "ordinary" probabilities interpreted as relative frequencies, let the symbols

$$\mathcal{P}(H_0) \text{ and } \mathcal{P}(H_1)$$

stand for these numbers, where $\mathcal{P}(H_0) + \mathcal{P}(H_1) = 1.00$.

Suppose that the experimenter is totally in the dark about the true situation, knowing only that either $H_0$ or $H_1$ must be true. If he is willing to bet with 50–50 odds that either hypothesis will turn out true, then

$$\mathcal{P}(H_0) = \mathcal{P}(H_1) = 1/2.$$

On the other hand, suppose that you bet with the experimenter about which will turn out eventually to be true, and he were willing to put up nine dollars to your one dollar on the bet that $H_1$ is true. In other words, he thinks that the correct odds are 9 to 1 against $H_0$ being true. In terms of personal probabilities, this is like saying

$$E(\$) = \$1\mathcal{P}(H_1) - \$9\mathcal{P}(H_0) = 0$$

so that

$$\mathcal{P}(H_1) = 9/10 \text{ and } \mathcal{P}(H_0) = 1/10,$$

if from his point of view this bet is fair.

Given the personal probabilities, it is possible to compare decision-rules in still another way. We can form the "subjective expected loss" for each decision-rule:

$$SE(u;D) = E(u;D,H_0)\mathcal{P}(H_0) + E(u;D,H_1)\mathcal{P}(H_1)$$

which is just a weighted sum of the expected losses for a given rule, the weights being the personal probabilities. For example, for decision-rule 1, Section 9.5,

$$SE(u;D_1) = 3.23(1/10) + (.065)(9/10)$$
$$= .382,$$

and for rule 2,

$$SE(u;D_2) = .34(1/10) + .83(9/10)$$
$$= .781.$$

Decision-rules may be compared by their subjective expected losses; the lower the subjective expected loss, the better the rule. In this case, given the loss-values, and given the personal probabilities, rule 1 is clearly superior to rule 2. Even though error has a fairly high probability by this rule when $H_0$ is true, the experimenter's own weighting of what he expects to be true of the situation tends to discount the likelihood of such errors.

In case you have forgotten again, we left our experimenter long ago, lost in thought and trying to decide how to decide between his two hypotheses. Now we have come up with an answer. Or have we? *Provided* that the experimenter can furnish us with the loss-values of the possible errors, and *provided* that we can find out his personal probabilities, then the subjective expected loss gives an unequivocal way for him to pick a decision-rule. Unfortunately, these two provisions introduce a problem as big as before.

### 9.9 THE FAILURE OF THE DECISION-THEORY APPROACH IN PSYCHOLOGICAL RESEARCH

This excursion into some of the rudiments of decision theory has been introduced to point up some of the shortcomings of hypothesis-testing in psychological research. In the sections to follow procedures will be given that are in common use in such research. Most such procedures use a rule for deciding when a result is significant that *might* be justified by a decision-making argument very similar to the one just given. The experimenter wants to avoid errors in inference, presumably because such errors lead to losses, at least in time and effort. Decision-rules differ in the expected losses they give, and it behooves the experimenter to choose a decision-rule that minimizes expected loss. The act of deciding on a region of rejection is the choice of a decision-rule, and should be subject to the same considerations.

Unfortunately, the cost of erroneous decisions is almost never considered in psychological research. Indeed, in most instances in psychological research it seems very unlikely that a numerical value could ever be assigned to the loss incurred in an erroneous decision. Just how bad is it to be wrong in a scientific inference? This problem is not so difficult in many other fields using statistical inference, especially in research on applied problems. In business decisions it is often possible to give a value in dollars to the outcomes that might result from various decisions, and statistical decision theory then provides guides for choosing an effective decision-rule. Even in some applied areas in psychology, losses involved in errors might be reckoned in the same general way. Thus, in studying methods for selecting people for various jobs the cost of an error may be a calculable thing, and the decision-rule may be chosen on that basis. Similarly, this possibility may exist for studies of diagnostic methods, of training effectiveness, and so on. By and large, however, most research psychologists would not know how to assign loss-values to decision errors.

In the same way, even if we admit the existence of personal probabilities or $\mathcal{P}$ values for the experimenter, seldom is he in a position to assess objectively what these values should be. Perhaps in the future a standard part of statistical analysis will be the statement of prior personal probabilities before the collection of the data. In principle, personal probabilities can be found by the odds the experimenter is willing to accept in betting on the truth of a hypothesis, and it might be possible to make this a standard part of statistical practice. Perhaps this will come about, but the point is that almost no one is prepared to begin reporting such a priori personal probabilities at this time.

In short, psychology uses much of the terminology of statistical decision theory without its main feature, the choice of a decision-rule having optimal properties for a given purpose. Instead, the psychologist uses conventional decision-rules, completely ignoring questions of the loss involved in errors and the degree of prior-certainty of the experimenter. These conventional rules can be justified by decision theory in some contexts, but they are surely not appropriate to every situation.

The author deplores this lack as much as anybody else. However, he sees very little chance for change in psychologists' behavior in the near future. Research psychologists apparently understand these conventions, and the majority seem to be able to work within them. The problem of error-loss is something that is different for different kinds of research questions, and any solution requires real effort that no one is yet willing to apply. Finally, the inclusion of personal probability in statistical decision making is by no means universally endorsed among statisticians. This question currently arouses considerable interest and study in mathematical statistics, but the matter is not resolved.

## 9.10   THE OPTION OF SUSPENDING JUDGMENT

Must the psychologist actually make a decision about what is true from his data? Naturally, choosing to suspend judgment and wait for more evidence is a decision to adopt a course of action. However, why cannot the psychologist adopt this time-honored strategy of the scientist more often than he apparently does? As we have seen, he is usually cut off from the possibility of choosing an appropriate decision-rule, using either the minimax principle or minimum subjective-expected-loss. He has no recourse except to fall back on some conventional rule. No convention can possibly be ideal or even sensible for all the problems to which it may be applied, as we shall illustrate below. If the psychologist cannot make up his mind how to decide in some rational way, then why *must* he decide that something is true or false?

Suppose that we give our experimenter the option of suspending judgment. That is, he does not have to decide that either $H_0$ or $H_1$ is true, but rather can suspend judgment until more evidence is collected. One rule he might adopt is

**Decision-rule 4:** If $P$ is .8 or more, decide $H_0$; if $P$ is .4 or less decide $H_1$; if $P$ is between .5 and .7 inclusive, then suspend judgment.

From Table 9.5.1, we can find that the probabilities of the various action-outcome possibilities are, by this rule,

|  | TRUE | |
|---|---|---|
|  | $H_0$ | $H_1$ |
| $H_0$ | .677 | .013 |
| DECIDE | | |
| $H_1$ | .007 | .633 |
| SUSPEND JUDGMENT | .316 | .354 |

The action "suspend judgment" is technically an error if either $H_0$ or $H_1$ is true, and assuredly there is going to be some loss connected with making such an error. However, it well could be that this loss is much less than that incurred by falsely concluding that either $H_0$ or $H_1$ is true. Suppose that the loss values were

|  | TRUE | |
|---|---|---|
|  | $H_0$ | $H_1$ |
| $H_0$ | 0 | 5 |
| DECIDE | | |
| $H_1$ | 10 | 0 |
| SUSPEND JUDGMENT | 1 | 1 |

Now in this case,

$$E(u;D_4,H_0) = (0)(.677) + (10)(.007) + (1)(.316) = .323$$
$$E(u;D_4,H_1) = (5)(.013) + (0)(.633) + (1)(.354) = .419.$$

Compare these expected losses with those in Table 9.7.1. When either $H_0$ or $H_1$ is true, the expected loss in using rule 4 is less than that for rule 2, and when $H_0$ is true, the expected loss is much less than that for rule 1 as well, although rule 1 has a smaller expected loss when $H_1$ is true. By the minimax-loss criterion, rule 4 is clearly superior to both rules 1 and 2 in this situation. In short, a rule involving suspension of judgment is relatively good here, and if the minimax criterion is adopted, is the best of those considered. It is entirely possible that the course of action represented by "no decision, suspend judgment" will be best in a given situation, especially if the penalty involved in waiting to decide is small compared to the loss involved in an incorrect decision.

On the other hand, in many applied situations the opportunity to suspend judgment is just not available to the experimenter. He must decide here and now on the basis of what little evidence he has. Fortunately, however, scientists often do have the privilege of waiting for more evidence.

The occurrence of a significant result in a significance test is not a command to decide something. All that the significance test per se can give is a probability statement about obtaining such and such result if the given hypothesis is true. If one is using the rule represented by the rejection region, then this probability statement is also a statement of the probability of one kind of error. But here the direct contribution of statistics stops; the actual decision should depend on other factors, such as potential losses and personal probabilities, that are not a part of the formal mechanism of the statistical test. It does not make much sense to go about making decisions among hypotheses when one has no idea about the goodness of the decision-rule he uses. If the psychologist has enough information about potential losses to be able to see that the conventional rule is not appropriate, then he should be able to figure out a better rule. On the other hand, if the situation in which he finds himself is so vague that he has no conception of the risk of loss through error, then how does he know that deciding among the hypotheses is better than suspending judgment regardless of the evidence? At least, suspending judgment is usually a conservative course of action.

Why, then, do psychologists bother with significance tests at all? *Regardless of what one is going to do with the information—change his opinion, adopt a course of action, or what not—he needs to know relatively how probable is a result like that obtained, given a hypothetical true situation. Basically, a significance test gives this information, and that is all.* The conventions about significance level and regions of rejection can be regarded as ways of defining "improbable." The occurrence of a significant result in terms of these conventions is really a signal: "Here is a direction and degree of deviation which falls among those relatively unlikely to occur given that the tested hypothesis is true, but which is relatively more likely given the truth of some other hypothesis." If one should decide to reject the original hypothesis on the basis of a significant result, then at least he knows the probability of error in doing so. This does not mean that he must decide against the hypothesis simply because some conventional level of significance was met. Other options, such as suspending judgment, may actually be better actions under the circumstances regardless of the result of the conventional significance test. Even more emphatically, the occurrence of a nonsignificant result does not mean that you must accept the hypothesis as true. As we shall see, one often has not the foggiest idea of the error probability in saying that the tested hypothesis is true; here, making a decision to accept the tested hypothesis is absurd in the light of the unknown, and perhaps very large, probability of such an error. On occasion, however, the probability of such an error can be assessed, and here one can feel safe in asserting that the tested hypothesis is true when this error-probability is small. In other circumstances where this probability of error cannot be found, and the experimenter is under no duress to make an immediate choice between hypotheses, then suspending judgment is a relatively safe way out. In still other circumstances the loss-values of errors may be so small that it really does not make much difference what the experimenter decides.

The thoughtless application of the decision-theory terminology to conventional significance-testing can introduce more problems than it solves. Thus, the student is advised to think of hypothesis testing in the way that it is actually used by most scientists: a conventional signalling device saying, for a significant result: "Here is something relatively unlikely given the situation initially postulated, but which is rendered relatively much more likely under an alternative situation. The probability is remote of this being a chance occurrence under the initial hypothesis, and something interesting may be here."

It is perfectly all right to discuss hypothesis testing in the decision-theoretic language, but the user is speaking as though the conventional rule were a good way to decide, which it may not be. *There is no God-given rule about when and how to make up your mind in general!*

## 9.11 DECIDING BETWEEN TWO HYPOTHESES ABOUT A MEAN

Before we leave the problem of deciding between two exact hypotheses, one more example will be given, this time involving the mean of a population. Furthermore, in this example, something about losses will be known, so that the applicability of a conventional rule to the problem can be studied.

A psychologist working in industry is assigned to study the possibility of using women in a certain job. Heretofore, only men have been used, and it is known that for the population of men on this job, the average performance score is 138, with a standard deviation of 20. If women perform exactly like men then the population of women should have the same mean and standard deviation as the men. On the other hand, if women have mean performance score of at least 142, a considerable profit will accrue to the management by employing them. From what the experimenter already knows about women's performance in other situations, he believes that one of these two possibilities will turn out to be true.

Accordingly, the experimenter frames two hypotheses, both of which deal with a population of women on this job:

$$H_0: \mu = 138$$
$$H_1: \mu = 142.$$

It is assumed that the population distribution in either situation will have a standard deviation of 20.

Now a sample of 100 women is to be drawn at random and put into this job situation on an experimental basis. The psychologist feels that this sample is large enough to permit using the normal approximation to the sampling distribution of the mean.

The following conventional rule is used:

If the sample result falls among the highest 5 percent of means in a normal distribution given $H_0$, then reject $H_0$; otherwise, reject $H_1$.

This region of rejection for $H_0$ is shown in Figure 9.11.1.

FIG. 9.11.1

In this instance, there are once again two kinds of errors that can be
made. The probabilities for each kind are labeled $\alpha$ and $\beta$ respectively:

<table>
<tr><td></td><td></td><td colspan="2" align="center">TRUE</td></tr>
<tr><td></td><td></td><td align="center">$H_0$</td><td align="center">$H_1$</td></tr>
<tr><td></td><td>$H_0$</td><td align="center">$1 - \alpha$</td><td align="center">$\beta$</td></tr>
<tr><td>DECIDE</td><td></td><td></td><td></td></tr>
<tr><td></td><td>$H_1$</td><td align="center">$\alpha$</td><td align="center">$1 - \beta$</td></tr>
</table>

In this situation with two *exact* hypotheses, it does make sense to talk about
accepting or deciding in favor of $H_0$, since both probabilities can be known. In
essence, the conventional rule says to fix $\alpha$ at .05, and the region of rejection
chosen does just that.

However, notice that assigning the value of .05 to the $\alpha$ probability
of error automatically fixes $\beta$ as well. Given that $H_0$ is true, then the region of rejection must be bounded by a $z_M$ score such that

$$F(z_M) = .95, \text{ or } 1 - F(z_M) = .05.$$

The normal tables show that this $z_M$ score is 1.65. In terms of a sample mean

$$z_M = \frac{M - 138}{\sigma_M} = \frac{M - 138}{2}.$$

Thus, the critical value of $M$ is

$$M = 138 + 1.65\sigma_M = 138 + 3.30 = 141.30.$$

However, what would the $z_M$ score for this critical mean be if $H_1$ were true?

$$z_M = \frac{141.3 - 142}{2} = -.35.$$

In a normal distribution, $F(-.35) = .36$, approximately, and so we can see that $\beta = .36$. Thus, the two error probabilities are

$$\alpha = .05$$
$$\beta = .36.$$

In short, the $\beta$ probability of making an error is much greater than $\alpha$. Our experimenter is rather unlikely to decide on $H_1$ when $H_0$ is true, but has considerable chance of concluding $H_0$ when $H_1$ is true. Nevertheless, he can draw his sample at random, compute the mean, and decide by this rule: if the sample has a mean that is more than 1.65 standard errors away from 138 then he concludes $H_1$ is true; otherwise $H_0$.

Suppose, however, that the possible losses to the management could be figured in this way: a decision that $H_1$ is true leads the management to hire women for the job, whereas women are not hired if the decision favors $H_0$. If the test indicates $H_1$ even though $H_0$ is true, the management is out the cost of the experiment, $10,000, but no other loss is incurred, since the women hired should perform like the men. On the other hand, if the second kind of error is made, and women are not hired even though they are really better than the men, the management is out not only the cost of the experiment but also the $80,000 profit that might have been made in a year by hiring the women, resulting in a total loss of $90,000. Clearly, the two errors do not have the same consequences for the management. And yet, this rule for decision almost guarantees that the less important error will not be made, while permitting large risk of making the expensive error.

This difficulty can be shown most clearly in terms of subjective expected loss. If the personal probabilities of the experimenter actually were

$$\mathcal{P}(H_0) = \mathcal{P}(H_1) = 1/2, \text{ then}$$
$$SE(u;D) = (10,000)(.05)(.5) + (90,000)(.36)(.5)$$
$$= \$16,250,$$

the subjective expected loss would be over sixteen thousand dollars.

On the other hand, suppose that another rule were adopted, where $\beta$ is set equal to .05, making $\alpha$ equal to .36. In this circumstance,

$$SE(u;D) = (10,000)(.36)(.5) + (90,000)(.05)(.5)$$
$$= \$4050.$$

Obviously, this second rule is more desirable than the first if the expected loss is to be low. Still better rules exist if the probability $\beta$ is made even smaller. In this situation, where losses can be considered, the adoption of an arbitrary decision-rule is not very wise.

On the other hand, if a sample does show a mean which is more than 1.65 standard errors away from 138, the experimenter can say that such samples are "improbable" given $\mu = 138$, regardless of whether or not this statement has any connection with a decision-rule he is actually going to use. If he *must* use the arbitrary rule, then the probability $\alpha$ is given by the probability of finding a sample mean in the rejection region for $H_0$. Nevertheless, the probability $\beta$ may be so big that this rule is unreasonable for the actual decision.

## 9.12  CONVENTIONAL DECISION-RULES

In psychology, given some hypothesis $H_0$ to be tested, the region of rejection is usually found as follows:

CONVENTION: Set $\alpha$, the probability of falsely rejecting $H_0$, equal to some small value. Then, in accordance with the alternative $H_1$, choose a region of rejection such that the probability of observing a sample value in that region is equal to $\alpha$ when $H_0$ is true. The obtained result is significant beyond the $\alpha$ level if the sample statistic falls within that region.

Ordinarily, the values of $\alpha$ used are .05 or .01, although, on occasion, larger or smaller values are employed. Even though only one hypothesis, $H_0$, may be exactly specified, and this determines the sampling distribution employed in the test, in choosing the region of rejection one acts as though there were two hypotheses, $H_0$ and $H_1$. The alternate hypothesis $H_1$ dictates which portion or **tail** of the sampling distribution contains the rejection region for $H_0$. In some problems, the region of rejection is contained in only one tail of the distribution, so that only extreme deviations in a given direction from expectation lead to rejection of $H_0$. In other problems, big deviations of either sign are candidates for the rejection region, so that the region of rejection lies in both tails of the sampling distribution.

In all that follows, these conventional rules will be used for finding a rejection region. Some hypothesis will be designated as $H_0$, and an arbitrary $\alpha$ value will be chosen, which, taken together with $H_1$, determines the sample values that lead to a possible rejection of $H_0$.

## 9.13  THE POWER OF A STATISTICAL TEST

Given only the one exact hypothesis $H_0$, and the required value of $\alpha$, one may still think of an inference involving two hypotheses:

$H_0$, the hypothesis actually being tested
$H_1$, the hypothesis, whatever it may be, that is true.

Once any true $H_1$ is specified, then we can determine $\beta$, the probability of an error in decision given the true $H_1$. Similarly, one may compute the probability $1 - \beta$, which is the probability of being right in rejecting $H_0$ given that $H_1$ is true. This probability, $1 - \beta$, is often called the **power** of the statistical test. It is literally the probability of finding out that $H_0$ is wrong, given the decision-rule and the true value under $H_1$.

For example, consider the hypotheses in the preceding problem. When $\alpha$ was set equal to .05, then the hypothesis actually being tested was $H_0$: $\mu = 138$. Suppose, however, that the true situation is represented by $H_1$: $\mu = 142$. By the rule used, $H_0$ is rejected when a sample exceeds 141.3. This gives a probability of error $\beta$ shown by the shaded region in Figure 9.13.1, if $H_1$ is true.

FIG. 9.13.1

The unshaded area under the curve is $1 - \beta$, or the power of the test, given $H_1$. In this instance the power is about .64, so that the chances of correctly rejecting $H_0$ are about six in ten. Notice, however that *the power of a test of $H_0$ cannot be found until some true situation $H_1$ is specified.*

## 9.14 Power of tests against various true alternatives

The power of a test of $H_0$ is not unlike the power of a microscope. It reflects the ability of a decision-rule to detect from evidence that the true situation differs from a hypothetical one. Just as a high-powered microscope lets us distinguish gaps in an apparently solid material that we would miss with low power or the naked eye, so does a high-powered test of $H_0$ almost insure us of detecting when $H_0$ is false. Pursuing the analogy further, any microscope will reveal "gaps" with more clarity the larger these gaps are; the larger the departure of $H_0$ from the true situation $H_1$, the more powerful is the test of $H_0$, other things being equal.

For example, suppose that the hypothesis to be tested is

$$H_0: \mu = \mu_0$$

but that the true hypothesis is

$$H_1: \mu = \mu_1.$$

Here, $\mu_0$ and $\mu_1$ symbolize two different possible numerical values for $\mu$. It will be assumed that under either hypothesis the sampling distribution of the mean is normal with $\sigma$ known. Suppose now that the $\alpha$ probability of error is set at .05, and the rejection region is on the *right tail* of the distribution. The decision-rule is such that the critical value of $M$ (the smallest $M$ leading to the rejection of $H_0$) is $\mu_0 + 1.65\sigma_M$. The power of the test can then be figured for any possible true $H_1$.

First of all, suppose that $\mu_1$ were actually $\mu_0 + \sigma_M$. Then in the distribution under $H_1$, the critical value of $M$ has a $z$ score given by

$$z_M = \frac{M - \mu_1}{\sigma_M}$$
$$= \frac{(\mu_0 + 1.65\sigma_M) - (\mu_0 + 1\sigma_M)}{\sigma_M} = .65.$$

The probability of a sample's falling into the region of rejection for $H_0$ is found from Table I to be .26. This probability is $1 - \beta$, the power of the test.

This may be clarified by Figure 9.14.1. The region of rejection for $H_0$ is the segment of the horizontal line to the right of $M = \mu_0 + 1.65\sigma_M$. The shaded

FIG. 9.14.1

portion under the curve for $\mu = \mu_0 + 1\sigma_M$ denotes $\beta$, the probability of *failing* to reject $H_0$, and the power is the unshaded part of the curve.

If another alternative hypothesis were true, say,

$$H_1: \mu_1 = \mu_0 + 3\sigma_M$$

then the power would be much larger. Here, relative to the sampling distribution based on the *true* mean, or $\mu_0 + 3\sigma_M$, the critical value of $M$ would correspond to a $z_M$ score of

$$z_M = \frac{(\mu_0 + 1.65\sigma_M) - (\mu_0 + 3\sigma_M)}{\sigma_M} = -1.35.$$

Table I shows us that above a $z$ score of $-1.35$ lie .91 of sample means in a normal sampling distribution, so that the power is .91.

The power of the test for any true value of $\mu_1$ can be found in the same way. Often, to show the relation of power to the true value of $\mu_1$, so called **power-functions** or **power curves** are plotted. One such curve is given in Figure 9.14.2, where the horizontal axis gives the possible values of true $\mu_1$ in terms of $\mu_0$ and $\sigma_M$, and the vertical axis the value of $1 - \beta$, the power for that alternative. Notice that for this particular decision-rule, the power curve rises for increasing values of $\mu_1$, and approaches 1.00 for very large values. On the other hand, for this decision-rule, when true $\mu_1$ is less than $\mu_0$ the power is very small, and approaches 0 for decreasing $\mu_1$ values. In any statistical test where the region of rejection is in the direction of the true value covered by $H_1$, the greater the discrepancy between the tested hypothesis and the true situation, the greater the power.

FIG. 9.14.2. Power curve for a one-sided test of a mean, $\alpha = .05$

## 9.15 POWER AND THE SIZE OF $\alpha$

Since $\beta$ will ordinarily be small for large $\alpha$, as we have seen in the discussion above, it follows that setting $\alpha$ larger makes for relatively more powerful tests of $H_0$. For example, the two power curves given below for the same

FIG. 9.15.1. Power curves for two tests with equal sample sizes but with different values of $\alpha$

decision-rule show that if $\alpha$ is set at .10 rather than at .05, the test with $\alpha = .10$ will be more powerful than that for $\alpha = .05$ over all possibly true values under alternative $H_1$ (note Figure 9.15.1). Making the probability of error in rejecting $H_0$ larger has the effect of making the test more powerful, other things being equal.

In principle, if it is very costly to make the mistake of overlooking a true departure from $H_0$, but not very costly to reject $H_0$ falsely, one could (and perhaps should) make the test more powerful by setting the value of $\alpha$ at .10, .20, or more. This is not ordinarily done in psychological research, however. There are at least two reasons why $\alpha$ is seldom taken to be greater than .05: In the first place, as observed in Section 9.9, the problem of relative losses incurred by making errors is seldom faced in psychological research; hence conventions about the size of $\alpha$ are adopted. The other important reason is that given some fixed $\alpha$ the power of the test can be increased either by increasing sample size or by reducing the standard error of the test statistic in some other way.

## 9.16    THE EFFECT OF SAMPLE SIZE ON POWER

Given a population with true standard deviation $\sigma$, the standard error of the mean depends inversely upon the square root of sample size $N$. That is,

$$\sigma_M = \frac{\sigma}{\sqrt{N}}.$$

When $N$ is large, then the standard error is smaller than when $N$ is small. Provided that $1 - \beta > \alpha$ to begin with, *increasing the sample size increases the power of a given test of $H_0$ against a true alternative $H_1$.*

For example, suppose that

$$H_0: \mu = 50$$
$$H_1: \mu = 60$$

where $H_1$ is true. Let us assume that true $\sigma = 20$. If samples of size 25 are taken, then

$$\sigma_M = \frac{20}{5} = 4.$$

Now the $\alpha$ probability for this test is fixed at .01, making the critical value of $M$ be

$$M = \mu_0 + 2.33\sigma_M = 50 + (2.33)(4) = 59.32.$$

In the true sampling distribution (under $H_1$) this amounts to a $z$ score of

$$z_M = \frac{59.32 - 60}{4} = \frac{-.68}{4} = -.17$$

so that .57 of all sample means should fall into the rejection region for $H_0$. The power here is thus .57.

Now let the sample size be increased to 100. This changes the standard error of the mean to

$$\sigma_M = \frac{20}{10} = 2$$

and the critical value of $M$ to

$$M = 50 + (2.33)(2) = 54.66.$$

The corresponding $z$ score when $\mu = 60$ is

$$z_M = \frac{54.66 - 60}{2} = -2.67$$

making the power now in excess of .99. With this sample size we would be almost certain to detect correctly that the $H_0$ is false when this particular $H_1$ is true. With only 25 cases, we are quite likely not to do so.

The disadvantages of an arbitrary setting of $\alpha$ can thus be offset, in part, by the choice of a large sample size. Other things being equal and regardless of the size chosen for $\alpha$, the test may be made powerful against any given

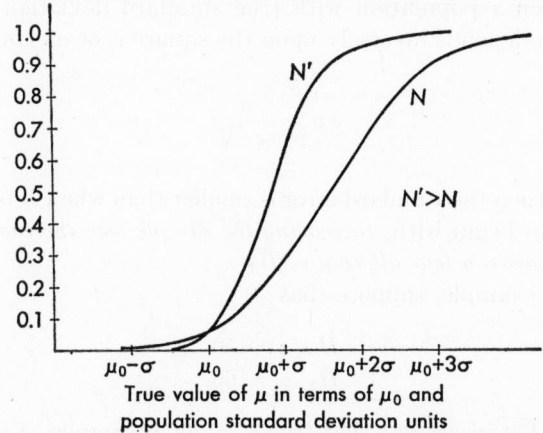

FIG. 9.16.1. Power curves for two tests with $\alpha = .05$ but with different sample sizes, $N' > N$.

alternative $H_1$ in the direction of the rejection region, provided that sample $N$ can be made very large. (See Figure 9.16.1.)

Once again, however, it is not always feasible to obtain very large samples. In most psychological research, samples of substantial size are costly for the experimenter, if not in money, then in effort. Our ability to attain power through large samples only partly offsets the failure to choose a decision-rule according to cost of error in such research; large samples may not really be necessary in some research using them, especially if the error thereby made improbable is actually not very important. This matter of sample size and power will be considered once again in Chapter 10.

## 9.17 POWER AND "ERROR VARIANCE"

Even given a fixed sample size, the experimenter has one more device for attaining power in tests of hypotheses. *Anything that makes $\sigma$, the population* *standard deviation, small will increase power, other things being equal.* This is one of the reasons for the careful control of conditions in good experimentation. By making conditions constant, the experimenter rules out many of the factors that contribute to variation in his observations. Statistically this amounts to a relative reduction in the size of $\sigma$ for some experimental population. When the experimenter rules out some of the error variance from his observations he is *decreasing* the standard error of the mean, and thus *increasing* the power of the test against whatever hypothesis $H_1$ is true. Experiments in which the variability attributable to experimental or sampling error is small are said to be **precise;** the result of such precision is that the experimenter is quite likely to be able to detect when something of interest is happening. The application of experimental controls is like restricting inferences to populations with smaller values of $\sigma^2$ than otherwise, and thus control over error variation through careful experimentation implies powerful statistical tests. It follows that controlled experiments in which there is little "natural" variation in the materials observed can attain statistical power with relatively few observations, while those involving extremely variable material may require many observations to attain the same degree of power.

## 9.18 TESTING INEXACT HYPOTHESES

The primary notions of errors in inference and the power of a statistical test have just been illustrated for an extremely artificial situation, in which a decision must be made between two exact alternatives. Such situations are almost nonexistent in psychological research. Instead, the experimenter is far more likely to be called on to evaluate inexact hypotheses, each of which encompasses a whole range of possibly true values. What relevance, then, does the discussion of the exact two-alternative case have to what psychologists actually do? The answer is that the researcher makes his inferences as though he were deciding between two exact alternatives, even though his interest lies in judging between inexact hypotheses. Thus, the mechanism we have been using for decisions between exact hypotheses is exactly the same as for any other set of alternatives.

An example will probably clarify this point. As a fairly plausible situation, imagine a psychologist who has constructed a new test of adult intelligence. This test has been very carefully standardized on a population of American adults. The standardization has been so carried out that the mean score is 100 and the standard deviation of the test is 15. Furthermore, the distribution of scores in the standardization population is approximately normal.

The psychologist is now interested in the application of the test to residents of England. From his knowledge of the abilities required by the test he has some reason to suspect that English adults may, on the average, score somewhat higher than American adults. So, in order to arrive at some idea if this may be the case, and especially to see if the test may require some scoring modification for administration in England, he decides to give the test to a sample of English adults. Basically, the question to be answered is "Do English adults tend to score higher on this test than Americans?" We will suppose that there is no reason to question the standard deviation of scores among the English, nor the general form of the distribution of scores.

The answer to his question is tantamount to a decision between two *inexact* hypotheses:

$$H_0: \mu \leq 100$$
$$H_1: \mu > 100$$

i.e., the English population has either a mean score less than or equal to the American mean, or a mean greater than the American mean.

In choosing the decision-rule he will use, the experimenter decides to set $\alpha$ equal to .01. A result greater than 100 tends to favor $H_1$, and so he takes as his region of rejection all $z$ scores greater than or equal to 2.33, since this value cuts off the highest 1 percent of sample means in a normal sampling distribution.

What, however, is the hypothesis actually being tested? As written, $H_0$ is inexact, since it states a whole region of possible values for $\mu$. One exact value is specified, however: this is $\mu = 100$. Actually, then, the hypothesis tested is $\mu = 100$ against some unspecified alternative greater than 100. In effect, the decision-rule can be put in the following form:

TRUE SITUATION

$\mu = 100$   $\mu > 100$

|  | $\mu = 100$ | $\mu > 100$ |
|---|---|---|
| $\mu = 100$ | .99 | $(\beta)$? |
| DECIDE | | |
| $\mu > 100$ | .01 | $(1 - \beta)$? |

The $\alpha$ probability of error can be specified in advance as .01, but $\beta$ and the power are unknown, depending as they do upon the true situation. The experimenter has no real interest in the hypothesis that $\mu = 100$; he may even feel extremely confident that the true mean is not precisely 100. Nevertheless, this is a useful dummy hypothesis, in the sense that *if he can reject $\mu = 100$ with $\alpha = .01$, then he can reject any other hypothesis that $\mu < 100$ with $\alpha < .01$.* In other words, by this decision-rule, if he can be confident that he is not making an error in rejecting the hypothesis actually tested, then he can be even more confident in rejecting any other hypothesis covered by $H_0$.

But what does this do to $\beta$? Given some true mean $\mu_1$ covered by $H_1$, *the power of the test of $\mu = 100$ is less than the power for any other hypothesis covered by $H_0$ with fixed $\alpha$.* If he had chosen to test any other exact hypothesis embodied in $H_0$, such as $\mu = 90$, then neither $\alpha$ nor $\beta$ would exceed those for $\mu = 100$. Testing the exact hypothesis with given $\alpha$ and $\beta$ probabilities can be regarded as testing *all* hypotheses covered by $H_0$, with *at most* $\alpha$ and $\beta$ probabilities of error (the $\beta$ depending on the *true* mean, of course). This is illustrated in Figure 9.18.1.

Suppose now that a sample of 200 cases yields a mean of 103.5. The standard error of the mean is

$$\sigma_M = \frac{15}{\sqrt{200}} = 1.06.$$

Thus, the $z$ score corresponding to the sample mean is

$$z_M = \frac{103.5 - 100}{1.06} = 3.30.$$

Since this $z$ score exceeds the critical value of 2.33, the hypothesis that $\mu = 100$ can be rejected with $\alpha < .01$, and any other hypothesis covered by $H_0$ can be rejected with $\alpha$ less than .01. If the experimenter decides that the true mean is greater than 100 he could be wrong in this decision, but the probability of such an error is less than .01. Notice that we did not say that the experimenter must decide in this way, but only that the $\alpha$ probability of error is slight should he make this decision.

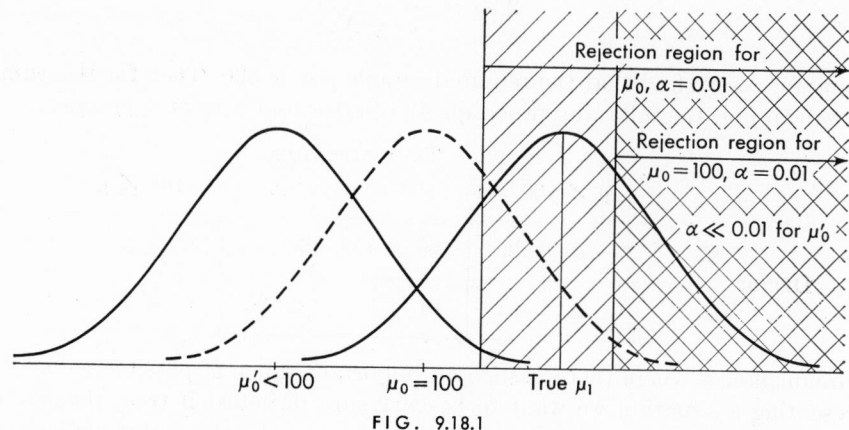

FIG. 9.18.1

On the other hand, suppose that the sample mean had been only 102. Here the $z_M$ score would have been only 1.89, which is not large enough to place the sample in the region of rejection for $H_0$ if the probability $\alpha$ is to be .01. Under the decision-rule using $\alpha = .05$ this would lead to a rejection of the hypothesis, but not by the rule originally decided upon.

The same problem can be put on a much more realistic basis, particularly with regard to sample size, if the experimenter has an idea of some minimal value of $\mu$ he would like to be very sure to detect as a significant result if true. That is, suppose the experimenter in this problem knows that it is absolutely essential that he restandardize the test if the mean for the population of English adults is *at least* 103. This is important enough to him that he wants the power of the test to be at least .95 when $\mu$ is at least 103. Does his choice of a sample size and of a rejection region meet this qualification?

For $N = 200$, the standard error of the mean is 1.06. Consequently, the critical value of the mean is

$$\text{critical } M = 2.33(1.06) + 100$$
$$= 102.47.$$

If the value of $\mu$ were actually 103, then in this sampling distribution under the true value of $\mu$ the critical value of $M$ would correspond to

$$z_M = \frac{102.47 - 103}{1.06} = -.5.$$

In a normal distribution, some 69 percent of cases must fall at or above $-.5$ standard errors from the mean. Hence, the power of this test against the true alternative $\mu = 103$ is only .69. If the experiment wants this power to be .95 for $\mu = 103$, then he must take a larger sample. In fact, the sample size required can be found from

$$-1.65 = \frac{M - 103}{\sigma/\sqrt{N}}$$

and

$$2.33 = \frac{M - 100}{\sigma/\sqrt{N}}.$$

Solving for $N$, we find that the required sample size is 396. Then for this sample size we can find the following probabilities of error and correct decisions:

|  |  | TRUE SITUATION | |  |
|---|---|---|---|---|
|  |  | $\mu \leq 100$ | $100 < \mu < 103$ | $103 \leq \mu$ |
| DECIDE | $H_0$ | $1 - \alpha \geq .99$ | $.99 > \beta > .05$ | $.05 \geq \beta$ |
|  | $H_1$ | $\alpha \leq .01$ | $.01 < 1 - \beta < .95$ | $.95 \leq 1 - \beta$ |

In circumstances where there *is* such an important range of possible values of $\mu$, representing a situation we want to be very sure to detect if true, then we can adjust the sample size or $\alpha$ value or both so as to make the power against such alternatives as great as necessary.

Obtaining a nonsignificant result (one not leading to a rejection of $H_0$ in favor of $H_1$) often puts the experimenter in a quandary. He cannot make the decision to reject $H_0$ and still stay within the bounds on $\alpha$ set by his decision-rule. Does this mean, however, that he must decide that $H_0$ is true? Most emphatically not! In the first place the experimenter does not have to decide anything; he may be content merely to report "$H_0$ not rejected," or "nonsignificant result," and let it go at that. On the other hand, he might want to adopt some more definite course of action, and here the decision to accept $H_0$ as true really makes sense only if the probability of error in such a decision is known. In the examples above, where the choice lay between two exact hypotheses, the probability for each kind of error could be calculated, and so the risk in accepting $H_0$ as true could be known. In examples such as the present one, the $\beta$ probability of error is unknown unless we are willing to postulate some exact value of $\mu$ as true. When one is operating with completely unknown error-probabilities, and the cost of an error may be great, then the decision to accept $H_0$ may be very unwise.

In the case of nonsignificant results a wise decision may be to suspend judgment and wait for more evidence. This is true particularly when the error of falsely accepting $H_0$ could be very costly. When the sample result is in the direction indicated by $H_1$, but is not sufficiently deviant from $H_0$ to warrant rejection, a mere increase in sample size might very well permit one to reject $H_0$. Thus, in many experimental contexts, failing to reject $H_0$ might appropriately be interpreted as suspension of judgment, since the experimenter has considerable stake in avoiding *either* kind of error, and wants to be sure to adopt a conservative course of action when $H_0$ cannot be rejected.

On the other hand, occasions exist when accepting $H_0$ makes quite good sense, even when the hypotheses are both inexact. In these circumstances the experimenter is able to calculate the probability of a sample such as the one he obtained, given that one of the values covered by $H_1$ were true. Here, he asks the probability of a sample result differing this much or more from expectation *in the direction of $H_0$*, given that a value covered by $H_1$ is true. Perhaps an example will make this point clear. Consider the developer of the intelligence test once again. Suppose that the sample mean turns out to be 98 in the test of $H_0: \mu \leq 100$, against $H_1: \mu > 100$. When it is true that $\mu = 100$ this sample result represents a standardized value of

$$z_M = \frac{98 - 100}{1.06} = -1.89.$$

This result falls quite far from the region of rejection, and so one does not accept $H_1$ as true; in fact, our best estimate of the value of $\mu$ is not 100, but rather 98, a value not even included in the hypothesis $H_1$. Each and every possible value of $\mu$ covered by $H_1$ is greater than 100, and so the $z_M$ value for any $\mu$ in $H_1$ must be *less* than $-1.89$.

Now suppose that the experimenter decides to *accept* $H_0: \mu \leq 100$ as true in the light of evidence such as this. How much risk is he taking? In a normal distribution, $F(-1.89)$ is approximately .03, so that the probability of error is *less* than .03 in saying that $H_0$ is true on evidence such as this when a value covered by $H_1$ is true. In other words, the experimenter who decides to accept $H_0$ on evidence this much or more in disagreement with $H_1$ is running very little risk of error. When the alternative hypothesis is "directional," as in this example, the experimenter may be quite justified in saying that $H_0$ is true, provided that he can assess the error probability involved in making this statement on this kind of evidence.

In summary, if there is no way at all to gain some idea of the risk run in falsely *accepting $H_0$*, and such errors are at all important, then suspension of judgment may be the best policy following a nonsignificant result. On the other hand, if the obtained result does agree with expectation under values covered by $H_0$, but would fall among the deviant and unlikely results given any value covered by $H_1$, then $H_0$ may very well be accepted as true. Either decision is possible, and how one interprets the occurrence of a nonsignificant result depends very much on what can be learned about the error-probabilities involved. There is really no rule about this; nevertheless, the experimenter is wise to make no actual decision between $H_0$ and $H_1$ unless he has some definite notion of the error probabilities involved. The risk run in accepting $H_1$ (rejecting $H_0$) is, of course, known to be $\alpha$, but the risk run in accepting $H_0$ (the probability $\beta$) is not, in general, known. For this reason, the decision to accept $H_0$ as true is reserved for situations where the experimenter has some idea of the risk he is taking.

### 9.19 TYPE I AND TYPE II ERRORS

The time has come to dignify with names the two kinds of errors we have been discussing. **Type I error is that made when** $H_0$ **(the tested hypothesis) is falsely rejected.** One makes a Type I error whenever the sample result falls into the rejection region even though $H_0$ is true. Thus the probability $\alpha$ gives the risk run of making a Type I error.

**The errors of Type II are those made by not rejecting** $H_0$ **when it is false.** When a sample result does not fall into the rejection region, even though some $H_1$ is true, we are led to make a Type II error. Thus for a given true alternative $H_1$, $\beta$ is the probability of Type II error. It follows that

$$\text{power} = 1 - \text{probability of Type II error.}$$

### 9.20 THE BASIS FOR THE CONVENTIONS ABOUT TYPE I ERRORS

The conventions about the permissible size of the $\alpha$ probability of Type I error actually grew out of a particular sort of experimental setting. Here it is known in advance that one kind of error is extremely important and is to be avoided. In this kind of experiment these conventional procedures do make sense when viewed from the decision-making point of view. Furthermore, designation of the hypothesis $H_0$ as the "null" hypothesis and the arbitrary setting of the level of $\alpha$ can best be understood within this context.

As an example of an experimental setting where Type I error is clearly to be avoided, imagine that one is testing a new medicine, with the goal of deciding if the medicine is safe for the normal adult population. By "safe" we will mean that the medicine fails to produce a particular set of undesirable reactions on all but a very few normal adults. Now in this instance, deciding that the medicine is safe when actually it tends to produce reactions in a relatively large proportion of adults is certainly an error to be avoided. Such an error might be called "abhorrent" to the experimenter and the interests he represents. Therefore, the hypothesis "medicine unsafe" or its statistical equivalent is cast in the role of the null hypothesis, $H_0$, and the value of $\alpha$ chosen to be extremely small, so that the abhorrent Type I error is very unlikely to be committed. A great deal of evidence against the null hypothesis is required before $H_0$ is to be rejected. The experimenter has complete control over Type I error, and regardless of any other feature his study of the medicine may have, he can be confident of taking very little risk of asserting that $H_1$, or "medicine safe" is true when actually $H_0$, or "medicine unsafe" is true.

In other words, the conventional practice of arbitrarily setting $\alpha$ at some very small level is based on the notion that one kind of error is extremely important and must be avoided if possible. This is quite reasonable in some contexts, such as the study of the safety of a new medicine.

On the other hand, the experimenter always has some control over the values of $\beta$ and the power of the test over the various possibly true alternatives. By the choice of an appropriate sample size and by exercising control over the size of $\sigma^2$ in the population considered, the value of $\beta$ for any possibly true alternative to $H_0$ may be made as small (or conversely, the power as large) as desired. If a number of different ways to test $H_0$ are available in terms of different sample statistics, some of these ways may give more powerful tests than others regardless of what the true situation actually is, and the experimenter chooses the best procedure among those available. However, the essential points are that the experimenter is absolutely free to set $\alpha$ at any level he chooses, and that the conventional levels are dictated by the notion that Type I errors are bad and must be avoided. The experimenter does not have this same freedom with respect to Type II errors; power must be bought in terms of sample size and other features of the test procedure. Power can always be made large against any given alternative, but only at some cost to the experimenter. An inappropriately small value of $\alpha$ makes it more difficult than otherwise to achieve a powerful test.

Within contexts such as the test of a new medication, where Type I error is abhorrent, setting $\alpha$ extremely small is manifestly appropriate. Here, considerations of Type II error are actually secondary. In some instances in psychology a similar situation exists, where one kind of error is clearly to be avoided, and from the outset the experimenter wants to be sure that this kind of error is very improbable. The designation of one hypothesis as $H_0$ should rest on which kind of error is to have the small probability $\alpha$. In the example of Section 9.11 the experimenter using the conventional rule should have designated $\mu = 142$ as $H_0$ for this very reason. On the other hand, in some psychological research it is very hard to see exactly why the particular hypothesis tested, or $H_0$, should be the one we are loath to abandon, and why Type I errors necessarily have this drastic character. Granting that scientific discretion is commendable, the mistaken conclusion that "something really happened" is not *necessarily* worse than overlooking a real experimental phenomenon. In some situations, perhaps, we should be far more attentive to Type II errors and the power of our tests, and less attentive to setting $\alpha$ at one of the conventional levels. Furthermore, if the conventional $\alpha$ levels are to be used, a little more thought might be given to deciding exactly what *is* the null hypothesis we want to be so careful not to reject falsely.

Incidentally, there is an impression in some quarters that the term "null hypothesis" refers to the fact that in experimental work the parameter value specified in $H_0$ is very often zero. Thus, in many experiments the hypothetical situation "no experimental effect" is represented by a statement that some mean or difference between means is exactly zero. However, as we have seen, the tested hypothesis can specify any of the possible values for one or more parameters, and this use of the word "null" is only incidental. It is far better for the student to think of the null hypothesis $H_0$ as simply designating that hypothesis actually being tested, the one which, if true, determines the sampling distribution actually referred to in the test, and which specifies the kind of error called Type I.

## 9.21 ONE-TAILED REJECTION REGIONS

In the example of Section 9.18 two inexact hypotheses were compared, having the form

$$H_0: \mu \leq \mu_0$$
$$H_1: \mu > \mu_0.$$

Here the entire range of possible values for the parameter under study (in this case, the population mean) was divided into two parts, that above and that below (or equal to) an exact value $\mu_0$. The interest of the experimenter lay in placing the true value of $\mu$ either above or below $\mu_0$.

In this instance the appropriate region of rejection for $H_0$ consists of values of $M$ relatively much larger than $\mu_0$. Such values have a rather small probability of representing true means covered by the hypothesis $H_0$, but are more likely to represent true means in the range of $H_1$. Such a rejection region consisting of sample values in a particular direction from the expectation given by the exact value included in $H_0$ are called **directional** or **one-tailed** rejection regions. For the particular hypotheses compared in Section 9.18, the rejection region was one-tailed, since only the right or "high-value" tail of the sampling distribution under $H_0$ was considered in deciding between the hypotheses.

For some questions, the two inexact hypotheses are of the form

$$H_0: \mu \geq \mu_0$$
$$H_1: \mu < \mu_0.$$

Once again the region of rejection is one-tailed, but this time the lower or left tail of the sampling distribution contains the region of rejection for $H_0$. The choice of the particular rejection region thus depends both on $\alpha$ and the alternative hypothesis $H_1$.

Tests of hypotheses using one-tailed rejection regions are also called **directional.** The direction or sign of the value of the statistic (such as $z_M$) is important in directional tests since the sample result must show not only an extreme departure from expectation under $H_0$ but also a departure in the right direction to be considered strong evidence against $H_0$ and for $H_1$.

Directional hypotheses are implied when the basic question involves terms like "more than," "better than," "increased," "declined." The essential question to be answered by the data has a clear implication of a difference or change in a specific direction. For example in the problem of Section 9.18 the experimenter wanted specifically to know if Englishmen make higher scores than Americans, indicating a directional hypothesis.

Many times, however, the experimenter goes into a problem without a clearly defined notion of the direction of difference to expect if $H_0$ is false. He asks "Did something happen?" "Is there a difference?" or "Was there a change?" without any specification of expected direction. Next we will examine techniques for nondirectional hypothesis-testing.

### 9.22  TWO-TAILED TESTS OF HYPOTHESES

Imagine a study carried out on the "optical dominance" of human subjects. There is interest in whether or not the dominant eye and the dominant hand of a subject tend to be on the same or different sides. Subjects are to be tested for both kinds of dominance, and then classified as "same side" or "different side" in this respect. We will use the letters "S" and "D" to denote these two classes of subjects.

From knowledge he already has about the relative frequency of each kind of dominance the experimenter reasons that if there actually is no tendency for eye dominance to be associated with hand dominance, then in a particular population of subjects he should expect 58 percent S and 42 percent D. However, he knows little about what to expect if there is some connection between the two kinds of dominance. To try to answer this question, our experimenter draws a random sample of 100 subjects, each with a full set of eyes and hands, and classifies them.

The question at hand may be put into the form of two hypotheses, one exact and one inexact:

$$H_0: p = .58$$
$$H_1: p \neq .58.$$

The first hypothesis represents the possibility of no connection between the two kinds of dominance, and the inexact alternative is simply a statement that $H_0$ is not true, since $H_1$ does not specify an exact value of population $p$.

FIG. 9.22.1

The $\alpha$ chosen is .05. The experimenter then is faced with the choice of a rejection region for the hypothesis $H_0$. Either a very high percentage of S subjects in his sample or a very low percentage would tend to discount the credibility of the hypothesis that $p = .58$, and would lend support to $H_1$. Thus he wants to arrange his rejection region so that the $H_0$ will be rejected when extreme departures from expectation of *either* sign occur. This calls for a rejection region on *both* tails of the sampling distribution of sample $P$ when $p = .58$. Since the sample size is relatively large the binomial distribution of sample $P$ may be approximated by a normal distribution, and the two rejection regions may be diagrammed as shown in Figure 9.22.1.

Since the total probability of Type I error has been set at .05, the rejection region on the upper tail of the distribution will contain *the highest 2.5 percent*, and the lower tail *the lowest 2.5 percent of sample proportions*, given that $p = .05$. In short, each region should contain exactly either $(1/2)\alpha$ or $\alpha/2$ proportion of all samples under $H_0$. Consequently, either a very large or very small sample $P$ will lead to a rejection of $H_0$, and the total probability of Type I error is .05. The $z$ score cutting off the upper rejection region is 1.96, and that for the lower is $-1.96$. Any sample giving a $z$ beyond these two limits will lead to a rejection of $H_0$.

Since the basic sampling distribution is binomial, the standard error of $P$ is

$$\sigma_P = \sqrt{\frac{pq}{N}} = \sqrt{\frac{(.58)(.42)}{100}}$$
$$= .049$$

when $H_0$ is true (Section 6.22). Using the normal approximation to the binomial we find

$$z = \frac{P - p}{\sigma_P}.$$

Now suppose that the proportion of S subjects is .69. Then

$$z = \frac{.69 - .58}{.049} = 2.24.$$

This value exceeds the critical $z$ score of 1.96, and so the result is said to be significant beyond the 5 percent level. If the experimenter concludes that eye and hand dominance do tend to be related then he runs a risk of less than .05 of being wrong.

Suppose, however, that the sample result had come out to be only .53. Then

$$z = \frac{.53 - .58}{.049} = -1.02$$

making the result nonsignificant. Here, the experimenter should most likely suspend judgment pending further evidence. He should not be willing to assert that $H_0$ is true: the risk in that assertion is unknown. Indeed, his best guess about the true value of $p$ is .53, not .58, and given enough sample observations, a $P$ value of .53 might be enough to warrant rejection. Thus, for a nonsignificant result such as this the experimenter cannot wisely accept $H_0$ as true. His best available choice may be to suspend judgment, and look for more evidence.

Although the example just concluded dealt with a hypothesis about a proportion, exactly the same procedure applies to two-tailed tests of means. An exact and an inexact hypothesis are opposed:

$$H_0: \mu = \mu_0$$
$$H_1: \mu \neq \mu_0.$$

The exact hypothesis is tested by forming two regions of rejection, each region containing exactly $\alpha/2$ proportion of sample results when $H_0$ is true, and lying in the higher and lower tails of the distribution. A sample result falling into either of these regions of rejection is said to be significant at the $\alpha$ level. If the result is not significant, then judgment is suspended.

## 9.23  RELATIVE MERITS OF ONE- AND TWO-TAILED TESTS

In deciding whether a hypothesis should be tested with a one- or two-tailed rejection region, the primary concern of the experimenter must be his original question. Is he looking for a directional difference between populations, or a difference only in kind or degree? By and large, most significance tests done

FIG . 9.23.1. Power curves for a two-tailed and a one-tailed test of a mean, $\alpha = .05$

in psychological research are nondirectional, simply because research questions tend to be framed this way. However, there are situations where one-tailed tests are clearly indicated by the question posed.

The powers of one- and two-tailed tests of the same hypothesis will be different, given the same $\alpha$ level and the same true alternative. If a one-tailed test is used, and the true alternative is in the direction of the rejection region, then the one-tailed test is more powerful than the two-tailed over all such possibly true values of $\mu$. In a way, we get a little statistical credit in the one-tailed test for asking a more searching question. On the other hand, if the true alternative happens to be on the tail opposite the rejection region in a one-tailed test, the power is very low; in fact, the power will always be less than $\alpha$ in the test of a mean. If you will, we are penalized for framing a stupid question. Power curves for one- and two-tailed tests for means are compared in Figure 9.23.1.

In many circumstances calling for one-tailed tests the form of the question or of the sampling distribution makes it clear that the only alternative of logical or practical consequence must lie in a certain direction. For example, when we turn to the problem of testing many means for equality simultaneously (Chapter 12) it will turn out that the only rejection region making sense lies on one tail of the particular sampling distribution employed. In other circumstances the question involves considerations of "which is better" or "which is more," where the discovery of a difference from $H_0$ in one direction may have real consequences for practical action, although a mean in another direction from $H_0$ may indicate nothing. For example, consider a treatment for some disease. The cure rate for the disease is known, and we want to see if the treatment *improves* the cure rate. We have not the slightest practical interest in a possible decrease in cures; this, like no change, leads to nonadoption of the treatment. The thing we want to be sure to detect is whether or not the new treatment is really better than what we have. Thus, we can safely ignore the low power for detecting a poorer treatment, so long as we have high power for detecting a really better treatment. In many such problems where different practical actions depend on the sign of the deviation from expectation, a one-tailed test is clearly called for. Otherwise, the two-tailed test is safest for the experimenter asking only "What happens?"

## 9.24 SOME REMARKS ON THE GENERAL THEORY UNDERLYING TESTS OF HYPOTHESES

For purposes of exposition the kinds of hypotheses considered in this chapter have been very elementary ones concerning the mean $\mu$ or the population proportion $p$. The hypotheses about $\mu$ have actually been composite as stated, but these have, in effect, been turned into simple hypotheses by our assumption that both $\sigma^2$ and the form of the population distribution are known. Working with these elementary examples has permitted us to use the familiar normal and binomial sampling distributions, and to illustrate decision-rules, error probabilities, and power in the simplest possible terms. Finally, and most important, we pretended that we knew that the best way to test a particular hypothesis was in terms either of the statistic $M$ or the statistic $P$; that is, the question of the relevant and appropriate statistic was not allowed to come up.

As it happens, $M$ and $P$ actually are the appropriate statistics for the particular hypotheses tested; however, as we shall see in succeeding chapters, in testing other hypotheses (particularly composite hypotheses) various other statistics that are not necessarily estimators for any population parameters may provide us the best ways of carrying out the tests. Such statistics, whose primary role is that of providing a test of some hypothesis, are usually called **test statistics,** and the hypothesis test itself is carried out in terms of the sampling distribution of the appropriate test statistic, rather than that of some estimator such as $M$, $\hat{s}^2$, or $P$.

In mathematical statistics a general theory of hypothesis testing exists that extends the elementary ideas discussed here to much more complex situations. Among other things this theory specifies desirable characteristics that a test statistic should have and indicates methods for finding such test statistics, all within the general framework outlined here: some particular $H_0$ and $H_1$ are formulated and a value of $\alpha$ is chosen arbitrarily by the experimenter; some appropriate test statistic is selected and the actual decision-rule is formulated in terms of rejection regions in the sampling distribution of this statistic. Much of the theory of hypothesis testing deals with the choice of the *right* statistic for the purpose.

Among the desirable properties of a test based on some statistic is that of **unbiasedness**: a test statistic (and decision-rule) is said to afford an unbiased test of the hypothesis $H_0$ if the use of this statistic (and rule) makes the probability of rejecting $H_0$ be at its smallest when $H_0$ is actually true. An unbiased test will have *minimum* power when $H_0$ is true.

Another property of a good test is **consistency**: in somewhat imprecise terms, a consistent test is one for which the probability of rejecting a *false $H_0$* approaches 1.00 as the sample size approaches $\infty$. That is, a consistent test always gains power against any true alternative as the sample size is increased.

Still another criterion of a good test is that it be **most powerful for the particular true alternative** to the hypothesis $H_0$. That is, among all of the different ways that one could devise to test some particular $H_0$ against some particular true alternative value covered by $H_1$, the most powerful test affords the smallest probability of Type II error, other things such as sample size being equal. **Uniformly most powerful tests** are those which give a smaller probability of Type II error than any other test regardless of the value which happens to be true among those covered by $H_1$, other things being equal.

The general theory of hypothesis testing first took form under the hand of Sir Ronald Fisher in the nineteen-twenties, but it was carried to a high state of development in the work of J. Neyman and E. S. Pearson, beginning about 1928. Neyman and Pearson introduced a device for finding "good" tests of hypotheses, a device known as the "likelihood ratio" test. This is a general procedure for finding the test statistic that will have optimal properties for testing any of a broad class of hypotheses, particularly the statistic that will give a most powerful test for a specific hypothesis. The theory underlying the likelihood ratio is very closely allied to the maximum-likelihood principle mentioned in Section 7.20, and involves the maximum likelihood of the particular sample result *given* the hypothesis $H_0$ relative to the maximum likelihood of the sample result over all possible values of the relevant parameters. Unfortunately, space and the mathematical level assumed here do not permit us to go further into this topic; the student with some command of the elementary calculus will find the likelihood ratio explained clearly in the text by Mood (1950). For the moment, suffice it to say that the "classical" tests of hypotheses to be discussed in Chapter 10 and thereafter are all equivalent to likelihood ratio tests. These are "best" available tests for the hypotheses considered, meaning that when the assumptions underlying these tests are true, no other available procedure would answer our question about $H_0$ and $H_1$ better than the one we will use.

## 9.25   CONFIDENCE INTERVALS

Hypothesis testing is but one form of statistical inference commonly used in psychological research. In many circumstances the primary purpose of data collection is not to test a hypothesis, but rather to obtain an estimate of some parameter. It was shown in Chapter 7 that the sample mean is an unbiased estimate of the population mean, and in the maximum-likelihood sense, the sample mean is our best estimate of its normal population counterpart.

Nevertheless, it is clear that sample mean ordinarily will not be equal to the true population value because of sampling error. It is necessary to qualify our estimate in some way to indicate the general magnitude of this error. Usually this is done by showing a confidence interval, which is **an estimated range of values with a given high probability of covering the true population value.** When there is a large degree of sampling error the confidence interval estimated from any sample will be large; the range of values likely to cover the population mean is wide. On the other hand, if sampling error is small the true value is likely to be covered by a small estimated range of values; in this case one can feel confident that he has "trapped" the true value within a small range of estimation for any sample.

In any normal distribution of sample means, with population mean $\mu$ and standard deviation $\sigma_M$, the following statement is true: **Over all samples of** $N$**, the probability is approximately .95 that**

$$-1.96\sigma_M \leq \mu - M \leq +1.96\sigma_M. \qquad [9.25.1^*]$$

That is, very nearly 95 percent of all possible sample means from the population in question must lie within 1.96 standard errors to either side of the true mean. You can check this for yourself from Table I.

However, the statement above is still true if we alter the inequality by adding $M$ to each term: **Over all sample values of** $M$**, the probability is approximately .95 that**

$$M - 1.96\sigma_M \leq \mu \leq M + 1.96\sigma_M. \qquad [9.25.2^*]$$

This is, over all possible samples, the probability is about .95 that the range between $M - 1.96\sigma_M$ and $M + 1.96\sigma_M$ will include the true mean, $\mu$.

This range of values between $M \pm 1.96\sigma_M$ is called the **95 percent confidence interval for** $\mu$. The two boundaries of the interval, or $M + 1.96\sigma_M$ and $M - 1.96\sigma_M$, are called **the 95 percent confidence limits.**

Although the best estimate of $\mu$ is $M$, of course, the confidence interval based on any sample can be thought of as a range of "good" estimates. One can think of the confidence interval as containing all the hypotheses about $\mu$ that could not be rejected at the .05 level (two-tailed) in the light of the evidence $M$.

Be sure to notice that $\mu$ is not a random variable and the probability statement is really not about $\mu$, but about *samples*. The population either does or does not have a $\mu$ equal to a given number, and if we use the ordinary relative-frequency definition of probability it does not make sense to say "the probability is such and such that the true mean takes on value $x$." Thus, one must be very careful about how he interprets the confidence interval. Before any sample mean is seen, one may decide to compute the 95 percent confidence interval for each and every sample. The actual range of numbers obtained for a sample will depend on the value of $M$. In short, over all possible samples, there will be many possible 95 percent confidence intervals. Some of these confidence intervals will represent the event "covers the true mean," and others will not. If one such confidence interval were sampled at random, then the probability is .95 that it covers the true mean.

**The 99 percent confidence interval for the mean is given by**

$$M - 2.58\sigma_M \leq \mu \leq M + 2.58\sigma_M. \qquad [9.25.3*]$$

Notice that the 99 percent confidence interval is larger than the 95 percent interval. More possible values are included, and thus one can assert with more confidence that the true mean is covered. A 100 percent confidence interval would be

$$M - \infty\sigma_M < \mu < M + \infty\sigma_M.$$

Here, one can be completely confident that the true value is covered, since the range includes all possible values of $\mu$. On the other hand, the 0 percent interval is simply $M$; for a continuous sampling distribution of $M$, the probability is zero that $M$ exactly equals $\mu$.

In the particular situation where the population $\sigma$ is known, then an analogy to the idea of finding confidence intervals for the mean is tossing rings of a certain size at a post. The size of the confidence interval is like the diameter of a ring, and random sampling is like random tosses at the post. The predetermined size of the ring determines the chances that the ring will cover the post on a given try, just as the size of the confidence interval governs the probability that the true value $\mu$ will be covered by the range of values in the estimated interval. Reducing the size of $\sigma_M$ by increasing $N$ is like improving our aim, since we are more likely to cover the true value with an interval of a given size in terms of $\sigma_M$. Later when we deal with situations where the population $\sigma$ is unknown, the analogy becomes that of tossing rings with a certain *distribution* of sizes at a post; here, the probability that the ring covers the post on a given try depends on the distribution of ring-sizes used, just as the probability that the confidence interval covers the true mean depends on the distribution of estimated confidence intervals over random samples. This idea will be elaborated upon in the next chapter.

It is interesting to note that, in principle, the 95 percent, or 99 percent, or any other confidence interval for a mean might be defined in other ways. For example, for a normal sampling distribution of $M$ it is true that the probability is approximate'y .95 that

$$-1.75\sigma_M \leq \mu - M \leq 2.33\sigma_M.$$

This implies that a 95 percent confidence interval might possibly be found with limits

$$M - 1.75\sigma_M \text{ and } M + 2.33\sigma_M.$$

In a similar way, still another 95 percent confidence interval might be found having limits

$$M - 2.06\sigma_M \text{ and } M + 1.88\sigma_M,$$

and so on. In principle, 95 percent confidence limits for $\mu$ might be found in any number of ways, since any number of ways exist to find areas in a normal distribution equivalent to probabilities of .95.

If so many different ways of defining the 95 percent confidence interval are possible, what is the advantage of defining this confidence interval to have limits

$$M - 1.96\sigma_M \text{ and } M + 1.96\sigma_M?$$

The answer is that, in the particular case of the mean, this way of defining the confidence interval gives the *shortest* possible range of values such that the probability statement holds. Naturally, there is an advantage in pinning the population parameter within the narrowest possible range with a given probability, and this dictates the form of the confidence interval we use. A secondary consideration is that this way of defining the confidence interval corresponds to the standard two-tailed test of the mean, so that a parameter value falling outside the 95 percent confidence interval for the mean for a particular sample would be rejected as a hypothesis (at the .05 level, two-tailed) in the light of this sample. Later, in Chapter 11, we will encounter standard confidence intervals for other parameters which, unfortunately, do not yield the shortest possible such intervals.

In many ways the presentation of a confidence interval in a data report is much more informative than reporting a hypothesis test or only a significance level. The reader can test any hypothesis he may entertain simply by looking at the confidence interval; only if the $\mu$ value in question lies outside the $100(1 - \alpha)$ percent confidence interval can the hypothesis be rejected beyond the $\alpha$ level in a two-tailed test. The confidence interval for $\mu$ not only specifies the unbiased estimate of the mean, but also includes the error variation qualifying that estimate.

As an example of a confidence interval for the mean when $\sigma_M$ is known, consider a sample of 50 cases giving a mean of 143. The population standard deviation, $\sigma$, is 35. The 95 percent confidence interval will be found. First of all,

$$\sigma_M = \frac{35}{\sqrt{50}} = 4.9.$$

Then the desired interval is

$$143 - (1.96)(4.9) \leq \mu \leq 143 + (1.96)(4.9)$$
$$133.39 \leq \mu \leq 152.60.$$

In succeeding sections methods for finding confidence intervals will be given not only for means, but also for proportions, for differences between means, and for variances. It is extremely good practice to compute and report confidence intervals, and the student should get in the habit of reporting them routinely for his data. Ordinarily, far more of interest is communicated to the reader of a research report by a confidence interval than by any other statistical summary of results.

### 9.26  APPROXIMATE CONFIDENCE INTERVALS FOR PROPORTIONS

Forming an exact confidence interval for a proportion is a considerably more complicated business than it is for a single mean. The trouble is that although the standard error of the mean does not depend upon the true mean's value, the standard error of a proportion $P$ does depend upon true $p$. From a sample, however, we have only $P$, an *estimate* of $p$, and so the true standard error is unknown unless $p$ is known.

However, when samples are large, so that the sampling distribution of the proportion is approximately normal, the $100(1 - \alpha)$ percent confidence limits for a proportion are given approximately by

$$\frac{N}{N + z^2}\left[ P + \frac{z^2}{2N} \pm z \sqrt{\frac{PQ}{N} + \frac{z^2}{4N^2}} \right] \qquad \text{[9.26.1\dag]}$$

where $z$ is the standard score in a normal distribution cutting off the *upper* $\alpha/2$ proportion of cases. These limits define the $100(1 - \alpha)$ percent confidence interval for $p$.

This rather mysterious-looking form for finding the confidence limits for a proportion can be justified as follows: Since the sampling distribution of $P$ for large samples can be assumed approximately normal, the appropriate confidence limits should be approximately

$$P - z\sqrt{\frac{(pq)}{N}} \text{ and } P + z\sqrt{\frac{(pq)}{N}}.$$

The possible values of $p$ corresponding to the limits thus satisfy the relation

$$\frac{N(P - p)^2}{(p - p^2)} = z^2.$$

Working out this quadratic equation in terms of $p$ we have

$$(N + z^2)p^2 - (2NP + z^2)p + NP^2 = 0.$$

Solving for $p$ by the rule for a quadratic equation,

$$\frac{-b \pm \sqrt{b^2 - 4ac}}{2a}$$

where $a = N + z^2$
$\quad b = -(2NP + z^2)$
$\quad c = NP^2$

and arranging terms gives expression **9.26.1**.

If $N$ is very large, this confidence interval may be replaced by the simpler approximation

$$P - z\sqrt{\frac{PQ}{N}} \leqq p \leqq P + z\sqrt{\frac{PQ}{N}}. \qquad \text{[9.26.2\dag]}$$

### 9.27 SAMPLE SIZE AND THE ACCURACY OF ESTIMATION OF THE MEAN

The width of any confidence interval for the mean $\mu$ depends upon $\sigma_M$, the standard error, and anything that makes $\sigma_M$ proportionately smaller reduces the width of the interval. Thus, any increase in sample size, operating to reduce $\sigma_M$, makes the confidence interval shorter. For example, the $\sigma$ value for some normal population is 45. When samples of size 9 are taken the 95 percent confidence interval based on any sample mean has limits

$$M - 1.96(15)$$

and

$$M + 1.96(15).$$

However, if samples of size 81 are taken, these limits come closer together,

$$M - 1.96(5)$$
$$M + 1.96(5),$$

so that the interval itself is smaller for any sample. Samples of 900 cases give a confidence interval which is relatively quite narrow: the limits are

$$M - 1.96(1.5)$$
$$M + 1.96(1.5).$$

Continuing in this way, if the sample size becomes extremely large, the width of the confidence interval approaches zero.

A practical result of this relation between the standard error of the mean and sample size is that *the population mean may be estimated within any desired degree of precision, given a large enough sample size.* This principle has already been introduced in terms of the Tchebycheff inequality (Section 7.11), but it can be stated even more strongly when the sampling distribution has some known form, such as the normal distribution. For instance, how many cases should one sample if he wants the probability to be .99 that his sample mean lies within $.1\sigma$ of the true mean? That is, the experimenter wants

$$\text{prob.}(|M - \mu| \leq .1\sigma) = .99.$$

Assuming that the sampling distribution is nearly normal, which it should be if sample size is large enough, this is equivalent to requiring that the 99 percent confidence interval should have limits

$$M - .1\sigma$$
$$M + .1\sigma.$$

and

However, this is the same as saying that

$$.1\sigma = 2.58\sigma_M$$

so that

$$.1\sigma = 2.58 \frac{\sigma}{\sqrt{N}}.$$

Solving for $N$, we find

$$\sqrt{N} = 25.8$$
$$N = 665.64.$$

In short, if the experimenter makes 666 independent observations, he can be sure that the probability of his estimate's being wrong by more than $.1\sigma$ is only one in one hundred. Notice that we do not have to say exactly what $\sigma$ is in order to specify the desired accuracy in $\sigma$ units, and to find the required sample size.

If the experimenter is willing to take a somewhat larger chance of an absolute error exceeding $.1\sigma$, then the required $N$ is smaller. If the probability of an error exceeding $.1\sigma$ in absolute magnitude is to be $.05$,

$$.1\sigma = 1.96\sigma_M$$
$$.1\sigma = 1.96 \frac{\sigma}{\sqrt{N}}$$

so that $N = 384$.

This idea may be turned around to find the accuracy *almost* insured by any given sample size. Given that $N$ is, say, 30, within how many $\sigma$ units of the true mean will the sample estimate fall with probability $.95$? Here, letting $k$ stand for the required number of $\sigma$ units,

$$k\sigma = 1.96 \frac{\sigma}{\sqrt{N}}$$

or

$$k = \frac{1.96}{\sqrt{30}} = \frac{1.96}{5.48} = .358.$$

For $N = 30$, the chances are about 95 in 100 that our estimate of $\mu$ falls within about $.36$ population standard deviations of the true value, provided that the sampling distribution is approximately normal.

It is obvious that the accuracy of estimation in a psychological experiment could be judged in this way. If the sample size is known, then one can judge how "off" the est mate of the mean is likely to be in terms of the population standard deviation. Furthermore, if one has some idea of the desirable accuracy of estimation, then he can set his sample size so as to attain that degree of accuracy with high probability. This is a very sensible and easy way to determine necessary sample size. Unfortunately, it does require the experimenter to think to some extent about the population he is sampling and what he is going to do with the result. For the problem at hand, just how much error in estimation can he tolerate?

## 9.28  AN EXAMPLE OF SAMPLE SIZE DETERMINED BY DESIRED ACCURACY OF ESTIMATION

The problem of determination of sample size is a most troublesome one in psychology. Unless one knows the accuracy with which he must estimate in some problem, or has an idea of the true departure from $H_0$ he must detect in a significance test, then there is simply no way to answer the question "How big a sample must I take?" Most psychologists would answer, "The bigger the better." In one sense this is right; as we have seen, we can always achieve relatively more power in a test and relatively more accurate estimation by increased sample size. Nevertheless, there is another consideration: anyone who has ever conducted a psychological study of any kind knows that random samples are extremely hard to obtain. Each increase in the number of observations may represent a large additional investment of the experimenter's time and funds. Particularly in experimental studies, it may not be possible to carry out a careful experiment with limited resources on a large number of subjects. Something has to "give" if the number of subjects is large, and it may be the quality of the experiment that suffers in the long run.

However, there are some instances where the result of the study is to be applied in some way and where the desired accuracy of estimation can be decided upon in terms of the intended application. One such instance is given below.

A psychologist in a large school system advocates that children studying a particular subject should be divided into two sections, based on their reading skills. He proposes that before children are assigned to a section, each should be given a reading test, with those falling at or above the reading-score mean going into the advanced section, and those below going into the slower section.

The school system is quite large, and the mean reading test-score for this particular population of children is not known. Consequently, the experimenter wants to estimate the population mean by drawing a random sample. This estimated mean will then be used to classify any child on the basis of his score.

Moreover, the psychologist knows something about the reading test itself as applied to children of that age. Let the score of any child on test be thought of as

$$X_S = T_S + e$$

where $T_S$ is the true reading score, and $e$ is random error. On any given occasion, the measurement of a child will be in error to some extent. In fact, independent measurements of any given child over different occasions should form a distribution, with mean $T_S$ and standard deviation $\sigma_S$. Furthermore, this distribution is thought of as normal (Fig. 9.28.1).

Studies of this test in the past have given an estimate of the *standard error of measurement*, which is the standard deviation of a child's hypothetical distribution of scores over measurement occasions. These studies have shown that the standard error of measurement should be about $.2\sigma$, where $\sigma$ is the population distribution's standard deviation. That is,

$$\sigma_S = .2\sigma.$$

Even if the population mean $\mu$ were known and actually used to classify any given child, there would still be a probability of misclassifying him because of the error in his obtained score. Thus, if $T_S$ fell below $\mu$, the child *ought* to go into the lower group. However, it would be possible for $X_S$ to fall above $\mu$ even though the child belongs in the lower group, and this would lead to a misclassification. Furthermore, if only the *estimate* $M$ is used for $\mu$, then there are two

FIG. 9.28.1. Hypothetical distribution of scores for a single individual over independent trials

reasons why a child may be misclassified: either his score contains error, or the mean used as a cutoff point is wrong (or both). Consider the possible distribution of scores for a child whose true reading ability is $T_S = \mu - .5\sigma$, as shown in Figure 9.28.2.

FIG. 9.28.2

Even though his score is compared with $\mu$, there is still some probability of a student's being misclassified. A misclassification occurs when $X_S$ turns out to equal or exceed $\mu$, so that the probability is found from

$$z = \frac{\mu - T_S}{\sigma_S} = \frac{\mu - (\mu - .5\sigma)}{.2\sigma}$$

$$= 2.5.$$

The probability is about .01 that this child will be placed in the wrong group. On the other hand, suppose that the *estimated* mean is actually $\mu - .4\sigma$, and this *estimate* $M$ is used in place of the unknown $\mu$. In this case, the $z$ score corresponding to $M$ in the *subject's* score distribution is

$$z = \frac{(\mu - .4\sigma) - (\mu - .5\sigma)}{.2\sigma}$$

$$= .5,$$

so that the probability of misclassification using the *sample* mean as the cutoff point is about .31. If the sample mean $M$ should fall even further below true $\mu$, then the probability of a misclassification is even larger.

The psychologist wants to be very sure that students who really are $.5\sigma$ or more below average in the population will be classified correctly. He wants no more than 5 in 100 such truly low students to be put into the high group. How many cases should he observe to estimate the population mean?

The requirement that the psychologist has set implies that $M$ must be quite close to $\mu$; in fact, he decides that he wants the probability to be only .01 that $M$ is more than $k\sigma$ away from $\mu$. These two requirements, the .05 probability of a misclassification, and the probability of a $k\sigma$ departure of $M$ from $\mu$, are equivalent to the following:

$$\frac{M - T_S}{\sigma_S} = \frac{(\mu - k\sigma) - (\mu - .5\sigma)}{.2\sigma} = 1.65$$

and
$$k\sigma = 2.58\sigma_M.$$

First of all, we solve for $k$:

$$\frac{\sigma(.5 - k)}{.2\sigma} = 1.65$$
$$.5 - k = .330$$
$$k = .17.$$

The estimate of the mean should be no more than $.17\sigma$ away from $\mu$. We want this to be true with probability .99. Now we solve for $N$:

$$.17\sigma = \frac{2.58\sigma}{\sqrt{N}}$$
$$\sqrt{N} = 15.18$$
$$N = 231, \text{ approximately.}$$

In short, if the experimenter wants to be this sure that he will get a sample mean close enough to $\mu$ to permit children $.5\sigma$ below $\mu$ to be classified correctly 95 percent of the time, he should observe at least 231 cases to estimate $\mu$. This sample size may exceed the psychologist's resources, and he may have to lower his sights somewhat. If he is willing to take more risk either of a misclassification, or of a deviant mean, then the required number of cases is, of course, smaller. On the other hand, if he can exceed this number of cases, he may be even more confident that his requirements are met.

Although this example is rather long and contrived, perhaps it will make clear that it is possible to set a lower bound on sample size by considering accuracy of estimation. This kind of procedure seems especially appropriate when the estimate is going to be used for individual classification or prediction of some kind. Quite often, experimenters have information letting them estimate the error variability in individual scores, especially the standard error of measurement, and this can provide a criterion for how precise the estimate of the mean must be in order to be accurate enough for the purpose.

## 9.29  EVIDENCE AND CHANGE IN PERSONAL PROBABILITY

In some research settings, a very good case can be made that the purpose of data collection is neither to permit an immediate decision to be made nor to obtain point-estimates of parameters. Instead, the purpose of data collection is to modify the experimenter's *degrees of belief* in the various situations that may exist. The experimenter starts out with various hypotheses about the true situation. He does not begin his experimentation in a state of total ignorance, however. For various theoretical and empirical reasons he has reason to believe in some of these hypotheses more strongly than others, *before* the data are seen. Then as a result of the data he adjusts his beliefs, so that some may be strengthened, some weakened, and still others unchanged. In short, some statisticians and psychologists would argue that scientific investigation does not usually deal with decision making, but rather with alteration in personal probabilities. As evidence accumulates some beliefs become so strong that these propositions are regarded as proved, and become part of the body of empirical science. Other beliefs fall away as evidence fails to support them.

The idea of personal probability has already been introduced in the discussion of decision-rules. Let us suppose once again that it is possible to assign numerical values to various hypotheses, each standing for the experimenter's personal probability that a given proposition is true.

For example, in the situation described in Section 9.5, the experimenter knows that the true population proportion is either

$$H_0: p = .80$$
or
$$H_1: p = .40,$$

so that we may regard the personal probability for any other $H$ to be zero. Suppose that in the light of what the experimenter already knows he has good reason to believe much more strongly in $H_0$ than in $H_1$. Imagine the personal probabilities assigned to these hypotheses are

$$\mathcal{P}(H_0) = .75$$
$$\mathcal{P}(H_1) = .25.$$

The experimenter is willing to give odds of three to one that $H_0$ is true. These personal probabilities of the experimenter are *prior*, since they reflect his degree of belief in the two alternatives before the evidence. After the data are observed, something should happen to these personal probabilities; the degree of belief in each of the hypotheses should change somewhat.

The personal probability for $H_0$, given the evidence $y$, will be designated by $\mathcal{P}(H_0|y)$, and that for $H_1$ by $\mathcal{P}(H_1|y)$. These are *posterior* values, since they *do* depend upon what is observed.

How should evidence affect the degree of belief in a given hypothesis? The key is given by Bayes' theorem, discussed in Section 4.5. If personal probabilities operate like ordinary, relative-frequency, probabilities, then by Bayes' theorem,

$$\mathcal{P}(H_0|y) = \frac{p(y|H_0)\mathcal{P}(H_0)}{p(y|H_0)\mathcal{P}(H_0) + p(y|H_1)\mathcal{P}(H_1)}.$$

The $p(y|H_0)$ and $p(y|H_1)$ are the usual probabilities dealt with in statistical inference: the conditional probability of evidence given that the particular hypothesis is true. Notice that, other things being equal, the more likely is $y$ given $H_0$, and the less likely is $y$ given $H_1$, the larger is $\mathcal{P}(H_0|y)$. Under this conception, evidence made likely by one hypothesis and not by the other always strengthens belief in the first, and weakens belief in the second.

However, the effective *strength* of the evidence also depends upon the *prior personal probabilities*. The amount that evidence changes degree of belief in $H_0$ and $H_1$ depends on the *prior* $\mathcal{P}(H_0)$ and $\mathcal{P}(H_1)$ values. For example, suppose that the experimenter observes a sample proportion $P$ of .6 among 10 cases. From the sampling distributions given in Section 9.5, we can see that

$$p(.6|H_0) = .088$$
$$p(.6|H_1) = .111.$$

Applying Bayes' theorem, we find

$$\begin{aligned}
\mathcal{P}(H_0|.6) &= \frac{p(.6|H_0)\mathcal{P}(H_0)}{p(.6|H_0)\mathcal{P}(H_0) + p(.6|H_1)\mathcal{P}(H_1)} \\
&= \frac{.066}{.066 + .028} \\
&= .70 \\
\mathcal{P}(H_1|.6) &= .30.
\end{aligned}$$

This evidence lowers the personal probability for $H_0$ somewhat, since it is less probable under $H_0$ than $H_1$. However, the posterior personal probability for $H_0$ is *still* much greater than for $H_1$, reflecting the original discrepancy in the degree of belief the experimenter holds for each.

On the other hand, suppose that the sample evidence is a $P$ of .3. Here,

$$p(.3|H_0) = .001; \; p(.3|H_1) = .215.$$

Notice that this value of $P$ is *very* improbable if $H_0$ were true. Now,

$$\begin{aligned}
\mathcal{P}(H_0|.3) &= \frac{(.001)(.75)}{(.001)(.75) + (.215)(.25)} \\
&= \frac{.00075}{.00075 + .05375} = .01 \\
\mathcal{P}(H_1|.3) &= 1 - (H_0|.3) = .99.
\end{aligned}$$

In spite of the original weighting given the evidence by the prior personal probabilities, this time the $P$ obtained is so unlikely given $H_0$ that the experimenter is almost certain that $H_1$ is true in the light of the evidence.

This way of evaluating evidence actually uses the raw materials of ordinary tests of hypotheses; as we have seen, the net result of any significance test is a conditional probability statement given that $H_0$ is true. However, a new ingredient is added: the prior personal probabilities of the experimenter. Intuitively, this approach has much to recommend it. In many ways it seems a far better description of what the scientist actually does with the statistical result than is the usual discussion of a significance test, burdened as it is with irrelevant decision terminology. In this conception, the scientist is viewed as changing his mind in the light of evidence, but he is not thought of as making some phony decision.

On the other hand, mathematical statisticians are not always enthusiastic about this approach. The general idea is very old, and at one time was carried to extreme and unreasonable lengths. Even metaphysical questions were treated by this general method. Much of modern theoretical statistics grew out of attempts to get away from the idea of prior probabilities, and it is not surprising that many statisticians look at such uses of Bayes' theorem with a jaundiced eye.

An elementary text is obviously no place to go into a detailed discussion of the procedures or of the relative merits of this form of inference. The interested student is referred to an informative book by Schlaifer (1961), which presents the Bayesian point of view in a modern setting and gives more advanced methods based on Bayes' theorem. It is certain that psychology has not heard the last of this matter, and perhaps students who have been exposed to the basic idea can take advantage of developments along this line when they occur. A major issue is, of course, the objective assessment of personal probabilities, which is a very real psychological problem as well. If this question can be settled, then perhaps the experimental psychologist of the future will use inferential methods such as this routinely.

## 9.30  SIGNIFICANCE TESTS AND COMMON SENSE

Stripped of the language of decision theory and of concern with personal probabilities, all that a significant result implies is that one has observed something relatively unlikely given the hypothetical situation, but relatively more likely given some alternative situation. Everything else is a matter of what one does with this information. Statistical significance is a statement about conditional probability, nothing else. It does not guarantee that something important, or even meaningful, has been found.

If a psychologist is seriously concerned with making a decision from his data, then he should pay attention to the possible losses the various outcomes represent for him. There is no guarantee that the use of any of the conventionalized rules for deciding significance is appropriate for his particular purpose. On the other hand, so long as the real costs of decision errors in scientific research remain as obscure as they are at present, then these conventions may not be a bad thing. In a young science, still mapping out its area of study, the error of pursuing a "phantom" result *is* costly, perhaps even more so than failing to recognize a real experimental effect when we see one. If these conventions are actually used to determine which lines of research are pursued and which are abandoned, then at least we tend to follow up the big departures from expectation that our data show.

However, conventions about significant results should not be turned into canons of good scientific practice. Even more emphatically, a convention must not be made a superstition. It is interesting to speculate how many of the early discoveries in physical science would have been statistically significant in the experiments where they were first observed. Even in the crude and poorly controlled experiment, some departures from expectation stand out simply because they are interesting and suggest things to us that we might not be able to explain. These are matters that warrant looking into further regardless of what the conventional rule says to decide. Statistics cannot do the scientist's basic job—looking and wondering and looking again.

It is a grave error to evaluate the "goodness" of an experiment only in terms of the significance level of its results. Regardless of the scientist's convictions about personal probability, even a little bit of evidence coming out of a careful experiment is far more persuasive than a great deal from a sloppy one. To what population of subjects do the conclusions refer? Has a significant result been "bought" by restricting the population so much that the result fails to have any generality at all? In an effort to achieve a large sample $N$ has the experimenter sacrificed all claim that his sample is random? Finally, how potent is the finding in a *predictive* sense: how much do these results permit us to reduce our uncertainty about the status of a given individual in this situation? This is by no means the same as statistical significance! As we shall see in later chapters, it is entirely possible for a highly significant result to contribute nothing to our ability to predict behavior, and for a nonsignificant result to mask an important gain in predictive ability.

It is very easy for research psychologists, particularly young psychologists, to become overconcerned with statistical method. Sometimes the problem itself seems almost secondary to some elegant method of data-analysis. Significant results are often confused with good results. But overemphasizing the role of statistical significance in research is like confusing the paintbrush with the painting. This form of statistical inference is a valuable tool in research, but it is never the arbiter of good research.

The remainder of this book is about statistical inference, and largely about significance tests. Since a text in statistics must necessarily deal mostly with statistics, there just is not room to discuss all the *if's, and's,* and *but's* that accompany the use of this tool in research. The skills of doing good research are acquired slowly, and often painfully, although a good share both of native curiosity and of common sense help matters along. Statistical texts can display the tools, but they cannot give a guide to their use in every conceivable situation. If the user has some idea of how the tool works perhaps he can see its uses and limitations in a given situation. Expert help is available and should always be sought. But if there is ever a conflict between the use of a statistical technique and common sense, then common sense comes first. Careful observation is the main business of empirical science, and statistical methods are useful only so long as they help, not hinder, the systematic exploration of data and the cumulation and coordination of results.

# INFERENCES ABOUT POPULATION MEANS

# 10

In this chapter we are going to discuss ways for making inferences about means, first for a single population and then for a difference between the means of two populations. The procedures and conventions of significance testing were emphasized in the previous chapter, and now we are going to apply these procedures to tests of hypotheses about means. Remember that a significant result will always be one falling among those that are extremely deviant from expectation and that are improbable if the null hypothesis were true, but that agree relatively well with expectation and have relatively higher probability if some situation covered by the alternative hypothesis were true. Before the test is carried out, some $\alpha$ level for significance is chosen as a specification of "improbable event, given $H_0$," for this situation. The conventional rules of the game determine which of the values of $\alpha$ are chosen.

## 10.1 LARGE-SAMPLE PROBLEMS WITH UNKNOWN POPULATION $\sigma^2$

In most of the examples of hypothesis testing up to this point we have actually "fudged" a bit on the usual situation: we have assumed that $\sigma^2$ is somehow known, so that the standard error of the mean is also known exactly. In these examples the author did not explain how $\sigma^2$ became known, largely because he could not think up a good reason. Now we must face the cold facts of the matter: for inferences about the population mean, $\sigma^2$ is seldom known. Instead, we must use the only substitute available for $\sigma^2$, which is our unbiased estimate $\hat{s}^2$, calculated from the sample.

Notice that this problem does not exist for hypotheses about a population proportion $p$, since the existence of an exact hypothesis about $p$ specifies what the value of the standard error of $P$, the sample proportion, must be. Therefore, the special techniques of this chapter apply only to inferences about means, and not to inferences about proportions.

From what we have already seen of the relation between sample size and accuracy of estimation, it makes sense that for large samples $\hat{s}^2$ should be a very good estimate of $\sigma^2$. *In general, for very large samples, there is rather little risk of a sizable error when one uses $\hat{s}$ in place of $\sigma$ in estimating the standard error of the mean.*

Hence, when the sample size is quite large, tests of hypotheses about a single mean are carried out in the same way as when $\sigma$ is known, except that the standard error of the mean is estimated from the sample:

$$\text{est. } \sigma_M = \frac{\hat{s}}{\sqrt{N}} = \frac{s}{\sqrt{N-1}}.$$

The standardized score corresponding to the sample mean is then referred to the normal distribution. This step is justified by the central limit theorem when $N$ is large, regardless of the population distribution's form.

For example, consider the following problem. A small rodent characteristically shows hoarding behavior for certain kinds of foodstuffs when the environmental temperature drops to a certain point. Numerous previous experiments have shown that in a fixed period of time, and given a fixed food supply, the mean amount of food hoarded by an animal is 9 grams. The experimenter is currently interested in possible effects that early food deprivation may have upon such hoarding behavior in the animal as an adult. So, the experimenter takes a random sample of 175 infant animals and keeps them on survival rations for a fixed period while they are at a certain age, and on regular rations thereafter. When the animals are adults he puts each one in an experimental situation where the lowered temperature condition is introduced. The amount of food each hoards is recorded, and a score is assigned to each animal.

What is the null hypothesis implied here? The basic experimental question is "Does the experimental treatment (deprivation) tend to affect the amount of food hoarded?" The experimenter has no special reason to expect either an increase or a decrease in amount, but is interested only in finding out if a difference from normal behavior occurs. This question may be put into the form of a null and an alternative hypothesis:

$$H_0: \mu_0 = 9 \text{ grams}$$
$$H_1: \mu \neq 9 \text{ grams}.$$

Suppose that the conventional level chosen for $\alpha$ is .01, so that the experimenter will say that the result is significant only if the sample mean falls among either the upper .005 or the lower .005 of all possible results, given $H_0$. Reference to Table I shows that .005 is the probability of $z$ score in a normal distribution falling at or below $-2.58$, and the probability is likewise .005 for a $z$ equal to or exceeding $+2.58$. Accordingly, the sample result will be significant only if

$$z_M = \frac{M - E(M)}{\text{est. } \sigma_M}$$

equals or exceeds 2.58 in absolute magnitude (disregarding sign). When the null hypothesis is true, $E(M) = 9$, and for a sample this large the value of the standard error of the mean should be reasonably close to $\dfrac{\hat{s}}{\sqrt{N}}$ or $\dfrac{s}{\sqrt{N-1}}$, the value of the sample estimate.

Everything is now set for a significance test except for the sample results. The sample shows a mean of 8.8 grams of food hoarded, with a standard deviation, $s$, of 2.3. The estimated standard error of the mean is thus

$$\text{est. } \sigma_M = \frac{2.3}{\sqrt{175 - 1}} = \frac{2.3}{13.19} = .174.$$

The standardized score of the mean is found to be

$$z_M = \frac{8.8 - 9}{.174} = \frac{-.2}{.174} = -1.149.$$

This result does not qualify for the region of rejection for $\alpha = .01$. Since the experimenter feels that he can afford to reject $H_0$ only if the $\alpha$ probability of error is no more than .01, then he cannot do so on the basis of this sample. On the other hand, the risk run in accepting $H_0$ is unknown, so he might well suspend judgment, pending more evidence.

## 10.2   Confidence intervals for large samples with unknown $\sigma^2$

Confidence intervals may also be found by the methods of Chapter 9. However, either when $\sigma^2$ is unknown, or when the population distribution has unknown form, a normal sampling distribution is assumed only for large samples. Just as in significance tests, the estimated standard error of the mean can be used in place of $\sigma_M$ in finding confidence limits when the sample is relatively large.

For example, the experimenter studying hoarding behavior computes the approximate 99 percent confidence limits in the following way:

$$M - 2.58 \, (\text{est. } \sigma_M)$$
and
$$M + 2.58 \, (\text{est. } \sigma_M)$$

so that for this problem, the numerical confidence limits are

$$8.8 - 2.58(.174) \text{ or } 8.35$$
and
$$8.8 + 2.58(.174) \text{ or } 9.25.$$

The experimenter can say that the probability is approximately .99 that the true value of $\mu$ is covered by an interval such as that between 8.35 and 9.25.

Notice that the value $\mu_0 = 9$ falls between these limits, reflecting the fact that the hypothesis $H_0$ cannot be rejected if $\alpha$ is set at .01 (two-tailed).

## 10.3 THE PROBLEM OF UNKNOWN $\sigma^2$ WHEN SAMPLE SIZE IS SMALL

Just as for any statistic used to estimate a parameter value, the estimated standard error of the mean will very likely not be exactly equal to $\sigma_M$. This is not a particular problem when sample size is large, since we can at least be sure that est. $\sigma_M$ is very likely to be close to the true $\sigma_M$ in value.

On the other hand, we simply cannot have this confidence in our estimate of the standard error when sample size is small. Our estimate is almost bound to be in error to some extent, and if the sample size is very small, we can expect the size of this error to be substantial in any given sample. This necessitates a different approach to the problem of testing hypotheses and establishing confidence intervals for the population mean for small samples.

In inferences about $\mu$, the ratio we would like to evaluate and refer to a normal sampling distribution is the standardized score

$$z_M = \frac{M - E(M)}{\sigma_M}. \qquad [10.3.1^*]$$

However, when we have only an *estimate* of $\sigma_M$, then the ratio we really compute and use is not a normal standardized score at all, although it has much the same form. The ratio actually used is

$$t = \frac{M - E(M)}{\text{est. } \sigma_M}. \qquad [10.3.2^*]$$

There is an extremely important difference between the two ratios, $z_M$ and $t$. For $z_M$, the numerator $(M - E(M))$ is a random variable, the value of which depends upon the particular sample drawn from a given population situation; on the other hand, the denominator is a constant, $\sigma_M$, which is the same regardless of the particular sample of size $N$ we observe. Now contrast this ratio with the ratio $t$: just as before, the numerator of $t$ is a random variable, but the denominator is also a random variable, since the particular value of $\hat{s}$— and hence the estimate of $\sigma_M$— is a sample quantity. Over several different samples, the same value of $M$ must give us precisely the same value of $z_M$; however, over different samples, the same value of $M$ will give us different $t$ values. Similar intervals of $t$ and $z_M$ values should have different probabilities of occurrence. For this reason it is risky to use the ratio $t$ as though it were $z_M$ unless the sample size is very large.

## 10.4 THE DISTRIBUTION OF $t$

The solution to the problem of the nonequivalence of $t$ and $z_M$ rests on the study of $t$ itself as a random variable. That is, suppose that the $t$ ratio were computed for each conceivable sample of $N$ independent observations drawn from some normal population distribution with true mean $\mu$. Each sample would have some $t$ value,

$$t = \frac{M - E(M)}{\text{est. } \sigma_M} = \frac{M - \mu}{s/\sqrt{N - 1}}.$$   [10.4.1*]

Over the different samples the value of $t$ would vary, of course, and the different possible values would each have some probability-density. A random variable such as $t$ is an example of a *test*-statistic, so called to distinguish it from an ordinary descriptive statistic or estimator, such as $M$ or $\hat{s}^2$. The $t$ value depends on other sample statistics, but is not itself an estimate of a population value. Nevertheless, such test-statistics have sampling distributions just as ordinary sample statistics do, and these sampling distributions have been studied extensively.

*In order to find the exact distribution of t, one must assume that the basic population distribution is normal.* The main reason for the necessity of this assumption is that only for a normal distribution will the basic random variables in numerator and denominator, sample $M$ and $s$, be statistically independent; this is a use of the important fact mentioned in Section 8.8. Unless $M$ and $s$ are independent, the sampling distribution of $t$ is extremely difficult to specify exactly. On the other hand, for the special case of normal populations, the distribution of the ratio $t$ is quite well known. In order to learn what this distribution is like, let us take a look at the rule for the density function associated with this random variable.

The density function for $t$ is given by the rule:

$$f(t) = G(\nu) \left[ 1 + \frac{t^2}{\nu} \right]^{-(\nu+1)/2}.$$   [10.4.2*]

Here, $G(\nu)$ stands for a constant number which depends *only* on the parameter $\nu$ (Greek nu), and how this number is found need not really concern us. Let us focus our attention on only the "working part" of the rule, which involves only $\nu$ and the value of $t$. This looks very different from the normal distribution function rule in Section 8.1. As with the normal function rule, however, a quick look at this mathematical expression tells us much about the distribution of $t$.

First of all, notice that the particular value of $t$ enters this rule only as a squared quantity, showing that the distribution of sample $t$ values must be symmetric, since a positive and a negative value having the same absolute size must be assigned the same probability-density by this rule. Second, since all the constants in the function rule are positive numbers, and the entire term involving $t$ is raised to a negative power, the largest possible density value is assigned to $t = 0$. Thus $t = 0$ is the distribution mode. If we inferred from the symmetry and unimodality of this distribution that the mean of $t$ is also 0, we should be quite correct. In short, the $t$ distribution is a unimodal, symmetric, bell-shaped distribution having a graphic form much like a normal distribution, even though the two function rules are quite dissimilar. Loosely speaking, the curve for a $t$ distribution differs from the standardized normal in being "plumper" in extreme regions and "flatter" in the central region, as Figure 10.4.1 shows. (Note that both $t$ and the standardized normal distribution have a mean of zero.)

The most important feature of the $t$ distribution will appear if we return for a look at the function rule. Notice that the only unspecified constants in the rule are those represented in **10.4.2** by $\nu$ and $G(\nu)$, which depends only on $\nu$. This is a **one-parameter distribution**: the single parameter is $\nu$, called *the degrees of freedom. Ordinarily, in most applications of the t distribution to problems involving a single sample, $\nu$ is equal to N − 1, one less than the number of independent observations in the sample.* For samples of $N$ independent observations from any normal population distribution, the exact distribution of sample $t$ values depends only on the degrees of freedom, $N - 1$. Remember, however, that the value of $E(M)$ or $\mu$ must be specified when a $t$ ratio is computed, although the true value of $\sigma$ need not be known.

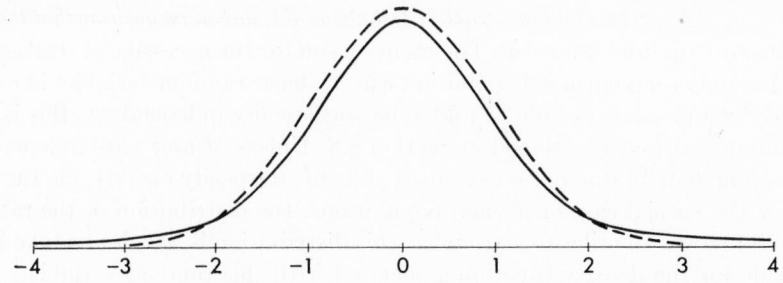

**FIG.** 10.4.1. Distribution of $t$ with $\nu = 4$, and standardized normal distribution

In principle, the value of $\nu$ can be any positive number, and it just happens that $\nu = N - 1$ is the value for the degrees of freedom for the particular $t$ distributions we will use first. Later we will encounter problems calling for $t$ distributions with other numbers of degrees of freedom. Like most theoretical distributions, the $t$ distribution is actually a family of distributions, with general form determined by the function rule, but with particular probabilities dictated by the parameter $\nu$. For any value of $\nu$, the mean of the distribution of $t$ is 0. For $\nu > 2$ the variance of the $t$ distribution is $\nu/(\nu - 2)$, so that the smaller the value of $\nu$ the larger the variance. As $\nu$ becomes large the variance of the $t$ distribution approaches 1.00, which is the variance of the standardized normal distribution.

Incidentally, the random variable $t$ is often called "Student's $t$," and the distribution of $t$, "Student's distribution." This name comes from the statistician W. S. Gosset, who was the first to use this distribution in an important problem, and who first published his results in 1908 under the pen-name "Student."

## 10.5 THE $t$ AND THE STANDARDIZED
### NORMAL DISTRIBUTION

As we have seen, the "shape" of the $t$ distribution is not unlike that of the normal distribution. Just as for the standardized normal, the mean of the distribution of $t$ is 0, although the variance of $t$ is greater than 1.00. Given any extreme interval of fixed size on either tail of the $t$ distribution, the probability associated with this interval in the $t$ distribution is larger than that for the corresponding normal distribution of $z_M$. The smaller the value of $\nu$, the larger is this discrepancy between $t$ and normal probabilities at the extreme ends of each distribution. This reflects and partly explains the danger of using a $t$ ratio as though it were a $z$ ratio: extreme values of $t$ are relatively more likely than comparable values of $z_M$. A small sample size corresponds to a small value of $\nu$, or $N - 1$, and thus there is serious danger of underestimating the probability of an extreme deviation from expectation when sample size is small. This is apparent in the illustration (Figure 10.4.1) showing the distribution of $t$ together with the standardized normal function.

Suppose that a sample of 5 observations is drawn, and from this sample we compute a ratio, $t$, using the estimate of $\sigma_M$ from the sample. Furthermore, suppose that

$$t = \frac{M - E(M)}{\text{est. } \sigma_M} \geq 2.13.$$

That is, we obtain a value for $t$ greater than or equal to 2.13. In the $t$ distribution for samples of size 5 ($\nu = 4$), this interval has probability of .05. That is, when sample size is 5, so that degrees of freedom are 4, the probability of obtaining a ratio in this interval of values is $1/20$. However, if the ratio is interpreted as a $z_M$ variable, then the normal probability for this interval is .0166. Incorrectly considering a $t$ ratio as a standardized normal variable leads one to underestimate the probability of values in extreme intervals, which are really the only intervals of interest in significance tests.

On the other hand, notice what should happen to the distribution of $t$ as $\nu$ becomes large (sample size grows large), as suggested both by Figure 10.4.1 and by the variance of a $t$ distribution. *As sample size $N$ grows large, the distribution of $t$ approaches the standardized normal distribution. For large numbers of degrees of freedom, the exact probabilities of intervals in the $t$ distribution can be approximated closely by normal probabilities.*

The practical result of this convergence of the $t$ and the normal probabilities is that the $t$ ratio *can* be treated as a $z_M$ ratio, provided that the sample size is substantial. The normal probabilities are quite close to—though not identical with—the exact $t$ probabilities for large $\nu$. On the other hand, when sample size is small the normal probabilities cannot safely be used, and instead one uses a special table based on the $t$ distribution.

How large is "large enough" to permit use of the normal tables? If the population distribution is truly normal, even forty or so cases permit a fairly accurate use of the normal tables in confidence intervals or tests for a mean. If really good accuracy is desired in determining interval probabilities, the $t$ distribution should be used even when the sample size is around 100 cases. Beyond this number of cases, the normal probabilities are extremely close to the exact $t$ probabilities.

Recall that the stipulation is made that the population distribution be *normal* when the $t$ distribution is used, even when the normal approximations are substituted for the exact $t$-distribution probabilities. As we have already seen, for a normal population the distribution of sample means must be normal anyway; the difficulty with the use of a normal sampling distribution for small $N$ comes solely from the fact that our estimate of the standard error is a random variable rather than a constant over samples, and this is the reason we must use the $t$ distribution. Thus the $t$ distribution is related to the normal distribution in two distinct ways: the parent distribution must be normal if $t$ probabilities are to be found exactly, and for sufficiently large $N$, the distribution of $t$ approaches the normal sampling distribution in form.

## 10.6 THE APPLICATION OF THE $t$ DISTRIBUTION WHEN THE POPULATION IS NOT NORMAL

It is apparent that the requirement that the population be normal limits the usefulness of the $t$ distribution, since this is an assumption that we can seldom really justify in practical situations. Fortunately, when sample size is fairly large, and provided that the parent distribution is roughly unimodal and symmetric, the $t$ distribution apparently still gives an adequate approximation to the exact (and often unknown) probabilities of intervals for $t$ ratios under these circumstances. However, one should insist on a relatively *larger* sample size the *less* confident that he is that the normal rule holds for the population, if he plans to use the $t$ distribution. In effect, if the sample size is large enough so that the normal probabilities are good approximations to the $t$ probabilities anyway, then the form of the parent distribution is more or less irrelevant. However, often the sample size is so small that the $t$ distribution must be used and here it *is* somewhat risky to make inferences from $t$ ratios unless the population is more or less normally distributed. This is an especially serious problem when one-tailed tests of hypotheses are made, since a very skewed population distribution can make the $t$ probabilities for one-tailed tests considerably in error. Once again, it is wise to plan on somewhat larger samples when one is considering a one-tailed test using the $t$ distribution and the population is not assumed normal.

## 10.7 TABLES OF THE $t$ DISTRIBUTION

Unlike the table of the standardized normal function, which suffices for all possible normal distributions, tables of the $t$ distribution must actually include many distributions each depending on the value of $\nu$, the degrees of freedom. Consequently, tables of $t$ are usually given only in abbreviated form; otherwise, a whole volume would be required to show all the different $t$ distributions one might need.

Table II in Appendix C shows selected percentage points of the distribution of $t$, in terms of the value of $\nu$. Different $\nu$ values appear along the left-hand margin of the table. The top margin gives values of $Q$, which is $1 - p(t \leq a)$, one minus the cumulative probability that $t$ is less than or equal to a specific value $a$, for a distribution within the given value for $\nu$. A cell of the table then shows the value of $t$ cutting off the upper $Q$ proportion of cases in a distribution for $\nu$ degrees of freedom.

This sounds rather complicated, but an example will clarify matters considerably: suppose that $N = 10$, and we want to know the value *beyond which* only 10 percent of all sample $t$ values should lie. That is, for the distribution of $t$ shown in Figure 10.7.1, we want the $t$ value that cuts off the shaded area in the curve, the upper 10 percent:

First of all, since $N = 10$, $\nu = N - 1 = 9$. So, we enter the table for the row marked 9. Now since we want the upper 10 percent, we find the column for which $Q = .1$. The corresponding cell in the table is the value of $t$ we are looking for, $t = 1.383$. We can say that in a $t$ distribution with 9 degrees of freedom,

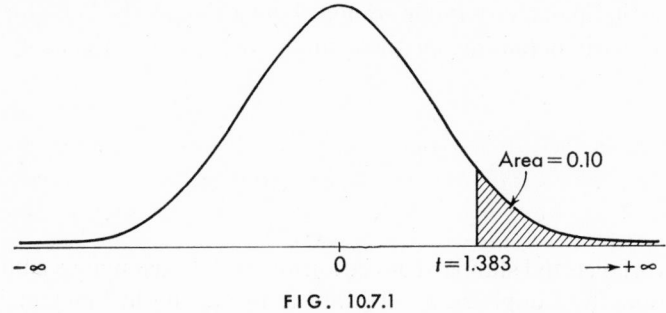

FIG. 10.7.1

the probability is .10 that a $t$ value *equals or exceeds* 1.383. Since the distribution is symmetric, we also know that the probability is .10 that a $t$ value *equals or falls below* $-1.383$. If we wanted to know the probability that $t$ equals or exceeds 1.383 in absolute value, then this must be $.10 + .10 = .20$, or $2Q$.

Suppose that in a sample of 21 cases, we get a $t$ value of 1.98. We want to see if this value falls into the upper .05 of all values in the distribution. We enter row $\nu = 21 - 1 = 20$, and column $Q = .05$; the $t$ value in the cell is 1.725. Our obtained value of $t$ is larger than this, and so the obtained value does fall among the top 5 percent of all such values. On the other hand, suppose that the obtained $t$ had been $-3$. Does this fall either in the top .001 or the bottom .001 of all such sample values? Again with $\nu = 20$, but this time with $Q = .001$, we find a $t$ value of 3.552. This means that at or above 3.552 lie .001 of all sample values, and also at or below $-3.552$ lie .001 of all sample values. Hence our sample value does not fall into either of these intervals; we can say that the sample value does not fall into the rejection region for $\alpha = .002$.

The very last row, marked $\infty$, shows the $z$ scores that cut off various areas in a normal distribution curve. If you trace down any given column, you find that as $\nu$ gets larger the $t$ value bounding the area specified by the column comes closer and closer to this normal deviate value, until finally, for an infinite sample size, the required value of $t$ is the same as that for $z$.

For one-tailed tests of hypotheses, the column $Q$ values are used to find the $t$ value which exactly bounds the rejection region. If the region of rejection is on the upper tail of the distribution, then $Q$ is the probability of a sample value's falling into the region greater than or equal to the tabled value of $t$. If the region is on the lower tail, the $t$ value in the table is given a negative sign, and $Q$ is the probability of a sample's falling at or below the negative $t$ value. If a two-tailed region is to be used, then the total $\alpha$ probability of error is $2Q$, and the number in the table shows the absolute value of $t$ that bounds the rejection region on *either* tail.

## 10.8 THE CONCEPT OF DEGREES OF FREEDOM

Before we proceed to the uses of the $t$ distribution, it is well to examine the notion of degrees of freedom. The degrees of freedom parameter reflects the fact that a $t$ ratio involves a sample standard deviation as the basis for estimating $\sigma_M$. Recall the basic definitions of the sample variance and the sample standard deviation:

$$s^2 = \frac{\Sigma(X - M)^2}{N}$$

and

$$s = \sqrt{\frac{\Sigma(X - M)^2}{N}}.$$

The sample variance and standard deviation are both based upon a sum of squared deviations from the sample mean. However, recall another fact of importance about deviations from a mean: in Section 6.6 it was shown that

$$\sum_i (X_i - M) = 0,$$

the sum of deviations about the mean must be zero.

These two facts have an important consequence: Suppose that you are told that $N = 4$ in some sample, and that you are to guess the four deviations from the mean $M$. For the first deviation you can guess any number, and suppose you say

$$d_1 = 6.$$

Similarly, quite at will, you could assign values to two more deviations, say

$$d_2 = -9$$
$$d_3 = -7.$$

However, when you come to the fourth deviation value, you are *no longer free* to guess any number you please. The value of $d_4$ *must* be

$$d_4 = 0 - d_1 - d_2 - d_3$$

or

$$d_4 = 0 - 6 + 9 + 7 = 10.$$

In short, given the values of any $N - 1$ deviations from the mean, which could be any set of numbers, the value of the last deviation is completely determined. Thus we say that there are $N - 1$ degrees of freedom for a sample variance, reflecting the fact that only $N - 1$ deviations are "free" to be any number, but that given these free values, the last deviation is completely determined. It is not the sample size per se that dictates the distribution of $t$, but rather the number of degrees of freedom in the variance (and standard deviation) estimate. We will consider the degrees of freedom again in the next chapter, where the variance will be studied in more detail, and also in Chapter 14.

## 10.9   SIGNIFICANCE TESTS FOR SINGLE MEANS USING THE $t$ DISTRIBUTION

For the moment you can relax; there is really nothing new to learn! When the null hypothesis concerns a single mean, then the test is carried out just as before, except that the table of $t$ (Appendix C, Table II) is used instead of the normal table (Appendix C, Table I). The $\alpha$ level is chosen, and the value (or values) of $t$ corresponding to the region of rejection can be determined from the $t$ table. The number of degrees of freedom used is simply $\nu = N - 1$. Then, the ratio

$$t = \frac{M - E(M)}{\text{est. } \sigma_M}$$   [10.9.1†]

obtained from the sample is compared with values in the rejection region specified by Table II. If the obtained $t$ ratio falls into the rejection region chosen, the sample result is said to be significant beyond the $\alpha$ level.

If the sample size is large, then the only difference in procedure is in the use of the normal tables to establish the region of rejection. Naturally, all the considerations hitherto discussed, especially the assumed normal distribution of the population, should be faced before the sample size and rejection region are decided upon. If large samples are available then the assumption of a normal population is relatively unimportant; on the other hand, this matter should be given some serious thought if you are limited to a very small sample size.

## 10.10   CONFIDENCE LIMITS FOR THE MEAN USING $t$ DISTRIBUTIONS

When sample size is so small that the normal approximation to the sampling distribution is not good, then the $t$ distribution is used to establish confidence limits for the mean. For some fixed percentage representing the confidence level, $100(1 - \alpha)$ percent, the sample confidence limits depend upon three things: the sample value of $M$, the estimated standard error, or est. $\sigma_M$, and the number of degrees of freedom, $\nu$. For some specified value of $\nu$, then the $100(1 - \alpha)$ percent

confidence limits are found from

$$M - t_{(\alpha/2;\,\nu)} \ (\text{est. } \sigma_M)$$
$$M + t_{(\alpha/2;\,\nu)} \ (\text{est. } \sigma_M).$$

[10.10.1 †]

Here, $t_{(\alpha/2;\,\nu)}$ represents the value of $t$ that bounds the upper $\alpha/2$ proportion of cases in a $t$ distribution with $\nu$ degrees of freedom. In Table II this is the value listed for $Q = \alpha/2$ and $\nu$. Thus, if one wants the 99 percent confidence limits, the value of $\alpha = .01$, and one looks in the table for $Q = .005$.

For example, imagine a study using 8 independent observations drawn from a normal population. The sample mean is 49 and the estimated standard error of the mean is 3.7. Now we want to find the 95 percent confidence limits. First of all, $\alpha = .05$, so that $Q = .025$. The value of $\nu$ is $N - 1$, or 7. The table shows a $t$ value of 2.365 for $Q = .025$ and $\nu = 7$, so that $t_{(\alpha/2;\,\nu)} = 2.365$. The confidence limits are

$$49 - (2.365)(3.7) = 40.25$$
$$\text{and} \quad 49 + (2.365)(3.7) = 57.75.$$

Over all random samples, the probability is .95 that the true value of $\mu$ is covered by an interval such as that between 40.25 and 57.75, the confidence interval calculated for this sample.

**FIG. 10.10.1.** Confidence intervals for means based on five independent samples

In summary, confidence limits are calculated in much the same way, and have the same general interpretation, when based on the $t$ distribution as for the normal distribution. The essential difference is that values of $t$ corresponding to $\alpha/2$ and $\nu$ must be used instead of normal $z$ values.

One important application of confidence intervals in psychology occurs when there is a set of some $J$ independent means, each based on a different sample given exactly one of a set of $J$ experimental treatments. In particular, the experimental treatments may represent some quantitative experimental variable (represented here by $X$), and the experimenter may be trying to infer the general form of relationship between the amount of treatment applied and the average or expected response of a subject in terms of variable $Y$. Here, he may choose to construct a confidence interval around *each* of the sample means on variable $Y$. Figure 10.10.1 represents a set of such means, with the 95 percent confidence interval shown for each. In this figure, the horizontal axis represents the different levels or quantities of the treatment administered, and the open circles the corresponding means of the samples on the dependent variable, $Y$. The vertical bars extending to either side of a mean point symbolize the 95 percent confidence interval based on that sample's mean. The experimenter's best guess about the general form of the function relating the experimental variable to the dependent variable is symbolized by the heavy line in the figure: this is simply a plot joining the sample means, since his best guess about the population mean under any given treatment is the sample mean. Nevertheless, it may well be true that the form of relationship in the population is something like that shown by the broken line. The experimenter has no basis at all for discounting the possibility of some such true relation on the basis of the obtained relation alone.

How sure can the experimenter be that the set of $J$ confidence intervals based on independent means all *simultaneously* cover the population values? In other words, how confident can he be that he has narrowed the possible relationships between the experimental and dependent variables to those symbolized by graphs joining points *within* the various intervals of Figure 10.10.1? A little thought should convince you that the probability is *not* .95 that all $J$ of the confidence intervals simultaneously cover the true means; we can, however, work out an approximation to the value of this probability.

Suppose that both the means and the estimated $\sigma_M$ values, and thus the obtained values for the confidence limits themselves, are independent across samples. We can consider the event "confidence interval covers true $\mu$" as though it were a "success" in a binomial experiment for any of the samples. The probability of any such success is .95 for a 95 percent confidence interval. Then the probability that all $J$ independent confidence intervals simultaneously cover the true means is simply the probability of exactly $J$ out of $J$ possible successes in a binomial experiment:

prob.(all $J$ of the 95 percent confidence intervals cover true values

$$\text{simultaneously}) = \binom{J}{J} (.95)^J (.05)^0$$
$$= (.95)^J.$$

For the example in Figure 10.10.1, $J = 5$, so that the probability that the true means all are covered by the indicated intervals is

$$(.95)^5 = .77.$$

The experimenter can have considerably less "confidence" in the statement that *all* of the confidence intervals simultaneously cover the true means than in the statement that *any one* confidence interval covers the true mean.

The probability of .77 calculated for this example was based on the assumption that each of the confidence limits obtained for a sample is independent of the corresponding limits obtained for the other samples. However, this is not a reasonable assumption in a great many instances, because the same estimated value of $\sigma$ or of $\sigma_M$ may be used for determining each of the confidence intervals. Nevertheless, even when the confidence limits for the various samples are not independent, the probability that all $J$ of the $100(1 - \alpha)$ percent confidence intervals simultaneously cover the true values must lie between $1 - \alpha$ and $1 - J\alpha$. Conversely, given any $J$ such confidence intervals, the probability that *at least one* fails to cover the true value is between $\alpha$ and $J\alpha$. For $J$ independent confidence intervals, the probability that at least one of the set fails to cover the true value is exactly $1 - (1 - \alpha)^J$. The practical implication is clear: given enough confidence intervals calculated from a set of data the probability can be quite high that *at least one* fails to cover the true parameter value. For similar reasons, given enough significance tests carried out on a set of data, each with some conventional value for $\alpha$, the probability can be much greater than $\alpha$ that *at least one* of these tests results in a Type I error. This point is an important one, and will recur in Chapters 12 and 14.

## 10.11 QUESTIONS ABOUT DIFFERENCES BETWEEN POPULATION MEANS

Examples of hypotheses about single means often sound rather "phony" in their experimental contexts, and the reason for this is not hard to find. In most experimental work it is not true that the experimenter knows about one particular population in advance and then draws a single sample for the purpose of comparing some experimental population to the known population. Rather, it is far more common to draw two samples, to only one of which the experimental treatment is applied; the other sample is given no treatment, and stands as a control group for comparison with the treated group. In other situations, two different treatments may be compared. The advantages of this method over the single sample procedure are obvious; the experimenter can exercise the same experimental controls on both samples, making sure that insofar as possible they are treated in exactly the same way, with the only systematic experimental difference being in the fact that something was done to representatives of one sample which was not done to members of the other. Then, if a very large difference appears between the two samples he can rest assured that the difference is a product of the experimental treatments and not just a peculiarity introduced by the way in which his data were gathered.

Each treatment group is a sample from a potential population of observations made under that treatment. A difference between the treatment populations should exist if the treatment is having an effect; but what can the experimenter infer from a sample difference? *His best estimate is that the population means are different to the same extent as the sample means. Regardless of the significance level given by any test he may apply, the actual difference obtained is always the best estimate he can make of the true difference between the population means.*

As always, this estimate is in error to some unknown extent, and although the obtained difference between the sample means is the best guess the experimenter can make, there is absolutely no guarantee that this estimate is exactly correct. It could well be true that the difference the experimenter observes has no real connection with the treatment administered, and is purely a chance result.

What is needed is a way of applying statistical inference to differences between means of samples representing two populations. First, large sample distributions of *differences* between sample means will be studied. Then, the application of the $t$ distribution to small sample differences will be introduced.

### 10.12 THE SAMPLING DISTRIBUTION OF DIFFERENCES BETWEEN MEANS

Suppose that we wished to test a hypothesis that two populations have means which differ by some specified amount, say 20 points. This is tested against the hypothesis that the population means do not differ by that amount. In our more formal notation:

$$H_0: \mu_1 - \mu_2 = 20$$
$$H_1: \mu_1 - \mu_2 \neq 20.$$

We draw a sample of size $N_1$ from population 1, and an *independent* sample of size $N_2$ from population 2, and consider the difference between their means, $M_1 - M_2$. Now suppose that we kept on drawing pairs of independent samples of these sizes from these populations. For each pair of samples drawn, the difference $M_1 - M_2$ is recorded. What is the distribution of such sample *differences* that we should expect in the long run? In other words, what is the sampling distribution of the difference between two means?

You may already have anticipated the form of the sampling distribution of the difference between two means, since all the groundwork for this distribution has been laid in Section 8.9. The difference between sample means drawn from independent samples is actually a linear combination:

$$(1)M_1 + (-1)M_2.$$

Let us apply the results of Sections 8.9 and 8.10 to this problem. In the first place,

$$E(M_1 - M_2) = E(M_1) - E(M_2) = \mu_1 - \mu_2, \qquad [10.12.1*]$$

which accords with principle **8.10.1** for any linear combination. Second, what is the standard error of the difference between two independent sample means? By principle **8.10.3**,

$$\text{var.}(M_1 - M_2) = (1)^2\sigma_{M_1}^2 + (-1)^2\sigma_{M_2}^2$$
$$= \sigma_{M_1}^2 + \sigma_{M_2}^2. \qquad [10.12.2*]$$

Hence, the standard error of the difference, $\sigma_{\text{diff.}}$, is

$$\sigma_{\text{diff.}} = \sqrt{\sigma_{M_1}^2 + \sigma_{M_2}^2} = \sqrt{\frac{\sigma_1^2}{N_1} + \frac{\sigma_2^2}{N_2}} \qquad [10.12.3*]$$

provided that samples 1 and 2 are completely independent.

Actually, we could have found this last result quite easily without invoking principle **8.10.2**. It may be instructive to do so.

By definition:

$$\text{var.}(M_1 - M_2) = E[(M_1 - M_2) - (\mu_1 - \mu_2)]^2$$
$$= E[(M_1 - \mu_1) - (M_2 - \mu_2)]^2.$$

For any given pair of samples, expanding the square gives

$$[(M_1 - \mu_1) - (M_2 - \mu_2)]^2 = (M_1 - \mu_1)^2 + (M_2 - \mu_2)^2 - 2(M_1 - \mu_1)(M_2 - \mu_2).$$

Now let us take the expectation of each of these terms separately:

$$E(M_1 - \mu_1)^2 = \sigma_{M_1}^2$$

and

$$E(M_2 - \mu_2)^2 = \sigma_{M_2}^2$$

by the definition of the variance of a sampling distribution of the mean. Furthermore,

$$E[(M_1 - \mu_1)(M_2 - \mu_2)] = 0$$

by rule 6, Appendix B, since $M_1$ and $M_2$ are independent. Thus, combining these results, we find that

$$\text{var.}(M_1 - M_2) = \sigma_{M_1}^2 + \sigma_{M_2}^2$$

or

$$\sigma_{\text{diff.}} = \sqrt{\frac{\sigma_1^2}{N_1} + \frac{\sigma_2^2}{N_2}}.$$

Notice that there is no requirement at all that the samples be of equal size. Regardless of the sample sizes, the expectation of the difference between two means is always the difference between their expectations, and the variance of the difference between two *independent* means is the *sum* of the separate sampling variances.

Furthermore, these statements about the mean and the standard error of a difference between means are true regardless of the form of the parent distributions. However, the form of the sampling distribution can also be specified under either of two conditions:

**If the distribution for each of two populations is normal then the distribution of differences between sample means is normal.**

This follows quite simply from principle 8.9 for linear combinations. When we can assume both populations normal, the form of the sampling distribution is known to be *exactly* normal.

On the other hand, one or both of the original distributions may not be normal; in this case the central limit theorem comes to our aid:

**As both $N_1$ and $N_2$ grow infinitely large, the sampling distribution of the difference between means approaches a normal distribution, regardless of the form of the original distributions.**

In short, when we are dealing with two very large samples, then the question of the form of the original distributions becomes irrelevant, and we can approximate the sampling distribution of the difference between means by a normal distribution.

## 10.13 AN EXAMPLE OF A LARGE-SAMPLE SIGNIFICANCE TEST FOR A DIFFERENCE BETWEEN MEANS

An experimenter working in the area of motivational factors in perception was interested in the effects of deprivation upon the perceived size of objects. Among the studies carried out was one done with orphans, who were com-pared with nonorphaned children on the basis of the judged size of parental figures viewed at a distance. Each child was seated at a viewing apparatus in which cut-out figures appeared. Each figure was actually of the same size and at the same distance from the viewer, although he was not told that the figures had the same size. A device was provided on which the child could actually judge the apparent sizes of the different figures in numerical terms. Several of the figures in the set viewed were obviously parents, whereas others were more or less neutral, such as milkmen, postmen, nurses, and so on. Each child was given a score, which was itself a difference in average judged size of parental and nonparental figures.

Now two independent randomly selected groups were used. Sample 1 was a group of orphaned children without foster parents. Sample 2 was a group of children having a normal family with both parents. Both populations of children sampled showed the same age level, sex distribution, educational level, and so forth.

The question asked by the experimenter was, "Do deprived children tend to judge the parental figures relatively larger than do the nondeprived?" In terms of a null and alternative hypothesis,

$$H_0: \mu_1 - \mu_2 \leq 0$$
$$H_1: \mu_1 - \mu_2 > 0.$$

The $\alpha$ level for significance decided upon was .05. The actual results were

|           *Sample 1*      |      *Sample 2*      |
|---------------------------|----------------------|
| $M_1 = 1.8$               | $M_2 = 1.6$          |
| $s_1 = .7$                | $s_2 = .9$           |
| $N_1 = 125$               | $N_2 = 150$          |

These sample sizes are rather large, and the experimenter felt safe in using the normal approximation to the sampling distribution, even though he had no idea about the distribution form for the two populations sampled. The $t$ ratio used was

$$t = \frac{(M_1 - M_2) - E(M_1 - M_2)}{\text{est. } \sigma_{\text{diff.}}} \qquad [10.13.1*]$$

In this problem, $E(M_1 - M_2) = 0$, under the hypothesis tested. It was obviously necessary for the experimenter to estimate the standard error of the difference, since both $\sigma_1$ and $\sigma_2$ were unknown to him. This estimate was found by first esti-mating $\sigma_{M_1}^2$ and $\sigma_{M_2}^2$:

$$\text{est. } \sigma_{M_1}^2 = \frac{s_1^2}{N_1 - 1} = \frac{.49}{124} = .004 \qquad [10.13.2\dagger]$$

$$\text{est. } \sigma_{M_2}^2 = \frac{s_2^2}{N_2 - 1} = \frac{.81}{149} = .005. \qquad [10.13.3\dagger]$$

Then,

$$\text{est. } \sigma_{\text{diff.}} = \sqrt{\text{est. } \sigma_{M_1}^2 + \text{est. } \sigma_{M_2}^2} = \sqrt{.004 + .005} = .095. \qquad [10.13.4\dagger]$$

On making these substitutions, the experimenter found

$$t = \frac{1.8 - 1.6}{.095} = 2.11.$$

The rejection region implied by the alternative hypothesis is on the *upper* tail of the sampling distribution. For a normal distribution the upper 5 percent is bounded by $z = 1.65$. Thus, the result is significant; deviations this far from zero have a probability of less than .05 of occurring by chance alone when the true difference is zero.

The experimenter may conclude that a difference exists between these two populations, *if* an $\alpha$ value less than .05 is a small enough probability of error to warrant this decision. However, the experimenter does not necessarily conclude that parental deprivation causes an increase in perceived size. The statistical conclusion suggests that it *might* be safe to assert that a particular direction of numerical difference exists between the mean scores of the two populations of children, but the statistical result is absolutely noncommittal about the reason for this difference, if such exists. The experimenter takes the step of advancing a reason at his own peril. The statistical test as a mathematical tool is absolutely neutral about what these numbers measure, the level of measurement, what was or was not represented in the experiment, and, most of all the cause of the experimenter's particular finding. As always, the test takes the numerical values as given, and cranks out a conclusion about the conditional probability of such numbers, given certain statistical conditions.

The general procedure for hypotheses about two means when sample size is quite large is represented by this example. The test statistic is

$$t = \frac{(M_1 - M_2) - E(M_1 - M_2)}{\text{est. } \sigma_{\text{diff.}}}.$$

This $t$ value may be referred to a normal distribution. The expected difference depends upon the hypothesis tested, and the estimated $\sigma_{\text{diff.}}$ is found directly from the estimate $\sigma_M^2$ for each sample by **10.13.4.**

The exact hypothesis actually tested is of the form

$$H_0: \mu_1 - \mu_2 = k,$$

where $k$ is any difference of interest. Quite often, as in the example, the experimenter is interested only in $k = 0$, but it is entirely possible to test any other meaningful difference value. The alternative hypothesis may be directional,

$$H_1: \mu_1 - \mu_2 > k$$
or
$$H_1: \mu_1 - \mu_2 < k,$$
or nondirectional,
$$H_1: \mu_1 - \mu_2 \neq k,$$

depending on the form of the original question.

As an illustration of a situation where some value other than zero figures in the null hypothesis, and also as an illustration of a one-tailed test, take the following example: a manufacturer is considering introducing a change in training procedure for his new employees. However, it is more expensive than the old, and he feels that he cannot afford it unless the average output of a man trained in the new way is more than 50 units per hour better than that of a man trained under the old procedure. The null hypothesis is

$$H_0: \mu_1 - \mu_2 \not> 50,$$

since the exact value that the null hypothesis requires is given by 50 units per hour. The alternative hypothesis states

$$H_1: \mu_1 - \mu_2 > 50.$$

Notice how the null and the alternative hypotheses are framed so as to correspond to the alternative practical decisions that our manufacturer may make: if the null hypothesis is true, he will not adopt the new training procedure since it does not meet the requirement he set up. He has no interest in the training procedure if it is less than 50 units better than the old. If, however, the alternative hypothesis is true, then he will adopt the new procedure. In this instance, where clear-cut courses of action depend on the evidence, the one-tailed test of a nonzero hypothesis makes sense. Subjects are assigned at random to two groups, one getting the new and the other the old training. Given large samples, the $t$ ratio is computed just as in the previous example, except that here $E(M_1 - M_2) = 50$. A significant result gives the manufacturer considerable assurance in saying that one procedure is on the average more than 50 units better than the other.

## 10.14   LARGE-SAMPLE CONFIDENCE LIMITS
### FOR A DIFFERENCE

When both samples are large, as in the example in Section 10.13, confidence limits are found exactly as for a single mean, except that $(M_1 - M_2)$ and est. $\sigma_{\text{diff}}$. are substituted for $M$ and est. $\sigma_M$ respectively. Thus, 95 percent confidence limits for a difference with large samples are

$$M_1 - M_2 - 1.96 \text{ (est. } \sigma_{\text{diff}}.) \qquad \text{[10.14.1*]}$$
$$M_1 - M_2 + 1.96 \text{ (est. } \sigma_{\text{diff}}.).$$

For the example in the preceding section, the 95 percent limits are

$$.2 - 1.96(.095)$$
$$.2 + 1.96(.095)$$

or .014 and .386. Notice that since the value $\mu_1 - \mu_2 = 0$ does not fall within these values this value can be rejected as a hypothesis beyond the .05 level (two-tailed).

## 10.15   USING THE $t$ DISTRIBUTION TO TEST
### HYPOTHESES ABOUT DIFFERENCES

Given the assumption that both populations sampled have normal distributions, any hypothesis about a difference can be tested using the $t$ distribution, regardless of sample size. However, one additional assumption becomes necessary: *in order to use the t distribution for tests based on two (or more) samples, one must assume that the standard deviations of both (or all) populations are equal.* The basis for this assumption will be discussed in the next chapter.

Given these assumptions, then the distribution of $t$ for a difference has the same form as for a single mean, except that the degrees of freedom are

$$\nu = N_1 - 1 + N_2 - 1 = N_1 + N_2 - 2.$$

When samples are drawn from populations with equal variance, then the estimated standard error of a difference takes a somewhat different form. First of all, when $\sigma_1 = \sigma_2 = \sigma$,

$$\sigma_{\text{diff.}} = \sqrt{\frac{\sigma^2}{N_1} + \frac{\sigma^2}{N_2}} = \sqrt{\sigma^2\left(\frac{1}{N_1} + \frac{1}{N_2}\right)}. \qquad [10.15.1*]$$

Now, as we showed in Section 7.15, when one has two or more estimates of the same parameter $\sigma^2$, the *pooled* estimate is actually better than either one taken separately. From **7.15.5** it follows that

$$\text{est. } \sigma^2 = \frac{N_1 s_1^2 + N_2 s_2^2}{N_1 + N_2 - 2}$$

is our best estimate of $\sigma^2$ based on the two samples. Hence

$$\text{est. } \sigma_{\text{diff.}} = \sqrt{\text{est. } \sigma^2\left(\frac{1}{N_1} + \frac{1}{N_2}\right)}$$

$$= \sqrt{\left(\frac{N_1 s_1^2 + N_2 s_2^2}{N_1 + N_2 - 2}\right)\left(\frac{N_1 + N_2}{N_1 N_2}\right)}. \qquad [10.15.2\dagger]$$

This estimate of the standard error of the difference ordinarily forms the denominator of the $t$ ratio when the $t$ distribution is used for hypotheses about a difference.

## 10.16 AN EXAMPLE OF INFERENCES ABOUT A DIFFERENCE FOR SMALL SAMPLES

Two random samples of subjects are being compared on the basis of their scores on a motor learning task. The subjects are allotted to two experimental groups, with five subjects in the first and seven in the second. In the first group a subject is rewarded for each correct move made, and in the second each incorrect move is punished. The score is the number of trials to reach a specific criterion of performance. The experimenter wishes to find evidence for the question, "Does the kind of motivation employed, reward or punishment, affect the performance?" This question implies the null and alternative hypotheses:

$$H_0: \mu_1 - \mu_2 = 0$$
$$H_1: \mu_1 - \mu_2 \neq 0.$$

The experimenter is willing to assume that the population distributions of scores are normal, and that the population variances are equal. The probability of Type I error decided upon is .01. Since this is a two-tailed test, a glance at Table II shows that for $N_1 + N_2 - 2$ or $5 + 7 - 2 = 10$ degrees of freedom, and for $2Q = .01$, the required $t$ value is 3.169. Thus an obtained $t$ ratio equaling or exceeding 3.169 in absolute value is grounds for rejecting the hypothesis of no difference between population means.

The sample results are

$$M_1 = 18 \qquad M_2 = 20$$
$$s_1^2 = 4.8 \qquad s_2^2 = 5.0.$$

The estimated standard error of the difference is found by the pooling procedure given in the last section:

$$\text{est. } \sigma_{\text{diff.}} = \sqrt{\text{est. } \sigma^2 \left( \frac{1}{N_1} + \frac{1}{N_2} \right)}$$
$$= \sqrt{\frac{(5)(4.8) + (7)(5.0)}{10} \left( \frac{12}{35} \right)}$$
$$= \sqrt{2.02}$$
$$= 1.42.$$

Thus, the $t$ ratio is

$$t = \frac{(M_1 - M_2) - E(M_1 - M_2)}{\text{est. } \sigma_{\text{diff.}}} = \frac{-2}{1.42} = -1.41.$$

This value comes nowhere close to that required for rejection, and thus if $\alpha$ must be no more than .01 the experimenter does not reject the null hypothesis. His best choice may be to suspend judgement, pending more evidence.

Confidence intervals are found just as for a single small sample mean: the limits are

$$(M_1 - M_2) - t_{(\alpha/2; \nu)} (\text{est. } \sigma_{\text{diff.}}) \qquad \text{[10.16.1*]}$$
$$(M_1 - M_2) + t_{(\alpha/2; \nu)} (\text{est. } \sigma_{\text{diff.}}).$$

For this example, the 99 percent limits are

$$-2 - (3.169)(1.42)$$

and

$$-2 + (3.169)(1.42)$$

or approximately $-6.5$ and $2.5$. The probability is .99 that the true *difference*, $\mu_1 - \mu_2$, is covered by an interval such as this. Once again, notice that this interval *does* contain the value 0, indicating the hypothesis entertained above is not rejected.

## 10.17   THE IMPORTANCE OF THE ASSUMPTIONS IN A $t$ TEST OF A DIFFERENCE

In order to justify the use of the $t$ distribution in problems involving a difference between means, one must make two assumptions: the populations sampled are normal, and the population variances are homogeneous, $\sigma^2$ having the same value for each population. Formally, these two assumptions are essential if the $t$ probabilities given by the table are to be exact. On the other hand, in practical situations these assumptions are sometimes violated with rather small effect on the conclusions.

The first assumption, that of a normal distribution in the populations, is apparently the less important of the two. So long as the sample size is even moderate for each group quite severe departures from normality seem to make little practical difference in the conclusions reached. Naturally, the results are more accurate the more nearly unimodal and symmetric the population distributions are, and thus if one suspects radical departures from a generally normal form then he should plan on larger samples. Furthermore, the departure from normality can make more difference in a one-tailed than in a two-tailed result, and once again some special thought should be given to sample size when one-tailed tests are contemplated for such populations. By and large, however, this assumption may be violated almost with impunity provided that sample size is not extremely small.

On the other hand, the assumption of homogeneity of variance is more important. In older work it was often suggested that a separate test for homogenity of variance be carried out before the $t$ test itself, in order to see if this assumption were at all reasonable. However, the most modern authorities suggest that this is not really worth the trouble involved. In circumstances where they are needed most (small samples), the tests for homogeneity are poorest. Furthermore, for samples of equal size relatively big differences in the population variances seem to have relatively small consequences for the conclusions derived from a $t$ test. On the other hand, when the variances are quite unequal the use of differ-ent sample sizes can have serious effects on the conclusions. The moral should be plain: given the usual freedom about sample size in experimental work, *when in doubt use samples of the same size.*

However, sometimes it is not possible to obtain an equal number in each group. Then one way out of this problem is by the use of a correction in the value for degrees of freedom. This is useful when one cannot assume equal population variances and samples are of different size. In this situation, however, the $t$ ratio is calculated as in Section 10.13, where the seperate standard errors are computed from each sample and the pooled estimate is not made. Then the corrected number of degrees of freedom is found from

$$\nu = \frac{(\text{est. } \sigma_{M_1}^2 + \text{est. } \sigma_{M_2}^2)^2}{(\text{est. } \sigma_{M_1}^2)^2/(N_1 + 1) + (\text{est. } \sigma_{M_2}^2)^2/(N_2 + 1)} - 2. \qquad [10.17.1\dagger]$$

This need not result in a whole value for $\nu$, in which case the use of the nearest whole value for $\nu$ is sufficiently accurate for most purposes. When somewhat greater accuracy is desired, the approximate formula for critical values of $t$ given in Section 14.17 is useful. When both samples are quite large, then both the assumptions of normality and of homogeneous variances become relatively unimportant, and the method of Section 10.13 can be used.

## 10.18   THE POWER OF *t* TESTS

The idea of the power of a statistical test was discussed in the preceding section only in terms of the normal distribution. Nevertheless, the same general considerations apply to the power of tests based on the *t* distribution. Thus, the power of a *t* test increases with sample size, increases with the discrepancy between the null hypothesis value and the true value of a mean or a difference, increases with any reduction in the true value of $\sigma$, and increases with any increase in the size of $\alpha$, given a true value covered by $H_1$.

Unfortunately, the actual determination of the power for a *t* test against any given true alternative is more complicated than for the normal distribution. The reason is that when the null hypothesis is false, each *t* ratio computed involves $E(M)$ or $E(M_1 - M_2)$, which is the exact value given by the null (and false) hypothesis. If the true value of the expectation could be calculated into each *t* ratio, then the distribution would follow the *t* function tabled in the appendix. However, when $H_0$ is false, each *t* value involves a false expectation; this results in a somewhat different distribution, called the **noncentral** *t* **distribution.** The probabilities of the various *t*'s cannot be known unless one more parameter, $\delta$, is specified beside $\nu$. This is the so-called noncentrality parameter

$$\delta = \frac{\mu - \mu_0}{\sigma_M},$$   [10.18.1]

which expresses the difference between the true expectation $\mu$ and that given by the null hypothesis, or $\mu_0$, in terms of $\sigma_M$. For a hypothesis about a difference and for samples of equal size,

$$\delta = \frac{(\mu_1 - \mu_2) - (\mu_{0_1} - \mu_{0_2})}{\sigma_{\text{diff.}}}.$$   [10.18.2]

This makes the determination of the power of a *t* test considerably more troublesome than for tests using the normal distribution. In particular, information about $\sigma$ for each population is required. However, for uses that most psychologists are likely to make of the power concept, especially in determining sample size, the normal approximation may still suffice. Consequently, in the discussion to follow we are going to assume that sample size is large enough that the normal approximations are sufficiently accurate, and we will not deal directly with the power of the *t* test. For more accurate work, most advanced texts in statistics give tables of the power function of *t*, in terms of both $\nu$ and $\delta$.

## 10.19   TESTMANSHIP, OR HOW BIG IS A DIFFERENCE?

When an experimenter assigns subjects at random to two experimental groups, giving a different treatment to subjects in each group, he is usually looking for evidence of a statistical relation. Here, the independent variable represents the various experimental treatments and the dependent variable is the score of any subject within a group. Each treatment group is a random sample of all potential subjects given that treatment. The sample space is conceived as the set of all possible treatment-subject combinations, and the statistical relation itself is defined in terms of this sample space.

As we saw in Chapter 4, the complete absence of a statistical relation, or no association, occurs only when the conditional distribution of the dependent variable is the same regardless of which treatment is administered. Thus if the independent variable is not associated at all with the dependent variable the population distributions must be identical over the treatments. If, on the other hand, the means of the different treatment populations *are* different, the conditional distributions themselves must be different and the independent and dependent variables must be associated. The rejection of the hypothesis of no difference between population means is tantamount to the assertion that the treatment given does have some statistical association with the dependent variable score.

However, the occurrence of a significant result says nothing at all about the strength of the association between treatment and score. A significant result leads to the inference that some association exists, but in no sense does this mean that an important degree of association necessarily exists. Conversely, evidence of a strong statistical association can occur in data even when the results are not significant. The game of inferring the true degree of statistical association has a joker: this is the sample size. The time has come to define the notion of the strength of a statistical association more sharply, and to link this idea with that of the true difference between population means.

Just as in our discussion of relations in Chapters 1 and 4, let us call the experimental variable (or the independent variable) $X$ once again. Here, $X$ may symbolize a number standing for a quantity of some treatment, or it may simply represent any one of a set of qualitatively different treatments. In either circumstance, $X$ stands for the status of the individual observation on the experimental factor, the condition manipulated by the experimenter. The dependent variable is $Y$, which here stands for a numerical score. If we conceive the sample space as comprising the outcomes of our observing all of a population of individuals under each of the possible set of treatments $X$, then each possible observation in the experiment is some $(X,Y)$ event. Furthermore, if individuals from the population of potential subjects are sampled at random, and assigned at random to the various possible treatments $X$ in the experiment, then the occurrence of any individual in the treatment $X$ has a probability $p(X)$. For our purposes, it will be convenient to assume that

$$p(X) = \frac{\text{number of individuals observed under treatment } X}{\text{total number of individuals observed}}.$$

When does it seem appropriate to say that a strong association exists between the experimental factor $X$ and the dependent variable $Y$? Over all of the different possibilities for $X$ there is a probability distribution of $Y$ values, which is the **marginal** distribution of $Y$ over $(X,Y)$ events. The existence of this distribution implies that we do not know exactly what the $Y$ value for any observation will be; we are always uncertain about $Y$ to some extent. However, given any particular $X$, there is also a **conditional** distribution of $Y$, and it may be that in this conditional distribution the highly probable values of $Y$ tend to "shrink" within a much narrower range than in the marginal distribution. If so, we can say that the information about $X$ tends to *reduce uncertainty* about $Y$. *In general we will say that the strength of a statistical relation is reflected by the extent to which knowing X reduces uncertainty about Y.*

One of the best indicators of our uncertainty about the value of a variable is $\sigma^2$, the variance of its distribution. The marginal distribution of $Y$ has variance $\sigma_Y^2$, and given any $X$, the conditional distribution has variance $\sigma_{Y|X}^2$. For the time being, let us assume that $\sigma_{Y|X}^2$ is the same regardless of which $X$ we specify. This is exactly the assumption of equal variances made in the $t$ test, since each population distribution is actually a conditional distribution, given some treatment specification. The reduction in uncertainty provided by $X$ is then proportional to

$$\sigma_Y^2 - \sigma_{Y|X}^2, \qquad [10.19.1^*]$$

the difference between the marginal and the conditional variance of $Y$.

It is convenient to turn this reduction in uncertainty into a **relative reduction** by dividing by $\sigma_Y^2$, giving

$$\omega^2 = \frac{\sigma_Y^2 - \sigma_{Y|X}^2}{\sigma_Y^2}. \qquad [10.19.2^*]$$

The relative reduction in uncertainty about $Y$ given by $X$ is shown by the index $\omega^2$ (Greek omega, squared). Sometimes the value $\omega^2$ is called **the proportion of variance in $Y$ accounted for by** $X$. Viewed either as a relative reduction in uncertainty, or as a proportion of variance accounted for, the index $\omega^2$ represents the strength of association between independent and dependent variables. (The index $\omega^2$ is almost identical to two other indices to be introduced later, *the intraclass correlation* and the *correlation ratio*, usually represented by the symbols $\rho_I$ and $\eta^2$ respectively. However, since these indices were developed for and are used in somewhat different contexts, it seems better to use the relatively neutral symbol $\omega^2$ here, to avoid later confusion.)

This index reflects the predictive power afforded by a relationship: when $\omega^2$ is zero, then $X$ does not aid us at all in predicting the value of $Y$. On the other hand, when $\omega^2$ is 1.00, this tells us that $X$ lets us know $Y$ exactly. All intermediate values of the index represent different degrees of predictive ability. Notice that for any functional relation, $\omega^2 = 1.00$, since there can be only one $Y$ for each possible $X$. A value less than unity tells us that precise prediction is not possible, although $X$ nevertheless gives *some* information about $Y$ unless $\omega^2 = 0$.

About now you should be wondering what the index $\omega^2$ has to do with the difference between population means. It can be shown, by methods we shall use in Chapter 12, that when $p(X_1) = p(X_2) = 1/2$,

$$\sigma_Y^2 = \sigma_{Y|X}^2 + \frac{(\mu_1 - \mu_2)^2}{4} \qquad [10.19.3^*]$$

where $\mu_1$ is the mean of population 1, $\mu_2$ that of population 2, and

$$\frac{\mu_1 + \mu_2}{2} = \mu,$$

the mean of the marginal distribution.

On substituting into **10.19.2,** we find

$$\omega^2 = \frac{(\mu_1 - \mu_2)^2}{4\sigma_Y^2}.$$

For two treatment-populations with equal variances the strength of the statistical association between treatment and dependent variable varies directly with the squared difference between the population means, relative to the unconditional, marginal, variance of $Y$.

When the difference $\mu_1 - \mu_2$ is zero, then $\omega^2$ must be zero. In the usual $t$ test for a difference, the hypothesis of no difference between means is equivalent to the hypothesis that $\omega^2 = 0$. On the other hand, when there is any difference at all between population means, the value of $\omega^2$ must be greater than 0. In short, a true difference is "big" in the sense of predictive power only if the square of that difference is large relative to $\sigma_Y^2$. However, in significance tests such as $t$, we compare the difference we get with an estimate of $\sigma_{\text{diff.}}$. The standard error of the difference can be made almost as small as we choose if we are given a free choice of sample size. Unless sample size is specified, there is no *necessary* connection between significance and the true strength of association.

This points up the fallacy of evaluating the "goodness" of a result in terms of statistical significance alone, without allowing for the sample size used. All significant results do not imply the same degree of true association between independent and dependent variables.

It is sad but true that researchers have been known to capitalize on this fact. There is a certain amount of "testmanship" involved in using inferential statistics. *Virtually any study can be made to show significant results if one uses enough subjects, regardless of how nonsensical the content may be.* There is surely nothing on earth that is completely independent of anything else. The strength of an association may approach zero, but it should seldom or never be exactly zero. If one applies a large enough sample of the study of any relation, trivial or meaningless as it may be, sooner or later he is almost certain to achieve a significant result. Such a result may be a valid finding, but only in the sense that one can say with assurance that some association is not exactly zero. The degree to which such a finding enhances our knowledge is debatable. If the criterion of strength of association is applied to such a result, it becomes obvious that little or nothing is actually contributed to our ability to predict one thing from another.

This kind of testmanship flourishes best when people pay too much attention to the significance test and too little to the degree of statistical association the finding represents. This clutters up the literature with findings that are often not worth pursuing, and which serve only to obscure the really important predictive relations that occasionally appear. The serious scientist owes it to himself and his readers to ask not only, "Is there any association between $X$ and $Y$?"

but also, "How much does my finding suggest about the power to predict $Y$ from $X$?" Much too much emphasis is paid to the former, at the expense of the latter, question.

## 10.20  ESTIMATING THE STRENGTH OF A STATISTICAL ASSOCIATION FROM DATA

It is quite possible to estimate the amount of statistical association implied by any obtained difference between means. The ingredients for this kind of estimation are essentially those used in a $t$ test. The problems connected with the sampling distribution of this estimate will be deferred until Chapter 12, and for the moment we shall consider only how this estimate is made and used.

For samples from two populations, each of which has the same true variance, $\sigma^2_{Y|X}$, a rough estimate of $\omega^2$ is provided by

$$\text{est. } \omega^2 = \frac{t^2 - 1}{t^2 + N_1 + N_2 - 1}. \qquad [10.20.1]$$

(A more general form for estimating $\omega^2$ will be given in Chapter 12.) Notice that if $t^2$ is less than 1.00, then this estimate is negative, although $\omega^2$ cannot assume negative values. In this situation the estimate of $\omega^2$ is set equal to zero.

Let us consider an example using this estimate. Imagine a study involving two groups of 30 cases each. Subjects are assigned at random to these two groups, and each set of subjects is given a different treatment. The results are

| Group 1 | Group 2 |
|---|---|
| $M_1 = 65.5$ | $M_2 = 69$ |
| $s^2_1 = 20$ | $s^2_2 = 28$ |
| $N_1 = 30$ | $N_2 = 30$ |

First of all the $t$ ratio is computed in the usual way (Section 10.16):

$$\text{est. } \sigma^2 = \frac{30(20) + 30(28)}{58} = 24.83$$

and

$$\text{est. } \sigma_{\text{diff.}} = \sqrt{\frac{24.83(2)}{30}} = 1.29.$$

Thus,

$$t = \frac{65.5 - 69}{1.29} = -2.71.$$

For a two-tailed test with 58 degrees of freedom, this value is significant beyond the .01 level. Thus, we are fairly safe in concluding that some association exists.

What do we estimate the true degree of association to be? Substituting into **10.20.1**, we find

$$\text{est. } \omega^2 = \frac{(2.71)^2 - 1}{(2.71)^2 + (60 - 1)} = .096.$$

Our best available estimate is that $X$ (the treatment administered) accounts for about 10 percent of the variance of $Y$ (the obtained score).

Suppose, however, that the groups had contained only 10 cases each, and that the results had been:

Group 1      Group 2

$M_1 = 65.5$      $M_2 = 69$

$s_1^2 = 5$      $s_2^2 = 7$

$N_1 = 10$      $N_2 = 10$

Here

$$\text{est. } \sigma^2 = \frac{10(5) + 10(7)}{18} = 6.67$$

$$\text{est. } \sigma_{\text{diff.}} = \sqrt{6.67\left(\frac{2}{10}\right)} = 1.15$$

so that

$$t = \frac{-3.5}{1.15} = -3.04.$$

For 18 degrees of freedom, this value is also significant beyond the .01 level (two-tailed), and once again we can assert with confidence that some association exists.

Again, we estimate the degree of association represented by this finding:

$$\text{est. } \omega^2 = \frac{(3.04)^2 - 1}{(3.04)^2 + 19} = .29.$$

Here, our best guess is that $X$ accounts for about 29 percent of the variance in $Y$. Even though the difference between the sample means is the same in these two examples, and both results are significant beyond the .01 level, the second experiment gives a much higher estimate of the true association than the first.

The point of this discussion should be evident by now: statistical significance is not the only, or even the best, evidence for a strong statistical association. A significant result implies that it is safe to say some association exists, but the estimate of $\omega^2$ tells how strong that association appears to be. It seems far more reasonable to decide to follow up a finding that is *both* significant *and* indicates a strong degree of association than to tie this course of action to significance level alone. Conversely, when a result fails to attain significance and there is no ready way to estimate the $\beta$ probability, the experimenter really has at least two courses of action: he can suspend judgment temporarily and actually collect more data, or he can suspend judgment permanently by forgetting the whole business. If the estimated strength of association is relatively small it may not be worthwhile to spend more time and effort in this direction. Regardless of the courses of action open to the experimenter, on the whole it is reasonable that a better decision can be made in terms of both significance level and estimated strength of relation than by either taken alone. In most experimental problems we want to find and refine relationships that "pay off," that actually increase our ability to predict behavior. When the results of an experiment suggest that the strength of an association is very low, then perhaps the experimenter should ask himself whether this matter is worth pursuing after all, regardless of the statistical significance he may attain by increased sample size or other refinements of the experiment.

## 10.21   STRENGTH OF ASSOCIATION AND SAMPLE SIZE

Of all the questions that psychologists carry to statisticians, surely the most frequently heard is, "How many subjects do I need in this experiment?" The response of the statistician is very likely to be unsatisfactory, the gist being "How big is a difference that you consider important?" This is a question that can be answered only by the psychologist, and then only if he has given the matter some serious thought. If the experimenter cannot answer this question the statistician really cannot help him. Perhaps framing the essential point in terms of strength of a relation rather than the size of a difference will make it a little easier to grasp.

Basically, the question of sample size depends upon the strength of association the experimenter *wants* to detect as significant. Actually, this matter is properly discussed in terms of the $t$ distribution, but for the kinds of rough determinations most psychologists need to make, the normal approximation will suffice.

Recall the basic definition of $\omega^2$ in terms of two population means:

$$\omega^2 = \frac{(\mu_1 - \mu_2)^2}{4\sigma_Y^2}.$$

From this definition, we can derive the fact that

$$\frac{|\mu_1 - \mu_2|}{\sigma_{Y|X}} = 2\sqrt{\frac{\omega^2}{1 - \omega^2}} = \Delta. \qquad\qquad [10.21.1^*]$$

Given any value of $\omega^2$, we can find the ratio of the absolute difference between population means to the standard deviation of either population. The symbol $\Delta$ (capital Greek delta) will stand for this absolute difference between means in standard deviation units.

If we want to discuss the difference between means in units of the standard error of the difference, then for samples of the same size, $n$,

$$\frac{|\mu_1 - \mu_2|}{\sigma_{\text{diff.}}} = \Delta\sqrt{\frac{n}{2}}.$$

Now suppose that an experiment is being planned which involves two groups, each of size $n$. The experimenter wants to be very sure that he will detect a significant difference if the true degree of association $\omega^2$ is $k$ or more in value. How large should $n$ be in each sample?

Several things must be specified: the value of $k = \omega^2$, the $\alpha$ probability, and the probability $1 - \beta$, which is the power of the test when the true degree of association is equal to $k$. Given these three specifications, then one can approximate the required size of $n$ by taking

$$\sqrt{\frac{n}{2}} = \frac{[z_{(1-\alpha/2)} - z_{(\beta)}]}{\Delta} \qquad \text{[10.21.2†]}$$

or

$$n = \frac{2[z_{(1-\alpha/2)} - z_{(\beta)}]^2}{\Delta^2} \qquad \text{[10.21.3†]}$$

where $z_{(1-\alpha/2)}$ is the value of a standardized score in a normal distribution cutting off the lower $(1 - \alpha/2)$ proportion of cases, and $z_{(\beta)}$ is the standardized score cutting off the lower $\beta$ proportion of cases. The value of $\Delta$ is found from the required value of $\omega^2$ by substitution into 10.21.1.

For example, suppose that the experimenter wants to be very sure to detect a true association when $X$ actually accounts for 25 percent or more of the variance of $Y$, so that $\omega^2$ is .25 or more. He wants the test to have a power of .99 when $\omega^2 = .25$, and he has already decided that $\alpha$ must be .01. How many cases should he include in each sample?

First of all, solving from 10.21.1 for $\Delta$, we find

$$\Delta = 2\sqrt{\frac{.25}{1 - .25}}$$

or

$$\Delta = 1.15.$$

The value of $z_{(1-\alpha/2)}$ is 2.58, and that for $z_{(\beta)} = -2.33$. Thus,

$$n = \frac{2(2.58 + 2.33)^2}{(1.15)^2} = 36.5.$$

In order to have $\alpha = .01$, and to have a test with power of about .99 for a significant result when $\omega^2 = .25$, the experimenter should plan on about 37 subjects in each sample, a total of 74 subjects in all.

This may be more subjects than the experimenter can manage to obtain. He can reduce his estimate of the required number either by *lowering* his requirements for the power of the test, making the power, say, .95 for $\omega^2 = .25$, or by *raising* the probability $\alpha$ to, say, .05. Suppose that he adopts the latter course, making $\alpha = .05$. In this instance, his revised estimate of sample size is given by

$$n = \frac{2(1.96 + 2.33)^2}{(1.15)^2} = 27.9$$

showing that these requirements are approximately satisfied if he takes around 28 subjects in each group, for a total of about 56 cases in all.

These estimates of required sample size are only approximate, since we use the normal rather than the $t$ distribution. They are to be regarded only as rough guides to the general sample sizes required. Unless the sample size estimates turn out rather large as in the example, and if it is important that the experimenter fulfill the requirements he has set himself about $\omega^2$, $\alpha$, and $1 - \beta$, he is very wise to take samples somewhat larger than his estimate suggests.

It is remarkable how few studies reported in psychology seem to be based on sample sizes chosen in any systematic way. Certainly there are situations where real limits exist about how large a sample can be, and here the experimenter merely does the best he can. However, there is usually some freedom of choice within fairly broad limits. One does not have to look very far to find the reason this question is often ignored: all too seldom is the experimenter prepared to state the strength of association that he feels he *must* be sure to detect as a significant result. To decide this requires a great deal of thought about the potential applications, or the experimental follow-up that should be implied by a significant finding. On the other hand, unless this thought is expended in planning a study there is simply no way to determine required sample size. If psychologists are going to use conventions for deciding significance of results then perhaps a few conventions are called for about the strength of association it is desirable to *detect* as significant.

Regardless of the sample size actually chosen, the experimenter can form a rough estimate of the sensitivity of the experiment for detecting statistical association. For two relatively large samples of equal size, the expression

$$\Delta^2 = \frac{2[z_{(1-\alpha/2)}]^2}{n} \qquad\qquad [10.21.4^*]$$

can be solved for $\Delta^2$. Then by the relation

$$\omega^2 = \frac{\Delta^2}{\Delta^2 + 4} \qquad\qquad [10.21.5^*]$$

one finds the strength of association for which the power is approximately .50. One can be reasonably sure that if the true degree of association is greater than the value of $\omega^2$ found by this procedure, then he has better than a fifty-fifty chance of detecting this fact as a significant result. Conversely, if the true association is less than the value of $\omega^2$ found the chances are about .50 or better that he will not detect this as a significant result.

For example, suppose that 25 subjects are used in each of two experimental groups. The $\alpha$ level chosen is .01, two-tailed. Then

$$\Delta^2 = \frac{2(2.58)^2}{25} = .53$$

so that

$$\omega^2 = \frac{.53}{.53 + 4} = .12.$$

The experimenter can say that if the true degree of association is about .12 or more he has about a fifty-fifty chance of detecting this as a significant result.

Had the experimenter used 100 subjects per group, then the value of $\omega^2$ in **10.21.4** would have been about .03. For this relatively large sample size the experimenter has about a fifty-fifty chance of detecting a significant difference when the experimental variable $X$ accounts for no more than about 3 percent of the variance of $Y$. The larger the sample size, the smaller the proportion of variance accounted for that we can safely expect to be detected as a significant result.

The discussion of sample size in this section has been conducted in terms of two-tailed tests, since these are most comon in psychological research. However, the same idea applies in approximating the required sample size for a one-tailed test as well. Instead of using $z_{(1-\alpha/2)}$ in the computations, one simply substitutes $z_{(1-\alpha)}$ where $\alpha$ is the chosen error probability in the one-tailed region. For one-tailed tests the statements made about degrees of association and their detection are valid only for differences in the direction of the region of rejection, of course.

## 10.22   CAN A SAMPLE SIZE BE TOO LARGE?

In one sense, even posing this question sounds like heresy! Psychologists are often trained to think that large samples are *good things*, and we have seen that the most elegant features within theoretical statistics actually are the limit theorems, each implying a connection between sample size and the goodness of inferences.

Nevertheless, it seems reasonable that sample size can never really be discussed apart from what the experimenter is trying to do, and the stakes that he has in the experiment. *So long as the experimenter's primary interest is in precise estimation, then the larger the sample the better.* When he wants to come as close as he possibly can to the true parameter values, he can always do better by increasing sample size.

This is not, however, the main purpose of some experiments. These studies are, in the strict sense, exploratory. The experimenter is trying to map out the main relationships in some area. His study serves as a guide for directions that he will pursue in further, more refined, studies. He wants to find those statistical associations that are relatively large and that give considerable promise that a more or less precise relationship is there to be discovered and refined. He does not want to waste his time and effort by concluding an association exists when the degree of prediction actually afforded by that association is negligible. In short, the experimenter would like a significant result to represent not only a nonzero association, but an association of considerable size.

When this is the situation it is advisable to look into the effects of sample size on the probability of finding a significant result given a *weak* association. For example, an experimenter has decided to use 30 subjects in each of two experimental groups. However, he does not want to waste his time with a significant result when the true degree of association is .01 or less. He decides that he wants the probability of a significant result to be .05 or less when the true $\omega^2$ is .01 or less. He has already decided that $\alpha$ must be .01, and he knows that this must be the probability of a significant result when $\omega^2 = 0$ (the true difference is zero). For a two-tailed test, he cannot make the power of the test less than $\alpha$. However, the experimenter's requirement is that his test have power of only .05 or less when $\omega^2$ is less than or equal to .01.

Using **10.21.1** from the previous section,

$$\Delta = 2 \sqrt{\frac{.01}{1 - .01}}$$
$$= 2(.10) = .2, \text{ approximately.}$$

In this problem, $1 - \beta = .05$, and so, by **10.21.3**,

$$n = \frac{2(2.58 - 1.65)^2}{(.2)^2}$$
$$= 43.$$

If he uses *no more* than about 43 subjects in each group then the experimenter can be quite sure that a significant result is not likely to occur when the true degree of association is .01 or less. However, if he uses more subjects, he cannot be this confident of *not* detecting a very small association.

What does setting maximum sample size at 43 dictate about the $\omega^2$ values he *will* detect as significant? How large a $\omega^2$ will he detect as a significant result 95 percent of the time? This is found from

$$\Delta^2 = \frac{2(2.58 + 1.65)^2}{43}$$
$$= .83$$

so that

$$\omega_1^2 = \frac{(.83)^2}{(.83)^2 + 4}$$
$$= .15.$$

Even with the sample size of 43 cases per group, the experimenter knows that there is a probability of about .95 of finding a significant result when the true proportion of variance accounted for is as small as .15. Thus, 43 cases per group is both large enough to let the experimenter be confident of detecting relatively strong associations, and small enough so that he is unlikely to detect very tiny associations as significant.

There is a real danger in detecting trivial associations as significant results when the sample size is very large. If the experimenter wants significance to be very likely to reflect a sizable association in his data, and also wants to be sure that he will not be led by a significant result into some blind alley, then he should pay attention to both aspects of sample size. Is the sample size *large* enough to give confidence that the big associations will indeed show up, while being *small* enough so that trivial associations will be excluded from significance?

## 10.23 PAIRED OBSERVATIONS

Sometimes it happens that subjects are actually sampled in pairs. Even though each subject is experimentally different in one respect (nominally, the independent variable) from his pair-mate and each has some distinct dependent variable score, the scores of the members of a pair are not necessarily independent. For instance, one may be comparing scores of husbands and wives; a husband is "naturally" matched with his wife, and it makes sense that knowing the husband's score gives us some information about his wife's, and vice versa. Or individuals may be matched on some basis by the experimenter, and within each matched pair the members are assigned at random to experimental treatments. This matching of pairs is one form of experimental control, since each member of each experimental group must be identical (or nearly so) to his pair-mate in the other group with respect to the matching factor or factors, and thus the factor or factors used to match pairs cannot be responsible for any observed difference in the groups.

Given two groups matched in this pairwise way, either by the experimenter or otherwise, it is still true that the difference between the means is an unbiased estimate of the population difference (in two matched populations):

$$E(M_1 - M_2) = \mu_1 - \mu_2.$$

However, the matching, and the consequent *dependence* within the pairs, changes the standard error of the difference. This can be shown quite simply: By definition, the variance of the difference between two sample means is

$$\sigma^2_{\text{diff.}} = E(M_1 - M_2 - \mu_1 + \mu_2)^2$$

which is the same as

$$E[(M_1 - \mu_1) - (M_2 - \mu_2)]^2.$$

Expanding the square, we have

$$E(M_1 - \mu_1)^2 + E(M_2 - \mu_2)^2 - 2E(M_1 - \mu_1)(M_2 - \mu_2).$$

The first of these terms is just $\sigma^2_{M_1}$, and the second is $\sigma^2_{M_2}$. However, what of the third term? From rule 6 Appendix B we find that the expectation of this product must be zero when the variables are independent. On the other hand, when variables are dependent the expectation is *not* ordinarily zero. Let us denote this last term above as cov.$(M_1, M_2)$, the **covariance** of the means. Then, for matched groups,

$$\sigma^2_{\text{diff.}} = \sigma^2_{M_1} + \sigma^2_{M_2} - 2\text{ cov.}(M_1, M_2).$$

In general, for groups matched by pairs, this covariance is a positive number, and thus the variance and standard error of a difference between means will usually be *less* for matched than for unmatched groups. This fact accords with the experimenter's purpose in matching in the first place: to remove one or more sources of variability, and thus to lower the sampling error.

This unknown value of cov.$(M_1, M_2)$ could be something of a problem, but actually it is quite easy to bypass this difficulty altogether. Instead of regarding this as two samples, we simply think of the data coming from one sample of *pairs*. Associated with each pair $i$ is a difference

$$D_i = (Y_{i1} - Y_{i2})$$

where $Y_{i1}$ is the score of the member of pair $i$ who is in group 1, and $Y_{i2}$ is the score of the member of pair $i$ who is in group 2. Then an ordinary $t$ test for a *single* mean is carried out using the scores $D_i$. That is,

$$M_D = \frac{\sum_i D_i}{N}$$

and

$$s_D^2 = \frac{\sum_i D_{1i}^2}{N} - M_D^2.$$

Then

$$\text{est. } \sigma_{M_D} = \frac{s_D}{\sqrt{N-1}}$$

and $t$ is found from

$$t = \frac{M_D - E(M_D)}{\text{est. } \sigma_{M_D}}$$

with $N - 1$ degrees of freedom. *Be sure to notice that here $N$ stands for the number of differences, which is the number of pairs.*

Naturally, the hypothesis is about the true value of $E(M_D)$, which is always $\mu_1 - \mu_2$. Thus any hypothesis about a difference can be tested in this way, provided that the groups used are matched *pairwise*. Similarly, confidence limits are found just as for a single mean, using $M_D$ and $\sigma_{M_D}$ in place of $M$ and $\sigma_M$.

## 10.24 SIGNIFICANCE TESTING IN MORE COMPLICATED EXPERIMENTS

Only in the very simplest experimental problems does the experimenter confine himself to two treatment groups. It is far more usual to find experiments that involve a number of qualitatively or quantitatively different treatments. However, the basic conception of what the experimenter is doing remains the same: he is looking for evidence of a statistical relation between experimental and dependent variables. When there are several groups it is no longer possible to make a simple and direct connection between the degree of statistical association and the difference between any pair of means; here there are any number of pairs of means that may be different and thus imply association, and the mechanism of the simple $t$ test breaks down. Thus, we will introduce this problem once again in somewhat different terms in Chapter 12. However, before we can discuss methods general enough to handle multi-group data, we need to study two more theoretical sampling distributions, both of which grow out of problems of inference about population variances. The next chapter is devoted to the study of these two distributions.

# THE CHI-SQUARE AND THE
# F DISTRIBUTIONS

*11*

The essential ideas of inferential statistics are most easily discussed in terms of inferences about means or proportions, and so attention has been focused almost exclusively on these matters in the preceding chapters. However, population distributions can be compared in terms of variability as well as central tendency, and it is important to have inferential methods for the variance at our disposal.

The three basic sampling distributions used so far (the binomial, the normal, and the $t$ distribution) no longer apply directly when the variance of a population is under study. Rather, we must turn to two new theoretical distributions. The first of these is called the **chi-square distribution,** or the distribution of the random variable $\chi^2$ (small Greek chi, squared). We will use this distribution first in making inferences about a single population variance, although it has many other applications. The second distribution we will consider is usually called the $F$ **distribution,** or the distribution of the random variable $F$ (after Sir Ronald Fisher, who developed the main applications of this distribution). The study of this theoretical distribution grows out of the problem of comparing two population variances. The uses of both of these distributions extend far beyond the problems for which they were originally developed, since, like the normal distribution, they provide good approximations to a large class of other sampling distributions that are not easy to determine exactly. These five theoretical distributions, the three already studied plus the two to be introduced in this chapter, make up the arsenal of theoretical functions from which the statistician draws most heavily; almost all the elementary methods of statistical inference rest on one or more of these theoretical distributions. Furthermore, these five theoretical functions have very close connections with each other, and after we conclude our discussion of the chi-square and $F$ distributions, some of these relationships will be pointed out.

*336*

## 11.1  The chi-square distribution

Suppose that there exists a population having a normal distribution of scores $Y$. The mean of this distribution is $E(Y) = \mu$, and the variance is

$$E(Y - \mu)^2 = \sigma^2.$$

Now cases are sampled from this distribution *one* at a time, $N = 1$. For each case sampled the **squared standardized score**

$$z^2 = \frac{(Y - \mu)^2}{\sigma^2} \qquad\qquad [11.1.1]$$

is computed. Let us call this squared standardized score $\chi^2_{(1)}$ so that

$$\chi^2_{(1)} = z^2. \qquad\qquad [11.1.2^*]$$

Now we will look into the sampling distribution of this variable $\chi^2_{(1)}$.

First of all, what is the range of values that $\chi^2$ might take on? The original normal variable $Y$ ranges over all real numbers, and this is also the range of the standardized variable $z$. However, $\chi^2_{(1)}$ is always a squared quantity, and so its range must be all the *nonnegative* real numbers, from zero to a positive infinity. We can also infer something about the form of this distribution of $\chi^2_{(1)}$; the bulk of the cases (about 68 percent) in a normal distribution of standardized scores must lie between $-1$ and $1$. Given a $z$ between $-1$ and $1$, the corresponding $\chi^2_{(1)}$ value lies between 0 and 1, so that the bulk of this sampling distribution will fall in the interval between 0 and 1. This implies that the form of the distribution of $\chi^2_{(1)}$ will be very skewed, with a high probability for a value in the interval from 0 to 1, and relatively low probability in the interval with lower bound 1 and approaching positive $\infty$ as its upper bound. The graph of the distribution of $\chi^2_{(1)}$ is represented in Figure 11.1.1.

$f(\chi^2_{(1)})$

$\chi^2_{(1)}$

FIG. 11.1.1.  The  distribution  of $\chi^2$ for $\nu = 1$

Figure 11.1.1 pictures **the chi-square distribution with one degree of freedom. The distribution of the random variable** $\chi^2_{(1)}$**, where**

$$\chi^2_{(1)} = \frac{(Y - \mu)^2}{\sigma^2},$$

**and** $Y$ **is normally distributed with mean** $\mu$ **and variance** $\sigma^2$ **is a chi-square distribution with 1 degree of freedom.**

Now let us go a little further. Suppose that samples of *two* cases are drawn independently and at random from a normal distribution. We find the squared standardized score corresponding to each observation:

$$z_1^2 = \frac{(Y_1 - \mu)^2}{\sigma^2}$$

$$z_2^2 = \frac{(Y_2 - \mu)^2}{\sigma^2}.$$

The *sum* of these two squared standardized scores is found and designated as the random variable $\chi_{(2)}^2$:

$$\chi_{(2)}^2 = \frac{(Y_1 - \mu)^2}{\sigma^2} + \frac{(Y_2 - \mu)^2}{\sigma^2} = z_1^2 + z_2^2. \qquad [11.1.3*]$$

If we look into the distribution of the random variable $\chi_{(2)}^2$ we find that the range of possible values extends over all nonnegative real numbers. However, since the random variable is based on *two* independent observations, the distribution is somewhat less skewed than for $\chi_{(1)}^2$; the probability is not so high that the sum of two squared standardized scores should fall between 0 and 1. This is illustrated in Figure 11.1.2. This illustrates a **chi-square distribution with two degrees of freedom.**

Finally, suppose that we took $N$ independent observations at random from a normal distribution with mean $\mu$ and variance $\sigma^2$ and defined

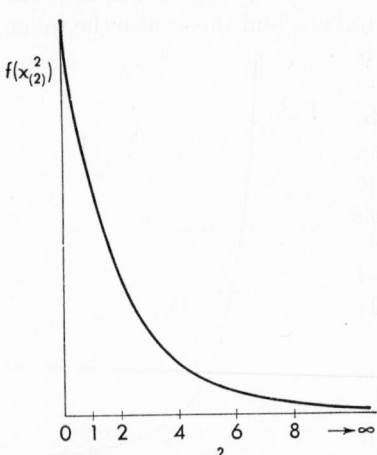

$$\chi_{(N)}^2 = \frac{\sum_{i}^{N} (Y_i - \mu)^2}{\sigma^2} = \sum_i z_i^2. \qquad [11.1.4*]$$

FIG. 11.1.2. The distribution of $\chi^2$ for $\nu = 2$

The distribution of this random variable will have a form that depends upon the number of independent observations taken at one time. **In general, for $N$ independent observations from a normal population, the sum of the squared standardized scores for the observations has a chi-square distribution with $N$ degrees of freedom.** Notice that the standardized scores must be relative to the *population mean* and the *population standard deviation*.

Another way of expressing the definition of a chi-square variable is as follows: **a random variable has a chi-square distribution with $N$ degrees of freedom if it has the same distribution as the sum of the squares of $N$ independent random variables, each normally distributed, and each having expectation 0 and variance 1.** Chi-square distributions for larger numbers of degrees of freedom have the form illustrated in Figure 11.1.3.

**FIG. 11.1.3.** The general form of the distribution of $\chi^2$ for larger numbers of degrees of freedom

## 11.2   THE FUNCTION RULE AND THE MEAN AND VARIANCE FOR A CHI-SQUARE DISTRIBUTION

The function rule assigning a probability density to each possible value of $\chi^2$ is given by

$$f(\chi^2) = h(\nu)e^{-\chi^2/2}(\chi^2)^{(\nu/2)-1}, \qquad \text{for } \chi^2 \gtreqless 0 \qquad [11.2.1*]$$
$$\nu > 0.$$

As shown in Figures 11.1.1 through 11.1.3, the plot of this density function always presents the picture of a very positively skewed distribution, at least for relatively small values of $\nu$, with a distinct mode at the point $\nu - 2$ for $\nu > 2$. However, as $\nu$ is increased, the form of the distribution appears to be less skewed to the right. In this function rule the value $h(\nu)$ is a constant depending only on the parameter $\nu$. Unlike the normal and the $t$ distributions, it is not so easy to infer the characteristics of the distribution of $\chi^2$ from this function rule. However, the thing to notice is that there is only one value other than $\chi^2$ that must be specified in order to find the density: this is the parameter $\nu$. Like the $t$ distribution, the distribution of $\chi^2$ depends only on the degrees of freedom, the parameter $\nu$. The family of chi-square distributions all follow this general rule, but the exact form of the distribution depends on the number of degrees of freedom, $\nu$. In principle, the value of $\nu$ can be any positive number, but in the applications we will make of this distribution in this chapter, $\nu$ will depend only on the sample size, $N$.

From the original definition of $\chi^2$, it is quite easy to infer what the mean of this distribution must be. For $N$ independent observations we defined

$$\chi^2_{(N)} = \frac{\sum_i^N (Y_i - \mu)^2}{\sigma^2} = \sum_i^N z_i^2$$

where the random variable $Y$ is normal. If we take the expectation of $\chi^2_{(N)}$ over all possible samples of $N$ independent observations, we find

$$E[\chi^2_{(N)}] = E\left(\sum_i^N z_i^2\right)$$
$$= \sum_i^N E(z_i^2). \qquad [11.2.2]$$

However, for any $i$, $E(z_i^2) = 1$, by the definition of a standardized score. Thus

$$E[\chi^2_{(N)}] = N. \qquad [11.2.3]$$

**If a chi-square variable has a distribution with $\nu$ degrees of freedom, then the expectation of the distribution is simply $\nu$.** In our derivation, $\nu = N$, the number of independent observations, and so the mean of the distribution is the number of degrees of freedom, or $N$.

The variance of a chi-square distribution with $\nu$ degrees of freedom is always

$$\text{var.}[\chi^2_{(\nu)}] = 2\nu. \qquad [11.2.4]$$

Giving the degrees of freedom $\nu$ actually gives all the information one needs to specify the particular chi-square distribution completely.

## 11.3 TABLES OF THE CHI-SQUARE DISTRIBUTION

Like the $t$ distribution, the particular distribution of $\chi^2$ depends on the parameter $\nu$, and it is difficult to give tables of the distribution for all values of $\nu$ that one might need. Thus, Table III in Appendix C, like Table II, is a condensed table, showing values of $\chi^2$ that correspond to percentage points in various

FIG. 11.3.1

distributions specified by $\nu$. The rows of Table III list various degrees of freedom $\nu$ and the column headings are probabilities $Q$, just as in the $t$ table. The numbers in the body of the table give the values of $\chi^2$ such that in a distribution with $\nu$ degrees of freedom, *the probability of a sample chi-square value this large or larger is $Q$* (Fig. 11.3.1).

For example, suppose that we are dealing with a chi-square distribution with 5 degrees of freedom. Find the row $\nu$ equal to 5, and the column headed .05. The value in this row and column is approximately 11.071, showing that for 5 degrees of freedom, random samples showing a chi-square value of 11.071 *or more* should in the long run occur about five times in a hundred. As another example, look at the row labeled $\nu = 2$ and the column headed .10. The entry in this combination of row and column indicates that in a distribution with 2 degrees of freedom, chi-square values of 4.605 or more should occur with probability of about 1 in 10, under random sampling. Finally, look at the row for $\nu = 24$, and the column for .001; the cell entry indicates that chi-square values of 51.179 or more occur with probability of only about .001 in a distribution with 24 degrees of freedom.

## 11.4 THE ADDITION OF CHI-SQUARE VARIABLES

When several independent random variables each have a chi-square distribution, then the distribution of the *sum* of the variables is also known. This is a most important and useful property of variables of this kind, and can be stated more precisely as follows:

If a random variable $\chi^2_{(\nu_1)}$ has a chi-square distribution with $\nu_1$ degrees of freedom, and an independent random variable $\chi^2_{(\nu_2)}$ has a chi-square distribution with $\nu_2$ degrees of freedom, then the new random variable formed from the sum of these variables

$$\chi^2_{(\nu_1 + \nu_2)} = \chi^2_{(\nu_1)} + \chi^2_{(\nu_2)} \qquad \text{[11.4.1*]}$$

has a chi-square distribution with $\nu_1 + \nu_2$ degrees of freedom.

In short, the new random variable formed by taking the sum of two independent chi-square variables is itself distributed as $\chi^2$, with degrees of freedom equal to the sum of those for the original distributions. A little thought will convince you that this must be so: if $\chi^2_{(\nu_1)}$ is the sum of squares of $\nu_1$ independent variables, each normally distributed with mean 0 and variance 1, and $\chi^2_{(\nu_2)}$ is based on the sum of $\nu_2$ independent such squares, then $\chi^2_{(\nu_1 + \nu_2)}$ must also be a sum of $\nu_1 + \nu_2$ squared values of independent normal variables each with mean 0 and variance 1. Therefore $\chi^2_{(\nu_1 + \nu_2)}$ qualifies as a chi-square variable by definition.

## 11.5 THE DISTRIBUTION OF THE SAMPLE VARIANCE FROM A NORMAL POPULATION

In this section, the sampling distribution of the sample variance will be studied. It will be assumed that the population actually sampled is normal, and the results in this section apply, strictly speaking, only when this assumption is true.

Recall that in Section 6.16 the sample variance was defined by

$$s^2 = \frac{\sum\limits_i^N (Y_i - M)^2}{N}.$$

Suppose, however, that we actually knew the value of $\mu$. For any single deviation from $\mu$, $(Y_i - \mu)$, it is true that

$$(Y_i - \mu) = (Y_i - M) + (M - \mu) \qquad \text{[11.5.1]}$$

since adding and subtracting the same number to any given number does not change the value. Now, for any squared deviation from $\mu$,

$$(Y_i - \mu)^2 = [(Y_i - M) + (M - \mu)]^2$$
$$= (Y_i - M)^2 + (M - \mu)^2 + 2(Y_i - M)(M - \mu). \quad [11.5.2]$$

Summing over all of the squared deviations from $\mu$ in the sample, we have

$$\sum_i^N (Y_i - \mu)^2 = \sum_i (Y_i - M)^2 + \sum_i (M - \mu)^2 + 2 \sum_i (Y_i - M)(M - \mu). \quad [11.5.3]$$

The value of $(M - \mu)^2$ is constant over all individuals $i$, so that

$$\sum_i^N (M - \mu)^2 = N(M - \mu)^2. \quad [11.5.4]$$

Furthermore, since $(M - \mu)$ is the same for all $i$, then

$$\sum_i^N (Y_i - M)(M - \mu) = (M - \mu) \sum_i (Y_i - M)$$
$$= 0, \quad [11.5.5]$$

because the sum of the deviations about a sample mean must be 0. Hence,

$$\sum_i (Y_i - \mu)^2 = \sum_i (Y_i - M)^2 + N(M - \mu)^2. \quad [11.5.6*]$$

If we divide the entire expression by $\sigma^2$, this becomes

$$\frac{\sum_i (Y_i - \mu)^2}{\sigma^2} = \frac{\sum_i (Y_i - M)^2}{\sigma^2} + \frac{N(M - \mu)^2}{\sigma^2}. \quad [11.5.7]$$

Now look at the term on the left in this expression: given $N$ independent cases from a normal population distribution,

$$\frac{\sum_i (Y_i - \mu)^2}{\sigma^2} = \chi^2_{(N)}, \quad [11.5.8]$$

so that this sum of squared deviations from $\mu$, divided by $\sigma^2$, qualifies as a chi-square variable with $N$ degrees of freedom.

Furthermore, if the population distribution is normal, the sampling distribution of $M$ must be normal, with mean $\mu$ and variance $\sigma^2/N$. Thus,

$$\frac{N(M - \mu)^2}{\sigma^2} = \frac{(M - \mu)^2}{(\sigma^2/N)} = \chi^2_{(1)}. \quad [11.5.9*]$$

It follows that the last term in **11.5.7** qualifies as a chi-square variable with 1 degree of freedom, since this is just $z_M^2$ from a normal distribution. Putting these two facts together, we have

$$\chi^2_{(N)} = \frac{\sum_i (Y_i - M)^2}{\sigma^2} + \chi^2_{(1)} \qquad\qquad [11.5.10]$$

or

$$\chi^2_{(N)} = \frac{Ns^2}{\sigma^2} + \chi^2_{(1)}. \qquad\qquad [11.5.11^*]$$

The term on the left is a chi-square variable with $N$ degrees of freedom, and the term on the extreme right is a chi-square variable with 1 degree of freedom. From this fact it can be shown, by use of the addition property of chi-square variables, that

$$\frac{Ns^2}{\sigma^2} = \chi^2_{(N-1)}, \qquad\qquad [11.5.12^*]$$

**the ratio $Ns^2/\sigma^2$ is a chi-square variable with $N - 1$ degrees of freedom.**
If, instead of $s^2$, we use the unbiased estimate $\hat{s}^2$, we find that

$$\frac{(N - 1)\hat{s}^2}{\sigma^2} = \chi^2_{(N-1)}, \qquad\qquad [11.5.13^*]$$

**meaning that the ratio of $(N - 1)\hat{s}^2$ to $\sigma^2$ is a random variable distributed as chi-square with $N - 1$ degrees of freedom.** This fact is the basis for inferences about the variance of a single normally distributed population.

This same idea applies to the sampling distribution of any estimate of a variance, provided that the basic population sampled is normal. Thus, it is also true that when the pooled estimate of $\sigma^2$ is made from two independent samples of $N_1$ and $N_2$ cases,

$$\frac{(N_1 + N_2 - 2) \text{ est. } \sigma^2}{\sigma^2} = \chi^2_{(N_1+N_2-2)}. \qquad\qquad [11.5.14^*]$$

The pooled sample estimate of $\sigma^2$, multiplied by the degrees of freedom and divided by the true value of $\sigma^2$, is a chi-square variable with $\nu = N_1 + N_2 - 2$.

The sampling distribution of the unbiased estimate $\hat{s}^2$ is actually the distribution of the variable

$$\hat{s}^2 = \frac{\chi^2_{(\nu)}\sigma^2}{\nu}, \text{ or } \frac{\text{est. } \sigma^2}{\sigma^2} = \frac{\chi^2_{(\nu)}}{\nu} \qquad\qquad [11.5.15^*]$$

a chi-square variable multiplied by $\sigma^2$ and divided by degrees of freedom. However, inferences are usually made in terms of the distribution of $\dfrac{(N - 1)\hat{s}^2}{\sigma^2}$ since this is just a chi-square variable; thus one can get by with only one chi-square table for this as well as for other uses of this distribution.

### 11.6 TESTING EXACT HYPOTHESES ABOUT A SINGLE VARIANCE

Just as for the mean, it is possible to test exact hypotheses about a single population variance (and, of course, a standard deviation). The exact hypothesis tested is

$$H_0: \sigma^2 = \sigma_0^2$$

where $\sigma_0^2$ is some specific positive number. The alternative hypothesis may be either directional or nondirectional, depending, as always, on the original question.

As usual, some value of $\alpha$ is decided upon, and a region of rejection adopted depending both on $\alpha$ and the alternative $H_1$. The test statistic itself is

$$\chi^2_{(N-1)} = \frac{(N-1)\hat{s}^2}{\sigma_0^2}. \qquad [11.6.1\dagger]$$

The value of this test statistic, computed from the $\hat{s}^2$ actually obtained and the $\sigma_0^2$ dictated by the null hypothesis, is referred to the distribution of $\chi^2$ for $N-1$ degrees of freedom.

For example, there is some evidence that women tend to be a less variable, more homogenous group than do men. One might ask this question about height: "It is well known that men and women in the United States differ in terms of their mean height; is it true, however, that women show less variability in height than do men?" Now let us assume that from the records of the Selective Service System we actually *know* the mean and standard deviation of height for American men between the ages of twenty and twenty-five years. However, such complete evidence is lacking for women. Assume that the standard deviation of height for the population of men twenty to twenty-five years is 2.5 inches. For this same age range, we want to ask if the population of women shows this same standard deviation, or if women are *less* variable, with their distribution having a smaller $\sigma$. The null and alternative hypotheses can be framed as

$$H_0: \sigma^2 \geq 6.25 \qquad (\text{or } [2.5]^2)$$
$$H_1: \sigma^2 < 6.25.$$

Imagine that we plan to draw a sample of 30 women at random, each between the ages of twenty and twenty-five years, and measure the height of each. The test statistic will be

$$\chi^2_{(29)} = \frac{(29)\hat{s}^2}{6.25}.$$

What, however is the region of rejection? Here, *small* values of $\chi^2$ tend to favor $H_1$, that women actually are less variable than men. Hence, we want to use a region of rejection on the left (or small-value) tail of the chi-square distribution with 29 degrees of freedom. If $\alpha = .01$, then from Table III in Appendix C, the value of $\chi^2$ leading to rejection of $H_0$ should be less than the value given by the row with $\nu = 29$, and the column for $Q = .99$. This value is 14.257.

Now the actual value of $\hat{s}^2$ obtained turns out to be 4.55, so that

$$\chi^2_{(29)} = \frac{(29)(4.55)}{6.25} = 21.11.$$

This value is larger than the critical value decided upon, and we cannot reject $H_0$ if $\alpha$ is to be .01.

This example illustrates that, as with the $t$ and the normal distribution, either or both tails of the chi-square distribution can be used in testing a hypothesis about a variance. Had the alternative hypothesis in this problem been

$$H_1 : \sigma^2 \neq 6.25,$$

then the rejection region would lie in both tails of the chi-square distribution. The rejection region on the lower tail of the distribution would be bounded by a chi-square value corresponding to $\nu = 29$ and $Q = .995$, which is 13.121; the rejection region on the upper tail would be bounded by the value for $\nu = 29$ and $Q = .005$, which is 52.336. Any obtained $\chi^2$ value falling *below* 13.121 or *above* 52.336 would let one reject $H_0$ beyond the .01 level.

## 11.7 CONFIDENCE INTERVALS FOR THE VARIANCE AND STANDARD DEVIATION

Finding confidence intervals for the variance is quite simple, provided that the normal distribution rule holds for the population.

Suppose that we had a sample of some $N$ independent observations, and we wanted the 95 percent confidence limits for $\sigma^2$. For samples from a normal distribution, it must be true that

$$\text{prob.} \left[ \chi^2_{(N-1;.975)} \leq \frac{(N-1)\hat{s}^2}{\sigma^2} \leq \chi^2_{(N-1;.025)} \right] = .95 \qquad [11.7.1^*]$$

where $\chi^2_{(N-1;.975)}$ is the value in a chi-square distribution with $N-1$ degrees of freedom cutting off the upper .975 of sample values, and $\chi^2_{(N-1;.025)}$ the value cutting off the upper .025 of sample values. This inequality can be manipulated to show that it is also true that

$$\text{prob.} \left[ \frac{(N-1)\hat{s}^2}{\chi^2_{(N-1;.025)}} \leq \sigma^2 \leq \frac{(N-1)\hat{s}^2}{\chi^2_{(N-1;.975)}} \right] = .95. \qquad [11.7.2^*]$$

That is, the probability is .95 that the true value of $\sigma^2$ will be covered by an interval with limits found by

$$\frac{(N-1)\hat{s}^2}{\chi^2_{(N-1;.025)}}$$

and

$$\frac{(N-1)\hat{s}^2}{\chi^2_{(N-1;.975)}}.$$

Suppose, for example, that a sample of 15 cases is drawn from a normal distribution. We want the 95 percent confidence limits for $\sigma^2$. The value of $\hat{s}^2$

is 10; this is our best single estimate of $\sigma^2$, of course. For $\nu = 14$ and for $Q = .025$, $\chi^2_{(14;.025)}$ is found from Table III to be 26.12, and the value of $\chi^2_{(14;.975)}$ is 5.63. Thus the confidence limits for $\sigma^2$ are

$$\frac{(14)(10)}{26.12} \text{ or } 5.36$$

and

$$\frac{(14)(10)}{5.63} \text{ or } 24.87.$$

We can say that the probability is .95 that an interval such as 5.36 to 24.87 covers the true value of $\sigma^2$.

In general, to find the $100(1 - \alpha)$ percent confidence limits, we take

$$\frac{(N - 1)\hat{s}^2}{\chi^2_{(N-1;\alpha/2)}}$$

and

$$\frac{(N - 1)\hat{s}^2}{\chi^2_{(N-1;1-\alpha/2)}}.$$

These limits can always be turned into confidence limits for $\sigma$ by replacing each limiting value by its square root.

On the other hand, this procedure for finding confidence limits for $\sigma^2$ contains a serious difficulty. When a confidence interval for $\mu$ is found by the methods of Section 9.25 or of Section 10.10, the confidence limits are taken to be equally distant from the obtained value of $M$. Since the normal sampling distribution of $M$ is symmetric, and the distribution of $t$ is also symmetric, these methods of constructing confidence intervals for $M$ give *shortest* intervals. As mentioned in Section 9.25, it is perfectly possible to construct 95 percent, 99 percent, or any other confidence intervals for $M$ in a variety of ways, but making the confidence limits equidistant from $M$ gives the shortest of all possible such intervals. In other words, by the methods of 9.25 and 10.10, we "pin down" the value of $\mu$ within the smallest possible estimated range of values.

Unfortunately, this is not true when we find a confidence interval for $\sigma^2$ by the method just introduced. Here, the confidence limits are determined by values of $\chi^2$ cutting off highest and lowest intervals having the same probability, $\alpha/2$, in the asymmetric chi-square distribution. This does make it true that the *failure* of the confidence interval to cover any hypothetical value of $\sigma_0^2$ is equivalent to the rejection of $\sigma_0^2$ as a hypothesis at the $\alpha$ level, two-tailed. It does *not*, however, make it true that we have the shortest possible such interval of possible values of $\sigma^2$ for a given value of $(1 - \alpha)$, nor that we have the shortest possible interval of "good bets" about the value of $\sigma^2$. For this reason, the confidence interval for $\sigma^2$, although corresponding to procedures for testing hypotheses about $\sigma^2$, is not particularly useful when our interest lies in obtaining the best possible estimates of $\sigma^2$ from the data. More advanced methods do exist for finding this shortest possible confidence interval for $\sigma^2$, and useful tables for finding these intervals are given in Tate and Klett (1959).

Regardless of whether confidence intervals are found by the method given here, or by a method giving shortest intervals, it is true that the larger the sample size, the narrower is the interval with a given probability of covering the true value of $\sigma^2$. For this reason, when we are estimating $\sigma^2$ for any purpose the larger the sample size the more confident we can be of coming close to the value of $\sigma^2$ with our sample estimate $\hat{s}^2$.

## 11.8  THE IMPORTANCE OF THE NORMALITY ASSUMPTION IN INFERENCES ABOUT $\sigma^2$

In the preceding chapter it was pointed out that although the rationale for the $t$ test demands the assumption of a normal population distribution of scores, in practice the $t$ test may be applied when the parent distribution is not normal, provided that sample $N$ is at least moderately large. *This is not the case for inferences about the variance, however.* One runs a considerable risk of error in using the chi-square distribution either to test a hypothesis about a variance or to find confidence limits unless the population distribution is normal, or approximately so. The effect of the violation of the normality assumption is usually minor for large $N$, but can be quite serious when inferences are made about variances, even for moderate $N$. This principle is an important one and will be emphasized several times in succeeding sections.

## 11.9  THE NORMAL APPROXIMATION TO THE CHI-SQUARE DISTRIBUTION

As the number of degrees of freedom grows infinitely large, the distribution of $\chi^2$ approaches the normal distribution. You should hardly find this principle surprising by now! Actually, the same mechanism is at work here as in the central limit theorem: for any $\nu$ greater than 1, the chi-square variable is equivalent to a *sum* of $\nu$ independent random variables. Thus, like the mean, $M$, given enough summed terms the sampling distribution approaches the normal form in spite of the fact that each component of the sum does not have a normal distribution when sampled alone.

This fact is of more than theoretical interest when very large samples are used. For very large $\nu$, the probability for any interval of values of $\chi^2_{(\nu)}$ can be found from the normal standardized scores

$$z = \frac{\chi^2_{(\nu)} - \nu}{\sqrt{2\nu}} \qquad [11.9.1*]$$

since the mean and variance of a chi-square distribution are $\nu$ and $2\nu$ respectively. However, this approximation is not good unless $\nu$ is extremely large. A somewhat better approximation procedure is to find the value of $\chi^2_{(\nu)}$ that cuts off the *upper Q* proportion of cases by taking

$$\chi^2_{(\nu;Q)} = \frac{1}{2}\{z_Q + \sqrt{2\nu - 1}\}^2. \qquad [11.9.2*]$$

This can be used to find chi-square values for $\nu$ greater than 100, which are not given in Table III. The necessary $z_Q$ values are listed at the bottom of Table III, and can also be found from Table I.

## 11.10 The $F$ distribution

It is rather rare to find a problem in psychology that centers on the value of a single population variance. Somewhat more common, however, is the situation where the variances of two populations are compared for equality. That is, we ask if the variability of population 1 is precisely equal to that of population 2, so that $\sigma_1^2 = \sigma_2^2$. The $F$ distribution is used to make inferences of this sort, although we will also use this same distribution for quite a different kind of problem in the next chapter.

Imagine two distinct populations, each showing a normal distribution of the variable $Y$. The means of the two populations may be different, but each population shows the same variance, $\sigma^2$. We draw two independent random samples: the first sample, from population 1, contains $N_1$ cases, and that from population 2 consists of $N_2$ cases. From each sample, an unbiased estimate of $\sigma^2$ is made, based on $\hat{s}_1^2$ and $\hat{s}_2^2$ for each pair of samples. From the results of Section 11.5 we know that

$$\frac{(N_1 - 1)\hat{s}_1^2}{\sigma^2} = \chi^2_{(N-1)}$$

so that

$$\hat{s}_1^2 = \frac{\sigma^2 \chi^2_{(\nu_1)}}{\nu_1}.$$

In the same way, we know that

$$\hat{s}_2^2 = \frac{\sigma^2 \chi^2_{(\nu_2)}}{\nu_2}.$$

For each possible pair of samples, one from population 1, and one from population 2, we take the *ratio* of $\hat{s}_1^2$ to $\hat{s}_2^2$ and call this ratio the random variable $F$:

$$F = \frac{\hat{s}_1^2}{\hat{s}_2^2} = \frac{\text{est. } \sigma_1^2}{\text{est. } \sigma_2^2}. \qquad [11.10.1^*]$$

What sort of distribution should the random variable $F$ actually have when the hypothesis that $\sigma_1^2 = \sigma_2^2$ is true? First of all notice that when we put the two variance estimates in ratio, this is actually the ratio of two independent chi-square variables, each divided by its degrees of freedom:

$$F = \frac{[\chi^2_{(\nu_1)}/\nu_1]}{[\chi^2_{(\nu_2)}/\nu_2]} \qquad [11.10.2^*]$$

since

$$\frac{\hat{s}_1^2}{\hat{s}_2^2} = \frac{(\hat{s}_1^2/\sigma_1^2)}{(\hat{s}_2^2/\sigma_2^2)}$$

*provided* that $\sigma_1^2 = \sigma_2^2$ (that is to say, the hypothesis of the equality of the population variances is true).

Showing $F$ as a ratio of two chi-square variables each divided by its $\nu$ is actually a way of defining the $F$ variable:

**A random variable formed from the ratio of two independent chi-square variables, each divided by its degrees of freedom, is said to be an $F$ ratio, and to follow the rule for the $F$ distribution.**

When this definition is satisfied, meaning that both parent populations are normal, have the same variance, and that the samples drawn are independent, then the theoretical distribution of $F$ values can be found.

The density function for $F$ is much too complicated to allow us to gain much idea of the form of the distribution by looking at its mathematical expression. Suffice it to say that the density function for $F$ depends only upon two parameters, $\nu_1$ and $\nu_2$, which can be thought of as *the degrees of freedom associated with the numerator and the denominator of the F ratio.* The range for $F$ is *nonnegative real numbers.* The expectation of $F$ is $\nu_2/(\nu_2 - 2)$. In general form, the distribution for any fixed $\nu_1$ and $\nu_2$ is nonsymmetric, although the particular "shape" of the function curve varies considerably with changes in $\nu_1$ and $\nu_2$.

Before we can apply this theoretical distribution to an actual problem of comparing two variances, the use of $F$ tables must be discussed.

## 11.11  THE USE OF $F$ TABLES

Since the distribution of $F$ depends upon two parameters $\nu_1$ and $\nu_2$, it is even more difficult to present tables of $F$ distributions than those of $\chi^2$ or $t$. Tables of $F$ are usually encountered only in drastically condensed form.

Such tables give only those values of $F$ that cut off the *upper* proportion $Q$ in an $F$ distribution with $\nu_1$ and $\nu_2$ degrees of freedom. The only values of $Q$ given are those that are commonly used as $\alpha$ in a test of significance (that is, the .05, the .025, and the .01 values). Table IV in Appendix C shows $F$ values required for significance at the $\alpha = Q$ level, given $\nu_1$ and $\nu_2$. The columns of each table give values of $\nu_1$, the degrees of freedom for the numerator, and the rows give values of $\nu_2$, the degrees of freedom for the denominator. Each separate table represents one value of $Q$. The entries in the body of the table are the values of $F$ required for significance at this level.

The use of Table IV can be illustrated in the following way: Suppose that two independent samples are drawn, containing $N_1 = 10$ and $N_2 = 6$ cases, respectively. The degrees of freedom associated with the two variances are $\nu_1 = 10 - 1 = 9$ and $\nu_2 = 6 - 1 = 5$. For the ratio

$$F = \frac{\hat{s}_1^2}{\hat{s}_2^2}$$

the degrees of freedom must be 9 for the numerator, and 5 for the denominator. Now suppose that the obtained $F = 7.00$. Does this fall into the upper .05 of values in an $F$ distribution, with 9 and 5 degrees of freedom? We turn to Table IV and find the page for .05. Then we look at the column for $\nu_1 = 9$ and the row for $\nu_2 = 5$. The tabled value is 4.77. Our obtained $F$ value of 7.00 exceeds 4.77, and thus our sample result falls among the upper 5 percent in an $F$ distribution.

As another example, suppose that $\nu_1 = 1$, and $\nu_2 = 45$. For the problem at hand, the rejection region contains the *upper* .01 proportion in an $F$ distribution. What value must our sample result equal or exceed in order to be significant? Table IV shows that for the .01 level, the required $F$ for this number of degrees of freedom is between 7.31 (the $F$ for $\nu_2 = 40$) and 7.08 (the $F$ for $\nu_2 = 60$). It is difficult to find the exact value of $F$ required, but we are reasonably sure that the required $F$ is somewhere around 7.3.

In both of these illustrations we have dealt only with the upper tail of the $F$ distribution. This would be appropriate if we were doing a one-tailed test, where $H_1: \sigma_1^2 > \sigma_2^2$. However, it is possible, although somewhat more difficult, to find $F$ values corresponding to two-tailed rejection regions.

Let $F_{(\nu_1; \nu_2)}$ stand for an $F$ ratio with $\nu_1$ and $\nu_2$ degrees of freedom, and let $F_{(\nu_2; \nu_1)}$ be an $F$ ratio with $\nu_2$ degrees of freedom in the *numerator*, and $\nu_1$ degrees of freedom in the *denominator*. The numbers of degrees of freedom in numerator and denominator are simply reversed for these two $F$ ratios. Then it is true that, for any positive number $C$,

$$p[C \leqq F_{(\nu_1; \nu_2)}] = p\left[F_{(\nu_2; \nu_1)} \leqq \frac{1}{C}\right] \qquad [11.11.1]$$

the probability that $F_{(\nu_1; \nu_2)}$ is greater than or equal to some number $C$ is the same as the probability that the reciprocal of $F_{(\nu_1; \nu_2)}$ is less than or equal to the *reciprocal* of $C$. Practically, this means that the *value required for $F$ on the lower tail of some particular distribution can always be found by finding the corresponding value required on the upper tail of a distribution with numerator and denominator degrees of freedom reversed, and then taking the reciprocal.*

For instance, we want the $F$ value that cuts off the *bottom* .05 of sample values in a distribution with 7 and 10 degrees of freedom. We find this by first locating the value which cuts off the *top* .05 in a distribution with 10 and 7 degrees of freedom: this is 3.64 from Table IV. Then the $F$ value we are looking for on the *lower* tail when 7 and 10 are the degrees of freedom is the reciprocal:

$$F_{(.95; 7, 10)} = \frac{1}{F_{(.05; 10, 7)}} = \frac{1}{3.64} = .27.$$

Any obtained $F$ value that has 7 and 10 degrees of freedom, and that has a value of .27 *or less* represents a result occurring no more than .05 of the time in this distribution of possible results.

Since the tables of $F$ given in the appendix are for the .05, .025, and the .01 significance levels, *one-tailed*, the only *two-tailed* $F$ values that can be found from these tables are the .10, the .05, and the .02 significance levels. Suppose that $\alpha = .05$ in a problem where $\nu_1 = 20$, and $\nu_2 = 30$. A two-tailed test is desired; what are the limits to the region of rejection? First of all, from Table IV for

$Q = .025$, we find that $F_{(20; 30)} = 2.20$, which is the boundary for the *upper* rejection region. Then we look up the value in the same table for $F_{(30; 20)}$, which is 2.35. The boundary value for the lower rejection region is found to be 1/2.35, or .43. Thus, if our sample $F$ ratio is larger than 2.20, or smaller than .43, the sample value falls in a region of rejection.

## 11.12   USING THE $F$ DISTRIBUTION TO TEST HYPOTHESES ABOUT TWO VARIANCES

In an investigation of the effect of stress on children's performance of a reasoning test, it is felt that competition with peers represents one form of stressful situation to a child. However, the experimenter suspects that competition has different effects on different children. He conjectures that bright children might be stimulated to do even better than otherwise by the competitive atmosphere, but that the relatively dull child will appear even more at a disadvantage. One implication of this notion is that if groups of children are sampled from a population having a normal distribution of ability, but the groups are given different amounts of "competitive stress," the group subjected to the greater stress should show a relatively *greater variance* among the scores.

Letting population 1 stand for the potential group of children tested under stress, and 2 for the control, or nonstressed, population, we frame the following hypotheses:

$$H_0: \sigma_1^2 \leq \sigma_2^2$$
$$H_1: \sigma_1^2 > \sigma_2^2.$$

The rejection region decided upon is one-tailed, reflecting the experimenter's prior "hunch" about effects of stress. The $\alpha$ level to be used is .05.

Thirty-two children are selected at random, and assigned at random to two experimental groups of sixteen cases each. Group 1 is given the stress treatment, and group 2 is not. The results are

$$\hat{s}_1^2 = 5.8, \ \hat{s}_2^2 = 1.7.$$

If the exact null hypothesis is true, so that both of these values are estimates of the same population value $\sigma^2$, the ratio

$$F = \frac{\hat{s}_1^2}{\hat{s}_2^2}$$

should be distributed as the $F$ distribution with $N_1 - 1 = 15$ and $N_2 - 1 = 15$ degrees of freedom. The value required for significance at the .05 level, one-tailed, is found from Table IV to be 2.40. However, the obtained value of $F$ is

$$F = \frac{5.8}{1.7} = 3.41,$$

which exceeds the value required. On this evidence we can reject the null hypothesis of equal variances at the .05 level. We are fairly safe in saying that the experimental increase in stress seems to increase the variability of scores.

Had the alternative hypothesis been two-tailed, then we would have had to consider the required value of $F$ on both tails of the distribution, of course. In this instance, the procedure given in the preceding section would be used.

## 11.13 THE ASSUMPTION OF THE NORMAL DISTRIBUTION IN TESTING HYPOTHESES ABOUT TWO VARIANCES

Despite the risk of needless repetition, it is well to emphasize the importance of the normal-distribution assumption in inferences about population variances. Neither the chi-square nor the $F$ distributions can safely be used for *variance* hypotheses unless the population distribution is normal or the sample sizes are quite large. This warning does not necessarily extend to all uses of these two distributions, but it is valid when the primary question to be answered is about one or more variances.

Occasionally you will find the $F$ test for equality of variance used along with a $t$ test, the experimenter's idea being to test the assumption of equal variances before doing the $t$ test itself. However, this is not an especially good idea, considering the sensitivity of the variance test to nonnormality. The variance-ratio test is least effective for this purpose when it is needed most: with small samples. What one really wants to find out is something about means, and this inference may be quite valid in *spite* of the evidence for unequal variances given by the $F$ test. This consideration applies with even greater force to inferences about several variances; methods exist for comparing several variances simultaneously, and sometimes one is advised to carry out such a test as a preliminary to the simultaneous comparison of several means (by use of the method we will study in the next chapter). Once again, however, the test of equality of variances is quite sensitive to nonnormality, although this apparently makes little difference in tests concerning means. Therefore, one can easily do himself a disservice if he interprets a significant result from a test of variances as a prohibition against the use of a test of means. Although assumptions about equal variances are made in the use of most methods for testing means, there does not seem to be much profit in trying routinely to test the validity of this assumption, at least by the methods generally available.

## 11.14 RELATIONSHIPS AMONG THE THEORETICAL DISTRIBUTIONS

Now that the major sampling distributions have been introduced, some of the connections among these theoretical distributions can be examined in more detail. Over and over again, the binomial, normal, $t$, chi-square, and $F$ distributions have proved their utility in the solution of problems in statistical inference. Remember, however, that none of these distributions is empirical in the sense that someone has taken a vast number of samples and found that the sample values actually do occur with exactly the relative frequencies given by the function rule. Rather, it follows mathematically (read "logically") that if we are drawing random samples from certain kinds of populations, various sample statistics *must* have distributions given by the several function rules. Like any other theory, the theory of sampling distributions deals with "if-then" statements. This is why the assumptions we have introduced are important; if we wish to apply the theory of statistics to making inferences from samples, then we cannot expect the theory necessarily to provide us with correct results unless the conditions specified in the theory hold true. As we have seen, from a practical standpoint these assumptions may be violated to some extent in our use of these theoretical distributions as approximations, especially for large samples. However, these assumptions are quite important for the *mathematical* justification of our methods, in spite of the possible applicability of the methods to situations where the assumptions are not met.

Apart from the general requirement of simple random sampling of independent observations, the most usual assumption made in deriving sampling distributions is that the population distribution is normal. The chi-square, the $t$, and the $F$ distributions all rest on this assumption. The normal distribution is, in a real sense, the "parent" distribution to these others. This, as mentioned in Chapter 8, is one of the main reasons for the importance of the normal distribution: the normal function rule not only provides probabilities that are often excellent approximations to other probability (density) functions, but it also has highly convenient mathematical properties for deriving other distribution functions based on normal populations.

The chi-square distribution rests directly upon the assumption that the population is normal. As you will recall from Section 11.1, the chi-square variable is basically a sum of squares of independent *normal* variables, each with mean 0 and with variance 1. At the elementary level, the problem of the distribution of the sample variance can be solved explicitly only for normal populations; this sampling distribution depends on the distribution of $\chi^2$, which in turn rests on the assumption of a normal distribution of single observations. Furthermore, in the limit the distribution of $\chi^2$ approaches a normal form.

There are close connections in theory between the $F$ distribution and both the normal and chi-square distributions. Basically, the $F$ variable is a ratio of two independent chi-square variables, each divided by its degrees of freedom. Since a chi-square variable is itself defined in terms of the normal distribution, then the $F$ distribution also rests on the assumption of two (or more) normal populations.

The $t$ distribution has links with the $F$, chi-square, and normal distributions. The $t$ ratio for a single mean can be written as

$$ t = \frac{(M - \mu)/\sigma}{\sqrt{(\hat{s}^2/N\sigma^2)}} = \frac{(M - \mu)/\sigma_M}{\sqrt{(\hat{s}^2/\sigma^2)}}. \qquad [11.14.1] $$

The numerator of the $t$ ratio is obviously merely $z_M$, a standardized score in the normal sampling distributions of means. However, consider the term in the denominator. Since, from Section 11.5 we know that

$$\frac{(N-1)\hat{s}^2}{\sigma^2} = \chi^2_{(N-1)}$$

$$\frac{\hat{s}^2}{\sigma^2} = \frac{\chi^2_{(N-1)}}{N-1},$$

it follows that

$$t = \frac{z_M}{\sqrt{\chi^2_{(N-1)}/(N-1)}}.$$
[11.14.2*]

**In general, a $t$ variable is a standardized normal variable $z_M$ in ratio to the square root of a chi-square variable divided by $\nu$.** Let us look at $t^2$ for a single mean in the light of this definition:

$$t^2 = \frac{z_M^2}{\chi^2/(N-1)}.$$
[11.14.3]

The numerator of $t^2$ is, by definition, a chi-square variable with 1 degree of freedom, and the denominator is a chi-square variable divided by its degrees of freedom, $\nu = N - 1$. Furthermore, these two chi-square variables are independent, by the principle stating that for a normal population, $\hat{s}^2$ is independent of $M$ (Section 8.8). Thus, for a single mean, $t^2$ qualifies as an $F$ ratio, with 1 and $N - 1$ degrees of freedom. In general,

$$t^2_{(\nu)} = F_{(1, \nu_2)} \qquad \nu = \nu_2;$$
[11.14.4*]

the square of $t$ with $\nu$ degrees of freedom is an $F$ variable with 1 and $\nu$ degrees of freedom.

You can check this for yourself by examining the column for 1 and $\nu_2$ degrees of freedom in the $F$ table. In the table of $F$ values required for significance at the .05 level, each of the entries in this column is simply the square of the entry in the $t$ table for $\nu = \nu_2$ and $t_{.025}$. Similarly, in the table for $\alpha = .01$, each entry in the column for 1 and $\nu_2$ degrees of freedom is the square of the corresponding entry for $t_{.005}$ in the distribution of $t$.

This relation between $t^2$ and $F$ lets us illustrate the importance of the assumption that the two populations have the same true $\sigma^2$ when a difference between means is tested. For $n$ cases in each of two independent groups, the value of $z^2$ represented by the numerator of $t^2$ must be

$$z^2_{\text{diff.}} = \frac{(M_1 - M_2)^2}{\sigma^2_{\text{diff.}}}.$$
[11.14.5]

When $\mu_1 = \mu_2$, this is a chi-square variable with one degree of freedom. Furthermore, the square of the denominator term in the $t$ ratio must correspond to

$$\frac{\text{est. } \sigma^2_{\text{diff.}}}{\sigma^2_{\text{diff.}}}$$
[11.14.6]

for this to be a chi-square variable divided by its degrees of freedom. When each population has the same true variance, $\sigma^2$, the denominator term we compute is equivalent to such a variable, and the value $t^2$ is then the square of the ratio we actually find:

$$t^2 = \frac{(M_1 - M_2)^2}{\text{est. } \sigma_{\text{diff.}}^2} = \frac{(\chi_{(1)}^2/1)}{(\chi_{(\nu_2)}^2/\nu_2)} = F. \qquad [11.14.7]$$

The ratio one calculates, not knowing the true $\sigma_{\text{diff.}}^2$, actually is distributed exactly as $t$ (or its square distributed as $F$) when the true variances are equal. However, if the values of the two variances are not the same, the ratio of the estimated $\sigma_{\text{diff.}}^2$ to the true $\sigma_{\text{diff.}}^2$ is equivalent to

$$\frac{\text{est. } \sigma_{\text{diff.}}^2}{\text{true } \sigma_{\text{diff.}}^2} = \frac{\chi_a^2 \sigma_1^2 + \chi_b^2 \sigma_2^2}{(n-1)(\sigma_1^2 + \sigma_2^2)} \qquad [11.14.8]$$

where $\chi_a^2$ and $\chi_b^2$ symbolize two possibly different values of a chi-square variable with $n - 1$ degrees of freedom. This ratio is not necessarily distributed as a chi-square variable divided by its degrees of freedom. Thus, when variances are unequal for the two populations, the ratio we compute is not really distributed *exactly* like the random variable $t$, since the square of the ratio we compute cannot be equivalent to an $F$ ratio. For this reason, a correction procedure, such as that in Section 10.17, is required when the variances are unequal and sample size is small.

The important relationships among these theoretical distributions are summarized in Table 11.14.1, showing how the distribution represented in the column depends for its derivation upon the distribution represented in the row.

**Table 11.14.1**

| Distribution | Chi-square | F | t |
|---|---|---|---|
| Normal | Parent, and limiting form as $\nu \to \infty$. Defined as sum of normal and independent $z^2$ values. | Parent, making values in numerator and denominator independent $\chi^2/\nu$ values. | Parent, and limiting form as $\nu \to \infty$. Numerator is normal $z$. |
| Chi-square | | Variables in numerator and denominator are independent $\chi^2/\nu$. | Denominator is $\sqrt{\chi^2/\nu}$. |
| F | | | $t_{(\nu)}^2 = F_{(1,\nu)}$ |

All four of these theoretical distributions will figure in the next three chapters as we work through the rationale for the analysis of variance and comparisons among means. Having some idea of the interrelations of these distributions will be of help in understanding how the $F$ distribution can be used to test a hypothesis about *several* means.

# THE ANALYSIS OF VARIANCE:
# MODEL I, FIXED EFFECTS

## 12

In the examples of Chapter 10, the presence of a statistical relation was inferred from the difference between only two sample means. Of course, such data come only from the simplest kinds of experiments, involving an experimental group and a control group, or perhaps two different experimental treatments. Most psychological experiments are far more complicated than this, employing several groups given different treatments, or groups given different combinations of treatments. However, the experimenter's problem is essentially the same: here he needs a method for the simultaneous comparison of many means in order to decide if some statistical relation exists between the experimental and the dependent variables. The most commonly used procedure for this purpose is the analysis of variance, which is the topic of this chapter.

Bear in mind that the independent or experimental variable $X$ may stand for a qualitatively different treatment administered to each group, or for a numerical amount of some treatment. Both in Chapter 10 and in this chapter we deal with the first instance, in which the different groups represent *qualitatively* distinct classes. The study of experiments involving a quantitative independent variable will be deferred until Chapter 15, although the basic ideas underlying the analysis of variance also will apply in that instance.

The methods and examples discussed in this chapter are a very small subset of the potential applications of the analysis of variance. Only two very simple kinds of experiments will be considered here: first to be considered are experiments having *one qualitative experimental variable or factor* and *one quantitative dependent variable*. In this situation, we will apply the *one-way* analysis of variance (that is to say, the problem is to compare sample groups differing systematically in only one way). Then we will consider the situation where each distinct group of $n$ cases is given a different combination of *two different qualitative* treatments. Here the *two-way* analysis of variance will apply (experimental groups may differ systematically in two ways). There are several good reasons for limiting this discussion to these simple experimental situations. In the first place, a beginning student in psychology is likely to be doing rather simple experiments, or at least his experiments *ought* to be simple if they are to be done with care. In the second place, treating the more complex applications of the analysis of variance must take us fairly far into experimental design, a topic quite capable of occupying a large book of its own. Third, the basic reasoning underlying our discussion of the simple one-way and two-way situations extends quite easily to more complicated situations, so that the student who can follow this discussion should have relatively little trouble with most elementary texts on experimental design and the applications of analysis of variance.

It is important to distinguish between two different sampling situations to which the analysis of variance applies. These differ both in the way that experimental treatments are selected and in the kinds of inferences one makes from the analysis. The formal statistical models applying to these two sampling situations have become known as "Model I" or the "fixed effects model," and "Model II," the "random effects model." The situations calling for these two different models will be compared briefly in the next section.

## 12.1  MODEL I: FIXED EFFECTS

Imagine a situation where several experimental treatments are to be administered. Suppose that there are $J$ different such treatments, and that each treatment is to be administered to one and only one experimental group. Each of the $J$ groups consists of individuals chosen at random and independently and assigned at random to the groups. For example, four different tranquilizing drugs are to be compared for the effect each has on driving skill. Some $N$ subjects are chosen at random and independently and allotted at random to four non-overlapping groups. The individuals in the first group are given drug 1, those in the second drug 2, and so on. Then the groups are to be compared on the dependent variable $Y$, a score on driving skill. Or, perhaps, six different methods of teaching second-grade arithmetic are known. School children from a specific population are sampled and allotted at random to six different groups, each group representing one of the six instructional methods. The groups are then compared on their average achievement after a year's instruction. In both examples, members of some small set of treatments are to be compared, and each treatment of interest is actually used in the experiment.

**Experiments to which Model I applies are distinguished by the fact that inferences are to be made only about differences among the $J$ treatments actually administered, and about no other treatments that might have been included.** In advance of the actual experiment, the experimenter decides that he wants to see if differences in effect exist among some fairly small set of treatments or treatment combinations. He is interested in these treatments or combinations, and *no* others. Each treatment of immediate interest to the experimenter is actually included in the experiment, and the set of treatments or treatment combinations applied exhausts the set of treatments about which the experimenter wants to make inferences. The effect of any treatment is "fixed," in the sense that it must appear in any complete repetition of the experiment on new subjects.

Two examples of experiments in which the fixed effects model does not apply may help clarify this distinction. Consider the problem of an experimenter studying the effect of administration of partial reinforcement on the learning-speed of rats. The independent variable is the particular proportion of reinforced trials the rat experiences. The experimenter is not interested in particular proportions of reinforced trials to which rats might be exposed, but rather in a whole range of such proportions, from 100 percent reinforcement to almost zero. It is perfectly clear that all conceivable levels of partial reinforcement cannot be represented in the experiment, and so the experimenter must somehow sample particular proportions of reinforced trials from among all the possibilities to which rats might be exposed. He is not, per se, particularly interested in the specific levels used in the experiment, but rather in all levels within the range sampled.

As another example to which the fixed effects model does not apply, consider an experiment involving a projective test. This test consists of ten different stimulus cards given in turn to the subject, who gives verbal responses to each. Among the things recorded about the behavior of a subject is the mean time between the presentation of a card and his first response. The experiment is designed to study the effect of the order of presentation of the cards to a subject upon his average first response time. However, there are 10! or 3,628,800 different possible orders of presentation of the cards. The experimenter takes a random sample of, say, twenty such orders, and tests a different group of randomly selected subjects under each. Here, the experimenter is not really interested in the twenty orders actually administered so much as he is in the possible effects of order *in general*. Thus, the fixed effects model is inappropriate for this problem.

**The random effects model (Model II) applies when the experiment involves only a random sample of the set of treatments about which the experimenter wants to make inferences.** The various treatments actually applied do not exhaust the set of all treatments of interest. Here, the effect of a treatment is not regarded as fixed, since any particular treatment itself need not be included each time the experiment is carried out: on each repetition of the entire experiment a new sample of treatments is to be taken. The experimenter may not actually plan to repeat the experiment, but conceptually each repetition involves a fresh sample of treatments. This second model will be considered in more detail in the next chapter. For the moment, we will confine our attention to Model I, for the fixed effects situation.

## 12.2 THE IDEA OF AN EFFECT

It is time to be more specific about the meaning of "effect" as used here. Common sense suggests that if various experimental treatments are having different systematic influences on groups, the means of the groups should tend to be different. In particular, if there really exists a functional relationship between treatment $X$ and the value of variable $Y$ when all possible other factors are controlled, and if the influence of any uncontrolled factors can be regarded as random error, "canceling out" in the long run, a functional relationship should exist between $X$ and *mean* $Y$ over the various treatment populations. The presence of different means for different experimental populations is, as we have seen, an indicator of a statistical relation between the experimental and dependent variables. As the term is used in analysis of variance, **an effect is a reflection of a difference among population means;** this idea will now be given a more formal statement.

If we think of a treatment population $j$ as the hypothetical set of all possible unit observations that might be made under treatment $j$, then the experimental group to which treatment $j$ is actually applied represents a sample from this hypothetical population. Let $M_j$ be the sample mean of the group to which treatment $j$ was actually applied, and let the mean of the potential treatment population be $\mu_j$. Furthermore, suppose that the different treatment populations could somehow be pooled; if an observation unit were equally likely to occur in any treatment population, the mean $\mu$ of this *total* population would be the mean of the $J$ different $\mu_j$ values:

$$\mu = \frac{\sum\limits_{j} \mu_j}{J}.$$

**The effect of treatment $j$ is defined as the deviation of the mean of population $j$, $\mu_j$, from the grand population mean, $\mu$:**

**effect of treatment $j = (\mu_j - \mu)$**

or
$$\alpha_j = (\mu_j - \mu). \qquad [12.2.1*]$$

This symbol $\alpha_j$ (*not* to be confused with the alpha standing for the probability of Type I error) will stand for the effect of any single treatment $j$.

Since the grand population mean $\mu$ is also the mean of all of the treatment population means, it follows that the sum of all of the effects must be zero:

$$\sum_{j} \alpha_j = \sum_{j} (\mu_j - \mu) = J\mu - J\mu = 0. \qquad [12.2.2*]$$

If there is absolutely no effect associated with any treatment, then

$$\alpha_j = 0 \qquad [12.2.3]$$

for each and every treatment population $j$. This is equivalent to the statement that

$$\mu_1 = \mu_2 = \cdots = \mu_J = \mu,$$

where the index numbers $1, 2, \cdots, J$ designate the various treatments. *The complete absence of effects is equivalent to the absolute equality of all of the population means.*

Notice that when there are no treatment effects

$$\sum_j \alpha_j^2 = 0, \qquad\qquad [12.2.4*]$$

and also that any weighted sum of the $\alpha_j^2$ must be zero, since each and every $\alpha_j$ is zero when no treatment effects exist.

## 12.3 THE LINEAR MODEL IN THE FIXED EFFECTS SITUATION

Now we are ready to state a model, or "theory," about the composition of any observed score $Y_{ij}$, corresponding to the $i$th individual observed in condition $j$. This is called a *linear* model, since it states that the score of any individual in any treatment group is composed from a simple sum:

$$Y_{ij} = \mu + \alpha_j + e_{ij}. \qquad\qquad [12.3.1*]$$

This model asserts that the score for observation $i$ in group $j$ is based on the sum of three components: the grand mean of all of the $J$ different treatment populations, the effect associated with the particular treatment $j$, and another part which is strictly peculiar to the $i$th observation made under treatment $j$. This last term, $e_{ij}$, is the random error associated with that particular treatment-subject combination.

Notice that any individual $i$ observed under treatment $j$ is a random sample of one from the corresponding treatment population $j$, so that the expectation over all individuals given treatment $j$ is

$$E(Y_{ij}) = \mu_j.$$

By the linear model, the expected score value over all individuals $i$ in population $j$ is

$$E(Y_{ij}) = \mu + \alpha_j + E(e_{ij}),$$

or

$$E(Y_{ij}) = \mu_j + E(e_{ij}).$$

Thus, for any population $j$, the expectation of $e_{ij}$ over all individuals is zero:

$$E(e_{ij}) = 0.$$

Furthermore, let $M_j$ be the mean of the sample given the particular treatment $j$, and let $M$ stand for the mean over all individuals in all treatments for the experiment. Then over all possible samples of $n_j$ individuals from population $j$,

$$E(M_j) = \mu + \alpha_j + E(M_{ej}),$$

where

$$M_{ej} = \frac{\sum_i e_{ij}}{n_j}.$$

That is, the expected value of $M_j$ depends on $\mu$, on the effect $\alpha_j$, and on the expected mean error over the $n_j$ observations in group $j$. Since

$$E(M_j) = \mu_j,$$

it must be true that

$$E(M_{ej}) = 0$$

for any group $j$. By the same line of reasoning, it must be true that over all samples and over all treatments

$$E(M) = \mu, \text{ and } E(M_e) = 0, \text{ where}$$

$$M_e = \frac{\sum_j \sum_i e_{ij}}{N},$$

the expectation of the average error over all observations in all treatments is zero.

Since both individual errors and mean errors have expectations of zero in this model, an unbiased estimate of the effect of any treatment $j$ can be found by taking

$$\text{est. } \alpha_j = (M_j - M) \qquad [12.3.2*]$$

so that

$$E(\text{est. } \alpha_j) = E(M_j - M) = \alpha_j. \qquad [12.3.3*]$$

To gain some feel for this linear model, imagine three samples consisting of three observations each. Suppose that these three samples represent identical population distributions, and that there is *no* variability (that is, no error) within any of the populations. If the mean of each of the populations were $\mu = 40$, then our sample results should look like this:

| *Sample 1* | *Sample 2* | *Sample 3* |
|:---:|:---:|:---:|
| 40 | 40 | 40 |
| 40 | 40 | 40 |
| 40 | 40 | 40 |

There should be no differences either between or within samples if this were the true situation. When this is true the linear model becomes simply

$$Y_{ij} = \mu,$$

since $\alpha_j = 0$, $e_{ij} = 0$ for all $i$ and $j$.

Now suppose that the three samples are given different treatments, and that treatment effects exist, but that there is once again no variability within a treatment population (again, no error). Our results might look like this:

| *Sample 1* | *Sample 2* | *Sample 3* |
|:---:|:---:|:---:|
| $40 - 2 = 38$ | $40 + 6 = 46$ | $40 - 4 = 36$ |
| $40 - 2 = 38$ | $40 + 6 = 46$ | $40 - 4 = 36$ |
| $40 - 2 = 38$ | $40 + 6 = 46$ | $40 - 4 = 36$ |

Here there are differences between observations in different treatments, but there are no differences within a treatment sample. The linear model here is

$$Y_{ij} = \mu + \alpha_j,$$

since $\alpha_j \neq 0$ while $e_{ij} = 0$, for any $i$ and $j$.

In actuality there is always variability in a population, so that there is sampling error. The actual data we might obtain would undoubtedly look something like this:

| Sample 1 | Sample 2 | Sample 3 |
|----------|----------|----------|
| $40 - 2 + 5 = 43$ | $40 + 6 - 5 = 41$ | $40 - 4 + 3 = 39$ |
| $40 - 2 + 2 = 40$ | $40 + 6 + 1 = 47$ | $40 - 4 - 2 = 34$ |
| $40 - 2 - 3 = 35$ | $40 + 6 + 8 = 54$ | $40 - 4 + 1 = 37$ |
| $M_1 = 39.3$ | $M_2 = 47.3$ | $M_3 = 36.7 \qquad M = 41.1$ |

Here, a random error component has been added to the value of $\mu$ and the value of $\alpha_j$ in the formation of each score. The linear model in this situation is

$$Y_{ij} = \mu + \alpha_j + e_{ij}.$$

Notice that not only do differences exist between observations in different treatments, but also between observations in the same treatment.

If we estimate the effect of treatment 1 by taking

$$\text{est. } \alpha_1 = M_1 - M = 39.3 - 41.1 = -1.8$$

it happens in this example that we are almost right, since the data were fabricated so that $\alpha_1 = -2$. Likewise, our estimate of $\alpha_2$ is in error by .2 and our estimate of $\alpha_3$ in error by $-.4$. Although these errors may seem rather slight in this example, there is no guarantee in any given experiment that they will not be very large. Thus we need to evaluate how much of the apparent effect of any experimental treatment is, in fact, due to error before we can decide that something systematic is actually occurring.

This example should suggest that evidence for experimental effects has something to do with the differences *between* the different groups relative to the differences that exist *within* each group. Next, we will turn to the problem of separating the variability among observations into two parts: the part that should reflect both experimental effects and sampling error, and that part that should reflect sampling error alone.

## 12.4 THE PARTITION OF THE SUM OF SQUARES FOR ANY SET OF $J$ DISTINCT SAMPLES

In this section we are going to leave the study of population effects for a while, and show how the variability in any set of $J$ experimentally different samples may be partitioned into two distinct parts. Actually, we will do this in terms of the sum of squared deviations about the grand mean for the samples, rather than the sample variance itself.

Any score $Y_{ij}$ in sample $j$ exhibits some deviation from the grand sample mean of all scores, $M$. The extent of deviation is merely

$$(Y_{ij} - M).$$

This deviation can be thought of as composed of two parts,

$$(Y_{ij} - M) = (Y_{ij} - M_j) + (M_j - M), \qquad \text{[12.4.1]}$$

the first part being the deviation of $Y_{ij}$ from the mean of group $j$, and the second being the deviation of the group mean from the grand mean. Notice that if the groups in question are actually entire populations, equation 12.4.1 is equivalent to the statement that

$$(Y_{ij} - \mu) = e_{ij} + \alpha_j.$$

Now suppose that we square the deviation from $M$ for each score in the entire sample (12.4.1), and sum these squared deviations across all individuals $i$ in all sample groups $j$:

$$\sum_j \sum_i (Y_{ij} - M)^2 = \sum_j \sum_i [(Y_{ij} - M_j) + (M_j - M)]^2$$
$$= \sum_j \sum_i (Y_{ij} - M_j)^2 + \sum_j \sum_i (M_j - M)^2$$
$$+ 2 \sum_j \sum_i (Y_{ij} - M_j)(M_j - M). \quad \text{[12.4.2]}$$

Now look at the last term on the right in equation 12.4.2 above:

$$2 \sum_j \sum_i (Y_{ij} - M_j)(M_j - M) = 2 \sum_j (M_j - M) \sum_i (Y_{ij} - M_j)$$
$$= 0$$

since the value represented by the term $(M_j - M)$ is the same for all $i$ in group $j$, and the sum of $(Y_{ij} - M_j)$ must be zero when taken over all $i$ in any group $j$. Furthermore,

$$\sum_j \sum_i (M_j - M)^2 = \sum_j n_j (M_j - M)^2$$

since, once again, $(M_j - M)$ is a constant for each individual $i$ figuring in the sum. Putting these results together, we have

$$\sum_j \sum_i (Y_{ij} - M)^2 = \sum_j \sum_i (Y_{ij} - M_j)^2 + \sum_j n_j (M_j - M)^2. \quad \text{[12.4.3*]}$$

This equality is usually called the "partition of the sum of squares," and is true for any set of $J$ distinct samples. Verbally, this fact can be stated as follows: the total sum of squared deviations from the grand mean can always be separated into two parts, the sum of squared deviations within groups, and the weighted

sum of squared deviations of group means from the grand mean. It is convenient
to call these two parts

$$\text{SS within} = \sum_j \sum_i (Y_{ij} - M_j)^2 \qquad [12.4.4]$$

for **sum of squares within groups,** and

$$\text{SS between} = \sum_j n_j (M_j - M)^2 \qquad [12.4.5]$$

for **sum of squares between groups.** Thus, it is a true statement that

$$\text{SS total} = \text{SS within} + \text{SS between.} \qquad [12.4.6\dagger]$$

The meaning of this partition of the sum of squares into two parts can easily be
put into common-sense terms: Individual observations in any sample will differ
from each other, or show variability. These obtained differences among individuals
can be due to two things. Some pairs of individuals are in different treatment
groups, and their differences are due either to the different treatments, or to
chance variation, or to both. The sum of squares between groups reflects the contribution of different treatments, as well as chance, to intergroup differences. On
the other hand, individuals in the *same* treatment groups can differ only because
of chance variation, since each individual within the group received exactly the
same treatment. The sum of squares within groups reflects these intragroup differences due only to chance variation. Thus, in any sample two kinds of variability can be isolated: the sum of squares between groups, reflecting variability
due to treatments *and* chance, and the sum of squares within groups, reflecting
chance variation alone.

## 12.5 ASSUMPTIONS UNDERLYING INFERENCES ABOUT TREATMENT EFFECTS

The partition of the sum of squares is possible for any set of $J$
distinct samples, and no special assumptions about populations or sampling are
necessary in its derivation. However, before we can use sample data to make
inferences about the existence of population effects, several assumptions must be
made. These are as follows.

1. For each treatment population $j$, the distribution of $e_{ij}$ is assumed normal
   (which in the fixed effects model also implies that the distribution of $Y_{ij}$ is
   normal).
2. For each population $j$, the distribution of $e_{ij}$ has a variance $\sigma_e^2$, which is assumed
   to be the same for each treatment population. (This implies that each
   population has the same variance of $Y$ scores.)
3. The errors associated with any pair of observations are assumed to be independent. A consequence of this assumption is that if $h$ and $i$ stand for
   any pair of observations, and $j$ and $k$ for any pair of treatments, then

$$E(e_{ij}e_{hj}) = 0$$

and
$$E(e_{ij}e_{hk}) = 0.$$

In short, we are going to regard our observations as independently drawn from normal treatment populations each having the same variance, and with error components independent across all pairs of observations.

## 12.6   The mean square between groups

The next question is how to use the partition of the sum of squares in making inferences about the existence of treatment effects. First of all, we will examine the expectation of the sum of squares between groups.

For any group $j$, a simple substitution from **12.3.1** above shows that

$$M_j = \frac{\sum_i Y_{ij}}{n_j} = \mu + \alpha_j + M_{ej}$$

and

$$M = \frac{\sum_j \sum_i Y_{ij}}{N} = \mu + M_e.$$

Thus, the deviation of any sample group mean from the grand sample mean is actually

$$(M_j - M) = \alpha_j + (M_{ej} - M_e).$$

From this it follows that

$$\text{SS between} = \sum_j n_j(M_j - M)^2 = \sum_j n_j[\alpha_j + (M_{ej} - M_e)]^2. \qquad \text{[12.6.1]}$$

On taking the expectation of the SS between, we find

$$E(\text{SS between}) = E\sum_j n_j[\alpha_j + (M_{ej} - M_e)]^2$$

$$= \sum_j n_j\alpha_j^2 + E\sum_j n_j(M_{ej} - M_e)^2, \qquad \text{[12.6.2]}$$

by virtue of the fact that each $\alpha_j$ is conceived as fixed over samples, and the fact that $E(e_{ij}) = 0$.

Now turn your attention for a moment to the last term on the right in expression **12.6.2**. First of all, on squaring and distributing the summation we find that

$$\sum_j n_j(M_{ej} - M_e)^2 = \sum_j n_j M_{ej}^2 - 2M_e \sum_j n_j M_{ej} + \sum_j n_j M_e^2 = \sum_j n_j M_{ej}^2 - NM_e^2$$

since
$$M_e = \frac{\sum_j n_j M_{ej}}{N}.$$

Hence $$E \sum_j n_j (M_{ej} - M_e)^2 = \sum_j n_j E(M_{ej}^2) - NE(M_e^2).$$

Because $E(M_{ej}) = E(M_e) = 0$, then for any $j$,

$$E(M_{ej}^2) = \sigma^2_{M_{ej}} = \frac{\sigma_e^2}{n_j}, \qquad [12.6.3]$$

the variance of the sampling distribution of *mean errors* for samples of size $n_j$.

Furthermore, $$E(M_e^2) = \sigma^2_{M_e} = \frac{\sigma_e^2}{N}, \qquad [12.6.4]$$

the variance of the sampling distribution of mean errors for samples of size $N$. Thus, combining the results of **12.6.3** and **12.6.4** we have

$$E \sum_j n_j (M_{ej} - M_e)^2 = \sum_j n_j \frac{\sigma_e^2}{n_j} - \frac{N\sigma_e^2}{N}$$

$$= (J - 1)\sigma_e^2. \qquad [12.6.5]$$

On making this substitution (into **12.6.2**) we finally arrive at the result we were seeking:

$$E(\text{SS between}) = \sum_j n_j \alpha_j^2 + (J - 1)\sigma_e^2. \qquad [12.6.6^*]$$

Ordinarily, we deal with the *mean square between*,

$$\text{MS between} = \frac{\text{SS between}}{J - 1}. \qquad [12.6.7\dagger]$$

Then

$$E(\text{MS between}) = \sigma_e^2 + \frac{\sum_j n_j \alpha_j^2}{J - 1}. \qquad [12.6.8^*]$$

**The mean square between groups is an unbiased estimate of $\sigma_e^2$, the error variance, plus a term that can be zero only when there are no treatment effects at all. When the hypothesis of no treatment effects is absolutely true, then,**

$$E(\text{MS between}) = \sigma_e^2. \qquad [12.6.9^*]$$

**If any true treatment effects at all exist, then,**

$$E(\text{MS between}) > \sigma_e^2. \qquad [12.6.10^*]$$

Accordingly, we can see that the mean square between groups gives one piece of the evidence needed to adjudge the existence of treatment effects. The sample value of MS between should be an unbiased estimate of error variance alone when no treatment effects exist. On the other hand, the value of MS between must be an estimate of $\sigma_e^2$ *plus* a positive quantity when any treatment effects exist.

Naturally, MS between is always a sample quantity, and thus it must have a sampling distribution. However, it is easy to see what this sampling distribution must be: when there are no treatment effects, MS between is an unbiased estimate of $\sigma_e^2$, and in Chapter 11 we found that for normal parent populations,

$$\frac{(\text{est. } \sigma_e^2)}{\sigma_e^2} = \frac{\chi_{(\nu)}^2}{\nu}.$$

The ratio of MS between to $\sigma_e^2$ must be a chi-square variable divided by degrees of freedom, *when* there are no treatment effects *and* the parent populations are normal (assumption 1, Section 12.5).

What is the number of degrees of freedom for MS between? There are really only $J$ different sample values that go into the computation of MS between: these are the $J$ values of $M_j$. Thus, *there are $J - 1$ degrees of freedom for MS between.*

As yet we have no idea of the value of $\sigma_e^2$, so that the sampling distribution of MS between cannot be used directly to provide a test of the hypothesis of no treatment effects. Now, however, let us investigate the sampling distribution of MS within.

## 12.7   THE MEAN SQUARE WITHIN GROUPS

What population value is estimated by the mean square within groups? Under the fixed effects model it is obvious that the treatments administered cannot be responsible for differences that occur among observations within any given group. This kind of within-groups variation should be a reflection of random error alone. Keeping this in mind, let us find the expectation of the sum of squares within groups.

$$E(\text{SS within}) = E\left[ \sum_j \sum_i (Y_{ij} - M_j)^2 \right].$$

For any given sample $j$,

$$E \frac{\left[ \sum_i (Y_{ij} - M_j)^2 \right]}{n_j - 1} = \sigma_e^2 \qquad [12.7.1]$$

since for any sample $j$ this value is an unbiased estimate of the population error variance, $\sigma_e^2$. Thus,

$$E(\text{SS within}) = \sum_j E \sum_i (Y_{ij} - M_j)^2$$

$$= \sum_j (n_j - 1)\sigma_e^2$$

$$= (N - J)\sigma_e^2. \qquad [12.7.2^*]$$

If we define

$$\text{MS within} = \frac{\text{SS within}}{N - J},\qquad \text{[12.7.3†]}$$

then

$$E(\text{MS within}) = \sigma_e^2.\qquad \text{[12.7.4*]}$$

**The expectation of MS within is** $\sigma_e^2$. The mean square within groups is thus an unbiased estimate of the error variance within each treatment population. This is true regardless of the possible existence of treatment effects.

## 12.8 THE SAMPLING DISTRIBUTION OF MS WITHIN

We have just shown that the mean square within groups is a pooled estimate of the value of the variance $\sigma_e^2$, which was assumed to be the same for each population. Thus, once again for normal populations, it must be true that

$$\frac{\text{MS within}}{\sigma_e^2} = \frac{\chi_{(\nu)}^2}{\nu}.$$

Here, however, the value of the degrees of freedom $\nu$ is quite different than that for MS between. This chi-square variable is actually a *sum* of independent chi-square variables, each of which has some $n_j - 1$ degrees of freedom. The addition property mentioned in Section 11.4 must apply, and so **the degrees of freedom for MS within is**

$$\sum_j (n_j - 1) = N - J.\qquad \text{[12.8.1†]}$$

Surely you can anticipate the turn the argument takes now! We have MS between, which estimates $\sigma_e^2$ when there are no treatment effects, but a value greater than $\sigma_e^2$ when effects exist. Moreover, we have another estimate of $\sigma_e^2$ given by MS within, which does *not* depend on the presence or absence of effects. Two variance estimates which *ought* to be the same under the null hypothesis suggest the $F$ distribution, and this is what we use to test the hypothesis.

## 12.9 THE $F$ TEST IN THE ANALYSIS OF VARIANCE

The usual hypothesis tested using the analysis of variance is

$$H_0: \mu_1 = \cdots = \mu_j = \cdots = \mu_J,$$

the hypothesis that all treatment population means are equal. The alternative is just

$$H_1: \text{not } H_0,$$

implying that some of the population means are different from others. As we have seen, these two hypotheses are equivalent to the hypothesis of no-effects and its contrary:

$$H_0: \alpha_j = 0, \text{ for all } j$$
$$H_1: \alpha_j \neq 0, \text{ for some } j.$$

The argument in Sections 12.6 through 12.8 has shown that *when* $H_0$ *is true,*

$$E(\text{MS between}) = \sigma_e^2$$

and

$$E(\text{MS within}) = \sigma_e^2,$$

both the mean square between and the mean square within are unbiased estimates of the same value, $\sigma_e^2$. On the other hand, *when the null hypothesis is false*, then

$$E(\text{MS within}) < E(\text{MS between}).$$

Since both of these mean squares divided by $\sigma_e^2$ are distributed as chi-square variables divided by their respective degrees of freedom when $H_0$ is true, it follows that their ratio should be distributed as $F$, provided that MS between and MS within are *independent* estimates of $\sigma_e^2$. Here, once again, the principle of Section 8.8 comes to our aid: **for** $J$ **samples of independent observations, each drawn from a normal population distribution, MS between and MS within are statistically independent.** For each sample, the mean $M_j$ is independent of the variance estimate $\hat{s}_j^2$, provided that the population distribution is normal. By an extension of the principle given in Section 8.8, MS between, based on the $J$ values $M_j$, must be independent of MS within, based on the several $\hat{s}_j^2$ values; each piece of information making up MS between is independent of the information making up MS within, given normal parent distributions.

Finally, we have all the justification needed in order to say that the ratio

$$\frac{(\text{MS between}/\sigma_e^2)}{(\text{MS within}/\sigma_e^2)} = \frac{\text{MS between}}{\text{MS within}} \qquad [12.9.1\dagger]$$

is distributed as $F$ with $J - 1$ and $N - J$ degrees of freedom, *when the null hypothesis is true.* This statistic is the ratio of two independent chi-square variables, each divided by its degrees of freedom, and thus is exactly distributed as $F$ when $H_0$ is true.

The $F$ ratio used in the analysis of variance always provides a *one-tailed* test of $H_0$ in terms of the sampling distribution of $F$. Evidence for $H_1$ must show up as an $F$ ratio greater than 1.00, and an $F$ ratio less than 1.00 can signify nothing except sampling error (or perhaps nonrandomness of the samples or failure of the assumptions). Therefore, for the analysis of variance, the $F$ ratio obtained can be compared directly with the one-tailed values given in Table IV.

An $\alpha$ level is chosen in advance, and this value determines the section of the table one uses to determine the significance of the obtained $F$ ratio.

## 12.10 COMPUTATIONAL FORMS FOR THE SIMPLE ANALYSIS OF VARIANCE

Although the argument given above dealt with sums of squares defined as follows:

$$\text{SS total} = \sum_j \sum_i (Y_{ij} - M)^2$$

$$\text{SS within} = \sum_j \sum_i (Y_{ij} - M_j)^2$$

$$\text{SS between} = \sum_j n_j (M_j - M)^2$$

most users of the analysis of variance find it more convenient to work with equivalent, but computationally simpler, versions of these sample values. These computational forms will be given below.

First of all, the total sum of squares can be shown to be equal to

$$\text{SS total} = \sum_j \sum_i Y_{ij}^2 - \frac{\left( \sum_j \sum_i Y_{ij} \right)^2}{N}. \qquad \text{[12.10.1†]}$$

It is easy to show that this is true:

$$\text{SS total} = \sum_j \sum_i (Y_{ij} - M)^2 = \sum_j \sum_i (Y_{ij}^2 - 2Y_{ij}M + M^2)$$

$$= \sum_j \sum_i Y_{ij}^2 - 2M \sum_j \sum_i Y_{ij} + \sum_j \sum_i M^2,$$

by rules 3 and 4 in Appendix A. This last expression reduces further to

$$\sum_j \sum_i Y_{ij}^2 - 2M(NM) + NM^2$$

or

$$\sum_j \sum_i Y_{ij}^2 - NM^2,$$

by the definition of the sample grand mean, $M = \sum_j \sum_i Y_{ij}/N$. Making one last substitution for $M$ gives the computing formula, **12.10.1**.

The computing formula for the sum of squares between groups can be worked out in a similar way:

$$\text{SS between} = \sum_j n_j(M_j - M)^2 = \sum_j n_j(M_j^2 - 2MM_j + M^2)$$

$$= \sum_j n_j M_j^2 - 2M \sum_j n_j M_j + M^2 \sum_j n_j$$

$$= \sum_j \frac{\left(\sum_i Y_{ij}\right)^2}{n_j} - 2NM^2 + NM^2$$

or

$$\text{SS between} = \sum_j \frac{\left(\sum_i Y_{ij}\right)^2}{n_j} - \frac{\left(\sum_j \sum_i Y_{ij}\right)^2}{N}. \qquad \text{[12.10.2†]}$$

Finally, the computing formula for the sum of squares within groups is found by

$$\text{SS within} = \text{SS total} - \text{SS between}$$

$$= \sum_j \sum_i Y_{ij}^2 - \frac{\left(\sum_j \sum_i Y_{ij}\right)^2}{N} - \sum_j \frac{\left(\sum_i Y_{ij}\right)^2}{n_j} + \frac{\left(\sum_j \sum_i Y_{ij}\right)^2}{N}$$

$$= \sum_j \sum_i Y_{ij}^2 - \sum_j \frac{\left(\sum_i Y_{ij}\right)^2}{n_j}. \qquad \text{[12.10.3†]}$$

Ordinarily, the simplest computational procedure is to calculate both the sum of squares total and the sum of squares between directly, and then to subtract SS between from SS total in order to find the SS within.

## 12.11   A COMPUTATIONAL OUTLINE FOR THE ONE-WAY ANALYSIS OF VARIANCE

It is natural for the beginner in statistics to be a little staggered by all of the arithmetic that the analysis of invariance involves. However, take heart! With a bit of organization and with the aid of a desk calculator simple analyses can be done quite quickly. The important thing is to form a clear mental picture of the different sample quantities you will need to compute, and how they combine. Below is an outline of the steps to follow:

1. Start with a listing of the raw scores separated by columns into the treatment groups to which they belong.
2. Square each score ($Y_{ij}^2$) and then add these squared scores over all individuals in all groups. The result is $\sum_j \sum_i Y_{ij}^2$. Call this quantity $A$.

3. Now sum the *raw* scores over all individuals in all groups to find $\sum_j \sum_i Y_{ij}$. Call the resulting value $B$ (on some desk calculators it is possible to find $A$ and $B$ simultaneously).

4. Now for a single group, say group $j$, sum all of the raw scores in that group and square the sum, to find $\left(\sum_i Y_{ij}\right)^2$. Divide by the number in that group: $\left(\sum_i Y_{ij}\right)^2 / n_j$.

5. Repeat step 4 for each group, and then sum the results across the several groups to find $\sum_j \dfrac{\left(\sum_i Y_{ij}\right)^2}{n_j}$. Call this quantity $C$.

6. The **sum of squares total** is found from $A - B^2/N$.

7. The **sum of squares between** is $C - B^2/N$.

8. The **sum of squares within** is

$$\text{SS total} - \text{SS between} = A - C.$$

9. Divide SS between by $J - 1$ to give **MS between.**

10. Divide SS within by $N - J$ to give **MS within.**

11. Divide MS between by MS within to find the $F$ **ratio.**

12. Carry out the test by referring the $F$ ratio to a table of the $F$ distribution with $J - 1$ and $N - J$ degrees of freedom.

## 12.12   THE ANALYSIS OF VARIANCE SUMMARY TABLE

It is customary to display the results of an analysis of variance in a table similar to Table 12.12.1.

Table 12.12.1

| Source | SS | df | MS | F |
|---|---|---|---|---|
| Treatments (between groups) | $\displaystyle\sum_j \frac{\left(\sum_i Y_{ij}\right)^2}{n_j} - \frac{\left(\sum_j \sum_i Y_{ij}\right)^2}{N}$ | $J - 1$ | $\dfrac{\text{SS between}}{J - 1}$ | $\dfrac{\text{MS between}}{\text{MS within}}$ |
| Error (within groups) | $\displaystyle\sum_j \sum_i Y_{ij}^2 - \sum_j \frac{\left(\sum_i Y_{ij}\right)^2}{n_j}$ | $N - J$ | $\dfrac{\text{SS within}}{N - J}$ | |
| Totals | $\displaystyle\sum_j \sum_i Y_{ij}^2 - \frac{\left(\sum_j \sum_i Y_{ij}\right)^2}{N}$ | $N - 1$ | | |

In practice, the column labeled SS in Table 12.12.1 contains the actual values of the sums of squares computed from the data. In the d.f. column appear the numbers of degrees of freedom associated with each sum of squares; these numbers of degrees of freedom must sum to $N - 1$. The MS column contains the values of the mean squares, each formed by dividing the sum of squares by its degrees of freedom. Finally, the $F$ statistic is formed from the ratio of the mean square between groups to the mean square within groups.

The student does well to form the habit of arranging the results of an analysis of variance in this way. Not only is it a good way to display the results for maximum clarity, but it also forms a convenient device for organizing and remembering the computational steps.

## 12.13  AN EXAMPLE

An experiment was carried out to study the effect of a small lesion introduced into a particular structure in a rat's brain on his ability to perform in a discrimination problem. The particular structure studied is bilaterally symmetric, so that the lesion could be introduced into the structure on the right side of the brain, the left side, both sides, or neither side (a control group). Four groups of randomly selected rats were formed, and given the various treatments. Originally the control group contained 7 rats and each of the experimental groups 14 rats, but due either to death or postoperative incapacity only the following numbers were actually observed in the discrimination situation. The experimenter assumed that the death or incapacity of a rat operated randomly over the treatments. The basic design of the experiment was then as follows:

*Group*

| I | II | III | IV |
|---|----|-----|-----|
| no lesion | left | right | both left and right |
| (7 rats) | (11 rats) | (13 rats) | (9 rats) |

After a period of postoperative recovery, each rat was given the same series of discrimination problems. The dependent variable score was the average number of trials it took each rat to learn the task to some criterion level.

The null hypothesis was that the four treatment populations of rats are identical in their average ability to learn this task:

$$H_0: \mu_1 = \mu_2 = \mu_3 = \mu_4,$$

as against the hypothesis that treatment differences exist:

$$H_1: \text{not } H_0.$$

The alpha level chosen for the experiment was .05. It was assumed that scores for each population of rats was normally distributed with the same variance. The data are shown in Table 12.13.1.

## Table 12.13.1

| | Group | | |
|---|---|---|---|
| *I* | *II* | *III* | *IV* |
| 20 | 24 | 20 | 27 |
| 18 | 22 | 22 | 35 |
| 26 | 25 | 30 | 18 |
| 19 | 25 | 27 | 24 |
| 26 | 20 | 22 | 28 |
| 24 | 21 | 24 | 32 |
| 26 | 34 | 28 | 16 |
| — | 18 | 21 | 18 |
| 159 | 32 | 23 | 25 |
| | 23 | 25 | — |
| | 22 | 18 | 223 |
| | — | 30 | |
| | 266 | 32 | |
| | | — | |
| | | 322 | |

Now the simple analysis of variance will be illustrated for these data. Given this listing of the raw scores according to treatment groups, we first square and sum over all individuals in all groups (step 2 above):

$$A = \sum_j \sum_i Y_{ij}^2 = 20^2 + 18^2 + \cdots + 18^2 + 25^2 = 24424.$$

Next, the raw scores over all observations are summed, and the result squared (step 3):

$$B = \left( \sum_j \sum_i Y_{ij} \right) = (20 + 18 + \cdots + 18 + 25) = 970$$

$$\frac{B^2}{N} = \frac{(970)^2}{40} = 23522.5.$$

Using steps 4 and 5 above we find

$$C = \sum_j \frac{\left( \sum_i Y_{ij} \right)^2}{n_j} = \frac{(159)^2}{7} + \frac{(266)^2}{11} + \frac{(322)^2}{13} + \frac{(223)^2}{9} = 23545.1.$$

Then (steps 6, 7, and 8),

$$\text{SS total} = A - \frac{B^2}{N} = 24424 - 23522.5 = 901.5$$

$$\text{SS between} = C - \frac{B^2}{N} = 23545.1 - 23522.5 = 22.6$$

$$\text{SS within} = 901.5 - 22.6 = 878.9.$$

Steps 9, 10, and 11 are represented in the following summary table:

| Source | SS | df | MS | F |
|---|---|---|---|---|
| Treatments (between groups) | 22.6 | 3 | 7.5 | $\dfrac{7.5}{24.4}$ |
| Error (within groups) | 878.9 | 36 | 24.4 | |
| Totals | 901.5 | 39 | | |

Ordinarily, at this point, the obtained $F$ ratio would be compared with the value shown in Table IV for 3 and 36 degrees of freedom and the specified $\alpha$ level. For $\alpha = .05$, the required $F$ is 2.84, with 40 degrees of freedom used as the value nearest to 36. However, this step is really not necessary for this example, since the obtained $F$ value is less than one, and the null hypothesis cannot be rejected. There is not enough evidence to warrant the conclusion that mean differences, or effects, truly exist among these treatment populations.

## 12.14  THE $F$ TEST AND THE $t$ TEST

When only two independent groups are being compared in the experiment, and a nondirectional alternative hypothesis is being considered, it makes no difference whether the analysis of variance or the $t$ test shown in Section 10.15 is used. As noted in Section 11.14, the square of a variable distributed as $t$ with $N - 2$ degrees of freedom will be distributed as $F$ with 1 and $N - 2$ degrees of freedom. A simple analysis of variance for two groups always yields an $F$ ratio that is the same as the *square* of the $t$ ratio calculated as in 10.15 for the same data. If the obtained $F$ value is significant for any $\alpha$, the corresponding value of $t = \sqrt{F}$ will be significant at the same $\alpha$ level in a two-tailed test. However, if the alternative hypothesis is directional, the sign of the difference between the two means must be considered; in this situation if $F$ is significant at the $\alpha$ level, the one-tailed $t$ test will show significance at the $\alpha/2$ level, provided that the sign of the obtained difference is appropriate to the alternative hypothesis.

This direct parallel between the $F$ test in the analysis of variance and the $t$ test for a difference in means holds only for the case of two groups, with an important exception that will be discussed in Chapter 14. One is never really justified in carrying out all the $\binom{J}{2}$ different $t$ tests for differences among $J$ groups, and then regarding this as some kind of substitute for the analysis of variance. Such $t$ tests carried out on all pairs of means must necessarily extract redundant, overlapping, information from the data, and as a result a complicated pattern of dependency must exist among the tests. Furthermore, the apparent levels of significance found from a set of such tests have neither a simple interpretation nor a simple connection with the hypothesis tested by the $F$ test in the analysis of variance. Thus, for example, one might suppose that the hypothesis of equality among the $J$ population means could be rejected if at least one of the $\binom{J}{2}$ $t$ tests between means turned out significant at the $\alpha$ level. However, even if each one of these tests were independent of each of the others, it would still be true that the probability of at least one significant result by chance alone would be $1 - (1 - \alpha)^G$, where $G = \binom{J}{2}$; this probability is closer to $G\alpha$ than to $\alpha$ when $\alpha$ is small. Furthermore, the tests, as pointed out above, are not independent, and thus the exact probability of one or more significant such results is not easy to determine. All in all, there is very little to recommend such a multiple $t$ test procedure.

Nevertheless, situations do arise when it is important for the experimenter to be able to compare certain means in the data, in order to answer particular questions about the experiment. Chapter 14 will be devoted to ways for making these individual comparisons among sets of means, either as a substitute for the analysis of variance, or as a supplement to a significant $F$ test.

## 12.15 ANOTHER EXAMPLE OF A SIMPLE, ONE-WAY, ANALYSIS OF VARIANCE

An experimenter is interested in "level of aspiration" as the dependent variable in an experiment. He has developed an experimental task consisting of a difficult game apparently involving motor skill, yielding a numerical score that can be attached to a person's performance. But this appearance is deceptive: unknown to the subject, the game is actually under the control of the experimenter, so that each subject is made to obtain exactly the same score. After a fixed number of trials, during which the subject unknowingly receives the preassigned score, he is asked to predict what his score will be on the next group of trials. However, before he predicts, the subject is given "information" about how his score compares with some fictitious norm group. In one experimental condition the subject is told that his performance is *above average* for the norm group, in the second that he is *average*, and in the third that he is *below average*. There are thus three possible experimental treatments or "standings" that might be given to any subject.

The actual dependent variable score $Y$ is based on the report the subject makes about his anticipated performance in the next group of trials. Since each subject has obtained the same score, this anticipated score on the next set of trials is treated as equivalent to a level of aspiration that the subject has set for himself. Each subject is tested privately, and no communication is allowed between subjects until the entire experiment is completed.

A random sample of sixty men in college is drawn, and the subjects are assigned individually and at random to the three experimental groups. It is decided to test the hypothesis of no treatment effects at the .05 level.

**Table 12.15.1**

INDIVIDUAL ANTICIPATED SCORES BY GROUPS, ACCORDING
TO INFORMATION GIVEN ABOUT STANDING

| Above average | Average | Below average |
|:---:|:---:|:---:|
| 52 | 28 | 15 |
| 48 | 35 | 14 |
| 43 | 34 | 23 |
| 50 | 32 | 21 |
| 43 | 34 | 14 |
| 44 | 27 | 20 |
| 46 | 31 | 21 |
| 46 | 27 | 16 |
| 43 | 29 | 20 |
| 49 | 25 | 14 |
| 38 | 43 | 23 |
| 42 | 34 | 25 |
| 42 | 33 | 18 |
| 35 | 42 | 26 |
| 33 | 41 | 18 |
| 38 | 37 | 26 |
| 39 | 37 | 20 |
| 34 | 40 | 19 |
| 33 | 36 | 22 |
| 34 | 35 | 17 |
| Totals   832 | 680 | 392 |

The data are given in Table 12.15.1. Note that here, $J = 3$, and $n_j = 20$ for each group $j$. We calculate

$$\sum_j \sum_i Y_{ij}^2 = 66872 = A$$

$$\sum_j \sum_i Y_{ij} = 1904 = B$$

$$\sum_j \frac{\left(\sum_i Y_{ij}\right)^2}{20} = \frac{(832)^2 + (680)^2 + (392)^2}{20} = 65414.4 = C.$$

$$\text{SS total} = A - \frac{B^2}{60} = 66872 - \frac{(1904)^2}{60} = 6451.7$$

$$\text{SS between} = C - \frac{B^2}{60} = 65414.4 - 60420.3 = 4994.1$$

$$\text{SS within} = A - C = 66872 - 65414.4 = 1457.6.$$

Finally, the analysis of variance is summarized in the following table:

| Source | SS | df | MS | F |
|--------|------|--------------|--------|------|
| Between groups | 4994.1 | $3 - 1 = 2$ | 2497.1 | 97.5 |
| Within groups | 1457.6 | $60 - 3 = 57$ | 25.6 | |
| Totals | 6451.7 | $60 - 1 = 59$ | | |

The hypothesis of no treatment effects can definitely be rejected, far beyond the .05 level chosen for $\alpha$. For the .05 level, with 2 and 57 degrees of freedom, an $F$ value of only about 3.2 is necessary, and the value for $F$ found here is very much greater than this. One can feel very confident in asserting that the "standing" information given to the subject has some effect on aspiration level, as reflected in the score each subject predicts for himself.

## 12.16 THE IMPORTANCE OF THE ASSUMPTIONS IN THE FIXED EFFECTS MODEL

In the development of the fixed effects model for the analysis of variance a number of assumptions were made. These assumptions help to provide the theoretical justification for the analysis and the $F$ test. On the other hand, it is sometimes necessary to analyze data when these assumptions clearly are not met; indeed, it seldom stands to reason that they are exactly true. In this section we will examine the consequences of the application of the analysis of variance and the $F$ test when these assumptions are not met.

In the first place, note that the inferences made in this chapter are about *means*. The models to be described in the next chapter provide inferences about *variances*, and *the remarks made in this section apply only to the fixed effects model*.

The first assumption listed in Section 12.5 specifies a normal distribution of errors, $e_{ij}$, for any treatment population $j$. This is equivalent to the assumption that each population has a normal distribution of scores, $Y_{ij}$. What are the consequences for the conclusions reached from the analysis when this assumption is not true? It can be shown that, other things being equal, *inferences made about means that are valid in the case of normal populations are also valid even when the forms of the population distributions depart considerably from normal, provided that the n in each sample is relatively large*. This is really but another instance of the principle underlying the central limit theorem, discussed in Section 8.11. Consequently, we need not worry unduly about the normality assumption so long as we are dealing with relatively large samples. In circumstances where the assumption of normality appears more or less unreasonable, the experimenter might do well to take a somewhat larger number of observations than otherwise. The more severely the population distributions are thought to depart from normal form, the relatively larger should the $n$ per sample be. In particular, when each population is supposed to have the same, nonnormal, form, the $F$ test is relatively unaffected.

The second assumption listed in Section 12.5 states that the error variance, $\sigma_e^2$, must have the same value for all treatment populations. Ordinarily, other things being equal, *this assumption of homogeneous variances can be violated without serious risk, provided that the number of cases in each sample is the same.* On the other hand, *when different numbers of cases appear in the various samples, violation of the assumption of homogeneous variances can have very serious consequences for the validity of the final inference.* The moral is again plain: whenever possible, an experiment should be planned so that the number of cases in each experimental group is the same, unless the assumption of equal population variances is eminently reasonable in the experimental context.

The third assumption in Section 12.5 requires statistical independence among the error components, $e_{ij}$. The assumption of independent errors is most important for the justification of the $F$ test in the analysis of variance, and, unfortunately, violations of this assumption have important consequences for the results of the analysis. *If this assumption is not met, very serious errors in inference can be made.* In general, great care should be taken to see that data treated by the fixed effects analysis of variance are based on independent observations, both within and across groups (that is, each observation in no way related to any of the other observations). This is most likely to present a problem in studies where repeated observations are made of the same experimental subjects, perhaps with each subject being observed under each of the experimental treatments. In some experiments of this sort there is good reason to believe that the performance of the subject on one occasion has a systematic effect on his subsequent performances under the same or another experimental condition. In the fixed effects model, such systematic connections or dependencies among observations amount to a lack of statistical independence among errors, in violation of the assumption. For this reason, some authors suggest that data based on repeated observations should never be treated under the fixed effects model for analysis of variance. However, this seems to be a point of experimental technique on which the statistician must tread very lightly. The circumstance that observations were repeated does not, ipso facto, imply that observations must be regarded as statistically dependent; a shrewd experimenter can sometimes get his subject into a stable state very early by pre-experimental warm-up techniques, and in such situations it may be quite reasonable to assume that repeated observations are statistically independent. In other kinds of experiments, still other grounds may exist for assuming independence of repeated observations. The point, as always, is that statistics is limited in its ability to legislate experimental practice. Statistical assumptions must not be turned into prohibitions against particular kinds of experiments, although these assumptions must be borne in mind by the experimenter exercising thought and care in matching the particular experimental situation with an appropriate form of analysis. More will be said about the problem of repeated observations in Chapter 13.

Some further comments are in order about the meaning of an obtained $F$ ratio with a value less than 1.00. When the null hypothesis is true, we should expect the $F$ ratio to have a value close to 1.00 (more precisely, a value given by $\nu_2/(\nu_2 - 2)$, where $\nu_2$ symbolizes the degrees of freedom for the denominator). Nonetheless, by chance alone it is entirely possible to obtain an $F$ ratio much less than 1.00, or even an $F$ value of exactly zero, regardless of whether $H_0$ or $H_1$ is true. Although such values can occur by chance, the occurrence of a very small $F$ ratio can also serve as a signal that the experimenter needs to think more carefully about the experimental situation itself. Very commonly, a close analysis of the experimental situation shows a systematic, but uncontrolled, factor to be in operation, resulting in a mean square within groups that reflects something other than error variation alone. The existence of such an uncontrolled but nonrandom factor is, of course, a failure of the assumptions, but before the experimenter appeals to chance or to some less obvious failure of assumptions, he might entertain the possibility that the experiment itself is open to suspicion.

Finally, a word about the general assumption embodied in the fixed effects model: each score is assumed to be a *sum*, consisting of a general mean, plus a treatment effect, plus an independent error component. The appealing simplicity of this model notwithstanding, many situations exist where we know that an additive model such as this is not realistic. For example, in some experimental problems it may be far more reasonable to suppose that random errors serve to multiply treatment effects, rather than add to them. In such instances, expert statistical advice should be sought. It is often possible to transform the original scores by, for example, taking their logarithms, so as to make the transformed scores correspond to the linear model. Such transformations should not be undertaken by the novice, however, without expert statistical guidance.

Other special problems arise when the observed scores are proportions, or rates, or time scores, or any of a wide variety of ratios. Once again, expert help should be sought in the choice of a transformation of the raw data making such scores correspond to the additive, fixed effects, model.

In summary, for ordinary numerical scores, regarded as a continuous random variable, the assumption of normality may safely be ignored when the $n$ in each sample is fairly large, and the assumption of equal variances appears to be relatively unimportant when the number of observations in each sample is the same. The assumption of independence of errors cannot, however, be ignored without severe risk of false conclusions. Each of these principles applies only to inferences about means under Model I, and need not hold for the analysis of variance models to be discussed in the next chapter.

## 12.17 THE PROBLEM OF TESTING FOR HOMOGENEITY OF VARIANCE

Since the analysis of variance is based on the assumption of equal variances, it may seem quite sensible to carry out a test for homogeneous variances on the sample data and then use to the result of that test to decide if the analysis of variance is legitimate. Such tests for the homogeneity of several variances exist, and some statistics books advocate these procedures. However, the standard tests for equality of several variances are extremely sensitive to any departure from normality in the populations. The statistician says that these tests with outcomes that depend heavily on incidental assumptions are not "robust." It could easily turn out that one would refrain from carrying out the analysis of variance because variances were apparently unequal, when a test of equality of *means* would actually be quite justifiable. Consequently, a test for homogeneity of variance before the analysis of variance has rather limited practical utility, and modern opinion holds that the analysis of variance can and should be carried on without a preliminary test of variances, especially in situations where the number of cases in the various samples can be made equal (see Box, 1953, 1954).

On the other hand, sometimes there is direct interest in a comparison among a set of variances, rather than in a comparison among means. The experimenter may be trying to find out if different treatments produce different degrees of variability. In such instances, it is sometimes possible to carry out an analysis of variance procedure on the logarithms of the sample variances. The reader is referred to Scheffé (1959, p. 83) for the details of this test, although help should be sought in its application.

## 12.18   ESTIMATING THE STRENGTH OF A STATISTICAL RELATION FROM THE ONE-WAY ANALYSIS OF VARIANCE

The size of the effect $\alpha_j$ associated with any treatment $j$ can always be estimated in the fixed effects model by taking

$$\text{est. } \alpha_j = M_j - M.$$

In the example of Section 12.15 the best available estimate of the effect of the "above average" information on the individual subject's score is

$$\text{est. } \alpha_1 = \frac{832}{20} - \frac{1904}{60} = 41.6 - 31.7 = 9.9.$$

In the same way, effects can be estimated for the other treatments.

However, it is useful to have some idea of the over-all strength of association between independent and dependent variables that a significant finding actually represents. The index $\omega^2$ introduced in Section 10.19 can be extended to serve this purpose when there are several distinct treatment groups or "levels" of the independent variable.

Just as before, we would like the index $\omega^2$ to represent the relative reduction in variance of $Y$ afforded by the information that an observation belongs in independent variable category $X$. Over all possible $(X,Y)$ events, the variance of the marginal distribution of $Y$ will be called, once again, $\sigma_Y^2$. The variance within any conditional distribution of $Y$ for a fixed $X$ category, $\sigma_{Y|X}^2$, will be assumed to equal $\sigma_e^2$, the variance within any treatment population.

Suppose that the probability of any observation unit's falling into the treatment category $X_j$ is $p(X_j)$. Then

$$\sigma_Y^2 = E(Y_{ij} - \mu)^2 = E(Y_{ij} - \mu_j + \alpha_j)^2$$
$$= \sigma_e^2 + \sum_j \alpha_j^2 p(X_j). \qquad [12.18.1*]$$

When each observation unit has equal probability of falling into each treatment category $X_j$, then $p(X_j) = 1/J$, and

$$\sigma_Y^2 = \sigma_e^2 + \sum_j \frac{\alpha_j^2}{J}. \qquad [12.18.2*]$$

On the other hand, if each of the *relative* sample sizes in the various treatment groups is the same as the probability of observing a case in the corresponding population, so that

$$p(X_j) = \frac{n_j}{N},$$

then

$$\sigma_Y^2 = \sigma_e^2 + \sum_j \frac{n_j \alpha_j^2}{N}. \qquad [12.18.3*]$$

In either circumstance, we can define

$$\omega^2 = \frac{\sigma_Y^2 - \sigma_e^2}{\sigma_Y^2}$$
$$= \frac{\sum_j \alpha_j^2 p(X_j)}{\sigma_e^2 + \sum_j \alpha_j^2 p(X_j)}. \qquad [12.18.4*]$$

This population index should reflect how much knowing the particular $X_j$ category represents in increased ability to predict the $Y$ value for an observation. Notice that if $\alpha_j$ is zero for each $j$, then $\omega^2$ must be zero.

In order to estimate the value of $\omega^2$ from sample data, we recall from Sections 12.6 and 12.8 that

$$E(\text{MS between}) = \sigma_e^2 + \sum_j \frac{n_j \alpha_j^2}{J - 1}$$

and

$$E(\text{MS within}) = \sigma_e^2.$$

Therefore, when the probability $p(X_j) = n_j/N$, so that the proportional representation of cases in the $J$ samples is the same as the proportions in the respective populations, a reasonable (though rough) estimate of $\omega^2$ is given by

$$\text{est. } \omega^2 = \frac{\text{SS between} - (J - 1) \text{ MS within}}{\text{SS total} + \text{MS within}}. \qquad [12.18.5\dagger]$$

(Actually, the $\omega^2$ introduced in Section 10.19 is estimated in precisely this way, with $t^2 = $ MS between/MS within, and $J = 2$.)

This estimate of the strength of the statistical relation can be *negative*, in which case the estimate of $\omega^2$ is set equal to zero; however, a significant $F$ guarantees a nonnegative estimate.

For example, let us apply the estimate of $\omega^2$ to the data of Section 12.15. Here, the result was very significant; how much does knowing the particular treatment group to which an individual belongs let us reduce our uncertainty about his $Y$ score? For this example,

$$\text{est. } \omega^2 = \frac{4994.1 - (2)(25.6)}{6451.7 + 25.6}$$
$$= .76.$$

The estimate implies that this statistical association is *very* strong. The independent variable $X$ (the norm information given) is estimated to account for 76 percent of the variance in the $Y$ scores. Naturally, this example is fabricated, and it is rather rare to find evidence for statistical association this strong in psychological data. Nevertheless, the example does show how the estimate of $\omega^2$ can reinforce the meaning of a significant finding: not only is there evidence for *some* association between independent and dependent variables; our rough estimate suggests that this association is very strong.

By way of contrast, suppose that another study employed 6 groups of 30 observations each, and that the analysis of variance turned out as follows:

| Source | SS | df | MS | F |
|---|---|---|---|---|
| Between groups | 1500 | 5 | 300 | 4.5 |
| Within groups | 11605.8 | 174 | 66.7 | |
| Totals | 13105.8 | 179 | | |

For 5 and 174 degrees of freedom, this $F$ value is significant just beyond the .01 level. Now we will see how much statistical association is apparently represented by this finding.

$$\text{est. } \omega^2 = \frac{1500 - 333.5}{13105.8 + 66.7} = .089.$$

In this instance, only between 8 and 9 percent of the variance in the dependent variable seems to be accounted for by the independent variable. This still may be enough to make the statistical association an important one from the experimenter's point of view, but the example shows, nevertheless, that a significant result need not correspond to a *very* strong association

The comments in Section 10.20 apply equally well to the analysis of variance situation. A result that is both significant *and* that gives an estimate of relatively strong association is usually far more informative than a significant result taken alone. Furthermore, even though a result is not significant, estimating whether or not a fairly high degree of association may in fact be present gives a clue to the experimenter about the advisability of a possible increase in sample size, or a refinement in the experimental procedure, when and if this experiment is repeated.

## 12.19 THE POWER OF THE $F$ TEST IN THE ANALYSIS OF VARIANCE

A few words are in order about the problem of determining the power of the $F$ test in the analysis of variance. This problem is not elementary, and there is little reason to go into great detail here. However, it may be informative to see what the basic problem is, and how it is handled.

The rationale for taking the ratio of MS between to MS within as the test statistic makes sense only if each of these sample quantities has the *same* expectation. That is, both MS between and MS within are unbiased estimates of $\sigma_e^2$ *when* the null hypothesis is true, and under these circumstances, their ratio *is* distributed exactly as an $F$ variable. On the other hand, when the null hypothesis is *not* true, the MS between has a different expectation, as we have seen, and sample ratios of MS between to MS within are *not* distributed as $F$.

Instead, when the null hypothesis is false, the sample ratio actually computed has a distribution known as *noncentral F*. This distribution rests on three parameters: the degrees of freedom, $\nu_1$ and $\nu_2$, corresponding to numerator and denominator respectively, and a so-called noncentrality parameter, $\delta$, where

$$\delta = \sqrt{\sum_j \frac{n\alpha_j^2}{\sigma_e^2}} \qquad [12.19.1*]$$

(given normal population distributions, each with variance $\sigma_e^2$, and samples of equal size $n$).

The distribution of noncentral $F$ depends on the value of $\delta$, which in turn depends on the sizes of the squared effects relative to $\sigma_e^2$. Unless one has some idea of this value $\delta$, he has no simple way to determine the power of the $F$ test, since a particular member of the family of noncentral $F$ distributions must be used to find the power, and the choice of the appropriate distribution depends upon what is true about the sizes of the squared effects relative to $\sigma_e^2$. In this light it is hardly surprising that most psychological reports employing the analysis of variance and the $F$ test have little to say about the power of the test.

Fairly extensive tables of noncentral $F$ exist, as well as power charts for the $F$ test, and these are to be found in more advanced books on statistics and experimental design. The chief use of these tables is in finding the sample size, $n$ per group, necessary to insure a certain amount of power against some specific alternative situation determining the value of $\delta$. If the experimenter has decided upon a value of $\delta$ representing a situation that he wants or needs to detect as significant, then these tables are relatively easy to use.

The obvious question is, "How does the experimenter know the value of $\delta$ to use?" A clue is given by our index $\omega^2$, the proportion of variance accounted for by the independent variable. The noncentrality parameter $\delta$ has a very close connection with $\omega^2$: for $J$ groups of equal size $n$,

$$\omega^2 = \frac{\delta^2}{nJ + \delta^2} \qquad \qquad [12.19.2*]$$

and

$$\delta^2 = \frac{nJ\omega^2}{1 - \omega^2}. \qquad \qquad [12.19.3*]$$

In other words, if the experimenter does have some idea of the strength of statistical association he wants to be sure to detect as significant, he can determine $\delta$ for various possible values of $n$, and then he has a way to choose sample size for the analysis of variance and $F$ test. Notice, however, the experimenter must decide about the strength of association that he *wants* to detect in his particular problem. If he can answer this question, any competent statistician can answer his question about sample size, but there is no one to help the experimenter who cannot decide on something he wants to detect as significant if true. Here, as in all aspects of experimental design, a great deal of preliminary study and planning is necessary before the data are seen if one is to make full use of the resources of statistics.

## 12.20   THE TWO-WAY ANALYSIS OF VARIANCE WITH REPLICATION

We now have enough background to discuss how the simple one-way analysis of variance can be extended to cover a more complicated experimental set-up in which there are two different sets of treatments. Suppose, once again, that an experimenter is interested in level of aspiration as the dependent variable, just as in Section 12.15. Just as before, the experimental game is under the control of the experimenter, so that each subject actually obtains the same score. After a fixed number of trials, during which the subject gets the preassigned score, he is asked to predict what his score will be on the next group of trials. Before he predicts, the subject is given "information" about how his score compares with some norm group. In one experimental condition he is told that his performance is above average for the norm group, in the second condition he is told that his score is average, and in the third condition he is told that his score is below average for the norm group. Once again, there are three experimental treatments in terms of "standings": "above average," "average," and "below average." However, unlike the previous example, this time *two different norm groups* are used in the information given subjects. One half of the subjects are told that they are being compared with college men, and the other half are told that they are being compared with professional athletes. Hence, there are two additional experimental treatments: "college norms," and "professional athlete norms."

In this example interest is focused on two distinct experimental factors: the information about standing that the subject is given, and the norm group used for comparison. Either or both of these experimental factors might possibly influence the value that a subject anticipates as his next score (his level of aspiration). A random sample of sixty male college students is selected and assigned at random to each of the six possible treatment *combinations*. This can be diagrammed as follows:

**Table 12.20.1**

ASSIGNMENT OF SUBJECTS TO TREATMENT COMBINATIONS,
BY NUMBERS IN EACH COMBINATION

|  |  | Above | Average | Below |
|---|---|---|---|---|
| NORM INFORMATION | Athlete | 10 | 10 | 10 |
|  | College | 10 | 10 | 10 |

STANDING

This experiment represents an instance where two different sets of experimental treatments are crossed, or given in every combination. Here there are six distinct sample groups, each group being given a particular combination of two kinds of treatments. *Three* questions are of interest:

1. Are there systematic effects due to experimental set alone (irrespective of norm group)?
2. Are there systematic effects due to norm information alone (irrespective of experimental set)?
3. Are there systematic effects due neither to norm information alone, nor to experimental set alone, but attributable only to the *combination* of a particular norm group with a particular experimental set?

Notice that this study could be viewed as two separate experiments carried out on the same set of subjects: There are three groups of twenty subjects each, differing only in experimental set or "standing"; exactly the same set of "norm-group" conditions are represented in each experimental "standing" group. On the other hand, looking at Table 12.20.1 by rows rather than by columns, we see that there are also two samples of thirty subjects each, differing systematically by "norm-group." Each "norm-group" sample has exactly the same representation of the other experimental conditions within it.

Question 3 above cannot, however, be answered by the comparison of "norm-groups" alone or by the comparison of experimental "set" groups alone. This is a question of "interaction," *the unique effects of combinations of treatments.* This is the important new feature of the two-way (or higher) analysis of variance: we will be able to examine *main effects* of the separate experimental variables or factors just as in the one-way analysis, as well as *interaction effects*, differences apparently due only to the unique combinations of treatments.

## 12.21 CROSSING AND NESTING IN EXPERIMENTS

Before we go further into the topic of experiments where two experimental factors are to be studied, two convenient terms should be introduced.

Consider the experiment described in the preceding section: two experimental factors are under study, the first being the "standing information" given the subject, and the second being the "norm information." Each subject is to get a combination of a category of "standing information" and a category of "norm information." In experiments such as this, where two experimental factors are present and each category or level of one factor occurs with each level of the other, the two factors are said to be **completely crossed**. All possible combinations of levels of two (or more) experimental factors occur in a completely crossed experiment. Furthermore, if all possible combinations of factor levels occur an equal number of times, the experiment is said to be **balanced**. Note that the experiment described above is thus completely crossed and balanced.

On the other hand, in some experiments categories or levels of one factor occur only *within* levels of another factor. Thus, we might be comparing three different teaching methods, and another factor of interest might be the particular classrooms in which the methods were tried. It is impracticable to cross the factors of methods and classrooms, and so it is decided to apply the same method to each of two different classrooms, for a total of six classrooms, two per method. Here, the factor of "classroom" is said to be **nested** within the factor of "teaching method." A particular classroom occurs in the experiment only in association with one particular method. In a nested experiment such as this, any comparison of methods that we make is also a comparison of sets of classrooms; the only meaningful evidence for the possible effects of classrooms, over and above the effects of the methods, must come from comparison of classrooms *within* the particular methods. Many experiments calling for a simple one-way analysis of variance can be thought of as nested designs, where a factor corresponding to "individual subjects" is nested within the main treatments factor of the experiment. For example, in the experiment of Section 12.13 a factor of "particular rats" can be thought of as nested within the factor corresponding to "type of lesion."

The remainder of this chapter will be devoted to experiments where there are two completely crossed and balanced factors, and then a different random sample of subjects is assigned to each particular *combination* of the other two factors: that is, each combination of treatments is administered to a separate and distinct set of randomly selected subjects. However, this is but one of the simplest kinds of experimental designs, and it is entirely possible to design and analyze a wide variety of experiments where different factors are either crossed or nested.

## 12.22   THE FIXED EFFECTS MODEL IN THE TWO-WAY ANALYSIS

Just as in the fixed effects model for the one-way analysis of variance, in the corresponding model for a two-way analysis it is assumed that each observed dependent variable score is a sum of systematic effects associated with experimental treatments, plus random error:

$$Y_{ijk} = \mu + \alpha_j + \beta_k + \gamma_{jk} + e_{ijk} \qquad [12.22.1*]$$

where $\alpha_j$ is the effect of treatment $j$

$$\alpha_j = \mu_j - \mu,$$ [12.22.2*]

and $\beta_k$ is the effect of treatment $k$

$$\beta_k = \mu_k - \mu.$$ [12.22.3*]

Here, $\mu_j$ is the mean of the population given treatment $j$ and pooled over all of the $K$ different treatments $k$, and $\mu_k$ is the mean of the population given treatment $k$ and pooled over all of the $J$ different treatments $j$. The grand mean $\mu$ is the mean of the population formed by pooling all of the different populations given the possible treatment combinations $j$ and $k$.

The new feature of equation 12.22.1 is the inclusion of a term representing the interaction effect, $\gamma_{jk}$ (small Greek gamma). The interaction effect is the experimental effect created by the combination of treatments $j$ and $k$ over and above any effects associated with treatments $j$ and $k$ considered separately:

$$\gamma_{jk} = \mu_{jk} - \mu - \alpha_j - \beta_k$$
$$= \mu_{jk} - \mu_j - \mu_k + \mu.$$ [12.22.4*]

The interaction effect $\gamma_{jk}$ is thus equal to the mean of the population given both of the treatments $j$ and $k$, minus the mean of the treatment population $j$, minus the mean of the population given treatment $k$, plus the grand mean.

Some intuition about the meaning of interaction effects may be gained by examining another set of artificial data. In the experiment outlined in Section 12.20, suppose that the only effect (that is nonzero effect) is associated with experimental "standing." Furthermore, suppose that the value of each error $e_{ijk}$ is zero. Then the *means* of each of the six groups given different treatment combinations should look something like this:

**Table 12.22.1**

|  | Above | Average | Below |
|---|---|---|---|
| College | 28 | 33 | 35 |
| Athlete | 28 | 33 | 35 |

NORM GROUP

Above Average Below  $M = 32$
STANDING

Here the effect associated with treatment "above" is $28 - 32 = -4$, the effect of the treatment "average" is $33 - 32 = 1$, and the effect of the treatment "below" is $35 - 32 = 3$. Note that the columns of the table differ from each other, but that the rows within each column show identical values. Each score is simply $Y_{ijk} = 32 + \alpha_j$.

On the other hand, it might turn out that effects exist only for the norm groups, so that no effects are associated with the column treatments or with the row by column interaction. Once again, if the data were errorless, we should observe something like:

**Table 12.22.2**

|  | College | 34 | 34 | 34 |
| NORM GROUP | | | | |
|  | Athlete | 30 | 30 | 30 |

Above   Average   Below
STANDING

Here the rows differ from each other, but the values for the columns within each row are identical. The effect of the first row is $34 - 32 = 2$, and that of the second row is $30 - 32 = -2$. Each score fits the rule

$$Y_{ijk} = 32 + \beta_k.$$

Now suppose that there were *both* column and row effects, but that no interaction or error effects exist. In this case

$$Y_{ijk} = 32 + \alpha_j + \beta_k,$$

so that the means for the groups each represent a sum of effects like this

**Table 12.22.3**

| | College | $32 + 2 - 4$ $= 30$ | $32 + 2 + 1$ $= 35$ | $32 + 2 + 3$ $= 37$ |
| NORM GROUP | | | | |
| | Athlete | $32 - 2 - 4$ $= 26$ | $32 - 2 + 1$ $= 31$ | $32 - 2 + 3$ $= 33$ |

Above          Average          Below
STANDING

In this instance the six treatment combinations yield means differing across the different **cells** of the table. However, the effect of a combination, $\mu_{jk} - \mu$, associated with cell $jk$, is exactly equal to the effect associated its row, $\beta_k$, plus the effect associated with its column $\alpha_j$, so that $Y_{ijk} = \mu + \alpha_j + \beta_k$. **When there is no interaction, effects are said to be additive, since the effect of a combination is the sum of the effects of the treatments involved.** Notice that the difference between a particular pair of columns is the same over the rows, and that any row difference is constant over columns, within Table 12.22.3 representing the condition of no interaction.

Finally, in the table below, interaction effects have also been added to the data of Table 12.22.3. Once again, assume that these data are errorless:

**Table 12.22.4**

| | College | $32 + 2 - 4 - 2$ $= 28$ | $32 + 2 + 1 + 6$ $= 41$ | $32 + 2 + 3 - 4$ $= 33$ |
| NORM GROUP | | | | |
| | Athlete | $32 - 2 - 4 + 2$ $= 28$ | $32 - 2 + 1 - 6$ $= 25$ | $32 - 2 + 3 + 4$ $= 37$ |

Above          Average          Below
STANDING

The effect associated with a combination of treatments is now no longer the simple sum of the effects of its row and its column, an indication that interaction effects are present. **Notice that columns are different in different ways within rows, and vice-versa, when interaction is present.**

Naturally, for any real data there will be random error as well. This implies that the problem is now threefold: we must find out (1) if there are effects of the treatments represented by the columns, (2) if there are effects of treatments represented by the rows, and (3) if there are effects which are attributable neither to rows (irrespective of columns) nor columns (irrespective of rows) but rather to interaction.

## 12.23 THE IMPORTANCE OF INTERACTION EFFECTS

The presence or absence of interaction effects, as inferred from the $F$ test for interaction, can have a very important bearing on how one interprets and uses the results of an experiment. When the presence of column effects is inferred, this implies that the populations represented by the columns have means that differ; the amount and direction of difference between sample means for any pair of columns provides an estimate of the corresponding difference between population means. When interaction effects are absent, differences among the means representing different column-treatment populations have the same size and sign, even though the populations are conceived as receiving still another treatment represented by one of the rows. This suggests that the difference between a pair of column means in the data is our best bet about the difference to be expected between a pair of individuals given different column treatments, quite irrespective of the particular row treatment that might have been administered. On the other hand, when interaction effects exist, *varying differences* exist between the means of populations representing different column treatments, depending on the particular row treatment that is applied. It is still true that differences between column means in the data provide an estimate of the difference we should expect between individuals given the particular treatments, but only on the average, over all of the different row treatments that might have been applied. When a particular row treatment is specified, it may be that quite another size and direction of difference should be expected between individuals given different column treatments. In short, interaction effects lead to a qualification on the estimate one makes of the differences attributable to different treatments; when interaction effects exist, the best estimate one can make of a difference attributable to one factor depends on the particular level of the other factor.

For example, suppose that an experimenter is comparing two methods of instruction in golf. Let us represent these two methods as the column treatments in the data table. The other factor considered is the sex of the student; the study employs a group of 50 boys and a group of 50 girls, with 25 subjects in each group taught by Method I and the remainder by Method II. After a fixed period of instruction by one or the other method, each member of the sample is given a proficiency test. Suppose that the sample means for the four subgroups turn out as follows:

For a small enough estimated error variance, such data would lead to the conclusion that no difference exists between boys and girls in terms of performance on the proficiency test, but that *both column effects and interaction effects do exist.* Now suppose that the experimenter wants to decide which method to use for the instruction of an individual student. If *low* scores indicate good performance, but he doesn't know or doesn't wish to specify the sex of the student, then Method II clearly is called for, since the experimenter's best estimate is that Method I gives a higher mean than Method II over both sexes. However, suppose that he knows that the individual to be instructed is a *girl:* in this case, the experimenter does *much* better to choose Method I, since he has evidence that *within the population of girls, mean II is higher than mean I.*

Significant interaction effects usually reflect a situation very like this: over-all estimates of differences due to one factor are fine as predictors of average differences over *all possible levels of the other factor,* but it will not necessarily be true that these are good estimates of the differences to be expected when information about the category on the other factor is given. Significant interaction serves as a warning: treatment differences *do* exist, but to specify exactly *how* the treatments differ, and especially to make good individual predictions, one must look *within* levels of the *other* factor. The presence of interaction effects is a signal that in any predictive use of the experimental results, effects attributed to particular treatments representing one factor are best qualified by specifying the level of the *other* factor. This is extremely important if one is going to try to use estimated effects in forecasting the result of applying a treatment to an individual; when interaction effects are present, the best forecast can be made only if the individual's status on *both* factors is known.

In the language of Chapter 1, tests for interaction permit one to decide if variable $Z$ is relevant to the relationship between $X$ and $Y$. If there is no interaction, then the relationship between $X$ and $Y$ does not depend upon the specification of $Z$, and that between $Z$ and $Y$ does not depend upon $X$. The presence of interaction effects suggests the contrary: a functional relation between $X$ and $Y$ will not appear unless $Z$ is controlled. The presence only of interaction suggests that the only nontrivial functional relationship between $X$ or $Z$ and $Y$ involves $(X,Z)$ *pairs* in relation to $Y$, or else control over variable $Z$. In a very real sense, the study of interaction sheds light on the relevancy of different variables in the search for predictive functional relationships.

For these reasons, the presence of interaction effects can be most important to the interpretation of the experiment. The estimated effects of any given treatment are not "best bets" about any randomly selected individual when interaction effects are present; the best prediction entails knowing the other treatment or treatments administered.

Although it is necessary to consider possible interaction effects even in fairly simple experiments, the subject of interaction and of the interpretation that should be given to significant tests for interaction is neither elementary nor fully explored. To a very large extent, the presence or absence of interactions in an experiment is governed by the scale of measurement used for the dependent variable. Thus, in terms of the original scale of measurement interaction may be present, but if, for example, the values are transformed into their respective logarithms, interaction effects may vanish. It is clear that in many circumstances evidence for interaction reflects not so much a state of nature as our own inability to find the proper measurement scales for the phenomena we study. Since simple additive models are so much more tractable theoretically and practically than models including all the qualifications introduced by interaction, it is often desirable to transform the original data to eliminate interactions. Such considerations are, however, far beyond our limited scope.

Interaction effects can be studied separately only in a two-way (or higher) analysis of variance with crossed factors, where the experiment is carried out **with replication**. Furthermore, the procedures we will develop in the remainder of this chapter apply only to the situation where the experimental design is **orthogonal**. We need to have a look at what these terms "with replication" and "orthogonal" imply about the way the experiment is designed.

## 12.24 THE IDEA OF REPLICATION

The discussion of the two-way analysis of variance will be limited here to replicated experiments. For our purposes this means that **within each treatment combination there are at least two independent observations made under identical experimental circumstances**. The requirement that the experiment be replicated is introduced here so that an error sum of squares will be available, permitting the study of tests both for treatment effects and for interaction. If there were only one observation for each treatment combination, we would not be able to test separately for interaction effects, since in this situation there is no direct way to estimate error variance apart from interaction effects. Occasionally, experiments are carried out where only one observation is made per treatment combination; under the fixed effects model this makes it necessary to know or to assume that no interaction effects exist if a test for main treatment effects is to be carried out. This assumption is often very questionable, and most circumstances requiring a nonreplicated experiment will fit into one of the models to be discussed in Chapter 13. For this reason, our discussion for the fixed effect model will be confined to replicated experiments.

## 12.25  Orthogonal designs for experiments

An orthogonal design for an experiment can be defined as a way of collecting observations that will permit one to estimate and test for the various treatment effects and for interaction effects separately. The potential information in the experiment can be "pulled apart" for study in an orthogonal design. Any experimental layout can be regarded as an orthogonal design provided that: (1) the observations within a given treatment *combination* are sampled at random and independently from a normal population, and (2) the number of observations in *each possible combination* of treatments is the same. Thus, the usual procedure in setting up an experiment to be analyzed by the two-way (or higher) analysis of variance is to assign subjects at random and independently to each combination of treatments so as to have an equal number in each combination. This means that in a table representing the experimental groups, such as Table 12.20.1, the cells of the table all contain the same number of observations. Let us call the number of "row" treatments $R$, and the number of "column" treatments $C$. For experiments of this sort where each cell in an $R \times C$ data-table contains the same number $n$ of cases, each *row* will contain $Cn$ cases, and each *column* $Rn$ cases. If at all possible, experiments should be set up in this way, not only to insure orthogonality, but also to minimize the effect of nonhomogeneous population variances should they exist (see Section 12.17).

It is also possible to design two-factor experiments that will be orthogonal even though the numbers of cases in the various cells differ, provided that **proportionality** holds within the cells of any given row or column. This means that for any treatment combination $jk$,

$$n_{jk} = \frac{n_j n_k}{N},$$

where $n_{jk}$ is the number of observations in the combination $j$ and $k$, $n_j$ is the total number of observations in treatment $j$, $n_k$ is the total number of observations in treatment $k$, and $N$ is the total number of observations in all. However, in this circumstance, the ordinary computational procedures for the analysis of variance must be altered somewhat. For the sake of simplicity, the discussion to follow is restricted to the case of *equal numbers of observations* in the cells of a $R \times C$ table. The beginning student is advised to seek expert help when his data do not conform to this pattern, especially when unequal cell numbers appear because of "lost" or otherwise missing data.

## 12.26  Sums of effects in the fixed model

Just as in the simple one-way analysis of variance under the fixed effects model, in the two-way situation it is assumed that the experimental treatments and treatment combinations are fixed, and that the only inferences to be made are about those treatments and treatment combinations actually represented in the experiment.

The following equalities are assumed true of the effects:

$$\sum_j \alpha_j = 0$$

$$\sum_k \beta_k = 0$$

$$\sum_j \gamma_{jk} = 0$$

$$\sum_k \gamma_{jk} = 0.$$

The effects, being deviations from a grand mean $\mu$, sum to zero over all the different "levels" of a given kind of treatment. However

$$\sum_j \alpha_j^2 > 0$$

unless $\alpha_j = 0$ for each $j$;

$$\sum_k \beta_k^2 > 0$$

unless $\beta_k = 0$ for each $k$;

$$\sum_j \sum_k \gamma_{jk}^2 > 0$$

unless $\gamma_{jk} = 0$ for each and every combination $j,k$.

## 12.27 THE PARTITION OF THE SUMS OF SQUARES FOR THE TWO-WAY ANALYSIS OF VARIANCE

Once more we start off by looking at how the total sum of squares can be partitioned for a set of data. For any individual $i$ in any treatment combination $jk$, the deviation of the score $Y_{ijk}$ from the sample grand mean $M$ can be written as

$$Y_{ijk} - M = (Y_{ijk} - M_{jk}) + (M_j - M) + (M_k - M)$$
$$+ (M_{jk} - M_j - M_k + M). \quad [12.27.1]$$

If the deviation for each score is squared, and these squares are summed over all individuals in all combinations $j$ and $k$, we have

$$\sum_j \sum_k \sum_i (Y_{ijk} - M)^2 = \sum_j \sum_k \sum_i (Y_{ijk} - M_{jk})^2$$
$$+ \sum_j n_j (M_j - M)^2 + \sum_k n_k (M_k - M)^2$$
$$+ \sum_j \sum_k n_{jk} (M_{jk} - M_j - M_k + M)^2. \quad [12.27.2]$$

(The algebraic argument for this statement is almost exactly the same as in Section 12.4 and will not be repeated here; the student, however, may find it profitable to try to derive this for himself.)

Now let us examine the various individual terms on the right of expression **12.27.2**. We call

$$\sum_j \sum_k \sum_i (Y_{ijk} - M_{jk})^2 = \text{SS error} \qquad [\textbf{12.27.3}]$$

the **sum of squares for error,** since it is based on deviations from a cell mean for individuals treated in exactly the same way; the only possible contribution to this sum of squares should be error variation.

Next, consider

$$\sum_j n_j (M_j - M)^2 = \text{SS columns}, \qquad [\textbf{12.27.4}]$$

which is the **sum of squares between columns.** Here the deviations of column treatment means from the grand mean make up this sum of squares. This sum of squares reflects two things: the treatment effects of the columns *and* error. Notice that this sum of squares is identical to the sum of squares between groups found in the one-way analysis, if the different experimental groups are regarded as columns in the table.

The third term is

$$\sum_k n_k (M_k - M)^2 = \text{SS rows}, \qquad [\textbf{12.27.5}]$$

which is the **sum of squares between rows.** It is based upon deviations of the row means from the grand mean, and thus reflects both row-treatment effects and error. This is the same as the sum of squares between groups if data were regarded as coming only from experimental groups corresponding to the rows.

Finally, the fourth term

$$\sum_j \sum_k n_{jk} (M_{jk} - M_j - M_k + M)^2 = \text{SS interaction} \qquad [\textbf{12.27.6}]$$

the **sum of squares for interaction.** This sum of squares involves only *interaction effects and error*.

The partition of the sum of squares for a two-way analysis can be written in the following schematic form:

SS total = SS error + SS columns + SS rows + SS interaction.   [**12.27.7†**]

Whereas in the one-way analysis the total sum of squares can be broken into only two parts, a sum of squares between groups and a sum of squares within groups (error), in the two-way analysis with replication the total sum of squares can be broken into *four* distinct parts. The principle generalizes to experimental layouts with any number of treatment and treatment combinations, but we shall stop with the two-way situation.

## 12.28  ASSUMPTIONS IN THE TWO-WAY FIXED EFFECTS MODEL

Before we turn to an examination of the sampling distribution of the various mean squares, the assumptions we must make to determine these sampling distributions will be stated:

1. The errors $e_{ijk}$ are normally distributed with expectation of zero for each treatment-combination population $jk$.
2. The errors $e_{ijk}$ have exactly the same variance $\sigma_e^2$ for each treatment-combination population.
3. The errors $e_{ijk}$ are independent, both within each treatment combination and across treatment combinations.

You will note that these are essentially the same assumptions made for the one-way model, except that now we deal with treatment-combination populations, the entire set of potential observations to be made under any combination of treatments.

## 12.29  THE MEAN SQUARES AND THEIR EXPECTATIONS

We begin by finding the expectation of the *error* sum of squares: substituting from **12.27.3**, we have

$$E \sum_j \sum_k \sum_i (Y_{ijk} - M_{jk})^2 = E \sum_j \sum_k \sum_i (\mu + \alpha_j + \beta_k + \gamma_{jk}$$
$$+ e_{ijk} - \mu - \alpha_j - \beta_k - \gamma_{jk} - M_{ejk})^2$$
$$= E \sum_j \sum_k \sum_i (e_{ijk} - M_{ejk})^2. \qquad [12.29.1]$$

By rule 5 of Appendix B, and by assumption 2, Section 12.28,

$$E \sum_j \sum_k \sum_i (Y_{ijk} - M_{jk})^2 = \sum_j \sum_k E \sum_i (e_{ijk} - M_{ejk})^2$$
$$= \sum_j \sum_k (n_{jk} - 1)\sigma_e^2$$
$$= RC(n - 1)\sigma_e^2. \qquad [12.29.2]$$

(Since the number $n_{jk}$ in each cell is assumed to be the same, hereafter $n$ will be written to signify this number. Remember that the $R$ represents the number of rows and the $C$ the number of columns; the number of observations in any row is $Cn$, and in any column is $Rn$.) Let

$$\text{MS error} = \frac{\text{SS error}}{RC(n - 1)}. \qquad [12.29.3\dagger]$$

Then, by **12.29.2** above,

$$E(\text{MS error}) = \frac{E(\text{SS error})}{RC(n-1)} = \frac{RC(n-1)\sigma_e^2}{RC(n-1)} = \sigma_e^2. \qquad [12.29.4^*]$$

The expected value of the mean square error is simply the error variance $\sigma_e^2$.

Now look at the mean square between columns. Since there are $C$ columns, the mean square between columns is found from

$$\text{MS columns} = \frac{\text{SS columns}}{C-1} \qquad [12.29.5\dagger]$$

in exactly the same way as for the MS between in a one-way analysis of variance. Then

$$E(\text{MS columns}) = E\left[\sum_j \frac{n_j(M_j - M)^2}{C-1}\right]. \qquad [12.29.6]$$

Since $\sum_k \beta_k = 0$ and $\sum_k \gamma_{jk} = 0$, it follows that

$$E(\text{MS columns}) = E\sum_j Rn\frac{(\alpha_j + M_{ej} - M_e)^2}{C-1} = \sigma_e^2 + \frac{Rn\sum_j \alpha_j^2}{C-1}. \qquad [12.29.7^*]$$

When the hypothesis of no column effects is true,

$$E(\text{MS columns}) = \sigma_e^2, \qquad [12.29.8^*]$$

but when the hypothesis is false,

$$E(\text{MS columns}) > \sigma_e^2. \qquad [12.29.9^*]$$

**The mean square between columns and the mean square error are independent and unbiased estimates of the same variance $\sigma_e^2$ when the null hypothesis of no column effects is true.** This hypothesis can be tested by the $F$ ratio,

$$F = \frac{\text{MS columns}}{\text{MS error}} \qquad [12.19.10\dagger]$$

with $C-1$ and $RC(n-1)$ degrees of freedom. The rationale is precisely the same as that given in Sections 12.6 through 12.9.

In the same way we examine the expectation of the mean square for rows:

$$\text{MS rows} = \sum_k \frac{Cn(M_k - M)^2}{R-1}. \qquad [12.29.11\dagger]$$

Since $\sum_j \alpha_j = 0$ and $\sum_j \gamma_{jk} = 0$, this expectation is

$$E(\text{MS rows}) = E\sum_k Cn\frac{(\beta_k + M_{ek} - M_e)^2}{R-1} = \sigma_e^2 + \frac{Cn\sum_k \beta_k^2}{R-1}. \qquad [12.29.12^*]$$

The expectation of the mean square rows can be exactly $\sigma_e^2$ only when the hypothesis of no row effects is true; otherwise,

$$E(\text{MS rows}) > \sigma_e^2. \qquad [12.29.13*]$$

**The mean square between rows is an unbiased estimate of $\sigma_e^2$ when the null hypothesis of no row effects is true, and it is independent of the mean square error.** The hypothesis of no row effects is then tested by the ratio

$$F = \frac{\text{MS rows}}{\text{MS error}} \qquad [12.29.14\dagger]$$

with $R - 1$ and $RC(n - 1)$ degrees of freedom.

Finally, the expectation of the sum of squares for interaction may be found, although this requires a little more work:

$$E \sum_j \sum_k n(M_{jk} - M_j - M_k + M)^2$$

$$= E\left[ \sum_j \sum_k n(\gamma_{jk} + M_{ejk} - M_{ej} - M_{ek} + M_e)^2 \right]$$

$$= \sum_j \sum_k n\gamma_{jk}^2 + E \sum_j \sum_k n(M_{ejk} - M_{ej} - M_{ek} + M_e)^2 \quad [12.29.15]$$

since the expectation of any of the error terms is always zero. Now consider the last term on the right in **12.29.15**:

$$E \sum_j \sum_k n(M_{ejk} - M_{ej} - M_{ek} + M_e)^2$$

$$= E \sum_j \sum_k nM_{ejk}^2 - E \sum_j RnM_{ej}^2 - E \sum_k CnM_{ek}^2 + E(RCnM_e^2)$$

$$= \frac{RCn\sigma_e^2}{n} - \frac{RCn\sigma_e^2}{Rn} - \frac{RCn\sigma_e^2}{Cn} + \frac{RCn\sigma_e^2}{RCn}$$

$$= \sigma_e^2(RC - C - R + 1) = \sigma_e^2(R - 1)(C - 1). \quad [12.29.16*]$$

If we define

$$\text{MS interaction} = \frac{\text{SS interaction}}{(R - 1)(C - 1)} \qquad [12.29.17\dagger]$$

then

$$E(\text{MS interaction}) = \frac{E(\text{SS interaction})}{(R - 1)(C - 1)}$$

$$= \sigma_e^2 + \frac{\displaystyle\sum_j \sum_k n\gamma_{jk}^2}{(R - 1)(C - 1)}. \qquad [12.29.18*]$$

When there are no interaction effects *at all*, then

$$E(\text{MS interaction}) = \sigma_e^2 \qquad [12.29.19*]$$

the mean square for interaction is also an unbiased estimate of the error variance $\sigma_e^2$. Otherwise,

$$E(\text{MS interaction}) > \sigma_e^2. \qquad [12.29.20*]$$

The mean square for interaction is independent of the mean square for error, and so the hypothesis of no interaction effects may be tested by

$$F = \frac{\text{MS interaction}}{\text{MS error}} \qquad [12.29.21\dagger]$$

with $(R-1)(C-1)$ and $RC(n-1)$ degrees of freedom.

Thus we see that it is possible to make separate tests of the hypothesis of no row effects, the hypothesis of no column effects, and the hypothesis of no interaction effects, all from the same data. Furthermore, under the fixed effects model, and given an orthogonal experimental design, estimates of the three different kinds of effects are independent of each other.

## 12.30  COMPUTING FORMS FOR THE TWO-WAY ANALYSIS WITH REPLICATIONS

In carrying out an analysis of variance the following computing forms are generally used. These sums of squares are algebraically equivalent to those given in Section 12.27.

$$\text{SS total} = \sum_j \sum_k \sum_i Y_{ijk}^2 - \frac{\left( \sum_j \sum_k \sum_i Y_{ijk} \right)^2}{N} \qquad [12.30.1\dagger]$$

$$\text{SS rows} = \frac{\sum_k \left( \sum_j \sum_i Y_{ijk} \right)^2}{Cn} - \frac{\left( \sum_j \sum_k \sum_i Y_{ijk} \right)^2}{N} \qquad [12.30.2\dagger]$$

$$\text{SS columns} = \frac{\sum_j \left( \sum_k \sum_i Y_{ijk} \right)^2}{Rn} - \frac{\left( \sum_j \sum_k \sum_i Y_{ijk} \right)^2}{N} \qquad [12.30.3\dagger]$$

$$\text{SS error} = \sum_j \sum_k \sum_i Y_{ijk}^2 - \frac{\sum_j \sum_k \left( \sum_i Y_{ijk} \right)^2}{n} \qquad [12.30.4\dagger]$$

$$\text{SS interaction} = \frac{\sum_j \sum_k \left( \sum_i Y_{ijk} \right)^2}{n} - \frac{\sum_k \left( \sum_j \sum_i Y_{ijk} \right)^2}{Cn}$$
$$- \frac{\sum_j \left( \sum_k \sum_i Y_{ijk} \right)^2}{Rn} + \frac{\left( \sum_j \sum_k \sum_i Y_{ijk} \right)^2}{N}$$

$$= \text{SS total} - \text{SS rows} - \text{SS columns} - \text{SS error}. \qquad [12.30.5\dagger]$$

Notice that the sum of squares for columns is calculated just as for a one-way analysis of data arranged into columns. Furthermore, the sum of squares for rows is identical to the sum of squares between groups when the data are arranged into a table where the experimental groups are designated by rows. The sum of squares total is also calculated in exactly the same way as for a one-way analysis. The only new features here are the computations for error and for interaction. Generally, the error term is calculated directly, and then the interaction term is found by subtracting the sum of squares, rows, columns, and error all from the sum of squares total.

### 12.31 A COMPUTATIONAL OUTLINE FOR THE TWO-WAY ANALYSIS UNDER THE FIXED EFFECTS MODEL

1. Arrange the data into an $R \times C$ table, in which the $R$ rows represent the $R$ different treatments of one kind, and the $C$ columns the $C$ different treatments of the other kind. Each cell in the table should contain the same number $n$ of observations. There are $N = RCn$ distinct observations in all.

2. Square each raw score and sum over all individuals in all cells to find $\sum_j \sum_k \sum_i Y_{ijk}^2$. Call this quantity $A$.

3. Sum the raw scores in a given *cell jk* to find $\sum_i Y_{ijk}$. Do this for *each cell*, and reserve these values for use in later steps.

4. Now sum the resulting values (step 3) over *all cells* to find $\sum_j \sum_k \sum_i Y_{ijk}$. Call this quantity $B$. Find the **sum of squares total** by $A - \dfrac{B^2}{N}$.

5. Next take the $RC$ different values found in step 3 and sum the cell totals for *a given row across columns* to find $\sum_j \sum_i Y_{ijk}$. The result for any row $k$ will be designated by $D_k$.

6. Having carried out step 5 for *each row*, square each of the $D_k$, sum over all of the various rows to find $\sum_k D_k^2$. Divide this quantity by $Cn$, the number of observations per row. Then

$$\frac{\sum_k D_k^2}{Cn} - \frac{B^2}{N}$$

is the **sum of squares for rows**.

7. Now return to the quantities found in step 3. This time sum the cell totals for *a given column across rows* to find $\sum_k \sum_i Y_{ijk}$ and call this value for column $j$, $G_j$.

8. Having carried out step 7 for each column, square each of the $G_j$ and sum across the various columns to find $\sum_j G_j^2$. Divide this quantity by $Rn$, the number of observations per column. Then

$$\frac{\sum_j G_j}{Rn} - \frac{B^2}{N}$$

   is the **sum of squares for columns**.

9. Once again return to the cell totals found in step 3. For a given cell $jk$ call the total $H_{jk}$. Now square $H_{jk}$ for each cell and sum across *all cells* to find $\sum_j \sum_k H_{jk}^2$. Divide this by $n$, the number of observations per cell. Then

$$A - \frac{\sum_j \sum_k H_{jk}^2}{n}$$

   is the **sum of squares for error**.

10. Find the **sum of squares for interaction** by taking

$$\text{SS total} - \text{SS rows} - \text{SS columns} - \text{SS error}$$

   or

$$\frac{\sum_j \sum_k H_{jk}^2}{n} - \frac{\sum_k D_k^2}{Cn} - \frac{\sum_j G_j^2}{Rn} + \frac{B^2}{N}.$$

11. Enter these sums of squares in the summary table.
12. Divide the SS rows by $R - 1$ to find MS rows.
13. Divide the SS columns by $C - 1$ to find MS columns.
14. Divide the SS interaction by $(R - 1)(C - 1)$ to find MS interaction.
15. Divide the SS error by $RC(n - 1)$ to find MS error.
16. The hypothesis of no row effects is tested by

$$F = \frac{\text{MS rows}}{\text{MS error}}$$

   with $R - 1$ and $RC(n - 1)$ degrees of freedom.

17. The hypothesis of no column effects is tested by

$$F = \frac{\text{MS columns}}{\text{MS error}}$$

   with $C - 1$ and $RC(n - 1)$ degrees of freedom.

18. The hypothesis of no interaction is tested by

$$F = \frac{\text{MS interaction}}{\text{MS error}}$$

   with $(R - 1)(C - 1)$ and $RC(n - 1)$ degrees of freedom.

## 12.32 THE SUMMARY TABLE FOR A TWO-WAY FIXED EFFECTS ANALYSIS OF VARIANCE WITH REPLICATIONS

For the fixed effects model, the results of a two-way analysis of variance are displayed in a summary table (Table 12.32.1).

### Table 12.32.1

| Source | SS | d.f. | MS | F |
|---|---|---|---|---|
| Rows | $$\dfrac{\sum\limits_{k}\left(\sum\limits_{j}\sum\limits_{i}Y_{ijk}\right)^2}{Cn} - \dfrac{\left(\sum\limits_{j}\sum\limits_{k}\sum\limits_{i}Y_{ijk}\right)^2}{N}$$ | $R-1$ | $\dfrac{\text{SS rows}}{R-1}$ | $\dfrac{\text{MS rows}}{\text{MS error}}$ |
| Columns | $$\dfrac{\sum\limits_{j}\left(\sum\limits_{k}\sum\limits_{i}Y_{ijk}\right)^2}{Rn} - \dfrac{\left(\sum\limits_{j}\sum\limits_{k}\sum\limits_{i}Y_{ijk}\right)^2}{N}$$ | $C-1$ | $\dfrac{\text{SS col.}}{C-1}$ | $\dfrac{\text{MS col.}}{\text{MS error}}$ |
| Inter-action | $$\dfrac{\sum\limits_{j}\sum\limits_{k}\left(\sum\limits_{i}Y_{ijk}\right)^2}{n} - \dfrac{\sum\limits_{k}\left(\sum\limits_{j}\sum\limits_{i}Y_{ijk}\right)^2}{Cn} - \dfrac{\sum\limits_{j}\left(\sum\limits_{k}\sum\limits_{i}Y_{ijk}\right)^2}{Rn} + \dfrac{\left(\sum\limits_{j}\sum\limits_{k}\sum\limits_{i}Y_{ijk}\right)^2}{N}$$ | $(R-1)(C-1)$ | $\dfrac{\text{SS int.}}{(R-1)(C-1)}$ | $\dfrac{\text{MS int.}}{\text{MS error}}$ |
| Error (within cells) | $$\sum\limits_{j}\sum\limits_{k}\sum\limits_{i}Y_{ijk}^2 - \dfrac{\sum\limits_{j}\sum\limits_{k}\left(\sum\limits_{i}Y_{ijk}\right)^2}{n}$$ | $RC(n-1)$ | $\dfrac{\text{SS error}}{RC(n-1)}$ | — |
| Totals | $$\sum\limits_{j}\sum\limits_{k}\sum\limits_{i}Y_{ijk}^2 - \dfrac{\left(\sum\limits_{j}\sum\limits_{k}\sum\limits_{i}Y_{ijk}\right)^2}{N}$$ | $RCn-1$ | — | — |

Naturally, when the summary table is used to report an analysis of actual data, the algebraic expressions and symbols are replaced by the corresponding values obtained.

## 12.33 AN EXAMPLE

Suppose that the experiment on level of aspiration, outlined in Section 12.20, had actually been carried out, and the data shown in Table 12.33.1 obtained. We wish to examine three null hypotheses: (1) there is no effect of the standing given the subject, corresponding to the hypothesis of no column effects; (2) the actual norm group given the subjects has no effect, corresponding to the hypothesis of no row effects; and (3) the norm–group–standing combination has no unique effect, corresponding to the hypothesis of no row-column interaction. The $\alpha$ level chosen for each of these three tests will be .05.

Table 12.33.1

| Norms | Standing | | |
| --- | --- | --- | --- |
| | *Above* | *Average* | *Below* |
| | 52 | 28 | 15 |
| | 48 | 35 | 14 |
| | 43 | 34 | 23 |
| | 50 | 32 | 21 |
| | 43 | 34 | 14 |
| College men | 44 | 27 | 20 |
| | 46 | 31 | 21 |
| | 46 | 27 | 16 |
| | 43 | 29 | 20 |
| | 49 | 25 | 14 |
| | 464 | 302 | 178 |
| | 38 | 43 | 23 |
| | 42 | 34 | 25 |
| | 42 | 33 | 18 |
| | 35 | 42 | 26 |
| Professional athletes | 33 | 41 | 18 |
| | 38 | 37 | 26 |
| | 39 | 37 | 20 |
| | 34 | 40 | 19 |
| | 33 | 36 | 22 |
| | 34 | 35 | 17 |
| | 368 | 378 | 214 |

Following the computational outline given in Section 12.31 we first find the square of each of the scores, and sum:

$$A = \sum_j \sum_k \sum_i Y_{ijk}^2 = (52)^2 + (48)^2 + \cdots + (22)^2 + (17)^2 = 66872.$$

The sum of the scores in each cell (step 3) is given in the table above. Taking the sum of the cell sums gives the total sum,

$$B = \sum_j \sum_k \sum_i Y_{ijk} = 464 + 302 + \cdots + 214 = 1904.$$

Hence the total sum of squares is

$$A - \frac{B^2}{N} = 66872 - \frac{(1904)^2}{60} = 6451.7.$$

Now the cell totals are summed for each row:

$$D_1 = \sum_j \sum_i Y_{ij1} = 464 + 302 + 178 = 944$$

$$D_2 = \sum_j \sum_i Y_{ij2} = 368 + 378 + 214 = 960.$$

The sum of squares for rows is found from

$$\frac{\sum_k D_k^2}{Cn} - \frac{B^2}{N} = \frac{(944)^2 + (960)^2}{30} - \frac{(1904)^2}{60}$$
$$= 4.2.$$

In a similar way, we find the sum of squares for columns by first summing cell totals for each column

$$G_1 = \sum_k \sum_i Y_{i1k} = 464 + 368 = 832$$

$$G_2 = \sum_k \sum_i Y_{i2k} = 302 + 378 = 680$$

$$G_3 = \sum_k \sum_i Y_{i3k} = 178 + 214 = 392.$$

The sum of squares for columns is found from

$$\frac{\sum_j G_j^2}{Rn} - \frac{B^2}{N} = \frac{(832)^2 + (680)^2 + (392)^2}{20} - \frac{(1904)^2}{60}$$
$$= 4994.1.$$

Next, the sum of squares for error will be calculated. We begin by squaring and summing the *cell totals:*

$$\sum_j \sum_k H_{jk}^2 = (464)^2 + (302)^2 + \cdots + (214)^2 = 662288.$$

The sum of squares for error is

$$A - \frac{\sum_j \sum_k H_{jk}^2}{n} = 66872 - \frac{662288}{10} = 643.2.$$

The only remaining value to be calculated is the sum of squares for interaction; this is done by subtraction, as follows:

SS total − SS rows − SS cols. − SS error = 6451.7 − 4.2 − 4994.1 − 643.2
SS interaction = 810.2.

Table 12.33.2 is the summary table for this analysis of variance.

**Table 12.33.2**

| *Source* | *SS* | *df* | *MS* | *F* |
|---|---|---|---|---|
| Rows (norm groups) | 4.2 | 1 | 4.2 | .35 |
| Columns (standings) | 4994.1 | 2 | 2497.05 | 209.8 |
| Interaction | 810.2 | 2 | 405.1 | 34.0 |
| Error (within cells) | 643.2 | 54 | 11.9 | |
| Totals | 6451.7 | 59 | | |

The hypothesis of no row effects cannot be rejected, since the $F$ value is less than unity. For the hypothesis of no column effects, an $F$ of approximately 3.15 is required for rejection at the 5 percent level; the obtained $F$ of 209 far exceeds this, and so may conclude with considerable confidence that column effects exist. In the same way, the $F$ for interaction effects greatly exceeds that required for rejecting the null hypothesis, and so there seems to be reliable evidence for such interaction effects.

Our conclusions from this analysis of variance make it reasonably safe to make the following assertions.

1. There is apparently little or no effect of norm group alone on level of aspiration.
2. The experimental standing does seem to affect level of aspiration when considered over the different norm groups.
3. There is apparently an interaction between norm group and standing, meaning that the magnitude and direction of the effects of standing differ for different norm groups.

In short, the standing one is told that he has makes a difference in his aspiration level, but the kind and extent of difference that it makes depends upon the norm group to which he is being compared.

The different column effects can be estimated from the column means and the over-all mean:

$$\text{est. } \alpha_1 = 41.6 - 31.7 = 9.9$$
$$\text{est. } \alpha_2 = 34.0 - 31.7 = 2.3$$
$$\text{est. } \alpha_3 = 19.6 - 31.7 = -12.1.$$

(Because of rounding error these do not quite total zero, as they should.) In a similar way, interaction effects may be estimated from the means of cells, the rows, and the columns:

$$\text{est. } \gamma_{11} = 46.4 - 31.4 - 41.6 + 31.7 = 6.1$$
$$\text{est. } \gamma_{12} = 30.2 - 31.4 - 34.0 + 31.7 = 3.1$$

and so on. The estimated total effect of the "above" treatment on a subject in the college norm group is thus

$$\text{est. } (\alpha_1 + \gamma_{11}) = 9.9 + 6.1 = 16.0.$$

Note that for an individual selected at random from group 1 ("above" standing) with unspecified norm group, the best guess we can make about the effect on *him* of this treatment is 9.9 units. However, if we are told that he belongs to the group given the "college men" norms, our best bet is 16.0 as the amount of effect. In the same way, the effect of any column treatment $j$ within a row-treatment population $k$ is estimated $\alpha_j + \gamma_{jk}$.

## 12.34 ESTIMATING STRENGTH OF ASSOCIATION FROM A TWO-WAY ANALYSIS OF VARIANCE

From the experimenter's point of view, it may be informative to assess the strength of association represented either by significant treatment or interaction effects. This may be done once again by rough estimates of the index $\omega^2$, although the form of the estimation is somewhat different, since there are three different such indices for a two-way experimental design.

Imagine a sample space in which there are three kinds of events $X$, $Y$, and $Z$, and each elementary event belongs to some joint event class $(X, Z, Y)$. The event $X$ stands for the column treatment given, the event $Z$ is the row treatment, and the event $Y$ is the value of the random variable standing for the dependent variable score. Suppose that the probability of an event $X_j$, the probability of an observation's being made in column treatment $j$, is $p(X_j) = 1/C$. Let $p(Z_k)$, the probability of an observation's being in row treatment $k$, be $1/R$. Furthermore, let the probability of an observation in the combination $jk$ be $p(X_j, Z_k) = 1/RC$.

Under these circumstances, for Model I the variance $\sigma_Y^2$ of the **marginal** distribution of $Y$ is

$$\sigma_Y^2 = \sigma_e^2 + \frac{\sum_j \alpha_j^2}{C} + \frac{\sum_k \beta_k^2}{R} + \frac{\sum_j \sum_k \gamma_{jk}^2}{RC}. \qquad [12.34.1*]$$

The definition of $\omega_{Y|X}^2$, the proportion of variance accounted for by $X$ alone in the population is

$$\omega_{Y|X}^2 = \frac{\left(\sum_j \alpha_j^2\right)/C}{\sigma_Y^2}. \qquad [12.34.2*]$$

Similarly, we can define

$$\omega_{Y|Z}^2 = \frac{\left(\sum_k \beta_k^2\right)/R}{\sigma_Y^2}, \qquad [12.34.3*]$$

and

$$\omega_{Y|XZ}^2 = \frac{\left(\sum_j \sum_k \gamma_{jk}^2\right)/RC}{\sigma_Y^2}. \qquad [12.34.4*]$$

This last index is the proportion of variance accounted for uniquely by the combination of *both* X and Z.

Given these definitions, and our results about the expectations of mean squares for the two-way analysis of variance (Section 12.29), we can estimate these values of $\omega^2$ by taking

$$\text{est. } \omega^2_{Y|X} = \frac{\text{SS columns} - (C-1)\text{ MS error}}{\text{MS error} + \text{SS total}} \qquad [12.34.5\dagger]$$

$$\text{est. } \omega^2_{Y|Z} = \frac{\text{SS rows} - (R-1)\text{ MS error}}{\text{MS error} + \text{SS total}} \qquad [12.34.6\dagger]$$

$$\text{est. } \omega^2_{Y|XZ} = \frac{\text{SS interaction} - (R-1)(C-1)\text{ MS error}}{\text{MS error} + \text{SS total}}. \qquad [12.34.7\dagger]$$

For the example in Section 12.33, these estimated values are

$$\text{est. } \omega^2_{Y|X} = \frac{4994.1 - (2)(11.9)}{11.9 + 6451.7} = .77$$

$$\text{est. } \omega^2_{Y|XZ} = \frac{810.2 - (2)(11.9)}{11.9 + 6451.7} = .12.$$

Since the F ratio shows a value less than 1.00 in the test for row differences, the estimate of $\omega^2_{Y|Z}$ is set equal to zero. These estimates suggest that a very strong association exists between the treatments symbolized by X and the dependent variable Y. Knowing X alone tends to reduce our "uncertainty" about Y by about 77 percent. Notice that this is almost the same estimated value found in Section 12.18, which was actually based on these same data. However, since here we are dealing with a two-way design, we can also find out something more: there is apparently a further accounting for around 12 percent of the variance of Y if one knows *both* of the categories represented by X and Z, the treatment combination. In other words, we may safely conclude not only that association exists between independent and dependent variables but also that this association is quite sizable in a predictive sense, for any population situation corresponding to our experiment.

As always, we cannot be sure that any association at all exists: the validity of this statement depends upon the assumptions being correct, and on these data not representing a chance result representing some really quite empty situation. However, the significance level assures us that the probability of error in such a statement is rather small, and our estimates of the strength of association are the best guesses we are able to make about the association's magnitude. Estimates of the size of effects and of strength of association are aids to the experimenter in trying to figure out what went on in the experiment and the meaning of the results. The F test per se is capable of indicating merely that something systematic seems to have happened. Only a careful examination of the data can make the meaning of the experiment clear, and this is why estimation of effects or of association-strength forms an important and informative part of any experimental analysis. (In Chapter 14 methods will be given for further exploration of differences in means after the analysis of variance has shown overall significance.)

### 12.35 The importance of the assumptions in the two-way (or higher) analysis of variance with fixed effects

The list of assumptions in Section 12.28 was an almost exact parallel to the list in Section 12.5. Similar assumptions are made for more complex experiments requiring a higher-order analysis, provided that the fixed effects model is appropriate.

As you may have anticipated, the same relaxation of assumptions is possible in the two- or multi-way analysis as in the one-way analysis. For experiments with a relatively large number of observations per cell, the requirement of a normal distribution of errors seems to be rather unimportant. In an experiment where it is suspected that the parent distributions of dependent variable values are very unlike a normal distribution, perhaps a correspondingly large number of observations per cell should be used.

When the data table represents an equal number of observations in each cell, the requirement of equal error variance in each treatment combination population may also be violated without serious risk. Consequently, there are two good reasons for planning experiments with equal $n$ per cell: the experimental design will thus be orthogonal (Section 12.25) and the possible consequences of nonhomogeneous variances will be minimized.

Regardless of the simplicity or complexity of the experiment, however, the error portions entering into the respective observations should be independent if the fixed effects model is to apply. This seems to be the one requirement that can be violated only with grave risk of erroneous conclusions. For this reason considerable caution must be exercised in the planning and analysis of experiments involving repeated observations of the same subjects or of subjects matched in certain ways if the methods of this chapter are to be used. Ordinarily, the methods to be discussed in the next chapter are preferable for the analysis of such data.

### 12.36 The analysis of variance as a summarization of data

It may appear that the main use of the analysis of variance, particularly for two-factor or multi-factor experiments, is in generating a number of $F$ tests on the same set of data, and that the partition of the sum of squares is only a means to this end. However, this is really a very narrow view of the role of this form of analysis in experimentation. The really important feature of the analysis of variance is that it permits the separation of all of the potential information in the data into distinct and nonoverlapping portions, each reflecting only certain aspects of the experiment. For example, in the simple, one-way analysis of variance, the mean square between groups reflects both the systematic differences among observations that are attributable to the experimental manipulations, as well as the chance, unsystematic differences attributable to all of the other circumstances of the experiment. On the other hand, the mean square within the groups reflects only these latter, unsystematic, features. Under the fixed effects model, these two statistics are independent, completely nonoverlapping, ways of summarizing the data. The information contained in one is nonredundant with the information contained in the other. Estimates of the effects of the treatments are independent of estimates of error-variability. The mechanics of the analysis of variance allow the experimenter to arrange and summarize his data in these nonredundant ways, in order to decide if effects exist and to estimate how large or important those effects may be.

Similarly, for a two-factor experiment we arrive at a mean square for one treatment factor, and a separate mean square for the other. These two mean squares reflect quite nonredundant aspects of the experiment, even though they were each based on the same basic data: the first sum of squares reflects only the effects attributable to the first experimental factor (plus error), and the second those effects attributable to the other (plus error). Under the statistical assumptions we make these two mean squares are independent of each other. Furthermore, the mean squares for interaction and for error are independent of each other and of the treatment mean squares. The analysis of variance lets the experimenter "pull apart" the factors that contribute to variation in his experiment, and identify them exclusively with particular summary statistics. For experiments of the orthogonal, balanced type considered here, the analysis of variance is a routine method for finding the statistics that reflect particular, meaningful, aspects of the data.

In short, it is useful to think of the analysis of variance as a device for "sorting" the information in an experiment into nonoverlapping and meaningful portions. As mentioned in Section 12.12, multiple *t* tests carried out on the same data do not provide this feature; the various differences between means do overlap in the information they provide, and it is not easy to assess the evidence for over-all existence or importance of treatment effects from a complete set of such differences. On the other hand, the analysis of variance packages the information in the data into neat, distinct "bundles," permitting a relatively simple judgment to be made about the effects of the experimental treatments. The real importance of the analysis of variance lies in the fact that it routinely provides such succinct over-all "packaging" of the data.

In Chapter 14 the information that goes into the various mean squares will be studied in more detail. We will find that each distinct degree of freedom in the analysis corresponds to one nonredundant, independent, nonoverlapping question that one *might* ask of the data via an estimate and accompanying *t* test, and that the *F* test itself provides an over-all or "omnibus" conclusion about a set of such questions. Furthermore, a significant *F* may be interpreted as a signal to look further into the data, to try to answer particular questions about what went on in the experiment. We will go much further into these matters in Chapter 14.

For the moment, however, let us consider the several *F* tests obtained from a two- or multi-factor experiment. The sums of squares and mean squares for columns, for rows, for interaction, and for error are all, under the assumptions made, independent of each other. However, are the three or more $F$ tests themselves independent? Does the level of significance shown by any one of the tests in any way predicate the level of significance shown by the others? Unfortunately, it can be shown that such $F$ tests are *not* independent. Some connection exists among the various $F$ values and significance levels. This is due to the fact that each of the $F$ ratios involves the same mean square for error in the denominator; the presence of this same value in each of the ratios creates some statistical dependency among them. The practical result is much the same as for the multiple confidence intervals discussed in Section 10.10. If three $F$ tests are carried out, and these tests actually are independent, then one should expect about 3(.05) or .15 of these tests to show significance at the .05 level by chance alone. Furthermore, the probability is $1 - (.95)^3$ or about .14 that *at least one* of the tests will show spurious significance. However, for the usual situation where the tests are not independent, one has no ready way to calculate the number that should be expected by chance, and one knows only that the probability that at least one is spuriously significant is somewhere between .05 and .15.

For really complicated analyses of variance, the problem becomes much more serious, since a fairly large number of $F$ tests may be carried out, and the probability may be quite large that one or more tests gives spuriously significant results. The matter is further complicated by the fact that the $F$ tests are not independent, and the number to be expected by chance is quite difficult to calculate exactly. For this reason, when large numbers of $F$ tests are performed, the experimenter should not pay too much attention to isolated results that happen to be significant. Rather, the pattern and interpretability of results, as well as the strength of association represented by the findings, form a more reasonable basis for the over-all evaluation of the experiment. When the number of degrees of freedom for the mean square error is very large, then the various $F$ tests may be regarded as approximately independent, and the number of significant results at the .05 level to be expected should be close to 5 percent. Even here, however, the importance of a particular result is very difficult to interpret on the basis of significance level alone. A great deal of thought must go into the interpretation of a complicated experiment, quite over and above the information provided by the significance tests.

## 12.37 ANALYZING EXPERIMENTS WITH MORE THAN TWO EXPERIMENTAL FACTORS

The essential features of any fixed effects analysis of variance have now been discussed. In experiments involving three or more different experimental factors, the total sum of squares is partitioned into even more parts, but the basic ideas of the partition, the mean squares, and the $F$ tests are the same. In a three-factor experiment, not only are there mean squares representing the interactions of particular pairs of the experimental factors, but also a mean square representing the simultaneous interaction of all three of the factors. The higher the order of the experimental design, the larger becomes the number of possible interactions representing every combination of two or more factors. Each and every significant interaction represents a new qualification on the meaning of the results. Moreover, as suggested above, if many significance tests are carried out on the same data, the probability of at least one spuriously significant result may be very large, and this probability, as well as the number of Type I errors to be expected by chance, cannot be determined routinely. For these reasons, very complicated experiments with many factors are somewhat uneconomical to perform, since they require a large number of observations as a rule, and a complete analysis of the data yields so many statistical results that the experiment as a whole is often very difficult to interpret in a statistical light. In planning an experiment, it is a temptation to throw in many experimental treatments, especially if the data are inexpensive and the experimenter is adventuresome. However, this is *not* always good policy if the psychologist is interested in finding meaning in his results; other things being equal, the simpler the psychological experiment the better will be its execution, and the more likely will one be able to decide what actually happened and what the results actually mean.

The two-way experiments discussed in this chapter as illustrating Model I are examples of "factorial" designs, since they involve several experimental "factors" each represented at several "levels." In a complete factorial experiment the set of experimental factors is completely crossed, so that every possible combination of factor levels is observed. The fixed effects model applies when the different levels of each factor are chosen in advance of the experiment and when the only conclusions to be drawn concern *those particular* levels and combinations. By far the most commonly encountered experiments are of this type, and the student is referred to the references at the end of this book giving a further exposition of the planning and analysis of factorial experiments. The varieties of experimental design are almost limitless, however, and many designs in common use are quite different from the factorial arrangement.

Far and away, the fixed effects analysis of variance is the statistical technique encountered most in current experimental psychology. Its advantages are many: the general technique is extremely flexible and applies to a wide variety of experimental arrangements. Indeed, the availability of a statistical technique such as the analysis of variance has done much to stimulate inquiry into the logic and economics of the *planning* of experiments. Statistically, the $F$ test in the fixed effects analysis of variance is relatively *robust;* as we have seen, the failure of at least two of the underlying statistical assumptions does not necessarily disqualify the application of this method in practical situations. Computationally the analysis is relatively simple and routine and provides a condensation of the main statistical results of an experiment into an easily understood form.

However, the application of the analysis of variance never transforms a sloppy experiment into a good one, no matter how elegant the experimental design appears on paper, nor how neat and informative the summary table appears to the reader. Furthermore, there are psychological experiments where the fixed effects model is manifestly inappropriate; as mentioned above, often these are experiments in which treatments are sampled, in which subjects are somehow matched within groups, or in which repeated observations are made on the same individuals. The techniques of analysis of variance and its connections with experimental design were first developed by Sir Ronald Fisher and others mainly for problems in the biological sciences, most notably in agriculture, where assumptions such as independence among errors are often simple to meet. The unique problems of psychological research are not always provided for either in analysis of variance assumptions or in standard experimental designs. Quite often, the psychologist is able to tailor his experimental problem to fit the methodology available to him *without losing the essence of the problem in so doing*. However, experiments should be planned so as to capture the phenomena under study in its clearest, most easily understood form, and this does not necessarily mean that one of the "textbook" experimental designs, nor a treatment by the analysis of variance will best clarify matters. The experimental *problem* must come first in planning, and not the requirements of some particular form of analysis, even though, ideally, both should be considered together from the outset. If it should come to a choice between preserving the essential character of the experimental problem, or using a relatively elegant technique such as the analysis of variance, then the problem should come first.

The point has been repeated several times, but it bears repetition: statistics should aid in the clarification of meaning in an experimental situation, but the production of a statistical summary in some impressive and elegant form should never be the primary goal of a research enterprise. If the analysis of variance does not fit the problem, do not use it. If *no* inferential statistical techniques are available to fit the problem, do not alter the problem in essential ways to make some pet or fashionable technique apply. Above all, do not "jam" the data willy-nilly into some wildly inappropriate statistical analysis simply to get a significance test; there is little or nothing to gain by doing this. Thoughtless application of statistical techniques makes the reader wonder about the care that went into the experiment itself. A really good experiment, carefully planned and controlled, often speaks for itself with little or no aid from inferential statistics.

# THE ANALYSIS OF VARIANCE: MODELS II AND III, RANDOM EFFECTS AND MIXED MODELS

## 13

In the preceding chapter, the analysis of variance was discussed only for the fixed effects model. At the beginning of that chapter it was mentioned that the fixed effects model is appropriate when the experimental treatments actually administered are thought of as exhausting all treatments of interest. That is, given any experimental factor, any "level" or category of that factor figuring in the experimental question is observed. The only inferences to be drawn from the experiment concern the effects of those levels actually represented. Similarly, in an experiment with two or more crossed factors, each combination of factor levels ordinarily is represented in the experiment, and the only inferences drawn concern those observed levels and their combinations.

Now we turn to a model for experiments in which inferences are to be drawn about an entire set of distinct treatments or factor levels, including some not actually observed. For such experiments, many more categories or levels of a factor are possible than actually occur as observations in the experiment itself. The experimenter is interested in the *whole range* of possible levels, and what he observes as factor levels or experimental treatments is only a random sample of the potential set he might have observed. Before the experiment a sample is drawn from among all possible levels of a particular experimental factor, and then inferences are made about the effects of all such levels from the sample of factor levels.

For example, suppose that in a psychological experiment we suspect that the personality of the experimenter himself may be having an effect on the results. In principle there are a vast number of people, each presumably having a distinct personality, who might possibly serve as the person who conducts the experiment. Obviously, it is reasonable to narrow this population of potential experimenters down to people having the requisite technical skills to conduct the experiment (for example, English-speaking psychologists), but even this leaves a great many people from which to choose. To put it mildly, trying out each such person in our experiment would complicate matters! So, instead, we draw a random sample from among English-speaking psychologists. Suppose that five different persons are chosen; each of the five persons conducts the experiment on a different sample of $n$ subjects assigned at random to him. Each experimenter constitutes an experimental treatment given to one group of subjects; in all other respects subjects are treated exactly the same. Since the experimental treatments employed are themselves a random sample, this experiment fits the random effects, rather than the fixed effects, model: an inference is to be made about experimenter effects in general from observation of only five experimenters sampled at random.

The random effects model will be given a more formal statement in succeeding sections, and will be illustrated first for a one-way analysis of variance, and then extended to the two-way case. It will be seen that, computationally, analyses using the fixed and random effects models are identical, but that the inferences drawn are different, and that the actual form of the $F$ test is different in the two-way analysis.

Parenthetically, the student is warned that designation of the random effects model as Model II, and the mixed model as Model III, though convenient for the organization adopted here, is not uniform across authors. It is probably better for the student to learn to think of these three models as "fixed effects," "random effects" (or "components of variance"), and "mixed" from the very outset, rather than relying on any number-designation alone.

## 13.1  MODEL II: RANDOM EFFECTS

In the study outlined in the section above, consider a particular experimenter, whom we will call, for the moment, experimenter $v$. When this particular experimenter is paired with a particular subject, say subject $i$, then some value of the dependent variable $Y$ is observed. Let us denote the value of $Y$ obtained for subject $i$ under experimenter $v$ by the symbol $Y_i(v)$. Over all possible subjects that might be paired with a particular experimenter $v$ there is some hypothetical distribution of possible values of $Y_i(v)$. That is, we can think of a distribution of values for a population of potential subjects, each observed under the same experimenter $v$. For the moment let us call the mean of this population distribution $\mathbf{\mu}(v)$. Then the score associated with any particular subject drawn from this population for experimenter $v$ is thought of as

$$Y_i(v) = \mathbf{\mu}(v) + e_i(v).$$

Here, $\mathbf{\mu}(v)$ is the mean of the population of all possible observations under this experimenter across subjects, $e_i(v)$ is the deviation from that mean, or the error, peculiar to subject $i$ observed under experimenter $v$.

However, there are a great many possible experimenters who might carry out this particular experiment. Suppose that the number of such possible experimenters is some large, but perhaps finite, number $V$. We select a random sample of some $J$ such experimenters for our particular study; note that this is tantamount to selecting some $J$ distinct populations of observations for representation in our experiment, since each experimenter $v$ that we might use is associated with a potential population of observations to be made. Any given experimenter either may or may not appear in our actual sample of $J$ experimenters. This situation is unlike the fixed effects model, where if a treatment (a particular population of potential observations) is represented once in an experiment, it is thought of as always being represented in any complete repetition of that experiment. In this new, random effects, model, whether or not a particular treatment (experimenter) appears in any repetition of the experiment is purely a matter of chance. In short, only a random selection of some $J$ of the total number $V$ of possible experimenters is actually used in the performance of the experiment, and consequently only $J$ of the $V$ populations of ultimate interest actually are represented in the data. When $J = V$, so that every population of interest actually is represented by observations in the experiment, the fixed effects and the random effects models are identical. On the other hand, when $J$ is less than $V$, so that only a subset of the treatments of interest (the experimenters) appear in any given repetition of the experiment, the fixed effects model no longer applies.

Now imagine a particular experimenter $v$ who happens to be among those sampled for the experiment proper, and who is the $j$th such experimenter actually observed; we will designate this experimenter as $v_j$. Experimenter $v_j$ is observed in association with a distinct random sample of some $n$ subjects. The score for any observation $i$ made in the experiment under the particular experimenter $v_j$ will be denoted by $Y_i(v_j)$. This score can also be thought of as composed of two components:

$$Y_i(v_j) = \mathbf{\mu}(v_j) + e_i(v_j).$$

However, the $j$ subscript here indicates only that the particular experimenter $v$ was the $j$th member of the sample of experimenters, and $\mathbf{\mu}(v_j)$ is merely the true mean associated with experimenter $v$, or $\mathbf{\mu}(v)$. If that experimenter were to be observed over all possible subjects, rather than for a limited sample of $n$ subjects, the mean value for such observations should be $\mathbf{\mu}(v)$.

In general, the thing to be remembered is that not only is a random sample of observations made under each of a set of $J$ different treatment populations, but also that the different treatment populations themselves are members of a random sample of a much larger set of *possible* treatment populations. The reason for the relatively complicated notation used here is this: any given treatment $v$ is itself associated with a potential population of observations with mean $\mathbf{\mu}(v)$, and the particular observation $i$ made under that treatment is sampled from that population. The treatments that actually are used in the experiment itself are, moreover, a random selection from a large set of possible such treatments. Any potential treatment $v$ may or may not appear in the actual experiment carried out; this is purely a matter of chance. But wherever it does appear, a population of potential observations associated with that treatment, having a mean $\mathbf{\mu}(v)$ and a variance $\mathbf{\sigma}^2(v)$, is represented by a sample in the experiment.

Now, over all of the $V$ possible experimenters who might have been included among the $J$ actually sampled, there is a general mean $\mu$. That is,

$$\mu = \frac{\sum_v \mathbf{\mu}(v)}{V}.$$

We may define the effect associated with a particular experimenter $v$ as the deviation of $\mathbf{\mu}(v)$ from this grand over-all mean:

$$\text{effect of experimenter } v = \boldsymbol{a}(v) = \mathbf{\mu}(v) - \mu.$$

Then the score associated with any observation $i$ that might be made under experimenter $v$ can be thought of as

$$Y_i(v) = \mu + \boldsymbol{a}(v) + \boldsymbol{e}_i(v). \qquad [13.1.1]$$

That is, the score $Y_i(v)$ may be thought of as a sum consisting of the general mean $\mu$, the effect associated with the particular experimenter $v$, and an error component associated uniquely with observation $i$ made under experimenter $v$. Similarly, for any experimenter $v$ included in the sample as the $j$th experimenter in the actual study, we can think of the effect $\boldsymbol{a}(v_j)$ associated with *that* experimenter. Any observation $i$ made in association with that experimenter should then have a score with a composition given by

$$Y_i(v_j) = \mu + \boldsymbol{a}(v_j) + \boldsymbol{e}_i(v_j). \qquad [13.1.2]$$

Since experimenter $v_j$ is a randomly chosen member of the population of $V$ experimenters, then $\boldsymbol{a}(v_j)$ is a randomly chosen value from the distribution of effects over the various possible experimenters. The effect associated with any observation $i$ made under the $j$th experimenter included is a value of a random variable, or a **random effect**. Recall that in the fixed effects model of Chapter 12, the composition of the score for individual observation $i$ in condition $j$ was thought of as

$$Y_{ij} = \mu + \alpha_j + e_{ij}$$

where $\alpha_j$ symbolizes the effect attributable to the $j$th treatment administered. In Model I, the particular treatment in the experiment represented by the subscript $j$ is conceived as fixed, since in any repetition of the experiment that treatment appears and is associated with the subscript $j$. On the other hand, in the random effects model, or Model II, the value represented by $\boldsymbol{a}(v_j)$ need not be the same from repetition to repetition of the experiment. The value $\boldsymbol{a}(v_j)$ is a value of a random variable, which depends upon the particular, randomly selected, experimenter who happens to appear as the $j$th experimenter actually employed. This is the reason for the "random effects" nomenclature: the particular experimenter under whom the observation is made is most definitely thought of as exerting a systematic influence on the obtained score, via the effect $\boldsymbol{a}(v)$ associated with him, but the opportunity for this experimenter to appear in the actual data as experimenter $v_j$, exerting effect $\boldsymbol{a}(v_j) = \boldsymbol{a}(v)$, is governed purely by a random process. Thus, $\boldsymbol{a}(v_j)$ is spoken of as a random variable, or random effect.

Although this discussion has been carried on so far in terms of particular experimenters sampled from a population of $V$ such persons, it should be obvious that the same argument applies to any set of $V$ potential treatments or levels from which some $J$ might be sampled for use in a given experiment. Any particular treatment $v$ may or may not appear in the actual experiment, but if it does appear, then there is an effect $a(v)$ associated with that treatment which should be the same each and every time that particular treatment shows up in the sample of $J$ such treatments.

In both the fixed effects and the random effects models, our first interest is in judging if there really are different effects associated with the different possible treatments. For the present study, we would like to see if "experimenter effects" exist. Recall that in the fixed effects analysis of variance the hypothesis to be tested can be stated as

$$H_0: \alpha_j = 0, \qquad \text{for all } j.$$

In a somewhat similar way the hypothesis for the random effects model can be stated:

$$H_0: a(v) = 0, \qquad \text{for all possible treatments } v.$$

In other words, we wish to see if any effects at all exist attributable to the treatments, including not only those actually sampled but also the potential treatments not appearing in the experiment actually carried out. In the fixed effects situation of Chapter 12, we found that a test of the hypothesis of no treatment effects was equivalent to a test that there was no variability among the effects of the $J$ treatments: that is,

$$\text{variance of effects} = \frac{\sum_j \alpha_j^2}{J} = 0$$

when the null hypothesis is true. In the random effects model, the population of potential treatments is thought of as generating a distribution of effects $a(v)$, with a mean of zero and a variance given by

$$\sigma_A^2 = E[a(v)]^2,$$

where the expectation is over all possible treatments $v$. The hypothesis of no treatment effects is true when, and only when, the value of $\sigma_A^2$ is zero. Our immediate task is to find a way to test the hypothesis that $\sigma_A^2 = 0$.

## 13.2   ASSUMPTIONS MADE IN THE RANDOM EFFECTS MODEL

Once the conceptual distinctions between Models I and II are clear, we can adopt a somewhat simpler notation. Let us define

$$a_j = a(v_j)$$
$$e_{ij} = e_i(v_j)$$
$$Y_{ij} = Y_i(v_j).$$

Then the basic model given by expression **13.1.2** becomes

$$Y_{ij} = \mu + a_j + e_{ij}. \qquad\qquad [13.2.1*]$$

Remember that $a_j$ represents a random variable, the value of which depends upon which one of the basic set of treatments is selected at random and denoted by the subscript $j$. Furthermore, $e_{ij}$ is a random variable that depends on the particular observation $i$ that happens to be made under the treatment designated by $v_j$. It has become conventional to use Roman letters such as $a_j$ to denote the random variables in Model II, in contrast to Greek letters such as $\alpha_j$ used for the comparable terms conceived as constants in the fixed effects model.

      The assumptions to be made in deriving a test of the hypothesis of no treatment effects are as follows:

1. The possible values $a_j$ represent a random variable having a distribution with a mean of zero, and a variance $\sigma_A^2$.
2. For any treatment $j$, the errors $e_{ij}$ are normally distributed with a mean of zero and a variance $\sigma_e^2$, which is the same for each possible treatment $j$.
3. The $J$ values of the random variable $a_j$ occurring in the experiment are completely independent of each other.
4. The values of the random variable $e_{ij}$ are completely independent.
5. Each pair of random variables $a_j$ and $e_{ij}$ are completely independent.

      You will note that here we are making assumptions about two different kinds of distributions. First of all there is a distribution of possible values for the effects $a_j$ that might appear in a given repetition of the experiment. For the experiment proper, a random sample is taken from among all possible such effects values when a random sample of treatments is drawn. For the time being, no special assumptions need be made about the distribution of effects from which the sample of effects is drawn, other than that the mean is zero and that the variance has some (finite) value $\sigma_A^2$. Later, when we discuss this model more generally, we will assume that the distribution of effects is normal. The second kind of distribution is that of errors within particular treatments. Just as in Model I, we assume errors to be normally and independently distributed, with the same variance irrespective of the particular treatment under which the observation is made. Notice that we are, at present, making no assumptions about the number $V$ of potential treatments from which a sample of $J$ is taken for the experiment, except that $V$ is greater than $J$. We are, however, assuming that within any given treatment population an infinite number of potential units for observation exist.

## 13.3    The mean squares for Model II

      In this section the mean squares for the one-way analysis will be examined. *The discussion will be restricted to the situation where exactly the same number of observations n are made under each treatment.* Although the treatments may have different numbers of sample observations in the one-way case for the fixed effects model, some difficulties arise in Model II unless the numbers of observations are equal.

The partition of the sum of squares for the random effects model is carried out in exactly the same way as for Model I. Furthermore, the mean squares are found just as before:

$$\text{MS between} = \frac{\text{SS between}}{J-1} = \frac{\sum_j n(M_j - M)^2}{J-1} \qquad \text{[13.3.1†]}$$

and

$$\text{MS within} = \frac{\text{SS within}}{N-J} = \frac{\sum_j \sum_i (Y_{ij} - M_j)^2}{N-J}. \qquad \text{[13.3.2†]}$$

Bear in mind that for any random sample of $J$ treatments or factor levels, there is a corresponding random sample of effects $a_j$. Let the sample mean of these effects be denoted by

$$M_a = \frac{\sum_j a_j}{J}.$$

Although the mean of the effects over all of the *possible* treatments must be zero, the value of $M_a$ need not be zero, since this is but the mean of a sample of effects actually occurring in the experiment.

In the same way, sample means for error may be defined:

$$M_{ej} = \frac{\sum_i^n e_{ij}}{n}$$

and

$$M_e = \frac{\sum_j \sum_i e_{ij}}{N} = \frac{\sum_j M_{ej}}{J}.$$

In these terms, $MS$ between groups becomes

$$\frac{\sum_j n(M_j - M)^2}{J-1} = \frac{\sum_j n(a_j + M_{ej} - M_a - M_e)^2}{J-1}.$$

Now suppose that we take the expectation of the mean square between groups, over all samples of subjects *and* over all samples of treatments:

$$E(\text{MS between}) = E \sum_j n \frac{(a_j + M_{ej} - M_a - M_e)^2}{J-1}.$$

or

$$E(\text{MS between}) = nE \sum_j \frac{(a_j - M_a)^2}{J - 1} + nE \sum_j \frac{(M_{ej} - M_e)^2}{J - 1}$$
$$+ 2n \sum_j E \frac{(a_j - M_a)(M_{ej} - M_e)}{J - 1}. \quad [13.3.3]$$

Consider the first term on the right in equation 13.3.3. Since the $J$ values $a_j$ are a sample from a population of effects, this first term

$$\sum_j \frac{(a_j - M_a)^2}{J - 1}$$

is an unbiased estimate of the *effects* variance $\sigma_A^2$, so that

$$nE \sum_j \frac{(a_j - M_a)^2}{J - 1} = n\sigma_A^2. \quad [13.3.4^*]$$

The last term on the right in expression 13.3.3 is zero because of the assumption that the $a_j$ and the $e_{ij}$ are independent. The middle term in 13.3.3 is simply

$$nE \sum_j \frac{(M_{ej} - M_e)^2}{J - 1} = \sigma_e^2$$

since it involves the unbiased pooled estimate of the variance of the mean error, $\sigma_e^2/n$. Finally, we see that

$$E(\text{MS between}) = n\sigma_A^2 + \sigma_e^2. \quad [13.3.5^*]$$

**The expected mean square between is the weighted sum of two variances, that of the population of treatment effects, and that of the error.**

Now we turn to the mean square within treatments:

$$E(\text{MS within}) = E \sum_j \sum_i \frac{(e_{ij} - M_{ej})^2}{J(n - 1)}. \quad [13.3.6\dagger]$$

For any $j$, $\sum_i \frac{(e_{ij} - M_{ej})^2}{n - 1}$ is an unbiased estimate of $\sigma_e^2$, the error variance, so that

$$E(\text{MS within}) = \sum_j \frac{\sigma_e^2}{J} = \sigma_e^2. \quad [13.3.7^*]$$

**Thus the mean square within is always an unbiased estimate of error variance alone.**

## 13.4 THE NULL HYPOTHESIS FOR MODEL II

In Model I, the null hypothesis is that each effect $\alpha_j$ is zero, which corresponds to the equality of all of the treatment-population means. We saw in Section 13.1 that, in Model II, if there are no treatment effects at all, either for those represented in the experiment or for any other possible treatment in the set sampled, $a(v) = 0$ for each possible treatment $v$, and $\sigma_A^2 = 0$. Hence the null hypothesis of no treatment effects for Model II is usually written

$$H_0: \sigma_A^2 = 0.$$

Now suppose that this null hypothesis were true. In this case

$$E(\text{MS between}) = \sigma_e^2 \qquad \text{[13.4.1*]}$$
$$E(\text{MS within}) = \sigma_e^2 \qquad \text{[13.4.2*]}$$

so that *both* mean squares are unbiased estimates of error variance alone.

The mean square between can be shown to be independent of the mean square within under the assumptions of Section 13.1, so that when $H_0$ is true the ratio

$$F = \frac{\text{MS between}/\sigma_e^2}{\text{MS within}/\sigma_e^2} = \frac{\text{MS between}}{\text{MS within}} \qquad \text{[13.4.3†]}$$

can be referred to the $F$ distribution with $J - 1$ and $N - J$ degrees of freedom, as a test of this null hypothesis. Significant values of $F$ lead to a rejection of $H_0: \sigma_A^2 = 0$ in favor of $H_1: \sigma_A^2 > 0$.

## 13.5 AN EXAMPLE

Suppose that the experiment described in the introduction to this chapter were actually carried out. Five experimenters chosen at random conduct the same experiment, each on a different set of eight subjects randomly sampled and assigned at random among the experimental groups. The data are as shown in Table 13.5.1.

The hypothesis that $\sigma_A^2 = 0$ (that there are no experimenter effects) is to be tested using $\alpha = .01$.

The computations are:

$$\text{SS total} = 1455.94 - \frac{(240.8)^2}{40} = 6.32$$
$$\text{SS between} = \frac{(44.0)^2 + \cdots + (49.3)^2}{8} - \frac{(240.8)^2}{40}$$
$$= 1453.09 - 1449.62 = 3.47$$
$$\text{SS within} = \text{total} - \text{between} = 6.32 - 3.47 = 2.85.$$

Table 13.5.1

|  | | *Experimenter* | | |
| 1 | 2 | 3 | 4 | 5 |
| 5.8 | 6.0 | 6.3 | 6.4 | 5.7 |
| 5.1 | 6.1 | 5.5 | 6.4 | 5.9 |
| 5.7 | 6.6 | 5.7 | 6.5 | 6.5 |
| 5.9 | 6.5 | 6.0 | 6.1 | 6.3 |
| 5.6 | 5.9 | 6.1 | 6.6 | 6.2 |
| 5.4 | 5.9 | 6.2 | 5.9 | 6.4 |
| 5.3 | 6.4 | 5.8 | 6.7 | 6.0 |
| 5.2 | 6.3 | 5.6 | 6.0 | 6.3 |
| 44.0 | 49.7 | 47.2 | 50.6 | 49.3 |

$$\sum_j \sum_i Y_{ij} = 240.8$$

Table 13.5.2 is the summary table. The $F$ value required for rejection at the .01 level for 4 and 35 degrees of freedom is between 4.02 and 3.83 (that is, between the values for 30 and 40 degrees of freedom denominator). Accordingly, the

Table 13.5.2

| Source | SS | df | MS | E(MS) | F |
| --- | --- | --- | --- | --- | --- |
| Between (experimenters) | 3.47 | 4 | .868 | $8\sigma_A^2 + \sigma_e^2$ | 10.72 |
| Within | 2.85 | 35 | .081 | $\sigma_e^2$ | |
| Total | 6.32 | 39 | | | |

hypothesis of no experimenter effects may be rejected. There is sufficient evidence to say that experimenter effects exist and contribute to the variance of $Y$.

## 13.6 ESTIMATION OF VARIANCE COMPONENTS IN A ONE-WAY ANALYSIS

Instead of estimating effects directly by taking differences of the treatment means from the grand mean, as in the fixed effects model, in Model II we will estimate $\sigma_A^2$, the true variance due to treatments. For the foregoing experiment, this is the true variance attributable to experimenters.

Since the expectation of the mean square between is

$$E(\text{MS between}) = n\sigma_A^2 + \sigma_e^2, \qquad [13.6.1]$$

an unbiased estimate of $\sigma_A^2$ may be found by taking

$$\frac{\text{MS between} - \text{MS within}}{n} = \text{est. } \sigma_A^2. \qquad \textbf{[13.6.2†]}$$

(Note: est. $\sigma_A^2 = 0$ when MS within $\geq$ MS between.)

For the example, this estimate is

$$\text{est. } \sigma_A^2 = \frac{.868 - .081}{8} = .098.$$

The variance of $Y_{ij}$ over the population of all possible potential observations is

$$\sigma_Y^2 = E(Y_{ij} - \mu)^2 = \sigma_A^2 + \sigma_e^2$$

so that the true variance consists of two independent parts or components: the variance due to treatments, and that due to error alone. The best estimate of the total variance $\sigma_Y^2$ is given by

$$\text{est. } \sigma_Y^2 = \text{est. } \sigma_A^2 + \text{est. } \sigma_e^2 = \frac{\text{MS between} + (n-1)\,\text{MS within}}{n}. \qquad \textbf{[13.6.3†]}$$

For the example,

$$\text{est. } \sigma_Y^2 = .098 + .081$$
$$= .179.$$

This fact that the total variance must consist of two components allows one to make a somewhat more informative use of the estimates of $\sigma_A^2$ and $\sigma_e^2$. We can take the ratio of the estimated $\sigma_A^2$ to the estimated total variance to find the estimated proportion of variance accounted for by the treatments,

$$\text{est. proportion of variance accounted for} = \frac{\text{est. } \sigma_A^2}{\text{est. } \sigma_Y^2} \qquad \textbf{[13.6.4†]}$$

$$\text{est. proportion of variance accounted for by experimenters} = \frac{(.098)}{.179}$$
$$= .55.$$

Here we estimate that over one half of the variance among observations seems to be due to experimenter differences. This would be a most important finding in a real experiment, as it would suggest that different experimenter's repetitions of this experiment would not be comparable. A change in experimental procedure or some better control over experimenter differences would clearly be called for.

In many other contexts as well it is highly informative to estimate variance components and to turn these estimates into proportions of variance accounted for. Such indices give one of the best ways to decide if a factor is a predictively important one relative to the dependent variable. We have already noted that it is entirely possible for a given factor to show up as statistically significant in a study, even though only a very small percentage of variance is attributable to that factor. This is most likely to happen if the sample $n$ is very large, of course. On the other hand, when there is both significant evidence for effects of a factor *and* evidence that the factor accounts for a relatively large percentage of variance, then this information may be an important key in interpreting the experiment or in deciding how the experimental findings might be applied. Thus, in Model II experiments, in which levels of a factor are sampled, it is good practice to estimate the components of variance, and judge the "predictive" significance of the factor on this basis in addition to the result of the $F$ test.

## 13.7 THE INTRACLASS CORRELATION COEFFICIENT

One way of expressing the idea that a factor accounts for a given amount of variance is by the index known as the population intraclass correlation coefficient:

$$\rho_I = \frac{\sigma_A^2}{\sigma_A^2 + \sigma_e^2}. \qquad [13.7.1*]$$

The intraclass correlation coefficient for the grand population will be zero only when $\sigma_A^2$ is zero, and will reach unity only when $\sigma_e^2 = 0$, given that $\sigma_Y^2 > 0$. Notice that this index is simply another way of expressing the proportion of variance attributable to the factor $A$. The population index $\rho_I$ is identical to $\omega^2$ in its general form and meaning, although $\rho_I$ applies to the random effects and $\omega^2$ to the fixed effects model so that slightly different estimation methods apply in the two situations.

Quite often the intraclass correlation is used to express the fact that observations in the same category are related, or tend on the average to be more like each other than observations in different categories. The larger the value of $\rho_I$, the more similar do observations in the same treatment category tend to be, relative to observations in different categories. For example, in a study of the similarity in intelligence of twins, a random sample of sets of twins might be taken, each pair of twins constituting a natural "treatment" with $n = 2$. An estimated intraclass correlation greater than zero would indicate that some of the variability in intelligence is accounted for variation among sets of twins, so that pairs of twins tend to be more alike in this respect than are pairs of nontwins.

Still another special application of this idea of an intraclass correlation occurs in the study of the reliability of repeated measurements of individuals. The reliability of a single measurement $Y_{ij}$ for an individual $j$ can be defined in a way equivalent to $\rho_I$ for a population of such individuals. The estimate of $\rho_I$ given by **13.6.4** is then an estimate of the true reliability for such measurements. A modern discussion of these methods for estimating reliability in terms of the random effects analysis of variance is given in Winer (1962, Chapter 4).

## 13.8 INTERVAL ESTIMATION FOR PROPORTION OF VARIANCE ACCOUNTED FOR

Under Model II, it is also possible to estimate intervals for the proportion of variance accounted for by a factor. Here, however, we must assume that the basic distribution of effects, $a(v)$, is normal. Given this assumption, the required limits can be found from the distribution of the quantity $\theta$, where

$$\theta = \frac{\sigma_A^2}{\sigma_e^2} \qquad\qquad \textbf{[13.8.1]}$$

and

$$\text{true proportion of variance accounted for} = \frac{\theta}{1 + \theta} = \rho_I. \qquad \textbf{[13.8.2]}$$

The required confidence interval is found as follows: Let $F'$ be the value in an $F$ distribution with $J - 1$ and $N - J$ degrees of freedom, cutting off the *upper* $(\alpha/2)$ proportion in the distribution, and let $F''$ be the value cutting off the *lower* $(\alpha/2)$. For this distribution, it must be true that

$$\text{prob.}(F'' \leq F \leq F') = 1 - \alpha.$$

Furthermore, regardless of the true value of $\sigma_A^2$, it will be true that the ratio

$$\frac{\text{MS between}/(\sigma_e^2 + n\sigma_A^2)}{\text{MS within}/(\sigma_e^2)} \qquad\qquad \textbf{[13.8.3]}$$

is distributed as an $F$ variable with $J - 1$ and $N - J$ degrees of freedom, since numerator and denominator *are* independent chi-square variables divided by degrees of freedom when Model II is true, and the basic distribution of effects is normal. This ratio is equivalent to

$$\left(\frac{\text{MS between}}{\text{MS within}}\right)\left(\frac{1}{1 + n\theta}\right), \qquad\qquad \textbf{[13.8.4]}$$

so that

$$\text{prob.}\left(F'' \leq \frac{\text{MS between}}{\text{MS within}}\frac{1}{1 + n\theta} \leq F'\right) = 1 - \alpha.$$

By algebraic operation on this inequality, it can be shown that the $100(1 - \alpha)$ percent confidence interval for $\theta$ is

$$\frac{1}{n}\left[\frac{\text{MS between}}{(\text{MS within})\ F'} - 1\right] \leq \theta \leq \frac{1}{n}\left[\frac{\text{MS between}}{(\text{MS within})\ F''} - 1\right]. \quad \textbf{[13.8.5†]}$$

This may be turned into a confidence interval for $\rho_I$ very easily by the relation

$$\rho_I = \frac{\theta}{1 + \theta}. \qquad\qquad \textbf{[13.8.6†]}$$

The value of $F'$ can be found directly from the $F$ tables for $(\alpha/2)$, and the degrees of freedom $J - 1$, and $N - J$. However, the value of $F''$ must be found by the methods of Section 11.11, for values on the *lower* tail of an $F$ distribution. Notice that since the distribution of $F$ is not symmetric, these confidence intervals, like those for $\sigma^2$ given in Chapter 11, need not be optimal.

As an example let us find the 95 percent confidence interval for $\theta$ and $\rho_I$ for the data of Section 13.5. Here,

$$\frac{\text{MS between}}{\text{MS within}} = 10.5.$$

The first thing we need is the value of $F'$, that value cutting off the *upper* 2.5 percent in an $F$ distribution with 4 and 35 degrees of freedom. Table IV shows this to be about 3.2. Next, we must find $F''$, the value on the lower tail of this same distribution cutting off the lower 2.5 percent. From the same table we take the value cutting off the *upper* 2.5 percent in a distribution *with 35 and 4 degrees of freedom:* this is about 8.4. Thus,

$$F'' = \frac{1}{8.4} = .119.$$

The approximate 95 percent confidence interval for $\theta$ is then

$$\frac{1}{8}\left[\frac{10.72}{3.2} - 1\right] \leqq \theta \leqq \frac{1}{8}\left[\frac{10.72}{.119} - 1\right]$$
$$.29 \leqq \theta \leqq 11.1.$$

The corresponding interval for $\rho_I$ is

$$\frac{.29}{1 + .29} \leqq \rho_I \leqq \frac{11.1}{1 + 11.1}$$

or
$$.224 \leqq \rho_I \leqq .917.$$

Over random samples the probability is approximately .95 that an interval such as this covers the true value of $\rho_I$. Notice that for this example the value 0 *does not* fall into the interval, reflecting the significance of the $F$ test carried out in Section 13.5. This procedure is applicable to the estimation of $\rho_I$, the proportion of variance accounted for, only in the random effects model, or Model II. *It does not apply to the estimation of $\omega^2$ in Model I, the fixed effects situation.*

When the $F$ ratio is small, the confidence intervals for $\theta$ and for $\rho_I$ may show negative values for the lower limit. When this happens, the lower limit for the confidence interval can be regarded as equal to zero, since neither true $\rho_I$ nor $\theta$ can be negative.

## 13.9 OTHER HYPOTHESES TESTABLE USING MODEL II

The hypothesis tested in the example above was that there exist no effects of the individual treatments, so that $\sigma_A^2 = 0$. The theory is not limited to this situation, however. When the distribution of effects can be assumed to be normal it is possible to test many other hypotheses about the ratio $\theta = \sigma_A^2/\sigma_e^2$, or, equivalently, about $\rho_I$.

In the general case, the hypothesis tested is

$$H_0: \theta \leqq \theta_0 \text{ versus } H_1: \theta_0 < \theta$$

where $\theta_0$ is any hypothetical value, $0 \leqq \theta_0$.

This general hypothesis is tested as follows: after $\alpha$ is chosen, we determine the $F$ value cutting off the upper $\alpha$ proportion of cases in a distribution with $J - 1$ and $N - J$ degrees of freedom. Call this value $F_\alpha$. Now we find the $F$ ratio for the sample in the usual way (Section 13.4). The hypothesis is rejected in favor of $H_1$ when

$$\frac{\text{MS between}}{\text{MS within}} \geqq (1 + n\theta_0)F_\alpha. \qquad \text{[13 9.1†]}$$

For example, suppose that in planning a study the experimenter was undecided about whether a given factor $A$ should be controlled or allowed to vary. The experimenter made up his mind that he would control for $A$ only if he could be confident that $A$ accounted for at least 10 percent of the variance in the dependent variable, as judged from a preliminary experiment. This is equivalent to a true $\rho_I$ of .10. The pilot experiment was carried out, with a random selection of seven levels of factor $A$ and three observations chosen at random in each level. The $F$ ratio for this experiment, with 6 and 14 degrees of freedom, turned out to be 4.0. The $F_\alpha$ value required for significance at the 5 percent level and for these degrees of freedom is 2.85.

Since the question involves a percentage of variance accounted for, or $\rho_I$, this must be turned into the equivalent value of $\theta_0$. If the variance accounted for were exactly .10 of the total, then

$$\frac{\sigma_A^2}{\sigma_e^2 + \sigma_A^2} = \frac{\theta_0}{1 + \theta_0} = .10$$

$$\theta_0 = \frac{1}{9}.$$

Hence,

$$F_\alpha(1 + n\theta_0) = 2.85\left(1 + \frac{3}{9}\right) = 3.80.$$

The obtained value of $F$ exceeds this, and so the experimenter concluded that more than 10 percent of the variance is attributable to $A$, and that the factor $A$ should be controlled in the experiment.

## 13.10  IMPORTANCE OF THE ASSUMPTIONS IN MODEL II

By now it should surely be clear that the actual *arithmetic* of the simple analysis of variance is the same regardless of the model adopted. The analysis of variance is, strictly speaking, only a way of arranging this arithmetic. However, the inferences made from the sample values are really quite different, depending on the model invoked. All the inferences made under Model I concern means (and differences between means). On the other hand, the inferences made using Model II deal with variances: that is, *the basic inference has to do with the variance of the population of effects actually sampled by the experimenter.* This distinction between the two models has an influence on the importance of the assumptions made in each.

In the first place, the assumption of normality can be quite important in Model II. Provided that one is concerned only with a test of the hypothesis $\sigma_A^2 = 0$, then slight departures from normality among the error distributions should have only minor consequences for the conclusions reached using reasonably large sample size. Here, no assumption at all about the distribution of the $a$ values need be made. On the other hand, for tests of the more general hypothesis given in Section 13.9, it is most important that the distributions *both* of effects and of errors be normal in form. In the same way, interval estimates for $\theta$ and for $\rho_I$ depend heavily upon the assumptions of normal distributions of the $a$ and the $e$ values for their validity.

The assumption of equality of variance has a somewhat different status in the random effects than in the fixed effects model. If the random effects model applies, and if the effects $a_j$ are independent of the errors $e_{ij}$, we need assume only one distribution of errors with variance $\sigma_e^2$, so that in a sense, the error variance for all possible observations given some treatment $j$ must be the same as for any other treatment. However, the important assumptions are those involving independence: the errors *must* be independent both of the particular treatment effects and of each other. The random effects model is not really applicable to data where the *errors* in observations must be related to the effect of the treatment applied, or to each other. Examples of situations where errors are related are most often those in which subjects are given repeated trials at some task, and some trial-related change such as learning occurs, making the observed scores depend on each other in some serial fashion. In many learning situations, the occurrence of an error makes the occurrence of another error of the same magnitude or direction less likely than otherwise, also introducing such a statistical dependence.

However, as always, we must be very careful not to let a purely statistical consideration intrude on experimental practice. The mere fact that an experiment involves repeated observations or observations on matched subjects does not necessarily imply a serious violation of the statistical assumptions. For example, in some situations the careful experimenter can plan his study in such a way that an initial "warm-up" or practice session does away with this form of dependency among observations, and then an analysis of variance may be fully applicable to the experimental data. In other situations, still other experimental devices may exist for controlling for such dependencies. These purely statistical requirements must not be interpreted as prohibitions against certain kinds of experiments, but only as warnings that special care should be taken in planning the experiment itself if a particular form of analysis is desired.

Although statistical dependency among the error components of scores creates a special problem in any analysis of variance, it is not true that the *observations themselves* must be completely independent for Model II to apply. We have just seen that the intraclass correlation coefficient expresses the degree of similarity or dependency among observations given the same treatment. When $\sigma_A^2$ is greater than zero some statistical relation must exist between pairs of score values within the possible treatment groups. As we saw in Section 13.9, hypotheses about the degree of relatedness can be tested via Model II. However, the form of relatedness that makes the simple Model II analysis inapplicable is most often a trend or serial relation, ordinarily implying nonindependence of the error terms. It is this sort of nonindependence that makes a special problem for studies involving repeated measurements of the same individuals.

Finally, it should be emphasized that the application of Model II analysis of variance depends on two kinds of random sampling: the treatments or factor levels themselves must be sampled at random, and then within each treatment group a random sample of individual observations must appear. The inferences drawn under this model are not strictly valid unless *both* forms of random sampling are actually carried out.

All in all, the Model II analysis of variance is more heavily dependent upon the assumption of normal distributions, both of treatment effects and of errors, than is Model I. In a way, one gets more for his money in a Model II one-way analysis: an inference is permitted that goes beyond the factor levels actually observed, interval estimates of strength of association can be made, and a general hypothesis about $\rho_I$ can be tested. None of these things have direct parallels in the fixed effects models. However, some of these "additional" inferences are paid for by relatively more restrictive assumptions.

## 13.11   TWO-FACTOR EXPERIMENTS WITH SAMPLING OF LEVELS

Now we turn to the analysis of experiments involving two factors, each of which is represented in the experiment only by a sample of its levels.

For example, suppose that a projective test involves ten cards administered individually to a subject. The subject must respond by giving as many free-associations to each card as he is able. These responses are scored in a number of ways, but the total number of responses is an important index of overall performance. The developer of this test has some idea that the *order* in which cards are presented has a bearing on the total number of responses given, and so he would like to see if this factor of order is an important one in accounting for variation in test performance. If it should turn out that order is important, he will try to find an order of presentation for the cards that will be optimal in evoking responses. Furthermore, this psychologist has worked out a standard set of instructions for test administrators, in the hope that administrator effects on performance are thereby made negligible. However, he would like to see if this is the case.

Here are two factors, order of presentation and test administrator, that may account for variance in total response to the test. Obviously, neither factor can be represented at all levels in any experiment, since there are exactly 3,628,800 different ways of presenting the ten cards, and a very large number of persons who might be trained to administer the test. Hence, the experimenter decides to conduct a study in which each of these factors will be sampled. From a single set of data he will be able to answer the question of the relative contribution to variance of each of the factors, as well as the secondary question of possible interaction between test administrator and order of presentation.

This hypothetical experiment will be developed as an example in Section 13.15. For the time being we will turn our attention to extending Model II to cover such situations.

## 13.12 MODEL II FOR TWO-FACTOR EXPERIMENTS

The two different factors in the experiment will be designated $A$ and $B$. A random sample of $C$ different levels of $A$ will be drawn, and shown as columns in the data table, and a random sample of $R$ different levels of $B$ will appear as the rows in the table. Within each combination shown by a cell of the data table, $n$ observations are to be made at random.

The score of individual $i$ in column $j$ and row $k$ of the table will be thought of as a sum:

$$Y_{ijk} = \mu + a_j + b_k + c_{jk} + e_{ijk}.$$

Here, $a_j$ is the random variable standing for the effect of the sample treatment appearing in the data table as column $j$, $b_k$ the random variable indicating the effect of the sample treatment in row $k$, and $c_{jk}$ is the random interaction effect associated with cell $jk$. The term $e_{ijk}$ is a random variable standing for the error effect of the observation of individual $i$ under the joint conditions indicated by column $j$ and row $k$. Observe that in this linear model all components of a score except the grand mean $\mu$ are values of *random variables*, the sampled effects.

The assumptions made are:

1. The $a_j$ are normally distributed random variables with mean zero and variance $\sigma_A^2$.
2. The $b_k$ are normally distributed with mean zero and variance $\sigma_B^2$.
3. The $c_{jk}$ are normally distributed with mean zero and variance $\sigma_{AB}^2$.
4. The $e_{ijk}$ are normally distributed with mean zero and variance $\sigma_e^2$.
5. The $a_j$, the $b_k$, the $c_{jk}$, and the $e_{ijk}$ are pair-wise independent.

## 13.13 THE MEAN SQUARES

The computations for the two-way analysis under Model II are exactly the same as for Model I (Section 12.28). Thus, the total sum of squares is partitioned into a sum of squares for rows, a sum of squares for columns, a sum of squares for interaction, and an error sum of squares.

On examining the mean squares, however, we will find that the expectations are quite different from those for Model I. Consider the mean square for rows. In terms of the model, Section 13.12,

$$\text{MS rows} = \frac{\sum_{k} Cn(M_k - M)^2}{R - 1}$$

where

$$M_k = \frac{\sum_{j} \sum_{i} (\mu + a_j + b_k + c_{jk} + e_{ijk})}{Cn}$$

$$= \mu + M_a + b_k + c_k + M_{ek} \qquad \text{[13.13.1]}$$

and

$$M_a = \frac{\sum_{j} a_j}{C} ; \qquad M_b = \frac{\sum_{k} b_k}{R}$$

$$b_k = \frac{\sum_{j} b_k}{C} ; \qquad a_j = \frac{\sum_{k} a_j}{R}$$

$$c_k = \frac{\sum_{j} c_{jk}}{C} ; \qquad c_j = \frac{\sum_{k} c_{jk}}{R}$$

$$M_{ek} = \frac{\sum_{j} \sum_{i} e_{ijk}}{Cn} ; \; M_{ej} = \frac{\sum_{k} \sum_{i} e_{ijk}}{Rn} .$$

Furthermore,

$$M = \frac{\sum_{k} \sum_{j} \sum_{i} (\mu + a_j + b_k + c_{jk} + e_{ijk})}{RCn}$$

$$= \mu + M_a + M_b + M_c + M_e \qquad \text{[13.13.2]}$$

where

$$M_c = \frac{\sum_{k} \sum_{j} c_{jk}}{RC} = \frac{\sum_{k} c_k}{R}$$

$$M_e = \frac{\sum_{k} \sum_{j} \sum_{i} e_{ijk}}{RCn} = \frac{\sum_{k} M_{ek}}{R} .$$

Then, for any row $k$,

$$(M_k - M)^2 = (b_k - M_b + c_k - M_c + M_{ek} - M_e)^2 . \qquad \text{[13.13.4*]}$$

At this point, one of the really important differences between Models I and II appears. You may recall that in Section 12.26 it was pointed out that for the fixed effects model the following things are assumed true of the interaction effects $\gamma_{jk}$:

$$\sum_j \gamma_{jk} = 0, \sum_k \gamma_{jk} = 0, \text{ and } \sum_j \sum_k \gamma_{jk} = 0.$$

That is, in Model I we assume that over the column treatments the interaction effects sum to zero, that over the row treatments interaction effects sum to zero, and that over both rows and columns these effects sum to zero. The net result is that in the sum of squares for, say, rows, only row effects and error can possibly be included:

$$(M_k - M)^2 = (\beta_k + M_{ek} - M_e)^2.$$

For the fixed effects model, any interaction effect cannot possibly contribute to the sum of squares for rows because this sum of squares is itself based on the data *summed* over columns, automatically making the interaction effects sum to zero. For the same reason, the sum of squares for columns does not include any of the interaction effects.

On the other hand, in Model II the set of $R$ row treatments represents a *sample* from a large set of possible such treatments, and the $C$ column treatments another sample from a large set. Here it is reasonable to assume that

$$E(c_{jk}) = 0$$
$$\phantom{E(c_{jk})} _j$$
$$E(c_{jk}) = 0$$
$$\phantom{E(c_{jk})} _k$$
$$E(c_{jk}) = 0.$$
$$\phantom{E(c_{jk})} _{jk}$$

That is, the expected value of the interaction term $c_{jk}$ is zero over *all possible* treatments that might have been selected for column $j$ with a fixed row treatment $k$. Furthermore, the expected value of the interaction term $c_{jk}$ is zero over all possible treatments that might have been selected for row $k$ with a fixed column treatment $j$. However, these requirements hold only when one considers *all possible* row or column treatments that might have been selected. Unlike the situation in the fixed effects model, *here there is no requirement at all that the interaction effects sum to zero over the particular set of $R$ row treatments or over the particular set of $C$ column treatments that just happened to appear in the sample.* For this reason, none of $c_k$ or $c_j$ or $M_c$ need be zero in any given set of data. The important consequence of this fact is that *the sum of squares for rows reflects deviations due not only to row treatment effects, but also to interaction effects.* In the same way *the sum of squares for columns includes both column and interaction effects.* This has a most important bearing on estimates and tests made under Model II, as we shall see.

Resuming the argument for the expected mean square for rows, we note that in expression **13.13.4** no term $a_j$ can appear in any one of the squares entering into the mean square, but that each such square includes a term $(c_k - M_c)$ due to interaction. As pointed out above, this is due to the fact that the values $c_{jk}$ summed over $j$ for any particular $k$ *need not* be zero. For this reason it can be shown that

$$E(\text{MS between rows}) = \sigma_e^2 + n\sigma_{AB}^2 + Cn\sigma_B^2. \qquad \textbf{[13.13.5*]}$$

Unlike the expectation for fixed effects, *here the mean square for rows estimates a weighted sum of the error variance, the variance due to row treatments, and the interaction variance,* $\sigma_{AB}^2$.

A parallel situation holds for factor $A$, represented by the columns:

$$E(\text{MS columns}) = E\,\frac{(\text{SS columns})}{C-1}$$
$$= \sigma_e^2 + n\sigma_{AB}^2 + Rn\sigma_A^2. \qquad [13.13.6*]$$

Turning to the expected value for the mean square interaction, we find that

$$E(\text{MS interaction}) = E\,\frac{(\text{SS interaction})}{(R-1)(C-1)}$$
$$= \sigma_e^2 + n\sigma_{AB}^2. \qquad [13.13.7*]$$

The expectation of the mean square error is, as always,

$$E(\text{MS error}) = E\,\frac{\left[\sum_j \sum_k \sum_i (e_{ijk} - M_e)^2\right]}{RC(n-1)} = \sigma_e^2. \qquad [13.13.8*]$$

## 13.14  HYPOTHESIS TESTING IN THE TWO-WAY ANALYSIS UNDER MODEL II

We have just seen that the expected values both for the mean square for rows and the mean square for columns are different in Model II from those in Model I. The practical implication of this fact is that the hypotheses of no row and no column effects are tested in a different way for this model than for Model I. Consider the test of the hypothesis

$$H_0\colon \sigma_A^2 = 0.$$

When this hypothesis is true, then

$$E(\text{MS columns}) = \sigma_e^2 + n\sigma_{AB}^2 \qquad [13.14.1*]$$

which is *not* the same as the expectation of mean square error, but rather that of *mean square interaction:*

$$E(\text{MS interaction}) = \sigma_e^2 + n\sigma_{AB}^2. \qquad [13.14.2*]$$

These two mean squares (MS columns and MS interaction) can be shown to be independent, and when each is divided by $\sigma_e^2 + n\sigma_{AB}^2$, each is distributed as $\chi^2$ divided by degrees of freedom. Thus, the hypothesis of no column effects is usually tested by

$$F = \frac{\text{MS columns}}{\text{MS interaction}} \qquad [13.14.3\dagger]$$

with $C-1$ and $(R-1)(C-1)$ degrees of freedom.

In the same way, the hypothesis

$$H_0: \sigma_B^2 = 0$$

is tested by a comparison of MS rows with the interaction MS, since if this hypothesis is true,

$$E(\text{MS rows}) = \sigma_e^2 + n\sigma_{AB}^2, \qquad \text{[13.14.4*]}$$

which is the same as the expected value of the mean square for interaction. The hypothesis is tested by the ratio

$$F = \frac{\text{MS between rows}}{\text{MS interaction}}, \qquad \text{[13.14.5†]}$$

with $R - 1$ and $(R - 1)(C - 1)$ degrees of freedom. The hypothesis of no interaction is tested just as for Model I:

$$H_0: \sigma_{AB}^2 = 0$$

tested by

$$F = \frac{\text{MS interaction}}{\text{MS error}} \qquad \text{[13.14.6†]}$$

with $(R - 1)(C - 1)$ and $RC(n - 1)$ degrees of freedom.

It should be emphasized that the test of row and column effects against interaction is really appropriate *only* when the factors have been randomly sampled, as in Model II (and in some instances of the mixed models introduced in sections to follow). When the experiment qualifies for Model I, the ratio of the mean square for a factor to the interaction mean square is *not necessarily* distributed as $F$, even when the null hypothesis is true. This is one of the major practical distinctions between the fixed effects and the random effects models.

There is one situation, however, when the main effects are not tested against interaction in Model II. This occurs when the experimenter has decided that the interaction variance $\sigma_{AB}^2$ is zero. There is either some theoretical or some empirical reason to believe that interaction effects should not occur, or there is *strong* evidence for no interaction in the data. Of course, there is a difficult problem involved in deciding when there really *is* strong evidence that interaction effects do not exist. When the mean square for interaction is equal to or less than the mean square for error, we are ordinarily quite justified in reaching this conclusion. However, a simple rule that applies to a broad class of situations is that due to Paull (1950): **when each of the mean squares for error and for interaction has a number of degrees of freedom greater than six, then pool these into a combined estimate of error when the $F$ ratio for interaction is less than 2.00.**

When there is sufficient evidence that no interaction effects exist, the two sums of squares, error and interaction, are pooled as follows:

$$\text{pooled MS error} = \frac{\text{SS interaction} + \text{SS error}}{(R - 1)(C - 1) + RC(n - 1)}. \qquad \text{[13.14.7†]}$$

When $\sigma_{AB}^2 = 0$, the expectation of this pooled MS error is $\sigma_e^2$. The expectation of

MS rows is also $\sigma_e^2$ under the hypothesis of no row effects, so that the test may be carried out by use of the ratio

$$F = \frac{\text{MS rows}}{\text{pooled MS error}}$$

[**13.14.8**†]

with $R - 1$ and $RCn - R - C + 1$ degrees of freedom. In the same way a test of no column effects is carried out by

$$F = \frac{\text{MS columns}}{\text{pooled MS error}},$$

[**13.14.9**†]

with $C - 1$ and $RCn - R - C + 1$ degrees of freedom. This procedure is *not* recommended, however, unless the evidence for no interaction effects is strong enough to satisfy a criterion such as Paull's.

## 13.15 AN EXAMPLE

Suppose that developer of the projective test mentioned in Section 13.11 actually carried out the experiment. Recall that this study was designed to test both for the presence of effects associated with order of presentation and with particular administrators of the test. Four persons were selected at random from among psychologists and trained to administer the test. Also, four orders of presentation of the test were selected at random. Each administrator gave the test to a different pair of randomly selected normal adults under each one of the selected order conditions, so that a total of thirty-two different test performances were observed in all. The dependent variable was the total number of responses a subject gave to the test cards. The experimenter was prepared to assume normal distributions of order effects, of administrator effects, of interaction effects, and

**Table 13.15.1**

| Order | Administrator | | | | |
| | 1 | 2 | 3 | 4 | *Totals* |
|---|---|---|---|---|---|
| I | 26 | 30 | 25 | 28 | |
| | 25 | 33 | 23 | 30 | 220 |
| II | 26 | 25 | 27 | 27 | |
| | 24 | 33 | 17 | 26 | 205 |
| III | 33 | 26 | 30 | 31 | |
| | 27 | 32 | 24 | 26 | 229 |
| IV | 36 | 37 | 37 | 39 | |
| | 28 | 42 | 33 | 25 | 277 |
| Totals | 225 | 258 | 216 | 232 | 931 |

of error. The data were as shown in Table 13.15.1. The $\alpha$ level chosen for the test of each hypothesis was .05.

The analysis proceeds in the usual manner for two-way designs (Section 12.31):

$$\text{SS total} = \sum_j \sum_k \sum_i Y_{ijk}^2 - \frac{\left(\sum_j \sum_k \sum_i Y_{ijk}\right)^2}{N}$$

$$= 27965 - \frac{(931)^2}{32}$$

$$= 878.7$$

$$\text{SS rows} = \frac{\sum_k \left(\sum_j \sum_i Y_{ijk}\right)^2}{Cn} - \frac{\left(\sum_j \sum_k \sum_i Y_{ijk}\right)^2}{N}$$

$$= \frac{(220)^2 + \cdots + (277)^2}{8} - \frac{(931)^2}{32} = 363.0$$

$$\text{SS columns} = \frac{\sum_j \left(\sum_k \sum_i Y_{ijk}\right)^2}{Rn} - \frac{\left(\sum_j \sum_k \sum_i Y_{ijk}\right)^2}{N}$$

$$= \frac{(225)^2 + \cdots + (232)^2}{8} - \frac{(931)^2}{32} = 122.3$$

$$\text{SS error} = \sum_j \sum_k \sum_i Y_{ijk}^2 - \frac{\sum_j \sum_k \left(\sum_i Y_{ijk}\right)^2}{n}$$

$$= 27965 - \frac{(51)^2 + (50)^2 + \cdots + (64)^2}{2}$$

$$= 310.5$$

$$\text{SS interaction} = \text{SS total} - \text{SS rows} - \text{SS columns} - \text{SS error}$$

$$= 878.7 - 363.0 - 122.3 - 310.5 = 82.9.$$

Table 13.15.2 summarizes the analysis.

**Table 13.15.2**

| Source | SS | df | MS | E(MS) | F |
|--------|-----|-----|------|--------|-----|
| Rows (orders) | 363.0 | 3 | 121.0 | $\sigma_e^2 + 2\sigma_{AB}^2 + 8\sigma_B^2$ | $\left(\dfrac{121.0}{15.7} = 7.7\right)$ |
| Columns (admin.) | 122.3 | 3 | 40.8 | $\sigma_e^2 + 2\sigma_{AB}^2 + 8\sigma_A^2$ | $\left(\dfrac{40.8}{15.7} = 2.6\right)$ |
| Interaction | 82.9 | 9 | 9.2 | $\sigma_e^2 + 2\sigma_{AB}^2$ | |
| Error | 310.5 | 16 | 19.4 | $\sigma_e^2$ | |
| Totals | 878.7 | 31 | | | |

Ordinarily, the tests both for row and for column effects would be carried out by dividing the mean square for rows or columns by mean square interaction. However, it is immediately apparent that here the mean square for error is larger than mean square for interaction, so that the estimate of $\sigma_{AB}^2$ is zero. Notice that the Paull criterion is also satisfied. Thus, we find

$$\text{pooled MS error} = \frac{82.9 + 310.5}{9 + 16} = 15.7,$$

which has $9 + 16$ or 25 degrees of freedom.

We test for row effects by finding

$$F = \frac{121.0}{15.7} = 7.7.$$

For 3 and 25 degrees of freedom, this value exceeds that required for the .05 level, and so the hypothesis of no row effects is rejected. The same procedure is carried out for columns, and he·e

$$F = \frac{\text{MS columns}}{\text{pooled MS error}} = 2.6$$

for 3 and 25 degrees of freedom. This fails to reach the value of 2.99 required to reject the null hypothesis. (These $F$ values are enclosed in parenthesis in the summary table to show that they are not obtained in the usual way. In reports of such data, the $F$ tests would usually be accompanied by an explanatory footnote to the summary table.)

The conclusions from the experiment are, then, as follows:

1. Order does seem to have an effect on the total number of responses given in the test.
2. There is insufficient evidence to determine if true administrator differences exist.
3. There is virtually no evidence for administrator-order interaction.

Incidentally, the comment in Section 12.36 about the statistical dependency of $F$ tests based on the same denominator mean square applies to these results. The prior probability that at least one of the three significance tests carried out leads to a Type I error is not equal to the nominal $\alpha$ value of .05, but rather is some undetermined value between .05 and .15. Similarly, the proportion of significant results representing Type I error need not be .05. There is no simple way of determining how much the significance level given by one of these tests depends on the levels given by the others.

## 13.16   POINT ESTIMATION OF VARIANCE COMPONENTS

The four expressions in the $E(\text{MS})$ column of the summary table allow us to estimate the components of variance, as follows:

$$\text{est. } \sigma_B^2 = \frac{\text{MS rows} - \text{MS interaction}}{Cn} \qquad [\textbf{13.16.1}\dagger]$$

$$\text{est. } \sigma_A^2 = \frac{\text{MS columns} - \text{MS interaction}}{Rn} \qquad [\textbf{13.16.2}\dagger]$$

$$\text{est. } \sigma_{AB}^2 = \frac{\text{MS interaction} - \text{MS error}}{n} \qquad [\textbf{13.16.3}\dagger]$$

$$\text{est. } \sigma_e^2 = \text{MS error.} \qquad [\textbf{13.16.4}\dagger]$$

If any of the first three estimates turn out to be negative in sign, then that component is estimated to be zero.

In the example above, the estimate of $\sigma_{AB}^2$ is zero, and the pooled MS error was taken to represent $\sigma_e^2$. Thus, to be consistent, one should estimate the other components as follows:

$$\text{est. } \sigma_B^2 = \frac{\text{MS rows} - \text{pooled MS error}}{Cn}$$

$$= \frac{121.0 - 15.7}{8} = 13.16$$

$$\text{est. } \sigma_A^2 = \frac{40.8 - 15.7}{8} = 3.14$$

$$\text{est. } \sigma_e^2 = 15.7.$$

The proportion of variance accounted for by factor $B$ (rows) is estimated from

$$\frac{\text{est. } \sigma_B^2}{\text{est. } (\sigma_e^2 + \sigma_{AB}^2 + \sigma_A^2 + \sigma_B^2)} = \frac{13.16}{15.7 + 0 + 13.16 + 3.14} = .41.$$

An estimated 41 percent of the variance in total response is attributable to order of presentation of this projective test.

For factor $A$ (columns) the estimated proportion of variance accounted for is

$$\frac{3.14}{15.7 + 0 + 13.16 + 3.14} = .098$$

so that if factor $A$ accounts for any variance at all, our best guess is that this is less than 10 percent of the total variance.

It is possible to find a confidence interval for

$$\theta = \frac{\sigma_A^2}{\sigma_e^2 + n\sigma_{AB}^2}$$

by the method of Section 13.8. Unfortunately, this confidence interval cannot be turned directly into a confidence interval for proportion of variance accounted for, as in the one-way case. Thus, its use is rather more limited. Approximate confidence intervals for the variance components $\sigma_A^2$, $\sigma_B^2$, and so forth, can be found by methods outlined in Scheffé (1959, pp. 231–235).

## 13.17   MODEL III: A MIXED MODEL

Multifactor experiments involving Model II are relatively rare in psychological research. It is far more common to encounter experiments where one or more factors have fixed levels and the remaining factors are sampled. This situation calls for a third model of data, in which each individual observation results in a score that is a sum of *both* fixed and random effects. Obviously, mixed models such as this apply only to experiments where two or more factors are under study.

As an example of an experiment fitting a mixed model, suppose that a study is concerned with the muscular tension induced in subjects by three different varieties of task. The subject performs using pencil and paper with the preferred hand, meanwhile holding the bulb of a sensitive pressure recording gauge in the other. The mean reading on this gauge during the performance provides the dependent variable score. Three separate kinds of tasks are administered: in one type the subject solves relatively complicated problems in arithmetic; in a second type he writes a short, imaginative, composition; and in the third he must make a careful tracing of a line drawing.

Now it is obvious that individual differences may exist among subjects with respect to the characteristic pressure each will exert with the non-preferred hand. Furthermore, over the three tasks, some systematic, trial-related, change might occur. For these reasons the experimenter decides to use the same subjects over all three tasks, and to give each type of task twice to each subject, making a total of six performances to be carried out by any subject. The actual order of presentation for these six performances is chosen at random and separately for each subject. After a preliminary period of practice on a neutral task designed to accustom him to the experimental arrangement, each subject carries out the six performances, two of each type, in the random order previously selected for him. Some six subjects are selected at random for participation in this experiment.

This experiment illustrates several things. In the first place, the experimenter is interested in three, and only three, types of task that might be given to the subject. Therefore the factor of "tasks" is properly considered to be composed of three fixed levels; this is a fixed effects factor. On the other hand, the experimenter is not at all interested in any particular subject or small set of subjects, but rather in the large set of potential subjects who might be observed under these task conditions. Granted that the only subjects about whom an inference is to be made are those of a certain age, sex, ability to understand instructions, and so forth, the experimenter would, nevertheless, like to extend his inference to all possible such subjects. The factor of "subjects" consists of a great many possible levels, from which only a few are selected at random for representation in the experiment. Hence, "subjects" corresponds to a random effects factor.

Notice that by giving each type of problem to each subject, a form of control over individual differences among subjects is introduced, since a possi-

bility such that all of the relaxed, easy-going subjects in the sample might acci-
dentally pile up in one experimental condition, and all of the nervous wrecks in
another, is thereby eliminated. We will have more to say about this form of
experimental control in succeeding sections.

Finally, the experimenter knows that the order in which a subject
receives the various tasks and repetitions of tasks might also account for variance
in the experiment. Since he cannot use enough subjects to introduce this factor
as a systematic feature of the experiment, he does the next best thing by giving
each subject a different, randomly selected, order of performance of the tasks
and their repetitions. In this way, the possible effects of order are effectively
"mixed up" with the possible effects of individual subjects; the sampled factor
actually may be regarded as "subject-order" combinations. However, this is irrelevant to the purposes of the experimenter, who is most interested in possible effects
associated with the tasks, rather than in the study of individual differences among
subjects.

This is a fairly straight-forward and typical example of an experiment calling for a mixed model of the analysis of variance. Next we will turn to
a study of the model itself before pursuing this example further. We shall find
that the combination of fixed and random effects in the same experiment requires
no change at all in the computational procedures for a simple two-factor design
such as this. However, it does make an important difference in the $F$ ratios
employed to test for the different effects.

### 13.18　A MIXED MODEL FOR A TWO-FACTOR EXPERIMENT

Let the factor having fixed levels be labeled $A$, and represented by
the columns of the table, and let the randomly sampled factor be $B$, and shown
by the rows of the data table. Now it is assumed that

$$Y_{ijk} = \mu + \alpha_j + b_k + c_{jk} + e_{ijk} \qquad [13.18.1*]$$

where $\alpha_j$ is the fixed effect of the treatment indicated by the column $j$, $b_k$ is the
random variable associated with the $k$th row, $c_{jk}$ the random interaction effect
operating in the cell $jk$, and $e_{ijk}$ is the random error associated with observation
$i$ in the cell $jk$. We make the following assumptions.

1. The $b_k$ and the $c_{jk}$ are jointly normal, each with mean of zero and with variances
   $\sigma_B^2$ and $\sigma_{AB}^2$ respectively.
2. The $e_{ijk}$ are normally distributed, with mean zero and variance $\sigma_e^2$.
3. The $e_{ijk}$ are independent of the $b_k$ and the $c_{jk}$.
4. Over the possible rows $k$, the degree of dependence between any pair of observations in different columns $j$ and $j'$ is the same for all pairs of columns.

This last assumption requires some elaboration. It will not, in general, be true that the observations within any *sampled* level (row) will be independent in this model. Observations in the same sample level from factor $B$ but

in different levels on factor $A$ (columns) may be dependent or related to some extent. Here we are assuming that over the possible levels of $B$, the degree of statistical relation is the same for observations in any pair of levels on $A$. This assumption is very questionable for many kinds of data, especially in psychological research, but it must be made to justify the test of $A$ effects given below. A much more advanced method of testing this hypothesis exactly without assumption 4 is given in Scheffé (1959, pp. 270–273). However, our discussion will be restricted to the case where assumption 4 is justified. When this assumption is very questionable, approximate, though conservative, procedures outlined in Winer (1962, p. 123) may be employed.

## 13.19 THE EXPECTED MEAN SQUARES IN A MIXED MODEL

The partition of the sum of squares and the calculation of the mean squares proceed exactly as for any two-way analysis of variance. However, let us look into the composition of the mean square between columns (the fixed effects factor) under the model outlined in Section 13.18. Basically, the mean square between columns is found from the squared deviations of column means from the general mean of the data. In the mixed model, the squared difference between $M_j$, the mean of a particular column $j$, and $M$, the general mean, can be thought of as having the following composition:

$$(M_j - M)^2 = (\alpha_j + M_b + c_j + M_{ej} - M_b - M_c - M_e)^2$$
$$= (\alpha_j + c_j - M_c + M_{ej} - M_e)^2.$$

Here, $M_b$, $c_j$, $M_{ej}$, and $M_e$ are all defined just as in Section 13.13. Notice that any deviation of a column mean from the grand mean includes not only the column effect and a mean error deviation, but also a deviation due to interaction effects, $c_j - M_c$. The reason for this is exactly the same as given for the occurrence of interaction effects in expression **13.13.4**: there is no requirement at all that interaction effects must sum to zero across rows when the row treatment effects, and thus the interaction effects, are only a random sample of such effects. Thus column means, formed by summing observations across rows, include not only the fixed column effects, but also some of the random interaction effects as well.

For this reason, given the mean square for columns calculated in the usual way, it can be shown that the expectation for this mean square is

$$E(\text{MS columns}) = \sigma_e^2 + n\sigma_{AB}^2 + \frac{Rn\left(\sum_j \alpha_j^2\right)}{C - 1}. \qquad \textbf{[13.19.1*]}$$

In Model III, the mean square for columns (the fixed effects factor) is an estimate of a weighted sum of the error variance, the sum of the squared effects associated with the column factor itself, *and* the interaction variance.

This often strikes students as a violation of intuition, but a little reflection should convince you that this is reasonable. Consider the example of Section 13.17 once again. Why should the means corresponding to the different tasks (columns) in the experiment tend to differ? In the first place there actually may be systematic differences between the population means, or effects, connected with the different tasks. Furthermore, since we deal only with sample means rather than with population means, a certain amount of random error may enter into the average differences we observe between the tasks. However, there is still another reason why the column means might differ in any sample. Any given subject might find one or two of the tasks quite stressful and tension-producing and the others quite easy. Furthermore, the pattern of such hard and easy tasks might vary over subjects, so that the effect that a task has *within* a particular subject might be different across subjects. Subject 1 finds arithmetic problems extremely challenging, although imaginative composition is a breeze for him. On the other hand, subject 2 finds arithmetic problems no challenge at all, but is brought to a standstill when faced with a writing task. Such systematic differences among the tasks *within* particular subjects, but differing from one subject to another, is what we mean by "subject by task interaction." Since subjects were sampled for the experiment, it is entirely possible for such interaction effects to tend to "pile up" in one or another of the columns of the data table, and thus to contribute to the apparent differences between means for the tasks; whether or not this happens depends on the particular sample of subjects we obtain. Such apparent differences among means need not be due to the main effects $\alpha_j$ of the tasks themselves, since interaction effects representing differences within *particular* subjects need not have any special connection with the differences between means for the tasks across *all possible* subjects. On the other hand, this is not the same as random error, since these differences do reflect systematic effects occurring in the experiment. The presence of interaction effects in the deviation of a column mean $M_j$ from the general mean $M$ is actually due to the circumstance that one set of factor levels (subjects) is sampled, so that the interaction effects are under no necessity to "cancel out" in the particular sample drawn.

Now let us examine the composition of the mean square for rows (the sampled factor). This mean square is based on the squared deviation of each row mean, $M_k$, from the general sample mean $M$. Applying the model of Section 13.18 once again we find that

$$(M_k - M)^2 = (b_k + M_{ek} - M_b - M_e)^2.$$

Here, the deviation depends only on row effects and upon error deviation; the interaction effects do not appear in any such deviation making up the mean square for rows.

The reason for the absence of interaction effects in the mean square for rows is really very simple. You may recall from Section 13.13 that when the interaction effects $c_{jk}$ were regarded as sampled, we assumed that the expected values for the interaction effects over rows, over columns, and row and column combinations, should be zero. The same assumption holds here, and in particular we are assuming that for a given row $k$

$$E(c_{jk}) = 0,$$
$$\quad_{j}$$

the expectation of $c_{jk}$ over all possible levels that might appear as column $j$ is zero. However, all possible column treatments under consideration are actually included among those used in the experiment. This implies that

$$E(c_{jk}) = \frac{\sum_{j} c_{jk}}{C} = 0.$$
$$\quad_{j}$$

Since this is true, then within any given row the sum of the $c_{jk}$ values taken over columns must be zero. Because the columns factor is *not* sampled, and each possible column treatment is actually represented in the experiment, interaction effects within rows *do* cancel out and sum to zero. Thus, $c_k = 0$ and $M_c = 0$ in the mixed model.

As a result it can be shown that

$$E(\text{MS rows}) = \sigma_e^2 + Cn\sigma_B^2, \qquad \text{[13.19.2*]}$$

the mean square for rows estimates a weighted sum of the error variance and the variance attributable to the sampled factor $B$.

The interaction variance is based on the squared difference between the deviation from $M$ for the mean of each cell $jk$ in the data table, and the corresponding row mean's and column mean's deviations:

$$[(M_{jk} - M) - (M_k - M) - (M_j - M)]^2 = (M_{jk} - M_k - M_j + M)^2.$$

In terms of our mixed model:

$$(M_{jk} - M_k - M_j + M)^2 = (\alpha_j + b_k + c_{jk} + M_{ejk} - b_k - M_{ek} - \alpha_j - c_j$$
$$- M_b - M_{ej} + M_b + M_e)^2$$
$$= (c_{jk} - c_j + M_{ejk} - M_{ek} - M_{ej} + M_e)^2.$$

Observe that any such deviation depends only on interaction effects and on error. Then it can be shown that

$$E(\text{MS interaction}) = \sigma_e^2 + n\sigma_{AB}^2. \qquad \text{[13.19.3*]}$$

That is, the interaction mean square is an estimate of a weighted sum of the error variance and the interaction variance.

When the hypothesis of no column effects is true, so that $\alpha_j = 0$ for each of the column treatments $j$, then

$$E(\text{MS columns}) = \sigma_e^2 + n\sigma_{AB}^2. \qquad \text{[13.19.4*]}$$

Notice that this is exactly the same as the expectation for the MS interaction. Under our assumptions (particularly assumption 4) the ratio

$$F = \frac{\text{MS columns}}{\text{MS interaction}} \qquad \text{[13.19.5†]}$$

with $C - 1$ and $(R - 1)(C - 1)$ degrees of freedom provides an appropriate test of the hypothesis of no column effects. *Be careful to notice that it is the fixed effects factor that is tested against interaction in this mixed model.*

On the other hand, when the hypothesis of no row effects is true,

$$E(\text{MS rows}) = \sigma_e^2, \qquad \text{[13.19.6*]}$$

which is the same as

$$E(\text{MS error}) = \sigma_e^2.$$

Then the test for the existence of row effects (that is a test of $H_0: \sigma_B^2 = 0$) is given by

$$F = \frac{\text{MS rows}}{\text{MS error}} \qquad \text{[13.19.7†]}$$

with $R - 1$ and $RC(n - 1)$ degrees of freedom.

Thus, we see that there are two distinctly different kinds of $F$ tests employed in the analysis of variance for this mixed model: the hypothesis that all the fixed effects are zero is tested by comparing the mean square for that factor against the mean square for interaction. On the other hand, the hypothesis associated with the random effects factor is tested by comparing its associated mean square with the mean square for error. *The important procedural differences among these three models thus have to do with the way in which hypotheses are tested, and especially with the denominators used in the various F ratios.*

The test for interaction in a two-way analysis is the same for all three models:

$$F = \frac{\text{MS interaction}}{\text{MS error}}, \qquad \text{[13 19.8†]}$$

with $(R - 1)(C - 1)$ and $RC(n - 1)$ degrees of freedom.

When there is good reason to believe that interaction effects do not exist, there is some advantage in pooling the interaction and the error sums of squares to get a new estimate of the error variance. This is done exactly as outlined in Section 13.14, and Paull's rule is a handy device for deciding when a pooled estimated of error should be used in this model as well.

## 13.20 An Example Fitting Model III

Suppose that the experiment outlined in Section 13.17 is carried out, and that the data turn out as shown in Table 13.20.1. In this table, the two values appearing for each combination of a subject with a task represent the two performances of that task by the subject. Although the task on each of these two trials is the same, the concrete problem given to the subject is different on the repetition of the task. Furthermore, since the order of all six performances is randomized individually for each subject, so that the two distinct problems within a task appear in a randomly chosen order, the experimenter is prepared to regard these scores as two independent observations under the same task condition. That is, the repetition of the task by a subject is regarded as constituting an independent replication of the experiment.

**Table 13.20.1**

| Subjects | Tasks | | | Total |
|---|---|---|---|---|
| | *I* | *II* | *III* | |
| 1 | 7.8 | 11.1 | 11.7 | |
| | 8.7 | 12.0 | 10.0 | |
| | 16.5 | 23.1 | 21.7 | 61.3 |
| 2 | 8.0 | 11.3 | 9.8 | |
| | 9.2 | 10.6 | 11.9 | |
| | 17.2 | 21.9 | 21.7 | 60.8 |
| 3 | 4.0 | 9.8 | 11.7 | |
| | 6.9 | 10.1 | 12.6 | |
| | 10.9 | 19.9 | 24.3 | 55.1 |
| 4 | 10.3 | 11.4 | 7.9 | |
| | 9.4 | 10.5 | 8.1 | |
| | 19.7 | 21.9 | 16.0 | 57.6 |
| 5 | 9.3 | 13.0 | 8.3 | |
| | 10.6 | 11.7 | 7.9 | |
| | 19.9 | 24.7 | 16.2 | 60.8 |
| 6 | 9.5 | 12.2 | 8.6 | |
| | 9.8 | 12.3 | 10.5 | |
| | 19.3 | 24.5 | 19.1 | 62.9 |
| Totals | 103.5 | 136.0 | 119.0 | 358.5 |

The .05 level is chosen for $\alpha$, and the analysis proceeds as follows:

$$\text{SS total} = (7.8)^2 + \cdots + (10.5)^2 - \frac{(358.5)^2}{36} = 123.57$$

$$\text{SS columns} = \frac{(103.5)^2 + (136.0)^2 + (119.0)^2}{12} - \frac{(358.5)^2}{36} = 44.04$$

$$\text{SS rows} = \frac{(61.3)^2 + \cdots + (62.9)^2}{6} - \frac{(358.5)^2}{36} = 6.79$$

$$\text{SS error} = (7.8)^2 + \cdots + (10.5)^2 - \frac{(16.5)^2 + \cdots + (19.1)^2}{2}$$

$$= 14.53$$

$$\text{SS interaction} = 123.57 - 44.04 - 6.79 - 14.53 = 58.21.$$

Table 13.20.2 is the summary table for this analysis.

**Table 13.20.2**

| Source | SS | df | MS | E(MS) | F |
|--------|----|----|----|----|----|
| Columns (tasks) | 44.04 | 2 | 22.02 | $\sigma_e^2 + 2\sigma_{AB}^2 + \dfrac{12\sum_j \alpha_j}{2}$ | 3.78 |
| Rows (subjects) | 6.79 | 5 | 1.36 | $\sigma_e^2 + 6\sigma_B^2$ | 1.68 |
| Interaction (tasks by subjects) | 58.21 | 10 | 5.82 | $\sigma_e^2 + 2\sigma_{AB}^2$ | 7.19 |
| Error | 14.53 | 18 | .81 | $\sigma_e^2$ | |
| Total | 123.57 | 35 | | | |

For 2 and 10 degrees of freedom an $F$ value of 4.10 is required for significance, so that the hypothesis of no column effects is *not* rejected. Notice that the $F$ ratio for columns is formed by dividing the column mean square by the mean square for interaction. If this experiment had been incorrectly analyzed under Model I, quite a different conclusion would have been reached; this illustrates the importance of using the proper model in testing hypotheses.

For 5 and 18 degrees of freedom an $F$ value of 2.77 is required in order to reject the null hypothesis at the 5 percent level. The $F$ ratio formed by the mean square for rows over the mean square error gives a value smaller than this, so that the hypothesis of no subject effects is also not rejected.

On the other hand, the $F$ test for interaction exceeds the required $F$ of 2.41, and the hypothesis of no interaction *is* rejected.

In summary, there is insufficient evidence to permit us to conclude either that there are task effects or that subject effects exist in this experiment. There is, however, fairly strong evidence for the presence of interaction effects. It stands to reason that there is something about the combination of a particular subject with a particular task that accounts for variance in the data. Thus, within subjects, task differences apparently exist, but these tend to be different for different subjects. Similarly, subject differences may exist within tasks, but these intersubject differences tend to vary across the three tasks. In this light, the findings of this study seem very trivial: they suggest that if you want to say how these tasks differ, you must specify the subject to whom the tasks are given. Of course, the usual qualification holds: this result might reflect only sampling error, or the influence of some uncontrolled aspect of the study.

## 13.21 VARIANCE ESTIMATION IN MODEL III

Just as in Model I, the best estimate of any one of the fixed effects is given by the difference between the treatment mean and the grand mean in the sample:

$$E(M_j - M) = \alpha_j.$$

Notice, however, that in the example given above, since interaction effects seem to exist with the *sampled* factor, such estimates of main effects have little or no practical use. In a two-way design such as the example the variance component associated with the random effects can be estimated by:

$$\text{est. } \sigma_B^2 = \frac{\text{MS rows} - \text{MS error}}{Cn} \qquad [13.21.1\dagger]$$

and that for interaction by:

$$\text{est. } \sigma_{AB}^2 = \frac{\text{MS interaction} - \text{MS error}}{n}. \qquad [13.21.2\dagger]$$

## 13.22   SOME CONNECTIONS AMONG THE THREE MODELS

Up to this point, the question of the number of possible treatments or levels from which we sample has been skimmed over rather lightly. However, the time has come to consider the situation where one actually knows the number of distinctly different levels of the factor from which he samples. This question was unimportant for our development of a test for the simple one-way analysis under the random effects model, although we later found it necessary to assume a normal distribution of effects, implying an infinite number of factor levels, in the tests and interval-estimation procedures of Sections 13.8 and 13.9. Similar normality assumptions are necessary in the two-factor situations for both Models II and III.

Now we will consider a possible situation where the two factors of the experiment are each represented by a sampling of levels, and where something is known of the number of the possible such levels for each. Suppose that the factor shown as columns in the data table is represented by some $C$ randomly selected levels from among a total of some $V$ possible levels. The factor shown as rows is represented by some $R$ levels selected at random from among some $U$ possibilities. Both $U$ and $V$ are here thought of as known, finite, numbers. Let any particular level that might be selected for inclusion among the columns be denoted by $v$, and any particular one of the possible levels for rows by $u$. Returning to the notation of Section 13.1 once again, a possible column effect can be symbolized by $a(v)$, and a possible row effect by $b(u)$. A possible interaction effect associated with a combination $(v,u)$ from among the $VU$ possible such combinations can be denoted by $c(v,u)$. Now suppose that we define the true variance due to the columns factor $A$ as

$$\sigma_A^2 = \frac{\sum_v [a(v)]^2}{V - 1},$$

that for the factor $B$ represented by the rows as

$$\sigma_B^2 = \frac{\sum_u [b(u)]^2}{U - 1},$$

and the true interaction variance as

$$\sigma_{AB}^2 = \frac{\sum_v \sum_u [c(v,u)]^2}{(U - 1)(V - 1)}.$$

Under these conditions the expectations of the mean squares become:

$$E(\text{MS columns}) = \sigma_e^2 + n\left(1 - \frac{R}{U}\right)\sigma_{AB}^2 + nR\sigma_A^2$$

$$E(\text{MS rows}) = \sigma_e^2 + n\left(1 - \frac{C}{V}\right)\sigma_{AB}^2 + nC\sigma_B^2$$

$$E(\text{MS interaction}) = \sigma_e^2 + n\sigma_{AB}^2$$

$$E(\text{MS error}) = \sigma_e^2$$

Viewing the expected mean squares in this way lets us show the connections between Models I, II, and III very simply. Suppose first of all that $V = C$ and $U = R$, so that the sample of $C$ column levels completely exhausts the set of possible levels for that factor, and the sample of $R$ row levels exhausts the possible levels for factor $B$. Then, letting

$$a(v) = a(v_j) = \alpha_j,$$

and

$$b(u) = b(u_k) = \beta_k,$$

the expectations given above become

$$E(\text{MS columns}) = \sigma_e^2 + \frac{nR \sum_j \alpha_j^2}{C - 1}$$

$$E(\text{MS rows}) = \sigma_e^2 + \frac{nC \sum_k \beta_k^2}{R - 1}$$

$$E(\text{MS interaction}) = \sigma_e^2 + \frac{n \sum_j \sum_k \gamma_{jk}^2}{(R - 1)(C - 1)}$$

$$E(\text{MS error}) = \sigma_e^2.$$

These are precisely the expected mean squares for the fixed effect Model I found in Chapter 12. This illustrates once again that when both sets of factor levels exhaust the possible levels that might appear in the experiment, Model I applies.

On the other hand, suppose that both $U$ and $V$ are thought of as infinitely large numbers, so that infinitely many possibilities exist both for the row levels and for the column levels. Here the expected mean squares become:

$$E(\text{MS columns}) = \sigma_e^2 + n\sigma_{AB}^2 + nR\sigma_A^2$$
$$E(\text{MS rows}) = \sigma_e^2 + n\sigma_{AB}^2 + nC\sigma_B^2$$
$$E(\text{MS interaction}) = \sigma_e^2 + n\sigma_{AB}^2$$
$$E(\text{MS error}) = \sigma_e^2.$$

These are the mean square expectations found in Section 13.13 for Model II, where we assumed that both rows and columns represented samples from possible sets of levels of (practically) infinite size.

Finally, suppose that the levels of factor $A$ (the columns) exhaust the possible levels for this factor, but that the levels for factor $B$ are a sample from among an infinite number of such levels. Then the expected mean squares are:

$$E(\text{MS columns}) = \sigma_e^2 + n\sigma_{AB}^2 + \frac{nR \sum_j \alpha_j^2}{C - 1}$$
$$E(\text{MS rows}) = \sigma_e^2 + nC\sigma_B^2$$
$$E(\text{MS interaction}) = \sigma_e^2 + n\sigma_{AB}^2$$
$$E(\text{MS error}) = \sigma_e^2.$$

These are the expectations for mean squares found in Section 13.19 under Model III, a mixed model.

This is a useful way to visualize the similarities and differences between these three models for the analysis of variance. The essential differences between these models depend on the conception each embodies of number of possible treatments or factor-levels that might be selected for inclusion in the actual experiment.

## 13.23 RANDOMIZATION IN EXPERIMENTS

The basic statistical tools of the experimenter are randomization and control. Randomization enters into the experiment in at least two different ways. The actual individuals observed in any sample may differ in any number of ways from the "typical" individual in the population as a whole. It is entirely possible to obtain a sample of $N$ individuals who are "peculiar" as compared with the population they represent, and the conclusions reached from this sample need not be indicative of what the population as a whole tends to be like. By sampling at random from the population, the experimenter is able to identify the peculiarities of his sample with random error, and to allow for the possibility of an atypical sample in his conclusions. Furthermore, given some sample it will always be true that factors other than the ones manipulated by the experimenter will contribute to the observed differences between subjects in the particular situation. If it should happen that some extraneous factor operates unevenly over several treatment groups or over different subjects, this can create spurious differences, or mask true effects in the data. Such a factor is a "nuisance-factor," playing a role analogous to "noise" in communication. Randomization of subjects over treatments is one device for "scattering" the effects of these nuisance factors through the data. Often, when particular nuisance factors are known, levels of these factors are scattered at random throughout the design. In order to randomize his experiment, the researcher uses some scheme such as a table of random numbers to allot individual subjects to experimental groups or nuisance levels to subgroups in a purely random, unsystematic, "chancy" way. By randomization, the possibility of "pile-ups" of nuisance effects in particular treatment groups is identified with random error, and the experimenter can rest assured that overall repetitions of his experiment under the same conditions, true effects will eventually emerge if they exist.

Every experiment is randomized to some extent. A study having one or more experimental factors and certain constant controls where every other factor contributing to variance is randomized is ordinarily called a **fully randomized** design: usually a random sample is drawn, and then subjects are allotted to treatments or treatment combinations purely at random. In addition, levels of one or more nuisance factors may be assigned at random. Most of the experiments used as examples in Chapter 12 were of this type. Furthermore, many other experiments fitting either the fixed effects or the random effects models can also be thought of in this way if nature or some other agency is conceived as carrying out the random assignment of individuals to groups.

On the other hand, sometimes it is advantageous to the experimenter *not* to randomize the effects of particular nuisance factors, but rather to represent them systematically in his experiment. These nuisance factors are treated as though they were experimental factors, when actually the purpose of representing them in the experiment in the first place is to control these factors and thereby reduce error variance. It should be obvious from our discussion of the indices $\omega^2$ and $\rho_I$ that deliberate introduction of any systematic effects that account for a portion of the variance $\sigma_Y^2$ must also *reduce* the error variance $\sigma_e^2$. That is, the true variance of any dependent variable is thought of as a sum of components:

$$\sigma_Y^2 = \text{(the variance attributable to systematic features of the experiment)}$$
$$+ \text{(the variance attributable to unsystematically represented factors).}$$

The more *relevant* factors that can be introduced into the experiment in a systematic way, the smaller will be the variance considered as error. Furthermore, the smaller the error variance, then the more precise will be the experiment, in that confidence intervals will be smaller and true effects more likely to be detected if present.

It follows that in multifactor experiments the introduction of each factor can serve two purposes: not only does the representation of the factor permit inferences to be drawn about *its* effects, but also it permits inferences to be made about other factors with relatively greater precision than otherwise. Often there is genuine interest in the possible effects and interaction effects of each factor. On the other hand, it is very common to find one or more factors introduced only as a device for reducing error variance, when little or no interest is taken in that factor per se. The experimenter somehow knows beforehand that certain nuisance factors do contribute to variance, and that introducing one or more of them systematically into the experiment will increase the precision of his inferences about the other factors of primary interest.

We are going to conclude our discussion of mixed models by considering one of the most common of the simple experimental designs involving matching as a device for increased precision. In this design there is one factor $A$ that is actually the experimental variable of interest. However, there is another factor $B$ that is primarily of a nuisance character. *The experimenter knows that factor B accounts for some variance in Y.* Each level or category of the nuisance factor consists of a group of subjects who are "matched," each showing the same status on this nuisance factor. Then *within* each such matched group, all the different levels of factor $A$ are represented.

The experiment analyzed in Section 13.20 represents one fairly extreme form of a matched-groups design. Here, each subject was effectively matched with himself over the conditions of the experiment. The nuisance factor was "subjects" (or, more properly, "subject-order combinations") while the experimental factor of real interest was "task." The experimenter really did not care about the possible effects attributable to subjects (or to subject-order combinations) in and of themselves. He was, however, interested in controlling for such effects, both as generators of between-treatment differences in the data and as contributors to his estimate of error variance. He hoped thereby to increase both the interpretability and precision of his experiment. Although the "subjects" factor was tested in the analysis given above, this was really for illustrative purposes, and the test for the sampled factor is sometimes omitted altogether when such a nuisance factor is involved. It is most important, however, that the sum of squares for such a factor be extracted from the over-all sum of squares; otherwise, the statistical advantage gained from matching or repeating observations is lost.

The purpose of the experimenter in introducing various factors into his design must be considered in the analysis and interpretation of the experiment. It is often a temptation to think of the shape of the data table as dictating the tests and interpretations to be made. However, factors introduced solely for the purpose of statistical control have quite a different status in the over-all evaluation of the results from that of the experimental factors of genuine concern to the experimenter. The fact that evidence exists for effects or interactions of some nuisance variable may contribute absolutely nothing to the interpretation of the experiment. The researcher had a pretty good idea that the nuisance factor contributed to variance in the first place, or otherwise he would not have troubled to introduce it into the experiment in a systematic way. Nevertheless, whether or not one intends to test for the effects of such deliberately introduced nuisance factors, he must allow for their presence in the over-all partition of the sum of squares.

Now we will return to the study of a simple and very common type of matched-group or repeated-observation design. This design will be discussed as another instance of a mixed model.

### 13.24  SIMPLE MATCHED-GROUPS EXPERIMENTS UNDER THE MIXED MODEL: RANDOMIZED BLOCKS

Consider an experiment in which some $J$ different treatments are to be compared. Each treatment corresponds to one level on the real experimental factor of interest. These effects are regarded as fixed. However, one or more nuisance factors exist, and suppose that previous work has shown considerable statistical association between these factors and the variable $Y$. The experimenter would like to represent levels or combinations of levels of those factors in his experiment. If all levels or combinations of levels for one or more nuisance factors can be represented, then the model he uses is that of the fixed effects analysis described in Chapter 12: the experimental treatments are observed under each of the nuisance levels, with subjects within each nuisance level being allotted at random to the treatments.

However, it most often happens that there are very many levels to the nuisance factor, or many combinations of factors, and the experimenter must sample from among these levels for a representation in his experiment. He draws a sample of $K$ nuisance levels, each containing some $nJ$ subjects. Each group representing a qualitatively different category on the nuisance factor or factors is called a **matched group,** or a **block** of subjects. Then within each block, subjects are allotted at random to the $J$ different treatments. Such a matched group design, with sampling of the nuisance factor levels, is often called a **randomized blocks design** (especially when there are $J$ observations per block, or one subject per treatment within a matched group).

It must be emphasized that whatever the model adopted there is no requirement that the various levels of the nuisance or matching factor be stages on some single continuum or attribute. Levels on the matching factor may represent qualitative differences of any kind, or combinations of factor levels. *The important point is that the factor or factors underlying the groupings must actually contribute to variance.* If the factors leading to the matching of subjects have nothing at all to do with the dependent variable, then this is not an economical way to design an experiment, since formation of matched groups is troublesome and "costly," and the experimenter gets nothing in return (or may actually lose something) for his extra effort.

For an example of a randomized blocks design, suppose that in an experiment on human performance at some motor task, the experimenter knows that sex, age, and type of occupation all contribute to the variance of scores. Therefore, he wishes to use subjects matched in these respects. However, it would manifestly be impossible to introduce each of these things in the experiment at all levels or combinations of levels. Instead, the experimenter samples at random from among age-sex-occupation groups, finding $J$ subjects who are alike in all three respects for each such combination sampled. Some $K$ different groups or blocks are sampled, each containing $J$ subjects. Then, within any age-sex-occupation grouping, the subjects are assigned *at random* to the $J$ experimental treatments, each treatment getting one and only one subject. Here, $N = JK$ for the experiment.

A randomized blocks experiment such as this is usually analyzed as a **mixed model design without replication**. The analysis of variance proceeds just as for any two-way analysis, except that the partition of the sum of squares contains only three terms:

$$\text{SS total} = \text{SS rows} + \text{SS columns} + \text{SS interaction}.$$

Notice that a separate SS error cannot be calculated, since there is only one observation per cell. Table 13.24.1 is the summary table for the analysis. Since there is only one individual per cell in this instance $(n = 1)$ the only $F$ test to be made is that for treatments, which involves the MS rows divided by the MS interaction. The rows (blocks or matched groups effects) cannot be tested unless at least 2 observations are made in each block and treatment combination.

**Table 13.24.1**

| Source | SS | df | MS | E(MS) | F |
|--------|----|----|----|-------|---|
| Columns (treatments) | | $J - 1$ | $\dfrac{\text{SS columns}}{J - 1}$ | $\sigma_e^2 + \sigma_{AB}^2 + \dfrac{K \sum\limits_{j} \alpha_j^2}{J - 1}$ | $\dfrac{\text{MS col.}}{\text{MS int.}}$ |
| Rows (blocks of matched individuals) | | $K - 1$ | $\dfrac{\text{SS rows}}{K - 1}$ | $\sigma_e^2 + J\sigma_B^2$ | |
| Interaction | | $(J - 1)(K - 1)$ | $\dfrac{\text{SS int.}}{(J - 1)(K - 1)}$ | $\sigma_e^2 + \sigma_{AB}^2$ | |
| Total | | $JK - 1$ | | | |

Matched group designs of the randomized-blocks type (one observation per cell) are extremely common in any number of research areas and especially in agriculture (hence the name, each "block" being a separate set of plots of ground). It is a highly efficient way of proceeding, provided that one can be reasonably sure that the factors on which individuals are matched actually are associated with the dependent variable; presumably this kind of information is available to the experimenter from his knowledge of the research area or from pilot studies for his experiment.

When blocks represents a randomly sampled factor, the assumptions of the mixed model must of course be met. It often makes much more sense to regard the matching variable as sampled than to limit the generality of the experiment only to certain levels actually represented in the experiment. However, a troublesome point then emerges: if the matching factor actually is sampled, then the expectation of MS between columns (the fixed effects factor) contains interaction variance, and the test for treatment effects should be carried out against the MS interaction. If there is a rather small variance attributable to the nuisance factor, but a considerable interaction variance component, then it may still take enormous treatment effects to show up as significant. This situation is illustrated in the example of Section 13.20. When variance due to blocks is small, but large variance due to interaction is present, one of the basic advantages usually gained by introducing matching in the first place is, in effect, lost, since the experiment may be relatively less precise for detecting over-all effects of the treatments than it would have been if the nuisance variable had simply been randomized over subjects. Consequently when the levels of the nuisance variable are to be sampled, the experimenter does well to think about possible interactions of this nuisance variable. If for some reason or other he can conclude that interaction effects will not exist, then the unreplicated matching scheme may be quite effective for increasing the precision of the experiment. Otherwise, if he anticipates quite sizable interaction variance he should either replicate the experiment and regard the matching factor levels as fixed, gaining some precision at the risk of losing some generality, or he should abandon the matching and be content with randomizing the nuisance variable. However, if his interest is in the *uniformity* of the treatments over the various nuisance-factor levels, the tendency for general effects to emerge in spite of the deliberately introduced interaction between treatments and levels of the nuisance factor, then the randomized blocks type of design is sufficient to the purpose, and the nuisance factor levels should be sampled.

Occasionally, the levels of the matching factor are not sampled, but rather are chosen deliberately to represent extreme degrees of the matching variable, or large qualitative differences among groups in one or more ways. In such designs the mixed model is really not appropriate, and the experiment should either be replicated (two or more subjects or observations per treatment in each matched group) and analyzed by Model I, or the experimenter must either know or be prepared to assume that no interaction effects exist in order to achieve a fully valid $F$ test. A test for interaction or "nonadditivity" exists for fixed effects unreplicated designs (Tukey, 1949), and this provides a basis for judgment about the appropriate test for treatment effects in this situation.

This is an area in which the beginner in experimentation may need considerable help in designing his particular study. The concerns just raised lie very close to the core of experimental psychology. Matched-group, and particularly repeated-observation, designs either of the replicated or unreplicated variety are enormously useful in many areas such as learning and psychophysics. Such designs are basic to studies where one is trying to establish the form of functional relation between the experimental and the dependent variable. But here the problem of interaction with a nuisance variable such as "subjects" becomes a serious one. How do you interpret a function that changes its form in an essential way from subject to subject? The answer seems to lie in the study of such interaction effects in and of themselves, and particularly in the search for ways to transform or rescale dependent variables so as to eliminate such interactions. In some situations interaction effects can be eliminated by an appropriate transformation of the dependent variable, and then general, interpretable, functional relations may appear. In other situations the problem of nuisance interactions may be resolved by the extraction of other components of variance in the analysis. These are not elementary considerations, however, and a text such as this is not the place to pursue them further. The essential point is that there is no way to design an experiment using matched groups, repeated observations, or any other form of control, that is guaranteed to make the results nice, neat, and interpretable unless the experimenter knows something about the relations of the nuisance variables themselves to the dependent variable.

This is also not the place to go into the actual mechanics for matching subjects for an experiment. There are a number of pitfalls to be avoided, and, as usual, the beginner does well to seek help. An introductory exposition of the problem is given in Lindquist (1953, Chapter 5).

The really important point to remember is that matching is often a good device for introducing controls into the experiment and for reducing error-variance estimates, thereby for achieving greater sensitivity to the presence of real treatment effects. However, matching accomplishes this aim only if the matching variable or variables actually *do* show a relatively strong association with the dependent variable in the experiment. To reiterate: here is one place where the experimenter must make full use of his knowledge about the area of study and previous findings about the strengths of association or proportions of variance accounted for among the several relevant variables. Knowledge of possible interaction effects can be particularly important. "Blind" matching, without the use of such information, can actually impair the efficiency of the experimental design.

## 13.25  REPEATED OBSERVATION OF THE SAME SUBJECTS

The practical limit to the strategy of matching subjects in an experiment is reached when each subject is matched with himself. Each subject is given each of the $J$ experimental treatments, with each individual being assigned to the treatments in some different, randomly chosen, order. Conceptually, each group of $J$ observations of a single subject is like a matched group of observations: any subject represents some constellation of "nuisance factor levels" that he brings to the experiment, and that are presumably constant over the treatments for him. A sampling of subjects is formally like a sampling of nuisance-factor combinations, just as when matched groups are sampled.

However, the resemblance between the randomized blocks design just discussed and repeated measurements designs is somewhat specious and misleading. When different individuals are given different treatments, even though the individuals are matched, it is still reasonable to assume the error portions of their scores to be independent. In the random and mixed models the possibility of a particular kind of statistical association or dependence between scores of individuals in the same group of repeated observations is allowed, but the error portions of those scores must be independent, both of each other and of the random effects in the model. Texts in statistics and experimental design sometimes leave the impression that all the problems introduced by repeated observations are solved when "subjects" appears as a factor in the experimental analysis, and the mixed or random effects model is employed. This is not necessarily true. It is true that the analysis of variance for these models can be applied when a *particular form* of dependency exists among the observations (strictly speaking, when the dependency involves equal *correlations* among pairs of observations within subjects). However, we have no good reason to believe that most repeated observation data have this character, and we have ample reason to believe that in some such data the error components of observations are dependent, particularly when the material is such that learning or other serial changes occur.

Nevertheless, these problems are not insurmountable for the experienced and competent researcher. As mentioned before, a well-designed experiment can eliminate some of the sources of dependency among observations, and various experimental devices exist for handling this problem in different situations. As usual, these statistical considerations should not be interpreted as prohibitions against repeated observation experiments. Quite the contrary; such experimental designs are especially well suited to the problems of the research psychologist. On the other hand, these statistical requirements should serve as guideposts in the process of matching a well-thought-out experiment with an appropriate analysis. The experimenter may have to exercise considerable thought and ingenuity in planning the experiment if he wants the analysis of variance and $F$ tests to be appropriate to the data. But there is nothing sacred or mandatory about the use of analysis of variance; the real concern of the experimenter must always be for the logic of the experiment and the interpretability of the data.

Incidentally, these problems of dependency do not ordinarily arise when the basic scores assigned to individuals are means or other summary measures over repeated trials under the *same* condition, and each individual is represented by one such score. So long as each subject is paired with only one score in the data to be analyzed, and errors for different subjects are independent, then one of the methods already discussed is usually applicable.

One very hopeful sign for the psychologist in his search for ways to handle such problems is the appearance of methods based directly on **randomization.** There is a growing body of evidence that procedures such as the analysis of variance and $F$ test may be justified by a different kind of mathematical rationale, based on the actual randomization performed in the experiment. This rationale is rather different from the "classical" or "normal-theory" models presented here. The probability statements made under such randomization models do not refer specifically to distributions over all samples, but rather to distributions over **all possible randomizations of the same sample** (an example of this general idea will be given in Chapter 17). The connection between the idea of randomization in the experiment and the use of the $F$ test is not a particularly simple one, and space and the mathematical level assumed do not permit our going further into this rationale here. Suffice it to say that in some instances this randomization model does permit one to analyze data by the analysis of variance and to make inferences using the $F$ test, when Models I, II, and the mixed model are, for various reasons, inappropriate. A modern discussion of randomization models is given in Scheffé (1959, Chapter 9), although this presentation is not elementary and the student is, as usual, advised to seek help in the use of such a model for his data.

### 13.26  THE GENERAL PROBLEM OF EXPERIMENTAL DESIGN

The factorial design mentioned in the last chapter and the randomized blocks design just discussed are but two of the many ways that the experimenter may choose to design his study. The literature of experimental design is full of ways for collecting and analyzing data for particular experimental situations. Many of these designs in common use in psychology are found in references such as Edwards (1960), Lindquist (1953), and particularly in Winer (1962). A more advanced treatment of the subject is given in Cochran and Cox (1957). An informative, nonmathematical introduction to design is given in D. R. Cox (1958).

From a broad point of view, the problem of choosing a design for an experiment is a problem in economics. The experimenter has some question or questions that he wants to answer. He wants to be sure of the following points.

1. The actual data collected will contain all the information that he needs to make inferences, and that this information can be extracted from the data.
2. The important hypotheses can be tested validly and separately.
3. The level of precision reached in estimation, and the power of his statistical tests, will be satisfactory for his purposes.

Consideration number 1 involves the actual selection of treatments and treatment combinations that the experimenter will observe. What are the factors of interest? How many levels of a factor will be observed? Will these levels be sampled or regarded as fixed? Which factors should be crossed and which nested in the design. Consideration 2 is closely related to the first: must all combinations of factors to be observed, or is there interest in only some treatment combinations? If only part of the possible set of treatment combinations can be observed, is it possible to make separate inferences about the various factors and combinations? Consideration 3 involves the choice of sample size and of experimental controls. Is the sample size contemplated large enough to give the precision of estimation or power (or both) that the experimenter feels is necessary to have for his inferences?

However, attendant to each of these considerations are parallel considerations of cost.

4. The more different treatments administered, necessitated by the more questions asked of the data, the more the experiment will cost in time, subjects, effort, and other expenses.
5. The more kinds of information the experimenter wants to gain the larger the set of assumptions he usually must make to obtain valid inferences.
6. The more hypotheses that can be tested validly and separately, the greater the number of treatment combinations necessary, and the larger may be the required number of subjects. Furthermore, the clarity of the statistical findings may be lessened, and the experiment as a whole may be harder to interpret.

7. The experimenter can increase precision and power by larger samples, or by exercising additional controls in his experiment, either as constant control, or by a matching procedure. Each possibility has its real costs in time, effort, and, perhaps, money.

Other things being equal, the experimenter would like to get by with as few subjects as possible. Even "approximately" random samples are extremely difficult to obtain, and often the sheer cost of the experiment in time and effort goes up with each slight increase in sample size. Furthermore, the experiment may not be carried out as carefully with a large number as with only a few subjects. Throwing in lots of ill-considered treatments just to see what will happen can be an expensive pastime for the serious experimenter. The number of treatment combinations can increase very quickly when many factors are added, and some of these combinations may be of no interest at all to the experimenter or add little or nothing to precision, so that he may be paying a high price for discovering "garbage" effects in his data. If a large sample is out of the question, power and precision can be bought at the price of constant or matching controls. However, remember that constant control reduces the generality of the conclusions the experimenter can reach from a set of data, and matching may be extremely hard to carry out.

All in all, there are several things the experimenter wants from his experiment and several ways to get them. Each desideratum has its price, however, and the experimenter must somehow decide if the gain in designing the experiment in a particular way is offset by the loss he may incur in so doing. This is why the problem of experimental design has strong economic overtones.

Texts in experimental design present ways of laying out the experiment so as to get "the most for the least" in a given situation. Various designs emphasize one aspect or another of the considerations and costs involved in getting and analyzing experimental data. Texts in design can give only a few standard types or layouts that study and experience have shown optimal in one or more ways, with, nevertheless, some price paid for using each design. Obviously, the best design for every conceivable experiment does not exist "canned" somewhere in a book, and experienced researchers and statisticians often come up with novel ways of designing an experiment for a special purpose. On the other hand, a study of the standard experimental designs is very instructive for any experimenter, if only to let him appreciate the strengths and weaknesses of different ways of laying out an experiment.

We can go no further into the question of experimental design here. However, a principle for the beginner to remember is, *keep it simple!* Concentrate on how well and carefully you can carry out a few *meaningful* manipulations on a few subjects, chosen, *if possible*, randomly from some well-defined population and *randomized* among treatments. The experiment and its meaning is the thing to keep in mind, and not some fancy way of setting up the experiment that has no real connection with the basic problem or the economics of the situation. Then, when the novice finally knows his way around in his experimental area, the refinements of design are open to him.

# INDIVIDUAL COMPARISONS
# AMONG MEANS

*14*

The true experimental scientist gains insights as well as pleasure from "snooping around" in his data. He is satisfied only when he feels that he understands what actually went on in the experiment and what the data actually show. In any sensibly planned experiment there will be clues that can widen understanding, and the good scientist searches them out.

Experimentation is almost never conducted in the hermetically sealed atmosphere that statistical reports often suggest. Most emphatically, good research requires all the care and control that the experimenter can provide in the actual experiment. But research hypotheses are not entertained or dismissed in the cavalier way that a statistics book may imply. These books set down the formal rules of the game, a set of prearranged signals from one scientist to another that he has found something worth looking into, or that his results contain sampling error. Research reports are written in this conventionalized language, and no doubt will continue to be until something better is devised. Nevertheless, the formal rules of the game should not be confused with the actual work of the scientist.

The novice in the use of statistics often feels that statistical tests somehow cut him off from the close examination of his data. There is something that seems so final about an analysis of variance summary table, for example, that one is tempted to regard this as some ultimate distillation of all meaning in the experiment. Nothing could be further from the truth. Statistical summaries and tests are certainly useful, but they are not *ends* of experimentation. The important part of data analysis often begins when the experimenter asks himself, "What accounts for the results I obtain?" and turns to the detailed exploration of the data.

Considered by themselves, all that the $F$ tests in an analysis of variance can tell you is that *something* seems to have happened. If the $F$ is significant, then some effects presumably exist that can be expected to occur again under similar circumstances; if the test is not significant, something notable still may have happened, but if treatment effects exist they are at least partially obscured by other variation. Other than this, a $F$ test alone tells almost nothing. If all experimenters were satisfied with the general statement that something did (did not) happen, then science would progress by slow stages indeed. Yet, in psychology, it is remarkable that published research papers so often emphasize over-all significance of results, and give little evidence either of the experimenter's prior planning or of the combing through data for meaning and potential application that is the heart of research.

Although statistical methods and principles cannot do the experimenter's basic job for him, important statistical aids nevertheless exist at all stages of the research enterprise. When the experimenter only *looks* at his data, combining and recombining them in different ways, a basic statistical principle assists him: the best estimates he can make of the true experimental effects are those he actually observes in his data, regardless of statistical significance. However, even more potent statistical tools are available for the detailed analysis of data.

The material in this chapter deals with two devices for analyzing data in more detail than that provided by the ordinary analysis of variance. Both methods are designed for comparing means or groups of means in a variety of ways. First, the technique of **planned comparisons** will be introduced. Here, instead of planning to analyze his data to see if any over-all experimental effects exist, the researcher at the outset has a number of particular questions he wants to answer separately. This technique of planned comparisons is used *instead of* the ordinary analysis of variance and $F$ test. Indeed, as will be shown, the usual analysis of variance actually summarizes the evidence for many possible such individual questions that might be asked of the data.

Next, the even more important technique of **incidental** or **post-hoc comparisons** will be discussed. Here, differences among means combined in any number of ways can be evaluated for significance, *after* the over-all $F$ test has shown significance. This procedure of post-hoc comparisons is an important supplement to the usual analysis of variance, and is very useful for the further exploration of data after the initial analysis has suggested the existence of real effects in the data.

Both techniques, planned and post-hoc comparisons, apply only to fixed effects or mixed model experiments. The inferences to be made concern particular population means combined in particular ways, and these methods make sense only when applied to treatment groups representing *fixed level, non-sampled, factors.*

## 14.1 ASKING SPECIFIC QUESTIONS OF DATA

In Section 8.9 the idea of linear combinations of random variables was introduced, and the sampling distribution of such a linear combination was explored. Our concern with linear combinations was justified by the fact that the evidence pertaining to particular experimental questions can often be found from various ways of combining the data; specifically, by linear combinations of means. In this section we will pursue this idea further, and see how special linear combinations are useful to the experimenter.

Consider a study of the influence of the manner of persuasion upon the tendency of persons to change their attitude toward some institution or group. The particular attitude studied is that toward a minority group, and the experimental modes of persuasion used were:

1. a motion picture favorable to the minority group;
2. a lecture on the same topic, also favorable to the minority group;
3. a combination of the motion picture and the lecture.

Subjects were to be assigned at random to the different experimental groups, each having first been given a preliminary attitude test. Following the experimental treatment, each subject was to be given the test once again; the dependent variable here is the *change* in attitude score. It was recognized, however, that the mere repetition of a test may have some influence on the individual's changing his score, and so a randomly selected control group was also to be used, in which the subjects were to be given no special experimental treatment.

However, during the design of the experiment the question arose, "Would the subjects perhaps change as a result of seeing *any* movie or hearing *any* lecture?" Thus it was decided to introduce two more control groups, the first to be shown a movie completely unrelated to the minority group, and the second given a lecture by the same person, but on a quite different topic.

The final experimental design can be diagrammed as follows:

| *Experimental groups* | | | *Control groups* | | |
|---|---|---|---|---|---|
| *I* | *II* | *III* | *IV* | *V* | *VI* |
| Movie | Lecture | Movie and lecture | Nothing | Neutral movie | Neutral lecture |

A total sample of thirty subjects was drawn at random, and subjects were assigned at random to the six conditions, with five subjects per condition.

In this study, the experimenter was not interested in the over-all existence of treatment effects. Rather, from the outset his interest lay in answering the following specific questions:

1. Do the experimental groups as a whole tend to differ from the control groups?
2. Is the effect of the experimental lecture-movie combination different from the average effect of either movie or lecture separately?
3. Is the effect of the experimental lecture different from the effect of the experimental movie?
4. Among the control groups, is there any effect of the neutral movie or lecture as compared with the group receiving no treatment?

In other words, the experimenter entertained a number of particular questions before the collection of the data, and he wished to analyze his data to answer those questions. An over-all analysis of variance and $F$ test would give indication of the existence of *any* systematic effects. However, he was interested only in the particular differences among population means corresponding to answers to these questions.

Notice that the evidence pertaining to each question comes from the various sample means combined in some special way. For example, the evidence for question 3 involves only the difference between the means for groups I and II. On the other hand, the evidence for question 2 involves both the difference between mean I and mean III *and* the difference between mean II and mean III. Still other combinations of means pertain to the other questions asked. Can one, however, attach a significance level to each of these comparisons among means, permitting a statement about such differences among the *population* means?

This is a problem of planned comparisons among means, and the technique used will now be outlined. Let it be emphasized that this procedure applies only when the experimenter has specific questions to be asked *before* the data are collected, and this method is used *instead of* the ordinary analysis of variance and $F$ test.

## 14.2 PLANNED COMPARISONS

The basic theory underlying planned comparisons has already been outlined in Sections 8.9 and 8.10. There it was noted that given normally distributed variables sampled independently and at random, values from any linear combination of those random variables will also be normally distributed. Furthermore, if the mean and variance for each variable is known, then the mean and variance of the sampling distribution of the linear combination is also known. Both these principles were used in Section 10.12 to establish the rationale for the $t$ test of independent differences. Now we will go far beyond the simple two-sample case and apply these principles for any linear combination of means.

First, we need to define a **population comparison or comparison among population means**: given the means of $J$ distinct populations, $\mu_1, \cdots, \mu_J$, a comparison among those means is any linear combination or weighted sum, with weights $c_j$ not all equal to zero:

$$\psi = c_1\mu_1 + c_2\mu_2 + \cdots + c_J\mu_J = \sum_j c_j\mu_j. \qquad \textbf{[14.2.1*]}$$

We will use the symbol $\psi$ (small Greek psi) to stand for the value of some particular *population* comparison. The weights for a comparison $\psi$ are *some set of real numbers* $(c_1, \cdots, c_J)$ *not all zero*.

In almost all applications of the theory, the requirement is made that the *sum* of the weights $c_j$ equals zero:

$$\sum_j c_j = 0. \qquad \textbf{[14.2.2*]}$$

In the following we will simply assume that this requirement is met, and defer giving the reason for this requirement until Section 14.9.

A **sample comparison** is defined exactly as for a population comparison, except that **sample means** are weighted and summed:

$$\hat{\psi} = c_1 M_1 + \cdots + c_J M_J = \sum_j c_j M_j \qquad [14.2.3*]$$

(the caret or "hat" over the psi will always indicate that this comparison is a sample value). Once again, we will require that $\sum_j c_j = 0$. Be sure to notice that the symbol for a comparison, either $\psi$ or $\hat{\psi}$, stands for a single number, since it equals a *weighted sum of numbers*.

### 14.3   ESTIMATES OF POPULATION COMPARISON VALUES

Some of the statistical properties of comparisons will now be viewed in the light of what we know about linear combinations. We know from Section 8.10 that since each sample comparison is a linear combination, it is true that

$$E(\hat{\psi}) = E\left(\sum_j c_j M_j\right) = \sum_j c_j E(M_j) = \psi. \qquad [14.3.1*]$$

**Any sample comparison is an unbiased estimate of the population comparison involving the same weights** $c_j$. If we wish to evaluate the weighted sum of population means, our best estimate is the weighted sum of sample means. In the example above, each question asked by the experimenter can be answered by some particular comparison among population means. His best evidence for each question is some weighted sum based on sample means.

### 14.4   THE SAMPLING VARIANCE OF PLANNED COMPARISONS

Suppose that each of the sample means $M_j$ is based on a different sample of $n_j$ cases drawn at random from a population with true mean $\mu_j$. Furthermore, suppose that each population has the same variance $\sigma_e^2$, so that the sampling distribution of $M_j$ values has a variance $\sigma_e^2/n_j$.

By the principle of Section 8.10, the sampling variance of a comparison $\hat{\psi}$ based on independent means must be

$$\text{var.}(\hat{\psi}) = \sum_j c_j^2 \, \text{var.}(M_j) = \sigma_e^2 \sum_j \frac{c_j^2}{n_j}. \qquad [14.4.1*]$$

Thus, for example, suppose that the weights in a sample comparison of five means were $(-2, -1, 3, 1, -1)$, so that

$$\hat{\psi} = (-2)M_1 + (-1)M_2 + (3)M_3 + (1)M_4 + (-1)M_5. \qquad [14.4.2]$$

Furthermore, suppose that each mean is based on 10 cases, so that $n = 10$ for all $j$. Provided that $\sigma_e^2$ is the variance of each population, then the sampling distribution of values of $\hat{\psi}$ must have a variance given by

$$\text{var.}(\hat{\psi}) = \sigma_e^2 \left[ \frac{(-2)^2 + (-1)^2 + (3)^2 + (1)^2 + (-1)^2}{10} \right]$$

$$= \sigma_e^2 \left( \frac{16}{10} \right)$$

$$= \frac{8\sigma_e^2}{5}. \qquad [14.4.3]$$

Obviously, in no practical situation will we know the value of $\sigma_e^2$. However, *the value of $\sigma_e^2$ can be estimated from the data in exactly the same way that it is estimated in the analysis of variance:*

$$\text{est. } \sigma_e^2 = \text{MS error.}$$

(Here, $\sigma_e^2$ is the same as $\sigma_e^2$ in the expected mean squares for analysis of variance, and mean square error is the same as mean square within groups in the one-way analysis.) Thus

$$\text{est. var.}(\hat{\psi}) = (\text{MS error}) \sum_j \frac{c_j^2}{n_j}. \qquad [14.4.4\dagger]$$

Now we have the three essential ingredients for statistical inference: an unbiased estimate $\hat{\psi}$ of some population value $\psi$, an estimate of the sampling variance of $\hat{\psi}$, and we know the form of the sampling distribution of $\hat{\psi}$ (normal if populations are normal). These facts taken together suggest the use of $t$ (Section 11.14). Next, the question of a test will be undertaken.

## 14.5 INTERVAL ESTIMATES AND TESTS FOR PLANNED COMPARISONS

Given the value of the planned sample comparison $\hat{\psi}$, a confidence interval for the population comparison value $\psi$ can be found from

$$\hat{\psi} - t_{(\alpha/2; \nu)} \sqrt{\text{est. var.}(\hat{\psi})} \leq \psi \leq \hat{\psi} + t_{(\alpha/2; \nu)} \sqrt{\text{est. var.}(\hat{\psi})}. \quad [14.5.1\dagger]$$

For the $100(1 - \alpha)$ percent confidence interval, the value of $t_{(\alpha/2; \nu)}$ represents the value cutting off the *upper* $\alpha/2$ proportion of sample values in a distribution of $t$ with $\nu$ degrees of freedom. The number of degrees of freedom is the same as the degrees of freedom for the mean square error used to estimate $\sigma_e^2$. Such a confidence interval for $\psi$ rests on the usual assumptions for a fixed effects analysis of variance: normally distributed populations, each with variance $\sigma_e^2$, and independent errors. As in the over-all $F$ test for such an analysis, the assumption of normality is relatively innocuous for reasonably large samples, and the homogeneity-of-variance assumption can be violated to some extent if sample $n$ is constant over all groups.

This confidence interval can be used to test any hypothetical value of $\psi$ at all. If some hypothetical value of $\psi$ fails to be covered by the confidence interval, then that hypothesis may be rejected beyond the $\alpha$ level (two-tailed).

In most instances, the only hypothesis of interest in planned comparisons is

$$H_0: \psi = 0.$$

Then a test for this hypothesis is given by

$$t = \frac{\hat{\psi}}{\sqrt{\text{est. var.}(\hat{\psi})}}, \qquad \text{[14.5.2†]}$$

distributed as $t$ with $N - J$ degrees of freedom (the degrees of freedom for mean square error). If the hypothesis is to be tested against a directional alternative, then the sign of the $t$ is considered, just as in the ordinary test for two means.

Notice that the $t$ test for a difference between two independent means (Section 10.15) is merely a test of a comparison

$$\hat{\psi} = (1)M_1 + (-1)M_2$$

where the two weights are 1 and $-1$ respectively. However, the $t$ test can be used to test any particular comparison, regardless of the number of groups involved. This is the exception in the use of $t$ for means, previously mentioned in Section 12.14.

When the hypothesis to be tested is nondirectional, the $t$ test for any planned comparison may be replaced by the equivalent $F$ test:

$$F = \frac{(\hat{\psi})^2}{\text{MS error} \left( \sum_j c_j^2 / n_j \right)} \qquad \text{[14.5.3†]}$$

with 1 and $N - J$ degrees of freedom. (Recall, once again, that $t^2$ is distributed as an $F$ variable.)

Although this discussion has referred to comparisons planned among a set of $J$ means for data in a one-factor experiment, exactly the same ideas apply when comparisons are planned in a two-factor (or higher) experiment fitting the fixed effects or mixed model. Thus, when the comparisons are to be made among the $J$ column means in a two-factor experiment with $K$ rows and $n$ per cell in the data table,

$$\text{est. var.}(\hat{\psi}) = (\text{MS error}) \left( \sum_j \frac{c_j^2}{Kn} \right)$$

since each mean is based on $Kn$ observations. The $t$ or $F$ value is computed just as in **14.5.2** or **14.5.3,** with $JK(n - 1)$ degrees of freedom for the denominator. The test has this form, however, only when the fixed effects model applies.

When the second factor, represented by the rows, is sampled, so that the mixed model applies, then any comparison among the column means has an estimated variance given by

$$\text{est. var.}(\hat{\psi}) = (\text{MS interaction})\left(\sum_j \frac{c_j^2}{Kn}\right)$$

and the number of degrees of freedom for $t$ or the denominator of $F$ is $(J - 1)$ times $(K - 1)$.

If, for some reason, cell means are to be compared in a two-way table, with $n$ per cell, the estimated variance for the comparison is given by

$$\text{est. var.}(\hat{\psi}) = (\text{MS error})\left(\frac{\sum_j \sum_k c_{jk}^2}{n}\right)$$

where the mean square error is the mean square within cells, and the degrees of freedom are found from $(JK)(n - 1)$.

## 14.6 INDEPENDENCE OF PLANNED COMPARISONS

A single planned comparison among means is usually tested by a simple $t$ ratio, as we have seen. However, seldom does an experimenter have interest in only one comparison on his data. Usually there are sets of questions he wants answered, each corresponding to some comparison among means. This brings up the very critical problem of the independence of comparisons.

Just as the possible answers to some questions may depend logically upon answers to others, so the values of some comparisons made on a given set of means may depend upon the values of other comparisons. This fact has serious consequences for estimates and tests of several comparisons, since the questions involved in the respective comparisons cannot be given separate and unrelated answers unless the comparisons are statistically independent of each other. Fortunately, a simple method exists for determining whether or not two comparisons are independent, given normal population distributions with equal variances $\sigma_e^2$. **The determination of the independence of two comparisons depends only on the weights each involve, and in no way on the means actually observed.** One can plan comparisons that will be independent *before* the data are collected.

The solution to the problem of independent comparisons rests on still another general principle having to do with linear combinations of variables. This principle is another instance of the extraordinary utility of the assumption of normal distributions in statistical theory. The principle may be stated as follows:

Given $J$ independent random variables, $Y_1, \cdots, Y_J$, each normally distributed with variance $\sigma_e^2$, and two linear combinations,

$$\hat{\psi}_1 = c_{11}Y_1 + \cdots + c_{1J}Y_J$$

with weights $(c_{11}, \cdots, c_{1J})$, and

$$\hat{\psi}_2 = c_{21}Y_1 + \cdots + c_{2J}Y_J$$

with weights $(c_{21}, \cdots, c_{2J})$, then the random variables $\hat{\psi}_1$ and $\hat{\psi}_2$ are themselves independent *provided* that

$$\sum_j c_{1j}c_{2j} = 0. \qquad\qquad [14.6.1^*]$$

In other words, **given independent and normally distributed random variables having the same variance, one can decide if two different linear combinations of those variables are independent simply by seeing if the products of the weights assigned to each variable sum to zero:**

$$c_{11}c_{21} + \cdots + c_{1J}c_{2J} = 0.$$

**This principle is necessarily true only for normally distributed variables with equal variances.**

Now suppose that we assume $J$ normally distributed populations with equal variance, and consider independent random samples of size $n$ from each population. Then from this principle, *two different sample comparisons* $\hat{\psi}_1$ *and* $\hat{\psi}_2$ *among means are independent only if*

$$\sum_j c_{1j}c_{2j} = 0, \qquad\qquad [14.6.2^*]$$

where the $c_{1j}$ are the weights used in the first comparison, $\hat{\psi}_1$, and $c_{2j}$ are the weights used in the second, $\hat{\psi}_2$.

Two comparisons satisfying this condition are said to be **orthogonal** comparisons; orthogonality of two comparisons is equivalent to the statistical independence of sample comparisons only when the populations are normal, however. When two comparisons are statistically independent, the information each provides is actually nonredundant and unrelated to the information provided by the other. The estimate $\hat{\psi}_1$ is unrelated to the estimate $\hat{\psi}_2$. Thus, seeing if comparisons are orthogonal lets the experimenter judge whether or not he is gaining unrelated, nonoverlapping pieces of information about his experiment. On the other hand, although separate confidence intervals and tests can be constructed for such comparisons, these intervals and tests ordinarily are *not* statistically independent, due to the fact that the estimate of $\sigma_e^2$ each involves is based on the mean square error for the whole experiment. This is precisely the same problem encountered before with $F$ ratios; the different values determining the numerators of several $F$ ratios in an analysis of variance usually are independent, but the $F$ ratios themselves are not independent if they involve the same denominator value. Only when the number of degrees of freedom for the mean square error is very large can the confidence intervals and tests for individual planned comparisons be regarded as independent. We will have more to say on this issue in the last section of this chapter.

When the $J$ distinct samples have different sizes, symbolized by $n_j$, the criterion for orthogonality for two comparisons among the means becomes

$$\sum_j \frac{c_{1j}c_{2j}}{n_j} = 0,$$

so that the product of comparison weights for each sample is weighted inversely by $n_j$ before the sum is taken. If this weighted sum of products is zero, then the comparisons may be regarded as orthogonal.

In somewhat more formal terms, given two or more mutually orthogonal comparisons with population values $\psi_1$, $\psi_2$, and so on, then

$$\frac{(\hat{\psi}_1 - \psi_1)^2}{\sigma^2 \sum_j c_{1j}^2/n_j}, \quad \frac{(\hat{\psi}_2 - \psi_2)^2}{\sigma^2 \sum_j c_{2j}^2/n_j}, \text{ etc.}$$

can be regarded as independent chi-square variables, each with 1 degree of freedom, under the usual assumptions of normality and equality of variances. This fact makes it possible to find separate confidence intervals for the various true $\psi$ values, or to test separate hypotheses about the comparison values.

In the following, the terms "independent" and "orthogonal" will be used interchangeably. However, this is proper only because normal distributions with homogeneous variances are assumed throughout the discussion.

## 14.7 An illustration of independent and nonindependent planned comparisons

Four treatment-groups were observed in an experiment, with a sample of six randomly assigned subjects in each. The means of the four groups were

$$\begin{array}{cccc} I & II & III & IV \\ 17 & 24 & 27 & 16. \end{array}$$

The mean square error, found by the usual method for a one-way analysis of variance, was 5.6, with $24 - 4$, or 20, degrees of freedom. Before the data were seen, the experimenter decided that he was interested basically in the following questions.

1. Does mean I differ from the average of means II, III, and IV?
2. Does mean II differ from the average of means III and IV?
3. Does mean III differ from mean IV?
4. Does the average of I and II differ from the average of III and IV?

It is assumed that each population is normally distributed, with the same variance in each. Now, each of the questions can be put into the form of comparisons among means by using the following sets of weights. In Table 14.7.1, the rows represent the various questions (comparisons) and the columns the various samples. In the cells the numbers are the weights $c_j$ to be assigned to a given sample mean for a given comparison:

Table 14.7.1

| | | Means | | |
|:---:|:---:|:---:|:---:|:---:|
| Question | I | II | III | IV |
| 1 | 1 | $-\dfrac{1}{3}$ | $-\dfrac{1}{3}$ | $-\dfrac{1}{3}$ |
| 2 | 0 | 1 | $-\dfrac{1}{2}$ | $-\dfrac{1}{2}$ |
| 3 | 0 | 0 | 1 | $-1$ |
| 4 | $\dfrac{1}{2}$ | $\dfrac{1}{2}$ | $-\dfrac{1}{2}$ | $-\dfrac{1}{2}$ |

There is certainly nothing mysterious about the way these weights were chosen. The first comparison is designed to investigate a difference between mean I and the *average* of means II, III, and IV. This calls for a weighting of mean I by unity, and finding the average of the three other means, which is tantamount to weighting each one by a *negative* 1/3 in the comparison with mean I. Similarly, mean I does not figure in the second question, and so gets weight 0, while mean II is contrasted with the *average* for means III and IV. The other weights are found in similar ways. Note that the sum of weights for each row in the table is zero, as it should be for comparisons among means.

　　Are these four comparisons orthogonal, and thus independent of each other? Consider the weights in rows 1 and 2; the sum of their products across columns is

$$\sum_j c_{1j}c_{2j} = (1)(0) + \left(\frac{-1}{3}\right)(1) + \left(\frac{-1}{3}\right)\left(\frac{-1}{2}\right) + \left(\frac{-1}{3}\right)\left(\frac{-1}{2}\right) = 0,$$

so that comparison 1 and comparison 2 are orthogonal and hence independent. In the same way, by computing the sum of the products of weights we see that comparison 2 and comparison 3, and comparison 1 and comparison 3 are also independent.

　　Now look at comparison 1 and comparison 4. Here the sum of the products of weights is

$$(1)\left(\frac{1}{2}\right) + \left(\frac{-1}{3}\right)\left(\frac{1}{2}\right) + \left(\frac{-1}{3}\right)\left(\frac{-1}{2}\right) + \left(\frac{-1}{3}\right)\left(\frac{-1}{2}\right) = \frac{2}{3}$$

so that comparisons 1 and 4 are not orthogonal. Neither are comparisons 2 and 4. On the other hand, comparisons 3 and 4 are orthogonal.

　　These judgments about the orthogonality and consequent independence of comparisons depend, of course, upon the assumption that the means *themselves* are independent over samples, and that the sampling distribution represented by each mean is normal with variance $\sigma_e^2/n$.

The computation and tests for the first three comparisons will next be illustrated. Presumably, our experimenter would not test comparison 4 separately because of its nonindependence of the others. The information he gains from comparison 4 is redundant, depending on the outcomes of the first three comparisons.

The value of comparison 1 is

$$\hat{\psi}_1 = (1)(17) + \left(\frac{-1}{3}\right)(24 + 27 + 16) = -5.3.$$

The estimated variance of this comparison is, from **14.4.4,**

$$\text{est. var.}(\hat{\psi}_1) = \frac{(5.6)}{6}\left[(1)^2 + \left(\frac{-1}{3}\right)^2 + \left(\frac{-1}{3}\right)^2 + \left(\frac{-1}{3}\right)^2\right].$$
$$= .93(1.33) = 1.24.$$

Under the hypothesis that $\psi_1 = 0$, the $t$ ratio is

$$t = \frac{-5.3}{\sqrt{1.24}} = -4.8.$$

For a nondirectional test, with 20 degrees of freedom, this result is significant beyond the 1 percent level, so that we reject the hypothesis that the true comparison value is zero. We can assert confidently that population mean I does differ from the average of means II, III, and IV.

In a similar fashion we find

$$\hat{\psi}_2 = (1)24 + \left(\frac{-1}{2}\right)(27) + \left(\frac{-1}{2}\right)(16) = 2.5$$

with

$$\text{est. var.}(\hat{\psi}_2) = \frac{5.6}{6}\left[(1)^2 + \left(\frac{-1}{2}\right)^2 + \left(\frac{-1}{2}\right)^2\right]$$
$$= 1.40.$$

Then

$$t = \frac{2.5}{\sqrt{1.40}} = 2.11.$$

This is just significant at the 5 percent level for a nondirectional test; mean **II** does differ significantly from means III and IV. Finally,

$$\hat{\psi}_3 = 27 - 16 = 11,$$

with

$$\text{est. var.}(\hat{\psi}_3) = \frac{5.6}{6}(1 + 1) = 1.87.$$

Here,

$$t = \frac{11}{\sqrt{1.87}} = 8.04,$$

which is very significant. We can say with confidence that population mean III is different from population mean IV.

Recall once again, however, that although these various comparisons' *values* may be regarded as independent estimates, the *tests* accompanying these estimates are not independent. There is no very satisfactory elementary way to determine how much our conclusion about any one of the comparisons depends upon our conclusions about any of the others. All we have really done by use of orthogonal, planned, comparisons is to package the data into nonoverlapping, informative, portions, affording separate tests.

## 14.8  MULTIPLE *t* TESTS ON A SET OF DATA

For the moment, let us return to the problem of many *t* tests carried out on the same set of data, first mentioned in Section 12.14. Now we can show more clearly why carrying out all *t* tests between pairs of means is not a very satisfactory way to package the data for maximum clarity of results.

Suppose that some *J* treatment groups exist, and the experimenter decides to carry out a *t* test in the ordinary way for each such pair of group means. The significance level for each test is reported just as though each were carried out in the absence of any of the others. Under these circumstances the comparisons tested by the *t* tests cannot be regarded as independent, and the various tests themselves refer to redundant, overlapping, aspects of the data. Some pattern of significant and nonsignificant results will undoubtedly result. How does one interpret this pattern? How much does the result of one such test dictate the findings on another? What do the significance levels mean, both alone and relative to each other? What correspondence does the pattern of significant results have to the significance level that would be found by use of one over-all *F* test for these means? None of these questions has a simple answer, it seems.

The interpretation of a set of such results is very difficult, particularly because of the nonindependence of various comparisons tested. This can be illustrated from the example of the preceding section. Each possible *t* ratio for a difference between means corresponds to a test of one of the comparisons in Table 14.8.1. Suppose that the *t* test corresponding to row 1 is carried out first, that for row 2 second, and so on. It can be seen immediately by the rule of Sec-

**Table 14.8.1**

| | Means | | | |
|:---:|:---:|:---:|:---:|:---:|
| Comparison | I | II | III | IV |
| 1 | 1 | −1 | 0 | 0 |
| 2 | 1 | 0 | −1 | 0 |
| 3 | 1 | 0 | 0 | −1 |
| 4 | 0 | 1 | −1 | 0 |
| 5 | 0 | 1 | 0 | −1 |
| 6 | 0 | 0 | 1 | −1 |

tion 14.6 that the comparison involved in the fourth $t$ test is not independent either of the first or of the second. As an illustration of why this is true, suppose that you were given the information that the difference between means I and II is $-7$, and that the difference between I and III is $-10$. Then what do you know of the difference between II and III? The answer is that you know it to be exactly $-3$; the values of comparisons 1 and 2 actually determine the value of comparison 4. When one considers the entire set of six comparisons and tests it becomes clear that a fairly complex pattern of dependency runs throughout the possible $t$ tests. It is absurd to regard each new comparison and test as somehow providing new information. Here, the information in the data is packaged in redundant ways, and this makes the determination of over-all significance levels for such results extremely difficult. One really has no simple way to tell how many of the significant results are due to chance alone, to the circumstance that several tests were carried out on the same data, or, most important, to the circumstance that some results dictate others. Hypothesis testing seems to lose most of its usual meaning when carried out in this "shotgun" fashion.

On the other hand, must the experimenter limit himself only to inferences corresponding to orthogonal comparisons in the data? Fortunately, the answer is "no," since there is a proper way of inspecting all differences or comparisons of interest, orthogonal or not, in a set of data, where the significance level attached to each comparison is quite meaningful. However, this method properly belongs under post-hoc rather than planned comparisons, and will be discussed in Section 14.15.

## 14.9 THE INDEPENDENCE OF SAMPLE COMPARISONS AND THE GRAND MEAN

In principle, any set of weights (not all zero) could be used in carrying out a comparison among several sample means; however, as we have seen one usually uses only sets of weights such that $\sum_{j} c_j = 0$ for each comparison.

Now the reason for this requirement can be shown: by insisting that the weights applied in any comparison sum to zero, we make each comparison value be independent of the value of the grand sample mean.

In Chapter 8 it was pointed out that the mean of any sample is a linear combination of random variables. Given $N$ individuals divided among $J$ sample groups, the grand mean over all individuals in all groups is a linear combination

$$M = \sum_{j} \sum_{i} \frac{Y_{ij}}{N}$$

where each score gets a weight of $1/N$. Furthermore, again in terms of the individual scores, any sample comparison can be written variously as

$$\hat{\psi} = \sum_{j} c_j M_j = \sum_{j} c_j \sum_{i} \frac{Y_{ij}}{n_j} = \sum_{j} \sum_{i} \left( \frac{c_j}{n_j} \right) Y_{ij}.$$

Each *individual* score $Y_{ij}$ actually gets a weight $(c_j/n_j)$, depending on the group $j$ to which it belongs.

In most instances, we want to ask questions about combinations of population means that will be unrelated to any consideration of what the over-all mean of the combined populations is estimated to be. Thus, we choose weights such that any comparison to be made is orthogonal to the linear combination standing for the grand mean. In terms of the basic scores, the principle of Section 14.6 implies that it should be true that

$$\sum_j \sum_i \left(\frac{1}{N}\right)\left(\frac{c_j}{n_j}\right) = 0,$$

which in turn implies that $\sum_j c_j = 0$.

## 14.10   THE NUMBER OF POSSIBLE INDEPENDENT COMPARISONS

It stands to reason that given any finite amount of data, only a finite set of questions may be asked of those data if one is to get nonredundant, nonoverlapping, answers. There is just so much information in any given set of data; once this information has been gained, asking further questions leads to answers that depend upon the answers already learned.

This idea of the amount of information in a set of data has a statistical parallel in the number of possible independent (orthogonal) comparisons to be made among $J$ means:

**Given $J$ independent sample means, there can be no more than $J - 1$ comparisons, each comparison being independent both of the grand mean and of each of the others.**

In other words, the experimenter can frame no more than $J - 1$ different comparisons standing for questions about his data, if he wishes these comparisons to be completely independent of each other and the grand mean. This does not say that many different sets of $J - 1$ mutually independent comparisons cannot be found for any set of data. It does say that once a set of $J - 1$ comparisons has been found where the comparisons are independent of each other and the grand mean, it is impossible to find one more comparison which is also independent both of the grand mean and all of the rest. Thus the number of questions the experimenter may ask his data as planned comparisons is limited, if the statistical answers are to be regarded as independent.

This was the difficulty in the example of Section 14.7. There were only four sample means, and four comparisons were planned; it is impossible to find four mutually orthogonal comparisons *whatever* the weights used, if they all are to be orthogonal to the grand mean in addition. This principle also illuminates the dependencies among multiple $t$ tests; given $J$ samples, there will be $(J)(J - 1)/2$ possible $t$ tests between pairs of means. If $J$ is greater than two, this will always be more than the number of possible independent comparisons.

It is no accident that the number of independent comparisons, $J - 1$, is also the number of degrees of freedom for between groups in the analysis of variance. This connection will be clarified in the next section.

## 14.11 PLANNED COMPARISONS AND THE ANALYSIS OF VARIANCE

There is a very intimate connection between analysis of variance and the technique of planned comparisons. **Each and every degree of freedom associated with treatments in any fixed effects analysis of variance corresponds to some possible comparison of means.** The number of degrees of freedom for the mean square between is the number of possible *independent* comparisons to be made on the means. Any analysis of variance is equivalent to a break-down of the data into *sets* of orthogonal comparisons.

In order to show how this is true, we need to define the **sum of squares for a comparison**: the sum of squares for any comparison $\hat{\psi}_g$ is

$$ SS\ (\hat{\psi}_g) = \frac{(\hat{\psi}_g)^2}{w_g} \qquad [14.11.1\dagger] $$

where

$$ w_g = \sum_j \frac{c_j^2}{n_j}. \qquad [14.11.2\dagger] $$

For any comparison $\hat{\psi}_g$ this sum of squares has *one* degree of freedom. It follows that

$$ MS\ (\hat{\psi}_g) = SS\ (\hat{\psi}_g). \qquad [14.11.3] $$

Notice that the $F$ ratio for a comparison $\hat{\psi}_g$ could be written as

$$ F = \frac{MS\ (\hat{\psi}_g)}{MS\ \text{error}}, \qquad [14.11.4\dagger] $$

with 1 and $N - J$ degrees of freedom.

Now suppose that we have two *independent* comparisons $\hat{\psi}_g$ and $\hat{\psi}_h$ on the same data. If we find the values of $SS\ (\hat{\psi}_g)$ and $SS\ (\hat{\psi}_h)$ and add them up we have

$$ SS\ (\hat{\psi}_g \text{ and } \hat{\psi}_h) = SS\ (\hat{\psi}_g) + SS\ (\hat{\psi}_h). \qquad [14.11.5] $$

Because $\hat{\psi}_g$ and $\hat{\psi}_h$ are independent, this new sum of squares has *two* degrees of freedom by the additive property of chi-square variables. Furthermore, we could use this sum of squares to test the hypothesis that *both* $\psi_g$ and $\psi_h$ (population values) simultaneously are zero:

$$ H_0\colon \psi_g = 0,\ \psi_h = 0. $$

The appropriate $F$ test is given by

$$ F = \frac{MS\ (\hat{\psi}_g \text{ and } \hat{\psi}_h)}{MS\ \text{error}} = \frac{[SS\ (\hat{\psi}_g) + SS\ (\psi_h)]/2}{MS\ \text{error}} \qquad [14.11.6\dagger] $$

with 2 and $N - J$ degrees of freedom. One can *either* test each comparison separately, *or* test both together via this $F$ ratio; one does not do both kinds of tests, however.

Extending this idea further, suppose that there were $J - 1$ independent comparisons on the data, and that the SS were calculated for each of them. Then

$$\text{SS (all } \hat{\psi}_g) = \text{SS } (\hat{\psi}_1) + \cdots + \text{SS } (\hat{\psi}_g) + \cdots + \text{SS } (\hat{\psi}_{J-1}) \qquad [14.11.7]$$

with $J - 1$ degrees of freedom.

If we wanted to test the hypothesis that *all* comparisons were simultaneously zero, in some set $G$ consisting of $J - 1$ mutually orthogonal comparisons,

$$H_0 : \psi_g = 0 \text{ for all } g \epsilon G,$$

then the $F$ test would be

$$F = \frac{\text{MS (all } \hat{\psi}_g)}{\text{MS error}} = \frac{\sum_g \text{SS } (\hat{\psi}_g)/(J - 1)}{\text{MS error}} \qquad [14.11.8\dagger]$$

with $J - 1$ and $N - J$ degrees of freedom. Again, a prior choice exists between separate or collective tests of these comparisons, but it makes no sense to test *both* the separate and the collective hypotheses in the usual way.

It can be shown that **for any set of $J - 1$ independent sample comparisons on any set of $J$ means,**

$$\text{SS (all } \hat{\psi}_g) = \sum_g \text{SS } (\hat{\psi}_g) = \text{SS between groups.} \qquad [14.11.9*]$$

**The total of the sum of squares for any $J - 1$ independent comparisons on $J$ means is always equal to the sum of squares between the $J$ groups.**

**In the fixed effects analysis of variance, the $F$ test between groups is always equivalent to a simultaneous test that all comparisons among means are zero.** The $F$ test is an "omnibus test" of all possible comparisons to be made among a particular set of means in the data. Each of an independent set of these comparisons can be tested separately instead of all together, if the experimenter has definite questions to ask about his data to begin with. If he has no such questions, then the overall $F$ test still permits him to ask "did *anything* happen?" On the other hand, a much more powerful test of a particular hypothesis may be possible by testing one or more comparisons separately than by the overall $F$ test. The important thing to remember is that for each degree of freedom in the sum of squares between groups or treatments, there is a potential prior question to be asked of the data. The $F$ test gives evidence to let us judge if all of a set of $J - 1$ such orthogonal comparisons are simultaneously zero in the populations. For this reason, if planned orthogonal comparisons are tested separately, the overall $F$ test is not carried out, and vice-versa.

The same idea extends to higher-order analyses of variance as well. Suppose that in a two-factor experiment, there are $R$ rows and $C$ columns in the data matrix. Then the SS rows is the sum of the $R - 1$ separate and independent sums of squares corresponding to orthogonal comparisons that might be made on row means. When the experimental design itself is orthogonal, each and every one of these $R - 1$ comparisons is itself orthogonal to any of the $C - 1$ independent comparisons that might be made on the column means. Thus, for an orthogonal design, the SS rows and SS columns are independent, since the values making up each sum are independent. For such a design, and given normal population distributions with equal variances, the mean square for rows and the mean square for columns are completely independent values. Furthermore, the $(R - 1)(C - 1)$ potential orthogonal comparisons summarized as mean square interaction are independent of those made on rows, of those made on columns, and of each other. A considerable part of the statistician's ability to formulate different kinds of experimental designs for different purposes comes from the general principle showing which potential comparisons are independent and which are not in a given way that data might be collected.

Incidentally, the same sort of argument used above can also shed some light on the concept of degrees of freedom in general. You should remember that the unbiased variance estimate $\hat{s}^2$ is said to have $N - 1$ degrees of freedom when computed from a sample of $N$ independent observations. Now the rationale given in Section 10.8 for this number of degrees of freedom is rather inadequate; although the $N$ different observed values are independent, the $N$ deviations from the sample mean going to make up $\hat{s}^2$ are *not* independent. Nevertheless, it is always possible to find $N - 1$ linear combinations of those $N$ values that will be orthogonal to each other and the sample mean. For normal populations, values of these $N - 1$ orthogonal linear combinations *are* independent. Furthermore, it can be shown that the value of $\hat{s}^2$ depends only on the values of $N - 1$ such independent linear combinations. Each such linear combination of scores can be turned into a squared and weighted value, much like the sum of squares for a comparison among means, and $\hat{s}^2$ is algebraically equivalent to the sum of these squared and weighted values divided by the number of degrees of freedom. Each single such squared value has 1 degree of freedom, since it was based on a single linear combination; the sum of these values has $N - 1$ degrees of freedom since the linear combinations themselves are orthogonal. In short, the degrees of freedom for $\hat{s}^2$ is properly thought of as the number of linear combinations of scores, mutually orthogonal and orthogonal to the mean, sufficient to determine the value of $\hat{s}^2$. Note the similarity of this formulation to that of mean square between as a value based on $J - 1$ linear combinations orthogonal to each other and to the grand sample mean; the underlying ideas are the same in both instances.

A simple example may help to clarify this point. Consider a random sample of three independent observations, yielding values $y_1$, $y_2$, and $y_3$. Three orthogonal linear combinations of these values are formed:

$$v_1 = \frac{y_1 + y_2 + y_3}{3}$$

$$v_2 = y_1 - y_2$$

and

$$v_3 = \frac{y_1 + y_2}{2} - y_3.$$

The first of these linear combinations is just the sample mean, and you can check for yourself that the other two combinations are orthogonal both to the sample mean and to each other. Now we take

$$SS = \frac{v_2^2}{2} + \frac{v_3^2}{1.5}$$

just as though these two $v$ values were based on means. However, in terms of the original $y$ values,

$$SS = \frac{(y_1 - y_2)^2}{2} + \frac{1}{1.5}\left(\frac{y_1 + y_2}{2} - y_3\right)^2,$$

so that on expanding this expression and turning SS into a mean square, we have

$$MS = \frac{SS}{2} = \frac{y_1^2 + y_2^2 + y_3^2 - y_1 y_2 - y_1 y_3 - y_2 y_3}{3}.$$

On the other hand, on taking $\hat{s}^2$ in the usual way, we have

$$\hat{s}^2 = \frac{\sum_i y_i^2 - \left(\sum_i y_i\right)^2 \Big/ 3}{2} = \frac{y_1^2 + y_2^2 + y_3^2 - y_1 y_2 - y_1 y_3 - y_2 y_3}{3}$$
$$= MS.$$

Thus, the mean square based on two orthogonal linear combinations, each orthogonal to the sample mean, is exactly equivalent to the unbiased estimate $\hat{s}^2$ calculated from the values for these three observations. This mean square has two degrees of freedom, since it is based on two out of the set of three possible orthogonal linear combinations of values for three observations.

## 14.12   POOLING THE SUMS OF SQUARES FOR "OTHER COMPARISONS"

Quite often it happens that no set of prior questions exists that would use up all the possible $J - 1$ independent comparisons in the data. The experimenter may have only one or two questions he particularly wants answered, and is content to lump all other comparisons into a single test, corresponding to "are there any other effects?" Then a combination of planned comparisons and analysis of variance techniques is possible.

Suppose that out of $J - 1$ possible comparisons the experimenter decides that only two are of overriding interest. Let us call these comparisons $\hat{\psi}_1$ and $\hat{\psi}_2$. He calculates SS $(\hat{\psi}_1)$ and SS $(\hat{\psi}_2)$ and carries out the tests for each. Now what of all the remaining $J - 1 - 2$ independent comparisons he might make? A very simple way exists for finding a SS value for those remaining. First of all, by the analysis of variance he calculates SS between groups in the ordinary way. Then

SS (all $\hat{\psi}$ independent of $\hat{\psi}_1$ and $\hat{\psi}_2$)
$$= \text{SS between} - \text{SS}(\hat{\psi}_1) - \text{SS}(\hat{\psi}_2). \quad [14.12.1\dagger]$$

In other words, one simply subtracts the sum of squares for comparisons 1 and 2 from the sum of squares between groups to find the sum of squares for *all remaining* comparisons independent of the first two. Instead of only one $F$ test, the experimenter now makes three tests: one for comparison 1, one for comparison 2, and one for all remaining comparisons, given by

$$F = \frac{\text{SS between} - \text{SS}(\hat{\psi}_1) - \text{SS}(\hat{\psi}_2)}{(J-3)\,\text{MS error}} \quad [14.12.2\dagger]$$

with $(J-3)$ and $(N-J)$ degrees of freedom.

Any subset of some total possible set of independent comparisons may be planned for in this way: the comparisons of special interest are checked for independence and then tested. All remaining comparisons independent to those tested are embodied in the difference between the SS between and the sum of the SS for the special comparisons tested. The $F$ test for "other comparisons" has its degrees of freedom reduced by one for each comparison tested separately. If this $F$ value is significant, then these comparisons of secondary interest can be examined individually by post-hoc methods.

This is a strategy in the analysis of experiments that is quite versatile and is used all too seldom in psychological research; this is partly the result of an unfortunate confusion between planned and post-hoc comparisons that often appears in psychology. The method is particularly effective where various control groups are introduced into the experiment, and the experimenter's interest in the control groups is quite different from his concern with the experimental treatments. It should be emphasized, however, that the various comparisons to be tested separately must be planned before the data are seen for the inferences to be valid. Comparisons are tested *instead of*, rather than as a supplement to, the ordinary "omnibus" $F$ test. Remember that it is essential to this method that the comparisons designed for separate testing be orthogonal according to the rule given in Section 14.6.

## 14.13 AN EXAMPLE USING PLANNED COMPARISONS

The experiment outlined in Section 14.1 was carried out with a total of 30 subjects, assigned at random into groups of 5. The weights for the comparisons representing the four basic questions are shown in Table 14.13.1. A check using the criterion for orthogonality (Section 14.6) shows that these comparisons can be regarded as independent.

**Table 14.13.1**

| Comparison | Treatments | | | Controls | | |
| --- | --- | --- | --- | --- | --- | --- |
| | Movie | Lecture | Movie & lecture | Nothing | Neutral movie | Neutral lecture |
| 1 | $\frac{1}{3}$ | $\frac{1}{3}$ | $\frac{1}{3}$ | $-\frac{1}{3}$ | $-\frac{1}{3}$ | $-\frac{1}{3}$ |
| 2 | $\frac{1}{2}$ | $\frac{1}{2}$ | $-1$ | 0 | 0 | 0 |
| 3 | 1 | $-1$ | 0 | 0 | 0 | 0 |
| 4 | 0 | 0 | 0 | 1 | $-\frac{1}{2}$ | $-\frac{1}{2}$ |

It was decided to test each of these comparisons at the .05 level. The data turned out as shown in Table 14.13.2. The numbers in the table are changes in attitude score for each person.

**Table 14.13.2**

| | Movie | Lecture | Movie & lecture | Nothing | Neutral movie | Neutral lecture | |
| --- | --- | --- | --- | --- | --- | --- | --- |
| | 6 | 3 | 7 | $-6$ | 5 | $-1$ | |
| | 10 | 6 | 9 | 0 | $-5$ | 3 | |
| | 1 | $-1$ | 4 | $-5$ | 3 | 2 | |
| | 6 | 5 | 9 | 2 | $-4$ | $-1$ | |
| | 4 | 2 | 3 | 2 | 5 | $-6$ | |
| Totals | 27 | 15 | 32 | $-7$ | 4 | $-3$ | 68 |
| Means | 5.4 | 3 | 6.4 | $-1.4$ | .8 | $-.6$ | |

The numerical computations for the ordinary one-way analysis of variance are first carried out; not only does this give the MS error needed for the comparisons tests, but also the SS between useful in testing any remaining comparisons.

$$\text{SS total} = 720 - \frac{(68)^2}{30} = 565.9$$

$$\text{SS between} = \frac{(27)^2 + \cdots + (-3)^2}{5} - \frac{(68)^2}{30} = 256.3$$

$$\text{SS error} = 309.6$$

$$\text{MS error} = \frac{309.6}{24} = 12.9.$$

Now for comparison 1:

$$\hat{\psi}_1 = \left(\frac{1}{3}\right)(5.4) + \left(\frac{1}{3}\right)(3) + \left(\frac{1}{3}\right)6.4 - \left(\frac{1}{3}\right)(-1.4) - \left(\frac{1}{3}\right)(.8) - \left(\frac{1}{3}\right)(-.6)$$

$$= \frac{16}{3} = 5.3$$

$$w_1 = \frac{1}{5}\left[\frac{1}{9} + \frac{1}{9} + \frac{1}{9} + \frac{1}{9} + \frac{1}{9} + \frac{1}{9}\right] = \frac{2}{15}$$

$$\mathrm{SS}(\hat{\psi}_1) = \frac{15(5.3)^2}{2} = 210.7.$$

The test for comparison 1 is given by

$$F = \frac{210.7}{12.9} = 16.3$$

which is significant far beyond the 5 percent level for 1 and 24 degrees of freedom. There does seem to be a reliable difference between experimental and control groups, in general.

For comparison 2,

$$\hat{\psi}_2 = \left(\frac{1}{2}\right)(5.4) + \left(\frac{1}{2}\right)(3) - (1)(6.4) = -2.2$$

$$w_2 = \frac{1}{5}\left[\left(\frac{1}{2}\right)^2 + \left(\frac{1}{2}\right)^2 + 1\right] = .3$$

$$\mathrm{SS}\,(\hat{\psi}_2) = \frac{(2.2)^2}{.3} = 16.1,$$

so that the $F$ test for this comparison is

$$F = \frac{16.1}{12.9} = 1.2.$$

This is not significant. There is not enough evidence to say that the combined movie-lecture effect is different from the average of their separate effects.

Comparison 3 gives

$$\hat{\psi}_3 = (1)(5.4) - 1(3) = 2.4$$

with

$$w_3 = \frac{1}{5}(1 + 1) = .4$$

so that

$$\mathrm{SS}\,(\hat{\psi}_3) = \frac{(2.4)^2}{.4} = 14.4.$$

The $F$ test for comparison 3 is then

$$F = \frac{14.4}{12.9} = 1.1,$$

again not significant. There is not enough evidence to say that a movie-lecture difference exists in the populations.

The value for comparison 4 is

$$\hat{\psi}_4 = (1)(-1.4) + \left(\frac{-1}{2}\right)(.8) + \left(\frac{-1}{2}\right)(-.6) = -1.5$$

with

$$w_4 = \frac{1}{5}\left[1 + \frac{1}{4} + \frac{1}{4}\right] = .3.$$

The sum of squares

$$\text{SS}\,(\hat{\psi}_4) = \frac{(-1.5)^2}{.3} = 7.5$$

is less than MS error, so that the $F$ test is definitely not significant.

Only four of the five possible independent comparisons have been made. The sum of squares for the fifth comparison can be found from

$$\text{SS between} - \text{SS}\,(\hat{\psi}_1) - \text{SS}\,(\hat{\psi}_2) - \text{SS}\,(\hat{\psi}_3) - \text{SS}\,(\hat{\psi}_4)$$
$$= 256.3 - 210.7 - 16.1 - 14.4 - 7.5 = 7.6.$$

This last comparison might be tested, but we can see that since its sum of squares is less than MS error, it cannot be significant.

The results of this analysis can be put into tabular form as shown in Table 14.13.3.

**Table 14.13.3**

| Source | SS | df | MS | F |
|---|---|---|---|---|
| Between groups | 256.3 | 5 | | |
| Comparison: | | | | |
| 1 | 210.7 | 1 | 210.7 | 16.3 |
| 2 | 16.1 | 1 | 16.1 | 1.2 |
| 3 | 14.4 | 1 | 14.4 | 1.1 |
| 4 | 7.5 | 1 | 7.5 | — |
| Remainder | 7.6 | 1 | 7.6 | — |
| Error (within groups) | 309.6 | 24 | 12.9 | — |
| Totals | 565.9 | 29 | | |

As always, however, we should bear in mind that for any set of several significance tests, the probability that at least one of tests will give significant results can be relatively large, even though the nominal $\alpha$ level used for each separate test is conventionally small. A related problem in the evaluation of a set of results is the now familiar principle that the several $F$ or $t$ ratios, even for a set of independent comparisons, need not be independent. This point will be discussed further in Section 14.17. The over-all meaning of a set of statistical results such as ours is rather difficult to assess. We have, however, at least arranged the data into portions pertaining to hypotheses we believe important and meaningful for the over-all interpretation of the experiment. This was the contribution of the analysis by planned comparisons.

## 14.14 THE CHOICE OF THE PLANNED COMPARISONS

Given any $J$ independent means, there are any number of ways to choose the $J - 1$ independent comparisons to be made among these means. The important thing is that the experimenter have definite prior questions that he wants answered, and that these questions can be framed as orthogonal, or independent comparisons. The experimenter must assure himself that he has collected data that will provide answers to his questions in terms of orthogonal comparisons. For example, in the experiment just analyzed, the experimenter might have had the following initial concerns:

1. Is there any effect of showing the experimental movie, as opposed to the initial lecture or nothing?
2. Is there any effect of the experimental lecture, as opposed to the experimental movie or nothing?
3. Is the effect of the experimental movie the same whether or not it is accompanied by a lecture?
4. Does the neutral movie have the same effect as the neutral lecture?

These four questions can be embodied in four comparisons quite different from those employed above (Table 14.14.1). A check shows that each of these

**Table 14.14.1**

| Comparisons | Movie | Lecture | Movie & lecture | Nothing | Neutral movie | Neutral lecture |
|:---:|:---:|:---:|:---:|:---:|:---:|:---:|
| 1 | $\frac{1}{2}$ | $-\frac{1}{2}$ | $\frac{1}{2}$ | $-\frac{1}{2}$ | 0 | 0 |
| 2 | $-\frac{1}{2}$ | $\frac{1}{2}$ | $\frac{1}{2}$ | $-\frac{1}{2}$ | 0 | 0 |
| 3 | $-\frac{1}{2}$ | $-\frac{1}{2}$ | $\frac{1}{2}$ | $\frac{1}{2}$ | 0 | 0 |
| 4 | 0 | 0 | 0 | 0 | 1 | $-1$ |

comparisons is independent of each of the others. Notice, however, that some of these comparisons are *not* independent of some of the first set.

This new set of orthogonal comparisons also illustrates another point: If the experimenter had conceived the study as a two-factor design, in which "experimental movie versus no experimental movie" constituted the levels of the first factor, and "experimental lecture versus no experimental lecture" the levels of the second, then the first three comparisons outlined above correspond exactly to the three degrees of freedom associated with main effects and interaction in such a design. That is, comparison 1 provides a SS value that is exactly the same as the SS for the first factor, comparison 2 gives a SS value that corresponds to the SS for the second factor, and comparison 3 provides a SS value that is identical to the SS for interaction in a two-factor design. The fourth comparison is, however, based on two groups not included in the two-way design. This illustrates the fact mentioned in Section 14.11: the single degrees of freedom included in the SS between groups for an analysis of variance each correspond to some potential comparison among means.

For any given experiment, there will undoubtedly be many interesting questions that could be framed as planned comparisons. Only the particular experimenter can decide, of course, which comparisons are of interest to him. As a rule, he should not try to think up a sensible question to correspond to each of the $J - 1$ degrees of freedom associated with $J$ means just because he can, in principle, do so. Rather, the technique of planned comparisons should be used only when there are a few important specific questions to ask of the data that will clarify the whole experiment if answered. Once these questions have been decided upon, they must be phrased so that the answer will be evident from some way of weighting and combining means. Usually, such questions resolve themselves into differences between groups of means, just as, in the last set of comparisons, the answer to question 1 depends upon the difference between the averages of two groups of means:

$$\frac{\text{(movie)} + \text{(movie \& lecture)}}{2} - \frac{\text{(lecture)} + \text{(nothing)}}{2}.$$

This difference weights the (movie) mean and the (movie & lecture) means each by $1/2$, and the (lecture) and (nothing) group means each by $-1/2$, so that this difference gives us our weights for that comparison. The same is true for each of the other comparisons discussed here. In general, the idea is to frame the question, determine what data are necessary for the answer, and then ask how the data may be combined to answer it. The questions of most importance should be formulated first, and then if other important questions can be framed as independent comparisons, well and good. However, if all the different questions cannot be framed as separate orthogonal comparisons, the more important may be tested directly and the others lumped into an over-all "other comparisons" $F$ test.

## 14.15  INCIDENTAL OR POST-HOC COMPARISONS IN DATA

Even though tests for planned comparisons form a useful technique in experimentation, it is far more common for the experimenter to have no special questions to begin with. His initial concern is to establish only that some real effects or comparison differences do exist in his data. Given a significant over-all test, his task is then to explore the data to find the source of these effects, and to try to explain their meaning.

*The technique for comparisons to be introduced now is applicable only to the situation where a preliminary analysis of variance and F test has shown over-all significance.* It is not a device for rescuing poor experiments by data-juggling. Instead, if the experimenter has found evidence for over-all significance among his experimental groups, he may use this method of post-hoc comparisons to evaluate *any* interesting comparisons among means.

The idea of a comparison here is exactly the same as defined in Section 14.2. A sample comparison $\hat{\psi}$ is a linear combination of sample means

$$\hat{\psi} = \sum_j c_j M_j$$

where $\sum_j c_j = 0$.

After the over-all $F$ has been found significant, then *any* comparison $\hat{\psi}$ may be made. *Unlike planned comparisons, there is no requirement that such post-hoc comparisons be independent.* Any and all comparisons of interest may be made. Most often the experimenter may be interested in examining all pairs of means, but any comparison $\hat{\psi}$ is legitimate.

There are a number of methods that have been devised for testing the significance of post-hoc comparisons, only one of which will be given here. This is the method due to Scheffé (1959), which has advantages of simplicity, applicability to groups of unequal sizes, and suitability for any comparison. This method is also known to be relatively insensitive to departures from normality and homogeneity of variance. The method due to Tukey (outlined in Winer, 1962) seems to be preferable to the Scheffé method when the various samples are of equal size and the experimenter's interest lies only in all possible pairwise differences between means. However, the Scheffé method is emphasized here because of its simplicity and versatility over a wide variety of situations.

Given any comparison $g$ made on the data after a significant $F$ has been found for the relevant factor, the significance of the comparison value $\hat{\psi}_g$ may be found by use of the following confidence interval:

$$\hat{\psi}_g - S \sqrt{V(\hat{\psi}_g)} \leq \psi_g \leq \hat{\psi}_g + S \sqrt{V(\hat{\psi}_g)} \qquad \text{[14.15.1†]}$$

where

$$\sqrt{V(\hat{\psi}_g)} = \sqrt{(\text{MS error})w_g} = \sqrt{\text{est. var.}(\hat{\psi})} \qquad \text{[14.15.2†]}$$

and

$$S = \sqrt{(J-1)F_\alpha}. \qquad \text{[14.15.3†]}$$

The $w_g$ is defined in Section 14.11, and $F_\alpha$ is the value required for significance at the $\alpha$ level, with $J-1$ and $N-J$ degrees of freedom (that is, the $F$ required for significance at the $\alpha$ level for an *over-all* test of the $J$ means). For any $\alpha$, this gives the $100(1-\alpha)$ percent confidence interval for $\psi_g$, the true value of the comparison. When the confidence interval fails to cover zero, the comparison is said to be significant, and identified as one possible contributor to the over-all significance of $F$.

The meaning of this confidence interval for post-hoc comparisons requires some special comment. If we consider all possible comparisons $\psi_g$ that might be carried out on the true means of the $J$ groups, then *the probability is $1 - \alpha$ that the statement* **14.15.1** *is true simultaneously for all $\psi_g$.* That is, if we could work out all possible comparisons on the data, and for each comparison calculate a 95 percent confidence interval, then the chances are 95 in 100 that every one of these confidence intervals would contain the true value for that comparison. There is only a 5 percent chance that one or more confidence intervals will not cover the corresponding true comparison value.

This is a somewhat different conception from the usual confidence-interval statement. When we make a 95 percent confidence interval for, say, a single mean $\mu$, we are correct in saying that if we took all possible random samples of size $N$ and calculated the interval for each, the interval would cover the true value of $\mu$ 95 percent of the time. For the post-hoc comparisons, however, we are referring to all possible comparisons that might be made on a given set of data, and the probability statement is about the event of all such intervals computed from a set of data covering the corresponding true values. For this reason it is important that the initial $F$ be significant, giving us prior reason to believe that reliable departures from zero exist to be found among the possible comparisons.

Note that one says that a comparison is significant at the $\alpha$ level if the confidence interval for that comparison does not cover zero. Any confidence interval for a comparison $\psi_g$ that includes zero within its limits is said to be nonsignificant.

**If the over-all $F$ test is significant at the $\alpha$ level, then some comparison $\hat{\psi}_g$ must be significant at or beyond the same level.** Indeed, a significant $F$ test can be interpreted as evidence that at least one true comparison value among all those possible is not zero. This does not mean that just because the over-all $F$ was significant you will necessarily find the significant comparisons, but only that they exist to be found. Hence our interpretation of a significant $F$ as a signal, "Something's here—start looking."

## 14.16   AN EXAMPLE OF POST-HOC COMPARISONS FOLLOWING A ONE-WAY ANALYSIS OF VARIANCE

In a psychological study subjects were assigned randomly to five different groups, representing five different experimental treatments. Twelve subjects were used in each group. The means of the various groups were

$$
\begin{array}{ccccc}
I & II & III & IV & V \\
63 & 82 & 80 & 75 & 70
\end{array}
$$

and the analysis of variance is summarized in Table 14.16.1. For an $\alpha$ of .05, the required $F$ for 4 and 55 degrees of freedom is approximately 2.53, so that this obtained value is significant. Hence, post-hoc comparisons may be tested for significance. The .05 level will be used in these tests as well.

**Table 14.16.1**

| *Source* | *SS* | *df* | *MS* | *F* |
|---|---|---|---|---|
| Between groups | 2851 | 4 | 712.8 | 4.0 |
| Error (within groups) | 9801 | 55 | 178.2 | |
| Totals | 12652 | 59 | | |

Now suppose that the experimenter wished to examine all pair-wise differences between means. It is convenient to put all ten such differences in a table, such as Table 14.16.2. (The difference in a cell is the mean represented by column subtracted from the mean represented by the row; thus $63 - 82 = -19$, and so on.)

Table 14.16.2

|  | Mean | *Group* | | | |
|---|---|---|---|---|---|
|  |  | *II* | *III* | *IV* | *V* |
| Mean |  | 82 | 80 | 75 | 70 |
| Group |  |  |  |  |  |
| I | 63 | $-19$ | $-17$ | $-12$ | $-7$ |
| II | 82 |  | 2 | 7 | 12 |
| III | 80 |  |  | 5 | 10 |
| IV | 75 |  |  |  | 5 |

The 95 percent confidence interval will be found for each of these differences, as follows.

First we note that each of the comparisons being made uses the same numbers as weights, and that each mean is based on the same number of subjects, twelve; hence

$$w_g = \frac{1}{12}(1 + 1) = \frac{1}{6}$$

and

$$\sqrt{V(\hat{\psi}_g)} = \sqrt{\frac{178.2}{6}} = 5.45 \text{ for each pair of means.}$$

Also

$$S = \sqrt{(4)F_{(.05)}} = \sqrt{4(2.53)} = 3.18.$$

The 95 percent confidence interval for each comparison difference is thus

$$\hat{\psi}_g - (3.18)(5.45) \leq \psi_g \leq \hat{\psi}_g + (3.18)(5.45)$$

or

$$\hat{\psi}_g - 17.33 \leq \psi_g \leq \hat{\psi}_g + 17.33.$$

For this interval to *exclude* zero for any of these differences, the obtained difference would have to be *greater* than 17.33 in absolute magnitude. One of the differences (between I and II) is this large, and so this pairwise comparison is significant (at the .05 level). We can say that this difference contributes to the over-all significance of $F$.

However, many other comparisons could be tested. Suppose that we compare the average of II and III with the average of I, IV, and V. Here the value of the comparison is

$$\hat{\psi}_g = \frac{82 + 80}{2} - \frac{63 + 75 + 70}{3}$$

$$= \left(\frac{1}{2}\right)(82) + \left(\frac{1}{2}\right)(80) - \left(\frac{1}{3}\right)63 - \left(\frac{1}{3}\right)75 - \left(\frac{1}{3}\right)(70) = 11.67.$$

Now the confidence interval is different, since

$$w_g = \frac{1}{12}\left(\frac{1}{4} + \frac{1}{4} + \frac{1}{9} + \frac{1}{9} + \frac{1}{9}\right) = \frac{5}{72} = .069,$$

and
$$\sqrt{V(\hat{\psi}_g)} = \sqrt{(178.2)(.069)} = 3.51.$$

The value of $S$ is still 3.18 for $\alpha = .05$. Therefore, the confidence interval for this comparison is

$$\hat{\psi}_g - (3.18)(3.51) \le \psi_g \le \hat{\psi}_g + (3.18)(3.51)$$

or

$$11.67 - 11.16 \le \psi_g \le 11.67 + 11.16.$$

This interval does *not* include zero, and so this comparison also is significant beyond the .05 level.

The mere fact that one can find a significant comparison does not insure that the comparison is a meaningful one. It is definitely not profitable to work out every conceivable comparison among the means and test each for significance, in hopes that something of meaning will emerge. Just the reverse procedure should be used: inspecting the data, the experimenter comes to tentative conclusions about where the large and interpretable effects lie. These tentative conclusions are then tested.

## 14.17  PLANNED VERSUS POST-HOC COMPARISONS

It is obvious that in any given experiment it is always possible either to plan comparisons to be tested in lieu of the over-all $F$ test, or to perform post-hoc comparisons should the over-all $F$ be significant. What are the arguments for and against these two ways of proceeding?

An important point in favor of planned comparisons is this: consider any true comparison $\psi$ among $J$ means ($J > 2$), such that $\psi \ne 0$. **The probability of a test's detecting that $\psi$ is not zero is greater with a planned than with an unplanned comparison on the same sample means.** In other words, for any particular comparison, the test is more powerful when the comparison is planned than when it is post-hoc.

This can be seen in a slightly different way by considering confidence intervals. As we have just seen, the confidence interval for a post-hoc comparison is

$$\hat{\psi}_g - S\sqrt{V(\hat{\psi}_g)} \le \psi_g \le \hat{\psi}_g + S\sqrt{V(\hat{\psi}_g)}.$$

where

$$S = \sqrt{(J-1)F_\alpha}.$$

The confidence interval for a planned comparison may be written as

$$\hat{\psi}_g - t_{(\alpha/2)}\sqrt{V(\hat{\psi}_g)} \le \psi_g \le \hat{\psi}_g + t_{(\alpha/2)}\sqrt{V(\hat{\psi}_g)}$$

where $t_{(\alpha/2)}$ is the value of $t$ required for two-tailed significance at the $\alpha$ level with $N - J$ degrees of freedom. It can be shown that for more than two means

$$t_{(\alpha/2)} < S,$$

so that **the confidence interval for any given comparison is shorter when that comparison is planned than when it is post-hoc.**

The practical implication is that the *importance* of the comparison should dictate whether or not it is tested by the planned or the post-hoc procedure. If the experimental question represented by the comparison is an important one for the interpretation of the experiment, and it is essential that a Type II error not be made in the accompanying test, then a planned comparison should be carried out. On the other hand, if the question is a minor one, and a considerable risk of overlooking a true non-zero value can be tolerated, then the post-hoc method suffices.

However, we have also seen that the number and variety of planned comparisons to be made and tested is limited by the independence requirement. No such requirement holds for the post-hoc method. The data may be only partly explored by the planned method, but fully by the post-hoc method.

One final but very mportant point must be made before we leave the subject of planned and post-hoc comparisons. This point applies both to the method of planned comparisons and to any technique such as the multiway analysis of variance, where some $K$ different significance tests are applied to the data. It is true that when comparisons are orthogonal or the experimental design itself is orthogonal these various tests may be carried out separately. Furthermore, they may be regarded as approximately independent when the degrees of freedom for error is very large. Under these circumstances, if each test is conducted with $\alpha$ set at some level, say .05, then one should expect about 5 percent of these tests to show significance by chance alone, even though each and every $H_0$ tested is true.

However, the temptation is very strong for the experimenter interpreting the entire set of significance tests and evaluating the experiment as a whole to focus on the several tests that did turn out significant, and to overlook the fact that many such tests were carried out. What is the probability that *at least one test* will show spurious significance out of $K$ tests carried out? We have already seen that for $K$ independent tests this can be found from

$$p(\text{one or more significant results, all } H_0 \text{ true}) = 1 - (1 - \alpha)^K$$

which for small $\alpha$ is approximately equal to $K\alpha$. Thus, as the number of different tests increases, the probability of at least one spuriously significant result tends to increase as well. Although this probability can be calculated exactly only for independent tests, this is a feature of *any* set of ordinary significance tests on the same set of data, whether of planned comparisons or for effects in a complicated analysis of variance. Perform enough tests and the probability is large that at least one will turn out significant by chance alone.

On the other hand, in carrying out post-hoc comparisons the situation is different. Here, the probability is $\alpha$ that at least one comparison will turn out to be spuriously significant at the $\alpha$ level, regardless of how many comparisons are made. It is true that, for any given comparison, the probability of *overlooking* a true difference from zero is greater in the post-hoc than in the planned method (in other words, the Type II error probability is greater). Nevertheless, the probability of committing a Type I error for *one or more* such post-hoc comparisons is exactly $\alpha$.

This fact has two important implications for us: In the first place, the multiple results one gets from a complicated experiment are hard to interpret from a statistical point of view. Given enough significance tests, you are almost bound to get at least one significant result, even though the experiment is the purest nonsense. The probability that at least one of your over-all conclusions is wrong is considerably greater than $\alpha$. This is not an argument against the use of planned comparisons any more than against the use of multifactor experimental designs; it is, however, an argument against the indiscriminate use of the $\alpha$ level from single significance tests as a means of evaluating the conclusions drawn from the experiment as a whole, and especially against the overinterpretation of single significant findings.

The second implication is that the importance of not committing a Type II error should have a great deal to do with the choice of planned versus post-hoc comparisons. Thus, casual inspection of the data seems to call for the post-hoc variety of comparison, whereas the "big guns" of planned comparisons should be reserved for the really important questions, where one wants to be almost sure to detect true differences from zero where they exist.

If, for some reason, the experimenter feels that he must have the probability equal $\alpha$ or less that *one or more* planned comparisons turn out significant by chance, then he may adopt the following procedure: Each of the $K$ separate comparisons may be tested at the $\alpha/K$ level, and then it will be true that the probability of one or more significant results by chance alone is no greater than $\alpha$. For example, suppose that given some 10 experimental groups, 5 comparisons are to be tested separately. The experimenter tests each at the .01 level. Then the probability that one or more turns out significant by chance alone is no more than 5(.01) or .05. When only a few out of relatively many possible comparisons are to be tested separately, this procedure gives the experimenter some control over the "error rate" for the separate tests, without completely sacrificing the gains in power and "neat packaging" of the data achieved by making planned rather than post-hoc comparisons.

Since the procedure outlined in the preceding paragraph will often require $t$ values for percentage points not listed in the standard tables, the following approximation is useful. In order to find the approximate value of $t$ cutting off the upper $\alpha$ proportion in a distribution with $\nu$ degrees of freedom, take

$$t_{(\alpha;\,\nu)} = z_\alpha + (z_\alpha^3 + z_\alpha)/4(\nu - 2),$$

where $z_\alpha$ is the corresponding value in a standardized normal distribution.

In summary, then, let it be said that the planned comparisons method is best suited for situations where a few overriding concerns dictate the interpretation of the whole experiment. Here one must have the most powerful tests possible for resolving these issues. The post-hoc method is suited for trying out hunches gained during the data analysis and for inferring the sources of the significant over-all $F$ test. We will return to the subject of planned and post-hoc comparisons in Chapter 16, where their applicability to still another kind of experiment will be pointed out.

# PROBLEMS IN LINEAR REGRESSION AND CORRELATION

## 15

So far the emphasis in this book has been upon problems of inferring population characteristics from samples, and of finding evidence for statistical relations between variables. There is, however, quite another aspect to the theory of statistical inference: the problem of predicting a score for the individual case, given some prior information about him. How does one *use* the statistical relations found in data? For example, a personnel officer in an industrial setting must decide whether or not to hire an individual for a specific job. He has some information about him, perhaps a score on trade-skills test, and in the light of this information he must "bet" or predict how the person will work out on a particular job. A vocational counselor must give some advice to a prospective college student about the course of study in which he is likely to find success. The counselor has the student's high-school record, as well as his intelligence and interest test scores—what is the best thing to advise the student? A physician examines a patient who exhibits certain symptoms and laboratory test results. What kind of treatment is the best bet to relieve these symptoms? In the real work-a-day world, the problem of using the results of statistical studies to make a decision about an individual case is not only one of the most common, but perhaps the most important, single use of statistical findings.

Quite apart from any practical application, the problem of prediction arises in a purely scientific study as well. Several times in the preceding discussion we have emphasized that the scientist is looking for evidence of stable relationships in his data, and that the idea of strength of a statistical relation is based on the extent to which knowing individual status on variable $X$ reduces uncertainty about status on $Y$, the thing predicted. The indices $\omega^2$ and $\rho_I$ both rest on this notion: statistical association is strong to the extent that specifying the event $X$ reduces the variance of the possible $Y$ values, so that, literally, information about $X$ tells us something about $Y$. Furthermore, we have noted

490

that if there is actually a functional relation between $X$ and $Y$, perfect prediction is possible, so that $X$ tells us *everything* about $Y$, other things being equal.

However, we have said very little about possible *rules* for prediction. There has been a very good reason for us to avoid the question of prediction rules: heretofore, $X$ has been treated categorically, as standing for any one of a set of qualitatively distinct categories into which an observation might fall. The analysis of variance, for instance, deals only with a set of different samples representing different populations of potential observations. The actual experimental basis for distinguishing among the different samples is, formally, immaterial; the samples may represent either qualitative or quantitative distinctions of any sort. In the simple analysis of variance, we acknowledge only that the different samples are somehow different in one experimental respect, and then we look for systematic differences in the dependent variable $Y$. However, rules for going from the *qualitative* status of an observation to some quantitative prediction are ordinarily very difficult to formulate, and so we have had to be content with discussing evidence for the existence of a statistical relation, and with forming estimates of its strength according to indices such as $\omega^2$.

Now, however, we are going to deal with situations where the independent variable $X$ actually takes on *numerical* values. The variable $X$ may stand for an amount of some treatment administered in an experiment, such as the dosage of a drug, or the number of trials given at a learning task, values fixed quite arbitrarily by the experimenter. Or, perhaps, $X$ may stand for some measured property of the individual himself, such as his height, his age, or his intelligence quotient. Associated with each possible $X$ value there is some distribution of $Y$ scores, the conditional distribution of $Y$ given $X$ (compare Section 4.7). Perfect prediction of $Y$ from $X$ will be possible only if the relation between the two variables is functional, of course. For a functional relation, each conditional distribution of $Y$ given $X$ consists of a single value. Nevertheless, regardless of whether or not the relation is actually a function, we can ask three questions of any set of data in which each individual observed represents the occurrence of some joint *numerical* event $(X,Y)$:

1. Does a statistical relation affording some predictability appear between the random variables $X$ and $Y$?
2. How strong is the apparent degree of the statistical relation, in the sense of possible predictive ability the relation affords?
3. Can a simple rule be formulated for predicting $Y$ from $X$, and if so, how good is this rule?

The ordinary statistical techniques we have studied apply to the first two of these questions, but the third is a new feature. In this chapter we are going to study the possibility of applying a *rule* for the prediction of $Y$ from $X$. We are going to act *as though* the true relation actually were a function, and, using a function rule, make predictions or "bets" about $Y$ values from knowledge of $X$ values. Then we are going to evaluate the *goodness* of this prediction rule in terms of how well one actually would do by predicting according to the rule. If the statistical relation actually is a function then some rule exists that affords perfect prediction; for the usual statistical relation, no rule permits perfect prediction, but some function rule may nevertheless provide a good "fit" to the relation under study. Proceeding in this fashion gives us two important advantages: quite often we are able to achieve a fair degree of predictive ability by adopting a particular function rule, even though the true relation itself is not really a function. Second, by studying our errors using this rule, we gain information about how the rule might be made better and how the general form of the relation might be specified more adequately.

The basic topic of this chapter is the study of prediction using a *linear* function rule. When pairs of $(X, Y)$ values fall exactly into a function that can be plotted as a straight line, the function is said to be linear. Such functions have extremely simple rules, which are always of the form

$$Y = bX + a$$

where $b$ and $a$ are two constant numbers. In this chapter we will see how prediction rules of this linear form can be applied, and how the fit of such a rule to a given relation can be evaluated.

The reasons for starting with linear rules for prediction are several: linear functions are the simplest to discuss and understand; such rules are often good approximations to other, much more complicated, rules; and we will find that in certain circumstances the only prediction rule that *can* apply is linear. However, do not jump to the conclusion that just because we deal first with linear prediction this is the only important way to predict, or that all real relationships must be more or less like linear functions. In the next chapter we will find that there are many other, nonlinear, function rules that might also be applied to a given problem.

## 15.1 REGRESSION AND CORRELATION PROBLEMS

At the very outset it must be emphasized that we are going to deal with two rather different sampling situations in this chapter. First, we will discuss techniques applicable to so-called **regression problems.** These are the problems and techniques that will ordinarily be of most interest to the experimental psychologist. The general ideas we will use are straightforward extensions of those underlying the analysis of variance, except now we will consider *numerical* experimental variables.

For example, a typical regression problem might be the following: an experimenter is interested in the effect of some tranquilizing drug on a subject's ability to solve reasoning problems. Individuals are assigned at random to different experimental groups, and the same drug is administered in different preassigned amounts to the various groups. These dosages were decided upon before the experiment, and the experimenter is concerned only with these fixed amounts. Then the groups are compared on the basis of scores on a reasoning task. The experimenter is interested not only in the existence of a possible statistical relation between the amount of drug administered and the reasoning

score, but also in the extent to which this relation may be approximated by the
use of a linear function rule.

Several things are important about this example. In the first place,
there is a clearly identified independent variable $X$, each value of which is an
amount of the drug administered. The possible values of this variable are fixed in
advance by the experimenter. The dependent variable $Y$ s the reasoning score for a
subject, and within each experimental group this variable is free to take on different
values. Furthermore, *both* the independent and dependent variables are *numerical:*
each subject in a group $j$ has the same $X$ score, the amount of drug administered,
although a particular subject $i$ in group $j$ has his own dependent variable score
$Y_{ij}$. Finally, our interest is in the *form* of the relation that occurs, and specifically,
on whether this relation can be approximated well by a linear function. In other
words, can one predict the value of $Y_{ij}$ from that of $X_j$ using such a linear rule?

In a later section we will discuss the meaning of the term "regression" as used here. For the moment, suffice it to say that in a problem in regression, one variable is clearly the independent or predictor variable, the thing
manipulated or known first by the experimenter. This variable $X$ is represented
at several arbitrary values in the experiment. Here the only interest is in the
possibility and degree of linear prediction of $Y$ from $X$.

The other application of the theory presented in this chapter occurs
in **problems of correlation.** In a correlation problem, there is no clear-cut distinction between two kinds of scores as to which is the independent or predictor
variable. Both variables are left completely free to take on any value for any
observed individual. A sample of $N$ individuals is drawn and each individual
observed represents the occurrence of a joint $(X,Y)$ event. The basic question
asked concerns the relation between the two variables: can $Y$ be predicted from
$X$ or $X$ predicted from $Y$ using a linear rule?

For example, suppose that 100 children are observed, and the height
$(X)$ and weight $(Y)$ of each child noted. The pair of values for each child is thus
a representative of some joint $(X,Y)$ event. Any possible height, any possible
weight, or any possible combination may occur in the data. There is no implication
that height is somehow "responsible" for weight, or weight for height. The experimenter wants only to see how well the relation between the two kinds of scores can
be thought of as a linear relation. Can *either* variable be predicted from the other
by a linear rule?

This distinction between the two kinds of problems is an important
one, and will be emphasized by our discussing the two types separately. Although
there are close theoretical connections between the methods appropriate to these
two kinds of problems, in practice the two situations differ in the way in which
samples are drawn, the status of one variable as *the* independent or predictor
variable, the assumptions one makes in significance testing, and in some circumstances, in the kinds of conclusions drawn. Thus, regression and correlation problems will be distinguished from each other much as we did the different models
for analysis of variance, where a roughly parallel situation exists.

In the next few sections, however, this distinction between regression and correlation problems is not important. We are going to lay the ground-

work for the descriptive statistics of regression, for how one actually finds a linear rule to use for prediction from some complete set of data. Then we will turn to problems of inference in the regression and the correlation situations, where the regression-correlation distinction *is* important.

## 15.2 THE DESCRIPTIVE STATISTICS OF REGRESSION AND CORRELATION

Just as we discussed how one could find and interpret the mean and variance as descriptions of particular aspects of a set of data, we will now turn to the problem of finding a linear rule that "fits" a given set of data as well as possible. For the moment, our interest is only in a specific set of data, the scores for some particular set of $N$ observed individuals.

Imagine this kind of situation: a teacher of a large introductory college course is interested in the possible relationship between the high-school preparation in mathematics that a student has and his success in the course. In a particular semester the teacher has a class of 91 students, and at the outset he asks each student to tell him the mathematics courses he has taken in high school (four years). The teacher weights these courses in a routine way and assigns scores running from 2 through 8 to the students. Let us call these "mathematics scores" $X$.

The teacher, however, files these reports away and does not look at them until after the final examination in the course has been given. The actual raw scores on this examination will be called the variable $Y$. After both scores for each student are known, the teacher asks this question: "To what extent is there a linear relation between the $X$ and the $Y$ scores?" In other words, how well does a simple linear rule allow one to predict the $Y$ score of a student drawn at random from this group, given the information about the $X$ score? The problem is to find the best possible linear rule for predicting from these data, and then to evaluate the goodness of such a rule.

Actually, the teacher is not especially interested in predicting the raw $Y$ score of a student so much as he is in the relative performance of the student in terms of $Y$. That is, he would like to be able to predict the standard score $z_Y$, given by

$$z_Y = \frac{Y - M_Y}{s_Y}.$$

This prediction is to be based on the standard score $z_X$, where

$$z_X = \frac{X - M_X}{s_X}.$$

Since a linear rule is to be used for this prediction, this means a rule of the form

$$z'_Y = bz_X + a \qquad \text{[15.2.1*]}$$

where $b$ and $a$ are constants. The predicted score is labeled as $z'_Y$ to indicate that it *need not* be the same as $z_Y$, the true standard score for any given individual.

Several individuals may have the same $z_X$ standard score, but quite different $z_Y$ scores; by use of the rule, however, *only one $z_Y'$ or predicted standard score will be given for each $z_X$ value.*

The problem is shown graphically in Figure 15.2.1. Here, the horizontal axis represents possible values for $z_X$, the vertical axis the possible values for $z_Y$, and any point within the plane defined by these two axes represents a pair of $z$ scores, $(z_X, z_Y)$, that might be associated with any individual observation. Points in the functional relation $z_Y' = bz_X + a$ lie along the straight line in the figure. For the particular value of $z_X$ represented in the figure, the linear rule affords a *predicted* value $z_Y'$; this *need not* correspond to the actual value $z_Y$ corresponding to any individual showing the particular value of $z_X$ shown in the figure. The extent of "miss" or error between the predicted value $z_Y'$ and $z_Y$ for an individual is represented by the vertical distance between the two points

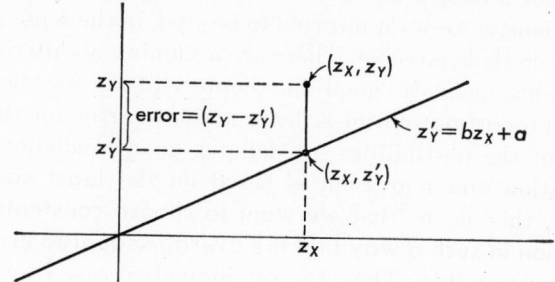

**FIG. 15.2.1.** Plot of a linear regression equation for the prediction of the standard score on Y from the standard score on X

$(z_X, z_Y)$ and $(z_X, z_Y')$. We would like our prediction rule to be such that, across all individuals, the fit between predicted and actual standard scores on $Y$ is as good as possible.

To recapitulate, the problem is to predict the $z_Y$ from $z_X$ *as though* these two numerical values were functionally related. The function rule to be used is a linear one, with constants chosen to give predictions that are, in some sense, "best." The user is perfectly well aware that the relation between the two kinds of scores is *not actually* a function (that is, any given value of $z_X$ can occur in pairs with any number of values of $z_Y$), but he does want to see how well the use of such a linear function rule allows him to guess the standard score on variable $Y$ given the standard score on $X$.

The reader may be puzzled by the use of the term "prediction" in this context; the teacher actually *has* the two scores for each of the 91 students. Why doesn't he merely look at the standardized $Y$ score for any student? Actually the methods to be developed here will apply to situations where the user wants to go beyond the immediate data, and to forecast the $Y$ or $z_Y$ score for an individual for which this information is not already available. However, the basis for these methods is best seen if one deals only with one intact group of $N$ cases, each having two scores, $X$ and $Y$. For the moment, "prediction" consists of drawing one case at random from this particular group, noting the $z_X$, and then finding a predicted value of $z_Y'$ by use of the linear rule

The first problem is to find constants $a$ and $b$ that will make the linear rule give the "best possible" predictions. We will find these constants by the method of "least squares" in the next section.

### 15.3 THE REGRESSION EQUATION FOR PREDICTING $z_Y$ FROM $z_X$

Given that we want to predict the relative status of an individual on variable $Y$, or $z_Y$, knowing only $z_X$, and that we must use the linear rule given by **15.2.1,**

$$z'_Y = bz_X + a,$$

how do we go about finding $b$ and $a$?

Obviously, we want our rule to be *good*, in the sense that it gives the best or closest predictions possible. There are a number of criteria that might be chosen to define what makes a "good" prediction: hitting the actual score on the nose the largest proportion of times, least absolute error on the average, and so on, are some of the possibilities for defining good prediction. However, the theory of correlation and regression is based on the **least squares** criterion. For our purposes, this means that **we want to choose constants for our linear prediction equation in such a way that the average squared error in prediction will be as small as possible.** Thus, for any individual case $i$ we will make some prediction, $z'_Y$; this need *not* be the same as the true value $z_{Yi}$ for that individual, and so some error will exist,

$$\text{error} = (z'_{Yi} - z_{Yi}).$$

The least-squares criterion requires that we choose $a$ and $b$ in such a way that the average squared error over individual predictions be as small as possible. Thus, given $N$ individuals $i$, we want to choose $a$ and $b$ so as to make

$$\frac{\sum\limits_i (z'_{Yi} - z_{Yi})^2}{N} \qquad [15.3.1*]$$

have its minimum possible value.

Now, first of all we will show that by the least-squares criterion, *if we are predicting standard scores, the value of the constant $a$ must be zero, so that the best linear rule is actually*

$$z'_Y = bz_X. \qquad [15.3.2*]$$

This can be shown as follows: Substituting **15.2.1** into **15.3.1** and rearranging terms we have

$$\frac{\sum\limits_i (z'_{Yi} - z_{Yi})^2}{N} = \frac{\sum\limits_i [(bz_{Xi} - z_{Yi}) + a]^2}{N}. \qquad [15.3.3]$$

On carrying out the square for each $i$ and summing, we have

$$\frac{\sum_i [(bz_{Xi} - z_{Yi}) + a]^2}{N} = \frac{\sum_i (bz_{Xi} - z_{Yi})^2}{N} + 2a\frac{\sum_i (bz_X - z_Y)}{N} + \frac{\sum_i a^2}{N}$$

$$= \frac{\sum_i (bz_{Xi} - z_{Yi})^2}{N} + a^2 \qquad [15.3.4]$$

since $a$ and $b$ are constants, and the mean of each set of $z$ scores must be zero.

Now, assuming $b$ fixed, for what value of $a$ can the expression on the right in **15.3.4** be at its smallest? The first term is a mean of squared numbers and hence must be positive, and $a^2$ must be positive as well; it follows that this expression can be at its smallest value *only* when $a$ is zero. Thus, the value of $a$ dictated by the least-squares criterion is zero.

Next, we will show that by the least-squares criterion the value of $b$ for predicting $z$ scores must be

$$b = \frac{\sum_i z_{Xi}z_{Yi}}{N}, \qquad [15.3.5^*]$$

that is, the constant $b$ must equal the average of the *products* of the standard scores across the $N$ individuals. This value of $b$ is actually the **correlation coefficient** (or Pearson product-moment correlation coefficient) $r_{XY}$, about which we will have much to say. By definition,

$$r_{XY} = \frac{\sum_i z_{Xi}z_{Yi}}{N}. \qquad [15.3.6^*]$$

Thus, by the criterion of least squares, our prediction rule must be

$$z'_Y = r_{XY}z_X. \qquad [15.3.7^*]$$

We can show as follows how the least-squares criterion dictates that $b = r_{XY}$ for the prediction of standard scores. Since we know that $a$ must be zero, this time we start by substituting expression **15.3.2** into **15.3.1**:

$$\frac{\sum_i (z'_{Yi} - z_{Yi})^2}{N} = \frac{\sum_i (bz_{Xi} - z_{Yi})^2}{N}. \qquad [15.3.8]$$

Expanding the square on the right hand of **15.3.8** and summing, we have

$$\frac{\sum_i (z'_{Yi} - z_{Yi})^2}{N} = \frac{b^2 \sum_i z_{Xi}^2}{N} - \frac{2b \sum_i z_{Xi}z_{Yi}}{N} + \frac{\sum_i z_{Yi}^2}{N}$$

$$= b^2 - 2br + 1 \qquad [15.3.9]$$

since the variance of standard scores is always 1. Now suppose that $b$ differed from $r$ by some amount $c$, either a positive or negative number:

$$b = r + c.$$

Substituting $r + c$ for $b$ in **15.3.9** above, we find

$$\frac{\sum_i (z'_{Yi} - z_{Yi})^2}{N} = (r + c)^2 - 2(r + c)r + 1$$
$$= r^2 + 2rc + c^2 - 2r^2 - 2rc + 1$$
$$= (1 - r^2) + c^2. \qquad [15.3.10]$$

When $b = r$, so that $c$ is zero, the mean squared error must be at its smallest,

$$\frac{\sum_i (z'_{Yi} - z_{Yi})^2}{N} = (1 - r^2), \qquad [15.3.11^*]$$

and for any $c \neq 0$, the value must be $(1 - r^2)$ *plus a positive number*, $c^2$. *Hence taking $b = r$ gives the least squared error in linear prediction, on the average, for standard scores.*

## 15.4 THE STANDARD ERROR OF ESTIMATE FOR STANDARD SCORES

In the preceding section, we used the idea of the mean squared error made in prediction of $z_Y$ from $z_X$, and we found that this mean squared error is at its minimum when the regression equation is given by **15.3.7**, or

$$z'_Y = r_{XY}z_X.$$

This notion of the mean squared error is an important one in its own right, and we will give it a special symbol and name. Let

$$s^2_{z_Y \cdot z_X} = \frac{\sum_i (z'_{Yi} - z_{Yi})^2}{N}$$
$$= 1 - r^2_{XY} \qquad [15.4.1^*]$$

be called the **sample variance of estimate for standard scores**. This variance of estimate reflects the *poorness* of the linear rule for prediction of standard scores, the extent to which squared error is, on the average, large.

Most often, however, this index is discussed in terms of its positive square root

$$s_{z_Y \cdot z_X} = \sqrt{1 - r^2_{XY}}, \qquad [15.4.2]$$

which is called the **sample standard error of estimate for predicting standard scores.**

Obviously, there is a close connection between the size of the standard error of estimate in a sample and the value of $r$ in the regression equation: **the larger the absolute value of $r_{XY}$, the smaller is the standard error of estimate.** Now we turn to some interpretations of the index $r_{XY}$.

## 15.5   INTERPRETATIONS OF THE CORRELATION COEFFICIENT IN A SAMPLE

The connection between the variance of estimate and the correlation coefficient shows us at once that $r_{XY}$ can take on values *only* between $-1$ and 1. Notice that the variance of estimate, being a weighted sum of squares, can be only a positive number or zero. If $r_{XY}$ were less than $-1$, or greater than $+1$, then the variance of estimate could not be positive. Hence, $-1 \leq r_{XY} \leq 1$.

What does it mean when $r_{XY}$ is exactly zero? When this is true, one predicts $z'_Y = 0$, corresponding to the mean $Y$, *regardless* of the value of $X$; for any $X$, the mean of $Y$ is the best linear prediction when the correlation is zero. Furthermore,

$$s^2_{z_Y \cdot z_X} = 1$$

for $r_{XY} = 0$. This means that when the correlation coefficient is zero the variance of estimate for standard scores is exactly the same as the variance of the standard scores $z_Y$ with $X$ *unspecified*. Thus, when $r_{XY}$ is zero, predicting by the linear rule *does not* reduce the variability of $z_Y$ below the variability present when $z_X$ is unknown. In short, the fact that $r_{XY}$ is zero means that if a predictive statistical relation exists for the set of data, it is not linear, and the linear rule gives no predictive power.

On the other hand, when $r_{XY}$ is either $+1$ or $-1$, the variance of error in prediction is zero, so that each prediction is exactly right. These maximum values for $r_{XY}$ can occur only when $X$ and $Y$ *are* functionally related, *and* follow a linear rule.

All intermediate values of $r_{XY}$ indicate that some prediction is possible using the linear rule, but that this prediction is not perfect, and some error in prediction exists. Any value of $r_{XY}$ between 0 and 1 in absolute magnitude indicates either that the relationship is not functional or that if it is a function, the rule is not exactly linear, although a linear rule does afford some predictability.

In the regression equation for standard scores the correlation coefficient plays the role of converting a standard score in $X$ into a predicted standard score in $Y$. Rather loosely, the correlation coefficient can be said to be "the rate of exchange," the value of a "standard deviation's worth" of $X$ in terms of *predicted* standard deviation units of $Y$. This becomes clearer if we look on a plot of the function given by the regression equation, as shown in Figure 15.5.1. This plot shows the pairing of $z_X$ and *predicted* $z_Y$, or $z'_Y$ values (do not fall into the mistake of thinking that such a plot shows *actual* $z_X$ and $z_Y$ pairings). The regression function is shown by the straight line plot generated by the regression equation. Regardless of the relationship between $X$ and $Y$, $z_X$ and $z'_Y$ will plot as a

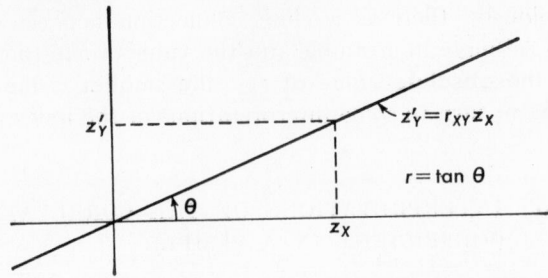

**FIG. 15.5.1.** The correlation coefficient as the slope of the regression line for predicting the value of $Z_Y$ from $Z_X$

straight line. Given a particular $z_X$, as shown in the figure, then the ratio of the predicted value to the known standard score value for $X$,

$$\frac{z'_Y}{z_X} = \tan \theta, \qquad [15.5.1]$$

the trigonometric tangent of the angle $\theta$. However, this ratio is also $r_{XY}$, so that

$$r_{XY} = \tan \theta, \qquad \left\{ \begin{array}{l} 0° \angle \theta \angle 45° \\ 135° \angle \theta \angle 180°. \end{array} \right. \qquad [15.5.2]$$

The tangent of the angle $\theta$ gives the *slope* of the regression line for predicting standard scores, and the value of $r_{XY}$ corresponds to the slope of this line. When $r_{XY}$ is between 0 and 1, the angle $\theta$ in such a plot must be between 0 and 45 degrees. For an $r_{XY}$ between 0 and $-1$, the angle $\theta$ must be between 135 and 180 degrees, so that in this instance a high standing on $X$ yields a prediction of low standing on $Y$, and vice versa.

## 15.6 THE IDEA OF REGRESSION TOWARD THE MEAN

The term *regression* has come to be applied to the general problem of prediction by use of a wide variety of rules, although the original application of this term had a very specific meaning, as we shall show. The term "regression" is a shortened form of **regression toward the mean in prediction.** The general idea is that **given any standard score $z_X$, the best linear prediction of the standard score $z_Y$ is one relatively nearer the mean of zero than is $z_X$.**

This can be illustrated quite simply from our regression equation **15.3.7.** Suppose that an individual has a standard score $z_X$ of 2. Also suppose that the regression equation we have found for the group to which he belongs is

$$z'_Y = .5 z_X.$$

Then we *predict* this individual to have a $z_Y$ score of 1, since

$$z'_Y = .5(2) = 1.$$

Notice that we predict him to fall relatively *nearer* the mean on $Y$ than he fell on $X$. That is, we predict in accordance with *regression toward the mean*. For another set of data, the regression equation might be

$$z'_Y = -.75z_X.$$

Now in this instance, suppose that the $z_X$ for some randomly selected individual were 1.5. Then

$$z'_Y = (-.75)(1.5) = -1.125.$$

Since the correlation coefficient is negative, the prediction is that this individual falls *below* the mean of $Y$, given that he falls *above* the mean on $X$. However, in absolute terms, we again predict that he falls relatively *closer* to the mean on $Y$ than he falls on $X$.

This principle of predicting relatively closer to the mean, or regression toward the mean, is a feature of any linear prediction rule that is best in the "least-squares" sense of Section 15.3. The idea is that if we are going to use such a linear rule for prediction, then it is always a good bet that an individual will fall *relatively closer to the group mean on the thing predicted than he does on the thing actually known*. This does *not* imply that an individual *must* fall relatively closer to the mean on $Y$ than he does on $X$, however, but only that our best *bet* about him is that he will do so. Regression toward the mean is not some immutable law of nature, but rather a statistical consequence of our choosing to predict in this linear way.

The idea of regression, and, indeed, most of the foundations for the theory of correlation and regression equations, came from the work of Sir Francis Galton in the nineteenth century. In his studies of hereditary traits, Galton pointed out the apparent regression toward the mean in the prediction of natural characteristics. In some biological traits, regression toward the mean does seem to occur just as the linear theory implies. However, the modern point of view in statistics is that regression toward the mean is built into the statistical assumptions and methods we use for prediction, and is not necessarily a feature of the natural world. Given the value of $z_X$, the *true* value of $z_Y$ for an individual observation can be anything, and regression toward the mean simply describes our best guess about the value of $z_Y$, when "best" is defined in terms of minimal squared error.

## 15.7  THE PROPORTION OF VARIANCE ACCOUNTED FOR BY LINEAR REGRESSION

In our discussion of the population indices of statistical relationship, $\omega^2$ and $\rho_I$, we found it convenient to define the over-all strength of relationship in terms of a proportional reduction in variance. Exactly the same idea may be applied in judging just how good a linear rule is for predicting $Y$ from $X$. In other words, we want an index to specify the strength of *linear* relationship in a set of data, showing how well a linear rule approximates the true form of the relation.

Because we are dealing with standard scores, the total variability of the $z_Y$ scores for $N$ individuals is 1.00. Furthermore, we have seen that the variance of estimate, $s^2_{z_Y \cdot z_X}$, is the average squared *error* in prediction using the linear rule. This can be thought of as representing the "left-over" variability, given the rule and the value of $z_X$. Thus, it makes sense to think of the proportional *reduction* in variance as

$$\frac{s^2_{z_Y} - s^2_{z_Y \cdot z_X}}{s^2_{z_Y}}$$

which is simply

$$\frac{1 - (1 - r^2)}{1} = r^2. \qquad [15.7.1*]$$

**The proportional reduction in variance of $Y$ given the linear rule and $X$ is $r^2_{XY}$, sometimes called the coefficient of determination.** You can always think of $r^2_{XY}$ as representing the strength of *linear* relationship in a given set of data.

Thus, if the value of a correlation coefficient is .50 (positive or negative in sign) then some .25 of the variability in $Y$ is accounted for by specifying the linear rule and $X$. If the correlation is .80, then 64 percent of the variance in $Y$ is accounted for in this way. A correlation of positive or negative 1.00 means that 100 percent of variability in $Y$ can be accounted for by the linear rule and $X$, but if $r_{XY} = 0$, none of the variability is thereby accounted for. All in all, not the correlation coefficient per se but the *square* of the correlation coefficient informs us of the "goodness" of the linear rule for prediction.

## 15.8 THE REGRESSION OF $z_X$ ON $z_Y$

There is really nothing in our discussion so far that has made it necessary to think of $X$ as the independent variable, or the value somehow known first or predicted from. It is entirely possible to consider a situation where one might want to predict $z_X$ from knowing $z_Y$. What does this do to the linear prediction rule, the correlation coefficient, and so on?

In the first place, the same argument used in Section 15.3 shows that for predicting $z_X$ from $z_Y$,

$$z'_X = r_{XY} z_Y, \qquad [15.8.1*]$$

where the correlation coefficient s just as before,

$$r_{XY} = \frac{\sum_i z_{Xi} z_{Yi}}{N}.$$

This equation **15.8.1** is for regression of $z_X$ on $z_Y$, or $z_X$ predicted from $z_Y$.

You may be wondering why the regression equation for predicting $z_X$ from $z_Y$ is not found by solving equation **15.3.7** for $z_X$, to give

$$z_X = \frac{1}{r_{XY}} (z'_Y). \qquad [15.8.2]$$

However, recall what the symbols $z'_Y$ and $z'_X$ actually represent. These are *predicted* values of $z_X$ and $z_X$, and do not necessarily symbolize the actual values of $z_Y$ and $z_X$ at all. Solving the expression **15.8.2** for $z_X$ *might* be useful if one wanted to know the value of $z_X$ *known*, given that $z'_Y$ were the predicted value, although it is hard to see why anyone would ordinarily want this information. The form of the regression equation used (**15.3.7** or **15.8.1**) depends strictly on which variable, $X$ or $Y$, is designated as the independent variable, or the thing known first in a prediction situation.

For prediction of $X$ from $Y$, the sample variance of estimate for standard scores is

$$s^2_{z_X \cdot z_Y} = 1 - r^2_{XY} \qquad \text{[15.8.3*]}$$

(notice the reversal in subscripts when $z_X$ is predicted from $z_Y$). The proportional variance in $X$ accounted for by $Y$ is, once again, $r^2_{XY}$.

This brings up the point that the correlation coefficient is a *symmetric* measure of linear relationship. *So long as we are talking about the correlation coefficient alone, it is immaterial which we designate as the independent and which the dependent variable; the measure of possible linear prediction is the same.* However, when we deal with the actual regression equations themselves, this symmetry is not usually present. As we shall see in the next section, it does make a difference whether you are predicting $Y$ from $X$ or $X$ from $Y$ when it comes to finding the regression equations and errors of estimate for *raw* scores.

## 15.9  THE REGRESSION EQUATIONS FOR RAW SCORES

Up to this point, we have considered only the problem of predicting standard scores from standard scores. Introducing regression and correlation in terms of standard scores makes the algebra somewhat easier, and the essential ideas somewhat simpler. Nevertheless, each feature of correlation and regression shown for standard score prediction is also valid for the prediction of raw scores. For any given set of data, each standard score corresponds uniquely to some raw score, and vice versa, so that linear prediction which is optimal in standard score terms is optimal in raw score terms as well.

It is quite simple to put the regression equation for prediction $z_Y$ from $z_X$ into raw score form. We start with

$$z'_Y = r_{XY} z_X,$$

which is exactly the same as

$$\frac{Y' - M_Y}{s_Y} = r_{XY} \frac{(X - M_X)}{s_X}$$

where $Y'$ is the *predicted raw score* for the individual, and $X$ is his *known* raw score on the independent variable. A little algebraic manipulation gives

$$Y' = \frac{r_{XY} s_Y}{s_X} (X - M_X) + M_Y. \qquad \text{[15.9.1†]}$$

This is the raw score form of the regression equation for prediction of $Y$ from $X$.

It will be convenient to write this regression equation as

$$Y' = b_{Y \cdot X}(X - M_X) + M_Y, \qquad [15.9.2\dagger]$$

where

$$b_{Y \cdot X} = \frac{r_{XY}s_Y}{s_X}. \qquad [15.9.3*]$$

The value $b_{Y \cdot X}$ is called the **sample regression coefficient** of $Y$ on $X$.

In an identical way, we can turn the regression equation for $z_X$ predicted from $z_Y$ into

$$X' = b_{X \cdot Y}(Y - M_Y) + M_X. \qquad [15.9.4\dagger]$$

This is the raw score form of the regression equation for predicting $X$ from $Y$. Here

$$b_{X \cdot Y} = \frac{r_{XY}s_X}{s_Y} \qquad [15.9.5*]$$

is the sample regression coefficient for predicting $X$ from $Y$.

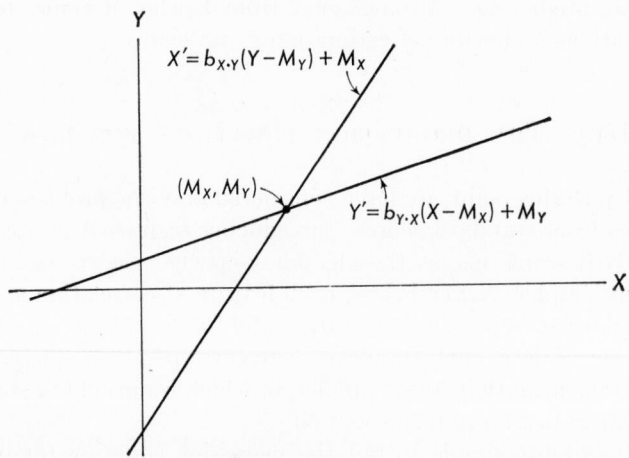

FIG. 15.9.1. Plot of the two regression lines for predicting Y from X and X from Y

Notice that when no specification is put on which is to be regarded as the independent or predictor variable, there are two possible sample regression coefficients, $b_{Y \cdot X}$ and $b_{X \cdot Y}$, and that

$$\sqrt{b_{Y \cdot X} b_{X \cdot Y}} = r_{XY}, \qquad [15.9.6]$$

the square root of the product of the two regression coefficients is the correlation coefficient.

Figure 15.9.1 shows the two raw score regression lines that might apply to a given set of data.

## 15.10 THE ERRORS OF ESTIMATE FOR RAW SCORES

When prediction of raw scores is to be carried out, the **sample variance of estimate** for predicting $Y$ from $X$ is

$$s_{Y \cdot X}^2 = s_Y^2 (1 - r_{XY}^2) \qquad \text{[15.10.1*]}$$

and the **sample standard error of estimate** is

$$s_{Y \cdot X} = s_Y \sqrt{1 - r_{XY}^2}. \qquad \text{[15.10.2*]}$$

Similarly, the sample variance of estimate for predicting $X$ from $Y$ is

$$s_{X \cdot Y}^2 = s_X^2 (1 - r_{XY}^2) \qquad \text{[15.10.3*]}$$

and the sample standard error of estimate is

$$s_{X \cdot Y} = s_X \sqrt{1 - r_{XY}^2}. \qquad \text{[15.10.4*]}$$

Finally, the proportion of variance accounted for by linear relationship (either in predicting $Y$ from $X$ or $X$ from $Y$) is $r_{XY}^2$, just as for standardized scores.

## 15.11 COMPUTATIONAL FORMS FOR $r_{XY}$ AND $b_{Y \cdot X}$

Although the sample correlation coefficient was actually defined in Section 15.3 as a summed product of standard scores (**15.3.6**), in practice the index is seldom computed in this way. An equivalent raw score computational form will now be found. We will show that the raw score form of the correlation coefficient is

$$r_{XY} = \frac{\left( \sum_i X_i Y_i / N \right) - M_X M_Y}{s_X s_Y}. \qquad \text{[15.11.1†]}$$

Starting with the definition **15.3.6**, and substituting the raw score equivalents of $z_X$ and $z_Y$, we have

$$
\begin{aligned}
r_{XY} &= \frac{\sum_i (X_i - M_X)(Y_i - M_Y)}{N s_X s_Y} \\
&= \frac{1}{N s_X s_Y} \left[ \sum_i X_i Y_i - \sum_i X_i M_Y - \sum_i Y_i M_X + N M_X M_Y \right] \\
&= \frac{1}{N s_X s_Y} \left[ \sum_i X_i Y_i - 2 N M_X M_Y + N M_X M_Y \right] \\
&= \frac{\left( \sum_i X_i Y_i / N \right) - M_X M_Y}{s_X s_Y}.
\end{aligned}
$$

Still another computing form for $r_{XY}$ that is useful when work is being done on a desk calculator is

$$r_{XY} = \frac{N \sum_i X_i Y_i - \left(\sum_i X_i\right)\left(\sum_i Y_i\right)}{\sqrt{\left[N \sum_i X_i^2 - \left(\sum_i X_i\right)^2\right]\left[N \sum_i Y_i^2 - \left(\sum_i Y_i\right)^2\right]}}. \qquad [15.11.2\dagger]$$

Various other methods for computing $r_{XY}$ are available. One method especially popular in past years is designed for data grouped into a joint frequency distribution or "scatter plot," and this version is to be found in many elementary statistics texts. However, when desk calculators are available this method is not usually so efficient as a method dealing directly with the raw scores, and we will not consider it here.

Given the correlation coefficient, it is possible to find the sample regression coefficient $b_{Y \cdot X}$ directly from

$$b_{Y \cdot X} = r_{XY}\left(\frac{s_Y}{s_X}\right).$$

However, for many problems in regression it is desirable to calculate $b_{Y \cdot X}$ without first finding $r_{XY}$. This may be done most simply by taking

$$b_{Y \cdot X} = \frac{\sum_i X_i Y_i - N M_X M_Y}{\sum_i X_i^2 - N M_X^2} \qquad [15.11.3\dagger]$$

or

$$b_{Y \cdot X} = \frac{N \sum_i X_i Y_i - \left(\sum_i X_i\right)\left(\sum_i Y_i\right)}{N \sum_i X_i^2 - \left(\sum_i X_i\right)^2}. \qquad [15.11.4\dagger]$$

Incidentally, it should be noted that the sample correlation coefficient is a *dimensionless* quantity, since it is not expressed directly either in units of $X$ or in units of $Y$. As we saw, the basic definition of the correlation coefficient (15.3.6) depends upon the individual $X$ and $Y$ *standard* scores, which are themselves in standard units. This fact makes it possible to simplify the computation of the correlation coefficient by transforming *either $X$ or $Y$ or both* into new variables $u$ and $v$ by the linear rules

$$u_i = cX_i + g$$
$$v_i = dY_i + h$$

where $c$ and $d$ are any positive constants, and $g$ and $h$ are any constant numbers at all. In other words, instead of carrying out the computations for $r_{XY}$ using $X$ and $Y$ values, we can carry these computations out using the transformed values $u$ and $v$. If $u$ and $v$ are both such positive linear functions of $X$ and $Y$, the standard scores for each individual are unchanged by this conversion to new scores, and thus the value of $r_{XY}$ is the same as the correlation value between $u$ and $v$. This principle is often used to cut down the labor in calculation for correlation coefficients, and will be illustrated in the problem of Section 15.28. Unlike $r_{XY}$, however, the value of $b_{Y \cdot X}$ is not invariant over such transformations of the scores.

## 15.12   AN EXAMPLE OF REGRESSION AND CORRELATION COMPUTATIONS FOR A SAMPLE

Consider once again the example of Section 15.3. The teacher collected data for a class of 91 students, obtaining for each a score $X$, based on the number of courses taken n high-school mathematics, and a score $Y$, the actual score on the final examination for the course. These data are shown in Table 15.12.1. The arrangement of data is similar to that used in a problem in regression: the columns of the table represent the various possible values of $X$, and within each column the different $Y$ values are shown. We will use $Y_{ij}$ to stand for a $Y$ value for individual $i$ in grouping $j$, and $X_j$ for the $X$ value common to all individuals in grouping $j$.

**Table 15.12.1**
FINAL EXAM SCORES $Y$ ARRANGED ACCORDING TO $X$ SCORE OBTAINED

| | | | | | | | | | | | | |
|---|---|---|---|---|---|---|---|---|---|---|---|---|
| | | | | 36 | | | | | | | | |
| | | | 34 | 35 | | | | | | | | |
| | | | 26 | 30 | | | | | | | | |
| | | | 25 | 27 | | | | | | | | |
| | 26 | | 23 | 25 | | | | | | | | |
| 22 | 23 | 29 | 23 | 25 | | | | | | | | |
| 17 | 18 | 26 | 22 | 24 | | | | | | | | |
| 16 | 18 | 26 | 22 | 21 | | | | | | | | |
| 14 | 16 | 24 | 19 | 20 | | | | | | | | |
| 10 | 13 | 24 | 18 | 19 | | | | 46 | | | | |
| 9 | 12 | 23 | 17 | 19 | | | | 38 | | | | |
| 7 | 10 | 22 | 17 | 18 | | 41 | | 34 | 44 | | 42 | 53 |
| 5 | 10 | 16 | 17 | 18 | 28 | 32 | 32 | 33 | 37 | 52 | 41 | 48 |
| 3 | 7 | 9 | 12 | 12 | 27 | 27 | 25 | 27 | 32 | 46 | 38 | 40 |
| 2 | 6 | 8 | 8 | 3 | 16 | 19 | 25 | 20 | 28 | 37 | 35 | 40 |
| | | | | *X* | | | | | | | | |
| 2 | 2.5 | 3 | 3.5 | 4 | 4.5 | 5 | 5.5 | 6 | 6.5 | 7 | 7.5 | 8 |
| | | | | *Freq.* | | | | | | | | |
| 10 | 11 | 10 | 14 | 15 | 3 | 4 | 3 | 6 | 4 | 3 | 4 | 4 |

The mean of the $Y$ values is

$$\frac{\sum_j \sum_i Y_{ij}}{N} = \frac{2169}{91} = 23.84$$

and that of the $X$ values is

$$\frac{\sum_j \sum_i X_j}{N_{\downarrow}} = \frac{\sum_j X_j(\text{freq.})}{N} = \frac{381.5}{91} = 4.19.$$

The two standard deviations are

$$s_X = \sqrt{\frac{\sum_j X_j^2(\text{freq.})}{N} - M_X^2} = \sqrt{\frac{1874.75}{91} - 17.56} = 1.74$$

$$s_Y = \sqrt{\frac{\sum_j \sum_i Y_{ij}^2}{N} - M_Y^2} = \sqrt{\frac{64043}{91} - 568.34} = 11.64.$$

The correlation coefficient will be computed next:

$$\frac{\sum_j \sum_i X_j Y_{ij}}{N} = \frac{(2)(22) + (2)(17) + \cdots + (8)(40) + (8)(40)}{91} = \frac{10580}{91} = 116.26$$

so that

$$r_{XY} = \frac{\sum_j \sum_i X_j Y_{ij}/N - M_X M_Y}{s_X s_Y}$$

$$= \frac{116.26 - (4.19)(23.84)}{(1.74)(11.64)}$$

$$= .81.$$

Thus, the regression equation for predicting $z_Y$ from $z_X$ for these data is

$$z_Y' = .81 z_X.$$

The raw score regression coefficient $b_{Y \cdot X}$ is

$$b_{Y \cdot X} = r_{XY} \frac{s_Y}{s_X}$$

$$= (.81) \frac{11.64}{1.74}$$

$$= 5.42.$$

Using this regression coefficient we find that the raw score regression equation for predicting $Y$ from $X$ is

$$Y_j' = (5.42)(X_j - 4.19) + 23.84.$$

For instance, given that an individual has a high-school mathematics score of 5, the teacher can predict that his score on the course examination is

$$Y' = (5.42)(5 - 4.19) + 23.84$$
$$= 28.23.$$

Figure 15.12.1 shows a plot of the regression equation, together with the actual $(X,Y)$ pairs for these data. Notice that although the actual pairs of scores do tend to cluster about the predicted $(X,Y')$ pairs, there is nevertheless

$$Y' = (5.42)(X - 4.19) + 23.48$$

FIG. 15.12.1. Plot of the data in Section 15.12, showing the regression line for predicting Y from X

some "scatter" of the actual $Y$ scores about the predicted value for each $X$. This, of course, is reflected in the fact that the obtained $r_{XY}$ is not 1.00.

For these data, the sample standard error of estimate is

$$s_{Y \cdot X} = s_X \sqrt{1 - r_{XY}^2}$$
$$= (11.64)(.586)$$
$$= 6.82.$$

## 15.13   ASSUMPTIONS MADE IN COMPUTING CORRELATION AND REGRESSION COEFFICIENTS FOR SAMPLE DATA

A few comments are in order about the propriety of computing correlations and regression equations for sample data. In some of the older literature in psychological research several misleading ideas appear about when it is proper to compute these indices and equations as *descriptive* statistics. The modern researcher needs to be clear about these matters. It is *not* necessary to make any assumptions at all about the form of the distribution, the variability of $Y$ scores within $X$ columns or "arrays," or the true level of measurement represented by the scores in order to employ linear regression and correlation indices to describe a given set of data. So long as there are $N$ distinct cases, each having two numerical scores, $X$ and $Y$, then the *descriptive* statistics of correlation and regression may be used. In so doing, we describe the data *as though* a linear rule were to be used for prediction, and this is a perfectly adequate way to talk about the tendency for *these* numerical scores to associate or "go together" in a linear way *in these data*.

The confusion has arisen because in inference about true linear relationships in populations, and in some applications of regression equations to predictions beyond the sample, assumptions do become necessary, as we shall see presently. However, one may apply correlation techniques to any set of paired-score data, and the results are valid descriptions of two things: the particular linear rule that best applies, and the goodness of the linear prediction rule as a summarization of the tendency of $Y$ scores to differ systematically with differences in $X$ *in these data*.

It is true, however, that the possible values that $r_{XY}$ may assume depend to some extent upon the forms of *marginal* distributions of both $X$ and $Y$ in the joint data-table. Unless the distributions for $X$ and $Y$ are similar in form, it is not necessarily true that the obtained value of $r_{XY}$ can range between $-1$ and $+1$. In fact, it is possible to produce examples where the forms of the distributions of $X$ and $Y$ are very different, and the maximum possible absolute value of $r_{XY}$ is only .3 or less. The fact that the value of the correlation coefficient can, in principle, range from $-1.00$ to $+1.00$ does not mean that the opportunity for a linear predictive relation to appear in a sample has nothing to do with the marginal distributions of the $X$ and $Y$ scores. In the same way, the actual possible range of the correlation in a population depends on the marginal distributions. This fact has very important implications for those who study the patterns of correlations in multivariate studies, and particularly for those who must employ some variant on, or approximation to, the correlation coefficient in such studies. An informative discussion of these issues is given in Carroll (1961).

A related problem with the value of $r_{XY}$ in a sample has to do with selection of cases to appear in the sample, and in particular with systematic restrictions on the range of $X$ (or of $Y$) values that appear. This introduces a bias into the value of $r_{XY}$ as an estimate of the correlation had this selection not been exercised. In particular, the absolute value of the correlation coefficient tends to be lowered by the introduction of such systematic selection reducing the possible range of one or both variables. These matters are also discussed by Carroll.

## 15.14 POPULATION CORRELATION AND REGRESSION

Imagine a population where each distinct elementary event qualifies for one and only one joint $(X,Y)$ event, where both $X$ and $Y$ are random variables.

Then indices of population correlation and regression can be defined in ways completely analogous to the sample indices.

In the first place, consider the expectation of the product of deviations from expectation:

$$E[(X - \mu_X)(Y - \mu_Y)] = \text{cov.}(X,Y). \qquad [15.14.1^*]$$

The expectation is taken over all individuals in the population, where

$$\mu_X = E(X)$$

and

$$\mu_Y = E(Y).$$

The expectation of this product, or cov.$(X,Y)$, is called the **population covariance** of $X$ and $Y$.

We have already used this idea of the population covariance several times. In rule 6 of Appendix B, it is stated that if two random variables are independent, then

$$E[(X - \mu_X)(Y - \mu_Y)] = 0,$$

so that cov.$(X,Y) = 0$. This rule has been applied a number of times, particularly in our discussion of the expectations for analysis of variance sums of squares. A corollary to this rule is that if

$$\text{cov.}(X,Y) \neq 0,$$

then $X$ and $Y$ are *not* statistically independent. It is obvious that the value of the covariance for two random variables must have something to do with possible association, or statistical relationship, between $X$ and $Y$. The absence of a statistical relation between $X$ and $Y$ implies that the covariance must be zero; however, the reverse implication does not necessarily hold, and **the fact that** cov.$(X,Y) = 0$ **does not necessarily mean that** $X$ and $Y$ **are independent.**

Notice that the **sample** parallel to the population covariance is

$$\frac{\sum_i (X_i - M_X)(Y_i - M_Y)}{N} = \frac{\sum_i X_i Y_i}{N} - M_X M_Y = \text{sample covariance.} \quad [15.14.2^*]$$

This is the term we calculate for the numerator in finding the *sample* correlation coefficient, so that the correlation coefficient for a sample may also be defined as

$$r_{XY} = \frac{\text{sample covariance}}{s_X s_Y}. \qquad [15.14.3^*]$$

In precisely this way we define the **population** correlation coefficient,

$$\rho_{XY} = \frac{\text{cov.}(X,Y)}{\sigma_X \sigma_Y}. \qquad [15.14.4^*]$$

The population correlation coefficient is the covariance of $X$ and $Y$, divided by the product of the population standard deviations for $X$ and $Y$.

Just as $r_{XY}$ must lie between $-1$ and $1$ inclusive, so must it be true that

$$-1 \leq \rho_{XY} \leq 1.$$

The population regression equations for predicting $Y$ from $X$ and $X$ from $Y$ are also parallels to the sample forms:

$$Y' = \rho_{XY} \frac{\sigma_Y}{\sigma_X} (X - \mu_X) + \mu_Y \qquad \text{[15.14.5*]}$$

and

$$X' = \rho_{XY} \frac{\sigma_X}{\sigma_Y} (Y - \mu_Y) + \mu_X. \qquad \text{[15.14.6*]}$$

The **population regression coefficients** are

$$\beta_{Y \cdot X} = \rho_{XY} \frac{\sigma_Y}{\sigma_X} \qquad \text{[15.14.7*]}$$

and

$$\beta_{X \cdot Y} = \rho_{XY} \frac{\sigma_X}{\sigma_Y}. \qquad \text{[15.14.8*]}$$

Finally, for any such population, we can discuss the *true* variance of estimate for $Y$ predicted from $X$:

$$\sigma_{Y \cdot X}^2 = \sigma_Y^2 (1 - \rho_{XY}^2) \qquad \text{[15.14.9*]}$$

as well as the true variance of estimate for $X$ predicted from $Y$

$$\sigma_{X \cdot Y}^2 = \sigma_X^2 (1 - \rho_{XY}^2). \qquad \text{[15.14.10*]}$$

The two **true standard errors of estimate** are thus

$$\sigma_{Y \cdot X} = \sigma_Y \sqrt{1 - \rho_{XY}^2} \qquad \text{[15.14.11*]}$$

and

$$\sigma_{X \cdot Y} = \sigma_X \sqrt{1 - \rho_{XY}^2}. \qquad \text{[15.14.12*]}$$

Notice that just as for a sample, one can interpret the square of the correlation coefficient as **the proportion of variance accounted for by linear regression**. That is, $\sigma_{Y \cdot X}^2$ is "error" variance in the use of the linear rule, the variability *not* accounted for by linear regression. Thus,

$$\sigma_Y^2 - \sigma_{Y \cdot X}^2$$

is the variance *accounted* for by linear regression, or the reduction in variance accomplished by using a linear prediction rule. It follows that

$$\rho_{XY}^2 = \frac{\sigma_Y^2 - \sigma_{Y \cdot X}^2}{\sigma_Y^2}, \qquad \text{[15.14.13*]}$$

the square of the correlation coefficient is the relative reduction in variance accomplished by the use of a linear prediction rule. (Notice the very close similarity in meaning among $\omega^2$, $\rho_I$, and $\rho_{XY}^2$; each is a relative reduction in population variance. However, $\omega^2$ and $\rho_I$ each stand for the reduction in variance of $Y$ obtained by specifying the $X$ **qualitative classification,** whereas $\rho_{XY}^2$ is the reduction in variance obtained by specifying the **numerical value** of $X$ and a **linear** least-squares prediction rule.)

All in all, the features describing correlation and the ability to predict $Y$ from $X$ using a linear rule can also be defined for populations of potential observations, in which each element represents some joint $(X,Y)$ event. As usual, we want to make inferences about these population characteristics from a sample. Consider our college teacher, once again. The real motive for his study of the class of students was to find some way of forecasting a student's degree of success in his course ahead of time. A student wants admission to the course. He is found to have a score of 4 in terms of high-school credits in mathematics. How good a bet is this student to do well in the course? Unfortunately, the only evidence the teacher has comes from a *sample* of students. The new student is a sample of 1 observation presumably from the same population as the class of 91 students already observed. How can the teacher actually use the information he has about the sample to make inferences about population and correlation, and then use the sample information to predict about new students?

In order to carry out this form of prediction, the teacher needs to estimate the true, or population, regression equation. What information about the regression equation appropriate to the population is contained in the regression equation found for a sample? Next we will consider ways to estimate the population regression equation given only the sample regression equation.

## 15.15  ESTIMATES OF THE PARAMETERS OF THE POPULATION REGRESSION EQUATION, AND STANDARD ERRORS

Given a random sample, the value of the sample regression coefficient $b_{Y \cdot X}$ is our best available estimate of $\beta_{Y \cdot X}$, the population regression coefficient. Moreover, the best estimate of $\beta_{Y \cdot X}(\mu_X)$ is given by $b_{Y \cdot X}(M_X)$. As usual, our best estimate of $\mu_Y$ is simply $M_Y$.

Since each of these estimates corresponds to a term in the sample regression equation, we can use the sample equation itself as our best estimate of the population regression equation; that is, our estimate of the population regression equation is given by

$$Y' = b_{Y \cdot X}(X - M_X) + M_Y.$$

In the example, the teacher *is* justified in using his sample regression equation to predict for new students drawn from the same population as the original class, *provided* that the class used to find this regression equation is actually a random sample from a population of such students.

In addition, an unbiased estimate of the *true* variance of estimate for predicting $Y$ from $X$ is given by

$$\text{est. } \sigma^2_{Y \cdot X} = \frac{N}{N-2} s^2_{Y \cdot X}.$$

The reason for the appearance of $N - 2$ in the denominator will be found in Section 15.19.

Before we consider the problem of confidence intervals for these estimates, and how a particular prediction might be made and itself qualified by a confidence interval, assumptions must be made about the nature of the population distribution of $(X, Y)$ pairs. This takes us directly into the study of problems in regression, which is our next topic. Here, for the first time, the essential differences between regression and correlation problems will be important in our discussion.

## 15.16 THE MODEL FOR SIMPLE LINEAR REGRESSION

Imagine a study of this kind: in an experiment on transfer of training some $N$ subjects were selected and assigned at random to $J$ different groups. Each of the experimental groups was given a different number of trials at learning a particular task, say task A. Then, given that experience, each individual in each group was put to work learning another performance, task B. The number of trials required by a subject to reach a criterion level of performance on B was noted. Here, the independent experimental variable $X$ is number of trials given on task A, and the dependent variable $Y$ is number of trials required to learn task B.

This is clearly an example of a regression problem. The possible values of $X$ to be represented in the experiment were chosen *in advance* by the experimenter, and each $X$ value decided upon was made to appear some prearranged number of times in the data. On the other hand, within each value of $X$, the data show some obtained distribution of $Y$ values. The experimenter's interest is primarily in evaluating the strength of linear relationship, if any, between $X$ and $Y$, and in estimating the linear regression equation.

Just as various models can be adopted for various kinds of situations in the analysis of variance, so in regression analysis different models are possible, and the form of analysis and the assumptions made depend on which model is used. Now the simplest model for regression analysis will be stated; this is, however, not the only model possible for analyzing such an experiment. An alternative, and in many instances better, model will be given in the next chapter.

For the moment, we are going to assume that any raw score $Y_{ij}$ has the following composition:

$$Y_{ij} = \mu_Y + \beta_{Y \cdot X}(X_j - \mu_X) + e_{ij} \qquad [15.16.1^*]$$

where $Y_{ij}$ is the score of individual $i$ in the $j$th treatment category, $X_j$ is the quantitative $X$ score associated with each individual in the $j$th category, and $e_{ij}$ is the random error associated with individual $i$ in category $j$.

Notice that within each category $j$, each and every individual exhibits the same value of $X$, or $X_j$. It will be assumed that the $J$ treatment categories are fixed, just as in fixed effects analysis of variance. This means that *the same sample distribution of $X_j$ values will appear in any exact repetition of the experiment for a different sample of $N$ individuals, although the distribution of $Y$ values within a category may differ from sample to sample.*

Notice also that this model is just another way of stating the linear regression equation for a population. Let

$$e_{ij} = Y_{ij} - Y'_j,$$

which is the miss or error in predicting $Y_{ij}$ given the value of $X_j$ and the *population* regression equation. Then

$$Y'_j = \mu_Y + \beta_{Y \cdot X}(X_j - \mu_X)$$

which is exactly the population regression equation, **15.14.5.**

The essential point, however, is that in adopting this model we are assuming that the linear regression equation is *true* as a description of the relation between $X$ and $Y$, and that any apparent deviation from this function rule is random error, the influence of other and uncontrolled factors obscuring this true functional relation. This model asserts that, basically, $Y$ *is* a linear function of $X$, could we but control the influence of all other factors. This need not really be true, of course, but in adopting this model we are assuming it true.

Given this linear model, and the fixed effects assumption for the categories $j$, then the true mean of $X$ for each category $j$ must be $X_j$, or

$$\mu_{X_j} = X_j.$$

This implies that the model may also be written

$$Y_{ij} = \mu_Y + \beta_{Y \cdot X}(\mu_{X_j} - \mu_X) + e_{ij}. \qquad [15.16.2*]$$

Be sure to notice the close similarity to the fixed-effects analysis of variance model; if we identify

$$\beta_{Y \cdot X}(\mu_{X_j} - \mu_X) = \alpha_j$$

we see this to be only a special version of Model I for the one-way analysis of variance.

## 15.17 THE SUMS OF SQUARES FOR REGRESSION PROBLEMS

In any regression problem, the deviation of a score $Y_{ij}$ from the grand mean $M_Y$ can be thought of as the sum of three parts:

$$(Y_{ij} - M_Y) = (Y_{ij} - M_{Y_j}) + (M_{Y_j} - Y'_j) + (Y'_j - M_Y). \qquad [15.17.1]$$

The first term $(Y_{ij} - M_{Y_j})$ is simply the deviation of the particular score from the mean of its group, $M_{Y_j}$. The second, $(M_{Y_j} - Y'_j)$, is the deviation of the mean of group $j$ from the score *predicted* by the *sample* regression equation from the $X_j$ for that group. The third part is the deviation of the predicted score itself from the grand mean.

By the now familiar argument used in Section 12.4 and elsewhere it can be shown that over all individuals in all groups, the total sum of squares can be partitioned into

$$\sum_j \sum_i (Y_{ij} - M_Y)^2 = \sum_j \sum_i (Y_{ij} - M_{Y_j})^2 + \sum_j n_j(M_{Y_j}^2 - Y_j'^2)$$
$$+ \sum_j n_j(Y_j' - M_Y)^2. \quad [15.17.2*]$$

The first of these parts is

$$\text{SS error} = \sum_j \sum_i (Y_{ij} - M_{Y_j})^2, \quad\quad\quad [15.17.3]$$

which is just the ordinary *SS within* found as for a one-way analysis of variance.

The second sum of squares is

$$\text{SS deviations from linear regression} = \sum_j n_j(M_{Y_j}^2 - Y_j'^2) \quad [15.17.4]$$

and the third part is

$$\text{SS linear regression} = \sum_j n_j(Y_j' - M_Y)^2. \quad\quad [15.17.5]$$

In short, for any regression problem it is true that

SS total = (SS error) + (SS deviations from lin. reg.)
$$+ \text{ (SS lin. reg.)}. \quad [15.17.6\dagger]$$

(Bear in mind that for any set of $J$ distinct groups it is *also* true that

SS total = (SS error) + (SS between groups)

as shown in Section 12.4. This fact will be used later.)

Now let us examine the expectations of the various sums of squares, beginning with the sum of squares for linear regression.

## 15.18 THE EXPECTATION OF THE SS FOR LINEAR REGRESSION

The sum of squares for linear regression can be put into a slightly more recognizable form by substituting from **15.9.2** for $Y_j'$:

$$\sum_j n_j(Y_j' - M_Y)^2 = \sum_j n_j[b_{Y \cdot X}(X_j - M_X) + M_Y - M_Y]^2$$
$$= b_{Y \cdot X}^2 \sum_j n_j(X_j - M_X)^2$$
$$= Nb_{Y \cdot X}^2 s_X^2. \quad\quad [15.18.1*]$$

That is, for a given sample $N$, the sum of squares for linear regression actually depends only upon $b_{Y \cdot X}^2$, the *sample* regression coefficient squared, and $s_X^2$, the *sample* variance of $X$.

Furthermore, since

$$b_{Y \cdot X} = r_{XY} \frac{s_Y}{s_X}$$

then

$$\text{SS linear regression} = N r_{XY}^2 s_Y^2 \qquad [15.18.2\dagger]$$

and also

$$\text{SS linear regression} = \frac{N[\text{sample cov.}(X,Y)]^2}{s_X^2} \qquad [15.18.3\dagger]$$

by **15.14.3**.

Look for a moment at the sample covariance,

$$\text{sample cov.}(X,Y) = \frac{\sum_j \sum_i X_j Y_{ij}}{N} - M_X M_Y. \qquad [15.18.4]$$

Since $X_j$ is the same for each individual $i$ in group $j$, the sample covariance in this instance is

$$\text{sample cov.}(X,Y) = \frac{\sum_j n_j (M_{Y_j})(X_j)}{N} - \frac{\sum_j n_j (M_{Y_j}) M_X}{N}$$

$$= \sum_j \frac{n_j (X_j - M_X)(M_{Y_j})}{N}. \qquad [15.18.5]$$

You are probably unaware of it, but we have just shown a most interesting fact: the sample covariance in a regression problem is a *linear combination* or comparison among the means $M_{Y_j}$ for $J$ samples, each mean being weighted by a value

$$c_j = \frac{n_j (X_j - M_X)}{N}. \qquad [15.18.6]$$

Furthermore,

$$\sum_j c_j = \sum_j \frac{n_j (X_j - M_X)}{N} = 0, \qquad [15.18.7]$$

since the sum of deviations of individual $X_j$ values about the $M_X$ must be zero for any sample. Thus, **formally, the sample covariance in a regression problem is simply a comparison among sample means.**

Now the information about comparisons in Section 14.11 can be used to find what the expectation of SS linear regression must be. For any sample comparison $\hat{\psi}$, we found that

$$\text{SS}(\hat{\psi}) = \frac{\hat{\psi}^2}{w}$$

is a sum of squares with 1 degree of freedom. For the covariance comparison

$$w = \sum_j \frac{c_j^2}{n_j} = \sum_j \frac{n_j^2 (X_j - M_X)^2}{n_j N^2}$$

$$= \frac{s_X^2}{N}. \qquad\qquad [15.18.8]$$

The sum of squares for the covariance comparison is thus

$$\frac{[\text{sample cov.}(X,Y)]^2}{(s_X^2/N)} = \frac{N[\text{sample cov.}(X,Y)]^2}{s_X^2}$$

$$= \text{SS linear regression.} \qquad [15.18.9*]$$

**The sum of squares for linear regression has one degree of freedom, since it corresponds to the sum of squares for a single comparison among sample means.**

If the true value for any comparison $\psi$ is zero, then

$$E(\text{SS } \hat{\psi}) = E(\text{MS } \hat{\psi}) = \sigma_e^2,$$

which provides the principle used in testing comparisons. Now this principle will be applied to the SS linear regression. When $\beta_{Y \cdot X}$ is truly zero, so that the true cov.$(X,Y)$ is zero, then

$$E(\text{SS linear regression}) = \sigma_e^2. \qquad [15.18.10*]$$

Furthermore, when each of the populations represented by the fixed $X_j$ values has a *normal* distribution of $Y$ values, with equal variance for each such population, then

$$\frac{\text{MS linear regression}}{\sigma_e^2} = \chi_{(1)}^2,$$

the ratio of MS linear regression to $\sigma_e^2$ is a chi-square variable with 1 degree of freedom, given that $\beta_{Y \cdot X}$ is zero. In short, the same situation exists as in any test of a planned comparison when the true comparison value is zero.

For the regression model, the weighting factor $w$ for the covariance comparison $\hat{\psi}$ is

$$w = s_X^2/N$$

so that

$$E(\text{MS linear regression}) = E(\hat{\psi}^2/w)$$

$$= \frac{N[\text{cov.}(X,Y)]^2}{s_X^2} + \sigma_e^2$$

$$= N\beta_{Y \cdot X}^2 s_X^2 + \sigma_e^2.$$

If we define

$$\rho^2 = \frac{\sigma_Y^2 - \sigma_{Y \cdot X}^2}{\sigma_Y^2},$$

the squared correlation coefficient as the proportion of variance accounted for by linear regression on the variable $X$ in the population, then

$$E(\text{MS linear regression}) = \sigma_e^2 + N\rho^2\sigma_Y^2.$$

(It might be mentioned that in the regression model adopted here, the correlation coefficient for the population, $\rho$, and the covariance, cov.$(X,Y)$, are not, strictly speaking, defined, since each is based on the notion of the expectation of the products of *two* random variables, $X$ and $Y$. In this model, $Y$ is a random variable, but $X$ is treated as a fixed constant. Nevertheless, it is useful to think of cov.$(X,Y)$ as a comparison $\psi$ among the population means, and of $\rho^2$ as the proportion of $\sigma_Y^2$ accounted for by linear regression.)

## 15.19  THE EXPECTATIONS OF THE OTHER SUMS OF SQUARES

Given the linear model we adopted at the outset, it must follow that the true mean for each population $j$ is the true value of $Y_j'$ found from the population regression rule. Thus any departure of $M_{Yj}$ from the sample $Y_j'$ can reflect only error. For this reason it can be shown that

$$\frac{E[\text{SS deviations from linear regression}]}{\text{degrees of freedom}} = \sigma_e^2. \qquad [15.19.1]$$

However, what are the degrees of freedom here? Recall that for any $J$ groups,

SS between = (SS linear regression) + (SS deviations from linear regression)

since the values of SS total and SS error remain unchanged regardless of whether we are doing an analysis of variance or a regression analysis on the same data. We saw in Section 14.11 that the SS between groups has only $J - 1$ degrees of freedom, and loses a degree of freedom for each particular orthogonal comparison sum of squares subtracted out. The sum of squares for deviations from regression must thus have only $J - 2$ degrees of freedom, and the expectation for this sum of squares is $(J - 2)\sigma_e^2$.

As usual, we assume equal variance $\sigma_e^2$ within each $X$ population, so that

$$E(\text{SS error}) = \sigma_e^2(N - J). \qquad [15.19.2]$$

Since for this model both MS deviations and MS error estimate only $\sigma_e^2$, the two SS values are pooled, giving

SS deviations and error = (SS error) + (SS deviations from linear regression).

Therefore, the mean square for deviations *and* error is

$$\text{MS deviations and error} = \frac{\text{SS deviations and error}}{N - 2}. \qquad [15.19.3\dagger]$$

The degrees of freedom associated with this mean square come from the sum of the degrees of freedom for deviations from regression, $J - 2$, and those for error, $N - J$:

$$N - 2 = J - 2 + N - J.$$

Under the assumption that each $X$ population has the same variance $\sigma_e^2$ (the assumption of *homoscedasticity*), then the population variance of estimate is the same as the value of $\sigma_e^2$:

$$\sigma_Y^2 = \rho^2 \sigma_Y^2 + \sigma_{Y \cdot X}^2$$
$$= \rho^2 \sigma_Y^2 + \sigma_e^2$$

and

$$\sigma_e^2 = \sigma_Y^2 (1 - \rho^2).$$

Hence, an unbiased estimated of $\sigma_{Y \cdot X}^2$ is provided by the unbiased estimate of $\sigma_e^2$:

$$\text{est. } \sigma_{Y \cdot X}^2 = \frac{\text{SS deviations and error}}{N - 2}$$
$$= \frac{N s_Y^2 (1 - r_{XY}^2)}{N - 2}.$$

## 15.20 Assumptions underlying a test using this regression model

For a genuine regression problem, where the various $X_j$ values are selected beforehand for observation, the following assumptions are made, in addition to the assumption of the general model:

$$Y_{ij} = \mu_Y + \beta_{Y \cdot X}(X_j - \mu_X) + e_{ij}$$

1. within each population $j$, the distribution of $Y_{ij}$ values is normal;
2. within each population $j$, the variance $\sigma_e^2$ is the same;
3. the errors $e_{ij}$ are completely independent.

In other words, the assumptions made here are identical to those for the fixed effects analysis of variance. Notice that absolutely no requirement is put on the distribution of $X$ values in the grand population, although if the fixed effects idea is to apply, presumably the relative proportions of the different $X_j$ values in the grand population is the same as in the sample. This need not trouble us unduly, since the main application of this procedure is to experimental situations where this question of the "actual" population distribution of $X$ values is irrelevant anyway.

## 15.21 Tests for zero linear regression

The hypothesis to be tested is of the form

$$H_0: \beta_{Y \cdot X} = 0$$

or, equivalently,

$$H_0: \rho_{Y \cdot X}^2 = 0.$$

Since the SS for linear regression has only one degree of freedom, we have the option of using either the $t$ or the $F$ ratio:

$$F = \frac{\text{MS linear regression}}{\text{MS error and deviations}} \qquad [15.21.1\dagger]$$

with 1 and $N - 2$ degrees of freedom. However, the $t$ ratio is ordinarily used, and can be put into a simple form: in terms of $b_{Y \cdot X}$,

$$t = \frac{b_{Y \cdot X} s_X \sqrt{N - 2}}{s_{Y \cdot X}} \qquad [15.21.2\dagger]$$

with $N - 2$ degrees of freedom.

In terms of $r_{XY}$, the test statistic is even simpler:

$$t = \frac{r_{XY} \sqrt{N - 2}}{\sqrt{1 - r_{XY}^2}} \qquad [15.21.3\dagger]$$

with $N - 2$ degrees of freedom. Either a directional or a nondirectional alternative may be used.

It is important to remember that in the model underlying this test it is assumed that if *any* possibility of prediction exists at all, then the linear rule completely specifies the predictive part of the relationship. Second, the hypothesis tested is that no prediction is possible even *using* the linear rule (that $\rho_{XY}^2$ or $\beta_{Y \cdot X}$ is zero). When we can reject $H_0$, we can feel confident that some prediction in the population is possible using a linear prediction rule. However, there is a difficulty with this model and the test it affords: the model itself may be wrong, as in a situation where almost perfect prediction is possible using *some* rule, but the linear rule gives very poor or no prediction. This leads to nonsignificant results which *do not* imply that no prediction is possible in the population. On the other hand, there may be a significant result, and the sample $r^2$ may be moderately large; this does not mean, however, that the $r^2$ obtained is an index of *possible* predictive power in the relationship, but only that there is a particular amount of predictive ability afforded by a *linear* rule. Some other rule may exist that greatly increases our ability to predict.

In the next chapter a somewhat different model for regression analysis will be explored, which permits one to evaluate both linear and other rules for describing and using a statistical relationship. For the moment, however, we will confine our attention to estimation methods within the linear regression model.

## 15.22   INTERVAL ESTIMATION IN REGRESSION PROBLEMS

Under the regression model, it is quite possible to form confidence intervals for $\beta_{Y \cdot X}$, the true regression coefficient. The $100(1 - \alpha)$ percent confidence interval is found from

$$b_{Y \cdot X} - \frac{\text{est. } \sigma_{Y \cdot X} t_{(\alpha/2)}}{s_X \sqrt{N}} \leq \beta_{Y \cdot X} \leq b_{Y \cdot X} + \frac{\text{est. } \sigma_{Y \cdot X} t_{(\alpha/2)}}{s_X \sqrt{N}} \qquad [15.22.1\dagger]$$

where

$$\text{est. } \sigma_{Y \cdot X} = \sqrt{\frac{N s_Y^2 - N b_{Y \cdot X}^2 s_X^2}{N - 2}} = \sqrt{\frac{N s_Y^2 (1 - r_{XY}^2)}{N - 2}},$$

or

$$\text{est. } \sigma_{Y \cdot X} = \sqrt{\text{MS deviations and error}} \qquad [15.22.2\dagger]$$

found from **15.19.3**. The $t_{(\alpha/2)}$ value is found for $N - 2$ degrees of freedom.

Occasionally, interval estimates are desired for the predicted values $Y'$ using the *population* regression rule, and some specific $X_j$ value. Remember that the predicted value $Y'$ found using a *sample* regression equation does not necessarily agree with the $Y'$ that would be found using the population regression equation. In a regression problem, there are *two* possible sources of disagreement between a sample $Y'$ and the true value: the sample mean $M_Y$ may be in error, and the sample estimate of $\beta_{Y \cdot X}$ may be wrong to some extent. Considering both of these sources of error, we have for a given score $X_j$ the following confidence interval for *predicted* $Y$ for population $j$:

$$Y_j' - t_{(\alpha/2)} \text{ est. } \sigma_{Y \cdot X} \sqrt{\frac{1}{N} + \frac{(X_j - M_X)^2}{N s_X^2}} \leq \text{true } Y_j'$$

$$\leq Y_j' + t_{(\alpha/2)} \text{ est. } \sigma_{Y \cdot X} \sqrt{\frac{1}{N} + \frac{(X_j - M_X)^2}{N s_X^2}}. \qquad [15.22.3*]$$

The number of degrees of freedom is again $N - 2$.

Be sure to notice the interesting fact that **the regression equation found for a sample is not equally good as an approximation to the population rule over all the different values of** $X_j$. The sample rule is at its best as a substitute for the population rule when $X_j = M_X$, the mean of the $X$ values, since the confidence interval is smallest at this point. However, as $X_j$ values grow increasingly deviant from $M_X$ in either direction, the confidence intervals grow wider. This indicates that for the more extreme values of $X_j$ we cannot really be sure that the value $Y_j'$ predicted for a sample for individuals each showing $X_j$ comes anywhere near the value we would predict if we knew the regression equation for the population.

However, you will also notice that three things operate to make the predicted $Y'$ values agree better with their population counterparts: large sample size; a *large* value of $s_X^2$, such as would be obtained by using a wide range of $X_j$ values each with equal $n$; and a *small* value of $s_Y^2$, such as would be attained by controls operating in the experiment as a whole.

Finally, if we wish, we can establish a confidence interval for the *actual score* (not the predicted score) of a *single* individual given that the over-all relationship is linear. This confidence interval is found from

$$Y'_j - t_{(\alpha/2)} \text{ est. } \sigma_{Y \cdot X} S_j \leq Y_{ij} \leq Y'_j + t_{(\alpha/2)} \text{ est. } \sigma_{Y \cdot X} S_j \qquad [15.22.4]$$

where

$$S_j = \sqrt{1 + \frac{1}{N} + \frac{(X_j - M_X)^2}{N s_X^2}}.$$

For small samples, this may be a very wide interval indeed, particularly for extreme values of $X_j$. On the other hand, if the regression equation actually is based on the entire population of potential observations, then the interval is merely:

$$Y'_j - z_{(\alpha/2)} \sigma_{Y \cdot X} \leq Y_{ij} \leq Y'_j + z_{(\alpha/2)} \sigma_{Y \cdot X} \qquad [15.22.5\dagger]$$

since we have assumed each of the populations $j$ normally distributed with the same variance $\sigma_{Y \cdot X}^2$.

The assumptions of normal distributions within each $X_j$ population and equality of variance within populations are quite important when one is using these interval estimation methods. *It is possible to make an estimate of the regression equation, and to use this equation for prediction without assuming anything except random sampling, but interval estimates depend heavily on these assumptions for their validity.*

On the other hand, the *test* of the hypothesis that $\beta_{Y \cdot X}$ is zero apparently shares the features of the fixed effects model, in that the assumptions of normality and of homogeneous variances are somewhat less important than in other situations. In particular, arranging to have an equal number of cases per $X_j$ grouping is good policy if one suspects that the equal variances assumption is not a reasonable one.

## 15.23  ESTIMATING THE STRENGTH OF LINEAR ASSOCIATION IN A REGRESSION PROBLEM

As mentioned in the preceding sections, the sample regression coefficient $b_{Y \cdot X}$ is an unbiased estimate of $\beta_{Y \cdot X}$, the population regression coefficient, and confidence limits may be established for the value of $\beta_{Y \cdot X}$ as well. On the other hand, in a *regression* problem, it is not so simple to estimate $\rho_{XY}^2$, the true proportion of variance accounted for by linear regression. In the population

$$\beta_{X \cdot Y}^2 = \frac{\rho_{XY}^2 \sigma_Y^2}{\sigma_X^2}$$

so that the point estimate of $\beta_{Y \cdot X}$ certainly has some bearing on the estimated value of $\rho_{XY}^2$. The value of $\sigma_X^2$ is presumably known, since this is given by $s_X^2$ for the distribution of $X$ values in the experiment; but the joker is $\sigma_Y^2$, which need not be the same as $s_Y^2$. However, a point estimate of sorts for $\rho_{XY}^2$ can be made much as for $\omega^2$ in the analysis of variance, by taking

$$\text{est. } \rho_{XY}^2 = \frac{(\text{MS regression}) - (\text{MS error and deviations})}{(\text{MS regression}) + (N - 1)(\text{MS error and deviations})}$$

$$= \frac{(N - 1)r_{XY}^2 - 1}{(N - 1) - r_{XY}^2}. \qquad \text{[15.23.1]}$$

For very large $N$ this is simply $r^2$. When MS regression is less than the pooled error mean square (as when the $F$ value is less than 1.00) then $\rho_{XY}^2$ is estimated to be zero. For regression problems using this model, simple interval estimates for $\rho_{XY}^2$ are apparently not possible.

## 15.24 AN EXAMPLE OF A REGRESSION PROBLEM

A social psychologist was interested in problem-solving carried out cooperatively by small groups of individuals. The theory upon which his experiments were based suggested that within a particular range of possible group sizes, the relationship between group size and average time to solution for particular kind of problem should be linear and negative: the larger the group, the less time on the average should it take for the problem to be solved. In order to check on this theory, the psychologist decided to form a set of experimental groups, ranging in size from groups consisting of a single individual to groups consisting of six individuals. Thus, 105 individuals were chosen at random from some specific population, and then formed at random into five groups consisting of 1 individual each, five groups each consisting of 2 individuals, five groups of 3, and so on until there were six different and nonoverlapping sets of five groups each, the last consisting of five groups each of size 6. Each individual subject participated in one and only one group in the study.

Each experimental group was given the same set of problems to solve, and given a score $Y$ based on the average time to solve the problems. (The normal distribution of such scores might be open to some question, but we'll simply ignore this problem.) Thus, the experimental unit of observation was a group, and the experimental design can be represented in terms of the following six samples of 5 groups each:

|  | *5 groups* | *5 groups* | *5 groups* | *5 groups* | *5 groups* | *5 groups* |
|---|---|---|---|---|---|---|
| Group size | 1 | 2 | 3 | 4 | 5 | 6 |

Notice that in this example $N = 30$, the number of distinct experimental *groups*.

Now the independent variable $X$ in this experiment is the group size; $X$ can take on only the whole values 1 through 6 in this experiment, and each value occurs with frequency 5. The dependent variable $Y$ is the score attached to each distinct group. Does a linear relation appear to exist between $X$ and $Y$ in this range of group sizes?

**Table 15.24.1**

GROUP SCORES ARRANGED ACCORDING TO GROUP SIZE

|  |  | $X$ |  |  |  |
| --- | --- | --- | --- | --- | --- |
| *1* | *2* | *3* | *4* | *5* | *6* |
| 32 | 30 | 27 | 19 | 23 | 20 |
| 29 | 30 | 26 | 21 | 19 | 19 |
| 30 | 26 | 24 | 20 | 20 | 16 |
| 28 | 27 | 24 | 20 | 22 | 18 |
| 26 | 26 | 23 | 18 | 18 | 16 |
| 145 | 139 | 124 | 98 | 102 | 89 |

The raw data were as shown in Table 15.24.1. Preliminary computations show that

$$\sum_j \sum_i X_j = (1)(5) + (2)(5) + (3)(5) + (4)(5) + (5)(5) + (6)(5) = 105$$

$$\sum_j \sum_i X_j^2 = (1)(5) + (4)(5) + \cdots + (36)(5) = 455$$

$$\sum_j \sum_i Y_{ij}^2 = (32)^2 + \cdots + (16)^2 = 16813$$

$$\sum_j \sum_i Y_{ij} = 697$$

$$\sum_j \sum_i Y_{ij}X_j = (32)(1) + (29)(1) + \cdots + (18)(6) + (16)(6)$$

$$= 2231.$$

Given these values, a simple substitution into **15.11.4** gives the sample value of $b_{Y \cdot X}$:

$$b_{Y \cdot X} = \frac{30(2231) - (105)(697)}{(30)(455) - (105)^2}$$

$$= \frac{-4024}{2625} = -1.53.$$

Notice the negative sign of $b_{Y \cdot X}$, indicating that the apparent linear relationship *is* negative.

Now $s_X^2$ is simply

$$s_X^2 = \frac{\sum_j \sum_i X_j^2}{30} - M_X^2$$

$$= \frac{455}{30} - (3.5)^2$$

$$= 2.92$$

so that from **15.18.1,**

$$\text{SS linear regression} = 30(1.53)^2(2.92)$$
$$= 205.06.$$

Since

$$\text{SS total} = 16813 - \frac{(697)^2}{30}$$
$$= 619.37$$

then

$$\text{SS deviations and error} = 619.37 - 205.06 = 414.31$$

and

$$\text{MS deviations and error} = \frac{414.31}{30-2} = 14.79.$$

Under the hypothesis of no linear regression the $F$ test **(15.21.1)** is given by

$$F = \frac{\text{MS linear regression}}{\text{MS deviations and error}}$$
$$= \frac{205.06}{14.79} = 13.86.$$

For 1 and 28 degrees of freedom this value is significant beyond the .01 level. On considering the sign of the regression coefficient one can say with considerable assurance that the null hypothesis of no linear regression is *not* true, and accept the alternative that some *negative* linear regression exists. Although we carried out the test in terms of $F$, we could just as well have used the (directional) $t$ test given by **15.21.2** or **15.21.3.**

Now suppose that we wished to find confidence limits for $\beta_{Y \cdot X}$, the true regression coefficient for this problem. First of all we find

$$\text{est. } \sigma_{Y \cdot X} = \sqrt{\text{MS deviations and error}}$$
$$= 3.85.$$

Then, by **15 .22.1,** the 95 percent confidence interval for $\beta_{Y \cdot X}$ is given by

$$-1.53 - \frac{(3.85)(2.048)}{\sqrt{(2.92)(30)}} \leq \beta_{Y \cdot X} \leq -1.53 + \frac{(3.85)(2.048)}{\sqrt{(2.92)(30)}}$$

or about

$$-2.37 \leq \beta_{Y \cdot X} \leq -.69.$$

In terms of the *sample* regression equation, the predicted $Y'$ score for a group with $X = 6$ is found from **15.9.2** to be

$$Y' = -1.53(6 - 3.5) + 23.23$$
$$= 19.41.$$

Now suppose that we wished to find the 95 percent confidence interval for the value to be predicted for this group of size 6 using the *population* regression equation; we would take confidence limits given by **15.22.3**:

$$19.41 \pm (2.048)(3.85) \sqrt{\frac{1}{30} + \frac{(6 - 3.5)^2}{(2.92)(30)}}$$

or $\qquad 19.41 \pm 2.55$.

In a similar way, we can form confidence limits for $Y'$ for any other value of $X$ represented in the experiment.

The sample correlation coefficient value obtained for these data is about $-.56$. In terms of population $\rho_{XY}^2$, we can estimate the strength of linear association in the way represented by **15.23.1,** which gives

$$\text{est. } \rho_{XY}^2 = \frac{205.06 - 14.79}{205.06 + (29)(14.79)}$$

$$= .31.$$

This estimate, that about 31 percent of the variance in $Y$ is accounted for by $X$ and the linear rule, lends assurance that a moderately strong *linear* relationship exists in the population represented by these data.

On the other hand, all these inferences about the existence and strength of linear relationship in the population strictly apply *only to this particular distribution of X values.* The experimenter has no assurance at all that the linear predictive relationship will hold this strongly, or at all, over a different range of $X$ possibilities. Consequently, his inferences do not necessarily extend to all possible distributions of $X$ values, but only to a distribution of $X$ values paralleling that actually used in the experiment.

## 15.25 PROBLEMS IN CORRELATION IN BIVARIATE NORMAL POPULATIONS

In a regression problem, the values of $X$ are selected in advance of the observation of the $Y$ values. However, quite frequently in psychological research a sample of $N$ individuals is drawn from some population where each individual "brings along" a pair of values $(X,Y)$. The experimenter exerts no direct control over either $X$ or $Y$ values for a given subject. Such a study is usually called a problem in correlation. The main interest actually focuses on the value of $r_{XY}$ itself, especially as an estimate of $\rho_{XY}$ for the population. Given a particular assumption about the population distribution of joint $(X,Y)$ events we can test not only if $X$ and $Y$ are linearly related, but also if any systematic relationship at all exists between the two variables.

In Chapter 4 it was pointed out that in a joint distribution of discrete random variables a probability is associated with each possible $X$ and $Y$ pair. Obviously, a similar conception holds when $X$ and $Y$ are continuous variables, and a probability is associated with any joint interval of values. Such joint distributions are called **bivariate.**

Although any number of theoretical bivariate distributions are possible in principle, by far the most studied is the **bivariate normal distribution.**

The density function for this joint distribution has a rather elaborate-looking rule. However, for standardized variables, this can be condensed to

$$f(z_X, z_Y) = \frac{1}{K} e^{-G}$$

where

$$G = \frac{(z_X^2 + z_Y^2 - 2\rho z_X z_Y)}{2(1 - \rho^2)}$$

and

$$K = 2\pi \sqrt{(1 - \rho^2)}.$$

Notice that in a bivariate normal distribution, the population correlation coefficient $\rho$ appears as a parameter in the rule for the density function. Thus, even though $z_X$ and $z_Y$ are both standardized variables, the particular bivariate distribution cannot be specified unless the value of the correlation $\rho$ is known.

In a bivariate normal distribution, the marginal distribution of $X$ over all observations is itself a normal distribution, and the marginal distribution of $Y$ is also normal. Furthermore, given any $X$ value, the *conditional* distribution of $Y$ is normal; given any $Y$, the conditional distribution of $X$ is normal. In other words, if a bivariate normal distribution is conceived in terms of a table of joint events (as in Section 4.10), where the number of possible $X$ values, of $Y$ values, and of possible joint $(X, Y)$ events is infinite, then within any possible row of the table one would find a normal distribution, a normal distribution also exists within any possible column, and the marginals of the table also exhibit normal distributions.

For our purposes, however, the feature of most importance in a bivariate normal distribution is this: **given that densities for joint $(X, Y)$ events follow the bivariate normal rule, then $X$ and $Y$ are independent if and only if** $\rho_{XY} = 0$. For *any* joint distribution of $(X, Y)$ the independence of $X$ and $Y$ implies that $\rho_{XY} = 0$, but it may happen that $\rho_{XY} = 0$ even though $X$ and $Y$ are *not* independent. However, *for this special joint distribution, the bivariate normal, $\rho_{XY} = 0$ both implies and is implied by the statistical independence of $X$ and $Y$.* The only predictability possible in a bivariate normal distribution is that based on a *linear* rule.

On the other hand, just because the distribution of $X$ and the distribution of $Y$ both happen to be normal, when considered as marginal distributions, this does *not* necessarily mean that the joint distribution of $(X, Y)$ values is bivariate normal. Hence, it is entirely possible for a nonlinear statistical relation to exist even though both $X$ and $Y$ are normally distributed when considered separately. It is not, however, possible for any but a linear relation to exist when $X$ and $Y$ jointly follow the bivariate normal law.

Most of the classical theory of inference about correlation and regression was developed in terms of the bivariate normal distribution. **If one can assume such a joint population distribution, inferences about correlation are equivalent to inferences about independence or dependence between two random variables.** For the kinds of problems here called **correlation problems,** the assumption of a bivariate normal distribution is usually made. When this assumption is valid, any inference about the value of $\rho$ is equivalent to an inference about the *independence*, or *degree of dependence* between two variables; this is not, however, a feature of regression problems, where the bivariate normal assumption need not be made. As always, by adopting more stringent assumptions about the form of the population distribution, one is able to make much more positive statements from sample results.

The general notion of the bivariate normal distribution has also been extended to the multivariate situation where any finite number of random variables are considered, and each observation represents a joint event such as $(X, Y, \ldots, Z, W)$. The same general form of density function is assumed to exist as for a bivariate normal distribution, except that in the density function rule for a multivariate normal distribution, the correlations $\rho_{XY}$ between each *pair* of variables appear as parameters. In a multivariate normal distribution, fixing one or more of the random variables at constant value still results in a multivariate normal, bivariate normal, or normal distribution of the "free" variables. This distribution will be important to our discussion in the second half of the next chapter; for the moment, we will confine our attention to the bivariate normal distribution, where there are only two random variables, $X$ and $Y$.

## 15.26   TESTS AND INTERVAL ESTIMATES IN CORRELATION PROBLEMS

For many correlation problems the hypothesis of interest is

$$H_0: \rho_{XY} = 0.$$

When this hypothesis is true and the population can be assumed to be bivariate normal in form, the distribution of the sample correlation coefficient tends, rather slowly, toward a normal distribution for increasing $N$. For $N$ extremely large, a test of the hypothesis that $\rho = 0$ might be made in terms of the normal distribution. On the other hand, it can be shown that even for relatively small $N$, a satisfactory test of this hypothesis in a bivariate normal population is given by the $t$ ratio:

$$t = \frac{r_{XY} \sqrt{N - 2}}{\sqrt{1 - r_{XY}^2}} \qquad [15.26.1\dagger]$$

with $N - 2$ degrees of freedom. This is precisely the same test statistic used in a regression problem to test the hypothesis that $\beta_{Y \cdot X}$ is zero, even though the rationale underlying these two tests is different, depending on the regression or correlation model adopted.

The various methods of interval estimation for $\beta_{Y \cdot X}$, for the mean predicted value of $Y$ for a fixed value of $X$, and for the value of a given observation in terms of $Y$, originally presented in Section 15.22, are also justified in a problem in correlation. Notice that when a bivariate normal distribution is assumed, the requirement of a normal conditional distribution of $Y$ values *given* any specific $X$ value is automatically met. The basic reasoning behind these methods of interval estimation is somewhat different in the regression and correlation problem models, but the form of interval estimation is the same in either instance.

Under the assumptions made in a problem in correlation, the value of $r_{XY}$ may be used directly as an estimator of $\rho_{XY}$ for the population. Although it is a sufficient and consistent estimator for $\rho_{XY}$, the sample correlation is slightly biased; however, the amount of bias involves terms of the order of $1/N$, and for most practical purposes can be ignored.

As mentioned earlier, for very large samples the distribution of the sample correlation coefficient may be regarded as approximately normal when $\rho_{XY} = 0$. Even for relatively small samples $(N > 4)$ this sampling distribution is unimodal and symmetric. However, when $\rho_{XY}$ is other than zero, the distribution of $r_{XY}$ tends to be very skewed. When $\rho_{XY}$ is greater than zero, the skewness tends to be toward the left, with intervals of high values of $r_{XY}$ relatively more probable than similar intervals of negative values. When $\rho_{XY}$ is negative, this situation is just reversed, and the distribution is skewed in the opposite direction. The fact that the particular form of the sampling distribution depends upon the value of $\rho_{XY}$ makes it impossible to use the $t$ test for other hypotheses about the value of the population correlation, or to set up confidence intervals for this value in some direct elementary way. Although the sampling distribution of $r_{XY}$ for $\rho_{XY} \neq 0$ has been fairly extensively tabled, it is much simpler to employ the following method.

R. A. Fisher showed that tests of hypotheses about $\rho_{XY}$, as well as confidence intervals, can be made from moderately large samples from a bivariate normal population if one uses a particular *function* of $r_{XY}$, rather than the sample correlation coefficient itself. The function used is known as the Fisher $r$ to $Z$ transformation, given by the rule

$$Z = \frac{1}{2} \log_e \left( \frac{1 + r_{XY}}{1 - r_{XY}} \right). \qquad [15.26.2^*]$$

The function is of the type called "one to one": for each possible value of $r$ there can exist one and only one value of $Z$, and for each $Z$, one and only one value of $r$. This fact makes it possible to convert a sample $r$ value to a $Z$ value, make inferences in terms of $Z$, and then to turn those inferences back into statements about correlation once again.

Fisher showed that for virtually any value of $\rho_{XY}$, for samples of moderate size the sampling distribution of $Z$ values is *approximately normal*, with an expectation given approximately by

$$E(Z) = \zeta = \frac{1}{2} \log_e \left( \frac{1 + \rho_{XY}}{1 - \rho_{XY}} \right). \qquad [15.26.3]$$

(The population value of $Z$, corresponding to $\rho$, is denoted by $\zeta$, small Greek zeta.) The sampling variance of $Z$ is approximately

$$\text{var. } (Z) = \frac{1}{N - 3}. \qquad [15.26.4^*]$$

The goodness of these approximations increases the *smaller* the absolute value of $\rho$, and the *larger* the sample size. For moderately large samples the hypothesis that $\rho_{XY}$ is equal to any value $\rho_0$ (not too close to 1 or $-1$) can be tested. This is done in terms of the test statistic

$$\frac{Z - \zeta}{\sqrt{1/(N - 3)}} \qquad\qquad [15.26.5\dagger]$$

referred to a *normal* distribution. The value taken for $E(Z)$ or $\zeta$ depends on the value given for $\rho_0$ by the null hypothesis:

$$\zeta = E(Z) = \frac{1}{2} \log_e \left( \frac{1 + \rho_0}{1 - \rho_0} \right)$$

and the sample value of $Z$ is taken from the sample correlation,

$$Z = \frac{1}{2} \log_e \left( \frac{1 + r_{XY}}{1 - r_{XY}} \right).$$

It should be emphasized that the use of this $r$ to $Z$ transformation *does* require the assumption that the $(X,Y)$ events have a bivariate normal distribution in the population. On the surface, this assumption seems to be a very stringent one, which may not be reasonable in some situations, though there is some evidence that the assumption may be relatively innocuous in others. However, the consequences of this assumption's not being met seem largely to be unknown. Perhaps the safest course is to require rather large samples in uses of this test when the assumption of a bivariate normal population is very questionable.

Table V in Appendix C gives the $Z$ values corresponding to various values of $r$. This table is quite easy to use, and makes carrying out the test itself extremely simple. Only positive $r$ and $Z$ values are shown, since if $r$ is negative, the sign of the $Z$ value is taken as negative also.

For example, suppose that we wanted to test the hypothesis that $\rho_{XY} = .50$ in some bivariate normal population. A sample of 100 cases drawn at random gives a correlation $r_{XY}$ of .35. The hypothesis is to be tested with $\alpha = .05$, two-tailed.

Then, from the Table V, we find that for $r_{XY} = .35$,

$$Z = .3654.$$

For $\rho_{XY} = .50$, we find

$$\zeta = E(Z) = .5493.$$

The test statistic is then

$$\frac{.3654 - .5493}{\sqrt{1/97}} = -1.81.$$

In a normal sampling distribution, a standard score of 1.96 in absolute value is required for rejecting the hypothesis at the .05 level, two-tailed. Thus, we do not reject the hypothesis that $\rho_{XY} = .50$ on the basis of this evidence. Observe that the test made in terms of $Z$ leads to an inference in terms of $\rho$.

Occasionally one has two *independent* samples of $N_1$ and $N_2$ cases respectively, where each is regarded as drawn from a bivariate normal distribution, and he computes a correlation coefficient for each. The question to be asked is, "Do both of these correlation coefficients represent populations having the *same* true value of $\rho$?" Then a test of the hypothesis that the two populations show equal correlation is provided by the ratio

$$\frac{Z_1 - Z_2}{\sigma_{(Z_1 - Z_2)}},$$ [15.26.6†]

where $Z_1$ represents the transformed value of the correlation coefficient for the first sample, $Z_2$ the transformed value for the second, and

$$\sigma_{(Z_1 - Z_2)} = \sqrt{\frac{1}{N_1 - 3} + \frac{1}{N_2 - 3}}.$$ [15.26.7†]

For reasonably large samples, this ratio can be referred to the normal distribution. Remember, however, that the two samples must be independent (in particular, not involving the same or matched subjects) and the population represented by each must be bivariate normal in form.

More generally, suppose that there are $J$ independent samples, each drawn from a bivariate normal distribution of $(X,Y)$ pairs. Each sample $j$ yields a sample correlation $r_j$ between $X$ and $Y$. Then the hypothesis that the true value $\rho_{XY}$ is the same for all of the populations can be tested by the statistic

$$V = \sum_j (n_j - 3)(Z_j - U)^2$$ [15.26.8†]

which is distributed as chi-square with $J - 1$ degrees of freedom when the null hypothesis that $\rho_1 = \rho_2 = \cdots = \rho_J$ is true. Here, $n_j$ is the number of observations in the sample $j$, and

$$U = \frac{\sum_j (n_j - 3)Z_j}{\sum_j (n_j - 3)}.$$

## 15.27 Confidence intervals for $\rho_{XY}$

If the population has a bivariate normal distribution of $(X,Y)$ events, then the $r$ to $Z$ transformation can be used to find confidence intervals, very much as for a mean of a large sample. It is approximately true that for random samples of size $N$, an interval such as

$$Z - z_{(\alpha/2)} \sqrt{\frac{1}{N-3}} \leq \zeta \leq Z + z_{(\alpha/2)} \sqrt{\frac{1}{N-3}} \qquad [15.27.1\dagger]$$

will cover the true value of $\zeta$ with probability $1 - \alpha$. Here, $Z$ is the sample value corresponding to $r_{XY}$, $\zeta$ is the $Z$ value corresponding to $\rho_{XY}$, and $z_{(\alpha/2)}$ (*definitely to be distinguished from $Z$*) is the value cutting of the upper $\alpha/2$ proportion in a normal distribution. Thus, the expression **15.27.1** above gives the $100(1 - \alpha)$ percent confidence interval for $\zeta$. On changing the limiting values of $Z$ back into correlation values, we have a confidence interval for $\rho_{XY}$.

In the example given in the preceding section,

$$Z = .3654$$
$$N = 100,$$

so that

$$\sqrt{\frac{1}{N-3}} = .1.$$

For $\alpha = .05$, $z_{(\alpha/2)} = 1.96$, so that the 95 percent confidence interval for $\zeta$ is given approximately by

$$.3654 - (1.96)(.1) \leq \zeta \leq .3654 + (1.96)(.1)$$

or

$$.1694 \leq \zeta \leq .5614.$$

The corresponding interval for $\rho_{XY}$ is then approximately

$$.168 \leq \rho_{XY} \leq .510$$

(the correlation values here are taken to correspond to the nearest tabled $Z$ values). We can assert that the probability is about .95 that sample intervals such as this cover the true value of $\rho_{XY}$.

## 15.28  AN EXAMPLE OF A CORRELATION PROBLEM

A study was made of the tendency of the height of a wife to be linearly related to that of her husband, and it was desired to find a sample correlation between husband and wife's heights, and to use this to test the hypothesis of no linear relationship.

A sample of 15 American *couples* was drawn at random, and the data are shown in Table 15.28.1.

For these data the computations for the correlation coefficient can be simplified by subtracting 60 from the height of each wife, and 70 from the height of each husband; this does not alter the value of $r_{XY}$ obtained (Section 15.11). Then the new scores are as shown in Table 15.28.2.

### Table 15.28.1

| | Heights in inches | |
|---|---|---|
| Couple | X (Wife's height) | Y (Husband's height) |
| 1 | 70 | 75 |
| 2 | 67 | 72 |
| 3 | 70 | 75 |
| 4 | 71 | 76 |
| 5 | 67 | 70 |
| 6 | 64 | 68 |
| 7 | 71 | 72 |
| 8 | 63 | 67 |
| 9 | 65 | 67 |
| 10 | 65 | 68 |
| 11 | 65 | 68 |
| 12 | 65 | 71 |
| 13 | 66 | 68 |
| 14 | 65 | 71 |
| 15 | 61 | 62 |

### Table 15.28.2

| | Transformed scores | | | | |
|---|---|---|---|---|---|
| Couple | $u$ | $v$ | $uv$ | $u^2$ | $v^2$ |
| 1 | 10 | 5 | 50 | 100 | 25 |
| 2 | 7 | 2 | 14 | 49 | 4 |
| 3 | 10 | 5 | 50 | 100 | 25 |
| 4 | 11 | 6 | 66 | 121 | 36 |
| 5 | 7 | 0 | 0 | 49 | 0 |
| 6 | 4 | −2 | −8 | 16 | 4 |
| 7 | 11 | 2 | 22 | 121 | 4 |
| 8 | 3 | −3 | −9 | 9 | 9 |
| 9 | 5 | −3 | −15 | 25 | 9 |
| 10 | 4 | −2 | −8 | 16 | 4 |
| 11 | 5 | −2 | −10 | 25 | 4 |
| 12 | 5 | 1 | 5 | 25 | 1 |
| 13 | 6 | −2 | −12 | 36 | 4 |
| 14 | 5 | 1 | 5 | 25 | 1 |
| 15 | 1 | −8 | −8 | 1 | 64 |
| | 94 | 0 | 142 | 718 | 194 |

The correlation coefficient computed by the formula **15.11.2** turns out to be

$$r_{XY} = \frac{(15)(142) - (94)(0)}{\sqrt{[(15)(718) - (94)^2][(15)(194) - (0)^2]}}$$

$$= \frac{2130}{\sqrt{(1934)(2910)}}$$

$$= .89.$$

On the evidence of the sample, we conclude that there is a very strong linear relation between the heights of wives and husbands.

If we wished only to test the hypothesis that the true correlation is zero, we would employ the $t$ test given in Section 15.26:

$$t = \frac{(.89)\sqrt{15 - 2}}{\sqrt{1 - (.89)^2}}$$

$$= \frac{3.209}{.456}$$

$$= 7.04.$$

This greatly exceeds both the values required for $\alpha = .05$ and for $\alpha = .01$ for a $t$ with 13 degrees of freedom (two-tailed).

Suppose, however, that the question had been, "Does the height of the wife and the linear relation account for more than 50 percent of the variance in the observed heights of husbands?" That is, we actually want to test the hypothesis

$$\rho_{XY}^2 \leq .50$$

against the alternative

$$\rho_{XY}^2 > .50.$$

Given the assumption that $\rho$ is positive, this is equivalent to the test of

$$H_0: \rho_{XY} \leq \sqrt{.50} \text{ or } H_0: \rho_{XY} \leq .707$$

against

$$H_1: \rho_{XY} > .707.$$

Here, the Fisher $r$ to $Z$ transformation is used to find the test statistic

$$\frac{Z - E(Z)}{\sqrt{1/(N - 3)}} = \frac{1.42 - .88}{\sqrt{1/12}}$$

$$= 1.87.$$

In a normal sampling distribution, this exceeds the value required for the 5 percent significance level, one-tailed. Thus we may safely conclude from this sample that more than 50 percent of the variance in $Y$ is accounted for by the apparent linear relation.

This example is made up, of course, and correlations this large are not usually found in psychological work. It does illustrate one thing, however. Even though the correlation found is sizable, it makes no sense at all to think of the height of the wife as "causing" the height of the husband, or that of the husband the height of the wife. These are simply two numerical measurements that happen to occur together in a more or less linear way, according to the evidence of this sample. The reason *why* this linear relation exists is completely out of the realm of statistics, and the correlation coefficient and tests shed absolutely no light on this problem. In this example, it is perfectly obvious that personal preferences and current standards of society cause *some* selection to occur in the process of mating, and these factors in turn underlie our observations that $(X,Y)$ pairs to occur in a particular kind of relationship. As a description of a population situation, our inferences may very well be valid, but this fact alone gives us no license to talk about the cause of the apparent linear relation.

## 15.29 RETROSPECT: REGRESSION AND CORRELATION PROBLEMS

By now it must be obvious that although both problems in correlation and those in regression involve the same machinery of *descriptive* statistics, the sampling procedures, the assumptions made, and the inferences drawn tend to be somewhat different in the two situations. In regression problems, the methods usual in any fixed-effects experiment are employed: the various values of $X$ to be observed are selected in advance, just as one selects factor levels or treatments for an experiment. Indeed, quite often the values of $X$ actually are amounts of some quantitative experimental treatment. No requirement is put on the experimental distribution of $X$, and only the usual Model I analysis of variance assumptions are made about the $Y$ values within each $X$ array. Then inferences are possible about *linear* regression, the ability to predict $Y$ from $X$ using a linear rule. It is not necessarily true, however, that *all* the ability to predict $Y$ from $X$ resides in some linear rule; small or zero regression coefficients are *not necessarily* indicators of independence between $X$ and $Y$ values.

In correlation problems, no explicit restrictions are put on the possible $X$ values to be observed in the sample. A sample of $N$ cases is drawn, and their $(X,Y)$ pairings noted. In making inferences, a bivariate normal distribution is assumed, and when this assumption *is valid* inferences about the population correlation are equivalent to inferences about the entire *strength* of predictive relationship possible in the population.

It is undoubtedly repetitious to say so, but the significance level obtained in either kind of problem is of small moment as compared with the estimate of our ability to predict, as given by an estimate of $\rho_{XY}^2$ such as the sample $r_{XY}^2$. Very tiny estimated values of $\rho_{XY}^2$ can come from extremely significant results, showing that the ability to predict $X$ from $Y$ linearly is not completely absent, but that there very well may be no practical advantage to be gained from knowing $X$ in the linear prediction of $Y$. Results deserving serious attention are those that are *both* significant and give estimated values of $\rho_{XY}^2$ indicating a really important percentage reduction in variance of $Y$, given $X$ and the regression equation.

In psychology, there is often a tendency to regard regression problems as somehow "better" than problems in correlation. This is largely because a problem in regression carries along all of the paraphernalia of the usual controlled experiment, and a problem in correlation, ordinarily, does not. This distinction is not altogether fair, either to the methods or to the people who use them. The important thing is the research question, and the selection of the best technique to shed light on that question. The theory of normal correlation, involving the bivariate normal assumption, grew out of biological problems and related applied situations. In problems where the variables $X$ and $Y$ symbolize measurements of biologically determined traits, the bivariate normal distribution assumption often makes sense. It was mentioned in Section 8.6 that the normal distribution of natural trait measurements is usually accounted for by an argument similar to that for the limiting form of the binomial distribution. It also happens that the bivariate or multivariate normal distribution can be shown to be the limiting form of a *multinomial* distribution; exactly the same kind of argument for normality can thus be applied to joint distributions of natural traits as to univariate distributions, and in this light the bivariate normal assumption is not quite so arbitrary as it first appears.

In one way, the correlational approach of drawing a random sample of $(X, Y)$ pairings is superior to the regression approach using fixed values, particularly if the main reason for the study is an intended use of a linear rule for prediction in some *existent* population. Notice that in the regression model, nothing was said about the distribution of $X$ values in some population; presumably, the relative frequencies for $X$ in the population are exactly like those in the sample. Now suppose that a study is done using the regression-problem procedure for sampling, where $X$ values are selected arbitrarily, but then the regression equation is actually used to make predictions for individuals in some existing population. *We can have no confidence that the sample regression equation is even remotely like the best way to predict for some population unless the proportional representation of $X$ values in the population is like that in the sample, or unless $X$ values themselves are sampled at random.* In most practical prediction situations, we simply do not know the probability of occurrence of any $X$ value, but we suspect that it is not the same as the relative frequency of $X$ in the sample. For a population of "natural" $(X, Y)$ events, where each individual sampled brings both an $X$ and a $Y$ value for observation, the regression sort of experiment ordinarily does not make much sense as a way to find a prediction rule for use outside the experimental situation itself.

However, in the correlation type of problem, the distribution of $X$ values in the sample need not have any particular connection with the distribution of $X$ in the population, other than describing a random sample from that population distribution. For correlation problems, the regression equation arrived at from the random sample is the best approximation one can make to the true linear regression equation for optimal prediction, *regardless* of the distribution of $X$ in the population. Hence, it seems reasonable then that the correlational approach should be used when interest lies in *actually predicting* an individual's status on one trait from his status on another in some "natural" population where the independent variable represents a natural or previously acquired characteristic of the individual.

Nevertheless, the regression approach is also useful. When some experimental treatment is given in quantity, such as the dosage of a drug, an amount of shock administered, amount of practice, and so on, the various $X$ values do not really "occur" in some real population of individuals, and it makes no particular sense to think of some existent distribution of $(X,Y)$ values. In this instance, where $X$ represents an amount of some experimental treatment administered, both the nature of the population $(X,Y)$ distribution and the character of the regression equation change. The population sampled in the experiment is potential or hypothetical. The population distribution of $X$ is whatever the experimenter chooses to make it; in estimating the regression equation he is saying, literally, "If I repeated this experiment, not on $J$ samples of individuals, but on $J$ distinct populations having a marginal distribution of $X$ like that in the sample, then the best rule for linear prediction of an individual $Y$ value given the $X$ value for the population should be thus and so." The predictions intended apply only to members of this potential grand population. In short, when $X$ is an amount of something actually *done* to a subject by the experimenter, and not a measure of something that the subject brings to the study as a natural or acquired trait, the regression scheme for sampling does lead to a sensible rule for linear prediction. Predictions can be made about an individual so treated, *within this hypothetical population*.

In summary, there is no value judgment to be put on regression as opposed to correlation problems. Each is appropriate to a particular kind of research enterprise: the correlation scheme applies especially to problems of linear prediction of natural traits, and the regression procedures to studies of the ability to predict results of quantitative *experimental* treatments using a linear function rule.

# OTHER TOPICS IN REGRESSION AND CORRELATION

## 16.1 CURVILINEAR REGRESSION

All the discussion in Chapter 15 was centered on linear regression, the use of a linear function rule for the prediction of $Y$ from $X$. However, the theory of "regression" is much more extensive than the preceding discussion of linear regression might suggest. Indeed, the linear rule for prediction is only the simplest of a large number of such rules that might apply to a given statistical relation. Linear regression equations may serve quite well to describe many statistical relations that are roughly like linear functions, or that may be treated as linear as a first approximation. Nevertheless, there is no law of nature requiring all important relationships between variables to have a linear form. It thus becomes important to extend the idea of regression equations to the situation where the relation is *not* best described by a linear rule. Now we are going to consider problems of curvilinear regression, problems where the best rule for prediction need not specify a simple linear function.

Our study of nonlinear prediction rules will be confined to *problems of regression*, as defined in the last chapter. An independent variable $X$ is identified, and various values of $X$ are chosen in advance to be represented in the experiment. Ordinarily, each $X$ value corresponds to an experimental treatment administered in some specific quantity. A regression problem where a curvilinear rule for prediction might make sense is the following: there is an investigation of the effect of environmental noise on the human subject's ability to perform a complex task. Several experimental treatments are planned, each treatment differing from the others only in the intensity of background noise present while the subject performs the task. Each treatment represents a one-step interval in the intensity of noise within a particular range. A group of some $N$ subjects chosen at random are assigned at random to the various groups, with $n$ subjects per group. In the experiment proper, each subject works on the same problem individually in the presence of the assigned intensity of background noise. The dependent variable is thus a subject's score on the task, and the independent variable is the noise intensity. The experimenter is interested not only in the possible existence of a linear relation between noise intensity and performance, but also a possible curvilinear relationship between $X$ and $Y$.

In the next section, a general model for dealing with curvilinear as well as linear regression will be explored. Using this model we will see first how a test may be made for the existence of a nonlinear relationship. Then we will deal with the problem of inferring the form of the statistical relation by use of planned comparisons among means. Finally, inferences about form of relation made from post hoc comparisons will also be considered.

## 16.2 THE MODEL FOR LINEAR AND CURVILINEAR REGRESSION

In Chapter 15, inferences about the existence and extent of linear regression were made in terms of the model

$$Y_{ij} = \mu_Y + \beta_{Y \cdot X}(X_j - \mu_X) + e_{ij},$$

which we saw to be an instance of the fixed effects model for analysis of variance. In adopting this model, we assume that the only systematic tendency of $Y$ to vary with $X$ is due to the linear regression of $Y$ on $X$.

Now we will extend this model to allow for the existence of other kinds of systematic dependence of $Y$ on $X$. The model we will use can be stated as follows:

$$Y_{ij} = \beta_0 + \beta_1(X_j - \mu_X) + \beta_2(X_j - \mu_X)^2 + \cdots \\ + \beta_{J-1}(X_j - \mu_X)^{J-1} + e_{ij}. \quad [16.2.1^*]$$

That is, we assume that the value of $Y$ might depend on the value of $(X_j - \mu_X)$, of $(X_j - \mu_X)^2$, and, indeed, on any power of $(X_j - \mu_X)$ up to and including the $J - 1$ power, each term weighted by a constant $\beta_1$, $\beta_2$, and so on.

Some intuitive feel for this model may be gained as follows. Suppose that it were really true that the best possible prediction of $Y_{ij}$ were afforded by

$$Y'_{ij} = \beta_0 + \beta_1(X_j - \mu_X) + \beta_2(X_j - \mu_X)^2.$$

However, the experimenter does not know this, and he applies the simple linear rule:

$$Y'_{ij} = \beta_1(X_j - \mu_X) + \mu_Y.$$

Does this describe all the predictability possible in the relationship? No, since if $\beta_2$ is not zero, the *deviations* of the predicted from the obtained values of $Y$ should be predictable using the rule

$$d_{ij} = (Y_{ij} - Y'_{ij}) = \beta_2(X_j - \mu_X)^2 + e_{ij} + (\beta_0 - \mu_Y).$$

In short, the deviations from linear regression here represent not only error, but also some further predictability depending on the *squared* value of $(X_j - \mu_X)$. We should expect that, when plotted, the deviations from linear regression for the various sample groups should tend to lie along a parabola, much as in Figure 16.2.1. The constant $\beta_2$ is a coefficient of **second-degree or quadratic regression.**

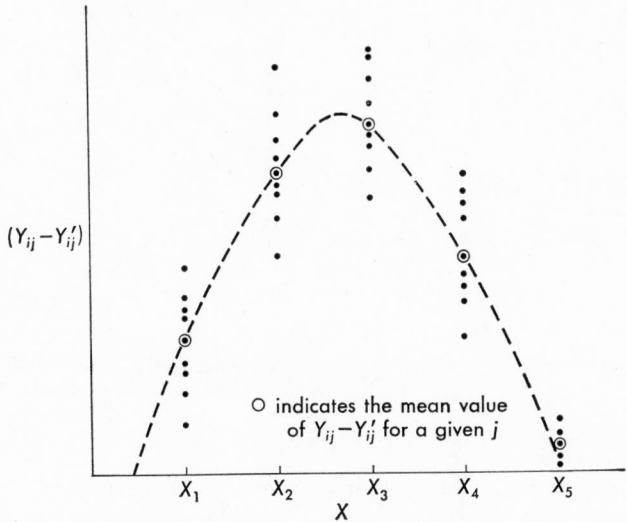

**FIG. 16.2.1.** Plot of deviations from linear regression, suggesting the presence of second-degree or quadratic regression

We need a way to decide if $\beta_2$ really is zero if we are going to tell whether or not the best prediction rule possible is at least of the second degree.

Extending this idea, suppose that the true relation between $X$ and $Y$ is given by the rule

$$Y_{ij} = \beta_0 + \beta_1(X_j - \mu_X) + \beta_2(X_j - \mu_X)^2 + \beta_3(X_j - \mu_X)^3 + e_{ij}.$$

However, the experimenter actually predicts using either a first- or a second-degree regression equation. Suppose that he uses an equation of the second degree. Then, nevertheless, the deviations from the predicted $Y_{ij}$ values will tend to be systematically related to $X$ values, since

$$(Y_{ij} - Y'_{ij}) = \beta_3(X_j - \mu_X)^3 + e_{ij} + \beta'_0.$$

Unless $\beta_3$ is zero, cubic trends exist between $X$ and $Y$, and the plot of deviations from prediction for the various populations should tend to fall into a cubic function, something like that shown in Figure 16.2.2.

The same general ideas hold for any number of experimental groups each associated with a fixed value $X_j$. A regression equation of the first, second, third, and so on up to the degree $J - 1$ is assumed possible. It can be shown, however, that for any finite number $J$ of groupings, each associated with some fixed value of $X_j$, the best prediction equation possible in this model is of *no higher*

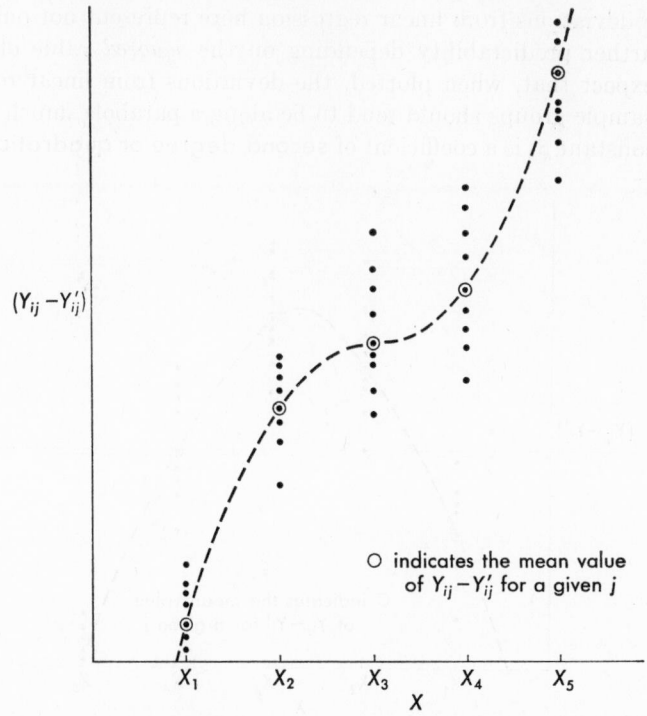

$(Y_{ij} - Y'_{ij})$

O indicates the mean value
of $Y_{ij} - Y'_{ij}$ for a given $j$

$X_1$  $X_2$  $X_3$  $X_4$  $X_5$

$X$

**FIG. 16.2.2.** Deviations from linear or quadratic regression, suggesting the presence of third-degree or cubic regression

*degree than* $J - 1$. Thus, a first-degree equation always suffices to describe the relation between $X$ values and *mean* $Y$ values for two groups, a second-degree equation suffices to describe the relation between $X$ and mean $Y$ for three groups, a third-degree equation for four groups, and so on.

Incidentally, the student who has had elementary calculus may recognize that this model corresponds to the expansion of a function $y = f(x)$ by a Taylor series. That is, for a large class of functions, the value of $y$ associated with any $x$ may be found from a sum of the form

$$f(x) = c_0 + c_1(x - a) + c_2(x - a)^2 + c_3(x - a)^3 + \cdot \cdot \cdot$$

where $a$, $c_0$, $c_1$, and so on are appropriately chosen constants. This fact has a bearing on how we interpret the results of an analysis under this model: when we infer the existence of a trend of a certain degree under this model, all we are really able to say is that a power series or expansion carried to a particular degree is capable of describing the relation obtained from the data. We are not really entitled to talk of the "real" function rule that may, in some sense, underlie what we observe, but only that when the function rule is expressed as a weighted sum of powers in $X$, an equation of a certain degree is sufficient to describe the relation we find. It is not necessarily true that the underlying process, whatever it may be, that generated the data is somehow conceptually equivalent to a sum of powers. This point will be important when we begin to discuss the various trends that appear to exist in a set of data, as in Section 16.8.

Regardless of the number $J$ of different $X_j$ groups, this model can still be regarded as a special version of the fixed effects analysis of variance model. Here, the effect $\xi$ (small Greek xi) associated with group $j$ can be thought of as

$$\xi_j = \sum_{k=0}^{J-1} \beta_k (X_j - \mu_X)^k$$

and

$$Y_{ij} = \mu_Y + \xi_j + e_{ij}.$$

This suggests that the machinery of fixed effects analysis of variance applies to problems of curvilinear as well as linear regression, and we will proceed in this way. However, an adequate justification of the $F$ tests here is somewhat beyond our scope, and we will have to be content with an analogy to the simple fixed-effects analysis of variance.

## 16.3   ANOTHER LOOK AT THE PARTITION OF THE SUM OF SQUARES FOR REGRESSION PROBLEMS

In Section 15.17 it was mentioned that for any regression problem at all,

SS total = (SS error) + (SS deviations from linear regression)
        + (SS linear regression).

Under the model used in the last chapter, nothing could contribute either to SS error or to SS deviations from linear regression except random errors, $e_{ij}$. Consequently, these two sums of squares were pooled and used to estimate $\sigma_e^2$.

Now, however, we have a different model, which permits other, nonlinear, kinds of relations to exist. Nevertheless, the SS error still should reflect only error variance in the data. Furthermore, the SS linear regression depends only on the true regression coefficient $\beta_1$ and error, just as before. On the other hand, the status of the SS deviations from linear regression changes in this new model: this sum of squares reflects all the possible *nonlinear* relations as well as random error.

We saw in Section 15.18 that the SS linear regression can be thought of as the sum of squares for a comparison among the means of the $J$ different groups. Now notice once again that for any set of distinct $J$ groups

SS between groups = (SS linear regression)
        + (SS deviations from linear regression)   [16.3.1†]

since SS total and SS error are found in the ordinary way regardless of whether the problem is one of regression or a simple analysis of variance. Since SS linear regression is based upon a comparison among means, SS deviations from regression represents all the $J - 2$ remaining comparisons among means *orthogonal* to the comparison for linear regression. In this model, the systematic differences between group means can reflect either linear or curvilinear association, and SS deviations from linear regression can reflect only *curvilinear* regression and error.

This can be shown in terms of the expected mean squares: in the discussion of the analysis of variance, we defined the index of *total* strength of relationship as

$$\omega^2 = \frac{\sigma_Y^2 - \sigma_e^2}{\sigma_Y^2} = \frac{\sum_j n_j \alpha_j^2}{N \sigma_Y^2}.$$

Furthermore, in Chapter 15, we found that the strength of linear relationship is indexed by

$$\rho_{XY}^2 = \frac{\sigma_Y^2 - \sigma_{Y \cdot X}^2}{\sigma_Y^2}.$$

It will always be true that $\omega^2 \geqq \rho_{XY}^2$.

**The strength of curvilinear relationship** must then be indexed by the difference

$$\omega^2 - \rho_{XY}^2, \qquad\qquad [16.3.2*]$$

the proportion of variance in $Y$ accounted for by $X$, but not by linear regression. From the results of Section 15.18 we can deduce that

$$E(\text{SS linear regression}) = \sigma_e^2 + N \rho_{XY}^2 \sigma_Y^2. \qquad [16.3.3]$$

We already know from Section 12.6 that

$$E(\text{SS between groups}) = (J - 1)\sigma_e^2 + \sum_j n_j \alpha_j^2, \qquad [16.3.4]$$

or, in terms of $\omega^2$,

$$E(\text{SS between groups}) = (J - 1)\sigma_e^2 + N\omega^2 \sigma_Y^2. \qquad [16.3.5]$$

Putting these two results, **16.3.3** and **16.3.5**, together we have

$$E(\text{SS deviations from linear regression}) = E(\text{SS between}$$
$$- \text{SS linear regression}) = (J - 2)\sigma_e^2 + (\omega^2 - \rho_{XY}^2)N\sigma_Y^2. \quad [16.3.6]$$

**The SS deviations from linear regression reflects only systematic differences between population group means not due to linear regression.** We should expect SS deviations from linear regression to reflect only error when $\beta_2$, $\beta_3$, and so on are *all* zero. If no curvilinear regression exists in the population, then

$$E(\text{MS deviations}) = \frac{E(\text{SS deviations})}{J - 2} = \sigma_e^2. \qquad [16.3.7*]$$

## 16.4 Testing for Linear and Nonlinear Regression

Given the usual assumptions for the one-way fixed effects analysis of variance it can be shown that an $F$ test for the hypothesis

$$H_0: \omega^2 - \rho_{XY}^2 = 0$$

becomes possible. In terms of the foregoing argument, this is the hypothesis of no *curvilinear* regression. This hypothesis may be tested apart from the hypothesis

$$H_0: \rho_{XY}^2 = 0,$$

so that one can ask *both* if any linear regression exists *and* if any curvilinear regression exists in the population (that is, predictability not afforded by a linear rule).

The actual $F$ test employed to test for linear regression is different in this model from that in Section 15.21. Here, we take

$$F = \frac{\text{MS linear regression}}{\text{MS error}} \qquad [16.4.1\dagger]$$

with 1 and $N - J$ degrees of freedom to test for the existence of linear regression ($\rho_{XY}^2 \neq 0$, or $\beta_1 \neq 0$).

The test for curvilinear regression is given by

$$F = \frac{\text{MS deviations from linear regression}}{\text{MS error}} \qquad [16.4.2\dagger]$$

with $J - 2$ and $N - J$ degrees of freedom.

A convenient way to find the SS linear regression directly is

$$\text{SS lin. reg.} = \frac{N \left[ \sum_j \sum_i X_j Y_{ij} - \left( \sum_j n_j X_j \right) \left( \sum_j \sum_i Y_{ij} \right)/N \right]^2}{N \left( \sum_j n_j X_j^2 \right) - \left( \sum_j n_j X_j \right)^2} \qquad [16.4.3\dagger]$$

although the method of Section 15.24 can be used. The separate calculation of the SS deviations from linear regression is actually the only new computational feature. The quantities needed for the analysis are

1. SS total (formula **12.10.1**)
2. SS between groups (formula **12.10.2**)
3. SS linear regression (formula **16.4.3**)
4. SS error = SS total − SS between
5. SS deviations from linear reg. = SS between − SS linear reg.

The analysis ordinarily is summarized in a table such as the following:

| Source | SS | df | MS | F |
|---|---|---|---|---|
| Between groups | | $J - 1$ | — | — |
| Linear regression | | 1 | $\dfrac{\text{SS lin.}}{1}$ | $\dfrac{\text{MS lin.}}{\text{MS error}}$ |
| Deviations from linear regression | | $J - 2$ | $\dfrac{\text{SS dev.}}{J - 2}$ | $\dfrac{\text{MS dev.}}{\text{MS error}}$ |
| Error | | $N - J$ | $\dfrac{\text{SS error}}{N - J}$ | |
| Total | | $N - 1$ | | |

A significant value for the first of these $F$ tests indicates that it is safe to conclude that some predictability is afforded by a linear rule. In the same way, a significant value for $F$ for the second test lets one conclude that some further prediction is possible using a curvilinear rule. However, neither of these tests guarantees that there exists either a strong linear nor a strong curvilinear relationship in the population sampled, but only that from the evidence, $\rho_{XY}^2 > 0$, and that $\omega^2 - \rho_{XY}^2 > 0$. Nevertheless, for regression problems we can form at least rough estimates for both of these population indices, as shown in Section 16.5.

Naturally, the simplest and most readily available estimate of the form of relation in the data is given by a plot of the $Y$ scores against the $X$ values. In many instances a regression curve drawn "by eye" on the scatter plot suffices to describe the general form of predictive relation that appears to exist. One can regard the test for curvilinear regression as a license to infer that the curvilinear regression line that appears to fit the data also is a good bet about the population. However, much more sophisticated methods exist for judging the form of the prediction equation after the test for curvilinear regression has proved significant. One of the simplest of these methods will be outlined in Section 16.12. A more general treatment of the problem of fitting curvilinear regression lines will be found in Lewis (1960).

## 16.5 ESTIMATION OF THE STRENGTH OF LINEAR AND CURVILINEAR RELATIONSHIP FROM DATA

Using the model of Section 16.2, we have seen that

$$E(\text{SS lin. regression}) = \sigma_e^2 + N\rho_{XY}^2\sigma_Y^2$$

and

$$E(\text{MS error}) = \sigma_e^2,$$

so that

$$E(\text{SS lin. reg.} - \text{MS error}) = N\rho_{XY}^2\sigma_Y^2.$$

Then an estimate of $\rho_{XY}^2$ may be found from

$$\text{est. } \rho_{XY}^2 = \frac{\text{SS lin. reg.} - \text{MS error}}{\text{SS total} + \text{MS error}}, \qquad \text{[16.5.1†]}$$

since

$$E(\text{SS total} + \text{MS error}) = N(\sigma_e^2 + \omega^2\sigma_Y^2) = N\sigma_Y^2.$$

Furthermore, by the same line of argument, a reasonable estimate of $\omega^2 - \rho_{XY}^2$, the proportion of variance accounted for by curvilinear regression, is given by

$$\text{est. } (\omega^2 - \rho_{XY}^2) = \frac{\text{SS deviations from lin. reg.} - (J - 2)\,\text{MS error}}{\text{SS total} + \text{MS error}}. \qquad \text{[16.5.2†]}$$

Once again, when MS deviation is less than MS error, so that the $F$ for curvilinear regression is less than 1.00, the estimate is taken to be zero.

Notice that

$$\text{est. } (\omega^2 - \rho^2_{XY}) + \text{est. } \rho^2_{XY} = \text{est. } \omega^2, \qquad \text{[16.5.3†]}$$

the estimated total strength of relationship.

## 16.6  THE CORRELATION RATIOS $\eta^2_{Y \cdot X}$ AND $\eta^2_{X \cdot Y}$

Our index $\omega^2$ has been defined only in terms of the strength of association between the independent and dependent variables in some population. Similarly, the difference $(\omega^2 - \rho^2_{XY})$ reflects the tendency toward a curvilinear relationship in the population considered.

However, for some purposes it is convenient to have a descriptive index of total relationship *in a given set of data*. For this purpose the index $\eta^2_{Y \cdot X}$ is sometimes used (Greek eta, squared). The definition of $\eta^2_{Y \cdot X}$ is

$$\eta^2_{Y \cdot X} = \frac{\sum\limits_{j} n_j (M_{Yj} - M_Y)^2}{\sum\limits_{j} \sum\limits_{i} (Y_{ij} - M_Y)^2} \qquad \text{[16.6.1*]}$$

which is exactly the same as

$$\eta^2_{Y \cdot X} = \frac{\text{SS between groups}}{\text{SS total}} \qquad \text{[16.6.2†]}$$

where each group corresponds to one $X_j$ value. The index $\eta^2_{X \cdot Y}$ is often called the **correlation ratio** for the relation of $Y$ to $X$.

If $Y$ is regarded as the independent variable, and the $X$ values in the data are arranged by $Y$ groupings, then another index $\eta^2_{X \cdot Y}$ may be found,

$$\eta^2_{X \cdot Y} = \frac{\sum\limits_{k} n_k (M_{Xk} - M_X)^2}{\sum\limits_{k} \sum\limits_{i} (X_{ik} - M_X)^2} \qquad \text{[16.6.3*]}$$

where $X_{ik}$ is the value of the $i$th individual in the $k$th category, corresponding to a $Y$ value $Y_k$. Ordinarily, these two indices will give different values for a given set of data, unless $r^2_{XY} = 1$, so that $r^2_{XY} = \eta^2_{Y \cdot X} = \eta^2_{X \cdot Y} = 1$.

**So long as the group we are dealing with is, in fact, the population, the two indices $\omega^2$ and $\eta^2_{X \cdot Y}$ are absolutely identical.** However, the utility of the correlation ratio is rather limited if one desires more than a descriptive statistic for a sample. This is the reason that the symbol $\omega^2$ has been used to discuss the *population* strength of total association in all of the foregoing: the correlation ratio $\eta^2_{Y \cdot X}$ usually applies only to a sample, and is usually discussed only when both variables $X$ and $Y$ are numerical. Applications of the two different $\eta^2$ indices make sense only when the sample is drawn as for a correlation problem. On the other hand the index $\omega^2$ applies only to a population, and can be discussed even when the independent variable is categorical in character.

The correlation ratio has a direct connection with the $F$ test for the presence of any association (i.e., $H_0$: true $\eta^2_{Y \cdot X} = 0$). Under this hypothesis,

$$F = \left(\frac{N - J}{J - 1}\right)\left(\frac{\eta^2_{Y \cdot X}}{1 - \eta^2_{Y \cdot X}}\right) \qquad [16.6.4*]$$

actually is distributed as $F$ with $J - 1$ and $N - J$ degrees of freedom. However, for the fixed effects or regression models, this is not true for any other hypothesis about the true correlation ratio.

Furthermore, the sample value of the correlation ratio is not an especially good way to estimate the true correlation ratio, and about the best one can do is to estimate $\omega^2$ as we have shown. In general, our estimate of $\omega^2$ gives a lower estimate of total association than does $\eta^2$; considering the error in the sample, this is not a bad feature of our estimate to have. Since $\eta^2_{Y \cdot X}$ makes most sense as a descriptive statistic, and since talking about degree of dependence *within a sample* has rather limited utility, we will continue to deal here only with the population quantity $\omega^2$.

## 16.7 AN EXAMPLE OF TESTS FOR LINEAR AND CURVILINEAR REGRESSION

Consider the example mentioned in Section 16.1. Six different levels of noise intensity are employed. Each level represents a one-step interval in a scale of intensity, although this need not be true in general for this procedure. The exact units of noise intensity need not bother us here, and we can represent the levels of $X$ as 1, 2, 3, and so on, since the different groupings represent equal intervals in noise intensity. The dependent variable is the score $Y_{ij}$ of a subject in a complex performance given the noise intensity level $X_j$. It is desired to test both for linear and for curvilinear regression, using $\alpha = .01$. The scores are shown in Table 16.7.1.

**Table 16.7.1**

| | *Noise intensity levels, $X_j$* | | | | |
|---|---|---|---|---|---|
| *1* | *2* | *3* | *4* | *5* | *6* |
| 18 | 34 | 39 | 37 | 15 | 14 |
| 24 | 36 | 41 | 32 | 18 | 19 |
| 20 | 39 | 35 | 25 | 27 | 5 |
| 26 | 43 | 48 | 28 | 22 | 25 |
| 23 | 48 | 44 | 29 | 28 | 7 |
| 29 | 28 | 38 | 31 | 24 | 13 |
| 27 | 30 | 42 | 34 | 21 | 10 |
| 33 | 33 | 47 | 38 | 19 | 16 |
| 32 | 37 | 53 | 43 | 13 | 20 |
| 38 | 42 | 33 | 23 | 33 | 11 |
| 270 | 370 | 420 | 320 | 220 | 140 |

The usual computations for a one-way analysis of variance are carried out first:

$$SS \text{ total} = (18)^2 + (24)^2 + \cdots + (11)^2 - \frac{(1740)^2}{60}$$

$$= 7252$$

$$SS \text{ between} = \frac{(270)^2 + \cdots + (140)^2}{10} - \frac{(1740)^2}{60}$$

$$= 5200$$

$$SS \text{ error} = SS \text{ total} - SS \text{ between} = 7252 - 5200 = 2052.$$

Next the SS for linear regression is found from equation **16.4.3.** Since $n_j = 10$ for each group, this becomes

$$SS \text{ lin. regression} = \frac{60 \left[ \sum_j \sum_i X_j Y_{ij} - \left( \sum_j 10 X_j \right) \left( \sum_j \sum_i Y_{ij} \right) / 60 \right]^2}{60 \left( \sum_j 10 X_j^2 \right) - \left( \sum_j 10 X_j \right)^2}.$$

Here

$$\sum_j \sum_i X_j Y_{ij} = \sum_j X_j \left( \sum_i Y_{ij} \right) = 1(270) + 2(370) + \cdots + 6(140) = 5490$$

$$\sum_j 10 X_j = 10(1) + \cdots + (10)(6) = 210$$

$$\sum_j 10 X_j^2 = 10(1 + 4 + \cdots + 36) = 910$$

so that

$$SS \text{ lin. reg.} = \frac{60[5490 - (210)(1740)/60]^2}{60(910) - (210)^2}$$

$$= 2057.1.$$

Then

$$SS \text{ dev. from lin. reg.} = SS \text{ between} - SS \text{ lin. reg.}$$
$$= 5200 - 2057.1$$
$$= 3142.9.$$

The completed summary table is thus

| Source | SS | df | MS | F |
|---|---|---|---|---|
| Between groups | 5200 | 5 | — | — |
| Linear reg. | 2057.1 | 1 | 2057.1 | 54.1 |
| Dev. from lin. | 3142.9 | 4 | 785.7 | 20.7 |
| Error | 2052 | 54 | 38 | |
| Totals | 7252 | 59 | | |

On evaluating these two $F$ tests, we find that each is significant far beyond the .01 level. In short, we can reject both the hypothesis

$$H_0: \rho_{XY} = 0,$$

*and* the hypothesis

$$H_0: \omega^2 - \rho_{XY}^2 = 0,$$

although we should recall from Section 14.26 that the probability of error in one or both of these conclusions is not necessarily .01. Nevertheless, here we may say with some confidence that both linear and curvilinear regression exist. The best rule for population prediction apparently involves both $X_j$ and powers of $X_j$, in terms of this model.

A plot of the $Y$ means for these data supports our findings (Figure 16.11.1). The sample means tend, roughly, to fall along a straight line with negative slope (the dotted line in the figure). However, they would cluster even more closely along a curved line suggesting a parabolic arc. The experimenter would be likely to conclude that, in the range studied, relatively low levels of noise intensity may actually facilitate the performance of subjects in this task, but that beyond a particular point (about level 3) average performance falls off rapidly with further increases in noise intensity.

We may apply our estimation methods (**16.5.1** and **16.5.2**) to obtain some idea of the strength of linear and curvilinear relationship in the population sampled. Using **16.5.1,** we find

$$
\begin{aligned}
\text{est. } \rho_{XY}^2 &= \frac{2057.1 - 38}{7252 + 38} \\
&= \frac{2019.1}{7290} \\
&= .28.
\end{aligned}
$$

From the evidence at hand, it appears that about 28 percent of the variance in $Y$ may be attributable to *linear* relationship with $X$, the noise levels.

Furthermore, using **16.5.2,** we have

$$
\begin{aligned}
\text{est. } (\omega^2 - \rho_{XY}^2) &= \frac{3142.9 - (4)(38)}{7290} \\
&= \frac{2990.9}{7290} \\
&= .41.
\end{aligned}
$$

Something on the order of 41 percent of the variance of $Y$ is attributable to *curvilinear* relationship with $X$. Notice that we estimate a considerably stronger curvilinear than linear relationship in the population, even though the $F$ tests were both very significant.

Finally, the total contribution of $X$ to the variance of $Y$, or $\omega^2$, is estimated to be

$$\text{est. } \omega^2 = \text{est. } \rho_{XY}^2 + \text{est. } (\omega^2 - \rho_{XY}^2) = .69$$

so that we infer quite a strong statistical association to exist between $X$ and $Y$.

## 16.8 PLANNED COMPARISONS FOR TREND:
### ORTHOGONAL POLYNOMIALS

The separation of sums of squares into components representing linear and nonlinear regression is but the simplest of the procedures that may be applied to problems of linear and curvilinear regression. Many times an experiment is set up to answer certain specific questions about the *form* of the relation existing between two variables. In general when the experimenter wants to look into the question of trend, or form of relationship, he has some prior ideas about what the population relation should be like. These hunches about trend often come directly from theory, or they may come from the extrapolation of established findings into new areas. At any rate, specific questions are to be asked about the *degree* of the regression equation sufficient to permit prediction.

The technique of planned comparisons studied in Chapter 14 lends itself directly to this problem. Given $J$ groups, each of which is associated with a value $X_j$ of the experimental variable, each of the $J - 1$ degrees of freedom for comparisons can be allotted to the study of *one question* about the form or degree of the predictive relation. In this discussion, we will restrict our attention to the situation where the following conditions are satisfied.

1. The various $X_j$ values represent *equally spaced unit intervals* on the $X$ dimension or continuum. The units may be anything, but the difference between each $X_j$ and $X_{j+1}$ is precisely one of these units.
2. The number of observations made, $n_j$, is the same for each value of $X_j$.
3. Inferences are to be made about a hypothetical population in which *only possible* values of $X_j$ are those actually represented in the experiment.

The first two of these requirements are not especially severe limitations, since this technique is ordinarily applied to experimental studies where one is free to choose the $X_j$ values and the $n$ per group quite arbitrarily. In such studies it is usually more convenient than otherwise to form equal spacings of $X_j$ values, and to assign individuals at random and equally among the groups. The third restriction is quite serious, however. In uses of this method, **really nothing can be said about values of $X_j$ that are not directly represented in the experiment, in so far as statistical inference is concerned.** The form of the relation may be quite different for $X$ outside of the range represented, or even for potential $X_j$ values intermediate to two actually represented. It is up to the experimenter to exercise caution and good scientific judgment in extrapolating beyond the $X_j$ values he has actually observed. The statistician cannot really help him here, since this is a question of scientific, not statistical, inference.

We have already seen (Section 15.18) that in the regression model the sum of squares for *linear* regression corresponds to the SS for one possible comparison among the sample means. Extending this idea, an orthogonal comparison can also be made reflecting second-degree or quadratic relationship. Still another orthogonal comparison can be carried out representing the third-degree, or cubic, relationship, and so on, until the experimenter has either investigated all the specific questions of interest, or $J - 1$ orthogonal comparisons have been made (whichever happens first). As for any set of *planned* comparisons, particular values from among the $J - 1$ possible comparisons are tested separately instead of the over all $F$ test of between group means. If any one of these comparisons is significant, then the experimenter has relatively strong evidence that the corresponding $\beta$ value in the population is not zero, and that the best prediction rule is at least of the degree represented by that comparison.

The weights which each trend comparison involves are completely dictated by $J$, the number of different $X_j$ groups, and by the degree of the particular trend investigated. That is, given any number of groups $J$, one standard set of weights exists for investigating linear, or first-degree, trends, an orthogonal set exists for second-degree, or quadratic, trends, another for cubic, or third-degree, trends, and so on, up to and including trends of degree $J - 1$. These standard sets of comparison weights are called **coefficients of orthogonal polynomials,** and the method itself is sometimes called **the method of orthogonal polynomials.**

The general theory underlying orthogonal polynomials is much too advanced for us to go into here. Suffice it to say that the **orthogonal polynomial coefficients are so derived that the particular comparisons among means each represent one and only one kind of possible trend or form of relationship in the data.** This sounds much more complicated than it actually is. Perhaps a simple example may clarify this point. For four groups, equally spaced with regard to the $X_j$ values, the three sets of standard orthogonal polynomial weights are

| Comparison | $M_1$ | $M_2$ | $M_3$ | $M_4$ |
|---|---|---|---|---|
| linear | $-3$ | $-1$ | $1$ | $3$ |
| quadratic | $1$ | $-1$ | $-1$ | $1$ |
| cubic | $-1$ | $3$ | $-3$ | $1$ |

The symbol $M_1$ denotes the mean $Y$ value for the group with the *lowest* $X$ value, or $X_1$, $M_2$ the mean $Y$ for the next lowest value of $X$, or $X_2$, and so on. Applying the weights given in the first row to the means, we get the first, or *linear* comparison:

$$\hat{\psi}_1 = -3(M_1) - 1(M_2) + 1(M_3) + 3(M_4).$$

The sample value of $\hat{\psi}_1$ is an unbiased estimate of the *population* comparison

$$\psi_1 = -3(\mu_1) - 1(\mu_2) + 1(\mu_3) + 3(\mu_4).$$

This population comparison can be zero *only if* $\beta_1 = 0$, so that there is no linear trend at all in the population. Otherwise $\psi_1$ cannot be zero.

By applying the weights of the second comparison to the sample means, we get

$$\hat{\psi}_2 = 1(M_1) - 1(M_2) - 1(M_3) + 1(M_4)$$

which estimates $\psi_2$, the same linear combination applied to the population means. This comparison value in the population can be zero only if $\beta_2 = 0$, so that no quadratic trend exists in the statistical relationship.

Finally, the comparison for cubic trends is

$$\hat{\psi}_3 = -1(M_1) + 3(M_2) - 3(M_3) + 1(M_4).$$

This comparison estimates $\psi_3$, which can be zero only if $\beta_3$ is zero, meaning that no cubic trend exists in the population relationship.

If all three comparisons, $\psi_1$, $\psi_2$, $\psi_3$, are zero when applied to population values, then $\omega^2 = 0$, and no predictive relationship at all exists in the data.

Now suppose that we apply these comparisons to some hypothetical population situations. First of all, suppose that it were really true that

$$Y_{ij} = \beta_0 + \beta_1(X_j - \mu_X) + e_{ij}$$

which implies that the predictive relationship is truly linear, and that the population means must fall on a straight line when plotted against the corresponding

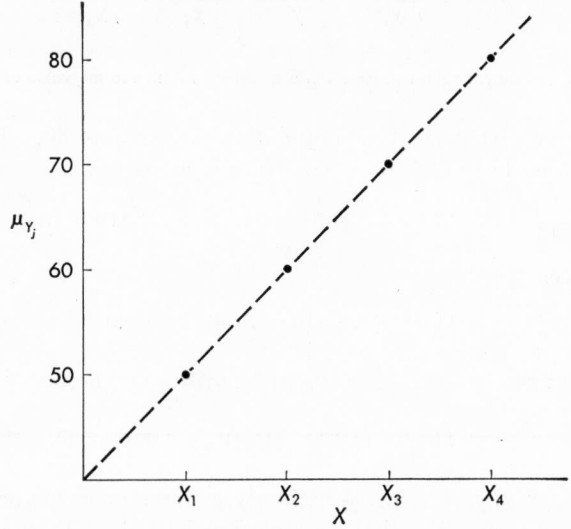

FIG. 16.8.1. Hypothetical population means in a linear relation to the value of X

$X_j$ values. Suppose that the true plot of $(X_j, \mu_{Y_j})$ pairs were as shown in Figure 16.8.1. Applying the standard weights for the linear comparison to the population means we have

$$\psi_1 = -(3)(50) - 1(60) + 1(70) + 3(80) = 100,$$

giving a large comparison value. However, if we apply the other two sets of weights to form the quadratic and the cubic comparisons, we find

$$\psi_2 = 1(50) - 1(60) - 1(70) + 1(80) = 0$$

and

$$\psi_3 = -1(50) + 3(60) - 3(70) + 1(80) = 0$$

reflecting the fact that the *only* predictive relation is linear.

However, suppose that it is really true that only a quadratic relation exists, following the rule

$$Y_{ij} = \beta_0 + \beta_2(X_j - \mu_X)^2 + e_{ij}.$$

Here, the true means must all lie on a *parabola* when plotted against $X_j$ values (Figure 16.8.2).

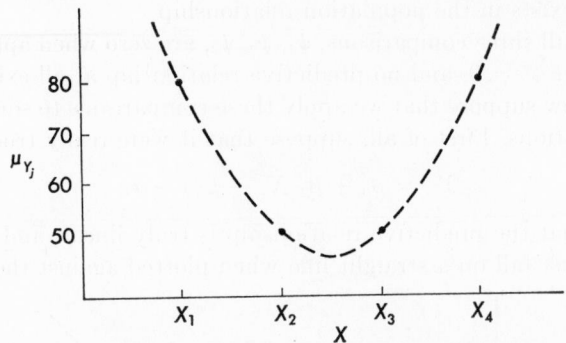

FIG. 16.8.2. Population means in a quadratic relation to the value of X

Suppose that the four population means were 80, 50, 50, and 80, as shown in the figure. Then the *linear* comparison gives

$$\psi_1 = -3(80) - 1(50) + 1(50) + 3(80) = 0$$

and the *cubic* gives

$$\psi_3 = -1(80) + 3(50) - 3(50) + 1(80) = 0.$$

However, in this instance, the *quadratic* comparison on the population means is

$$\psi_2 = 1(80) - 1(50) - 1(50) + 1(80) = 60,$$

showing that the predictive relation is purely of the second degree.

Finally, imagine that the relation is such that prediction from $X$ to $Y$ is afforded by a rule of the third or cubic degree, such as

$$Y_{ij} = \beta_0 + \beta_3(X_j - \mu_X)^3 + e_{ij}.$$

As a fairly extreme example, suppose that the plot of population means against $X_j$ values showed the form pictured in Figure 16.8.3. In this figure the population means are 60, 80, 50, and 70. Then we have

$$\psi_1 = -3(60) - 1(80) + 1(50) + 3(70) = 0$$
$$\psi_2 = 1(60) - 1(80) - 1(50) + 1(70) = 0$$
$$\psi_3 = -1(60) + 3(80) - 3(50) + 1(70) = 100$$

reflecting only the cubic trend in the relationship.

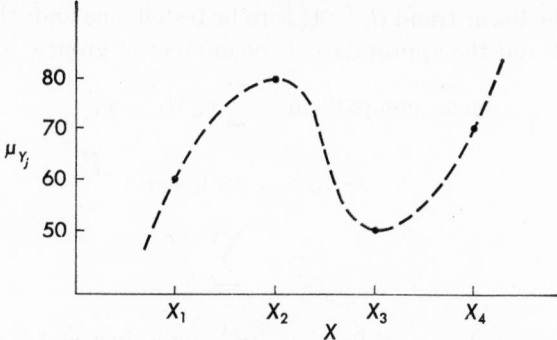

FIG. 16.8.3. A pronounced cubic trend among population means

This example may give you some feel for how these particular comparisons among sample means, used as estimates for population comparisons, give information about the general form of the predictive relationship, if any, between $X$ and $Y$. Large and significant sample comparison values are evidence that a trend of that particular degree *does* exist in the population relation.

One more thing should be pointed out: these weights used in the example are bona fide comparison weights, since the weights for each comparison sum to zero. Furthermore, the comparisons are all orthogonal, since the summed products of weights for any two comparisons is also zero. Thus the theory we have studied for any set of planned orthogonal comparisons applies perfectly well to trend comparisons of this type.

Table VI in Appendix C gives the required weights for trend comparisons for $J = 3$ through $J = 15$, and for trends through the sixth degree, which certainly should cover most psychological research on such problems. One simply finds the appropriate section of the table, and reads off the required weights. Within each section, the rows represent the $X_j$ groupings, with the lowest value of $X_j$ shown as the first or topmost row. The columns represent the *degree* of trend to be examined. Then the entry in any row $j$ and column $h$ gives the weight applied to the mean of the $j$th group in the comparison for a trend of degree $h$. A larger table of required weights is given in *Biometrika Tables for Statisticians* (1954).

## 16.9  COMPUTATIONS FOR TREND ANALYSIS USING ORTHOGONAL POLYNOMIALS

In planned comparisons for trend made on data from single-factor experiments, one proceeds just as for any problem involving planned comparisons. First, an ordinary one-way analysis of variance is performed, although the over-all $F$ test for the analysis is not carried out. The SS error is needed for testing the individual trend comparisons, and the SS between is useful either as an over-all check or for finding the pooled SS for all comparisons not of special interest by themselves.

If the linear trend ($h = 1$) is to be tested, one finds the set of weights $c_{1j}$ from Table VI and the appropriate $J$, or number of groups. Then

$$\text{linear comparison} = \sum_j c_{1j}M_j = \hat{\psi}_1 \qquad [16.9.1\dagger]$$

and

$$\text{SS}(\hat{\psi}_1) = \text{SS linear} = \frac{\hat{\psi}_1^2}{w_1} \qquad [16.9.2\dagger]$$

where

$$w_1 = \sum_j \frac{c_{1j}^2}{n}. \qquad [16.9.3\dagger]$$

The SS linear has *one* degree of freedom, of course, just as for any comparison among means.

Then if there is interest in testing for quadratic trends ($h = 2$) one finds the set of weights $c_{2j}$ from Table VI. The comparison is

$$\text{quadratic comparison} = \sum_j c_{2j}M_j = \hat{\psi}_2 \qquad [16.9.4\dagger]$$

$$\text{SS}(\hat{\psi}_2) = \text{SS quadratic} = \frac{\hat{\psi}_2^2}{w_2} \qquad [16.9.5\dagger]$$

where

$$w_2 = \sum_j \frac{c_{2j}^2}{n}. \qquad [16.9.6\dagger]$$

The number of degrees of freedom is again 1.

This general procedure is followed until as many of the comparisons as have a-priori interest for the experimenter have been made. These comparisons should actually be *planned* before the data are seen, and should really correspond to questions that are germane to the experimental problem and will clarify the interpretation of the experiment by their separate examination. For more than four or five experimental groups, it is seldom practical or useful to work out all the possible $J - 1$ trend comparisons. Usually, there is little understanding to be gained by finding, for example, that a sixth-degree or higher trend is significant. Ordinarily one stops after the cubic or perhaps quartic comparison, and then relegates all other trend effects to the pooled sum of squares:

$$\text{SS other trends} = \text{SS between} - \sum_{h=1}^{G} \text{SS}(\hat{\psi}_h) \qquad [16.9.7*]$$

where $h$ symbolizes any from the $G$ comparisons made separately. Thus, for five groups, one might be interested only in linear and quadratic trends. He would then find the pooled SS for other trends from

$$\text{SS (cubic and quartic)} = \text{SS between} - \text{SS lin.} - \text{SS quad.}$$

which has $4 - 2$ or 2 degrees of freedom.

In some applications of this method to problems of curve-fitting, in which one desires to find the trend of the lowest possible degree fitting the data satisfactorily, each successive comparison is tested against pooled SS for all comparisons representing trends of higher degree than the one tested. This method is presented quite clearly in Graybill (1961, page 182) but we shall not go into it here. In our example the value obtained for SS error will be used in the test for each trend comparison.

## 16.10  AN EXAMPLE OF PLANNED COMPARISONS FOR TREND

Suppose that the experiment on noise intensity-level and performance had actually been planned as a study of trend. The experimenter is especially interested in judging if linear and quadratic trends exist in the relation between $X$ and $Y$. We will pretend that the data in Section 16.7 had been collected specifically for this purpose.

The SS total, the SS between, and the SS error are found just as before, of course. However, let us list the group means and find the linear and

**Table 16.10.1**

|  | Group | | | | | |
|---|---|---|---|---|---|---|
|  | *1* | *2* | *3* | *4* | *5* | *6* |
| Means | 27 | 37 | 42 | 32 | 22 | 14 |
| Weights | | | | | | |
| linear | −5 | −3 | −1 | 1 | 3 | 5 |
| quadratic | 5 | −1 | −4 | −4 | −1 | 5 |

quadratic comparison values. Table 16.10.1 gives the six means and the weights that apply to each for linear and quadratic comparisons, as found from Table VI. The comparison values themselves are

$$\hat{\psi}_1 = -5(27) - 3(37) - 1(42) + 1(32) + 3(22) + 5(14)$$
$$= -120,$$

and

$$\hat{\psi}_2 = 5(27) - 1(37) - 4(42) - 4(32) - 1(22) + 5(14)$$
$$= -150.$$

The $w$ values for the corresponding sums of squares are found from

$$w_1 = \frac{25 + 9 + 1 + 1 + 9 + 25}{10} = 7$$

and

$$w_2 = \frac{25 + 1 + 16 + 16 + 1 + 25}{10} = 8.4$$

so that

$$\text{SS linear} = \frac{(-120)^2}{7} = 2057.1$$

$$\text{SS quad.} = \frac{(-150)^2}{8.4} = 2678.6.$$

(Notice that SS linear agrees exactly with the SS linear regression found in Section 16.7.) Then

$$\text{SS other trends} = 5200 - 2057.1 - 2678.6 = 464.3$$

with $\quad J - 1 - 2 = 3$ degrees of freedom.

The summary table for this analysis is

| *Source* | *SS* | *df* | *MS* | *F* |
|---|---|---|---|---|
| Between | 5200 | 5 | — | — |
| Linear | 2057.1 | 1 | 2057.1 | 54.1 |
| Quadratic | 2678.6 | 1 | 2678.6 | 70.5 |
| Other trends | 464.3 | 3 | 154.8 | 4.0 |
| Error | 2052 | 54 | 38 | |
| Totals | 7252 | 59 | | |

The $F$ tests for both linear and quadratic trend greatly exceed the value required for the .01 level of significance, but the over-all test for other trends does not reach the .01 level. Thus, we can be fairly sure that in the population predictive association does exist between $X$ and $Y$, and that the general rule for prediction includes both linear and quadratic components. We cannot, however, really be sure that the population prediction rule does not include higher order components as well. Even so, we infer from these data that a curvilinear regression equation affording at least some prediction has the general form

$$Y'_{ij} = \beta_0 + \beta_1(X_j - \mu_X) + \beta_2(X_j - \mu_X)^2$$

where the $\beta_1$ and $\beta_2$ are the linear and quadratic regression coefficients in the population.

## 16.11 ESTIMATION OF A CURVILINEAR PREDICTION FUNCTION

Sometimes it is convenient to find the actual pairings of $X_j$ and predicted $Y'_j$ values given by the curvilinear regression equation estimated from a sample. The experimenter may be interested in examining the departures his data tend to show from this estimated function, or perhaps in displaying in graphic form the relation suggested by the significant trends in his data. This is rather tedious to do in terms of the original $X_j$ values, but when the $X_j$ values are equally spaced a very simple substitute exists, involving the orthogonal polynomial coefficients once again. Instead of finding the predicted $Y$ directly as a function of $X_j$, we can represent $Y'$ as a function of the *polynomial weights* given to group $X$, and then use these predicted $Y$ values to find and plot all $(X_j, Y'_j)$ pairs.

**FIG.** 16.11.1. Linear and quadratic functions fitted to the data of Section 16.10

more or less parallel the systematic differences among the sample means. By way of contrast, the predictions using the linear regression equation alone correspond to points falling on the dotted line; it is apparent that adding a quadratic component to the prediction equation greatly improves our description of the relationship between $X$ and $Y$ exhibited in this sample, since the various means depart considerably from the regression line. On the other hand, if we added cubic, quartic, and quintic terms to our prediction equation, then we would find a curve on which the mean points for each group would fall exactly. There is not much profit in this, however, as the best description of a set of data is a curve fitting the points most nearly with a *simple* function rule (one of the lowest possible degree). Any set of means from $J$ sampled groups can be fitted with a curve of at most degree $J - 1$.

This device for actually obtaining predicted points using a curvilinear regression equation is quite easy to apply after a trend analysis, since most of the computations have already been done. It is useful as a way to visualize how the kind of trend suggested by the significant comparisons might actually appear in a plot, as well as a device to dramatize the predictive strength, or the weakness, of the relation inferred from the data. Remember, however, that such an obtained regression curve is actually only a description of *these* data. *It can be regarded as an estimate of the population regression function only for hypothetical populations showing exactly the same representation of X values as used in the sample.* Free and easy extrapolation outside these values is done at the user's peril!

This example of a simple analysis for trend has been carried out in terms of a single set of distinctly different samples, each corresponding to one fixed value of the experimental variable $X$. Obviously, however, in many psychological settings this sort of question is studied more naturally within a more complex design, perhaps one in which repeated observations on the same subjects are made. This requires some special considerations that we will not be able to pursue here, and the reader is referred to the book by Winer (1962) for details.

A word of caution: curve fitting by use of orthogonal polynomials is but the simplest approach to the problem of fitting a function to a set of data. A number of other approaches to this problem exist. In particular, it must be borne in mind that the curvilinear regression function determined by this method depends on our ability to represent a functional relation by a power series, or Taylor expansion. Merely because we can reproduce the general form of relation in the data by, say, a function of the third degree, it does not follow that the true relation is best expressed in these terms. It may well be that another, and perhaps simpler, form of function rule best describes the relation, with parameters that can be linked to the psychological factors involved. In particular, when one has definite ideas about the mathematical form of the relation, and he wishes to estimate parameters for this function, other methods are called for. The book by Lewis (1960) gives a useful introduction to the general subject of curve-fitting for various purposes.

## 16.12 TREND ANALYSIS IN POST-HOC COMPARISONS

It should be mentioned that the trend comparisons can perfectly well be made *after* the over-all analysis of variance has shown significant evidence for effects of the experimental variable. In particular, it may be informative to investigate trends of various degrees after significant evidence for over-all curvilinear regression has been found. The Scheffé method discussed in Chapter 14 applies to any post-hoc comparison among means, and one can use the orthogonal polynomial weights in the usual way to make post-hoc trend comparisons. However, just as for any set of post-hoc comparisons, the probability of our detecting a true trend as a significant result is ordinarily less in the test for a post-hoc than in the test for a planned comparison for that trend. Even so, post-hoc trend comparisons provide a most useful device for exploring data after the over-all $F$ for between groups has shown significance, when the independent variable groupings are equally spaced quantitative distinctions. Unless the experimenter has definite questions about particular trends prior to the data, he ordinarily tests for trend by the post-hoc method. Estimation of the function can then be carried out as in Section 16.11.

## 16.13 OTHER USES OF REGRESSION THEORY

We have considered only the barest rudiments of the theory of regression in this and the preceding chapter. The ideas of linear and curvilinear regression are capable of great extension and application to a wide variety of experimental problems. A very few of the directions of application of this general theory will be mentioned in this section.

In the first place, we have considered only relations following a linear prediction rule or those representable by rules involving powers of $X$ (a *power series* in $X$). Obviously, many forms of relation may exist among variables, such as those predictable from the rules

$$Y = m[v^X]$$
or
$$Y = B \log (X) + a, \qquad X > 0,$$

to take only two simple examples. The methods of regression analysis can often be extended to the study of such relations as well. Usually, some transformation is made of the $Y$ values to make the linear or power models fit: thus

$$\log_e Y = X(\log_e v) + \log_e m$$

may be studied by ordinary linear regression methods, even though

$$Y = m[v^X]$$

cannot. The basic methods of regression analysis can be extended in this way to cover many kinds of possible relations in data.

Another very important use of regression theory is also beginning to appear in psychological research. This involves the problem of testing a quantitative theory about two or more variables. Suppose that some theory exists which permits the deduction that the value of $Y$ should be a function of $X$, or $Y = g(X)$, other things being equal. The theory is sufficiently advanced for the quantitative rule for this function to be stated, and predicted values of $Y$ obtained. The experimenter wants to check this deduction, but, obviously, other things will not be equal in his experiment, and so random error will exist, making his predicted and obtained values disagree. However, if the theory is true, and the uncontrolled variation is random, there should appear a strong *linear* relation between theoretical values of $g(X)$ and the obtained values of $Y$. Each experimental group has some $X$ value, and hence affords a known value of $g(X)$ within the theory. Instead of testing for linear regression between $Y$ and $X$, the experimenter tests for a linear relation between $Y$ and the values given by the function of $X$, or $g(X)$ values. Then, a significant result and an estimated strong degree of association in the data is direct evidence for the theory's giving a good fit to data. Estimation is also applied to suggest ways in which the theory might be improved to give an even better fit. Evidence for curvilinear relationship between $Y$ and $g(X)$ sheds even further light on the range within which the theoretical deduction seems to apply, and gives evidence for changes that might improve the goodness of the theory as a predictor of actual human or animal behavior. When dealing with an actual quantitative theory capable of precise deductions about $Y$ values, this often is a far more sensible way for the experimenter to proceed than to cast the theory in the role of the null hypothesis. When the theoretical deduction itself corresponds to the null hypothesis a positive statement usually comes from significant results only if the theory is poor; proceeding by regression analysis between the predicted and obtained values makes significant linear association support the theory, and the experimenter can say something definite following a significance test and estimation procedure.

Nothing has been said so far about the comparisons of trends *among* populations. It may well be that the form of relation is different among different populations of experimental subjects, and the experimenter wants to discover this fact, if true. Especially important is the comparison of the form of apparent relationship between $X$ and $Y$ obtained in different variations of the same experiment. We have noted several times that the discovery and mathematical specification of functional relations involves weeding out variables that are irrelevant to the true relationship; if the form of obtained relation remains exactly the same over levels of some other variable, presumably that variable is irrelevant to the general form of relationship of $X$ and $Y$. On the other hand, if the relation between $X$ and $Y$ shows a different form when another factor $W$ is varied as well, then $W$ *is* relevant, and the ability to predict $Y$ in general may require knowledge of $X$ *and* $W$. Observing the difference in form of relation across experiments or across populations is an important step in building up and testing a quantitative theory. Fortunately, the theory of planned comparisons among trends extends directly to this problem of intersample comparisons of trends, and so this question may also be studied statistically. This problem of cross-level comparison of trend is essentially that of *interaction* in a two-way or higher analysis of variance with quantitative factors. An introduction to this problem and elementary methods for its solution are given in Lewis (1960).

The model for linear (or indeed, curvilinear) regression can be combined with that of the analysis of variance to yield methods for multifactor experiments where some of the experimental factors are qualitative and some are quantitative. This combined form of regression and variance analysis is often called the **analysis of covariance.** The analysis of covariance is useful not only in the mixed qualitative-quantitative situation, but also when quantitative nuisance or "matching" factors are introduced into an experiment designed primarily to study qualitative factors. Most advanced texts in statistics and experimental design consider simple analysis of covariance.

All of these extensions rest ultimately on the general ideas introduced here, however, and all were developed basically for the kinds of experiments we have called **problems in regression.** The novice experimental psychologist owes it to himself to develop some feel for regression techniques, and to become acquainted with some of the resources along these lines offered by modern statistics, although he always does well to seek expert help in applying the more advanced techniques. The book by Lewis (*op. cit.*) provides a good departure for the study of more advanced techniques in regression analysis and curve-fitting, and a fairly extensive survey of regression methods appears in Bennett and Franklin (1954), and in Anderson and Bancroft (1952). A thorough, though advanced, treatment of topics in regression theory is given by Graybill (1961, Chapters 8, 9, and 10).

## 16.14   LINEAR VERSUS CURVILINEAR REGRESSION

Past work in psychology dealing with statistical relations and the possibility of prediction has been cast largely in terms of linear regression. There have been several reasons for this. As a practical first approximation to a complicated relationship, a linear function rule often serves quite well. Psychologists have often been satisfied with assuming only linear regression because of the crude state of many of our measurement techniques; it seems rather pointless to read much meaning into the form of the relationship when the $X$ and $Y$ scores themselves have some undetermined relationship to the quantities the psychologist hopes to measure. The needs of practical prediction may be met quite well by a simple linear regression equation. In fact, the psychologist may even be lucky if he can answer the question "Is any prediction at all possible?" without going into the niceties of the form of the function rule that might serve best to predict $Y$ from $X$.

Another reason for the emphasis on linear prediction is that the theory of correlation is extremely well developed along certain lines, some of which will be explored in the next few sections. As we have seen, under the bivariate or multivariate normal assumptions, the absence of a linear relation is the absence of any systematic relation. In the theory of normal correlation, linear relations are really all one needs to study. Unfortunately, the distinction between regression and correlation studies is not always a sharp one, and many psychologists seem unaware of the dependence of the classical theory of correlation on normal theory. Some psychologists seem to operate on the principle that the study of correlations must lead to the discovery of all important predictive relations running through data; in some areas this may well be true, but it is not necessarily true in general, and seems an especially inappropriate assumption in many experimental studies.

Finally, the theory of correlation and linear regression has important ties to several branches of psychological methodology not considered here, such as test theory and factor analysis. This fact alone is sufficient to keep psychologists preoccupied with linear regression and correlation for some time to come.

Nevertheless, the beginner in psychological research should not discount the possibility of important and predictive nonlinear relations between variables. Current practice and practical necessity should not be confused with the way nature or man behaves. There is no guarantee that all psychological relationships of theoretical or applied interest must be linear in form. Presumably, as our science emerges from its rather primitive beginnings into a truly quantitative experimental discipline, we will turn increasingly away from the crude "Did anything happen?" approach to experimentation and toward problems of form of relation and refinement of prediction. This seems to have been true in the evolution of the other experimental sciences, and the author, for one, believes that it is beginning to happen in psychology. The time seems to be approaching for more estimation and quantitative specification of results in psychology, with less emphasis upon the "Gee Whiz" or "shotgun" sort of study where everything turns out both significant and meaningless.

On the other hand, at this stage of the game it is well for the experimenter to have good a-priori reasons for expecting particular kinds of predictive relations in the data before he spends much time and effort in analyzing trends. Especially, the importance of a trend in a single set of data must not be overemphasized. The same comment applies with even more force to the practice of fitting functions to data; these are nice ways to display findings, and the function obtained does describe *those data*, but means for any old set of data can always be fit perfectly with *some* function rule. Even the fact that some or all trends are found significant does not guarantee that the best description of the data is even remotely like the true form of relation. Functions fitted to data, like all other statistical devices, are only as good as the data to which they are applied. Careful study must be given to theory and great rigor must be exercised in the conduct of the experiment if the application of these relatively advanced methods is to uncover valid and predictive relations. Nonrandom samples and experimental errors can make monumental differences in conclusions reached about the form of a relationship from data. Furthermore, even with the most carefully collected data, the experimenter must be very leery about extending his findings beyond the domain actually studied in the sample. Functions that fit the values obtained perfectly can be wildly inappropriate over a larger range of $X$ values, or even a more finely divided set of $X$ intervals in the same range. Only if the experimenter has both good empirical evidence and sound theoretical reasons for doing so should he attempt to generalize beyond the range of $X$ studied. Finally, the "true" form and the parameters entering into a relation are not always apparent from the data. A great deal of evidence must accumulate before firm statements about the precise form of relation and the relevant parameters of a predictive rule can be made. And yet, the situation is not hopeless; evidence *does* cumulate and theories *do* exist. Used with prudence, these methods for studying the possibility of prediction and functional form can give us hunches and insights to pursue, and from just such hunches and insights a quantitative and predictive science will eventually grow.

## 16.15 SOME RUDIMENTS OF MULTIPLE REGRESSION THEORY

In practical prediction situations, it is seldom that only one item of prior information is known about the individual subject. Usually several tests are given in an employment interview before the decision to hire or not to hire an applicant is made. The admissions officer in a college may have college entrance scores, high-school achievement records, educational level of parents, and a great many other items of information about a college applicant each of which may figure in the prediction made about his probable success in college. In other words, there are often several variables, with known values, each of which may contribute to the prediction about the value of the dependent variable.

In the same way, in multifactor experiments where each experimental factor is quantitative it may be desirable to investigate the extent to which all the factors considered together account for variance in $Y$. Furthermore, it may be important to be able to predict the value of $Y$ given the *combination* of quantitative factor levels or experimental treatments administered to a subject.

The ability to predict from several variables considered simultaneously is studied in the theory of **multiple regression.** In this section we will consider only the barest rudiments of this theory, especially as it applies to a special kind of rule for predicting $Y$ from values of several variables; we are going to consider only simple extensions of linear regression equations, and so this part of the theory is appropriately called **multiple linear regression.** In principle, multiple curvilinear regression can be studied as well, but this is far beyond our scope.

Some changes in notation will be necessary in discussing multiple regression. Imagine a set of $K$ different variables, $\{X_k\}$, distinguished by the subscripts

$$(1, \cdots, k, \cdots, K).$$

The first of these variables, $X_1$, will be thought of, quite arbitrarily, as the dependent variable, and the others, $X_2, \cdots, X_K$, as the experimental or predictor variables for some particular problem. Similarly, relative to some fixed set of data, the standard score corresponding to $X_1$ will be denoted by $z_1$, that for $X_2$ by $z_2$, and so on.

Now we want to generalize the simple linear regression equation for one predictor variable to the situation where there are some $K - 1$ predictor variables. In our new notation, the linear regression equation found in Section 15.3 for standard scores becomes

$$z_1' = b_{1 \cdot 2} z_2, \qquad\qquad \textbf{[16.15.1]}$$

where the constant $b_{1 \cdot 2}$ turns out to be $r_{12}$.

Suppose, however, that instead of two variables we were dealing with three: $X_1$, the dependent variable, and the two other variables $X_2$ and $X_3$. Then the linear rule for predicting the standard score on variable 1 from both the standard scores on 2 and 3 is simply

$$z_1' = b_{12 \cdot 3} z_2 + b_{13 \cdot 2} z_3. \qquad\qquad \textbf{[16.15.2*]}$$

Here there are two constants, $b_{12 \cdot 3}$, reflecting the weight given the $z_2$ in predicting $z_1$, and $b_{13 \cdot 2}$, reflecting the weight given to $z_3$.

Just as in the two-variable situation, our job is to find values of these constants that will give the best predictions in the "least-squares" sense, making the average squared error in prediction a minimum. It is difficult to show the rationale for the required constants in terms of elementary methods alone, but we can at least suggest in a fairly crude way how these "best" values of $b_{12 \cdot 3}$ and $b_{13 \cdot 2}$ are determined.

Suppose that this prediction rule exists and that we find the covariance between the predicted values $z_1'$ and the obtained values of $z_2$ for all individuals $i$; or

$$\text{cov.}(z_1', z_2) = \frac{\sum_i z_{1i}' z_{2i}}{N}. \qquad [16.15.3]$$

Each $z_1'$ is thought of as a true $z_1$ plus some error: if these errors themselves have mean zero and are not correlated with $z_2$, then it must be true from **16.15.3** that

$$\text{cov.}(z_1', z_2) = \frac{\sum_i (z_{1i} + e_{1i})(z_{2i})}{N}$$

$$= \frac{\sum_i z_{1i} z_{2i}}{N}$$

or

$$\text{cov.}(z_1', z_2) = r_{12}, \qquad [16.15.4]$$

the covariance between the predicted $z_1$ scores and $z_2$ equals the correlation between $z_1$ and $z_2$. However, taken together with **16.15.2**, this implies that across individuals $i$,

$$r_{12} = \frac{\sum_i z_{1i}' z_{2i}}{N} = \frac{\sum_i z_{2i}(b_{12 \cdot 3} z_{2i} + b_{13 \cdot 2} z_{3i})}{N}$$

$$= \frac{\sum_i (b_{12 \cdot 3}) z_{2i}^2}{N} + \frac{\sum_i (b_{13 \cdot 2})(z_{2i} z_{3i})}{N}. \qquad [16.15.5]$$

Expression **16.15.5** reduces to

$$r_{12} = b_{12 \cdot 3} + b_{13 \cdot 2}(r_{23}), \qquad [16.15.6]$$

since the variance of a set of $z$ scores is 1, and $\sum_i z_{2i} z_{3i}/N$ actually defines $r_{23}$, the correlation between $X_2$ and $X_3$ for this group of individuals.

Applying this same argument to the correlation $r_{13}$, we find that

$$r_{13} = b_{12 \cdot 3}(r_{23}) + b_{13 \cdot 2}. \qquad [16.15.7]$$

Given **16.15.6** and **16.15.7**, and the actual values of the three correlation coefficients, $r_{12}$, $r_{13}$, and $r_{23}$, found for any given set of data, the required $b$ values can be found. That is, we have two equations in two unknowns:

$$b_{12 \cdot 3}(r_{23}) + b_{13 \cdot 2} = r_{13} \qquad [16.15.8^*]$$
$$b_{12 \cdot 3} + b_{13 \cdot 2}(r_{23}) = r_{12}.$$

Solving these equations for $b_{12 \cdot 3}$ and $b_{13 \cdot 2}$ gives us the constants we need for the actual regression equation. *These constants guarantee a least-squares fit between the predicted and the actual $X_1$ values for a given set of data.*

It is very simple to illustrate the way in which values of these constants are found for three-variable problems. Suppose that a personnel officer in an industrial plant has two items of information about each and every applicant for some specialized job; his score on a standard intelligence test $(X_2)$ and his score on a particular trade-skills test $(X_3)$. Each person employed can, after a time, be given a proficiency score $(X_1)$ indicating how he works out on the job. It is desired to find a regression equation for predicting standing on job proficiency from intelligence level and the trade-skills score. From the set of $N$ people who have already been employed, the personnel officer finds that

$$r_{12} = .20$$
$$r_{13} = .40$$
$$r_{23} = .30.$$

Thus, the weights entering into the regression equation must be the solutions to the simultaneous linear equations represented by **16.15.8**:

$$b_{12 \cdot 3} + .30(b_{13 \cdot 2}) = .20$$
$$.30(b_{12 \cdot 3}) + b_{13 \cdot 2} = .40.$$

On solving these equations we have

$$3.333b_{12 \cdot 3} + b_{13 \cdot 2} = .667$$
$$.300b_{12 \cdot 3} + b_{13 \cdot 2} = .400$$

$$\overline{\phantom{3.333b_{12 \cdot 3} + b_{13 \cdot 2} = .667}}$$

$$3.033b_{12 \cdot 3} \qquad = .267$$
$$b_{12 \cdot 3} \qquad = .088$$

and

$$b_{13 \cdot 2} \qquad = .374.$$

Thus, the regression equation is found to be

$$z_1' = (.088)z_2 + (.374)z_3.$$

The regression weights $b$ entering into this equation suggest that for optimal linear prediction of the standard score in work proficiency, the standard score on intelligence $(z_2)$ should be weighted by much less (.088) than that $(z_1)$ for trade skills (.374). Should a man show a standard score in intelligence of 1.5, and a trade-skills standard score of $-.3$, then the predicted standard score on job performance is found to be

$$z_1' = (.088)(1.5) + (.374)(-.3)$$
$$= .02,$$

almost at the mean. On the other hand, when $z_2 = -.3$ and $z_3 = 1.5$, $z_1' = .53$; the predicted score is considerably higher. The relative standing on trade skills is literally weighted more in prediction than is intelligence standing.

In general, for any finite number of variables $K$, the same general scheme is employed. An equation for predicting standard scores on $X_1$ is desired, of the form

$$z_1' = z_2(b_{12 \cdot 3 \cdots K}) + z_3(b_{13 \cdot 2 \cdots K}) + \cdots + z_K(b_{1K \cdot 2 \cdots K-1}). \qquad \text{[16.15.9*]}$$

The predicted value of $z_1$ is to be a weighted sum of $z$ values for variables 2 through $K$. The required weights are found from the simultaneous solutions to the $K - 1$ equations beginning with

$$(b_{12 \cdot 3 \cdots K}) + r_{23}(b_{13 \cdot 2 \cdots K}) + \cdots + r_{2K}(b_{1K \cdot 2 \cdots K-1}) = r_{12}$$

and ending with

$$r_{2K}(b_{12 \cdot 3 \cdots K}) + r_{3K}(b_{13 \cdot 2 \cdots K}) + \cdots + (b_{1K \cdot 2 \cdots K-1}) = r_{1K}.$$

The big computational chore in multiple regression problems with several variables consists of first finding all of the $\binom{K}{2}$ correlations needed, and then solving the $K - 1$ equations. Most older statistics books give considerable space to ways of solving these equations by hand. However, all signs point to such problems being handled by electronic computers in the future (as they already are in many research settings). Thus, we will not devote more space to the actual mechanics of solving large sets of simultaneous equations.

### 16.16 THE COEFFICIENT OF MULTIPLE CORRELATION

For a two-variable problem, we saw that $r_{XY}^2$ describes the proportion of variance in $Y$ accounted for by linear regression on $X$. It is also possible to give $r_{XY}$ a slightly different interpretation, however. Suppose that we found the correlation between the predicted $Y'$ scores and the *actual* values of $Y$ across all $N$ subjects $i$:

$$r_{(Y'Y)} = \frac{\sum_i z'_{Yi} z_{Yi}}{N s_{z_{Y'}}} = \frac{\sum_i (r_{XY} z_{Xi} z_{Yi})}{N \sqrt{r_{XY}^2}}$$

$$= r_{XY}. \qquad [16.16.1^*]$$

Thus the correlation coefficient between $X$ and $Y$ is also the correlation between predicted and obtained values $Y'$ and $Y$ of the dependent variable.

Now we can extend this idea to define a **multiple-correlation coefficient**. For three variables, $X_1$, $X_2$, and $X_3$, suppose that predictions of $X_1$ were made according to **16:15.2**. Now we take the correlation between the predicted value $z'_1$ and the actual value $z_1$ over all individuals $i$:

$$r_{(z_1' z_1)} = \frac{\sum_i z'_{1i} z_{1i}}{N s_{z_1'}} = \frac{\sum_i (b_{12 \cdot 3} z_{2i} + b_{13 \cdot 2} z_{3i}) z_{1i}}{N s_{z_1'}}.$$

Although we shall not prove this result, it can be shown that

$$s_{z_1'} = \sqrt{b_{12 \cdot 3} r_{12} + b_{13 \cdot 2} r_{13}}$$

so that

$$r_{(z_1' z_1)} = \left( \sum_i b_{12 \cdot 3}(z_{2i} z_{1i}) + \sum_i b_{13 \cdot 2}(z_{3i} z_{1i}) \right) \Big/ N \sqrt{b_{12 \cdot 3} r_{12} + b_{13 \cdot 2} r_{13}}$$

$$= \sqrt{b_{12 \cdot 3} r_{12} + b_{13 \cdot 2} r_{13}}$$

$$= R_{1 \cdot 23}. \qquad [16.16.2^*]$$

The correlation of predicted and obtained scores for variable $X_1$ is the multiple-correlation coefficient, denoted by $R_{1 \cdot 23}$. The value of the multiple-correlation coefficient itself is found from **16.16.2** to be

$$R_{1 \cdot 23} = \sqrt{b_{12 \cdot 3} r_{12} + b_{13 \cdot 2} r_{13}}. \qquad [16.16.3^*]$$

For our three variable examples of Section 16.15, the multiple-correlation coefficient is

$$
\begin{aligned}
R_{1 \cdot 23} &= \sqrt{(.088)(.20) + (.373)(.40)} \\
&= \sqrt{.0176 + .1492} \\
&= \sqrt{.1668} \\
&= .408.
\end{aligned}
$$

In general, in $K$-variable problems, the squared value of the multiple-correlation coefficient turns out to be

$$R^2_{1 \cdot 2 \ldots K} = (b_{12 \cdot 3 \ldots K}) r_{12} + \cdots + (b_{1K \cdot 2 \ldots K-1}) r_{1K} \qquad [16.16.4^*]$$

the weighted sum of the correlation coefficients of each variable with variable 1, each coefficient weighted by the regression weight applied to that variable in the regression equation. Then the value of $R$ is merely the positive square root of this $R^2$ value.

## 16.17  THE STANDARD ERROR OF ESTIMATE AND THE INTERPRETATION OF $R^2$

In a two-variable problem the sample standard error of estimate for predicting the $z$ score of the dependent variable is, in our new notation,

$$s^2_{z_1 \cdot z_2} = \frac{\displaystyle\sum_i (z'_{1i} - z_{1i})^2}{N} = 1 - r^2_{12}. \qquad [16.17.1]$$

If we applied precisely the same idea to predictions using a multiple regression equation, we could find

$$
\begin{aligned}
s^2_{z_1 \cdot z_2 \ldots z_K} &= \frac{\displaystyle\sum_i (z'_{1i} - z_1)^2}{N} \\
&= 1 - R^2_{1 \cdot 2 \ldots K}. \qquad [16.17.2^*]
\end{aligned}
$$

This is the **sample variance of estimate for $z$ scores.** The corresponding **sample standard error of estimate** is thus

$$s_{z_1 \cdot z_2 \ldots z_K} = \sqrt{1 - R^2_{1 \cdot 2 \ldots K}}. \qquad [16.17.3^*]$$

Just as in the two-variable situation, the value of the variance of estimate reflects the "poorness" of prediction, or *the proportion of variance in variable 1 not accounted for by variables 2, 3, and so on in terms of a linear prediction rule.* Hence, it must be true that the proportion of variance accounted for is given by

$$1 - s^2_{z_1 \cdot z_2 \cdots z_K} = 1 - (1 - R^2_{1 \cdot 2 \cdots K}) = R^2_{1 \cdot 2 \cdots K}. \qquad [16.17.4^*]$$

Just as for $r^2$, **the squared multiple correlation coefficient indicates the proportion of variance in** $X_1$ **accounted for by the set of** $K - 1$ **remaining variables, in terms of predictions using this form of linear rule.** The index $R^2$ is sometimes called the **coefficient of multiple determination.**

We can never do less well in linear predictions using several variables than the best we can do using a single variable. This means that the value of $R^2$ is always greater than or equal to the largest value of $r^2$ between any single independent variable and the dependent variable. That is,

$$R^2_{1 \cdot 2 \cdots K} \geqq r^2_{1k} \qquad [16.17.5^*]$$

for any variable $k$ in the set of $K - 1$ *predictor* variables.

This fact lets us evaluate how much we have gained in ability to predict by the addition of more items of prior information. For example, in Section 16.15 we found that the value of $R_{1 \cdot 2 \cdots K}$ was only .408, so that the squared value is close to .17. However, the original correlation between the job-proficiency and trade-skills scores was .40, giving a value of .16 to $r^2_{13}$. This says that almost nothing is contributed to the ability to predict by the addition of an intelligence-test score to the trade-skills score. The personnel officer would apparently do about as well using the trade-skills score alone for prediction as he would using the multiple-regression equation.

## 16.18 MULTIPLE REGRESSION EQUATIONS FOR RAW SCORES

Although the multiple-regression equation and the multiple-correlation coefficient have been presented here only in standard scores form, the same idea applies to raw scores. The raw score equivalent of formula **16.15.9** is

$$X'_1 = M_1 + b_{12 \cdot 3 \cdots K} \left( \frac{s_1}{s_2} \right) (X_2 - M_2) + b_{13 \cdot 2 \cdots K} \left( \frac{s_1}{s_3} \right) (X_3 - M_3)$$
$$+ \cdots + b_{1K \cdot 2 \cdots K-1} \left( \frac{s_1}{s_K} \right) (X_K - M_K). \qquad [16.18.1^*]$$

For *raw* scores, the sample standard error of estimate is

$$s_{1 \cdot 2 \cdots K} = s_1 \sqrt{1 - R^2_{1 \cdot 2 \cdots K}}. \qquad [16.18.2^*]$$

The value of the multiple-correlation coefficient is exactly the same, however, regardless of whether raw scores or standard scores are involved.

## 16.19  INFERENCES ABOUT MULTIPLE REGRESSION AND CORRELATION

Exactly as in our discussion of the descriptive statistics of simple correlation and regression, *one intact set of data are presumed in definitions of the descriptive statistics of multiple regression and correlation.* The regression equation, the value of $R$, and the standard error of estimate all refer to *this* set of data. The same ideas can be applied to a population, however, and we could define the true multiple-regression equation and the true $R$ in terms of this population. The status of the sample regression equation relative to the population is the same as in two-variable problems: the sample regression equation is usually the best guess we can make about the particular rule that applies in the population, but we have no assurance that the multiple linear predictive relationship (or lack thereof) in the sample is not a chance result rather than a true reflection of the population situation. Thus, considerations of sampling become important, and under certain assumptions we can make inferences about the population.

Just as for simple regression theory, different assumptions and different kinds of inferences can be made, depending on whether the problem is one of regression or of correlation. The general fixed effects model of analysis of variance extends directly to multiple-regression problems, and permits a test of the hypothesis that true $R$ is zero. It is far more usual, however, to regard the $N$ cases as a sample from a *multivariate normal distribution*, each case representing an occurrence of some joint event $(X_1, X_2, \cdots, X_K)$. Under this assumption it can be shown that the ratio

$$F = \left(\frac{R^2}{1 - R^2}\right)\left(\frac{N - K}{K - 1}\right) \qquad [16.19.1\dagger]$$

is distributed as $F$ with $K - 1$ and $N - K$ degrees of freedom, provided that true $R^2$ is zero. Here, $N$ is the number of subjects, and $K$ is the number of variables. This ratio tests only the hypothesis that the true value of $R^2$ is zero, however, which is ordinarily not a hypothesis of overwhelming interest. Methods exist for testing some other hypotheses about multiple regression, especially those having to do with increase in $R^2$ with the addition of more independent variables, but these methods are beyond our scope.

It must be emphasized that population $R^2$, like $\rho^2$, represents the strength only of a particular kind of relation among variables. If each and every variable from $X_2$ through $X_K$ is statistically independent of $X_1$, then true $R^2$ must be zero. However, if the population distribution is not normal it is entirely possible for true $R^2$ to be zero even though some statistical relationship, and thus predictability, exists. Statements about association derived from multiple correlation and regression analyses apply only to this particular linear way of predicting $X_1$ from the other variables, and do not necessarily imply that all possible predictability is thereby summarized, unless the multivariate normal assumption holds.

## 16.20 PARTIAL CORRELATION

Complementary to the notion of multiple correlation is that of the partial correlation between two variables, with the effects of some third variable being held constant. That is, consider three variables $X_1$, $X_2$, and $X_3$. The three correlation coefficients $r_{12}$, $r_{13}$, and $r_{23}$ are presumably known for the sample. However, in the computation of $r_{12}$, the value of $X_3$ is left completely free to vary; given the $X_1$ and $X_2$ values for an individual his $X_3$ score could, in principle, be anything.

Suppose, however, that the value of $X_3$ were fixed at some constant level. What would happen to the correlation between $X_1$ and $X_2$? This correlation might be different, because some of the apparent linear predictability of $X_1$ from $X_2$ (and vice versa) may be due to the association of each with $X_3$. For example, there is undoubtedly some positive correlation between body weight and the ability to read among normal school children. However, it is patently true that the tendency for such scores to covary arises in part from another factor strongly related to each, the child's chronological age. Could we hold chronological age constant, then this correlation between weight and reading ability should vanish, or at least be appreciably lowered. For studies centered on the influence of some extraneous variable (or variables) on the tendency of two other variables either to correlate or fail to correlate, the partial correlation coefficient is a very useful descriptive device.

The partial correlation coefficient $r_{12\cdot3}$ is the correlation between $X_1$ and $X_2$ adjusted for the linear regression of each on $X_3$. The partial correlation can be defined in this way: Suppose that $z_1$ were predicted from $z_3$, by

$$z_1' = r_{13}z_3.$$

Then the error in that prediction must represent the operation of all factors associated with variance in $X_1$ other than the linear association with factor 3. The variance of such errors is the variance in $X_1$ unaccounted for by the correlation $r_{13}$. In standard score terms, this variance is just

$$s_{z_1 \cdot z_3}^2 = 1 - r_{13}^2.$$

Similarly, the error in prediction of $z_2$ from $z_3$ must reflect factors other than linear association with factor 3.

Then the tendency for linear association between variables 1 and 2, free of the linear association each has with variable 3, must be represented in the correlation of these errors in predicting each variable from variable 3. Using **15.11.1,** we can define the partial correlation as a correlation between errors in prediction by writing

$$r_{12\cdot3} = \frac{\sum\limits_i (z_{1i}' - z_{1i})(z_{2i}' - z_{2i})}{N(s_{z_1 \cdot z_3})(s_{z_2 \cdot z_3})} \qquad [16.20.1*]$$

where both $z_{1i}'$ and $z_{2i}'$ are predicted from the individual's standard score $z_{3i}$. A little algebra lets us put this partial correlation coefficient in terms of the original correlations:

$$r_{12\cdot3} = \frac{\sum_i r_{13}r_{23}z_{3i}^2 - \sum_i r_{13}z_{3i}z_{2i} - \sum_i r_{23}z_{3i}z_{1i} + \sum_i z_{1i}z_{2i}}{N\sqrt{(1 - r_{13}^2)(1 - r_{23}^2)}}$$

$$= \frac{(r_{13}r_{23}) - (r_{13}r_{23}) - (r_{13}r_{23}) + r_{12}}{\sqrt{(1 - r_{13}^2)(1 - r_{23}^2)}} \qquad [16.20.2]$$

or

$$r_{12\cdot3} = \frac{r_{12} - (r_{13}r_{23})}{\sqrt{(1 - r_{13}^2)(1 - r_{23}^2)}}. \qquad [16.20.3\dagger]$$

This last expression is the usual computational form for a partial correlation coefficient based on the three original correlations. Obviously, we can define $r_{13\cdot2}$ and $r_{23\cdot1}$ in an analogous way.

Be sure to notice that the interpretation of the partial correlation coefficient as reflecting the extent of linear association between 1 and 2 with 3 held constant makes sense only if all the predictive relations among the variables are linear to begin with. Quite different relations between $X_1$ and $X_2$ may exist for different constant values of $X_3$ when the basic interrelations among the variables are not linear.

The partial correlation coefficient may be extended to four or more variables in the same general way. However, we shall not take the space to do this here, since these formulas can be found in many statistics books.

There is an intimate connection between partial correlation and multiple regression. The multiple-regression equation for three variables in Section 16.15 can also be written as

$$z_1' = (r_{12\cdot3})\left(\frac{s_{z_1\cdot z_3}}{s_{z_2\cdot z_3}}\right)(z_2) + (r_{13\cdot2})\left(\frac{s_{z_1\cdot z_2}}{s_{z_3\cdot z_2}}\right)(z_3). \qquad [16.20.4]$$

Observe that the $b$ weight that a score $z_2$ receives depends upon the partial correlation between 1 and 2 with 3 held constant, and that for $z_3$ depends on the partial correlation $r_{13\cdot2}$. Each variable is weighted in terms of its unique linear contribution to the variance of $X_1$. Furthermore, it follows that partial correlations can be found directly from particular multiple-regression weights. For three variables, once again,

$$r_{12\cdot3} = \sqrt{(b_{12\cdot3})(b_{21\cdot3})} \qquad [16.20.5]$$

where $b_{12\cdot3}$ is the weight applied to $z_2$ in the multiple-regression equation for predicting $z_1$, and $b_{21\cdot3}$ is the weight applied to $z_1$ in the equation for predicting $z_2$. (Notice the similarity to the expression **15.9.6.**)

When a random sample of $N$ cases can be assumed to come from a multivariate normal distribution, then it is permissible to use Fisher's $r$ to $Z$ transformation just as in Section 15.26 to test hypotheses and find confidence limits for the true value of the partial correlation. However, the standard error of $Z$ becomes

$$\sigma_Z = \frac{1}{\sqrt{N - 3 - (K - 2)}},$$

where $K$ is the total number of variables considered. Thus, for three variables ($K = 3$), when the partial correlation $r_{12\cdot3}$ is used to test the hypothesis that $\rho_{12\cdot3}$ is, say 0, the value of $r_{12\cdot3}$ is changed to a corresponding $Z$ value via Table V, and the test is carried out using the normal distribution of the statistic

$$\frac{Z - 0}{[1/\sqrt{N - 3 - (3 - 2)}]} = Z[\sqrt{(N - 4)}].$$

If this statistic shows a value significant at the $\alpha$ level, then the hypothesis that $\rho_{12\cdot3} = 0$ can be rejected at the $\alpha$ level. All in all, when the problem is one of *correlation*, and the assumption of a multivariate normal population is tenable, any procedure using the $r$ to $Z$ transformation applicable to a simple correlation also applies to a partial correlation, provided that the standard error of $Z$ is adjusted. However, the assumption of a multivariate normal distribution (all variables normally distributed, all pairwise joint events such as $(X_1, X_2)$ bivariate normal, and so on) is very unreasonable in many instances, and such tests should not be undertaken lightly.

## 16.21 TESTING SIGNIFICANCE FOR INTERCORRELATIONS

Before we leave the topic of correlation, a word must be said about significance tests for intercorrelations. It is quite common to find research in psychology where a number of different variables are studied in the same sample, and all sample intercorrelations are found among these variables. For example, a study may concern three variables, $X_1$, $X_2$, and $X_3$, and values are found for $r_{12}$, $r_{13}$, and $r_{23}$. This in itself is fine as a description of linear relations in the data, and is the first step in virtually any multivariate analysis, such as finding a multiple-regression equation or carrying out a factor analysis.

However, one often finds the experimenter testing the significance of each one of these $\binom{K}{2}$ intercorrelations by the method of Section 15.26, as though each one were based on a different sample. The resulting significance levels are largely meaningless, for reasons much like those making $t$ tests for all differences among a set of means a dubious procedure. In the first place, even for independent tests of significance, when so many tests are carried out the probability that some Type I errors are being made may be very high. Even worse, the $t$ tests for correlations are quite redundant and are not statistically independent when carried out on a table of intercorrelations. Consequently, the set of results can be grossly misleading. In particular, one should ordinarily expect *more* than $\binom{K}{2}\alpha$ such tests to show significance by chance alone.

It is simple to illustrate that restrictions exist in a table of inter-correlations. Consider a sample of $N$ cases, each of which gives three scores, $X_1$, $X_2$, and $X_3$. Imagine that $r_{12}$ turns out to be $-.80$ and $r_{13}$ is also $-.80$. What is the *smallest* value that $r_{23}$ can be? In this instance, it is not possible for $r_{23}$ to be $-1.00$, or $-.8$, or $-.5$, or indeed, any negative value at all. The very smallest value that $r_{23}$ can show for these data is .10. Fixing the value of two of the correlations determines the necessary lower limit for the third. The values of inter-correlations are dependent upon each other in a given sample.

In general, for $K$ variables, the average of the $\binom{K}{2}$ intercorrelations among these variables must be greater than (or equal to) $-1/(K-1)$. It follows that given the values of some of the intercorrelations, the average lower limit for all the other correlations is not $-1$, but some number greater than $-1$. The larger $K$ is, the closer this lower limit comes to 0. Hence, it is somewhat pointless to treat each of the correlations in turn as though the sampling distribution of values could extend from $-1$ through $+1$, when with each successive value of $r$ known from the sample the possible lower limit to the next set of values is raised. One should either not test for significance in the ordinary way in dealing with intercorrelations found for a single sample, or he should interpret the significance levels with *considerable* latitude.

It is rather hard to see why anyone would want to know if all the true intercorrelations among a set of variables are zero anyway. If these variables are to be used to predict some other variable, then a test of significance for $R^2$ is much more meaningful. If some other regression method is contemplated, appropriate tests may also exist for the results of applying this method. Tracing relationships among variables is the legitimate business of the scientist, but simply asking if *anything* relates linearly to anything else in a large set of variables is a pretty crude way to do business.

# COMPARING ENTIRE DISTRIBUTIONS:
# CHI-SQUARE TESTS

*17*

Heretofore, problems of hypothesis testing and interval estimation have centered very largely on summary characteristics of one or more population distributions. That is, we have been concerned with the value of a population mean, the differences among two or more population means, the equality of two population variances, the value of a population regression coefficient, and so on. In almost every instance the hypothesis tested was composite, so that the null hypothesis itself did not really specify the population distribution or distributions exactly. Of course, it was necessary to make assumptions about the population distribution in order to arrive at the appropriate test statistics and sampling distributions for these various hypotheses. Nevertheless, our interest was really in comparing population values with hypothetical values, or several populations in particular ways. With the exception of problems dealing with a single proportion (the two-class "Bernoulli" situation) we have not really considered hypotheses about the **identity** of two or more population distributions.

You may recall, however, that in Chapter 4 the basic ideas of the independence of variables and of attributes were introduced in terms of the *absolute identity* of two or more distributions. Most of the statistical tests we have discussed for experimental problems really do pertain to this question of independence of variables or attributes, but they actually do so because of assumptions such as normality and homogeneous variances; the assumptions make the hypotheses tested about, say, means, be equivalent to hypotheses about identical distributions. If the populations can be said to differ in any summary characteristic, then their distributions cannot be identical.

There are research problems in which one wants to make direct inferences about two or more distributions, either by asking if a population distribution has some particular specifiable form, or by asking if two or more population distributions are identical. These questions occur most often when *both* varia-

578

bles in some experiment are qualitative in character, making it impossible to carry out the usual inferences in terms of means or variances. In these instances we need methods for studying independence or association from categorical data. Other situations exist, however, when we wish to ask if a population distribution of a random variable has some precise theoretical form, such as the normal distribution, without having any special interest in summary properties such as mean and variance.

The methods considered in this chapter all pertain in one way or another to this central problem: how does one make inferences about a population *distribution* in terms of the distribution obtained in the sample? Remember that population distributions may have some random variable as the domain, as in all the examples in Chapters 10 through 16, or the distribution may consist of a probability assigned to each of a set of mutually exclusive and exhaustive qualitative classes. As suggested in Chapter 4, such a set of mutually exclusive and exhaustive *qualitative* events is often called an **attribute.** The methods of this chapter were originally developed for the study of theoretical distributions on attributes, and especially for the problem of independence or association of attributes. However, as we shall see, even the distribution of a random variable may be studied by these methods if the domain of the distribution is thought of as divided into a set of distinct class intervals.

It stands to reason that the best evidence one has about a population distribution grouped into qualitative classes is the sample distribution, grouped in the same way. Presumably the discrepancy between sample and theoretical distribution should have some bearing on the "goodness" of the theory in the light of the evidence. Furthermore, the comment made at the end of Chapter 5 was not altogether casual: in principle, exact probabilities for various possible sample distributions can always be found by use of the multinomial or hypergeometric rules, given some discrete population distribution. As we shall see, the rationale for the tests in this chapter is based essentially on this idea.

The first topic of this chapter is the comparison of a sample with a hypothetical population distribution. We would like to infer whether or not the sample result actually does represent some particular population distribution. We will deal only with discrete or grouped population distributions, and our inference will be made through an *approximation* to the exact multinomial probabilities. Such problems are said to involve "goodness of fit" between a single sample and a single population distribution.

Next, we will extend this idea to the simultaneous comparison of several discrete distributions. Ordinarily, the reason for comparing such distributions in the first place is to find evidence for **association** between two qualitative attributes. In short, we are going to employ a test for independence between attributes, which can be regarded as based on the comparison of *sample* distributions.

Finally, we will take up the problem of measuring the strength of association between two attributes from sample data. Tests and measures of association for qualitative data are very important for psychology, where many of the most important distinctions made are, essentially, categorical or qualitative in character. The methods in this chapter are widely used, both because of the kinds of data psychologists collect, and because of the computational simplicity of their application. However, the theory underlying these tests is not simple, and misapplication of these tests is very common. For this reason a good deal of space will be devoted to discussing some of the basic ideas underlying these methods, and some pains will be taken to emphasize their inherent limitations.

### 17.1 COMPARING SAMPLE AND POPULATION DISTRIBUTIONS: GOODNESS OF FIT

Suppose that a study of educational achievement of American men were being carried on. The population sampled is the set of all normal American males who are twenty-five years old at the time of the study. Each subject observed can be put into one and only one of the following categories, based on his *maximum* formal educational achievement:

1. college graduate;
2. some college;
3. high-school or preparatory-school graduate;
4. some high school or preparatory school;
5. finished eighth grade;
6. did not finish eighth grade.

These categories are mutually exclusive and exhaustive: each man observed must fall into one and only one classification.

The experimenter happens to know that ten years ago the distribution of educational achievement on this scale for twenty-five-year-old men was:

| Category | Relative frequency |
|:--------:|:------------------:|
| 1 | .18 |
| 2 | .17 |
| 3 | .32 |
| 4 | .13 |
| 5 | .17 |
| 6 | .03 |

He would like to ask if the present population distribution on this scale is exactly like that of ten years ago. Therefore the hypothesis of "no change" in the distribution for the present population specifies the exact distribution given above. The alternative hypothesis is that the present population does differ from the distribution given above, in some unspecified way.

A random sample of 200 subjects is drawn from the current population of twenty-five-year-old males, and the following frequency distribution obtained:

| Category | $f_{oj}$ (obtained frequency) | $f_{ej}$ (expected frequency) |
|:--------:|:------:|:------:|
| 1 | 35 | 36 |
| 2 | 40 | 34 |
| 3 | 83 | 64 |
| 4 | 16 | 26 |
| 5 | 26 | 34 |
| 6 | 0 | 6 |
|   | 200 | 200 |

(These figures *are* hypothetical!) The last column on the right gives the *expected* frequencies under the hypothesis that the population has the same distribution as ten years ago. For each category, the expected frequency is

$$Np_j = f_{ej} = \text{expected frequency}$$

where $p_j$ is the relative frequency for category $j$ dictated by the hypothesis.

How well do these two distributions, the obtained and the expected, agree? At first blush, you might think that the difference in frequency obtained and expected across the categories, or

$$\sum_j (f_{oj} - f_{ej}),$$

would describe the difference in the two distributions. However, it must be true that

$$\sum_j (f_{oj} - f_{ej}) = \sum_j f_{oj} - \sum_j f_{ej}$$
$$= N - N$$
$$= 0,$$

so that this is definitely not a satisfactory index of disagreement.

On the other hand, the sum of the *squared* differences in observed and expected frequencies does begin to reflect the extent of disagreement:

$$\sum_j (f_{oj} - f_{ej})^2.$$

This quantity can be zero only when the fit between the obtained and expected distributions is perfect, and must be large when the two distributions are quite different.

An even better index might be

$$\sum_j \frac{(f_{oj} - f_{ej})^2}{f_{ej}}, \qquad\qquad [17.1.1]$$

where each squared difference in frequency is weighted inversely by the frequency expected in that category. This weighting makes sense if we consider that a departure from expectation should get relatively more weight if we expect rather few individuals in that category than if we expect a great many. Somehow, we are more "surprised" to get many individuals where we expected to get few or none, than when we get few or none where we expected many; thus, the departure from expectation is appropriately weighted in terms of the frequency expected in the first place, when an index of over-all departure from expectation is desired.

Remember, however, the real purpose in the comparison of these distributions is to test the hypothesis that the expectations are correct, and that the current distribution actually is the same as ten years ago. One might proceed in this way: given the probabilities shown as relative frequencies for the hypothetical population distribution, the exact probability of any sample distribution can be found. That is, given the hypothesis and the assumption of independent random sampling of individuals (with replacement), the exact probability of a particular sample distribution can be found from the **multinomial** rule (Section 5.17). Thus, in terms of the hypothetical population distribution, the probability of a sample distribution exactly like the one observed is

$p$ (obtained distribution$|H_0$)

$$= \frac{200!}{35!\ 40!\ 83!\ 16!\ 26!\ 0!}\ (.18)^{35}(.17)^{40}(.32)^{83}(.13)^{16}(.17)^{26}(.03)^0.$$

With some effort we could work this value out exactly. However, we are not really interested in the probability of exactly this sort of obtained distribution, but rather in all possible sample results this much or more deviant from expectation according to an index such as expression **17.1.1.** The idea of working out a multinomial probability for each possible such sample result is ridiculous for $N$ and $J$ this large, as an absolutely staggering amount of calculation would be involved.

When the theoretical statistician finds himself in this kind of impasse he usually begins looking around for an approximation device. In this particular instance, it turns out that the multivariate normal distribution provides an approximation to the multinomial distribution for very large $N$, and thus the problem can be solved. We will not go into this derivation here, as it is far beyond our capabilities; suffice it to say that the basic rationale for this test does depend on the possibility of this approximation, and that the approximation itself is really good only for very large $N$. Then the following procedure is justified:

We form the statistic

$$\chi^2 = \sum_j \frac{(f_{oj} - f_{ej})^2}{f_{ej}} \qquad\qquad [17.1.2\dagger]$$

which is known as the Pearson $\chi^2$ statistic (after its inventor, Karl Pearson). Given that the exact probabilities for samples follow a multinomial distribution, and given a very large $N$, **when $H_0$ is true this statistic $\chi^2$ is distributed approximately as chi-square with $J - 1$ degrees of freedom.** Probabilities arrived at using this statistic are *approximately* the same as the exact multinomial probabilities we would like to be able to find for samples as much or more deviant from expectation as the sample obtained. The larger the sample $N$, the better should this approximation be.

Note that the number of degrees of freedom here is $J - 1$, the number of distinct categories in the sample distribution, or $J$, minus 1. You may have anticipated this from the fact that the sum of the differences between observed and expected frequencies is zero; given any $J - 1$ such differences, the remaining difference is fixed. This is very similar to the situation for deviations from a sample mean, and the mathematical argument for degrees of freedom here would be much the same as for degrees of freedom in a variance estimate.

To return to our example, the value of the $\chi^2$ statistic is

$$
\begin{aligned}
\chi^2 &= \sum_j \frac{(f_{oj} - f_{ej})^2}{f_{ej}} \\
&= \frac{(35 - 36)^2}{36} + \frac{(40 - 34)^2}{34} + \frac{(83 - 64)^2}{64} \\
&\quad + \frac{(16 - 26)^2}{26} + \frac{(26 - 34)^2}{34} + \frac{(0 - 6)^2}{6} \\
&= 18.30.
\end{aligned}
$$

This value is referred to in the chi-square table (Table III) for $J - 1 = 6 - 1 = 5$ degrees of freedom. We are interested only in the upper tail of the chi-square distribution in such problems, because the only reasonable alternative hypothesis (disagreement between true population and hypothetical distribution) must be reflected in *large values* of $\chi^2$. Table III shows that for 5 degrees of freedom, a value of 11.07 cuts off the upper .05 of the distribution, and a value of 15.09 corresponds to the upper .01. The hypothesis that the current distribution of educational achievement is exactly like that of ten years ago may thus be rejected, either at the .05 or at the .01 level, as we choose.

Tests such as that in the example, based on a single sample distribution, are called "goodness-of-fit" tests.

Chi-square tests of goodness of fit may be carried out for any hypothetical population distribution we might specify, provided that the population distribution is discrete, or is thought of as grouped into some relatively small set of class intervals. However, in the use of the Pearson $\chi^2$ statistic to approximate multinomial probabilities, it *must* be true that:

1. each and every sample observation falls into one and only one category or class interval;
2. the outcomes for the $N$ respective observations in the sample are independent;
3. sample $N$ is large.

The first two requirements stem from the multinomial sampling distribution itself: the multinomial rule for probability holds only for mutually exclusive and exhaustive categories, and for independent observations in a sample (random sampling with replacement). The third requirement comes from the use of the chi-square distribution to approximate these exact multinomial probabilities: this approximation is good only for large sample size. Furthermore, unless $N$ is infinitely large, the Pearson $\chi^2$ itself is not distributed exactly as the chi-square variable.

The fact that when $H_0$ is true the Pearson $\chi^2$ statistic for goodness of fit is not distributed exactly as the random chi-square variable can be seen from the expected value and the variance of the Pearson $\chi^2$, where $\nu$ symbolizes the degrees of freedom, $J - 1$:

$$E(\chi^2) = \nu \qquad\qquad\qquad [17.1.3]$$

$$\text{var.}(\chi^2) = 2\nu + \frac{1}{N}\left(\sum_j \frac{1}{p_j} - \nu^2 - 4\nu - 1\right). \qquad [17.1.4]$$

Recall that we learned in Chapter 11 that the expected value of a chi-square variable with $\nu$ degrees of freedom is $\nu$, and that the variance is $2\nu$. Although the expected value of the Pearson $\chi^2$ statistic is also $\nu$, the variance of this statistic need not equal the variance of the random variable chi-square, unless $N$ is infinitely large. This implies that the Pearson $\chi^2$ is not ordinarily distributed as the chi-square variable for samples of finite size. Note that the expression for the variance of the Pearson $\chi^2$ indicates that the goodness of the chi-square distribution as an approximation to the distribution of the Pearson statistic depends on several things, including not only the size of $N$ but also the true probabilities $p_j$ associated with the various categories and the number of degrees of freedom.

How large should sample size be in order to permit the use of the Pearson $\chi^2$ goodness-of-fit tests? Opinions vary on this question, and some fairly sharp debate has been raised by this issue over the years. Many rules of thumb exist, but as a conservative rule one is usually safe in using this chi-square test for goodness of fit if each *expected* frequency, $f_{ej}$, is 10 or more when the number of degrees of freedom is 1 (that is, two categories), or if the expected frequencies are each 5 or more where the number of degrees of freedom is greater than 1 (more than two categories). We will have more to say about sample size and Pearson $\chi^2$ tests in Section 17.7.

Be sure to notice, however, that *these rules of thumb apply to expected, not observed, frequencies per category.*

## 17.2 THE RELATION TO LARGE-SAMPLE TESTS OF A SINGLE PROPORTION

The goodness-of-fit test with 1 degree of freedom is formally equivalent to the large-sample test of a proportion, based on the normal approximation to the binomial. That is, imagine a distribution with only two categories.

| Category $j$ | Expected frequency | Obtained frequency | Expected proportion | Obtained proportion |
|:---:|:---:|:---:|:---:|:---:|
| 1 | $f_{e1}$ | $f_{o1}$ | $p$ | $P$ |
| 2 | $f_{e2}$ | $f_{o2}$ | $q$ | $Q$ |
|  | $N$ | $N$ | $1.0$ | $1.0$ |

Suppose that the normal approximation to the binomial is to be used to test the hypothesis that the true population proportion in category 1 is $p$. Then we would form the test statistic

$$z = \frac{NP - Np}{\sqrt{Npq}} = \frac{-(NQ - Nq)}{\sqrt{Npq}} \qquad [17.2.1]$$

or

$$z = \frac{f_{o1} - f_{e1}}{\sqrt{f_{e1}(N - f_{e1})/N}}. \qquad [17.2.2]$$

For very large $N$, this can be regarded as a standardized normal variable. Now consider the *square* of this standardized variable $z$:

$$z^2 = \frac{N(f_{o1} - f_{e1})^2}{f_{e1}(N - f_{e1})}$$

$$= \frac{(f_{o1} - f_{e1})^2}{f_{e1}} + \frac{(f_{o1} - f_{e1})^2}{N - f_{e1}}.$$

Since $(f_{o1} - f_{e1}) = -(f_{o2} - f_{e2})$, we may write

$$z^2 = \frac{(f_{o1} - f_{e1})^2}{f_{e1}} + \frac{(f_{o2} - f_{e2})^2}{f_{e2}}$$

$$= \chi^2. \qquad [17.2.3*]$$

**When the frequency distribution has only two categories, the Pearson $\chi^2$ statistic has exactly the same value as the square of the standardized variable used in testing for a single proportion, using the normal approximation to the binomial.** From the definition of a chi-square variable with 1 degree of freedom (Section 11.1), it can be seen that if $E(P) = p$, and if $N$ is very large, then sample values of $\chi^2$ should be distributed approximately as a chi-square variable with 1 degree of freedom. For a large sample and so long as a two-tailed test is desired, it is immaterial whether we use the normal-distribution test for a single proportion or the Pearson $\chi^2$ test for a two-category problem. Furthermore, the square root of this $\chi^2$ value gives the equivalent $z$ value if one does desire a one-tailed test. This direct equivalence between $z$ and $\sqrt{\chi^2}$ holds only for 1 degree of freedom, however.

Again, for 1 degree of freedom, the Pearson $\chi^2$ test may be improved somewhat if the test statistic is found by taking

$$\chi^2 = \frac{(|f_{o1} - f_{e1}| - .5)^2}{f_{e1}} + \frac{(|f_{o2} - f_{e2}| - .5)^2}{f_{e2}} \qquad [17.2.4\dagger]$$

so that the *absolute value* of the difference between observed and expected frequencies is reduced by .5 for each category before the squaring is carried out. This is known as **Yates' correction** and depends on the fact that the binomial is a discrete, and the normal a continuous, distribution. However, Yates' correction applies only when there is 1 degree of freedom.

### 17.3  A special problem: a goodness-of-fit test for a normal distribution

One use of the Pearson goodness-of-fit $\chi^2$ test is in deciding if a continuous population distribution has a particular form. That is, we might be interested in seeing if a sample distribution of scores might have arisen from some theoretical form such as the normal distribution. It is important to recall that like most theoretical distributions useful in statistics, the normal is a family of distributions, particular distributions differing in the parameters entering into the rule as constants; for the normal distribution, these parameters are $\mu$ and $\sigma$, of course. It is also important to remember that although such a distribution is continuous, it is necessary to think of the population as grouped into a finite number of distinct class intervals if the Pearson $\chi^2$ test is to be applied.

For example, suppose that there is good reason to believe that intelligence scores on some test are normally distributed among American men in general. However, we are curious about the distribution of such intelligence scores for men serving time in prison. Is it reasonable to believe that this distribution is also approximately normal? The question refers not to the mean, nor to the variance of this distribution, but rather to the distribution's form. We decide to draw a random sample of 400 men in prison to test the hypothesis of a normal population distribution.

However, the population distribution must be thought of as grouped into class intervals. Furthermore, it is necessary that the number expected in each class interval be relatively large. Therefore, the experimenter must first decide on the number of class intervals he will use to describe both theoretical and obtained distributions. He would like to have intervals insuring a fairly "fine" description, as well as a sizable number expected in each interval. Suppose that for our problem we decide to think of the population distribution as divided into eight class intervals, in such a way that each interval should include exactly one eighth of the population. What would the limits of these eight intervals be? From Table I we find the limits shown in Table 17.3.1. Notice that this arrangement into class intervals refers to the *population* distribution, assumed to be normal under the null hypothesis, and that this choice of class intervals is made before the data are seen. This arrangement is quite arbitrary, and some other number of class intervals might have been chosen; in fact, with a sample size this large, an experimenter would be quite safe in taking many more intervals with a much smaller probability associated with each. Notice also that the population is thought of as divided into class intervals of unequal size, in order to give equal probability of intervals. On the other hand, it is perfectly possible to decide on some arbitrary

**Table 17.3.1**

| Class limits in terms of z for class interval j | Approx. $p_j$ | $f_{ej}$ |
|---|---|---|
| 1.15 and above | 1/8 | 50 |
| .68 to   1.15 | 1/8 | 50 |
| .32 to   .68 | 1/8 | 50 |
| .00 to   .32 | 1/8 | 50 |
| −.32 to   .00 | 1/8 | 50 |
| −.68 to −.32 | 1/8 | 50 |
| −1.15 to −.68 | 1/8 | 50 |
| below −1.15 | 1/8 | 50 |
| | | — |
| | | 400 |

class-interval size in $z$ score terms, and then allow the various probabilities to be unequal. Our way of proceeding has two possible advantages: departures from normality in the middle of the score range are relatively more likely to be detected in this way than otherwise, and computations are simplified by having equal expectations for each class interval in the distribution. Furthermore, when the population is conceived as divided into class intervals having equal probability of occurrence, we can see from expression **17.1.4** that the sampling variance of the Pearson $\chi^2$ statistic should be relatively closer to that of a chi-square variable; thus, when $\nu = J - 1$ and $p_j = 1/J$, we find that

$$\text{var.}(\chi^2) = \frac{2\nu(N - 1)}{N}.$$

A relatively better approximation should be afforded when intervals giving equal expected frequencies are chosen, other things being equal. However, grouping in this way may not be especially advantageous in some studies, and other ways of thinking of the population as grouped may be more desirable. The point is that this step is *arbitrary*, even though the conclusions reached from the analysis may depend heavily upon how the population is regarded as grouped. A rejection of the normal-distribution hypothesis based on a certain grouping leads to the conclusion that the population is not normally distributed; however, a failure to reject, based on a particular grouping, does not imply that some other grouping would not have led to a rejection of this hypothesis. The point should be clear: in testing for a normal population distribution, the experimenter must give considerable prior thought to how he wants to regard the population as grouped, within the limitation that he must have a sizable expectation for frequencies within each category.

Now to proceed with the example. Before the sample distribution can be grouped into the same categories as the population, something must be known about the population mean and standard deviation. Our best evidence comes from the sample estimates, $M$ and $\hat{s}$, and so these are used in place of the unknown $\mu$ and $\sigma$. In the actual data for this example suppose that it turned out that the sample mean, $M$, is 98, and the estimate $\hat{s}$ is 8.4. Then these values are used as estimates of the true values of $\mu$ and $\sigma$ for this population.

Using these estimates, we turn each score for an individual in the sample into a standard score. In terms of the arbitrary class intervals decided upon, the distribution of these *sample* standard scores is shown in Table 17.3.2.

### Table 17.3.2

| Interval | $f_{oj}$ | $f_{ej}$ |
|---|---|---|
| 1.15 and above | 14 | 50 |
| .68 to 1.15 | 17 | 50 |
| .32 to .68 | 76 | 50 |
| .00 to .32 | 105 | 50 |
| − .32 to .00 | 71 | 50 |
| − .68 to −.32 | 76 | 50 |
| −1.15 to −.68 | 31 | 50 |
| below −1.15 | 10 | 50 |

Now the $\chi^2$ test for goodness of fit is carried out:

$$\chi^2 = \frac{(14 - 50)^2}{50} + \frac{(17 - 50)^2}{50} + \frac{(76 - 50)^2}{50} + \frac{(105 - 50)^2}{50}$$
$$+ \frac{(71 - 50)^2}{50} + \frac{(76 - 50)^2}{50} + \frac{(31 - 50)^2}{50} + \frac{(10 - 50)^2}{50}$$
$$= 183.3.$$

Before the significance level is ascertained, however, an adjustment must be made in the degrees of freedom. Two parameters had to be estimated in order to carry out this test: the mean and the standard deviation of the population. *One degree of freedom is subtracted from $J - 1$ for each separate parameter estimated in such a test.* Therefore, the correct number of degrees of freedom here is

$$\nu = J - 1 - 2 \text{ or } 5.$$

For 5 degrees of freedom, Table III shows that this obtained $\chi^2$ value far exceeds that required for significance at either the .05 or .01 level. The experimenter can feel quite confident in saying that scores in this population are not normally distributed.

Once again, let it be repeated that **the arrangement into population class intervals is arbitrary.** It may seem more reasonable to group the obtained distribution into convenient class intervals, and then to ask the question about the population distribution grouped in the same way. However, remember that the expected frequency in each interval must be relatively large, say 5 or more. In most instances this will require some combining of extreme class intervals to make the expected frequencies large enough to permit the test and *this combining operation amounts to a tinkering with the randomness of the sample.* Combining was not necessary in our example because we determined the required grouping ahead of time so as to guarantee large expected frequencies in each class.

## 17.4   PEARSON $\chi^2$ TESTS OF ASSOCIATION

The general rationale for testing goodness of fit also extends to tests of independence (or lack of statistical association) between categorical attributes. Quite often situations arise where $N$ independent observations are made, and each and every observation is classified in two qualitative ways. One set of mutually exclusive and exhaustive classes can be called the $A$ attribute. Any one of the $C$ distinct classes making up this attribute can be labeled $A_j$, where $j$ runs from 1 through $C$. Thus $A = \{A_1, \cdots, A_j, \cdots A_C\}$. Furthermore, on some other attribute $B$, there are some $R$ mutually exclusive and exhaustive classes.

$$B = \{B_1, \cdots, B_k, \cdots, B_R\}.$$

Each observation then represents the occurrences of one joint event $(A_j, B_k)$. The entire set of data can be shown as a **contingency table,** with the $C$ classes of attribute $A$ making up the columns, and the $R$ classes of attribute $B$ the rows; each and every possible $(A_j, B_k)$ joint event thus is shown by a cell in the table. Be sure to notice that each distinct observation can represent only one joint event, and thus *each observation qualifies for one and only one cell in the table.*

For example, suppose that a random sample of 100 school children is drawn. Each child is classified in two ways: the first attribute is the sex of the child, with two possible categories:

$$\text{male} \quad = A_1$$
$$\text{female} = A_2.$$

The second attribute, $B$, is the stated preference of a child for two kinds of reading materials:

$$\text{fiction} = B_1$$
$$\text{nonfiction} = B_2$$

(we will assume that each child can be given one and only one preference-classification). The entire set of data could be arranged into a joint-frequency distribution, or contingency table, symbolized by

|   | $A_1$ | $A_2$ |
|---|---|---|
| $B_1$ | $(A_1, B_1)$ | $(A_2, B_1)$ |
| $B_2$ | $(A_1, B_2)$ | $(A_2, B_2)$ |

$$N$$

Each cell of this table contains the frequency among the $N$ children for the joint event represented by that cell. The data might, for example, turn out to be

|   | male $A_1$ | femal $A_2$ |   |
|---|---|---|---|
| prefer fiction $B_1$ | 19 | 32 | 51 |
| prefer nonfiction $B_2$ | 29 | 20 | 49 |
|   | 48 | 52 | $100 = N$ |

This table shows that exactly 19 observations represent the joint event (male, prefers fiction), 32 the joint event (female, prefers fiction) and so on.

In general, for some $C$ classes making up the attribute $A$ and some $R$ classes the attribute $B$, the joint-frequency distribution is represented in an $R \times C$ table, each cell of which shows the frequency for one possible joint event in the data. The sum of frequencies over cells must be $N$, and each possible observation qualifies for one and only one cell in the table.

Corresponding to the joint-frequency distribution for a sample, there is a joint *probability* distribution in the population. For the example

|  | $A_1$ | $A_2$ |  |
|---|---|---|---|
| $B_1$ | $p(A_1,B_1)$ | $p(A_2,B_1)$ | $p(B_1)$ |
| $B_2$ | $p(A_1,B_2)$ | $p(A_2,B_2)$ | $p(B_2)$ |
|  | $p(A_1)$ | $p(A_2)$ | 1.00 |

Suppose that we had some hypothesis where the probability of each possible joint event is specified. We might want to ask how this hypothetical *joint* distribution actually fits the data. Just as for the simple frequency distribution considered in Section 17.1, the hypothesis about the joint distribution tells us what to expect for each *joint* event's frequency. That is, for cell $(A_1,B_1)$ we should expect exactly $Np(A_1,B_1)$ cases to occur in a random sample; for cell $(A_1,B_1)$ our expectation is $Np(A_1,B_2)$ and so on for the other cells. Given this *complete specification* of the population joint distribution, then for sufficiently large $N$ we could apply the Pearson $\chi^2$ test of goodness of fit. Just as for any goodness-of-fit test where no parameters are estimated, the number of degrees of freedom would be the number of distinct event classes minus 1. Since there are $RC$ *joint* events in this instance, $RC - 1$ is the degrees of freedom for a goodness-of-fit test for such a joint distribution.

However, exact hypothesis about joint distributions are quite rare in psychology. Very seldom would one want to carry out such a test even though it is possible. Instead, the usual null hypothesis is that the two attributes $A$ and $B$ are independent. If the hypothesis of independence can be rejected, then we say that the attributes $A$ and $B$ are statistically related or associated.

In Section 4.7 it was stated that two discrete attributes are considered independent *if and only if*

$$p(A_j,B_k) = p(A_j)p(B_k)$$

for *all possible* joint events $(A_j,B_k)$. Given that the hypothesis of independence is true, and given the *marginal* distributions showing $p(A_j)$ and $p(B_k)$, we know what the joint probabilities *must* be.

On the other hand, this fact alone does us little good, because independence is defined in terms of the *population* probabilities, $p(A_j)$ and $p(B_k)$, and these we do not know. What can we use instead? **The best estimates we can make of the unknown marginal probabilities are the sample marginal proportions:**

$$\text{est. } p(A_j) = \frac{\text{freq. of } A_j}{N}$$

## 17.5   An example of a test for independence in a larger table

There is no reason at all why the number of categories in either *A* or *B* must be only 2, as in the preceding example. Any number of rows and any number of columns can be used for classifying observations into a contingency table. Provided that there is a sufficiently large random sample of independent observations where each occurs in one and only one cell, a $\chi^2$ test can be carried out. However, for larger tables sample *N* must be rather large if a sufficiently large expected frequency is to be associated with each cell (this problem will be discussed in the next section).

Not only will the example in this section involve a larger table, but also it will illustrate that the row or column classes need not be qualitative in their original character, *if* the experimenter is willing to treat the data only in qualitative terms. That is, either the attribute *A* or the attribute *B* may represent numerical measurements grouped into class intervals. Under these conditions the $\chi^2$ test is still an adequate way to answer the question of association between *A* and *B*, but in using a $\chi^2$ test the experimenter is actually ignoring the numerical information in the scores and is treating the different class intervals simply as qualitative distinctions.

Consider an experiment where a psychologist is studying the possible inheritance of patterns of emotional response in rats. He has noticed that four strains of rats tend to differ in their tendency toward emotional response in a new situation. These four strains are each isolated and carefully inbred until, after several generations, a large number of representatives of four pure strains are available for study. Each rat is put individually into a new and presumably fear-inducing situation, and left for a fixed amount of time. By some standard procedure, each individual rat is given a "score" on emotional response, based on a composite of a number of behavior indices. The experimenter is looking for evidence of association between the emotionality score and the strain the rat belongs to. Some 25 rats are selected at random from each of the four pure strains, giving a total of 100 individuals in all. Within each strain used in the experiment

### Table 17.5.1

| Scores | Group | | | | Total |
|---|---|---|---|---|---|
| | *1* | *2* | *3* | *4* | |
| 9 and over | 5 | 8 | 6 | 4 | 23 |
| 6–8 | 10 | 7 | 8 | 6 | 31 |
| 3–5 | 5 | 4 | 7 | 8 | 24 |
| 0–2 | 5 | 6 | 4 | 7 | 22 |
| | 25 | 25 | 25 | 25 | 100 |

a grouped frequency distribution of "emotionality scores" is found, the same class intervals being used for each distribution. These frequency distributions for the four groups are shown in Table 17.5.1. *Because of his previous experience with such scores, the experimenter was able to set up these four class intervals in advance of his seeing the data.*

Basically, the experimenter is interested in comparing the four populations in terms of their distributions of scores. Looked at in this way, the problem is the comparison of four grouped frequency distributions, each based on the same grouping scheme. However, this can also be framed as a problem in testing the independence of two attributes.

Let us call rat population (pure breed) $j$ the class $A_j$, and let us call any class interval of scores $B_k$. Now if all the populations were exactly *alike* in their score distributions, it should be true that

$$p(B_k|A_j) = p(B_k).$$

That is, the probability of any rat's showing a score in the class interval $B_k$ given that he belongs to the population $A_j$ should be the same as the probability in general associated with that class interval. This is tantamount to the independence of the attribute $A$ (breeds) and the attribute $B$ (scores arranged in class intervals). Therefore the problem of the simultaneous comparison of a number of frequency distributions is basically the same as the problem of testing for independence.

Going ahead on this basis, we carry out the $\chi^2$ test for this table. The expected frequencies, each found by multiplying the column frequency by the row frequency and dividing by $N$, are shown in Table 17.5.2.

### Table 17.5.2

| Scores | Group 1 | 2 | 3 | 4 | Total |
|--------|------|------|------|------|------|
| 9 and over | 5.75 | 5.75 | 5.75 | 5.75 | 23 |
| 6–8 | 7.75 | 7.75 | 7.75 | 7.75 | 31 |
| 3–5 | 6.00 | 6.00 | 6.00 | 6.00 | 24 |
| 0–2 | 5.50 | 5.50 | 5.50 | 5.50 | 22 |
|  | 25.00 | 25.00 | 25.00 | 25.00 | 100 |

Observe that for these *expected* frequencies, the relative frequency distribution in each column is precisely the same as for the column marginal total. If there are no differences between the population distributions, we expect each sample to show exactly the same frequency distribution. The estimate of this expected distribution within a column is provided by the pooled sample frequency distribution (the $B_k$ marginals).

The $\chi^2$ test is given by

$$\chi^2 = \frac{(5 - 5.75)^2}{5.75} + \frac{(8 - 5.75)^2}{5.75} + \cdots + \frac{(7 - 5.5)^2}{5.5}$$
$$= 4.97.$$

Here there are $(4 - 1)(4 - 1) = 9$ degrees of freedom, and the value required for significance at the .05 level is 16.92, making the result clearly not significant. The experimenter does not have enough evidence to say whether or not the breed is associated with the score a rat gets on emotionality level.

This example should illustrate the fact that $\chi^2$ tests can be used to compare entire frequency distributions grouped in the same way. The grouping should, however, be decided upon in advance of the actual data. The only inference drawn from a significant result is that the different samples do not represent the same population distribution. Be very sure to notice, however, that this is rather different from the question asked in the analysis of variance, where several samples are also compared. In the analysis of variance, the numerical scores themselves are used as the basis for comparison in terms of means; in the $\chi^2$ analysis, the scores play a role only in the grouping of observations into qualitatively distinct categories. The fact that these groupings are class intervals of a numerical score distribution is quite immaterial in the test itself. Population differences of any sort may show up as a significant result, and the experimenter can conclude only that the population distributions are not identical when the test is significant. Furthermore, given that the underlying assumptions are met, the conclusions reached in analysis of variance are about population means; the experimenter can conclude not only that the populations differ, but also how and by how much they differ. The introduction of the scores themselves into the analysis makes for relatively stronger conclusions. Nevertheless, there are situations where several frequency distributions are to be compared directly, class intervals can be formed in advance of the data, and the sample size is relatively large. In this instance it is possible to use the $\chi^2$ test for independence, provided that the experimenter realizes that he is not using all of the information in the data and that his conclusions will not be directly comparable to those of the analysis of variance. In general, the Pearson $\chi^2$ analysis is best reserved for the truly qualitative data for which it is most appropriate.

## 17.6   THE SPECIAL CASE OF A FOURFOLD TABLE

Two-by-two contingency or joint-frequency tables are especially common in psychological research. For such fourfold tables, computations for the Pearson $\chi^2$ test can be put into a very simple form. Consider the following table:

| | | |
|---|---|---|
| $a$ | $b$ | $a + b$ |
| $c$ | $d$ | $c + d$ |
| $a + c$ | $b + d$ | $N$ |

Here, the small letters $a$, $b$, $c$, and $d$ represent the frequencies in the four cells, respectively. Then, the value of $\chi^2$ can be found quite easily from

$$\chi^2 = \frac{N(ad - bc)^2}{(a + b)(c + d)(a + c)(b + d)} \qquad [17.6.1\dagger]$$

with, of course, one degree of freedom.

This value of $\chi^2$ is usually corrected to give a somewhat better approximation to the exact multinomial probability. With the correction, the value is found from

$$\chi^2 = \frac{N(|ad - bc| - N/2)^2}{(a + b)(c + d)(a + c)(b + d)} \qquad [17.6.2\dagger]$$

which is compared with Table III (1 degree of freedom) in the usual way. This is another instance of **Yates' correction for continuity,** which we encountered first in Section 17.2. This correction should be applied only when the number of degrees of freedom is one, however.

## 17.7 The assumptions in $\chi^2$ tests for association

Chi-square tests are among the easiest for the novice in statistics to carry out, and they lend themselves to a wide variety of psychological data. This computational simplicity is deceptive, however, as the use of the chi-square approximation to find multinomial probabilities is based on a fairly elaborate mathematical rationale, requiring a number of very important assumptions. This rationale and the importance of these assumptions has not always been understood, even by experienced researchers, and there is probably no other statistical method that has been so widely misapplied.

In the first place, since the exact probabilities to be approximated are assumed to follow the multinomial rule, each and every observation categorized should be independent of each other observation. In particular, this means that caution may be required in the application of $\chi^2$ tests to data where dependency among observations may be present, as is sometimes the case in repeated observations of the same individuals. As always, however, it is not the mere fact that observations were repeated, but rather the nature of the experiment and the type of data, that let one judge the credibility of the assumption of independent observations. Nevertheless, the novice user of statistical methods does well to avoid the application of Pearson $\chi^2$ tests to data where each individual observed contributes more than a single entry to the joint frequency table.

In the second place, the joint-frequency table must be complete, in the sense that each and every observation made must represent one and only one joint-event possibility. This means that each distinct observation made must qualify for one and only one row, one and only one column, and one and only one cell in the contingency table.

The stickiest question of all concerns sample size and the minimum size of expected frequency in each cell. Probabilities found from the chi-square tables for such tests are always approximate. Only when the sample size is infinite must these probabilities be exact. The larger the sample size, the better this approximation generally is, but the goodness of the approximation also depends on such things as true marginal distributions of events, the number of cells in the contingency table, and the significance level employed. *Furthermore, there are no hard and fast rules that are sufficient to cover all the things which can influence the goodness of the chi-square approximation.* Rules of thumb for sample size do exist, but even these vary in different statistics texts; the simple reason for this is that statisticians themselves vary in their standards for a "good" approximation. This makes it very hard for the user of statistics, since a rule of thumb that may be fine for one kind of problem may not be advisable for another.

Without going further into the complexities of the matter, we will simply state a rule that is at least current, fairly widely endorsed, and generally conservative. **For tables with more than a single degree of freedom, a minimum expected frequency of 5 can be regarded as adequate, although when there is only a single degree of freedom a minimum expected frequency of 10 is much safer.** This rule of thumb is ordinarily conservative, however, and circumstances may arise where smaller expected frequencies can be tolerated. In particular, if the number of degrees of freedom is large, then it is fairly safe to use the $\chi^2$ test for association even if the minimum expected frequency is as small as 1, provided that there are only a few cells with small expected frequencies (such as one out of five or fewer). On the whole, however, it may be wise for the beginner using this technique to err, if he must, on the conservative side, and apply Pearson $\chi^2$ tests only to data having fairly large expected frequencies. When you find yourself in a situation where relatively many expected frequencies tend to be small and sample size cannot be made large, ask for expert advice. In some instances it may be possible to carry out an exact test of the hypothesis of independence, as suggested in Section 17.9.

A word must be said about the practice of pooling categories to attain large expected frequencies after the data are seen. This has been done routinely for many years, and many statistics texts advise this as a way out of the problem. However, this may amount to trading the devil for the witch! The whole rationale for the chi-square approximation rests on the randomness of the sample, and that the categories into which observations may fall are chosen in advance. When one starts pooling categories after the data are seen he is doing something to the randomness of the sample, with unknown consequences for his inferences. The manner in which categories are pooled can have an important effect on the inferences one draws. This practice is to be avoided if at all possible; better the risk of a poor approximation to the exact probabilities than a result without any statistical interpretation at all.

## 17.8  LIKELIHOOD RATIO TESTS FOR CATEGORICAL DATA

The method of the likelihood ratio mentioned in Chapter 9 has been applied to the problems of tests both of goodness of fit and of association for categorical data. Like the $\chi^2$ tests, the likelihood ratio methods are based ultimately on the multinomial rule for the distribution of sample results, given some hypothesis about a discrete distribution. However, the actual form of the test provided by the likelihood ratio method differs somewhat from the familiar $\chi^2$ statistic. For a goodness-of-fit test, the test statistic for large $N$ is

$$\chi^2 = 2 \sum_{j=1}^{J} n_j(\log_e n_j - \log_e p_j) - 2N \log_e N \qquad \text{[17.8.1]}$$

where $n_j$ is the observed number in category $j$, $p_j$ is the probability for that category as specified by the null hypothesis, and the logarithmns are to the base $e$. The value of this statistic is referred to chi-square table for $J - 1$ degrees of freedom.

For tests of association, the likelihood ratio test is given by

$$\chi^2 = 2N \log_e N + 2 \sum_{j}^{C} \sum_{k}^{R} n_{jk} \log_e n_{jk} - 2 \sum_{j}^{C} n_j \log_e n_j - 2 \sum_{k}^{R} n_k \log_e n_k \qquad \text{[17.8.2]}$$

where $n_j$ is the number observed in column $j$, $n_k$ is the number observed in row $k$, $n_{jk}$ is the observed frequency in cell $j,k$, and the logarithmns are again taken to the base $e$. This statistic is referred to in the distribution of chi-square with $(R - 1)(C - 1)$ degrees of freedom.

For very large $N$, these likelihood ratio tests become equivalent to the ordinary Pearson $\chi^2$ tests introduced earlier. However, there is some reason to believe that these tests may be somewhat less affected by small sample size than are the Pearson $\chi^2$ tests, particularly when the number of degrees of freedom is greater than one. Thus, for moderately large samples these procedures may be slightly superior. For very large samples, these methods and the $\chi^2$ tests presented earlier should give virtually identical results. The assumptions having to do with the completeness of the data and of the independence of observations are, however, just as essential for these methods based on the likelihood ratio as for the others. A discussion of these methods is given in Mood (1950).

## 17.9 THE POSSIBILITY OF EXACT TESTS FOR GOODNESS OF FIT AND FOR ASSOCIATION

As we have mentioned, the Pearson $\chi^2$ tests of association and of goodness of fit give approximations to exact probabilities, which, in principle, may be found using the multinomial (or in some instances, the hypergeometric) rule. The basic reason for using the chi-square approximation is that actual computation of these exact probabilities is extremely laborious or downright impossible. However, in some situations where the sample size is so small that the use of the $\chi^2$ tests is ruled out, it may be practicable to compute probabilities exactly. This will be illustrated only for a simple test of association, although other possibilities exist.

The test we will discuss is commonly known as **Fisher's exact test** for a $2 \times 2$ contingency table. This is not appropriately called a $\chi^2$ test, since it does not use the chi-square approximation at all. Instead, the exact probability is computed for a sample's showing as much or more evidence for association than that obtained, given only the operation of chance.

There are at least two somewhat different rationales one might advance for this exact test, but the one we will adopt is based on the principle of randomization. This general idea has been referred to already in Section 13.25.

Suppose that some $N$ subjects are categorized into the following $2 \times 2$ table:

|         | $A_1$ | $A_2$ |         |
|---------|-------|-------|---------|
| $B_1$   | $a$   | $b$   | $a + b$ |
| $B_2$   | $c$   | $d$   | $c + d$ |
|         | $a + c$ | $b + d$ | $N$ |

Now suppose for a moment that the $N$ subjects actually make up the population, and that the distribution in the population shows $a + c$ individuals in the first *column* category, $A_1$, and $b + d$ individuals in the second column category, $A_2$. Some $n = a + b$ individuals are sampled at random and *without* replacement. What is the probability that in *this sample* exactly $a$ individuals fall into $A_1$ and $b$ into $A_2$? In Section 5.19 it was mentioned that the probability of a sample drawn *without* replacement from a finite population can be found by the *hypergeometric* rule. Applying the rule, we find that the probability of $a$ in $A_1$ and $b$ in $A_2$ *within the sample represented by row $B_1$* is just

$$\frac{\binom{a + c}{a}\binom{b + d}{b}}{\binom{N}{a + b}}$$

which is the same as

$$\frac{(a + b)! \, (c + d)! \, (a + c)! \, (b + d)!}{N! \, a! \, b! \, c! \, d!}.$$

Now consider the marginals of the sample table as fixed, so that regardless of the arrangement within the table we know the totals in rows and columns. Imagine that occurrences of the events represented by the rows and columns have absolutely nothing to do with each other, so that the two attributes are independent. Any sample result in the cells of the table occurs as though individuals in the columns were assigned to the rows at random. Then the probability of any particular random arrangement is given by the use of the hypergeometric rule, just as for the probability found above. *If one finds the probability of the arrangement actually obtained, as well as every other arrangement giving as much or more evidence for association, then one can test the hypothesis that the obtained result is purely a product of chance by taking this probability as the significance level.* This amounts to finding both the probability of the obtained table, and every other table (with the same marginals) showing more disproportion between cells *a* and *c* than in the table obtained.

An example may make this idea seem more reasonable. Imagine a study involving 10 individuals. Each individual observation fell into one and only one cell of the following contingency table:

|  | $A_1$ | $A_2$ |  |
|---|---|---|---|
| $B_1$ | 1 | 4 | 5 |
| $B_2$ | 3 | 2 | 5 |
|  | 4 | 6 | 10 |

Now assume that regardless of how else the individuals were categorized we would have got 4 cases in $A_1$, 6 cases in $A_2$, 5 cases in $B_1$, and 5 cases in $B_2$. Also assume that the arrangement obtained in the cells of the table is purely a result of chance. What is the probability of this result (the arrangement actually obtained)? Since

$$a = 1$$
$$b = 4$$
$$c = 3$$
$$d = 2$$

this is

$$\frac{4!\ 6!\ 5!\ 5!}{10!\ 1!\ 4!\ 3!\ 2!}$$

or

$$p(\text{obtained arrangement}) = .238.$$

Actually, we could stop at this point, since for $\alpha = .05$ or less, we definitely could not reject the hypothesis of a random arrangement, since the probability is at least .238 of a sample this "systematic" or more so by chance alone. However, we will continue in order to show the method.

An even more systematic-looking result that might have occurred is

|  | $A_1$ | $A_2$ |
|---|---|---|
| $B_1$ | 0 | 5 |
| $B_2$ | 4 | 1 |

where $a = 0$, $b = 5$, $c = 4$, $d = 1$. Notice that if this result had occurred, then there would be even more discrepancy between the obtained distributions in rows $B_1$ and $B_2$. In other words, the relative frequencies in cells *a* and *c* are even more different than before. The probability of this result is

$$\frac{4!\ 6!\ 5!\ 5!}{10!\ 0!\ 5!\ 4!\ 1!} = .024.$$

Thus, the probability of our result or one *more* suggestive of association is

$$.238 + .024 = .262.$$

This is not as small as the conventional levels set for $\alpha$, and so the hypothesis that the apparent association is the product of chance is *not* rejected. Notice, however, that if the actual result had corresponded to the table given last, we could have rejected the hypothesis for any $\alpha \geqq .024$.

Unlike the $\chi^2$ test, the Fisher exact test is essentially one-tailed. The probabilities are calculated for all possible results departing as much or more in a specific direction from the marginal distribution of $A$ as does our sample. When the rows (or columns) have equal frequencies (as in the example) the final probability can be doubled to arrive at the two-tailed significance level. However, when both the two rows and the two columns have unequal marginal frequencies, the probability should be found for each possible table where the absolute difference

$$\left| \frac{a}{a+b} - \frac{c}{c+d} \right|$$

is as great or greater than in the table actually obtained.

Convenient tables are available for the Fisher exact test, so that it is not usually necessary to carry out all the computations given here in order to perform this test. These tables are available in the *Biometrika Tables for Statisticians* (1954) and in Siegel (1956) among other places.

It must be emphasized that the reasoning underlying this test is rather different from that for $\chi^2$ tests. Here, one actually refers his sample result to the distribution over possible randomizations of that sample. The hypothesis is that chance is the determiner of the apparent association in the table. This hypothesis is rejected as the actual table obtained falls among those unlikely to occur over all random assignments of subjects in columns to the rows. This rationale makes the test especially suitable for experiments where subjects actually *are* assigned to groups at random. Small sample size is no restriction for this test; indeed, small samples actually make the computations quite simple, although very strong association must exist to show up as significant when sample size is quite small.

Conceptually, no special difficulty exists in extending the exact test idea to larger tables, although there are two obvious problems that arise: the computations required mount up very rapidly as the size of the table increases, and one must have some sort of index (such as the Pearson $\chi^2$ statistic) to evaluate the apparent evidence for association in each possible sample. Thus, exact tests are not in common use for larger tables. However, if it should be very important to have a test for a small sample in some problem, it is well to remember that these exact procedures are possible, even for larger tables.

## 17.10   A TEST FOR CORRELATED PROPORTIONS IN A TWO-BY-TWO TABLE

A problem that often arises in psychological research is somewhat different from the problem of association between attributes. As an illustration of this problem, suppose that some $N$ individual subjects are each observed by two independent judges. Each judge places each subject into one of two mutually exclusive and exhaustive categories, such as "high leadership potential" versus "low leadership potential." It is assumed that a judge's ratings of different individuals are independent. Let us call these categories simply "$H$" and "$L$" for the moment. We would like to ask if these two judges, given all possible subjects in the population, would show the same true proportion of individuals rated in category "$H$." In other words, in the population of all subjects to be rated, does $p_1(H) = p_2(H)$, where $p_1(H)$ is the proportion rated in category $H$ by judge 1, and $p_2(H)$ is the proportion rated in that category by judge 2?

This is a problem of **correlated proportions,** since each of the two sample proportions will be based in part on the same individuals. A test due to McNemar (1955) applies to this situation. Suppose that the sample of $N$ individuals were arranged into the following $2 \times 2$ table:

JUDGE 1

$H$      $L$

|             |     | $H$ | $L$ |
|-------------|-----|-----|-----|
|             | $H$ | $a$ | $b$ |
| JUDGE 2     |     |     |     |
|             | $L$ | $c$ | $d$ |

An *exact* test of the hypothesis that $p_1(H) = p_2(H)$ is possible using binomial distribution. Under this hypothesis, the probability of a given sample result, showing a particular pair of cell frequencies $b$ and $c$, is just

$$\binom{b + c}{b} (.5)^{b+c}. \qquad [17.10.1*]$$

To carry out the exact test, let $g$ equal the smaller of the two frequencies, $b$ or $c$. Then one takes the sum of probabilities

$$2 \sum_{h=0}^{g} \binom{b + c}{h} (.5)^{b+c}. \qquad [17.10.2*]$$

If this number is less than or equal to the value chosen for $\alpha$, then the null hypothesis may be rejected (two-tailed).

When $N$ is relatively large, the exact probability may be approximated by use of $\chi^2$, where

$$\chi^2 = \frac{(|b - c| - 1)^2}{b + c} \qquad [17.10.3\dagger]$$

with one degree of freedom.

For our example, a significant result would let one conclude that the *true* distributions of judgments for the two judges differ. Be sure to notice that this is not an ordinary test of association for a contingency table, but rather a test of the equality of two proportions where each sample proportion involves some of the same observations, making the two sample proportions dependent.

Obviously, this test can be applied in contexts other than two judges' categorizations of subjects, although this is a fairly common problem in psychology; another common example is the difference in difficulty of two test items administered to the same subjects. This test has been extended to more complicated situations by Cochran; the procedure is discussed in Section 18.5.

## 17.11   MEASURES OF ASSOCIATION IN CONTINGENCY TABLES

One of the oldest problems in descriptive statistics is that of indexing the strength of statistical association between qualitative attributes. Although a number of simple and meaningful indices exist to describe association in a fourfold table, this problem grows more complex for larger tables, and has perhaps never been solved to everyone's real satisfaction.

Why should there be any special problem in indexing the strength of association between qualitative or categorical attributes? As we have seen, most of our notions of the strength of a statistical association rest on the concept of the variance of a random variable. Thus, indices such as $\rho^2$, $\rho_I$, $\eta^2$, and our index $\omega^2$, all rest on the idea of a proportional reduction in variance in the dependent variable afforded by specifying the value of the independent variable. However, when the independent and dependent variables are each categorical in nature, the variance per se is not defined. Something else must be used in specifying how knowledge of the $A$ category to which an observation belongs increases our ability to predict the $B$ category.

Three somewhat different approaches to this problem will be discussed here. The first rests directly on the notion of statistical independence between two attributes, defined by $p(A_j,B_k) = p(A_j)p(B_k)$. In this approach, the strength of association is measured basically in terms of the difference

$$|p(A_j,B_k) - p(A_j)p(B_k)|,$$

the extent to which the probability of a joint occurrence differs from the probability that would be true if the attributes $A$ and $B$ were independent. As we shall see, this conception is adequate from a statistical point of view but seems to lack a simple interpretation in terms of how one *uses* the statistical relation.

Another and much more recent approach deals with **predictive association**. Association between categorical attributes is indexed by the reduction in the probability of error in prediction afforded by knowing the status of the individual on one of the attributes. This way of defining association makes intuitive good sense, but is not as directly tied to tests of association as the first approach.

Finally, a brief mention will be made of still another point of view on this problem, based on concepts from information theory. Here an analogue to the variance does exist for categorical data. This makes it possible to define the strength of association in contingency tables in a way very similar to the usual indices for numerical data.

### 17.12 THE PHI-COEFFICIENT AND INDICES OF CONTINGENCY

Before we go into the problem of describing statistical association in a sample, a general way of viewing statistical association in a population will be introduced. This is the **index of mean square contingency,** originally suggested by Karl Pearson, the originator of the $\chi^2$ test for association. Imagine a *discrete joint probability distribution* represented in a table with $C$ columns and $R$ rows. The columns represent the qualitative attribute $A$, and the rows $B$. Then the mean square contingency is defined to be

$$\varphi^2 = \sum_j \sum_k \frac{p(A_j, B_k)^2}{p(A_j)p(B_k)} - 1 \qquad [17.12.1*]$$

This population index $\varphi^2$ (small Greek phi, squared) can be zero only when there is complete independence, so that

$$p(A_j, B_k) = p(A_j)p(B_k)$$

for each joint event $(A_j, B_k)$. However, when there is *complete association* in the table, the value of $\varphi^2$ is given by

$$\text{max. } \varphi^2 = L - 1,$$

where $L$ is the *smaller* of the two numbers $R$ or $C$ (number of rows or columns in the table). Thus, a convenient index of strength of association in a population is provided by

$$\varphi' = \sqrt{\frac{\varphi^2}{L-1}}, \qquad [17.12.2*]$$

which will always lie between the values 0 and 1.

For the special case in which $R = C = 2$ (a $2 \times 2$ table) then $\varphi$ is itself an index of association, since $\varphi = \varphi'$. Except in a $2 \times 2$ table the sign of $\varphi$ is always taken as positive, and even in $2 \times 2$ tables the sign is meaningless unless the categories are regarded as ordered.

Now consider a sample of data arranged into a fourfold contingency table, as in Section 17.6. The *sample* value of $\varphi$ is given by

$$\varphi = \frac{(bc - ad)}{\sqrt{(a + b)(c + d)(a + c)(b + d)}}. \qquad [17.12.3\dagger]$$

Notice that this is almost exactly the square root of the expression for $\chi^2$ in a $2 \times 2$ table, given by **16.6.1.** In fact

$$\chi^2 = N\varphi^2 \qquad [17.12.4\dagger]$$

and

$$\varphi = \sqrt{\frac{\chi^2}{N}}. \qquad [17.12.5\dagger]$$

Since both $\chi^2$ and population $\varphi$ reflect the degree to which there is nonindependence between $A$ and $B$, a test for the hypothesis

$$H_0: \text{true } \varphi = 0$$

is provided by the ordinary $\chi^2$ test for association in a 2 × 2 table.

In a 2 × 2 table there is an interesting link between sample $\varphi$ and the correlation coefficient $r$. Let the categories within each attribute $A$ and $B$ be thought of as *ordered*. Suppose that the individuals $i$ in the categories are assigned numerical scores are follows:

$$X_i = 1 \text{ if } i \text{ falls in the higher category of } A$$
$$X_i = 0 \text{ if } i \text{ falls in the lower category of } A$$
$$Y_i = 1 \text{ if } i \text{ falls in the higher category of } B$$
$$Y_i = 0 \text{ if } i \text{ falls in the lower category of } B.$$

The data in the table would then be of this form

|  | 1 | $a$ | $b$ |
|---|---|---|---|
| $Y$ | 0 | $c$ | $d$ |
|  |  | 0 | 1 |

$$X$$

Suppose that the correlation between these scores were computed across the $N$ individuals $i$. We would find that

$$r_{XY} = \frac{\sum_i X_i Y_i / N - M_X M_Y}{s_X s_Y}$$
$$= \frac{Nb - (b+d)(a+b)}{\sqrt{(a+b)(c+d)(a+c)(b+d)}}$$
$$= \frac{ab + b^2 + bc + bd - ab - b^2 - ad - bd}{\sqrt{(a+b)(c+d)(a+c)(b+d)}}$$
$$= \varphi.$$

What we have shown is that the coefficient $\varphi$ may be regarded as the correlation between the attributes $A$ and $B$ when the categories are associated with "scores" of 0 and 1. If the categories are ordered for each attribute, and 1 means a higher category than does 0 on $A$, and similarly on $B$, then the sign of the $\varphi$ coefficient becomes meaningful: a positive sign implies a tendency for the high category on $A$ to be associated with the high category of $B$, and vice-versa. On the other hand, a negative value implies a tendency for a high category on one attribute to be associated with a low category on the other. Because of this connection with $r$, $\varphi$ is often called the **fourfold point correlation**.

The idea of $\varphi^2$ extends to samples in larger contingency tables as well. For a set of data arranged into an $R \times C$ table, the *sample* value of $\varphi^2$ is simply

$$\varphi^2 = \frac{\chi^2}{N}.$$

A convenient way to describe the apparent strength of association in a sample is to find

$$\varphi' = \sqrt{\frac{\varphi^2}{L-1}} = \sqrt{\frac{\chi^2}{N(L-1)}} \qquad [17.12.6\dagger]$$

which must lie between 0, reflecting complete independence, and 1, showing complete dependence, of the attributes. The Pearson $\chi^2$ is computed in the ordinary way as for a test of association (**17.4.2**) and $L$ is the *smaller* of $R$, the number of rows, or $C$, the number of columns.

This index $\varphi'$ (Cramér's statistic) is not to be confused with the ordinary *coefficient of contingency*, sometimes used for the same purpose. The coefficient of contingency is defined by

$$C_{AB} = \sqrt{\frac{\chi^2}{N + \chi^2}}.$$

This last index has the disadvantage that it cannot attain an upper limit of 1.00 unless the number of categories for $A$ and $B$ is infinite. Obviously, this limits the usefulness of $C_{AB}$ as a descriptive statistic, and the index given by $\varphi'$ is superior.

The sample coefficient $\varphi'$ gives a way to discuss the apparent strength of statistical association in any contingency table, and there is a direct connection with $\chi^2$ tests making it possible to test the significance of any obtained $\varphi'$ value from a sufficiently large sample. However, it is rather hard to put the meaning of $\varphi'$ in common-sense terms, particularly for larger tables. Our other indices of association such as $\omega^2$ do have such an interpretation in terms of reduction in variance, or variance accounted for, but this idea is not directly applicable to the $\varphi'$ indices.

Now we turn to an index of association in the *predictive* sense. How much does knowing the classification $A$ improve one's ability to predict the classification on $B$?

## 17.13 A MEASURE OF PREDICTIVE ASSOCIATION FOR CATEGORICAL DATA

Suppose that for some population, the joint-probability distribution of $(A_j, B_k)$ events were as follows:

|       | $A_1$ | $A_2$ |       |
|-------|-------|-------|-------|
| $B_1$ | .20   | .15   | .35   |
| $B_2$ | .10   | .30   | .40   |
| $B_3$ | .10   | .15   | .25   |
|       | .40   | .60   | 1.00  |

That is, $p(A_1, B_1) = .20$, $p(A_2, B_1) = .15$, and so on.

Now suppose that, knowing these probabilities, you were asked to predict the $B$ category for some case drawn at random. You know *absolutely nothing* about which $A$ category this particular case belongs to. Which $B$ category should you bet on? Your probability of being exactly right is largest if you bet on $B_2$, since this category has the largest probability of occurrence. Let us symbolize this largest probability in the marginal distribution for $B$ by $\max_k p(B_k)$, the maximum $p(B_k)$ over all the possible events $B_k$. In this instance,

$$\max_k p(B_k) = .40.$$

In this way of predicting, *not knowing* the $A$ classification, the probability of an *error* in prediction is

$$p(\text{error}|A_j \text{ unknown}) = 1 - \max_k p(B_k).$$

For this particular example,

$$p(\text{error}|A_j \text{ unknown}) = .60.$$

Now, however, suppose that a case is drawn at random and you were *told* the $A$ group into which he falls. Given this information, you must predict the $B$ class. Assume that the case came from group $A_1$; what should you predict? The largest *conditional* probability, $\max_k p(B_k|A_1)$, occurs for category $B_1$:

$$\max_k p(B_k|A_1) = \frac{.20}{.40} = .50.$$

Thus, given $A_1$, category $B_1$ should be predicted, and the probability of an error in this instance is

$$p(\text{error}|A_1) = 1 - \max_k p(B_k|A_1) = .50.$$

On the other hand, if the information were that the case belongs to $A_2$, then category $B_2$ would be predicted, since

$$\max_k p(B_k|A_2) = p(B_2|A_2)$$
$$= \frac{.30}{.60} = .50.$$

An error in this prediction has probability of

$$p(\text{error}|A_2) = 1 - \max_p p(B_k|A_2).$$

Under this model of prediction, *on the average*, over all cases, the probability of error is, then

$$p(\text{error}|\text{given } A) = p(\text{error}|A_1)p(A_1) + p(\text{error}|A_2)p(A_2)$$
$$= 1 - \max_k p(A_1B_k) - \max_k p(A_2B_k)$$
$$= 1 - .20 - .30$$
$$= 1 - .50$$
$$= .50.$$

Notice that when $A$ is not specified, then the probability of an error in prediction is .60, but when $A$ is specified, this average probability of an error is only .50. This shows that there is *predictive* association between $A$ and $B$; the $A$ category quite literally tells one something about how to bet on $B$, since the probability of error is reduced when the particular $A$ category is known.

This idea is the basis for an **index of predictive association.** This index, which was developed by Goodman and Kruskal (1954), will be called $\lambda_B$, (small Greek lambda, sub $B$):

$$\lambda_B = \frac{p(\text{error}|A_j \text{ unknown}) - p(\text{error}|A_j \text{ known})}{p(\text{error}|A_j \text{ unknown})}. \qquad [17.13.1*]$$

This index shows the proportional reduction in the *probability* of error afforded by specifying $A_j$. If the information about the $A$ category does not reduce the probability of error at all, the index is zero, and one can say that there is no predictive association. On the other hand, if the index is 1.00, no error is made given the $A_j$ classification, and there is complete predictive association.

It must be emphasized that this idea is not completely equivalent to independence and association as reflected in $\chi^2$ and $\varphi'$. It is quite possible for some statistical association to exist even though the value of $\lambda_B$ is zero. In this situation, $A$ and $B$ are not independent, but the relationship is not such that giving $A_j$ causes one to change his bet about $B_k$; the index $\lambda_B$ is other than 0 only when *different* $B_k$ categories would be predicted for different $A_j$ information.

On the other hand, if there is complete proportionality throughout the table, so that $\varphi'$ is zero, then $\lambda_B$ must be zero. Furthermore, when there is complete association, so that perfect prediction is possible, both $\lambda_B$ and $\varphi'$ must be 1.00.

Sample values of $\lambda_B$ can be calculated quite easily from a contingency table. Here, the sample is regarded as though it were the population, and probabilities are taken from the relative frequencies in the sample. Thus we interpret $\lambda_B$ as the proportional reduction in the probability of error in prediction for cases drawn at random from *this* sample, or, if you will, a population exactly like this sample in its joint distribution.

In terms of the frequencies in the sample, we find

$$\lambda_B = \frac{\sum_j \max_k f_{jk} - \max_k f_{.k}}{N - \max_k f_{.k}} \qquad [17.13.2\dagger]$$

where

$f_{jk}$ is the frequency observed in cell $(A_j, B_k)$

$\max_k f_{jk}$ is the *largest* frequency in column $A_j$

$\max_k f_{.k}$ is the largest *marginal* frequency among the rows $B_k$.

When two or more cells in any column have the same frequency, larger than any others in that column, then the frequency belonging to any single one of those cells is used as the maximum value for the column. Similarly, if several row marginals each exhibit the same frequency, which is largest among the rows, that frequency is used.

As an example, suppose that some 40 observations were grouped into the following $3 \times 4$ contingency table:

|  | $A_1$ | $A_2$ | $A_3$ | $A_4$ |  |
|---|---|---|---|---|---|
| $B_1$ | 0 | 2 | 3 | 5 | 10 |
| $B_2$ | 7 | 6 | 1 | 1 | 15 |
| $B_3$ | 3 | 2 | 6 | 4 | 15 |
|  | 10 | 10 | 10 | 10 | 40 |

The value of $\lambda_B$, for predictions of $B$ from $A$, is found to be

$$\lambda_B = \frac{7 + 6 + 6 + 5 - 15}{40 - 15}$$
$$= .36.$$

By way of contrast, consider the values of $\chi^2$ and of $\varphi'$:

$$\chi^2 = 17.97$$

which for 6 degrees of freedom is significant beyond the .01 level. The sample value of $\varphi'$ is

$$\varphi' = \sqrt{\frac{17.97}{(40)(2)}}$$
$$= .48$$

which apparently indicates a considerable degree of association.

However, the index of predictive association is .36, apparently somewhat less than indicated by $\varphi'$. Although it is rather difficult to give an exact meaning to $\varphi'$, the meaning of $\lambda_B$ is quite clear: in predictions of $B$ from $A$, information about the $A$ category reduces the probability of error by some 36 percent on the average.

The index $\lambda_B$ is an *assymetric* measure, much like $\omega^2$ and $\eta^2$. It applies when $A$ is *the* independent variable, or the thing ordinarily known first, and $B$ is the thing predicted. However, for the same set of data, it is entirely possible to reverse the roles of $A$ and $B$, and obtain the index

$$\lambda_A = \frac{p(\text{error}|B_k \text{ unknown}) - p(\text{error}|B_k \text{ known})}{p(\text{error}|B_k \text{ unknown})}, \qquad [17.13.3*]$$

which is suitable for predictions of $A$ from $B$. In terms of frequencies:

$$\lambda_A = \frac{\sum_k \max_j . f_{jk} - \max_j . f_{j.}}{N - \max_j . f_{j.}}. \qquad [17.13.4\dagger]$$

In general, the two indices $\lambda_B$ and $\lambda_A$ will not be identical; it is entirely possible to have situations where $B$ may be quite predictable from $A$, but not $A$ from $B$.

Finally, in some contexts it may be desirable to have a *symmetric* measure of the power to predict, where neither $A$ nor $B$ is specially designated as the thing predicted from or known first. Rather, we act as though sometimes the $A$ and sometimes the $B$ information is given beforehand. In this circumstance the index $\lambda_{AB}$ can be computed from

$$\lambda_{AB} = \frac{\sum_j \max_k f_{jk} + \sum_k \max_j f_{jk} - \max_k f_{.k} - \max_j f_{j.}}{2N - \max_k f_{.k} - \max_j f_{j.}}. \qquad [17.13.5\dagger]$$

In the example, the symmetric measure is

$$\lambda_{AB} = \frac{7 + 6 + 6 + 5 + 5 + 7 + 6 - 15 - 10}{2(40) - 15 - 10}$$

$$= .31.$$

This says that knowing *either* the $A$ or $B$ classification considerably improves our ability to predict the other category, in that the probability of error is reduced by about 31 percent. The value of $\lambda_{AB}$ will, incidentally, always lie between $\lambda_A$ and $\lambda_B$.

These measures of *predictive* association form a valuable adjunct to the tests given by $\chi^2$ methods. When the value of $\chi^2$ turns out significant one can say with confidence that the attributes $A$ and $B$ are not independent. Nevertheless, the significance level alone tells almost nothing about the strength of association. Usually we want to say something about the predictive strength of the relation as well. If there is the remotest interest in actual predictions using the relation studied, then the $\lambda$ measures are worthwhile. Statistical relations so small as to be almost nonexistent can show up as highly significant $\chi^2$ results, and this is especially likely to occur when sample size is large. All too often the experimenter then "kids himself" into thinking that he has discovered some relationship observable to the "naked eye," which will be applicable in some real-world situation. Plainly, this is not necessarily true. The $\lambda$ indices do, however, suggest just how much the relationship found implies about real predictions, and how much one attribute actually does tell us about the other. Such indices are a most important corrective to the experimenter's tendency to confuse statistical significance with the importance of results for actual prediction. Virtually any statistical relation will show up as highly significant given a sufficient sample size, but it takes a relation of considerable strength to enhance our ability to predict in real, uncontrolled, situations. It can happen that even though a $\chi^2$ test is significant, the predictor's *behavior* is not changed one whit by this new information. The $\lambda$ measures show how one is led to predict *differentially* in the light of the relationship.

## 17.14 INFORMATION THEORY AND THE ANALYSIS OF CONTINGENCY TABLES

A few words must be said about still another development for the description of the relation exhibited in a contingency table. These ideas come from information theory, and suggest analogies to the classical statistics based on variance, but applicable to the qualitative situation. Unfortunately, space does not permit a thorough discussion of these notions, and so only the barest sketch will be given.

Imagine a discrete probability distribution based on, say, four categories

$$
\begin{array}{ll}
A_1 & p(A_1) \\
A_2 & p(A_2) \\
A_3 & p(A_3) \\
A_4 & p(A_4).
\end{array}
$$

Consider a particular case $x$ drawn at random from this distribution. The probability that this case falls in category $A_1$ is $p(A_1)$; in category $A_2$, $p(A_2)$; and so on. Now, however, you find out that the particular case $x$ belongs to category $A_1$. *How much information have you gained?* Before this information was supplied, some probability value less than 1 was attached to each possible category, but afterward, these probabilities are

$$
\begin{array}{l}
p(x \text{ in } A_1|\text{data}) = 1 \\
p(x \text{ in } A_2|\text{data}) = 0 \\
p(x \text{ in } A_3|\text{data}) = 0 \\
p(x \text{ in } A_4|\text{data}) = 0.
\end{array}
$$

Your distribution of probabilities relative to the occurrence of that case, $x$, has changed. There was some amount of uncertainty before the exact category was known, but afterward there was no uncertainty.

In information theory, the *average prior amount of uncertainty* over all possible such cases $x$ is defined to be

$$
H(A) = - \sum_j p(A_j) \log p(A_j). \qquad [17.14.1]
$$

Thus, given any prior distribution for the possible cases $x$, the average uncertainty can be calculated. However, after the information about the category for any particular case is given, there is *no* uncertainty, and

$$
\text{posterior } H(A) = 0.
$$

Thus, the average amount of information gained by the occurrence of particular cases is the *reduction* in average uncertainty, which is

$$
\text{average amount of information} = H(A) - \text{posterior } H(A) = H(A).
$$

From a purely statistical point of view, the interesting thing about this formulation is that the index $H(A)$ is a very close analogue to the *variance* $\sigma^2$ of a distribution. When $p(A_j) = 1.00$ for some $j$, then $H(A) = 0$; similarly, if there is only one possible value for a random variable, $\sigma^2 = 0$. On the other hand, when there is a wide range of possible events, $H(A)$ tends to be large; indeed, the more evenly spread are the probabilities over the various possible events, the larger will $H(A)$ be. In the same way, $\sigma^2$ is large when the distribution of a random variable is "spread-out." In short, $H(A)$ is a variance-like index that can be computed for any discrete distribution, even though the event-classes are purely qualitative.

Furthermore, for any joint-probability distribution, one can define the average *joint* uncertainty

$$H(A,B) = -\sum_j \sum_k p(A_j,B_k) \log p(A_j,B_k) \qquad [17.14.2]$$

and the average conditional uncertainties

$$H(A|B) = -\sum_k \sum_j p(A_j,B_k) \log p(A_j|B_k) \qquad [17.14.3]$$

and

$$H(B|A) = -\sum_j \sum_k p(A_j,B_k) \log p(B_k|A_j). \qquad [17.14.4]$$

Now given these variance-like measures for *qualitative* data, indices of strength of association much like $\rho^2$ and $\omega^2$ may be formed:

$$\text{relative reduction in uncertainty in } B \text{ given } A = \frac{H(B) - H(B|A)}{H(B)}. \qquad [17.14.5^*]$$

Notice the similarity between this index and $\omega^2$: if $B$ is thought of as the dependent variable, this index gives the proportion by which knowing the $A$ category reduces uncertainty about $B$, just as $\omega^2$ tells the extent to which fixing $X$ reduces the variance in $Y$.

A symmetric measure of association highly analogous to $\rho^2$ is

$$\frac{H(A) + H(B) - H(A,B)}{\text{minimum } [H(A), H(B)]} \qquad [17.14.6^*]$$

indicating the relative strength of association between both variables.

These indices can be computed from the relative frequencies in sample contingency tables, and used purely as descriptive statistics if one so desires. Furthermore, a sampling theory exists for these statistics, and tests for zero association are possible. This sampling theory is highly related to the likelihood ratio tests of Section 17.8. Their main contribution to statistical method lies, however, in the possibility of extending the familiar notions having to do with variance and factors accounting for variance to qualitative data situations. We will not go further into this topic, but the interested student is advised to look into the books by Attneave (1959) and Garner (1962), where these possibilities are discussed in detail. It is safe to say that in the future this information-analysis approach will provide many new links between methods developed for numerical data, and those based on qualitative distinctions; some important ideas for extending the standard experimental designs to cover the qualitative measurement situation have already come from this approach.

## 17.15 RETROSPECT: THE $\chi^2$ TESTS AND MEASURES OF ASSOCIATION

The problems to which the Pearson $\chi^2$ tests apply are basically those of comparing distributions: in tests of goodness of fit, the null hypothesis states that some theoretical distribution obtains, and the question itself is one of "fit" between the hypothetical and the obtained distributions in terms of the same event categories or groupings. Tests for association may be regarded in a similar way: the hypothesis of independence between two attributes dictates a particular relationship we should expect to hold between the cell frequencies and the marginal frequencies in the obtained joint distribution. Divergence between the expected and obtained frequencies is regarded as evidence against independence.

On the face of the matter, $\chi^2$ tests are simple and appealing. They are almost the only methods most psychologists know for handling qualitative data. On the other hand, $\chi^2$ tests are always approximate, and the evidence at hand suggests that the goodness of the approximation varies with a number of factors, not all of which can be taken into account in a simple rule of thumb. Most prominent among the requirements for a satisfactory use of $\chi^2$ tests is a large sample size, but even here statisticians are in disagreement about a sufficient number of cases to permit use of these tests. About the only advice that can be given the beginner in statistics in using these tests is caution: the Pearson $\chi^2$ tests look easy, but probably nowhere in statistical inference is it more important to recognize the "if–then" nature of the conclusions.

Chi-square tests have been used wholesale in many areas in psychology, and in studies of the most varied kinds of problems. In the light of the statistical requirements for these tests, a large proportion of these applications are doubtless unjustified. However, even granting that the test is justified in the first place, what does the use of a $\chi^2$ test for association actually tell the psychologist? If $N$ is very large, as it should be for the best application of the test, virtually any "degree" of true statistical relationship between attributes will show up as a significant result. The test detects virtually any departure from strict independence between the attributes for these large sample sizes. Given the significant result, the experimenter can say that the two attributes are not independent, but is that his real interest? It has been said before, but it bears saying again: surely nothing on earth is completely independent of anything else. Given a large enough sample size, the chances are very good that the psychologist can demonstrate the association of any two qualitative attributes via a $\chi^2$ test.

It seems to this author that the really important thing is some measure of the *strength* of association between the attributes studied. Such measures do take account of sample size, and do give some indication of how knowledge of one attribute can contribute to prediction of status on the other. Especially useful in this regard are the measures of predictive association and the information measures mentioned above. Such measures actually tell the psychologist much more about the possible importance and meaning of a given relationship than can any $\chi^2$ test alone. Thus, perhaps the emphasis in many such studies should be shifted from the sheer significance of the test to an appraisal of the strength of relationship represented. How much of a real increase in ability to *predict* does this finding seem to represent?

Admittedly, this is not always the experimenter's problem. There are circumstances where for theoretical or other reasons the experimenter wants merely a comparison between distributions, either sample and theoretical, or for two samples. Provided that the distributions considered are of some random variable, so that the obtained distributions can be put into cumulative form, then methods superior to $\chi^2$ tests exist. Most notable are the so-called Kolmogorov-Smirnoff tests, either for one or two samples. These tests provide a direct comparison between distributions, and thus handle one aspect of the problem to which a Pearson $\chi^2$ test is often applied, without some of the objectionable features of such a test. A description of the Kolmogorov-Smirnoff tests is given in Siegel (1956). Other tests are also possible when data are numerical in form, as will be shown in the next chapter.

All in all, the use of $\chi^2$ tests is not a panacea for the problems of the psychologist; far from it! Granted that psychologists do want to study qualitative data, and do want to make inferences about possible relations, the price paid in using $\chi^2$ tests for finding out only that "something" goes with "something" is fairly high, and may not be worth it. On the other hand, regardless of sample size, there *is* information in qualitative data about the *strength* of statistical relationship, and in many problems this is where the emphasis in data analysis should fall. In the light of its somewhat complicated statistical character, a significant Pearson $\chi^2$ test may mean next to nothing, but an apparent *predictive* relationship in the data is usually worth looking into.

# SOME ORDER STATISTICS

## 18

So far in our discussion of statistical inference we have dealt with three different kinds of experimental situations. In the first situation the experimental factor is thought of as a set of qualitative distinctions, and the dependent variable as some numerical measure. Tacitly we assumed that each $Y$ score represented some interval-scale measurement of a property of interest, and that the basic question had to do with the possible effects of the experimental manipulation on the underlying property under study. However, as pointed out in Chapter 3, the question of level of measurement represented by the numerical values $Y$ has to do with the *interpretation* put on the experiment, and statistical considerations enter in terms of the population distribution of the random variable $Y$, whatever these values actually represent. The classic methods, such as $t$ and $F$ tests, require that assumptions such as normality of parent distributions and homogeneity of variances be made; for this reason, such tests are often called "parametric," since their derivation involves explicit assumptions about population distributions and parameters. However, it is entirely possible to have an experimental situation fitting this general pattern where it is quite unreasonable to make these assumptions. Here, the study of association between experimental and dependent variables clearly must be approached in some other way.

In the second kind of experimental situation, both variables $X$ and $Y$ are numerical scores: these are the problems of regression and of correlation. Once again, the statistical methods per se are neutral about what these scores really represent, but the interpretation of the experiment may depend very heavily on whether interval scale or some other level of measurement holds for $X$ and $Y$. For instance, it may well be true that, considered simply as numerical scores, the values of $X$ and $Y$ exhibit a more or less linear relationship. However, if either $X$ or $Y$ is *not* an interval-scale representation of the magnitude of some underlying property, we have no basis at all for saying that the "real" psychological variables they represent have this particular form of relationship. Furthermore, significance tests and confidence intervals for regression and correlation are *parametric* methods, since they derive their validity from assumptions having to do with populations, such as the assumptions of homogeneous variances and bivariate normal distributions. Nevertheless, sometimes an experimenter wants to know if there *is* a statistical relation between two psychological factors, even though he can commit himself neither about the interval-scale character of the numerical values themselves nor about the population distribution of the scores.

Finally, in the preceding chapter we discussed situations where both variables in an experiment are treated qualitatively. Each observation is thought of as a representative of some qualitative *joint* event, and the essential question concerns the statistical association between two qualitative attributes (that is, nominal scales). Here, it is necessary to assume very little about the population sampled, but a great deal is necessary in terms of sample size, independence of observations, and so on, if we are to get a valid and workable test of the hypothesis of nonassociation or independence. Tests such as $\chi^2$ are appropriately called "nonparametric" since they require almost no "gratuituous" assumptions about the population sampled. However, such tests are *not assumption-free;* far from it! Rather, tests such as $\chi^2$ are actually based on discrete sampling distributions, which, in principle, can be worked out exactly by application of elementary rules of probability. When discrete sampling distributions are involved, and exact probabilities can be found for sample results, it is usually possible to dispense with some of the assumptions made in deriving tests based on continuous sampling distributions. Even when the actual test statistic, such as $\chi^2$, gives only an approximation to the exact results, the basic rationale nevertheless involves rather simple probability theory. As we saw in the preceding chapter, difficulties with the Pearson $\chi^2$ statistic arise mostly from its use to *approximate* multinomial probabilities; the argument for the multinomial distribution of possible sample results is straightforward. In Chapter 17 it was also pointed out that in some situations tests such as $\chi^2$ use only part of the potential information in the data, and the user may pay for this waste of information by being unable to make particular kinds of inferences from his result. Furthermore, the relative freedom from assumptions in such tests is offset in part by the large sample size necessary to justify the use of approximate methods.

In this chapter we are going to discuss methods based primarily on the **order relations** among observations in a set of data. The reasoning behind each of these tests involves relatively simple applications of probability theory; it happens that discrete sampling distributions often can be found in particularly simple ways if only the order features of the data are considered. In particular, many of these tests rest on the idea of the possible randomizations of the data. Perhaps the preceding discussion has suggested two reasons why we should be interested in analyzing data in terms of ordinal properties: In the first place, the only relevant information in a set of numerical scores may actually be ordinal. That is, it may well be true that the operation used to measure some psychological property actually is valid only at the ordinal level, so that the numerical scores obtained actually give information only about relative magnitudes of the underlying property, and arithmetic differences between scores have no particular meaning in terms of this underlying property. This is a common situation in psychological measurement. When the experimenter knows this to be true of his measurement operation, he wants only the relevant order information in the data to figure in the analysis. Even if he can assume only that the observed score is some unknown function of the underlying variable he hoped to represent, he may still be able to reach a judgment about independence or association of underlying variables by an ordinal analysis of the data (see Section 4.9).

An equally common reason for using order methods is that one or more assumptions about the population distributions, strictly necessary for the parametric method to apply, may be quite unreasonable. Rather than use the parametric method anyway and wonder about the validity of his conclusion, the experimenter prefers to change the question in such a way that another method does apply. Ordinarily, adoption of such a method will require that only certain features of the raw numerical data be considered if the objectionable assumptions are to be avoided, so that all of the numerical information in the scores is not used. Consequently, the experimenter may lose something by deciding to use the nonparametric method: the question answered by the nonparametric method is seldom exactly the same as that answered by the corresponding parametric method, and for a given sample size the nonparametric test may represent a considerably "weaker" use of the evidence.

Because of their direct dependency on elementary probability theory, and their comparative freedom from assumptions about population distributions and parameters, order techniques are usually classified among the nonparametric methods. However, not all nonparametric techniques involve considerations of order, nor are all order methods completely free of assumptions about distributions and parameters. Therefore, in this chapter, the author prefers to limit discussion to a few methods based on order, and more or less beg the complicated question of "parametric" versus "nonparametric." This chapter simply shows some techniques that are often found useful, and that happen to involve order. Nevertheless, a few comments will be made apposite to the use of these techniques in situations where other techniques such as $t$ and $F$ might also apply.

## 18.1 ORDER TECHNIQUES AS SUBSTITUTES FOR THE CLASSICAL METHODS

In the past few years, a great deal of study has been given to relative merits of parametric and nonparametric tests in situations where both types of methods apply. These studies show clearly that advantages and drawbacks exist in the use of any of these methods. However, research workers, and especially psychologists, sometimes gain the impression that they "get away with something" by using an order method or some other nonparametric technique in preference to one of the classic statistical tests. In some miraculous way, using such a technique is supposed to solve all the problems raised by unknown measurement level, objectionable assumptions, and so on (including, some apparently believe, sloppy data). If this is true, this is the only known example of something for nothing in statistics or anywhere else. Just as with any statistical method, there are both potential gains and losses in the decision to use a nonparametric technique, and the choice among methods can be evaluated only in the light of what the experimenter wants to do and the price he is willing to pay.

Clearly a word of warning is called for in the use of order methods as stand-ins for the classical methods in situations where both kinds of methods are appropriate. At least two things must be borne in mind:

*First,* the actual hypothesis tested by a given order method is seldom exactly equivalent to the hypothesis tested by a parametric technique. For example, when the usual assumptions for the simple analysis of variance are true, then the hypothesis that the means of the populations are equal *both implies and is implied by* the absolute identity of the population distributions. Under these assumptions, the test statistic is distributed as $F$ when and only when the null hypothesis is true. On the other hand, in order methods designed for the comparison of $J$ experimental groups, the actual null hypothesis ordinarily is that all possible orderings of observations by their scores in the data are equally likely. This is implied by the hypothesis of identical populations, so that if the equal-likelihood hypothesis is rejected, the hypothesis of identical populations can also be rejected. Thus, these order tests can be regarded essentially as testing the hypothesis of identical population distributions. Regardless of how well the actual test statistic agrees with expectation, however, the population distributions still *might* be different in particular ways. In most order tests the sampling distribution implied by a true $H_0$ can also obtain when $H_0$ is not true in various ways. Departures from strict identity among the population distributions may exist to which the order methods are very insensitive. If one is willing to make only minimal assumptions about the population distributions, then the kinds of true differences among populations that the test fails to detect may be quite unknown. Of course, various additional assumptions can be made about the population distributions, and then the sensitivity of these tests to various alternatives can be studied. Nevertheless, these gratuitous assumptions may be fully as offensive as the assumptions the test was designed to avoid in the first place. It is sad but true: the specificity of our final conclusion is more or less bought in terms of what we already know or can at least assume to be true. If we do not know or assume anything, we cannot conclude very much.

*Second,* when both the order method and a parametric method actually do apply (that is, when the parametric assumptions are true), the power of the two kinds of tests may be compared, given $\alpha$, the sample $N$, and the true situation. Order techniques share with other nonparametric methods the disadvantage of being relatively low-powered as compared with parametric tests. This means that, other things such as $\alpha$ and $N$ being equal, one is taking more risk of a Type II error in using the order method. If Type II errors are to be avoided, then a relatively larger sample size (or a larger $\alpha$ value) is required in the use of the order technique as compared to the parametric method.

In connection with the second point, a useful concept in the comparison of tests of hypotheses is that of "power-efficiency." The general idea may be given in this way: Suppose that there is some null hypothesis to be tested, and that either of two tests (methods of testing $H_0$), test $U$ and test $V$, might appropriately be applied. The power of test $U$ and of test $V$ against any alternative to $H_0$ will depend upon several things, of course, one of which is sample size. For a given degree of power against a specific true alternative, test $U$ may require $N_U$ cases, whereas test $V$ may require $N_V$ cases. In general, for different tests, $N_U$ and $N_V$ will be different for the same power level.

Now suppose that $N_U$ is the more powerful test, in the sense that it requires fewer cases to detect a true alternative to $H_0$ for some fixed $\alpha$ and $1 - \beta$ probabilities. Then the **power-efficiency** of test $V$ relative to test $U$ is

$$\text{power-efficiency of } V = \frac{(100)N_U}{N_V}.$$

The more cases $N_V$ that test $V$ requires to attain the same power as test $U$ with $N_U$ cases, the smaller is the power-efficiency of test $V$ relative to test $U$.

For instance, if test $U$ requires 20 cases to reach power of .95 for a given true situation and $\alpha = .05$, and test $V$ requires 40 cases to reach the same power under the same conditions, then the power efficiency of $V$ relative to $U$ is

$$\frac{100(20)}{40} = 50 \text{ percent.}$$

In this way nonparametric statistics (such as order methods) may be compared with parametric methods such as the $t$ test and the analysis of variance. Results of such comparisons show that **order methods generally have less than 100 percent power-efficiency when used in situations where the most powerful parametric tests such as $t$ and $F$ apply.** Order methods require more evidence than parametric methods to yield comparable conclusions.

These remarks should not be construed as holding against all applications of order statistics, however. The comments on power hold only where the appropriate "high-powered" methods can appropriately be applied. If the data are collected as order data in their own right, perhaps because no higher-level measurement operation is available, then this objection does not necessarily hold; the concept of comparative power between parametric and nonparametric tests is useless here since the experimenter really has no choice to make. Similarly, comparative power is difficult or impossible to study when the assumptions underlying parametric tests are not true. For data that are essentially ordinal, or when assumptions are manifestly untrue, some of the tests described here may be about as powerful as can be devised. Furthermore, since order methods apply to all sorts of population distributions, their applicability is considerably more general than the parametric methods. Note well, however: this refers to the generality of *application* of the method, and not to the *generalizability* of the results from a sample, which depends on how the sample was drawn and randomized. It is not clear at all that the use of a nonparametric technique makes *conclusions* more general.

The decision to use or not to use order methods in a given problem cannot be given a simple prescription. This is but another place where the experimenter has to think about what he wants to accomplish and how. It is wrong to conclude that statistical assumptions are bad, that only bona fide interval-scale data can be subjected to the classical statistical treatment, that tests with relatively low power-efficiency are useless, and so on. None of these statements is necessarily true in all situations. Through practice and all the help he can get the experimenter must learn to pick and choose among all of the various methods available, finding the one that most clearly, economically, and reasonably sheds light on the particular question he wants answered. This is not a simple task, and a brief discussion such as this can only begin to suggest some of these issues.

In the sections to follow, several types of order statistics and tests will be discussed. First of all, tests will be mentioned that are appropriate to experimental data where the experimental factor is categorical and the dependent variable is treated at the ordinal level. Then some correlation-like methods for ordinal data will be surveyed, and finally an index of association for ordered classes will be discussed.

## 18.2　COMPARING TWO OR MORE INDEPENDENT GROUPS: THE MEDIAN TESTS

One of the simplest of the order methods involves the comparison of several samples on the basis of deviations from the median rather than from the mean. We assume that the underlying variable on which the populations are to be compared is continuous, and that the probability of a tie between two observations in actual value of the underlying variable is, in effect, zero.

The null hypothesis to be tested is that the $J$ different populations are absolutely identical in terms of their distributions. The alternative is simply the contrary of $H_0$. If we wish to add the assumption that whatever the differences in central tendency that may exist among the distributions, they are at least identical in *form*, then the test actually becomes one of central tendency; however, it is hard to see why such an assumption would ordinarily be justified in a situation where an order method such as this is called for. Thus, in this method, as well as in most of the methods to follow, the null hypothesis will state only that the distributions are identical. The median test will be sensitive to differences in central tendency for the various population distributions, but failure to reject $H_0$ does not necessarily imply that the distributions are, in fact, identical, unless one is willing to make other assumptions.

The method is as follows: The $J$ different sample groups are combined into a single distribution and the grand median for the sample, $Md$, is obtained. Now each score in each group is compared with $Md$. If the particular score is above the grand median, the observation is assigned to a "plus" category; if the particular score is not above the grand median, the observation is assigned to a "minus" category. Let $a_j$ be the number of "plus" observations in group $j$, and let $n_j - a_j$ represent the number of "minus" observations. Then the data are arranged into a $2 \times J$ table such as the following:

| | GROUP | | | | | |
|---|---|---|---|---|---|---|
| | 1 | ... | $j$ | ... | $J$ | *Total* |
| PLUS | $a_1$ | | $a_j$ | | $a_j$ | $a$ |
| | | ... | | ... | | |
| MINUS | $n_1 - a_1$ | | $n_j - a_j$ | | $n_J - a_J$ | $N - a$ |
| | $n_1$ | ... | $n_j$ | ... | $n_J$ | $N$ |

Notice that this is simply a joint-frequency or contingency table, where one attribute is "group" and the other is "plus or minus."

Now, if the value $Md$ actually divides each of the populations in exactly the same way there should be a binomial distribution of the sample numbers $a_j$ for random samples from population $j$. That is, the probability of exactly $a_j$ "plus" observations in group $j$ is

$$\binom{n_j}{a_j} p^{a_j} q^{n_j - a_j}$$

where $p$ is the probability of an observation's falling into the "plus" category and $q = 1 - p$. Under the null hypothesis, the probability $p$ should be the same for each and every population, since any value $Md$ should divide the population distributions identically.

However, we want the probability of the obtained *sample* result, conditional to the fact that the *marginal* frequency of "plus" observations is $a$. Under the null hypothesis, the probability of exactly $a$ observations above the value $Md$ is $\binom{N}{a} p^a q^{n-a}$. Then the conditional probability for a particular arrangement in the table works out to be

$$\frac{\binom{n_1}{a_1} \binom{n_2}{a^2} \cdots \binom{n_j}{a_j} \cdots \binom{n_J}{a_J}}{\binom{N}{a}}.$$

This is the probability of this *particular* sample result conditional to this particular value of $a$. Since this probability can be found for any possible sample result, the significance level can be found by exact methods, involving finding all possible sample results differing this much or more among the $J$ groups. Such exact probabilities may be very laborious to work out, of course, unless $J$ is only 2 or 3.

For large samples a fairly good approximation to the exact significance level is found from the statistic

$$\chi^2 = \frac{(N - 1)}{a(N - a)} \sum_{j=1}^{J} \frac{(Na_j - n_j a)^2}{N n_j}. \qquad \text{[18.2.1†]}$$

For reasonably large samples ($N \geqq 20$, $n_j \geqq 5$ for each $j$), this statistic is distributed *approximately* as chi-square with $J - 1$ degrees of freedom.

Rejection of the null hypothesis lets us assert that the populations represented are *not* identical.

One difficulty with this test is that it is based on the assumption that ties in the data will not occur. Naturally, this is most unreasonable since tied scores ordinarily will occur. This is really a problem only if several scores are tied at the over-all median, $Md$, since other ties have no effect on the test statistic itself. When ties occur at the median, several things may be done to remove this difficulty, but the safest general procedure seems to be to allot the tied scores (those tied with the grand median) within each group in such a way that $a_j$ is as close as possible to $n_j - a_j$. This at least makes the test relatively conservative. Remember that this $\chi^2$ method gives an approximate test, and really should be used only when the sample size within each group is fairly large. In principle, exact probabilities may be computed, as suggested above, when sample $N$ is small.

As an example, consider the following problem. An experimenter was interested in the effect which the difficulty of admission to a club has on the desire of a person to become a member. Thus, he decided to form four experimental "social clubs" at a large college. A sample of 100 girls was drawn and each was assigned at random to one of four experimental groups. Each girl was sent a letter asking her to come for an interview as a prospective member of a service club having secret membership. In experimental treatment I, the goals of the club were outlined, and quite easy membership requirements stated. In treatment II, exactly the same information was given, but with somewhat harder requirements to be met. Treatments III and IV included severe and truly formidable entrance requirements respectively. After a standard "dummy" interview, each girl was asked to rate on a 12-point scale just how eager she was to join such a group. On this scale 1 represented *most* eager, and 12 *least* eager to join. The data are shown in Table 18.2.1.

### Table 18.2.1

| | | Group | | |
|---|---|---|---|---|
| Rating | I | II | III | IV |
| 12 | 0 | 0 | 0 | 0 |
| 11 | 3 | 2 | 1 | 0 |
| 10 | 7 | 3 | 4 | 1 |
| 9 | 5 | 5 | 4 | 4 |
| 8 | 5 | 5 | 1 | 0 |
| 7 | 3 | 6 | 3 | 10 |
| 6 | 2 | 2 | 5 | 8 |
| 5 | 0 | 2 | 4 | 1 |
| 4 | 0 | 0 | 3 | 1 |
| 3 | 0 | 0 | 0 | 0 |
| | 25 | 25 | 25 | 25 $N = 100$ |

The experimenter wanted to test the hypothesis that these groups represented four potential populations having identical distributions of ratings. The combined distribution of ratings was as follows:

|    | $f$ | $cf$ |
|----|-----|------|
| 12 | 0   | 100  |
| 11 | 6   | 100  |
| 10 | 15  | 94   |
| 9  | 18  | 79   |
| 8  | 11  | 61   |
| 7  | 22  | 50   |
| 6  | 17  | 28   |
| 5  | 7   | 11   |
| 4  | 4   | 4    |

$$Md = 7.5$$

When each rating was compared to the value of $Md$, the following results emerged:

|       | $I$ | $II$ | $III$ | $IV$ | |
|-------|-----|------|-------|------|-------------|
| plus  | 20  | 15   | 10    | 5    | $50 = a$     |
| minus | 5   | 10   | 15    | 20   | $50 = N - a$ |

$$\chi^2 = \frac{(99)}{(50)(50)}\left\{\frac{[(100)(20) - (25)(50)]^2}{2500} + \cdots \right.$$
$$\left. + \frac{[(100)(5) - (25)(50)]^2}{2500}\right\}$$
$$= 19.8$$

For 3 degrees of freedom, this value exceeds the $\chi^2$ value for the .01 level, and so the experimenter can say that the populations are not identical. The hypothesis tested is not about any particular characteristic of the populations considered, but rather about the absolute identity of their distributions. Some departure from strict identity of population distributions is inferred from this significant result, and the experimenter has evidence that the experimental treatment is associated with the rated attraction of a club for a girl.

## 18.3   THE MEDIAN TEST FOR MATCHED GROUPS

It is possible to extend the idea of the median test to situations where the various groups are not independent random samples, but rather are matched in terms of one or more factors. The method outlined below is especially appropriof each pair belongs to experimental (or natural) treatment 1 and the other to treatment 2. Here, the only relevant information given by the two scores for pair is taken to be the **sign of the difference** between them. If the two treatments actually represent identical populations, and chance is the only determiner of which member of a pair falls into which treatment, we should expect an equal number of differences of plus and of minus sign. The theoretical probability of a "plus" sign is .5, and so the probability of a particular number of plus (or minus) signs can be found by the binomial rule with $p = .5$ and $N$. Notice, however, that we must assume either that the population distributions are continuous so that exact equality between scores has probability zero, or that ties are otherwise impossible. Ordinarily, pairs showing zero differences are simply dropped from the sample, although this makes the final conclusion have a conditional character, "In a population of untied pairs . . . ," and so on. The test is carried out as follows:

First, the direction of the difference (that is, the sign of the difference) between the two observations in each pair is noted, with the same order of subtraction always maintained. Thus each *pair* is given a classification of Plus or Minus, according to the sign of the difference between scores. If the null hypothesis of no difference between the two matched populations were true, one would expect half the nonzero differences to show a positive sign, and half to show a negative sign. Thus, one may simply take the *proportion* of plus differences, and test the hypothesis that the sample proportion arose from a true proportion of .50.

The normal approximation to the binomial can be used if the num ber of sample pairs is large (10 or more):

$$z = \frac{|P - p| - 1/(2N)}{\sqrt{pq/N}} = \frac{|P - .50| - 1/(2N)}{\sqrt{(.50)(.50)/N}}. \qquad [18.4.1\dagger]$$

Here, $1/2N$ is a correction for continuity, as in Section 17.2. Although this form holds for a two-tailed test, either a one- or a two-tailed test may be carried out, depending on the alternative hypothesis appropriate to the particular problem. Naturally, in the one-tailed test the sign of the difference between $P$ and .5 is considered.

If the sample size is fewer than 10 pairs, the binomial distribution should be used to give an exact probability. That is, the binomial table with $p = .5$ should be used to find the probability that the *obtained frequency* of the *more frequent sign* should be equaled or exceeded by chance give a true $p$ of .50. These tables of exact probabilities are given in Siegel (1956) as well as many other places, although the binomial probabilities are not hard to work out. For a one-tailed test, one also checks that the more frequent sign accords with the alternative hypothesis before carrying out the test, of course. For a two-tailed test, this one-tailed binomial probability is doubled.

As an example of the sign test, consider this situation: It was desired to see the effect that a frustrating experience might have upon the "social age" of a child. Each child could be age-rated from his play by a trained observer.

Each of a random sample of preschool children was first rated by the observer according to the social-age level of his play during a free-play period. Pairs of children were then formed having the same rated "social age." One randomly chosen member of each pair was frustrated by being allowed to play with a desirable toy that was then taken away, while the pair-mates were not frustrated. The observer did not know which children were frustrated, and the children were given these experimental conditions separately. Finally, in a postexperimental session the children were again rated at free play. Suppose that twenty pairs were used, and that the postexperimental ratings were as shown in Table 18.4.1.

**Table 18.4.1**

| *Pair* | *Frustrated* | *Not frustrated* | *Sign of diff.* |
|--------|--------------|------------------|-----------------|
| 1 | 32 | 36 | + |
| 2 | 35 | 34 | − |
| 3 | 33 | 34 | + |
| 4 | 36 | 40 | + |
| 5 | 44 | 42 | − |
| 6 | 41 | 40 | − |
| 7 | 32 | 35 | + |
| 8 | 38 | 40 | + |
| 9 | 37 | 38 | + |
| 10 | 35 | 35 | 0 |
| 11 | 29 | 35 | + |
| 12 | 34 | 32 | − |
| 13 | 50 | 51 | + |
| 14 | 40 | 38 | − |
| 15 | 39 | 42 | + |
| 16 | 31 | 33 | + |
| 17 | 47 | 46 | − |
| 18 | 41 | 42 | + |
| 19 | 30 | 29 | − |
| 20 | 35 | 35 | 0 |

The final rating of the frustrated child was subtracted from that of his pair-mate in order to find the sign of the difference between them. Eleven pairs showed a positive sign, seven showed a negative sign, and two showed a zero difference. Did presence or absence of frustration seem to be related to the difference in rated social age? The null and alternative hypotheses are

$$H_0: p = .5$$
$$H_1: p \neq .5$$

where $p$ is the population proportion of plus changes among pairs (plus being the more frequent sign of change in the sample). The statistic for this test is thus

$$z = \frac{|11/18 - .50| - 1/36}{\sqrt{(.50)(.50)/18}} = \frac{.611 - .500 - .028}{.118} = .70.$$

Note that the two pairs showing no difference were excluded from the number of pairs figuring in the test, so that $N$ is reduced to 18. When referred to a normal distribution, this $z$ value leads to the conclusion of no significant difference. There is not enough evidence to conclude that frustration did lead to a difference in social-age rating.

## 18.5 COCHRAN'S TEST

A test that seems to stand midway between methods designed for contingency-table data and methods based on order is due to Cochran (1950). This test can be viewed as a generalization of the McNemar two-sample test mentioned in Section 17.10, and it is appropriate in an experiment involving repeated observations (or matched groups) where the dependent variable can take on only two values:

$Y_{jk} = 1$ (for "success," "pass," and so on, recorded for individual $k$ in treatment $j$).

$Y_{jk} = 0$ (for "fail," and so on, recorded for individual $k$ in treatment $j$).

For example, suppose that in some experiment $K$ subjects were observed in a standard situation where each subject performed individually under each of $J$ different experimental conditions. Each subject was assigned the conditions in some random order. In each condition, the task of the subject was to solve one of a set of simple reasoning problems. If the problem was solved correctly within one minute, the performance was recorded as a "success," and as a "failure" otherwise. Suppose that the interest of the experimenter was in seeing if the problems had equal difficulty for the subjects; that is, if the true proportion of successes was constant over the problems. In this situation the Cochran test would apply.

As usual, let the experimental treatments (problems, in the example) be shown as columns in the data table. The subjects are shown as the rows. Then the entry in the cell formed by column $j$ and row $k$ contains $Y$, which is 1 for a success and 0 for a failure. Let

$$Y_k = \sum_j Y_{jk}$$

be the marginal total for row $k$ and let

$$Y_j = \sum_k Y_{jk}$$

be the marginal total for column $j$. Finally, let

$$\bar{T} = \frac{\sum_j Y_j}{J}.$$

Then the statistic for Cochran's test is given by

$$Q = \frac{J(J-1) \sum_{j=1}^{J} (Y_j - \bar{T})^2}{J \left( \sum_k Y_K \right) - \left( \sum_k Y_k^2 \right)}.$$ [18.5.1†]

For relatively large $K$, this is distributed approximately as chi-square with $J - 1$ degrees of freedom, when the hypothesis is true that the probability of a "success" is constant over all treatments $J$.

Table 18.5.1

| | | Problem | | | |
|---|---|---|---|---|---|
| Subject | 1 | 2 | 3 | 4 | $Y_k$ |
| 1 | 1 | 1 | 1 | 0 | 3 |
| 2 | 0 | 1 | 1 | 1 | 3 |
| 3 | 0 | 0 | 1 | 0 | 1 |
| 4 | 1 | 1 | 1 | 1 | 4 |
| 5 | 0 | 1 | 0 | 0 | 1 |
| 6 | 0 | 0 | 1 | 0 | 1 |
| 7 | 1 | 0 | 0 | 0 | 1 |
| 8 | 0 | 0 | 1 | 1 | 2 |
| 9 | 0 | 0 | 0 | 0 | 0 |
| 10 | 1 | 0 | 0 | 0 | 1 |
| 11 | 1 | 0 | 1 | 0 | 2 |
| 12 | 0 | 0 | 1 | 1 | 2 |
| 13 | 0 | 1 | 0 | 1 | 2 |
| 14 | 1 | 0 | 0 | 0 | 1 |
| 15 | 0 | 1 | 0 | 0 | 1 |
| 16 | 1 | 0 | 1 | 1 | 3 |
| 17 | 0 | 1 | 0 | 0 | 1 |
| 18 | 0 | 0 | 1 | 0 | 1 |
| 19 | 0 | 1 | 1 | 0 | 2 |
| 20 | 0 | 0 | 1 | 1 | 2 |
| $Y_j$ | 7 | 8 | 12 | 7 | 34 |

$\bar{T} = \dfrac{34}{4} = 8.5$

$\sum_k Y_k^2 = 76$

$$Q = \frac{(4)(3)[(7 - 8.5)^2 + \cdots + (7 - 8.5)^2]}{4(34) - 76}$$

$$= 3.40$$

To continue the example, suppose that the experiment outlined above had been carried out. Twenty randomly selected subjects were given each of four problems, and each subject got the problems in some different, randomly chosen, order. A "1" was recorded for a successful solution, and a "0" for a failure. The data turned out to be as shown in Table 18.5.1. For 3 degrees of freedom, the $\chi^2$ table shows this value not significant at either the .05 or .01 level. Thus, the hypothesis of no difference between problems is not rejected.

So far, all the tests discussed in this chapter have actually depended on some way of arranging the observations into only two ordered classes: above or below the median in the median tests, plus or minus differences in the sign test, 1 and 0 categories in the Cochran test. The only role of the numerical scores has been to assign individuals to one of these two categories. When numerical data are reduced to only two categories, it is obvious that much of the possible information in the data is sacrificed. However, other techniques exist which use somewhat more of the information in the scores themselves; that is, observations are rank-ordered in terms of their scores in these methods. Next we turn to one of the simplest of the tests where the numerical score serves to give each observation a place in order.

## 18.6 THE WALD-WOLFOWITZ "RUNS" TEST FOR TWO SAMPLES

This test applies to the situation where two unmatched samples are to be compared, and each observation is paired with a numerical score. The underlying variable that these scores represent is assumed to be continuously distributed.

Suppose that the numbers of observations in the two experimental groups are $N_1$ and $N_2$ respectively. All of the $N_1 + N_2$ observations in these samples are drawn independently and at random. For convenience, we will call any observation appearing in sample 1 an "A" and any observation in sample 2 a "B." Now suppose that all these sample observations, irrespective of group, are arranged in order according to the magnitude of the scores shown. Then there will be some *arrangement* or pattern of A's and B's in order. In particular there will be *runs* or "clusterings" of the A's and B's. This is easily illustrated by an example.

Suppose that in some two-sample experiment the data turned out as shown in Table 18.6.1. When these scores are combined into a single set and arranged in order of magnitude, we get the following

$$\begin{array}{cccccccccccccccccccc} B & B & B & A & A & A & B & B & A & A & B & A & A & B & B & A & A & B & B & A \\ \backslash 1 & 1 & 2/ & \backslash 3 & 4 & 4/ & \backslash 5 & 5/ & \backslash 6 & 6/ & \backslash 7/ & \backslash 8 & 8/ & \backslash 12 & 13/ & \backslash 14 & 15/ & \backslash 18 & 19/ & \backslash 20/ \end{array}$$

$$\begin{array}{cccccccccc} 1 & 2 & 3 & 4 & 5 & 6 & 7 & 8 & 9 & 10 \end{array}$$

Above each observation's score is an A or a B, denoting the group to which that observation belongs. Now notice that there are runs of A's and B's. That is, the

**Table 18.6.1**

| Sample 1(A) | Sample 2(B) |
|:---:|:---:|
| 8 | 12 |
| 6 | 13 |
| 8 | 19 |
| 4 | 18 |
| 14 | 7 |
| 4 | 2 |
| 15 | 1 |
| 20 | 1 |
| 3 | 5 |
| 6 | 5 |

ordering starts off with a run of three B's . . . this run is underlined and numbered 1. Then there is a run of three A's, which is run number 2. Proceeding in this way, and counting the beginning of a new run whenever an A is succeeded by a B or vice versa, we find that there are 10 runs.

It should be obvious that there must be at least two runs in any ordering of scores from two groups. If the groups are of equal size $N$ there can be no more than $2N$ runs in all. In general, the number of runs cannot exceed $N_1 + N_2$.

Now suppose that the two groups were random samples from *absolutely identical population distributions*. In this instance we should expect many runs, since the values for the two samples should be well "mixed up" when put in order. On the other hand, if the populations differ, particularly in central tendency, we should expect there to be less tendency for runs to occur in the sample ordering. This principle provides the basis for a test based on fairly simple probability considerations.

For the moment, let $R$ symbolize the total number of runs appearing for the samples. Then it can be shown that if $R$ is any *odd* number, $2g + 1$, the probability for that number of runs is

$$\text{prob.}(R = 2g + 1) = \frac{\binom{N_1 - 1}{g - 1}\binom{N_2 - 1}{g} + \binom{N_1 - 1}{g}\binom{N_2 - 1}{g - 1}}{\binom{N_1 + N_2}{N_1}}$$

when all arrangements in order are equally likely.

If $R$ is an *even* number, $2g$, then

$$\text{prob.}(R = 2g) = \frac{2\binom{N_1 - 1}{g - 1}\binom{N_2 - 1}{g - 1}}{\binom{N_1 + N_2}{N_1}}.$$

On this basis, the exact sampling distribution of $R$ can be worked out, given equal probability for all possible arrangements of A and B observations. It turns out that for fairly large samples the distribution of $R$ can be approximated by a normal distribution with

$$E(R) = \frac{2N_1 N_2}{N_1 + N_2} + 1$$

and

$$\sigma_R^2 = \frac{2N_1 N_2 (2N_1 N_2 - N_1 - N_2)}{(N_1 + N_2)^2 (N_1 + N_2 - 1)}.$$

Thus, an approximate large sample test is given by

$$z = \frac{R - E(R)}{\sigma_R}$$

referred to a normal distribution. Since the usual alternative hypothesis entails "too few" runs, the test is ordinarily *one-tailed*, with only negative values of $z$ leading to rejection of the hypothesis of identical distributions.

For sample size less than or equal to 20 in *either* sample, exact values of $R$ required for significance are given in Siegel (1956).

There is some reason to believe that the runs test generally has rather low power-efficiency, compared either with a $t$ test for means or with other order tests for identical populations. However, it is mentioned here because of its utility in various problems where other methods may not apply. Actually, A and B may designate any dichotomy within a *single* sample, and any principle at all that gives an ordering to A's and B's may be used. For example, it may be of interest to see if there is a time-related trend such as learning in a *single* set of data. In this instance, we might find the over-all median for the set of scores, calling above the median A and below B. Here time is used as the ordering principle, and the occurrence of few runs is treated as evidence that time trends do exist. In any problem where the data may be given a dichotomous classification in one respect and then simply ordered in another respect, the runs test gives a way to answer the question of possible association between the basis for the ordering and the categorization. This makes the runs test useful in a variety of problems where other tests do not apply directly, and especially to problems where the *experimental* variable is ordinal and the *dependent* variable categorical.

A major technical problem with this test is the treatment of ties. In principle ties should not occur if the scores themselves represent a continuous random variable. But, of course, ties do occur in actual practice, since we seldom represent the underlying variable directly or precisely in the data. If tied scores all occur among observations in the *same* group (as in the example above), then there is no problem; the value of $R$ is unchanged by any method of breaking these ties. However, if members of *different* groups show tied scores, the number of runs depends upon how these ties are resolved in the final ordering. One way of meeting this problem is to break all ties in a way *least* conducive to rejecting the null hypothesis (so that the number of runs is made as large as possible). This at least makes for a conservative test of $H_0$. However, if cross-group ties are very numerous, this test is really inapplicable.

## 18.7   THE MANN-WHITNEY TEST FOR TWO INDEPENDENT SAMPLES

Unlike the runs test, this test employs the actual *ranks* of the various observations directly as a device for testing hypotheses about the identity of two population distributions. It is apparently a good and relatively powerful alternative to the usual *t* test for equality of means.

The Mann-Whitney test can best be justified in a way somewhat different from the tests previously discussed. The rationale for this test can be based directly on the method of randomization, alluded to in our discussion of the Fisher exact test (Section 17.9), and in Chapter 13. That is, probability statements actually refer directly to all possible randomizations of the *same* sample of $N$ subjects among the various treatment. However, we will not go further into this rationale here; suffice it to say that one can evaluate Type I error probability by referring to the sample space of all possible results of randomizing the same set of data provided that the original random sample is itself representative of the population to be investigated. The Mann-Whitney test, the Wilcoxen test (18.8), and, indeed, most of the order tests can be justified in terms of possible randomizations of the same sample.

We assume that the underlying variable on which two groups are to be compared is continuously distributed. The null hypothesis to be tested is that the two population distributions are identical. Then we proceed as follows:

The scores from the combined samples are arranged in order (much as in the runs test). However, now we assign a *rank* to each of the observations, in terms of the magnitude of the original score. That is, the lowest score gets rank 1, the next lowest 2, and so on. Now choose one of the samples, say sample 1, and find the *sum* of the ranks associated with observations in that sample. Call this $T_1$. Then find

$$U = N_1 N_2 + \frac{N_1(N_1 + 1)}{2} - T_1. \qquad \text{[18.7.1†]}$$

If the resulting value of $U$ is *larger* than $N_1 N_2 / 2$, take

$$U' = N_1 N_2 - U.$$

The statistic used is the *smaller* of $U$ or $U'$. (Incidentally, this choice of the smaller of the two values for $U$ is important in using tables to find significance for small samples, but is really immaterial in the large sample test to be described later.)

As an example, consider the following data:

| Sample 1(A) | Sample 2(B) |
| --- | --- |
| 8 | 1 |
| 3 | 7 |
| 4 | 9 |
| 6 | 10 |
|   | 12 |

Arranged in order and ranked, these data become

|       | B | A | A | A | B | A | B | B  | B  |
|-------|---|---|---|---|---|---|---|----|----|
| Score | 1 | 3 | 4 | 6 | 7 | 8 | 9 | 10 | 12 |
| Rank  | 1 | 2 | 3 | 4 | 5 | 6 | 7 | 8  | 9  |

The sum of the ranks for the $A$ observations (group 1) is

$$T_1 = 2 + 3 + 4 + 6 = 15.$$

This is turned into a value of $U$ by taking

$$U = 4(5) + \frac{4(5)}{2} - 15$$
$$= 15.$$

This is larger than $\frac{(4)(5)}{2}$ or 10, and so we take

$$U' = 20 - 15 = 5$$

as the value we will use.

Now notice that given these 9 *scores*, the value of $U$ depends only on how the $A$'s and $B$'s happen to be arranged over the rank order. The number of possible random arrangements is just $\binom{N_1 + N_2}{N_1}$, and if the hypothesis of completely identical populations is true, the random assignment of individuals to groups should be the only factor entering into variation among obtained $U$ values. Under the null hypothesis, all arrangements should be equally likely, and this gives the way for finding the probability associated with various values of $U$. For large samples, this sampling distribution of $U$ is approximately normal, with

$$E(U) = \frac{N_1 N_2}{2}$$

and

$$\sigma_U^2 = \frac{N_1 N_2 (N_1 + N_2 + 1)}{12}.$$

Thus, for large samples, the hypothesis of no difference in the population distributions is tested by

$$z = \frac{U - E(U)}{\sigma_U}.$$

For a two-tailed test, either $U$ or $U'$ may be used, since the absolute value of $z$ will be the same for either. However, if the alternative hypothesis is such that one of the populations should tend to have a lower average than the other (assuming distributions of similar *form*), then a one-tailed test is appropriate, and the sign of the $z$ should be considered.

For situations where the larger of the two samples is 20 or more and the samples are not too different in size, the normal approximation given above should suffice. However, when the larger sample contains fewer than 20 observations, tables given in Siegel (1956) should be used to evaluate significance of $U$.

This test is one of the best of the nonparametric techniques with respect to power and power-efficiency. It seems to be very superior to the median test in this respect, and compares quite well with $t$ when assumptions for both tests are met. For some special situations, it is even superior to $t$. This makes it an extremely useful device for the comparison of two independent groups.

Ordinarily, ties are treated in the Mann-Whitney test by giving each of a set of tied scores the *average* rank for that set. Thus, if three scores are tied for fourth, fifth, and sixth place in order, each of the scores gets rank 5. If two scores are tied for ninth and tenth place in order, each gets rank 9.5, and so on. This introduces no particular problem for large sample size when the normal approximation is used and ties are relatively infrequent. However, when ties exist $\sigma_U^2$ becomes

$$\sigma_U^2 = \frac{N_1 N_2}{12}\left[ N_1 + N_2 + 1 - \frac{\sum_{i=1}^{G}(t_i^3 - t_i)}{(N_1 + N_2)(N_1 + N_2 - 1)}\right],$$

where there are some $G$ distinct *sets* of tied observations, $i$ represents any *one* such set, and $t_i$ is the number of observations tied in set $i$. For a small number of ties and for large $N_1 + N_2$, this correction to $\sigma_U^2$ can safely be ignored.

## 18.8   THE WILCOXEN TEST FOR TWO
### MATCHED SAMPLES

As we saw in Section 18.4, the problem of comparing two matched samples can be treated by the sign test if the only feature of the data considered is the sign of the difference between each pair. However, this still overlooks one other important property of any pair of scores: not only does a difference have a direction, but also a size that can be ranked in order among the set of all such differences. The Wilcoxen test takes account of both features in the data, and thus uses somewhat more of the available information in paired scores than does the sign test. This procedure has very close ties with the Mann-Whitney test; both are based essentially on the randomization idea. The Wilcoxen test also has very high power-efficiency compared to other methods designed specifically for the matched-pair situation.

The mechanics of the test are very simple: the signed difference between each pair of observations is found, just as for the $t$ test for matched groups (Section 10.23). Then these differences are rank-ordered in terms of their absolute size. Finally, the sign of the difference is attached to the rank for that difference. The test statistic is $T$, the *sum of the ranks with the less frequent sign*.

Suppose that in some experiment involving a single treatment and one control group, subjects were first matched pairwise, and then one member of each pair was assigned to the experimental group at random. In the experiment proper, each subject received some $Y$ score. Perhaps the data turned out as shown in Table 18.8.1. Here, the differences are found, their absolute size ranked, and then the sign of the difference attached to the rank. The less frequent sign is minus, and so

$$T = 3.5 + 1 + 3.5 + 7 = 15.$$

### Table 18.8.1

| Pair | Treatment | Control | Difference | Rank | Signed rank |
|------|-----------|---------|------------|------|-------------|
| 1 | 83 | 75 | 8 | 8 | 8 |
| 2 | 80 | 78 | 2 | 2 | 2 |
| 3 | 81 | 66 | 15 | 10 | 10 |
| 4 | 74 | 77 | −3 | 3.5 | −3.5 |
| 5 | 79 | 80 | −1 | 1 | −1 |
| 6 | 78 | 68 | 10 | 9 | 9 |
| 7 | 72 | 75 | −3 | 3.5 | −3.5 |
| 8 | 84 | 90 | −6 | 7 | −7 |
| 9 | 85 | 81 | 4 | 5 | 5 |
| 10 | 88 | 83 | 5 | 6 | 6 |

The hypothesis tested by the Wilcoxen test is that the two populations represented by the respective members of matched pairs are identical. When this hypothesis is true, then each of the $2^N$ possible sets of *signed* ranks obtained by arbitrarily assigning $+$ or $-$ signs to the ranks 1 through $N$ is *equally* likely. The random assignment of subjects to experimental versus control group in the example is tantamount to such a random assignment of signs to ranks when the null hypothesis is true. On this basis, the exact distribution of $T$ over all possible randomizations can be worked out. For large $N$ (number of pairs), the sampling distribution is approximately normal with

$$E(T) = \frac{N(N + 1)}{4}$$

and

$$\sigma_T^2 = \frac{N(N + 1)(2N + 1)}{24}$$

so that a large sample test is given by

$$z = \frac{T - E(T)}{\sigma_T}.$$

This test can be either directional or nondirectional, depending on the alternative hypothesis. However, a directional test usually makes sense only if one is prepared to assume that the distributions have the same form, and that a signed deviation of $T$ from $E(T)$ is equivalent to a particular difference in central tendency between the two populations. For samples larger than about $N = 8$, this normal approximation is adequate. For very small samples, a table given in the book by Siegel (1956) should be used. Since only one set of differences is ranked, ties present no special problem unless they occur for zero differences. If an *even* number of zero differences occur, each zero difference is assigned the average rank for the set (zero differences, of course, rank lowest in absolute size), and then half are arbitrarily given positive and half negative sign. If an odd number of zeros occur, one randomly chosen zero difference is discarded from the data, and the procedure for an even number of zeros followed, except that $N$ is reduced by 1, of course. For other kinds of tied differences, the method used in the example may be followed. Be sure to notice that even when several pairs are tied in absolute size so that they all receive the midrank for that set, the sign given to that midrank for different pairs may be different. For fairly large samples with relatively few ties, this procedure of assigning average ranks introduces negligible error.

All in all, the Mann-Whitney and the Wilcoxen tests are generally regarded as the best of the order tests for two samples. They both compare favorably with $t$ in the appropriate circumstances, and when the assumptions for $t$ are not met they may even be superior to this classical method. However, each is fully equivalent to a classical test of the hypothesis that the *means* of two groups are equal only when the assumptions appropriate to $t$ are true. Unless additional assumptions are made, these tests refer to the hypothesis that two population distributions of unspecified form are *exactly* alike. In many instances, this is the hypothesis that the experimenter wishes to test, especially if he is interested only in the possibility of statistical independence or of association between experimental and dependent variables. However, if he wants to make particular kinds of inferences, particularly about population *means*, then other assumptions become necessary. Without these assumptions, the rejection of $H_0$ implies only that the populations differ in *some* way, but the test need not be equally sensitive to all ways that population distributions might differ.

## 18.9  THE KRUSKAL-WALLIS "ANALYSIS OF VARIANCE" BY RANKS

The same general argument for the Mann-Whitney test may be extended to the situation where $J$ independent groups are being compared. The version of a $J$-sample rank test given here is due to Kruskal and Wallis (1952). This test has very close ties to the Mann-Whitney and Wilcoxen tests just discussed, and can properly be regarded as a generalized version of the Mann-Whitney method.

Imagine some $J$ experimental groups in which each observation is associated with a numerical score. As usual, we assume that the underlying variable is continuously distributed. Now, just as in the Mann-Whitney test, the scores from all groups are pooled, arranged in order of size, and ranked. Then the rank-sum attached to *each separate group* is found. Let us denote this sum of ranks for group $j$ by the symbol $T_j$

$$T_j = \text{sum of ranks for group } j.$$

For example, suppose that three groups of small children were given the task of learning to discriminate between pairs of stimuli. Each child was given a series of pairs of stimuli, in which each pair differed in a variety of ways. However, attached to the choice of one member of a pair was a reward, and within an experimental condition, the cue for the rewarded stimulus was always the same. On the other hand, the experimental treatments themselves differed in the *relevant* cue for discrimination: in treatment I, the cue was form, in treatment II, color, and in treatment III, size. Some 36 children of the same sex and age were chosen at random and assigned at random to the three groups, with 12 children per group. The dependent variable was the number of trials to a fixed criterion of learning. Suppose that the data turned out to be as shown in Table 18.9.1.

Table 18.9.1

| | Treatment | |
|---|---|---|
| *I* | *II* | *III* |
| 6 (1) | 31 (34.5) | 13 (10) |
| 11 (7) | 7 (2) | 32 (36) |
| 12 (9) | 9 (4) | 31 (34.5) |
| 20 (19) | 11 (7) | 30 (33) |
| 24 (23) | 16 (14) | 28 (31) |
| 21 (20) | 19 (17.5) | 29 (32) |
| 18 (16) | 17 (15) | 25 (24) |
| 15 (13) | 11 (7) | 26 (26.5) |
| 14 (11.5) | 22 (21) | 26 (26.5) |
| 10 (5) | 23 (22) | 27 (29.5) |
| 8 (3) | 27 (29.5) | 26 (26.5) |
| 14 (11.5) | 26 (26.5) | 19 (17.5) |
| $T_j$   139.0 | 200.0 | 327.0 |
| $T = 666$ | | |

Here, the numbers in parentheses are the ranks assigned to the various score values in the entire set of 36 cases. Then the sum of the ranks for each particular group $j$ is found, and designated $T_j$. The value of $T$ is the sum of these rank sums; if the ranking has been done correctly, it will be true that

$$T = \frac{N(N + 1)}{2}.$$

Note here that

$$T = \frac{(36)(37)}{2} = 666.$$

For large samples, a fairly good approximate test for identical populations is given by

$$H = \frac{12}{N(N + 1)} \left[ \sum_j \frac{T_j^2}{n_j} \right] - 3(N + 1).$$

This value of $H$ can be referred to the chi-square distribution with $J - 1$ degrees of freedom for a test of the hypothesis that all $J$ population distributions are identical.

For the example,

$$H = \frac{12}{36(37)} \left[ \frac{(139)^2 + (200)^2 + (327)^2}{12} \right] - 3(37)$$
$$= 13.81.$$

However, since there were ties involved in the ranking, this value of $H$ really should be corrected by dividing through by a value found from

$$C = 1 - \left( \frac{\sum_{i}^{G} (t_i^3 - t_i)}{N^3 - N} \right)$$

where $G$ is the number of sets of tied observations, and $t_i$ is the number tied in any set $i$. For the example, there are 4 sets of two tied observations, 1 set of three ties, and one set of four tied observations. Thus,

$$C = 1 - \left( \frac{4[(2)^3 - 2] + [(3)^3 - 3] + [(4)^3 - 4]}{(36)^3 - 36} \right)$$

so that

$$C = .997.$$

Finally, the corrected value of $H$ is

$$H' = \frac{H}{C} = \frac{13.81}{.997} = 13.85.$$

Unless $N$ is small, or unless the number of tied observations is very large, relative to $N$, this correction will make very little difference in the value of $H$. Certainly, this was true here. Furthermore, when each set of tied observations lie within the same experimental group, the correction becomes unnecessary.

In terms of Table III, for 2 degrees of freedom the value of $H$ exceeds that required for the .01 level, and so the experimenter can be quite confident in saying that the population distributions are not identical. Apparently there is some association between the type of cue given in the discrimination problem and the number of trials to criterion.

It is somewhat difficult to specify the class of alternative hypotheses appropriate to the $J$ sample rank test, and so the question of power is somewhat more obscure than for the Mann-Whitney test. However, there is reason to believe that this test is about the best of the $J$-sample order methods. Certainly it should be superior in most situations to the median test discussed in Section 18.2. In comparisons with $F$ from the analysis of variance, the Kruskal-Wallis test shows up extremely well.

When sample size is relatively small within the groups, the tables given by Siegel should be consulted.

## 18.10 THE FRIEDMAN TEST FOR $J$ MATCHED GROUPS

Much as the Kruskal-Wallis test represents an extension of the Mann-Whitney test, so the Friedman test is related to the Wilcoxen matched-pairs procedure. Furthermore, we shall see that this test is related to the methods of Section 18.17. The Friedman test is appropriate when some $K$ sets of matched individuals are used, where each set contains $J$ individuals assigned at random to the $J$ experimental treatments. It also applies when each of $K$ individuals is observed under each of $J$ treatments in random order. Thus, it is useful in situations where data are collected much as in the randomized-blocks experiments mentioned in Section 13.24.

The data are set up in a table as for a two-way analysis of variance with one observation per cell. The experimental treatments are shown by the respective columns, and the matched sets of individuals by the rows. Within each row (matched group) a rank order of the $J$ scores is found. Then the resulting ranks are summed by columns, to give values of $T_j$.

For example, in an experiment with four experimental treatments ($J = 4$), 11 groups of 4 matched subjects apiece were used. Within each matched group the four subjects were assigned at random to the four treatments, one subject per treatment. The data can be represented as in Table 18.10.1.

### Table 18.10.1

| Groups | I | II | III | IV |
|--------|-----|------|------|------|
| 1 | 1 (2) | 4 (3) | 8 (4) | 0 (1) |
| 2 | 2 (2) | 3 (3) | 13 (4) | 1 (1) |
| 3 | 10 (3) | 0 (1) | 11 (4) | 3 (2) |
| 4 | 12 (3) | 11 (2) | 13 (4) | 10 (1) |
| 5 | 1 (2) | 3 (3) | 10 (4) | 0 (1) |
| 6 | 10 (3) | 3 (1) | 11 (4) | 9 (2) |
| 7 | 4 (1) | 12 (4) | 10 (2) | 11 (3) |
| 8 | 10 (4) | 4 (2) | 5 (3) | 3 (1) |
| 9 | 10 (4) | 4 (2) | 9 (3) | 3 (1) |
| 10 | 14 (4) | 4 (2) | 7 (3) | 2 (1) |
| 11 | 3 (2) | 2 (1) | 4 (3) | 13 (4) |
| $T_j$ | 30 | 24 | 38 | 18 |

$$T = \frac{K(J)(J + 1)}{2}$$
$$= 110$$

It is important to remember that the ranks are given to the scores *within* rows. Then the $T_j$ values are simply the sums of those ranks within columns.

The rationale for this test is really very simple. Suppose that within the population represented by a row, the distribution of values for all the *treatment* populations were identical. Then, under random sampling and randomization of observations, the probability for any given permutation of the ranks 1 through $J$ within a given row should be the same as for any other permutation. Furthermore, across rows, each and every one of the $J!$ possible permutations of ranks across columns should be equally probable. This implies that we should expect the column sums of ranks to be identical under the null hypothesis. However, if there tend to be pile-ups of high or low ranks in particular columns, this is evidence against equal probability for the various permutations, and thus against the null hypothesis.

The test statistic for large samples is given by

$$\chi_r^2 = \frac{12}{KJ(J + 1)} \left[ \sum_j T_j^2 \right] - 3K(J + 1)$$

distributed approximately as chi-square with $J - 1$ degrees of freedom.

For the example, we would take

$$\chi_r^2 = \frac{12}{11(4)(5)} [(30)^2 + (24)^2 + (38)^2 + (18)^2] - 3(11)(5)$$
$$= 11.79.$$

For 3 degrees of freedom, this is just significant at the .01 level, and so the experimenter may say with some assurance that the treatment populations differ.

If ties in ranks within rows should occur, a conservative procedure is to break the ties so that the $T_j$ values are as close together as possible.

This test may well be the best alternative to the ordinary two-way (matched-groups) analysis of variance. Once again, there is every reason to believe this test, much like the Kruskal-Wallis test for one-factor experiments, is superior to the corresponding median test, and from the little evidence available, the result should compare well with $F$ when both the classical and order methods apply.

The chi-square approximation given above is good only for fairly large $K$. However, the test should be satisfactory when $J \geq 4$ and $K \geq 10$. As usual, tables giving significance levels for small samples can be found in the book by Siegel.

## 18.11 RANK-ORDER CORRELATION METHODS

The tests discussed so far in this chapter are designed for situations where the experimental variable is categorical and the dependent variable is in ordinal terms, as given either by the original measurement procedure or by a transformation of the scores into ordered classes or ranks. In this section, measures and tests of association will be described for situations where *both* variables are represented in ordinal terms. First of all, two somewhat different measures of "agreement" or association between rank orders will be introduced. Next, a measure of association will be given for the special situation where both variables take the form of ordered classes. Finally, the problem of indexing simultaneous agreement among several rank orders will be treated.

It is customary to call some of these rank-order statistics "correlations," but this usage deserves some qualification. The Spearman rank correlation to be introduced next actually *is* a correlation coefficient computed for numerical values that happen to be ranks. However, the next index to be considered, Kendall's tau, is not a correlation coefficient at all. Neither of these indices is closely connected with the classical theory of *linear* regression: as we shall see, under some circumstances the Spearman correlation can be used as an estimator of the population correlation coefficient, but one is seldom interested in the possibility of linear regression equations for predicting rank on $Y$ from rank on $X$, particularly since the degree of possible linear relationship between ranks tells little about the form of relationship between the *underlying* variables. If it is true that scores $X$ and $Y$ have a strong linear relationship, and both $X$ and $Y$ are interval-scale representations of their respective underlying variables, then we can also infer that the underlying variables show this same degree of linear relationship. However, if the numerical values analyzed are ranks, the correlation between the ranks may tell relatively little about the degree of *linear* relationship between the underlying variables. Especially the *square* of a correlation-like index on ranks is not to be interpreted in the usual way as a proportion of variance accounted for in the underlying variables.

Instead, it is somewhat better to think of both the Spearman and the Kendall indices only as showing "concordance" or "agreement," the tendency of two rank orders to be similar. As descriptive statistics, both indices serve this purpose very well, although the definition of "disagree" is somewhat different for these two statistics.

Still another interpretation can also be put on the use of these rank-order measures of association. Even though the Spearman and the Kendall statistics cannot ordinarily be thought of as showing the extent of *linear* relation between the variables underlying the ranks, they can be considered as indices of the general "monotonicity" of the underlying relation. A function $(Y = f(X))$ is said to be **monotone-increasing** if an increase in the value of $X$ in the domain of the function always is accompanied by an increase in the corresponding value of $Y$. A **monotone-decreasing** function has the opposite property: an increase in the value of $X$ in the domain is accompanied by a decrease in the value of $Y$. Linear functions are always monotone, but so are many other functions that are definitely not linear $(Y = X^3, Y = \log X$, and so on). On the other hand, a function that plots as a parabola is **nonmonotone;** in part of the domain of $X$, increases in $X$ lead to increases in $Y$, and in another part, increases in $X$ lead to decreases in $Y$ by the function rule. In general, any functional relation between numbers with a plot showing one or more distinct "peaks" or "valleys" is nonmonotone.

The size of either the Spearman or the Kendall coefficient does tell something about the tendency of the underlying scores to relate in a *monotone* way. High absolute values of either index give evidence that the basic form of the relation between $Y$ and $X$ is monotone. Positive values suggest that the relation tends to be monotone-increasing, and negative values monotone-decreasing. On the other hand, much like $r_{XY}$, small absolute or zero values of these indices suggest *either* that the two variables are not related *at all*, or that the form of the relation is nonmonotone. In short, rank-order measures of association between variables do not reflect *exactly* the same characteristics as $r_{XY}$ (or more properly $r_{XY}^2$). They do not necessarily show the tendency toward linear regression, per se, for either of the numerical variables underlying the ranks, but rather show a more general characteristic, which includes linear regression as a special case: these indices reflect the **tendency toward monotonicity,** and the **direction of relationship** that appears to exist. Thus, rank-order measures of association stand somewhere between indices such as $\varphi$ and $r_{XY}$: $\varphi$ gives evidence for *some unspecified departure from independence*, rank-order measures tell something of the *monotonicity of the relationship*, and $r_{XY}$ reflects *the tendency toward linear relationship* between variables. Unfortunately, values given by these different statistics are not directly comparable with each other, but this difference among the statistics is a point to bear in mind when thinking about what the different rank-order indices actually "tell" about the underlying relationship. These various indices of "correlation" imply different things about the relation between variables, and are seldom interchangeable.

## 18.12   THE SPEARMAN RANK CORRELATION COEFFICIENT

Imagine a group of $N$ cases drawn at random as for a problem in correlation. However, instead of having an $X$ score for each individual, we have only his *rank* in the group on variable $X$ (say for low to high, the ranks 1 through $N$). In the same way, for each individual we have his rank in the group on variable $Y$. The question to be asked is "How much does the ranking on variable $X$ tend to agree with the ranking on variable $Y$?" and a measure is desired to show the extent of the agreement. Or, perhaps, we have two judges who each rank the same set of $N$ objects. We wish to ask, "How much does judge A agree with judge B?" In either instance, there are two distinct rank orders of the same $N$ things, and these rank orders are to be compared for their agreement with each other. Furthermore, when these objects or individuals constitute a random sample from some population, we may wish to test the hypothesis that the true agreement in ranks is zero.

Two simple ways for comparison of two rank orders for agreement have already been mentioned: the first, and older, method is the Spearman rank correlation, commonly symbolized $r_S$ (although $\rho$ is sometimes used, this symbol $r_S$ will be used here to avoid confusion with the population correlation); the second method is the Kendall "tau" statistic, which will be discussed in the following section. Regardless of whether the data are two rank orders representing scores shown by individuals in a sample, or rankings of objects given by two judges, we can apply $r_S$. Suppose that in either circumstance we call the things ranked "individuals," and the two bases for ranking, the "variables." We can take the point of view that if rank orders agree, the ranks assigned to individuals should *correlate* positively with each other, whereas disagreement should be reflected by a negative correlation. A zero correlation represents an intermediate condition; no particular connection between the rank of an individual on one variable and his rank on the other.

For a descriptive index of agreement between ranks, the ordinary correlation coefficient can be computed on the *ranks* just as for any numerical scores, and this is how the Spearman rank correlation for a sample is defined:

$$r_S = \text{correlation between ranks over individuals.}$$

However, since the numerical values entering into the computation of the correlation coefficient actually are ranks in this instance, $r_S$ can be given a very simple computational form when no ties in rank exist:

*[handwritten: May not be used if are ties in rankings]*

$$r_S = 1 - \left[ \frac{6 \left( \sum_i D_i^2 \right)}{N(N^2 - 1)} \right]. \qquad \text{[18.12.1†]}$$

Here $D_i$ is the *difference* between ranks associated with the particular individual $i$, and $N$ is the number of individuals observed.

The basis for this way of calculating $r_S$ can be shown very easily, given two simple mathematical facts:

1. Given the whole numbers $1, 2, \cdots, N$, the sum of this set of numbers is $N(N + 1)/2$.
2. Given the whole numbers $1, 2, \cdots, N$, the sum of *squares* of these numbers is $(N)(N + 1)(2N + 1)/6$.

It follows quite easily that for *each* of the two sets of ranks, the mean rank is

$$M = \frac{N(N + 1)}{2N} = \frac{(N + 1)}{2}, \qquad \text{[18.12.2]}$$

and the variance of the ranks is

$$s^2 = \frac{N(N + 1)(2N + 1)}{6N} - \frac{(N + 1)^2}{4}$$

$$= \frac{N^2 - 1}{12}. \qquad \text{[18.12.3]}$$

For the moment, let us symbolize the rank of individual $i$ on variable $X$ by $x_i$, and the rank of $i$ on variable $Y$ by $y_i$. Furthermore, let

$$D_i = (x_i - y_i).$$

Now, if we took the sum of the squares of these differences, we would find

$$\sum_i D_i^2 = \sum_i (x_i - y_i)^2 = \sum_i x_i^2 + \sum_i y_i^2 - 2 \sum_i x_i y_i. \qquad \text{[18.12.4]}$$

Using expression **18.12.4** and the second of the mathematical principles listed above, we have

$$\frac{\sum\limits_i x_i y_i}{N} = \frac{\sum\limits_i x_i^2}{2N} + \frac{\sum\limits_i y_i^2}{2N} - \frac{\sum\limits_i D_i^2}{2N}$$

$$= \frac{(N+1)(2N+1)}{6} - \frac{\sum\limits_i D_i^2}{2N}. \qquad [18.12.5]$$

On substituting **18.12.2, 18.12.3,** and **18.12.5** into the equation for the correlation coefficient and carrying out a little algebra, we have

$$r_S = \frac{\sum\limits_i x_i y_i / N - M_x M_y}{s_x s_y}$$

$$= \frac{(N^2 - 1)/12 - \sum\limits_i D_i^2 / 2N}{(N^2 - 1)/12} = 1 - \left( \frac{6 \sum\limits_i D_i^2}{N(N^2 - 1)} \right).$$

The Spearman rank correlation is thus very simple to compute when ranks are untied. All one needs to know is $N$, the number of individuals ranked, and $D_i$, the difference in ranking for each individual. In spite of the different computations involved, $r_S$ is only an ordinary correlation coefficient calculated on ranks.

The computation of $r_S$ will be illustrated in a problem dealing with agreement between judge's rankings of objects. In a test of fine weight discrimination, two judges each ranked 10 small objects in order of their judged heaviness. The results are shown in Table 18.12.1. Did the judges tend to agree?

Table 18.12.1

| Object | Judge I | Judge II | $D_i$ | $D_i^2$ |
|--------|---------|----------|-------|---------|
| 1      | 6       | 4        | 2     | 4       |
| 2      | 4       | 1        | 3     | 9       |
| 3      | 3       | 6        | 3     | 9       |
| 4      | 1       | 7        | 6     | 36      |
| 5      | 2       | 5        | 3     | 9       |
| 6      | 7       | 8        | 1     | 1       |
| 7      | 9       | 10       | 1     | 1       |
| 8      | 8       | 9        | 1     | 1       |
| 9      | 10      | 3        | 7     | 49      |
| 10     | 5       | 2        | 3     | 9       |
|        |         |          |       | 128     |

$$r_S = 1 - \frac{6(128)}{10(10^2 - 1)} = .224.$$

The Spearman rank correlation is only .224, so that agreement between the two judges was not very high, although there was some slight tendency for similar ranks to be given to the same objects by the judges.

Incidentally, notice that if the relative true weights of the objects are known, we could also find the agreement of each judge with the true ranking. When some criterion ranking is known, it may be useful to compare a judged ranking with this criterion to evaluate the accuracy or "goodness" of the judgments—this is not the same as the agreement of judges with each other, of course.

Formula **18.12.1** may not be used if there are ties in either or both rankings, since the means and variances of the ranks then no longer have the simple relationship to $N$ present in the no-tie case. When ties exist, perhaps the simplest procedure is to assign mean ranks to sets of tied individuals; that is, when two or more individuals are tied in order, each is assigned the mean of the ranks they would otherwise occupy. Next an ordinary correlation coefficient is computed, using the ranks as though they were simply numerical scores. The result is a Spearman rank correlation that can be regarded as corrected for ties. On the other hand, if a test of the significance of $r_S$ is the main object of the analysis, a conservative course of action is to find a way to break the ties that will make the absolute value of $r_S$ as small as possible.

When no ties in rank exist, the exact sampling distribution of $r_S$ can be worked out for small samples. Exact tests of significance for $r_S$ are based on the idea that if one of the two rank orders is known, and the two underlying variables are independent, then each and every permutation in order of the individuals is equally likely for the other ranking. On this basis, the exact distribution of $\sum_i D_i^2$ can be found, and this can be converted into a distribution of $r_S$. Exact probability tables for $\sum_i D_i^2$ and $r_S$ based on small $N$ are to be found in books by Kendall (1955), Siegel (1956), and others.

The exact distribution of $r_S$ is rather peculiar. Although the distribution is unimodal and symmetric when the rankings are independent, the plot of the distribution has a curious jagged or serrated appearance due to particular constraints on the possible values of $\sum_i D_i^2$ for a given $N$. With $N$ large, the distribution does approach a normal form, but relatively slowly, so that for samples of small to moderate size the normal approximation is not very good.

The hypothesis of the independence of the two variables represented by rankings can also be given an approximate, large-sample, test in terms of $r_S$. This test has a form very similar to that for $r_{XY}$:

$$t = \frac{r_S \sqrt{N-2}}{\sqrt{1 - r_S^2}}$$

with $N - 2$ degrees of freedom. This test is really satisfactory, however, only when $N$ is fairly large; $N$ should be at least greater than or equal to 10.

Remember that if inferences are to be made about the form of relation holding between two continuous underlying variables, one can fail to reject the null hypothesis either because the variables are independent or because the relation is nonmonotone. Furthermore, the rejection of the hypothesis does not necessarily let one conclude that linear association exists between the underlying variables, but only that some more or less monotone relation holds.

Under particular assumptions, especially that of a bivariate normal distribution, the value of $r_S$ from a large sample can be treated as an estimate of the value of $\rho$ for the variables underlying the ranks. When the population is bivariate normal with $\rho = 0$, values of $r_S$ and $r_{XY}$ correlate very highly over samples. On the other hand, these assumptions are rather special, and the status of $r_S$ as an estimator of $\rho$ *in general* is open to considerable question.

## 18.13   THE KENDALL TAU COEFFICIENT

A somewhat different approach to the problem of agreement between two rankings is given by the $\tau$ coefficient (small Greek tau) due to M. G. Kendall (1955). Instead of treating the ranks themselves as though they were scores and finding a correlation coefficient, as in $r_S$, in the computation of $\tau$ we depend only on the number of *inversions* in order for pairs of individuals in the two rankings. A single inversion in order exists between *any pair* of individuals b and c when b > c in one ranking and c > b in the other. When two rankings are *identical*, no inversions in order exist. On the other hand, when one ranking is exactly the reverse of the other, an inversion exists for *each pair* of individuals; this means that complete disagreement corresponds to $\binom{N}{2}$ inversions. If the two rankings *agree* (show noninversion) for as many pairs as they disagree about (show inversion) the tendency for the two rank orders to agree or disagree should be exactly zero.

This leads to the following definition of the $\tau$ statistic:

$$\tau = 1 - \left[ \frac{2(\text{number of inversions})}{\text{number of pairs of objects}} \right]. \qquad [18.13.1\dagger]$$

This is equivalent to

$$\tau = \frac{(\text{number of times rankings agree about a pair}) - (\text{number of times rankings disagree})}{\text{total number of pairs}}.$$

It follows that the $\tau$ statistic is essentially a difference between two proportions: the proportion of pairs having the *same* relative order in both rankings minus the proportion of pairs showing *different* relative order in the two rankings.

Viewed as coefficients of agreement, $r_S$ and $\tau$ thus rest on somewhat different conceptions of "disagree." In the computation of $r_S$, a disagreement in ranking appears as the *squared* difference between the ranks themselves over the individuals. In $\tau$, an inversion in order for any *pair* of objects is treated in the same way as evidence for disagreement. Although these two conceptions are related, they are not identical: the process of squaring differences between rank values in $r_S$ places somewhat different weight on *particular* inversions in order, whereas in $\tau$ all inversions are weighted equally by a simple frequency count. Values of the statistics $r_S$ and $\tau$ are correlated over successive random samples from the same population, but the extent of the correlation depends on a number of things, including sample size and the character of the relation between the underlying variables in the population. Nevertheless, the two statistics are closely connected, and a number of mathematical inequalities must be satisfied by the values of the two statistics. For example,

$$-1 \leq 3\tau - 2r_S \leq 1.$$

It will be convenient to discuss the numerator term in the $\tau$ coefficient separately, and thus we will define

$S$ = (number of agreements in order) − (number of disagreements in order)

$$= \binom{N}{2} - 2(\text{number of inversions}).$$

Various methods exist for the computation of $S$ and $\tau$, but the simplest is a graphic method. In this method, all one does is to list the individuals or objects ranked, once in the order given by the first ranking, and again in the order given by the second. For example, suppose that in some problem there were seven objects {a,b,c,d,e,f,g} ranked by each of two judges, and that the rankings came out like this:

|  |  | | | *Rank* | | | |
|---|---|---|---|---|---|---|---|
|  | *1* | *2* | *3* | *4* | *5* | *6* | *7* |
| Judge 1 | c | a | b | e | d | g | f |
| Judge 2 | a | c | e | b | f | d | g |

Now straight lines are drawn connecting the same objects in the two parallel rankings, thus:

Then *the number of times that pairs of lines cross is the number of inversions in order.* Here, the number of crossings is 4, and so

$$S = \binom{7}{2} - (2)(4)$$
$$= 21 - 8$$
$$= 13.$$

The sample value of $\tau$ is

$$\tau = \frac{13}{21}$$
$$= .62.$$

Although $r_S$ from a sample has a rather artificial interpretation as a correlation coefficient, the interpretation of the obtained value of $\tau$ is quite straightforward: if a *pair* of objects is drawn at random from among those ranked, the probability that these two objects show the *same* relative order in both rankings is .62 *more* than the probability that they would show different order. In other words from the evidence at hand it is a considerably better bet that the two judges will tend to order a randomly selected pair in the *same* way than in a different way.

This graphic method of computing $\tau$ is satisfactory only when no ties in ranking exist. For nontied rankings, however, it is very simple to carry out, even when moderately large numbers of individuals have been ranked. Notice that although both the examples of computations for $r_S$ and $\tau$ featured judges' rankings of objects, exactly the same methods apply when the ranking principle is provided by scores shown by individuals on each of two variables.

Still another way of computing $S$ will be mentioned, since we will find an extension of this method very convenient when ties exist in one or both rankings. The data are organized as in Table 18.13.1. Notice that this is really just a joint-frequency table based on ranks. Each distinct observation (object) has a pair of rank numbers, and this determines the cell in the table in which that observation falls. As a convention for the procedure described below, the ranks along the margins of the table are listed with the lowest ranks in the upper left-hand corner, as shown here.

**Table 18.13.1**

JUDGE 1

|  |  | 1 | 2 | 3 | 4 | 5 | 6 | 7 |
|---|---|---|---|---|---|---|---|---|
|  | 1 |  | 1(a) |  |  |  |  |  |
|  | 2 | 1(c) |  |  |  |  |  |  |
|  | 3 |  |  |  | 1(e) |  |  |  |
| JUDGE 2 | 4 |  |  | 1(b) |  |  |  |  |
|  | 5 |  |  |  |  |  |  | 1(f) |
|  | 6 |  |  |  |  | 1(d) |  |  |
|  | 7 |  |  |  |  |  | 1(g) |  |

Now $S$ is found as follows: we compute a value $S_+$ by first taking any cell with nonzero frequency and, ignoring its row and column, *counting the number of entries to the right and below that cell.* Thus, for the cell containing the object c, there are five entries to the right and below. For the cell with object b, there are three entries to the right and below, and so on. Then $S_+$ is the sum of these numbers over cells. Over all nonzero cells, the value of $S_+$ is found to be:

$$
\begin{aligned}
&5 \text{ (for cell a)}\\
&5 \text{ (for cell c)}\\
&3 \text{ (for cell e)}\\
&3 \text{ (for cell b)}\\
&1 \text{ (for cell d)}\\
&0 \text{ (for cell f)}\\
&0 \text{ (for cell g)}\\
\hline
\end{aligned}
$$

$$S_+ = 17.$$

Then

$$S = 2(S_+) - \binom{N}{2} = 34 - 21 = 13$$

and

$$\tau = .62.$$

As we shall see, this general method is advantageous when ties exist in the data, or when the data are put into ordered classes rather than ranks.

Notice that we might also compute a value $S_-$ by taking the sum of the frequencies to the left and below the various nonzero cells. Then

$$S = \binom{N}{2} - 2(S_-)$$

since

$$(S_+) + (S_-) = \binom{N}{2},$$

when there are no tied ranks.

The exact test of significance for $\tau$ is based on the assumption that the variables underlying the ranks are continuously distributed, so that ties are impossible. Alternatively, one can imagine random sampling of complete rank orders of $N$ things from a potential population of such rankings. In either instance, one assumes that if there is no true relationship between the pairs of rank orders observed, then given the first rank order, all possible permutations in order are equally likely to occur as the second rank order. This makes finding the exact sampling distribution of $S$ or of $\tau$ for fixed $N$ relatively simple.

However, for our purposes, the fact of importance is that the exact sampling distribution of $\tau$ approaches a normal distribution very quickly with successive increases in the size of $N$. Even for fairly small values of $N$, the distribution of $\tau$ is approximated relatively well by the normal distribution. Of course, this is true only when $H_0$ is true, so that the rankings are each equally likely to show any of the $N!$ permutations in order, and $E(\tau) = 0$. The distribution of $\tau$ is not simple to discuss when other conditions hold, and so we will test only the hypothesis of independence between rankings (implying equal probability of occurrence for each and every possible ordering of $N$ observations on the second variable given their ordering on the first).

For $N$ of about 10 or more, the test is given by

$$z = \frac{\tau}{\sigma_\tau}$$

referred to a normal distribution, where

$$\sigma_\tau^2 = \frac{2(2N + 5)}{9N(N - 1)}.$$

Equivalently, in terms of $S$,

$$z = \frac{S}{\sigma_S}$$

where

$$\sigma_S^2 = \frac{N(N - 1)(2N + 5)}{18}.$$

For small $N$, the exact tables in terms of $S$ given by Kendall (1948) or Siegel (1956) can be used.

This approximate test can be improved if a correction for continuity is made. The correction for continuity involves subtraction of $1 \Big/ \binom{N}{2}$ from the absolute value of $\tau$, or 1 from the absolute value for $S$, before the $z$ statistic is formed.

## 18.14 KENDALL'S TAU VERSUS THE SPEARMAN RANK CORRELATION

The Spearman rank correlation is the traditional way to treat the problem of association between ranks. However, there is reason to believe that the $\tau$ coefficient may be superior for many purposes.

In the first place, $\tau$ can be given a very simple interpretation as a descriptive statistic, whereas the Spearman coefficient is meaningful, at least at an elementary level, only by analogy with the ordinary correlation coefficient. By the graphic method shown above, the value of $\tau$ is certainly as easy to compute as that of $r_S$, although either index can be troublesome for large samples.

From the definition of sample $\tau$ as a difference between two proportions, of the general form $P - Q$, it is easy to see that $\tau$ for a population can be defined as a corresponding difference between probabilities. For this reason, sample $\tau$ provides an unbiased estimate of its population counterpart. On the other hand, $r_S$ is usually regarded as an estimator of the population correlation $\rho$, although studies have shown that its properties as an estimator of $\rho$ vary considerably with the form of the population distribution and with the true value of $\rho$. Recently, however, Kruskal (1958) showed that $\rho_S$, the Spearman coefficient, can also be defined for a population, and has a very reasonable interpretation as an index of strict monotonicity of relation. Under this view, $r_S$ can be shown to be biased as an estimator of $\rho_S$, and the curious circumstance emerges that an unbiased estimate of $\rho_S$ involves *both* sample $r_S$ and $\tau$:

$$\text{unbiased estimate of } \rho_S = \frac{N+1}{N-2} r_S - \frac{3}{N-2} \tau.$$

For large $N$, however, this is virtually the same value as $r_S$. At any rate, it is becoming evident that each index supplies information of importance about the general monotone relation that may exist between variables, quite irrespective of the true value of the correlation coefficient $\rho$.

The big argument in favor of the use of $\tau$ in the test of the hypothesis of independence is the fairly rapid convergence of its sampling distribution to a normal form, as opposed to the somewhat slower convergence and other peculiarities of the distribution of $r_S$. For moderately large samples, where the exact tables of the sampling distributions cannot be used, $\tau$ seems to provide a better test of the hypothesis of no-association than does $r_S$.

## 18.15 Kendall's tau with ties

The determination of the exact sampling distribution of $S$ (or $\tau$) depends on the assumption of *no* ties. However, if the underlying model is altered in a particular way, $\tau$ can be computed and tested even though ties occur in one or both rankings. First of all, we will consider the method for finding $S$ when ties occur, and then turn to the problem of a significance test.

The simplest method for finding $S$ and $\tau$ when ties occur is to use the joint-frequency–table method suggested in Section 18.13. However, here it will occur that more than one entry will fall into a particular row, column, or cell. This method is best shown by example.

Suppose that some 12 subjects were observed, and ranked on each of two variables, so that the ranked data were as shown in Table 18.15.1. A table is formed in which the first ranking is represented by the columns and the second

### Table 18.15.1

| Subject | X ranking | Y ranking |
|---|---|---|
| 1 | 5 | 8.5 |
| 2 | 7 | 11 |
| 3 | 5 | 12 |
| 4 | 1 | 8.5 |
| 5 | 2 | 8.5 |
| 6 | 3 | 6 |
| 7 | 5 | 5 |
| 8 | 11.5 | 8.5 |
| 9 | 11.5 | 2 |
| 10 | 9.5 | 2 |
| 11 | 9.5 | 2 |
| 12 | 8 | 4 |

ranking by the rows. (Actually, the score values themselves could have been used to form this table, since the actual rank values are not used at all after the data are tabled.) Table 18.15.2 shows these data.

**Table 18.15.2**

|  |  | 1 | 2 | 3 | 5 | 7 | 8 | 9.5 | 11.5 | Total |
|---|---|---|---|---|---|---|---|---|---|---|
|  | 2 |  |  |  |  |  |  | 2 | 1 | 3 |
|  | 4 |  |  |  |  |  | 1 |  |  | 1 |
|  | 5 |  |  |  | 1 |  |  |  |  | 1 |
| $Y$ | 6 |  |  | 1 |  |  |  |  |  | 1 |
| RANKING | 8.5 | 1 | 1 |  | 1 |  |  |  | 1 | 4 |
|  | 11 |  |  |  |  | 1 |  |  |  | 1 |
|  | 12 |  |  |  | 1 |  |  |  |  | 1 |
| Total |  | 1 | 1 | 1 | 3 | 1 | 1 | 2 | 2 | 12 |

*X* RANKING , *Y* RANKING (row label at left)

Now we proceed to find $S_+$ just as above, except that the number of cases to the right and below a given cell is weighted by the number of cases in that cell. For example, for the cell given by the row labeled 2 and the column labeled 9.5, there is only 1 case to the right and below; however, since there are 2 cases *in* the cell, in the sum for $S_+$ we enter 2(1) or 2 for this cell. Proceeding in this way over all of the cells with nonzero frequencies, we have

$$S_+ = 2(1) + 1 + 1(2) + 1(4) + 1(2) + 1(2) + 1(1)$$
$$= 14.$$

Now we find a value $S_-$, computed exactly as for $S_+$ except that we find the number of cases to the *left and below* a given cell, and weight this number by the cell frequency. Here

$$S_- = 2(8) + 1(8) + 1(7) + 1(3) + 1(2) + 1(2) + 1(1)$$
$$= 39.$$

Then,

$$S = S_+ - S_-$$

so that for this example

$$S = 14 - 39 = -25.$$

Kendall suggests calculating the denominator of $\tau$ by taking

$$\sqrt{\left(\frac{N(N-1)}{2} - T_1\right)\left(\frac{N(N-1)}{2} - T_2\right)}$$

where

$$T_1 = \frac{\sum_j n_j(n_j - 1)}{2}$$

$n_j$ = the marginal total of column $j$

$$T_2 = \frac{\sum_k n_k(n_k - 1)}{2}$$

$n_k$ = the marginal total for row $k$.

(A simpler method for finding a "tau-like" index will be given in the next section, however.)

For this example,

$$T_1 = \frac{1}{2}[3(2) + 2(1) + 2(1)]$$
$$= 5$$

and

$$T_2 = \frac{1}{2}[3(2) + 4(3)]$$
$$= 9.$$

Then

$$\tau = \frac{S}{\sqrt{\left(\frac{N(N-1)}{2} - T_1\right)\left(\frac{N(N-1)}{2} - T_2\right)}}$$

$$= \frac{-25}{\sqrt{(66 - 5)(66 - 9)}}$$

$$= \frac{-25}{59}$$

$$= -.42.$$

The apparent degree of agreement between these two rankings is a *negative* .42.

A large-sample test of significance for tau with ties can be constructed along the lines given in Section 18.13. That is, one forms a ratio

$$z = \frac{S}{\sigma_S}$$

and refers this to a normal distribution. However, it must be emphasized that when ties exist in either or both rankings, this test is *conditional* to the distribution of ties, and the significance level refers to a probability of occurrence among samples each showing *exactly* the same distribution of ties as appeared in the sample actually obtained. When ties exist, the sampling variance of $S$, or $\sigma_S^2$, is found from

$$\sigma_S^2 = \frac{N(N-1)(2N+5) - \sum_j n_j(n_j-1)(2n_j+5) - \sum_k n_k(n_k-1)(2n_k+5)}{18}$$

$$+ \frac{\left[\sum_j n_j(n_j-1)(n_j-2)\right]\left[\sum_k n_k(n_k-1)(n_k-2)\right]}{9(N)(N-1)(N-2)}$$

$$+ \frac{\left[\sum_j n_j(n_j-1)\right]\left[\sum_k (n_k)(n_k-1)\right]}{2(N)(N-1)}.$$

After this rather forbidding-looking calculation for $\sigma_S^2$ has been carried out, the value of $z$ may be found and referred to a normal table, provided that $N$ is rather sizable. Unless $N$ is quite large and ties are infrequent, a correction for continuity is required; this is given in Kendall (1955).

It is interesting to observe that even when ties exist, one really does not have to assign ranks at all in order to compute $\tau$; we are really dealing with ordered categories of observations, and when we assign the midrank to a set of observations we are, in effect, allotting them to the same ordered category. Thus, in principle this procedure may be carried out on a joint *grouped* frequency distribution; the actual computations, however, really involve only the *ordinal* properties of the scores on which the distributions were based, and the class intervals are treated as ordered classes.

Furthermore, even when data are grouped in this way, the $\tau$ index can be regarded as reflecting monotonicity in the relationship between the underlying scores. Large values of $\tau$ lead to the conclusion that the relationship tends to be monotone, and small absolute values may indicate either that there is no statistical association, or that the form of the relationship tends to be nonmonotone.

### 18.16  A MEASURE OF ASSOCIATION IN ORDERED CLASSES

It has just be suggested that the method for computing $S$ when the rankings contain ties is tantamount to arranging the data into ordered classes. Unfortunately, the value of the $\tau$ statistic itself does not seem to have a very simple interpretation when ties are present in either ranking. This difficulty is removed if one uses the $\gamma$ (Greek gamma) statistic suggested by Goodman and Kruskal (1954) specifically for data arranged into ordered classes. Actually, this statistic $\gamma$ has the same numerator term as $\tau$, and the $S$ value is computed in exactly the same way. However, its denominator differs from that of $\tau$, and permits $\gamma$ to have a simpler interpretation.

In terms of the quantities $S_+$ and $S_-$ computed above, the statistic $\gamma$ is just

$$\gamma = \frac{S_+ - S_-}{S_+ + S_-}.$$  [18.16.1†]

For the example above, this is

$$\gamma = \frac{-25}{14 + 39}$$
$$= -.47.$$

This value can be interpreted as follows: suppose that a pair of subjects were drawn at random from the 12 actually observed. Given that these subjects were tied in neither of the rankings, is it a better bet that they show the same or a different ordering on $X$ and $Y$? The value of $\gamma$ shows that it is a much better bet that an untied pair has different ordering on the two variables, since the probability of finding a pair with a different ordering is .47 *more* than the probability of a pair with the same ordering, among all possible untied pairs we might draw. Put more formally,

$$\gamma = p(\text{same ordering}|\text{untied pairs}) - p(\text{different ordering}|\text{untied pairs})$$

for a pair chosen at random with replacement from among these 12 subjects.

If there are no tied ranks, then

$$\gamma = \tau.$$

The index $\gamma$ has the same basic interpretation as $\tau$: a difference in probability for same versus different ordering on the underlying variables for a randomly selected pair. The only difference is that $\gamma$ is conditional to the set of *untied* such pairs. The index $\gamma$ is much like the $\lambda$ measures for categorical data (Section 17.13), since it has a simple interpretation in a predictive sense, although $\gamma$ refers to *ordered* categories and thus reflects the general tendency toward monotonicity in the relationship, while $\lambda$ reflects *any* form of predictive relationship.

## 18.17 KENDALL'S COEFFICIENT OF CONCORDANCE

Sometimes we want to know the extent to which members of a set of $m$ distinct rank orderings of $N$ things tend to be similar. For example, in a beauty contest each of 7 judges $(m = 7)$ gives a simple rank order of the 10 contestants $(N = 10)$. How much do these rank orders tend to agree, or show "concordance"?

This problem is usually handled by application of Kendall's statistic, $W$, the "coefficient of concordance." As we shall see, the coefficient $W$ is closely related to the average $r_S$ among the $m$ rank orders.

The coefficient $W$ is computed by putting the data into a table with $m$ rows and $N$ columns. In the cell for column $j$ and row $k$ appears the rank number assigned to individual object $j$ by judge $k$. Table 18.17.1 might show the data for the judges and the beauty contestants. It is quite clear that the judges did not agree perfectly in their rankings of these contestants. However, what should the column totals of ranks, $T_j$, have been if the judges had agreed exactly? If each judge had given exactly the same rank to the same girl, then one column should total to 7(1), another to 7(2), and so on, until the largest sum should be 7(10). On the other hand, suppose that there were complete disagreement among the judges, so that there was no tendency for high or low rankings to pile up in particular columns. Then we should expect each column sum to be about the same. In this example, the column sums of ranks are not identical, so that apparently some agreement exists, but neither are the sums as different as they should be when absolutely perfect agreement exists.

**Table 18.17.1**

| Judges | Contestants | | | | | | | | | |
|--------|----|----|----|----|----|----|----|----|----|----|
|        | *1* | *2* | *3* | *4* | *5* | *6* | *7* | *8* | *9* | *10* |
| 1 | 8 | 7 | 5 | 6 | 1 | 3 | 2 | 4 | 10 | 9 |
| 2 | 7 | 6 | 8 | 3 | 2 | 1 | 5 | 4 | 9 | 10 |
| 3 | 5 | 4 | 7 | 6 | 3 | 2 | 1 | 8 | 10 | 9 |
| 4 | 8 | 6 | 7 | 4 | 1 | 3 | 5 | 2 | 10 | 9 |
| 5 | 5 | 4 | 3 | 2 | 6 | 1 | 9 | 10 | 7 | 8 |
| 6 | 4 | 5 | 6 | 3 | 2 | 1 | 9 | 10 | 8 | 7 |
| 7 | 8 | 6 | 7 | 5 | 1 | 2 | 3 | 4 | 10 | 9 |
| $T_j$ | 45 | 38 | 43 | 29 | 16 | 13 | 34 | 42 | 64 | 61 |

$$T = \frac{m(N)(N+1)}{2}$$

$$= 385$$

This idea of the extent of variability among the respective sums of ranks is the basis for Kendall's $W$ statistic. Basically,

$$W = \frac{\text{variance of rank sums}}{\text{maximum possible variance of rank sums}}.$$

Because the mean rank and the variance of the ranks each depend only on $N$ and $m$, this reduces to

$$W = \left( \frac{12 \sum_j T_j^2}{m^2 N(N^2 - 1)} \right) - \frac{3(N+1)}{N-1}.$$

For the example, we find

$$W = \left( \frac{12[(45)^2 + \cdots + (61)^2]}{49(10)(99)} \right) - \frac{3(11)}{9}$$
$$= 4.28 - 3.66$$
$$= .62.$$

There is apparently a moderately high degree of "concordance" among the judges, since the variance of the rank sums is 62 percent of the maximum possible. Note that by its definition, $W$ cannot be negative, and its maximum value is 1.

The value of the concordance coefficient is somewhat hard to interpret directly in terms of the tendency for the rankings to agree, but an interpretation can be given in terms of the average value of $r_S$ over all possible *pairs* of rank orders. That is

$$\text{average } r_S = \frac{mW - 1}{m - 1}.$$

For the example,

$$\text{average } r_S = \frac{7(.62) - 1}{7 - 1}$$
$$= .56.$$

If we took all of the possible $\binom{7}{2}$ or 21 *pairs* of judges, and found $r_S$ for each such pair, the average rank correlation would be about .56. Thus, on the average, judge-pairs do tend to give relatively similar rankings. The advantage of reporting this finding in terms of $W$ rather than average $r_S$ is that

$$\frac{-1}{m - 1} \leq \text{average } r_S \leq 1$$

whereas, regardless of the values for $N$ or $m$,

$$0 \leq W \leq 1.$$

This makes $W$ values more immediately comparable across different sets of data. Nevertheless, the clearest interpretation of $W$ seems to be in terms of average $r_S$.

Recall that this is essentially the idea employed in the Friedman test for matched groups. In the Friedman procedure a matched group takes the place of a judge, and the rank order of scores for different treatments within a group is like an ordering of objects of judgment. Then, if the scores for different treatments tended to show up in substantially the same order for the various groups, a true difference in treatments is inferred.

An exact test is possible for the hypothesis that there is no actual agreement among judges (see Kendall, 1955; and Siegel, 1956, for tables). For $m$ of at least 8, an approximate test is given by

$$\chi^2 = m(N - 1)W$$

referred to the chi-square distribution with $N - 1$ degrees of freedom. This test is really a good one only for fairly sizable $m$ and $N$, however.

# RULES OF SUMMATION

APPENDIX *A*

## SUBSCRIPTS

In the discussion to follow, let $X$ and $Y$ stand for numerical variables. Ordinarily, the numerical values for these variables are scores in some given set of data, where each individual observed in a group of $N$ cases is paired either with a single score, $X$, or with a pair of scores $(X,Y)$.

The *subscript* notation is useful in keeping track of the various score values across the different individuals or observations. For the moment, we will consider $N$ distinct individuals, arbitrarily indexed by the set of numbers $(1, \cdots, i, \cdots, N)$. The "running subscript" $i$ denotes any one of these individuals. Then, $X_i$ denotes the particular value of $X$ associated with any particular individual $i$. That is, the variable $X_i$ ranges only over the set of particular values

$$(X_1, X_2, \cdots, X_N).$$

Now we need a way to discuss the *sum* of these particular values of $X$ over the entire set of $N$ different individuals $i$. The symbol $\Sigma$ (capital Greek sigma) stands for the operation "the sum of," referring to the values symbolized immediately after the summation sign. Thus,

$$\sum_{i=1}^{N} X_i$$

is read as "the sum of the $N$ values $X_i$, beginning with $i = 1$ and ending with $i = N$." That is,

$$\sum_{i=1}^{N} X_i = X_1 + X_2 + \cdots + X_N.$$

Suppose, for example, that $N = 4$, and the actual values associated with the four different individuals were

$$6, 8, 3, 11.$$

Then,

$$\sum_{i=1}^{N} X_i = 6 + 8 + 3 + 11 = 28.$$

In many simple contexts where it is clear that the sum extends across *all* of a set of $N$ individuals, the subscripts and superscripts on the summation sign are simplified or omitted. Thus, we often write:

$$\sum_i X_i$$

to indicate the sum of values across all $N$ individuals $i$, or even

$$\Sigma X_i$$

to stand for this sum. However, the subscript is usually omitted only in very simple expressions where the set of values to be included in the sum is perfectly clear.

Quite frequently, symbols for values corresponding to individual observations are given two (or more) subscripts. That is, it happens that sometimes we want to discuss individual observations arranged into several groupings or cross-classifications. Then two (or more) sets of index numbers are used. For example, suppose that there were some $J$ different *groups* of observations; these different groups are identified by being paired arbitrarily with the numbers

$$(1, \cdots, j, \cdots, J).$$

Furthermore, within any particular group, $j$, there is some number $n_j$ of distinct individuals or observations, each of which is associated with an $X$ score. Then, the particular value of the score for the $i$th individual in the group $j$ is symbolized by $X_{ij}$. If we wanted to symbolize the sum of the scores for the particular group $j$, then we would write

$$\sum_{i=1}^{n_j} X_{ij}$$

which stands for "the sum of values for all of the $n_j$ different individuals in the particular group labeled $j$." Where it is clear that all individuals scores in a particular group $j$ are to be summed, this can be abbreviated to

$$\sum_i X_{ij}.$$

Notice that this quite literally is the symbol for "sum over $i$" for a set of scores $X_{ij}$; the fact that $j$ appears as a subscript for $X$ but that $i$ alone appears below the sigma is a cue that all the scores summed in this particular operation *must* have the same subscript $j$ (that is, must be in the same group of observations).

However, often one wants to indicate the sum of $X_{ij}$ over *all* individuals in *all* groups. Written out in full, this would be symbolized by

$$\sum_{j=1}^{j} \sum_{i=1}^{n_j} X_{ij} = (X_{11} + X_{21} + \cdots + X_{n_{j-1},J} + X_{n_j,J}).$$

This *double* summation is interpreted as "Take a particular group $j$, and sum scores over all the $n_j$ different observations in that group; then, having done this for each of the $J$ different groups, sum the results over all of these groups." Once again, this can be simplified to

$$\sum_{j} \sum_{i} X_{ij}$$

when the meaning of the symbol is perfectly clear in terms of which values are to be summed.

This idea can be extended, although in our discussions a *triple* summation is the largest such symbol used. In some problems, each individual $i$ belongs simultaneously to *two* groupings. That is, suppose that all the scores in a set of data were arranged into a table with $K$ rows, $J$ columns, and $JK$ cells, and that each individual observation belongs to one and only one row, one and only one column, and one and only one cell in the data table. Now let the various *column* groupings be symbolized by the numbers

$$(1, \cdots, j, \cdots, J).$$

The *rows* of the data table are indexed by the set of numbers

$$(1, \cdots, k, \cdots, K).$$

Then any cell of the table is indexed by a *pair* of numbers $jk$. The score of the $i$th individual in the cell $jk$ of the data table is thus $X_{ijk}$. The number of individuals in the cell $jk$ is shown by $n_{jk}$.

Now, when there are three subscripts like this,

$$\sum_{j=1}^{J} \sum_{k=1}^{K} \sum_{i=1}^{n_{jk}} X_{ijk},$$

the following is symbolized: "Take a particular cell, $jk$, and sum the scores of all individuals $i$ in that cell; then, still within a particular column $j$, sum the results of doing this for each row $k$ over the $K$ respective rows; finally, sum the results for each column $j$ over the $J$ respective columns." A little thought should convince you that this is simply the sum of all individual scores in all cells, or the sum of all scores in the table.

In this instance, it is immaterial whether we write the sum for the rows or the sum for the columns first, since the total number symbolized is the same. However, this is not universally true, and order of the summation signs can be important.

Sometimes we want to symbolize only the sum for a particular cell, row, or column: First of all, letting $n_{jk}$ stand for the number in cell $j,k$, we write

$$\sum_{i=1}^{n_{jk}} X_{ijk} = (X_{1jk} + \cdots + X_{njk}).$$

This denotes the sum of all individual scores in the *single* cell $jk$. If we write

$$\sum_{j=1}^{J} \sum_{i=1}^{n_{jk}} X_{ijk} = (X_{11k} + X_{21k} + \cdots + X_{nJk}),$$

we intend that first the sum of individuals in a particular cell in column $j$ and row $k$ shall be taken, and then, still within the particular row $k$, the result for all the different columns $j$ shall be summed. This amounts to the sum of all scores within the particular row $k$. On the other hand, if we want the sum of all the scores in a particular column $j$, we could write

$$\sum_{k=1}^{K} \sum_{i=1}^{n_{jk}} X_{ijk} = (X_{1j1} + \cdots + X_{njK})$$

indicating the sum for a particular cell $jk$, and then the sum over the results for all rows $k$ within the particular column $j$. In short, *unless a subscript appears both in the symbol for the X values and under the summation sign, the total value symbolized pertains to some particular set of observations, represented by that subscript not appearing under the summation symbol*. Notice that when the sum of all observations in a particular row $k$ of the data table was intended, the sum was indicated over $i$ and over $j$, but *not* over $k$. On the other hand, when the sum of observations in some column $j$ was desired, the sum was indicated over $i$ and over $k$, but not over $j$.

In learning to work with summation signs, it is well to start the habit of reading the summation symbols from *right to left*, and from *inside the punctuation outward*. The *innermost* summation indicated in a mathematical expression is ordinarily to be carried out first, then the next summation symbolized to the left, and then finally the summation appearing closest to the margin on the left.

## RULES OF SUMMATION

A few simple rules can help one learn to interpret and carry out the computations symbolized by statistical expressions involving summations. Furthermore, elementary statistical derivations almost always involve one or more of these summation rules used as an algebraic equivalence. First of all, some simple rules will be given that apply when values for only one variable are being summed, and then we will consider situations involving two or more variables.

**R U L E  1.** If $a$ is some constant value over the $N$ different observations $i$, then

$$\sum_{i=1}^{N} a = Na.$$

For example, suppose that 5 observations are considered, and paired with each observation is the constant number 10. Then

$$\sum_{i} a = 10 + 10 + 10 + 10 + 10 = (5)(10).$$

Any time that, in the particular sum indicated, each and every individual observation entering into the sum is paired with exactly the same constant value $a$, then the sum is equal to the number of individuals considered times the value of $a$. Extending this rule to double or triple summations, we have

$$\sum_{j=1}^{J} \sum_{i=1}^{n_j} a = \sum_{j=1}^{J} (n_j)a$$

$$\sum_{k=1}^{K} \sum_{j=1}^{J} \sum_{i=1}^{n_{jk}} a = \sum_{k=1}^{K} \sum_{j=1}^{J} (n_{jk})a$$

and so on.

**R U L E  2.** Given the value $a$, which is constant over all individuals entering into the summation, then

$$\sum_{i=1}^{N} aX_i = a \sum_{i=1}^{N} X_i.$$

For example, consider the five individual scores

$$6, 7, 3, 9, 20.$$

Suppose that each of these scores is multiplied by the constant 2. Then

$$\sum_{i} 2X_i = 2(6) + 2(7) + 2(3) + 2(9) + 2(20)$$

$$= 2(6 + 7 + 3 + 9 + 20) = 2 \sum_{i} X_i.$$

Once again, this rule can be applied to several sums:

$$\sum_{j=1}^{J} \sum_{i=1}^{n_j} aX_{ij} = a \sum_{j=1}^{J} \sum_{i=1}^{n_j} X_{ij}.$$

Notice here that the $a$ symbol has no subscript, and thus may be regarded as a constant over the sum. However, it might happen that the sum is such that $a_j$ appears instead of $a$, meaning that $a_j$ is a constant for all observations $i$ in the *same* group $j$, but is different for different groups. Then,

$$\sum_{j=1}^{J} \sum_{i=1}^{n_j} a_j X_{ij} = \sum_{j=1}^{J} a_j \left( \sum_{i=1}^{n_j} X_{ij} \right).$$

One must be sure to notice the set of observations for which some value *is* constant in multiple summations.

RULE 3.   If some operation is to be carried out on the individual values of $X$ before the summation, this is indicated by mathematical punctuation, such as parentheses, or equivalent symbols having the force of punctuation. Unless the summation symbol is included within this punctuation, the summation is to be done after the other operation: for example

$$\sum_i (X_i)^2 = \sum_i X_i^2 = (X_1^2 + X_2^2 + \cdots + X_N^2)$$

$$\sum_i \sqrt{X_i} = \sqrt{X_i} + \sqrt{X_2} + \cdots + \sqrt{X_N}.$$

However,

$$\left( \sum_i X_i \right)^2 = (X_1 + \cdots + X_N)^2$$

$$\sqrt{\sum_i X_i} = \sqrt{X_1 + \cdots + X_N}.$$

Be sure to notice that where the parentheses (or other symbols such as exponent and radical signs having the same force of parentheses) happen to appear makes a big difference in the sum symbolized. In general,

$$\sum_i X_i^2 \neq \left( \sum_i X_i \right)^2$$

$$\sum_i \sqrt{X_i} \neq \sqrt{\sum_i X_i}$$

$$\log \left( \sum_i X_i \right) \neq \sum_i \log X_i,$$

and so on.

This is especially important when there is multiple summation. For example,

$$\sum_{j=1}^{n} \left( \sum_i X_{ij} \right)^2 = \sum_j (X_{1j} + \cdots + X_{nj})^2.$$

The notation here tells us *first* to take the sum of all the individual values in a single group $j$; then, having done this for each group $j$, we square the *sum* for each group; finally, the sum of the *squared* sums for the various groups is found. Squaring at the wrong place in this sequence of steps will give quite a different result.

**R U L E 4.** If the only operation to be carried out before a sum is taken is itself a sum (or difference), then the summation may be distributed. Thus,

$$\sum_i (X_i - 4) = \sum_i X_i - \sum_i 4$$

$$\sum_i (X_i^2 + 3X_i + 10) = \sum_i X_i^2 + \sum_i 3X_i + \sum_i 10.$$

This rule is very important in algebraic manipulations on expressions involving sums. For example, using this rule we can make the following algebraic changes:

$$\sum_{j=1}^{J} \sum_{i=1}^{n_j} (X_{ij} - m)^2 = \sum_{j=1}^{J} \sum_{i=1}^{n_j} (X_{ij}^2 - 2mX_{ij} + m^2)$$

$$= \sum_{j=1}^{J} \sum_{i=1}^{n_j} X_{ij}^2 - \sum_{j=1}^{J} \sum_{i=1}^{n_j} 2mX_{ij} + \sum_{j=1}^{J} \sum_{i=1}^{n_j} m^2.$$

Invoking rules 1 and 2, we can reduce this expression to

$$\sum_j \sum_i X_{ij}^2 - 2m \sum_j \sum_i X_{ij} + m^2 \sum_j n_j.$$

The value represented by this last expression is algebraically equivalent to the value of the first expression, but it may be far more convenient actually to compute this number in the second way, or to use this second expression in a mathematical argument.

## Summation rules for two or more variables

So far we have acted as though each distinct individual or observation were associated with one and only one numerical score. However, it may be that two distinct values $X_i$ and $Y_i$ are paired with each individual or observation $i$. Then the rules given above may be extended:

**R U L E 5.** If each of $N$ distinct individuals $i$ has two scores, $X_i$ and $Y_i$, then

$$\sum_{i=1}^{N} X_i Y_i = X_1 Y_1 + X_2 Y_2 + \cdots + X_N Y_N.$$

Notice that this symbol means that *the product of the pair of scores belonging to any given individual i is to be found first,* and then when this has been done for the entire set of individuals, *the sum of these products is to be found.* Be sure to notice that *in general*

$$\sum_i X_i Y_i \neq \left( \sum_i X_i \right) \left( \sum_i Y_i \right).$$

The other rules extend quite easily to the situation where two (or more) variables are considered:

**RULE 6.** $\displaystyle\sum_i aX_iY_i = a\sum_i X_iY_i.$

**RULE 7.** Given the constants $a$ and $b$,

$$\sum_i (aX_i + bY_i) = a\sum_i X_i + b\sum_i Y_i.$$

Sometimes it happens that when observations are arranged into groups, all observations $i$ in the same group $j$ will have the same value $X_j$ on one variable, but different values $Y_{ij}$ on the other. Then, the following rule applies:

**RULE 8.** $\displaystyle\sum_{j=1}^{J}\sum_{i=1}^{n_j} X_jY_{ij} = \sum_j X_j\left(\sum_i Y_{ij}\right).$

All of these rules may be extended by obvious analogy when there are more than three variables involved, or when there is multiple summation.

Like most of the mechanical skills of mathematics, real facility in algebraic manipulation of summations comes only with practice. However, when puzzled or in doubt about the equivalence to two sums, you can usually check this equivalence by actually writing out the terms in the sums symbolized.

# THE ALGEBRA OF EXPECTATIONS

APPENDIX $\mathcal{B}$

A very prominent place in theoretical statistics is occupied by the concept of the mathematical expectation of a random variable $X$. If the distribution of $X$ is discrete, then the expectation (or expected value) of $X$ is defined to be

$$E(X) = \sum_X Xp(X)$$

where the sum is taken over all of the different values that the variable $X$ can assume, and

$$\sum_X p(X) = 1.00.$$

For a continuous random variable $X$ ranging over all the real numbers, the expectation is defined by

$$E(X) = \int_{-\infty}^{\infty} Xf(X)\, d(X)$$

where

$$\int_{-\infty}^{\infty} f(X)\, d(X) = 1.00.$$

In essence, the expectation defined in either of these ways is a kind of weighted sum of values, and thus the rules of summation have very close parallels in the rules for the algebraic treatment of expectations. These rules apply either to discrete or to continuous random variables if particular boundary conditions exist; for our purposes these rules can be used without our going further into these special qualifications.

RULE 1. If $a$ is some constant number, then

$$E(a) = a.$$

That is, if the same constant value $a$ were associated with each and every elementary event in some sample space, the expectation or mean of the values would most certainly be $a$.

**R U L E 2.** If $a$ is some constant real number and $X$ is a random variable with expectation $E(X)$, then

$$E(aX) = aE(X).$$

Suppose that a new random variable is formed by multiplying each value of $X$ by the constant number $a$. Then the expectation of the new random variable is just $a$ times the expectation of $X$. This is very simple to show for a discrete random variable $X$: By definition

$$E(aX) = \sum_X aX p(aX).$$

However, the probability of any value $aX$ must be exactly equal to the probability of the corresponding $X$ value, and so

$$E(aX) = \sum_X aX p(X) = a \sum_X X p(X) = aE(X).$$

**R U L E 3.** If $a$ is a constant real number and $X$ is a random variable, then

$$E(X + a) = E(X) + a.$$

This can be shown very simply for a discrete variable. Here,

$$E(X + a) = \sum_X (X + a) p(X + a)$$

$$= \sum_X X p(X + a) + a \sum_X p(X + a).$$

However, $p(X + a) = p(X)$ for each value of $X$, so that

$$E(X + a) = E(X) + a \sum_X p(X) = E(X) + a.$$

The expectations of functions of random variables, such as

$$E[(X + 2)^2]$$
$$E(\sqrt{X + b})$$
$$E(b^X),$$

to give only a few examples, are subject to the same algebraic rules as summations. That is, the operation indicated within the punctuation is to be carried out *before* the expectation is taken. It is most important that this be kept in mind during any algebraic argument involving summations. In general,

$$E[(X + 2)^2] \neq [E(X) + E(2)]^2$$
$$E(\sqrt{X}) \neq (\sqrt{E(X)})$$
$$E(b^X) \neq b^{E(X)}$$

and so forth.

The next few rules concern two (or more) random variables, symbolized by $X$ and $Y$.

**RULE 4.** If $X$ is a random variable with expectation $E(X)$, and $Y$ is a random variable with expectation $E(Y)$, then

$$E(X + Y) = E(X) + E(Y).$$

Verbally, this rule says that the expectation of a sum of two random variables is the sum of their expectations. Once again, the proof is simple for two discrete variables $X$ and $Y$. Consider the new random variable $(X + Y)$. The probability of a value of $(X + Y)$ involving a *particular* $X$ value and a *particular* $Y$ value is the joint probability $p(X,Y)$. Thus,

$$E(X + Y) = \sum_X \sum_Y (X + Y)p(X,Y).$$

Notice that here the expectation involves the sum over all possible *joint* events $(X,Y)$. This could be written as

$$E(X + Y) = \sum_X \sum_Y (X + Y)p(X,Y)$$
$$= \sum_X \sum_Y Xp(X,Y) + \sum_X \sum_Y Yp(X,Y).$$

However, for any fixed $X$,

$$\sum_Y p(X,Y) = p(X)$$

and for any fixed $Y$,

$$\sum_X p(X,Y) = p(Y).$$

Thus,

$$p(X + Y) = \sum_X Xp(X) + \sum_Y Yp(Y) = E(X) + E(Y).$$

In particular, one of the random variables may be in a functional relation to the other. For example, let $Y = 3X^2$. Then

$$E(X + Y) = E(X + 3X^2)$$
$$= E(X) + E(3X^2)$$
$$= E(X) + 3E(X^2).$$

This principle lets one *distribute* the expectation over an expression which itself has the form of a sum. We will make a great deal of use of this principle.

This rule may also be extended to any finite number of random variables:

**RULE 5.** Given some finite number of random variables, the expectation of the sum of those variables is the sum of their individual expectations. Thus,

$$E(X + Y + Z) = E(X) + E(Y) + E(Z)$$

and so on.

In particular, some of the random variables may be in functional relations to others. Let $Y = 6X^4$, and let $Z = \sqrt{2X}$. Then

$$E(X + 6X^4 + \sqrt{2X}) = E(X) + 6E(X^4) + E(\sqrt{2X}).$$

The next rule is a most important one that applies only to *independent* random variables (see Chapter 4):

**RULE 6.** Given random variable $X$ with expectation $E(X)$ and the random variable $Y$ with expectation $E(Y)$, then if $X$ and $Y$ are independent

$$E(XY) = E(X)E(Y).$$

This rule states that if random variables are *statistically independent*, the expectation of the product of these variables is the product of their separate expectations. An important corollary to this principle is:

If $E(XY) \neq E(X)E(Y)$, the variables $X$ and $Y$ are not independent.

The basis for rule 6 can also be shown fairly simply for discrete variables. Since $X$ and $Y$ are independent, $p(X,Y) = p(X)p(Y)$. Then,

$$E(XY) = \sum_X \sum_Y (XY)p(X)p(Y) = \sum_X \sum_Y Xp(X)Yp(Y).$$

However, for any fixed $X$, $Yp(Y)$ is perfectly free to be any value, so that

$$E(XY) = \sum_X Xp(X) \sum_Y Yp(Y) = E(X)E(Y).$$

By extension of rule 6 to any finite number of random variables we have:

**RULE 7.** Given any finite number of random variables, if all the variables are independent of each other, the expectation of their product is the product of their separate expectations: thus,

$$E(XYZ) = E(X)E(Y)E(Z),$$

and so on.

Incidentally, we will have occasion to use the idea of the *covariance* of two random variables, defined by

$$\text{cov.}(X,Y) = E[(X - E(X))(Y - E(Y))].$$

When $X$ and $Y$ are independent,

$$\text{cov.}(X,Y) = E[X - E(X)]E[Y - E(Y)]$$

by the rule given above. Since it is obvious that

$$E[X - E(X)] = E(X) - E(X) = 0$$

from rule 1 and rule 3, it follows that *when random variables are independent, their covariance is zero.* However, it is not necessarily true that zero covariance implies that the variables are independent.

Two more useful rules involve the variance of a random variable. The variance is defined by

$$\text{var.}(X) = \sigma_X^2 = E[X - E(X)]^2$$

or

$$\sigma_X^2 = E(X^2) - [E(X)]^2.$$

**RULE 8.** If $a$ is some constant real number, and if $X$ is a random variable with expectation $E(X)$ and variance $\sigma_X^2$, then the random variable $(X + a)$ has variance $\sigma_X^2$.

This can be shown as follows:

$$\text{var.}(X + a) = E[(X + a)^2] - [E(X + a)]^2.$$

By rule 3 above, and expanding the squares, we have

$$E[(X + a)^2] - [E(X + a)]^2 = E[(X^2 + 2Xa + a^2)] - [E(X) + a]^2$$
$$= E(X^2 + 2aX + a^2) - [E(X)]^2 - 2aE(X) - a^2.$$

Then by rules 4 and 1, we have

$$\text{var.}(X + a) = E(X^2) + 2aE(X) + a^2 - [E(X)]^2 - 2aE(X) - a^2$$
$$= E(X^2) - [E(X)]^2$$
$$= \sigma_X^2.$$

**RULE 9.** If $a$ is some constant real number, and if $X$ is a random variable with variance $\sigma_X^2$, the variance of the random variable $aX$ is

$$\text{var.}(aX) = a^2\sigma_X^2.$$

In order to show this, we take

$$\text{var.}(aX) = E[(aX)^2] - [E(aX)]^2$$
$$= a^2E(X^2) - a^2[E(X)]^2$$
$$= a^2(E(X^2) - [E(X)]^2)$$
$$= a^2\sigma_X^2.$$

In short, adding a constant value to each value of a random variable leaves the variance unchanged, but multiplying each value by a constant multiplies the variance by the square of the constant.

# TABLES

APPENDIX C

## Table I

### CUMULATIVE NORMAL PROBABILITIES

| z | F(z) | z | F(z) | z | F(z) | z | F(z) |
|---|------|---|------|---|------|---|------|
| .00 | .5000000 | .21 | .5831662 | .42 | .6627573 | .63 | .7356527 |
| .01 | .5039894 | .22 | .5870604 | .43 | .6664022 | .64 | .7389137 |
| .02 | .5079783 | .23 | .5909541 | .44 | .6700314 | .65 | .7421539 |
| .03 | .5119665 | .24 | .5948349 | .45 | .6736448 | .66 | .7453731 |
| .04 | .5159534 | .25 | .5987063 | .46 | .6772419 | .67 | .7485711 |
| .05 | .5199388 | .26 | .6025681 | .47 | .6808225 | .68 | .7517478 |
| .06 | .5239222 | .27 | .6064199 | .48 | .6843863 | .69 | .7549029 |
| .07 | .5279032 | .28 | .6102612 | .49 | .6879331 | .70 | .7580363 |
| .08 | .5318814 | .29 | .6140919 | .50 | .6914625 | .71 | .7611479 |
| .09 | .5358564 | .30 | .6179114 | .51 | .6949743 | .72 | .7642375 |
| .10 | .5398278 | .31 | .6217195 | .52 | .6984682 | .73 | .7673049 |
| .11 | .5437953 | .32 | .6255158 | .53 | .7019440 | .74 | .7703500 |
| .12 | .5477584 | .33 | .6293000 | .54 | .7054015 | .75 | .7733726 |
| .13 | .5517168 | .34 | .6330717 | .55 | .7088403 | .76 | .7763727 |
| .14 | .5556700 | .35 | .6368307 | .56 | .7122603 | .77 | .7793501 |
| .15 | .5596177 | .36 | .6405764 | .57 | .7156612 | .78 | .7823046 |
| .16 | .5635595 | .37 | .6443088 | .58 | .7190427 | .79 | .7852361 |
| .17 | .5674949 | .38 | .6480273 | .59 | .7224047 | .80 | .7881446 |
| .18 | .5714237 | .39 | .6517317 | .60 | .7257469 | .81 | .7910299 |
| .19 | .5753454 | .40 | .6554217 | .61 | .7290691 | .82 | .7938919 |
| .20 | .5792597 | .41 | .6590970 | .62 | .7323711 | .83 | .7967306 |

*Table I* | *673*

Table I (continued)

| z | F(z) | z | F(z) | z | F(z) | z | F(z) |
|---|------|---|------|---|------|---|------|
| .84 | .7995458 | 1.32 | .9065825 | 1.79 | .9632730 | 2.26 | .9880894 |
| .85 | .8023375 | 1.33 | .9082409 | 1.80 | .9640697 | 2.27 | .9883962 |
| .86 | .8051055 | 1.34 | .9098773 | 1.81 | .9648521 | 2.28 | .9886962 |
| .87 | .8078498 | 1.35 | .9114920 | 1.82 | .9656205 | 2.29 | .9889893 |
| .88 | .8105703 | 1.36 | .9130850 | 1.83 | .9663750 | 2.30 | .9892759 |
| .89 | .8132671 | 1.37 | .9146565 | 1.84 | .9671159 | 2.31 | .9895559 |
| .90 | .8159399 | 1.38 | .9162067 | 1.85 | .9678432 | 2.32 | .9898296 |
| .91 | .8185887 | 1.39 | .9177356 | 1.86 | .9685572 | 2.33 | .9900969 |
| .92 | .8212136 | 1.40 | .9192433 | 1.87 | .9692581 | 2.34 | .9903581 |
| .93 | .8238145 | 1.41 | .9207302 | 1.88 | .9699460 | 2.35 | .9906133 |
| .94 | .8263912 | 1.42 | .9221962 | 1.89 | .9706210 | 2.36 | .9908625 |
| .95 | .8289439 | 1.43 | .9236415 | 1.90 | .9712834 | 2.37 | .9911060 |
| .96 | .8314724 | 1.44 | .9250663 | 1.91 | .9719334 | 2.38 | .9913437 |
| .97 | .8339768 | 1.45 | .9264707 | 1.92 | .9725711 | 2.39 | .9915758 |
| .98 | .8364569 | 1.46 | .9278550 | 1.93 | .9731966 | 2.40 | .9918025 |
| .99 | .8389129 | 1.47 | .9292191 | 1.94 | .9738102 | 2.41 | .9920237 |
| 1.00 | .8413447 | 1.48 | .9305634 | 1.95 | .9744119 | 2.42 | .9922397 |
| 1.01 | .8437524 | 1.49 | .9318879 | 1.96 | .9750021 | 2.43 | .9924506 |
| 1.02 | .8461358 | 1.50 | .9331928 | 1.97 | .9755808 | 2.44 | .9926564 |
| 1.03 | .8484950 | 1.51 | .9344783 | 1.98 | .9761482 | 2.45 | .9928572 |
| 1.04 | .8508300 | 1.52 | .9357445 | 1.99 | .9767045 | 2.46 | .9930531 |
| 1.05 | .8531409 | 1.53 | .9369916 | 2.00 | .9772499 | 2.47 | .9932443 |
| 1.06 | .8554277 | 1.54 | .9382198 | 2.01 | .9777844 | 2.48 | .9934309 |
| 1.07 | .8576903 | 1.55 | .9394292 | 2.02 | .9783083 | 2.49 | .9936128 |
| 1.08 | .8599289 | 1.56 | .9406201 | 2.03 | .9788217 | 2.50 | .9937903 |
| 1.09 | .8621434 | 1.57 | .9417924 | 2.04 | .9793248 | 2.51 | .9939634 |
| 1.10 | .8643339 | 1.58 | .9429466 | 2.05 | .9798178 | 2.52 | .9941323 |
| 1.11 | .8665005 | 1.59 | .9440826 | 2.06 | .9803007 | 2.53 | .9942969 |
| 1.12 | .8686431 | 1.60 | .9452007 | 2.07 | .9807738 | 2.54 | .9944574 |
| 1.13 | .8707619 | 1.61 | .9463011 | 2.08 | .9812372 | 2.55 | .9946139 |
| 1.14 | .8728568 | 1.62 | .9473839 | 2.09 | .9816911 | 2.56 | .9947664 |
| 1.15 | .8749281 | 1.63 | .9484493 | 2.10 | .9821356 | 2.57 | .9949151 |
| 1.16 | .8769756 | 1.64 | .9494974 | 2.11 | .9825708 | 2.58 | .9950600 |
| 1.17 | .8789995 | 1.65 | .9505285 | 2.12 | .9829970 | 2.59 | .9952012 |
| 1.18 | .8809999 | 1.66 | .9515428 | 2.13 | .9834142 | 2.60 | .9953388 |
| 1.19 | .8829768 | 1.67 | .9525403 | 2.14 | .9838226 | 2.70 | .9965330 |
| 1.20 | .8849303 | 1.68 | .9535213 | 2.15 | .9842224 | 2.80 | .9974449 |
| 1.21 | .8868606 | 1.69 | .9544860 | 2.16 | .9846137 | 2.90 | .9981342 |
| 1.22 | .8887676 | 1.70 | .9554345 | 2.17 | .9849966 | 3.00 | .9986501 |
| 1.23 | .8906514 | 1.71 | .9563671 | 2.18 | .9853713 | 3.20 | .9993129 |
| 1.24 | .8925123 | 1.72 | .9572838 | 2.19 | .9857379 | 3.40 | .9996631 |
| 1.25 | .8943502 | 1.73 | .9581849 | 2.20 | .9860966 | 3.60 | .9998409 |
| 1.26 | .8961653 | 1.74 | .9590705 | 2.21 | .9864474 | 3.80 | .9999277 |
| 1.27 | .8979577 | 1.75 | .9599408 | 2.22 | .9867906 | 4.00 | .9999683 |
| 1.28 | .8997274 | 1.76 | .9607961 | 2.23 | .9871263 | 4.50 | .9999966 |
| 1.29 | .9014747 | 1.77 | .9616364 | 2.24 | .9874545 | 5.00 | .9999997 |
| 1.30 | .9031995 | 1.78 | .9624620 | 2.25 | .9877755 | 5.50 | .9999999 |
| 1.31 | .9049021 | | | | | | |

## Table II
### UPPER PERCENTAGE POINTS OF THE $t$ DISTRIBUTION

| $\nu$ | $Q = 0.4$ $2Q = 0.8$ | 0.25 0.5 | 0.1 0.2 | 0.05 0.1 | 0.025 0.05 | 0.01 0.02 | 0.005 0.01 | 0.001 0.002 |
|---|---|---|---|---|---|---|---|---|
| 1 | 0.325 | 1.000 | 3.078 | 6.314 | 12.706 | 31.821 | 63.657 | 318.31 |
| 2 | .289 | 0.816 | 1.886 | 2.920 | 4.303 | 6.965 | 9.925 | 22.326 |
| 3 | .277 | .765 | 1.638 | 2.353 | 3.182 | 4.541 | 5.841 | 10.213 |
| 4 | .271 | .741 | 1.533 | 2.132 | 2.776 | 3.747 | 4.604 | 7.173 |
| 5 | 0.267 | 0.727 | 1.476 | 2.015 | 2.571 | 3.365 | 4.032 | 5.893 |
| 6 | .265 | .718 | 1.440 | 1.943 | 2.447 | 3.143 | 3.707 | 5.208 |
| 7 | .263 | .711 | 1.415 | 1.895 | 2.365 | 2.998 | 3.499 | 4.785 |
| 8 | .262 | .706 | 1.397 | 1.860 | 2.306 | 2.896 | 3.355 | 4.501 |
| 9 | .261 | .703 | 1.383 | 1.833 | 2.262 | 2.821 | 3.250 | 4.297 |
| 10 | 0.260 | 0.700 | 1.372 | 1.812 | 2.228 | 2.764 | 3.169 | 4.144 |
| 11 | .260 | .697 | 1.363 | 1.796 | 2.201 | 2.718 | 3.106 | 4.025 |
| 12 | .259 | .695 | 1.356 | 1.782 | 2.179 | 2.681 | 3.055 | 3.930 |
| 13 | .259 | .694 | 1.350 | 1.771 | 2.160 | 2.650 | 3.012 | 3.852 |
| 14 | .258 | .692 | 1.345 | 1.761 | 2.145 | 2.624 | 2.977 | 3.787 |
| 15 | 0.258 | 0.691 | 1.341 | 1.753 | 2.131 | 2.602 | 2.947 | 3.733 |
| 16 | .258 | .690 | 1.337 | 1.746 | 2.120 | 2.583 | 2.921 | 3.686 |
| 17 | .257 | .689 | 1.333 | 1.740 | 2.110 | 2.567 | 2.898 | 3.646 |
| 18 | .257 | .688 | 1.330 | 1.734 | 2.101 | 2.552 | 2.878 | 3.610 |
| 19 | .257 | .688 | 1.328 | 1.729 | 2.093 | 2.539 | 2.861 | 3.579 |
| 20 | 0.257 | 0.687 | 1.325 | 1.725 | 2.086 | 2.528 | 2.845 | 3.552 |
| 21 | .257 | .686 | 1.323 | 1.721 | 2.080 | 2.518 | 2.831 | 3.527 |
| 22 | .256 | .686 | 1.321 | 1.717 | 2.074 | 2.508 | 2.819 | 3.505 |
| 23 | .256 | .685 | 1.319 | 1.714 | 2.069 | 2.500 | 2.807 | 3.485 |
| 24 | .256 | .685 | 1.318 | 1.711 | 2.064 | 2.492 | 2.797 | 3.467 |
| 25 | 0.256 | 0.684 | 1.316 | 1.708 | 2.060 | 2.485 | 2.787 | 3.450 |
| 26 | .256 | .684 | 1.315 | 1.706 | 2.056 | 2.479 | 2.779 | 3.435 |
| 27 | .256 | .684 | 1.314 | 1.703 | 2.052 | 2.473 | 2.771 | 3.421 |
| 28 | .256 | .683 | 1.313 | 1.701 | 2.048 | 2.467 | 2.763 | 3.408 |
| 29 | .256 | .683 | 1.311 | 1.699 | 2.045 | 2.462 | 2.756 | 3.396 |
| 30 | 0.256 | 0.683 | 1.310 | 1.697 | 2.042 | 2.457 | 2.750 | 3.385 |
| 40 | .255 | .681 | 1.303 | 1.684 | 2.021 | 2.423 | 2.704 | 3.307 |
| 60 | .254 | .679 | 1.296 | 1.671 | 2.000 | 2.390 | 2.660 | 3.232 |
| 120 | .254 | .677 | 1.289 | 1.658 | 1.980 | 2.358 | 2.617 | 3.160 |
| ∞ | .253 | .674 | 1.282 | 1.645 | 1.960 | 2.326 | 2.576 | 3.090 |

This table is condensed from Table 12 of the *Biometrika Tables for Statisticians*, Vol. 1 (ed. 1), edited by E. S. Pearson and H. O. Hartley. Reproduced here with the kind permission of E. S. Pearson and the trustees of *Biometrika*.

*Table III* | *675*

## Table III
### UPPER PERCENTAGE POINTS OF THE $\chi^2$ DISTRIBUTION

| $\nu$ \ $Q$ | 0.995 | 0.990 | 0.975 | 0.950 | 0.900 | 0.750 | 0.500 |
|---|---|---|---|---|---|---|---|
| 1 | $392704 \cdot 10^{-10}$ | $157088 \cdot 10^{-9}$ | $982069 \cdot 10^{-9}$ | $393214 \cdot 10^{-8}$ | 0.0157908 | 0.1015308 | 0.454937 |
| 2 | 0.0100251 | 0.0201007 | 0.0506356 | 0.102587 | 0.210720 | 0.575364 | 1.38629 |
| 3 | 0.0717212 | 0.114832 | 0.215795 | 0.351846 | 0.584375 | 1.212534 | 2.36597 |
| 4 | 0.206990 | 0.297110 | 0.484419 | 0.710721 | 1.063623 | 1.92255 | 3.35670 |
| 5 | 0.411740 | 0.554300 | 0.831211 | 1.145476 | 1.61031 | 2.67460 | 4.35146 |
| 6 | 0.675727 | 0.872085 | 1.237347 | 1.63539 | 2.20413 | 3.45460 | 5.34812 |
| 7 | 0.989265 | 1.239043 | 1.68987 | 2.16735 | 2.83311 | 4.25485 | 6.34581 |
| 8 | 1.344419 | 1.646482 | 2.17973 | 2.73264 | 3.48954 | 5.07064 | 7.34412 |
| 9 | 1.734926 | 2.087912 | 2.70039 | 3.32511 | 4.16816 | 5.89883 | 8.34283 |
| 10 | 2.15585 | 2.55821 | 3.24697 | 3.94030 | 4.86518 | 6.73720 | 9.34182 |
| 11 | 2.60321 | 3.05347 | 3.81575 | 4.57481 | 5.57779 | 7.58412 | 10.3410 |
| 12 | 3.07382 | 3.57056 | 4.40379 | 5.22603 | 6.30380 | 8.43842 | 11.3403 |
| 13 | 3.56503 | 4.10691 | 5.00874 | 5.89186 | 7.04150 | 9.29906 | 12.3398 |
| 14 | 4.07468 | 4.66043 | 5.62872 | 6.57063 | 7.78953 | 10.1653 | 13.3393 |
| 15 | 4.60094 | 5.22935 | 6.26214 | 7.26094 | 8.54675 | 11.0365 | 14.3389 |
| 16 | 5.14224 | 5.81221 | 6.90766 | 7.96164 | 9.31223 | 11.9122 | 15.3385 |
| 17 | 5.69724 | 6.40776 | 7.56418 | 8.67176 | 10.0852 | 12.7919 | 16.3381 |
| 18 | 6.26481 | 7.01491 | 8.23075 | 9.39046 | 10.8649 | 13.6753 | 17.3379 |
| 19 | 6.84398 | 7.63273 | 8.90655 | 10.1170 | 11.6509 | 14.5620 | 18.3376 |
| 20 | 7.43386 | 8.26040 | 9.59083 | 10.8508 | 12.4426 | 15.4518 | 19.3374 |
| 21 | 8.03366 | 8.89720 | 10.28293 | 11.5913 | 13.2396 | 16.3444 | 20.3372 |
| 22 | 8.64272 | 9.54249 | 10.9823 | 12.3380 | 14.0415 | 17.2396 | 21.3370 |
| 23 | 9.26042 | 10.19567 | 11.6885 | 13.0905 | 14.8479 | 18.1373 | 22.3369 |
| 24 | 9.88623 | 10.8564 | 12.4011 | 13.8484 | 15.6587 | 19.0372 | 23.3367 |
| 25 | 10.5197 | 11.5240 | 13.1197 | 14.6114 | 16.4734 | 19.9393 | 24.3366 |
| 26 | 11.1603 | 12.1981 | 13.8439 | 15.3791 | 17.2919 | 20.8434 | 25.3364 |
| 27 | 11.8076 | 12.8786 | 14.5733 | 16.1513 | 18.1138 | 21.7494 | 26.3363 |
| 28 | 12.4613 | 13.5648 | 15.3079 | 16.9279 | 18.9392 | 22.6572 | 27.3363 |
| 29 | 13.1211 | 14.2565 | 16.0471 | 17.7083 | 19.7677 | 23.5666 | 28.3362 |
| 30 | 13.7867 | 14.9535 | 16.7908 | 18.4926 | 20.5992 | 24.4776 | 29.3360 |
| 40 | 20.7065 | 22.1643 | 24.4331 | 26.5093 | 29.0505 | 33.6603 | 39.3354 |
| 50 | 27.9907 | 29.7067 | 32.3574 | 34.7642 | 37.6886 | 42.9421 | 49.3349 |
| 60 | 35.5346 | 37.4848 | 40.4817 | 43.1879 | 46.4589 | 52.2938 | 59.3347 |
| 70 | 43.2752 | 45.4418 | 48.7576 | 51.7393 | 55.3290 | 61.6983 | 69.3344 |
| 80 | 51.1720 | 53.5400 | 57.1532 | 60.3915 | 64.2778 | 71.1445 | 79.3343 |
| 90 | 59.1963 | 61.7541 | 65.6466 | 69.1260 | 73.2912 | 80.6247 | 89.3342 |
| 100 | 67.3276 | 70.0648 | 74.2219 | 77.9295 | 82.3581 | 90.1332 | 99.3341 |
| $z_Q$ | $-2.5758$ | $-2.3263$ | $-1.9600$ | $-1.6449$ | $-1.2816$ | $-0.6745$ | 0.0000 |

## Table III (continued)

| $\nu$ \ $Q$ | 0.250 | 0.100 | 0.050 | 0.025 | 0.010 | 0.005 | 0.001 |
|---|---|---|---|---|---|---|---|
| 1 | 1.32330 | 2.70554 | 3.84146 | 5.02389 | 6.63490 | 7.87944 | 10.828 |
| 2 | 2.77259 | 4.60517 | 5.99147 | 7.37776 | 9.21034 | 10.5966 | 13.816 |
| 3 | 4.10835 | 6.25139 | 7.81473 | 9.34840 | 11.3449 | 12.8381 | 16.266 |
| 4 | 5.38527 | 7.77944 | 9.48773 | 11.1433 | 13.2767 | 14.8602 | 18.467 |
| 5 | 6.62568 | 9.23635 | 11.0705 | 12.8325 | 15.0863 | 16.7496 | 20.515 |
| 6 | 7.84080 | 10.6446 | 12.5916 | 14.4494 | 16.8119 | 18.5476 | 22.458 |
| 7 | 9.03715 | 12.0170 | 14.0671 | 16.0128 | 18.4753 | 20.2777 | 24.322 |
| 8 | 10.2188 | 13.3616 | 15.5073 | 17.5346 | 20.0902 | 21.9550 | 26.125 |
| 9 | 11.3887 | 14.6837 | 16.9190 | 19.0228 | 21.6660 | 23.5893 | 27.877 |
| 10 | 12.5489 | 15.9871 | 18.3070 | 20.4831 | 23.2093 | 25.1882 | 29.588 |
| 11 | 13.7007 | 17.2750 | 19.6751 | 21.9200 | 24.7250 | 26.7569 | 31.264 |
| 12 | 14.8454 | 18.5494 | 21.0261 | 23.3367 | 26.2170 | 28.2995 | 32.909 |
| 13 | 15.9839 | 19.8119 | 22.3621 | 24.7356 | 27.6883 | 29.8194 | 34.528 |
| 14 | 17.1170 | 21.0642 | 23.6848 | 26.1190 | 29.1413 | 31.3193 | 36.123 |
| 15 | 18.2451 | 22.3072 | 24.9958 | 27.4884 | 30.5779 | 32.8013 | 37.697 |
| 16 | 19.3688 | 23.5418 | 26.2962 | 28.8454 | 31.9999 | 34.2672 | 39.252 |
| 17 | 20.4887 | 24.7690 | 27.5871 | 30.1910 | 33.4087 | 35.7185 | 40.790 |
| 18 | 21.6049 | 25.9894 | 28.8693 | 31.5264 | 34.8053 | 37.1564 | 42.312 |
| 19 | 22.7178 | 27.2036 | 30.1435 | 32.8523 | 36.1908 | 38.5822 | 43.820 |
| 20 | 23.8277 | 28.4120 | 31.4104 | 34.1696 | 37.5662 | 39.9968 | 45.315 |
| 21 | 24.9348 | 29.6151 | 32.6705 | 35.4789 | 38.9321 | 41.4010 | 46.797 |
| 22 | 26.0393 | 30.8133 | 33.9244 | 36.7807 | 40.2894 | 42.7956 | 48.268 |
| 23 | 27.1413 | 32.0069 | 35.1725 | 38.0757 | 41.6384 | 44.1813 | 49.728 |
| 24 | 28.2412 | 33.1963 | 36.4151 | 39.3641 | 42.9798 | 45.5585 | 51.179 |
| 25 | 29.3389 | 34.3816 | 37.6525 | 40.6465 | 44.3141 | 46.9278 | 52.620 |
| 26 | 30.4345 | 35.5631 | 38.8852 | 41.9232 | 45.6417 | 48.2899 | 54.052 |
| 27 | 31.5284 | 36.7412 | 40.1133 | 43.1944 | 46.9630 | 49.6449 | 55.476 |
| 28 | 32.6205 | 37.9159 | 41.3372 | 44.4607 | 48.2782 | 50.9933 | 56.892 |
| 29 | 33.7109 | 39.0875 | 42.5569 | 45.7222 | 49.5879 | 52.3356 | 58.302 |
| 30 | 34.7998 | 40.2560 | 43.7729 | 46.9792 | 50.8922 | 53.6720 | 59.703 |
| 40 | 45.6160 | 51.8050 | 55.7585 | 59.3417 | 63.6907 | 66.7659 | 73.402 |
| 50 | 56.3336 | 63.1671 | 67.5048 | 71.4202 | 76.1539 | 79.4900 | 86.661 |
| 60 | 66.9814 | 74.3970 | 79.0819 | 83.2976 | 88.3794 | 91.9517 | 99.607 |
| 70 | 77.5766 | 85.5271 | 90.5312 | 95.0231 | 100.425 | 104.215 | 112.317 |
| 80 | 88.1303 | 96.5782 | 101.879 | 106.629 | 112.329 | 116.321 | 124.839 |
| 90 | 98.6499 | 107.565 | 113.145 | 118.136 | 124.116 | 128.299 | 137.208 |
| 100 | 109.141 | 118.498 | 124.342 | 129.561 | 135.807 | 140.169 | 149.449 |
| $z_Q$ | +0.6745 | +1.2816 | +1.6449 | +1.9600 | +2.3263 | +2.5758 | +3.0902 |

*Table IV* | 677

## Table IV

### PERCENTAGE POINTS OF THE $F$ DISTRIBUTION
### UPPER 5% POINTS

| $\nu_2 \backslash \nu_1$ | 1 | 2 | 3 | 4 | 5 | 6 | 7 | 8 | 9 | 10 | 12 | 15 | 20 | 24 | 30 | 40 | 60 | 120 | ∞ |
|---|---|---|---|---|---|---|---|---|---|---|---|---|---|---|---|---|---|---|---|
| 1 | 161.4 | 199.5 | 215.7 | 224.6 | 230.2 | 234.0 | 236.8 | 238.9 | 240.5 | 241.9 | 243.9 | 245.9 | 248.0 | 249.1 | 250.1 | 251.1 | 252.2 | 253.3 | 254.3 |
| 2 | 18.51 | 19.00 | 19.16 | 19.25 | 19.30 | 19.33 | 19.35 | 19.37 | 19.38 | 19.40 | 19.41 | 19.43 | 19.45 | 19.45 | 19.46 | 19.47 | 19.48 | 19.49 | 19.50 |
| 3 | 10.13 | 9.55 | 9.28 | 9.12 | 9.01 | 8.94 | 8.89 | 8.85 | 8.81 | 8.79 | 8.74 | 8.70 | 8.66 | 8.64 | 8.62 | 8.59 | 8.57 | 8.55 | 8.53 |
| 4 | 7.71 | 6.94 | 6.59 | 6.39 | 6.26 | 6.16 | 6.09 | 6.04 | 6.00 | 5.96 | 5.91 | 5.86 | 5.80 | 5.77 | 5.75 | 5.72 | 5.69 | 5.66 | 5.63 |
| 5 | 6.61 | 5.79 | 5.41 | 5.19 | 5.05 | 4.95 | 4.88 | 4.82 | 4.77 | 4.74 | 4.68 | 4.62 | 4.56 | 4.53 | 4.50 | 4.46 | 4.43 | 4.40 | 4.36 |
| 6 | 5.99 | 5.14 | 4.76 | 4.53 | 4.39 | 4.28 | 4.21 | 4.15 | 4.10 | 4.06 | 4.00 | 3.94 | 3.87 | 3.84 | 3.81 | 3.77 | 3.74 | 3.70 | 3.67 |
| 7 | 5.59 | 4.74 | 4.35 | 4.12 | 3.97 | 3.87 | 3.79 | 3.73 | 3.68 | 3.64 | 3.57 | 3.51 | 3.44 | 3.41 | 3.38 | 3.34 | 3.30 | 3.27 | 3.23 |
| 8 | 5.32 | 4.46 | 4.07 | 3.84 | 3.69 | 3.58 | 3.50 | 3.44 | 3.39 | 3.35 | 3.28 | 3.22 | 3.15 | 3.12 | 3.08 | 3.04 | 3.01 | 2.97 | 2.93 |
| 9 | 5.12 | 4.26 | 3.86 | 3.63 | 3.48 | 3.37 | 3.29 | 3.23 | 3.18 | 3.14 | 3.07 | 3.01 | 2.94 | 2.90 | 2.86 | 2.83 | 2.79 | 2.75 | 2.71 |
| 10 | 4.96 | 4.10 | 3.71 | 3.48 | 3.33 | 3.22 | 3.14 | 3.07 | 3.02 | 2.98 | 2.91 | 2.85 | 2.77 | 2.74 | 2.70 | 2.66 | 2.62 | 2.58 | 2.54 |
| 11 | 4.84 | 3.98 | 3.59 | 3.36 | 3.20 | 3.09 | 3.01 | 2.95 | 2.90 | 2.85 | 2.79 | 2.72 | 2.65 | 2.61 | 2.57 | 2.53 | 2.49 | 2.45 | 2.40 |
| 12 | 4.75 | 3.89 | 3.49 | 3.26 | 3.11 | 3.00 | 2.91 | 2.85 | 2.80 | 2.75 | 2.69 | 2.62 | 2.54 | 2.51 | 2.47 | 2.43 | 2.38 | 2.34 | 2.30 |
| 13 | 4.67 | 3.81 | 3.41 | 3.18 | 3.03 | 2.92 | 2.83 | 2.77 | 2.71 | 2.67 | 2.60 | 2.53 | 2.46 | 2.42 | 2.38 | 2.34 | 2.30 | 2.25 | 2.21 |
| 14 | 4.60 | 3.74 | 3.34 | 3.11 | 2.96 | 2.85 | 2.76 | 2.70 | 2.65 | 2.60 | 2.53 | 2.46 | 2.39 | 2.35 | 2.31 | 2.27 | 2.22 | 2.18 | 2.13 |
| 15 | 4.54 | 3.68 | 3.29 | 3.06 | 2.90 | 2.79 | 2.71 | 2.64 | 2.59 | 2.54 | 2.48 | 2.40 | 2.33 | 2.29 | 2.25 | 2.20 | 2.16 | 2.11 | 2.07 |
| 16 | 4.49 | 3.63 | 3.24 | 3.01 | 2.85 | 2.74 | 2.66 | 2.59 | 2.54 | 2.49 | 2.42 | 2.35 | 2.28 | 2.24 | 2.19 | 2.15 | 2.11 | 2.06 | 2.01 |
| 17 | 4.45 | 3.59 | 3.20 | 2.96 | 2.81 | 2.70 | 2.61 | 2.55 | 2.49 | 2.45 | 2.38 | 2.31 | 2.23 | 2.19 | 2.15 | 2.10 | 2.06 | 2.01 | 1.96 |
| 18 | 4.41 | 3.55 | 3.16 | 2.93 | 2.77 | 2.66 | 2.58 | 2.51 | 2.46 | 2.41 | 2.34 | 2.27 | 2.19 | 2.15 | 2.11 | 2.06 | 2.02 | 1.97 | 1.92 |
| 19 | 4.38 | 3.52 | 3.13 | 2.90 | 2.74 | 2.63 | 2.54 | 2.48 | 2.42 | 2.38 | 2.31 | 2.23 | 2.16 | 2.11 | 2.07 | 2.03 | 1.98 | 1.93 | 1.88 |
| 20 | 4.35 | 3.49 | 3.10 | 2.87 | 2.71 | 2.60 | 2.51 | 2.45 | 2.39 | 2.35 | 2.28 | 2.20 | 2.12 | 2.08 | 2.04 | 1.99 | 1.95 | 1.90 | 1.84 |
| 21 | 4.32 | 3.47 | 3.07 | 2.84 | 2.68 | 2.57 | 2.49 | 2.42 | 2.37 | 2.32 | 2.25 | 2.18 | 2.10 | 2.05 | 2.01 | 1.96 | 1.92 | 1.87 | 1.81 |
| 22 | 4.30 | 3.44 | 3.05 | 2.82 | 2.66 | 2.55 | 2.46 | 2.40 | 2.34 | 2.30 | 2.23 | 2.15 | 2.07 | 2.03 | 1.98 | 1.94 | 1.89 | 1.84 | 1.78 |
| 23 | 4.28 | 3.42 | 3.03 | 2.80 | 2.64 | 2.53 | 2.44 | 2.37 | 2.32 | 2.27 | 2.20 | 2.13 | 2.05 | 2.01 | 1.96 | 1.91 | 1.86 | 1.81 | 1.76 |
| 24 | 4.26 | 3.40 | 3.01 | 2.78 | 2.62 | 2.51 | 2.42 | 2.36 | 2.30 | 2.25 | 2.18 | 2.11 | 2.03 | 1.98 | 1.94 | 1.89 | 1.84 | 1.79 | 1.73 |
| 25 | 4.24 | 3.39 | 2.99 | 2.76 | 2.60 | 2.49 | 2.40 | 2.34 | 2.28 | 2.24 | 2.16 | 2.09 | 2.01 | 1.96 | 1.92 | 1.87 | 1.82 | 1.77 | 1.71 |
| 26 | 4.23 | 3.37 | 2.98 | 2.74 | 2.59 | 2.47 | 2.39 | 2.32 | 2.27 | 2.22 | 2.15 | 2.07 | 1.99 | 1.95 | 1.90 | 1.85 | 1.80 | 1.75 | 1.69 |
| 27 | 4.21 | 3.35 | 2.96 | 2.73 | 2.57 | 2.46 | 2.37 | 2.31 | 2.25 | 2.20 | 2.13 | 2.06 | 1.97 | 1.93 | 1.88 | 1.84 | 1.79 | 1.73 | 1.67 |
| 28 | 4.20 | 3.34 | 2.95 | 2.71 | 2.56 | 2.45 | 2.36 | 2.29 | 2.24 | 2.19 | 2.12 | 2.04 | 1.96 | 1.91 | 1.87 | 1.82 | 1.77 | 1.71 | 1.65 |
| 29 | 4.18 | 3.33 | 2.93 | 2.70 | 2.55 | 2.43 | 2.35 | 2.28 | 2.22 | 2.18 | 2.10 | 2.03 | 1.94 | 1.90 | 1.85 | 1.81 | 1.75 | 1.70 | 1.64 |
| 30 | 4.17 | 3.32 | 2.92 | 2.69 | 2.53 | 2.42 | 2.33 | 2.27 | 2.21 | 2.16 | 2.09 | 2.01 | 1.93 | 1.89 | 1.84 | 1.79 | 1.74 | 1.68 | 1.62 |
| 40 | 4.08 | 3.23 | 2.84 | 2.61 | 2.45 | 2.34 | 2.25 | 2.18 | 2.12 | 2.08 | 2.00 | 1.92 | 1.84 | 1.79 | 1.74 | 1.69 | 1.64 | 1.58 | 1.51 |
| 60 | 4.00 | 3.15 | 2.76 | 2.53 | 2.37 | 2.25 | 2.17 | 2.10 | 2.04 | 1.99 | 1.92 | 1.84 | 1.75 | 1.70 | 1.65 | 1.59 | 1.53 | 1.47 | 1.39 |
| 120 | 3.92 | 3.07 | 2.68 | 2.45 | 2.29 | 2.17 | 2.09 | 2.02 | 1.96 | 1.91 | 1.83 | 1.75 | 1.66 | 1.61 | 1.55 | 1.50 | 1.43 | 1.35 | 1.25 |
| ∞ | 3.84 | 3.00 | 2.60 | 2.37 | 2.21 | 2.10 | 2.01 | 1.94 | 1.88 | 1.83 | 1.75 | 1.67 | 1.57 | 1.52 | 1.46 | 1.39 | 1.32 | 1.22 | 1.00 |

**Table IV (continued)**
UPPER 2.5% POINTS

| $\nu_2$ \ $\nu_1$ | 1 | 2 | 3 | 4 | 5 | 6 | 7 | 8 | 9 | 10 | 12 | 15 | 20 | 24 | 30 | 40 | 60 | 120 | ∞ |
|---|---|---|---|---|---|---|---|---|---|---|---|---|---|---|---|---|---|---|---|
| 1 | 647.8 | 799.5 | 864.2 | 899.6 | 921.8 | 937.1 | 948.2 | 956.7 | 963.3 | 968.6 | 976.7 | 984.9 | 993.1 | 997.2 | 1001 | 1006 | 1010 | 1014 | 1018 |
| 2 | 38.51 | 39.00 | 39.17 | 39.25 | 39.30 | 39.33 | 39.36 | 39.37 | 39.39 | 39.40 | 39.41 | 39.43 | 39.45 | 39.46 | 39.46 | 39.47 | 39.48 | 39.49 | 39.50 |
| 3 | 17.44 | 16.04 | 15.44 | 15.10 | 14.88 | 14.73 | 14.62 | 14.54 | 14.47 | 14.42 | 14.34 | 14.25 | 14.17 | 14.12 | 14.08 | 14.04 | 13.99 | 13.95 | 13.90 |
| 4 | 12.22 | 10.65 | 9.98 | 9.60 | 9.36 | 9.20 | 9.07 | 8.98 | 8.90 | 8.84 | 8.75 | 8.66 | 8.56 | 8.51 | 8.46 | 8.41 | 8.36 | 8.31 | 8.26 |
| 5 | 10.01 | 8.43 | 7.76 | 7.39 | 7.15 | 6.98 | 6.85 | 6.76 | 6.68 | 6.62 | 6.52 | 6.43 | 6.33 | 6.28 | 6.23 | 6.18 | 6.12 | 6.07 | 6.02 |
| 6 | 8.81 | 7.26 | 6.60 | 6.23 | 5.99 | 5.82 | 5.70 | 5.60 | 5.52 | 5.46 | 5.37 | 5.27 | 5.17 | 5.12 | 5.07 | 5.01 | 4.96 | 4.90 | 4.85 |
| 7 | 8.07 | 6.54 | 5.89 | 5.52 | 5.29 | 5.12 | 4.99 | 4.90 | 4.82 | 4.76 | 4.67 | 4.57 | 4.47 | 4.42 | 4.36 | 4.31 | 4.25 | 4.20 | 4.14 |
| 8 | 7.57 | 6.06 | 5.42 | 5.05 | 4.82 | 4.65 | 4.53 | 4.43 | 4.36 | 4.30 | 4.20 | 4.10 | 4.00 | 3.95 | 3.89 | 3.84 | 3.78 | 3.73 | 3.67 |
| 9 | 7.21 | 5.71 | 5.08 | 4.72 | 4.48 | 4.32 | 4.20 | 4.10 | 4.03 | 3.96 | 3.87 | 3.77 | 3.67 | 3.61 | 3.56 | 3.51 | 3.45 | 3.39 | 3.33 |
| 10 | 6.94 | 5.46 | 4.83 | 4.47 | 4.24 | 4.07 | 3.95 | 3.85 | 3.78 | 3.72 | 3.62 | 3.52 | 3.42 | 3.37 | 3.31 | 3.26 | 3.20 | 3.14 | 3.08 |
| 11 | 6.72 | 5.26 | 4.63 | 4.28 | 4.04 | 3.88 | 3.76 | 3.66 | 3.59 | 3.53 | 3.43 | 3.33 | 3.23 | 3.17 | 3.12 | 3.06 | 3.00 | 2.94 | 2.88 |
| 12 | 6.55 | 5.10 | 4.47 | 4.12 | 3.89 | 3.73 | 3.61 | 3.51 | 3.44 | 3.37 | 3.28 | 3.18 | 3.07 | 3.02 | 2.96 | 2.91 | 2.85 | 2.79 | 2.72 |
| 13 | 6.41 | 4.97 | 4.35 | 4.00 | 3.77 | 3.60 | 3.48 | 3.39 | 3.31 | 3.25 | 3.15 | 3.05 | 2.95 | 2.89 | 2.84 | 2.78 | 2.72 | 2.66 | 2.60 |
| 14 | 6.30 | 4.86 | 4.24 | 3.89 | 3.66 | 3.50 | 3.38 | 3.29 | 3.21 | 3.15 | 3.05 | 2.95 | 2.84 | 2.79 | 2.73 | 2.67 | 2.61 | 2.55 | 2.49 |
| 15 | 6.20 | 4.77 | 4.15 | 3.80 | 3.58 | 3.41 | 3.29 | 3.20 | 3.12 | 3.06 | 2.96 | 2.86 | 2.76 | 2.70 | 2.64 | 2.59 | 2.52 | 2.46 | 2.40 |
| 16 | 6.12 | 4.69 | 4.08 | 3.73 | 3.50 | 3.34 | 3.22 | 3.12 | 3.05 | 2.99 | 2.89 | 2.79 | 2.68 | 2.63 | 2.57 | 2.51 | 2.45 | 2.38 | 2.32 |
| 17 | 6.04 | 4.62 | 4.01 | 3.66 | 3.44 | 3.28 | 3.16 | 3.06 | 2.98 | 2.92 | 2.82 | 2.72 | 2.62 | 2.56 | 2.50 | 2.44 | 2.38 | 2.32 | 2.25 |
| 18 | 5.98 | 4.56 | 3.95 | 3.61 | 3.38 | 3.22 | 3.10 | 3.01 | 2.93 | 2.87 | 2.77 | 2.67 | 2.56 | 2.50 | 2.44 | 2.38 | 2.32 | 2.26 | 2.19 |
| 19 | 5.92 | 4.51 | 3.90 | 3.56 | 3.33 | 3.17 | 3.05 | 2.96 | 2.88 | 2.82 | 2.72 | 2.62 | 2.51 | 2.45 | 2.39 | 2.33 | 2.27 | 2.20 | 2.13 |
| 20 | 5.87 | 4.46 | 3.86 | 3.51 | 3.29 | 3.13 | 3.01 | 2.91 | 2.84 | 2.77 | 2.68 | 2.57 | 2.46 | 2.41 | 2.35 | 2.29 | 2.22 | 2.16 | 2.09 |
| 21 | 5.83 | 4.42 | 3.82 | 3.48 | 3.25 | 3.09 | 2.97 | 2.87 | 2.80 | 2.73 | 2.64 | 2.53 | 2.42 | 2.37 | 2.31 | 2.25 | 2.18 | 2.11 | 2.04 |
| 22 | 5.79 | 4.38 | 3.78 | 3.44 | 3.22 | 3.05 | 2.93 | 2.84 | 2.76 | 2.70 | 2.60 | 2.50 | 2.39 | 2.33 | 2.27 | 2.21 | 2.14 | 2.08 | 2.00 |
| 23 | 5.75 | 4.35 | 3.75 | 3.41 | 3.18 | 3.02 | 2.90 | 2.81 | 2.73 | 2.67 | 2.57 | 2.47 | 2.36 | 2.30 | 2.24 | 2.18 | 2.11 | 2.04 | 1.97 |
| 24 | 5.72 | 4.32 | 3.72 | 3.38 | 3.15 | 2.99 | 2.87 | 2.78 | 2.70 | 2.64 | 2.54 | 2.44 | 2.33 | 2.27 | 2.21 | 2.15 | 2.08 | 2.01 | 1.94 |
| 25 | 5.69 | 4.29 | 3.69 | 3.35 | 3.13 | 2.97 | 2.85 | 2.75 | 2.68 | 2.61 | 2.51 | 2.41 | 2.30 | 2.24 | 2.18 | 2.12 | 2.05 | 1.98 | 1.91 |
| 26 | 5.66 | 4.27 | 3.67 | 3.33 | 3.10 | 2.94 | 2.82 | 2.73 | 2.65 | 2.59 | 2.49 | 2.39 | 2.28 | 2.22 | 2.16 | 2.09 | 2.03 | 1.95 | 1.88 |
| 27 | 5.63 | 4.24 | 3.65 | 3.31 | 3.08 | 2.92 | 2.80 | 2.71 | 2.63 | 2.57 | 2.47 | 2.36 | 2.25 | 2.19 | 2.13 | 2.07 | 2.00 | 1.93 | 1.85 |
| 28 | 5.61 | 4.22 | 3.63 | 3.29 | 3.06 | 2.90 | 2.78 | 2.69 | 2.61 | 2.55 | 2.45 | 2.34 | 2.23 | 2.17 | 2.11 | 2.05 | 1.98 | 1.91 | 1.83 |
| 29 | 5.59 | 4.20 | 3.61 | 3.27 | 3.04 | 2.88 | 2.76 | 2.67 | 2.59 | 2.53 | 2.43 | 2.32 | 2.21 | 2.15 | 2.09 | 2.03 | 1.96 | 1.89 | 1.81 |
| 30 | 5.57 | 4.18 | 3.59 | 3.25 | 3.03 | 2.87 | 2.75 | 2.65 | 2.57 | 2.51 | 2.41 | 2.31 | 2.20 | 2.14 | 2.07 | 2.01 | 1.94 | 1.87 | 1.79 |
| 40 | 5.42 | 4.05 | 3.46 | 3.13 | 2.90 | 2.74 | 2.62 | 2.53 | 2.45 | 2.39 | 2.29 | 2.18 | 2.07 | 2.01 | 1.94 | 1.88 | 1.80 | 1.72 | 1.64 |
| 60 | 5.29 | 3.93 | 3.34 | 3.01 | 2.79 | 2.63 | 2.51 | 2.41 | 2.33 | 2.27 | 2.17 | 2.06 | 1.94 | 1.88 | 1.82 | 1.74 | 1.67 | 1.58 | 1.48 |
| 120 | 5.15 | 3.80 | 3.23 | 2.89 | 2.67 | 2.52 | 2.39 | 2.30 | 2.22 | 2.16 | 2.05 | 1.94 | 1.82 | 1.76 | 1.69 | 1.61 | 1.53 | 1.43 | 1.31 |
| ∞ | 5.02 | 3.69 | 3.12 | 2.79 | 2.57 | 2.41 | 2.29 | 2.19 | 2.11 | 2.05 | 1.94 | 1.83 | 1.71 | 1.64 | 1.57 | 1.48 | 1.39 | 1.27 | 1.00 |

*Table IV* | 679

## Table IV (continued)
### UPPER 1% POINTS

| $\nu_2 \backslash \nu_1$ | 1 | 2 | 3 | 4 | 5 | 6 | 7 | 8 | 9 | 10 | 12 | 15 | 20 | 24 | 30 | 40 | 60 | 120 | ∞ |
|---|---|---|---|---|---|---|---|---|---|---|---|---|---|---|---|---|---|---|---|
| 1 | 4052 | 4999.5 | 5403 | 5625 | 5764 | 5859 | 5928 | 5982 | 6022 | 6056 | 6106 | 6157 | 6209 | 6235 | 6261 | 6287 | 6313 | 6339 | 6366 |
| 2 | 98.50 | 99.00 | 99.17 | 99.25 | 99.30 | 99.33 | 99.36 | 99.37 | 99.39 | 99.40 | 99.42 | 99.43 | 99.45 | 99.46 | 99.47 | 99.47 | 99.48 | 99.49 | 99.50 |
| 3 | 34.12 | 30.82 | 29.46 | 28.71 | 28.24 | 27.91 | 27.67 | 27.49 | 27.35 | 27.23 | 27.05 | 26.87 | 26.69 | 26.60 | 26.50 | 26.41 | 26.32 | 26.22 | 26.13 |
| 4 | 21.20 | 18.00 | 16.69 | 15.98 | 15.52 | 15.21 | 14.98 | 14.80 | 14.66 | 14.55 | 14.37 | 14.20 | 14.02 | 13.93 | 13.84 | 13.75 | 13.65 | 13.56 | 13.46 |
| 5 | 16.26 | 13.27 | 12.06 | 11.39 | 10.97 | 10.67 | 10.46 | 10.29 | 10.16 | 10.05 | 9.89 | 9.72 | 9.55 | 9.47 | 9.38 | 9.29 | 9.20 | 9.11 | 9.02 |
| 6 | 13.75 | 10.92 | 9.78 | 9.15 | 8.75 | 8.47 | 8.26 | 8.10 | 7.98 | 7.87 | 7.72 | 7.56 | 7.40 | 7.31 | 7.23 | 7.14 | 7.06 | 6.97 | 6.88 |
| 7 | 12.25 | 9.55 | 8.45 | 7.85 | 7.46 | 7.19 | 6.99 | 6.84 | 6.72 | 6.62 | 6.47 | 6.31 | 6.16 | 6.07 | 5.99 | 5.91 | 5.82 | 5.74 | 5.65 |
| 8 | 11.26 | 8.65 | 7.59 | 7.01 | 6.63 | 6.37 | 6.18 | 6.03 | 5.91 | 5.81 | 5.67 | 5.52 | 5.36 | 5.28 | 5.20 | 5.12 | 5.03 | 4.95 | 4.86 |
| 9 | 10.56 | 8.02 | 6.99 | 6.42 | 6.06 | 5.80 | 5.61 | 5.47 | 5.35 | 5.26 | 5.11 | 4.96 | 4.81 | 4.73 | 4.65 | 4.57 | 4.48 | 4.40 | 4.31 |
| 10 | 10.04 | 7.56 | 6.55 | 5.99 | 5.64 | 5.39 | 5.20 | 5.06 | 4.94 | 4.85 | 4.71 | 4.56 | 4.41 | 4.33 | 4.25 | 4.17 | 4.08 | 4.00 | 3.91 |
| 11 | 9.65 | 7.21 | 6.22 | 5.67 | 5.32 | 5.07 | 4.89 | 4.74 | 4.63 | 4.54 | 4.40 | 4.25 | 4.10 | 4.02 | 3.94 | 3.86 | 3.78 | 3.69 | 3.60 |
| 12 | 9.33 | 6.93 | 5.95 | 5.41 | 5.06 | 4.82 | 4.64 | 4.50 | 4.39 | 4.30 | 4.16 | 4.01 | 3.86 | 3.78 | 3.70 | 3.62 | 3.54 | 3.45 | 3.36 |
| 13 | 9.07 | 6.70 | 5.74 | 5.21 | 4.86 | 4.62 | 4.44 | 4.30 | 4.19 | 4.10 | 3.96 | 3.82 | 3.66 | 3.59 | 3.51 | 3.43 | 3.34 | 3.25 | 3.17 |
| 14 | 8.86 | 6.51 | 5.56 | 5.04 | 4.69 | 4.46 | 4.28 | 4.14 | 4.03 | 3.94 | 3.80 | 3.66 | 3.51 | 3.43 | 3.35 | 3.27 | 3.18 | 3.09 | 3.00 |
| 15 | 8.68 | 6.36 | 5.42 | 4.89 | 4.56 | 4.32 | 4.14 | 4.00 | 3.89 | 3.80 | 3.67 | 3.52 | 3.37 | 3.29 | 3.21 | 3.13 | 3.05 | 2.96 | 2.87 |
| 16 | 8.53 | 6.23 | 5.29 | 4.77 | 4.44 | 4.20 | 4.03 | 3.89 | 3.78 | 3.69 | 3.55 | 3.41 | 3.26 | 3.18 | 3.10 | 3.02 | 2.93 | 2.84 | 2.75 |
| 17 | 8.40 | 6.11 | 5.18 | 4.67 | 4.34 | 4.10 | 3.93 | 3.79 | 3.68 | 3.59 | 3.46 | 3.31 | 3.16 | 3.08 | 3.00 | 2.92 | 2.83 | 2.75 | 2.65 |
| 18 | 8.29 | 6.01 | 5.09 | 4.58 | 4.25 | 4.01 | 3.84 | 3.71 | 3.60 | 3.51 | 3.37 | 3.23 | 3.08 | 3.00 | 2.92 | 2.84 | 2.75 | 2.66 | 2.57 |
| 19 | 8.18 | 5.93 | 5.01 | 4.50 | 4.17 | 3.94 | 3.77 | 3.63 | 3.52 | 3.43 | 3.30 | 3.15 | 3.00 | 2.92 | 2.84 | 2.76 | 2.67 | 2.58 | 2.49 |
| 20 | 8.10 | 5.85 | 4.94 | 4.43 | 4.10 | 3.87 | 3.70 | 3.56 | 3.46 | 3.37 | 3.23 | 3.09 | 2.94 | 2.86 | 2.78 | 2.69 | 2.61 | 2.52 | 2.42 |
| 21 | 8.02 | 5.78 | 4.87 | 4.37 | 4.04 | 3.81 | 3.64 | 3.51 | 3.40 | 3.31 | 3.17 | 3.03 | 2.88 | 2.80 | 2.72 | 2.64 | 2.55 | 2.46 | 2.36 |
| 22 | 7.95 | 5.72 | 4.82 | 4.31 | 3.99 | 3.76 | 3.59 | 3.45 | 3.35 | 3.26 | 3.12 | 2.98 | 2.83 | 2.75 | 2.67 | 2.58 | 2.50 | 2.40 | 2.31 |
| 23 | 7.88 | 5.66 | 4.76 | 4.26 | 3.94 | 3.71 | 3.54 | 3.41 | 3.30 | 3.21 | 3.07 | 2.93 | 2.78 | 2.70 | 2.62 | 2.54 | 2.45 | 2.35 | 2.26 |
| 24 | 7.82 | 5.61 | 4.72 | 4.22 | 3.90 | 3.67 | 3.50 | 3.36 | 3.26 | 3.17 | 3.03 | 2.89 | 2.74 | 2.66 | 2.58 | 2.49 | 2.40 | 2.31 | 2.21 |
| 25 | 7.77 | 5.57 | 4.68 | 4.18 | 3.85 | 3.63 | 3.46 | 3.32 | 3.22 | 3.13 | 2.99 | 2.85 | 2.70 | 2.62 | 2.54 | 2.45 | 2.36 | 2.27 | 2.17 |
| 26 | 7.72 | 5.53 | 4.64 | 4.14 | 3.82 | 3.59 | 3.42 | 3.29 | 3.18 | 3.09 | 2.96 | 2.81 | 2.66 | 2.58 | 2.50 | 2.42 | 2.33 | 2.23 | 2.13 |
| 27 | 7.68 | 5.49 | 4.60 | 4.11 | 3.78 | 3.56 | 3.39 | 3.26 | 3.15 | 3.06 | 2.93 | 2.78 | 2.63 | 2.55 | 2.47 | 2.38 | 2.29 | 2.20 | 2.10 |
| 28 | 7.64 | 5.45 | 4.57 | 4.07 | 3.75 | 3.53 | 3.36 | 3.23 | 3.12 | 3.03 | 2.90 | 2.75 | 2.60 | 2.52 | 2.44 | 2.35 | 2.26 | 2.17 | 2.06 |
| 29 | 7.60 | 5.42 | 4.54 | 4.04 | 3.73 | 3.50 | 3.33 | 3.20 | 3.09 | 3.00 | 2.87 | 2.73 | 2.57 | 2.49 | 2.41 | 2.33 | 2.23 | 2.14 | 2.03 |
| 30 | 7.56 | 5.39 | 4.51 | 4.02 | 3.70 | 3.47 | 3.30 | 3.17 | 3.07 | 2.98 | 2.84 | 2.70 | 2.55 | 2.47 | 2.39 | 2.30 | 2.21 | 2.11 | 2.01 |
| 40 | 7.31 | 5.18 | 4.31 | 3.83 | 3.51 | 3.29 | 3.12 | 2.99 | 2.89 | 2.80 | 2.66 | 2.52 | 2.37 | 2.29 | 2.20 | 2.11 | 2.02 | 1.92 | 1.80 |
| 60 | 7.08 | 4.98 | 4.13 | 3.65 | 3.34 | 3.12 | 2.95 | 2.82 | 2.72 | 2.63 | 2.50 | 2.35 | 2.20 | 2.12 | 2.03 | 1.94 | 1.84 | 1.73 | 1.60 |
| 120 | 6.85 | 4.79 | 3.95 | 3.48 | 3.17 | 2.96 | 2.79 | 2.66 | 2.56 | 2.47 | 2.34 | 2.19 | 2.03 | 1.95 | 1.86 | 1.76 | 1.66 | 1.53 | 1.38 |
| ∞ | 6.63 | 4.61 | 3.78 | 3.32 | 3.02 | 2.80 | 2.64 | 2.51 | 2.41 | 2.32 | 2.18 | 2.04 | 1.88 | 1.79 | 1.70 | 1.59 | 1.47 | 1.32 | 1.00 |

This table is abridged from Table 18 of the *Biometrika Tables for Statisticians*, Vol. 1 (ed. 1), edited by E. S. Pearson and H. O. Hartley. Reproduced by the kind permission of F. S. Pearson and the trustees of *Biometrika*.

## Table V
### THE TRANSFORMATION OF $r$ TO $Z$

| $r$ | \.000 | .002 | .004 | .006 | .008 | $r$ | .000 | .002 | .004 | .006 | .008 |
|---|---|---|---|---|---|---|---|---|---|---|---|
| .00 | .0000 | .0020 | .0040 | .0060 | .0080 | .35 | .3654 | .3677 | .3700 | .3723 | .3746 |
| 1 | .0100 | .0120 | .0140 | .0160 | .0180 | 6 | .3769 | .3792 | .3815 | .3838 | .3861 |
| 2 | .0200 | .0220 | .0240 | .0260 | .0280 | 7 | .3884 | .3907 | .3931 | .3954 | .3977 |
| 3 | .0300 | .0320 | .0340 | .0360 | .0380 | 8 | .4001 | .4024 | .4047 | .4071 | .4094 |
| 4 | .0400 | .0420 | .0440 | .0460 | .0480 | 9 | .4118 | .4142 | .4165 | .4189 | .4213 |
| .05 | .0500 | .0520 | .0541 | .0561 | .0581 | .40 | .4236 | .4260 | .4284 | .4308 | .4332 |
| 6 | .0601 | .0621 | .0641 | .0661 | .0681 | 1 | .4356 | .4380 | .4404 | .4428 | .4453 |
| 7 | .0701 | .0721 | .0741 | .0761 | .0782 | 2 | .4477 | .4501 | .4526 | .4550 | .4574 |
| 8 | .0802 | .0822 | .0842 | .0862 | .0882 | 3 | .4599 | .4624 | .4648 | .4673 | .4698 |
| 9 | .0902 | .0923 | .0943 | .0963 | .0983 | 4 | .4722 | .4747 | .4772 | .4797 | .4822 |
| .10 | .1003 | .1024 | .1044 | .1064 | .1084 | .45 | .4847 | .4872 | .4897 | .4922 | .4948 |
| 1 | .1104 | .1125 | .1145 | .1165 | .1186 | 6 | .4973 | .4999 | .5024 | .5049 | .5075 |
| 2 | .1206 | .1226 | .1246 | .1267 | .1287 | 7 | .5101 | .5126 | .5152 | .5178 | .5204 |
| 3 | .1307 | .1328 | .1348 | .1368 | .1389 | 8 | .5230 | .5256 | .5282 | .5308 | .5334 |
| 4 | .1409 | .1430 | .1450 | .1471 | .1491 | 9 | .5361 | .5387 | .5413 | .5440 | .5466 |
| .15 | .1511 | .1532 | .1552 | .1573 | .1593 | .50 | .5493 | .5520 | .5547 | .5573 | .5600 |
| 6 | .1614 | .1634 | .1655 | .1676 | .1696 | 1 | .5627 | .5654 | .5682 | .5709 | .5736 |
| 7 | .1717 | .1737 | .1758 | .1779 | .1799 | 2 | .5763 | .5791 | .5818 | .5846 | .5874 |
| 8 | .1820 | .1841 | .1861 | .1882 | .1903 | 3 | .5901 | .5929 | .5957 | .5985 | .6013 |
| 9 | .1923 | .1944 | .1965 | .1986 | .2007 | 4 | .6042 | .6070 | .6098 | .6127 | .6155 |
| .20 | .2027 | .2048 | .2069 | .2090 | .2111 | .55 | .6184 | .6213 | .6241 | .6270 | .6299 |
| 1 | .2132 | .2153 | .2174 | .2195 | .2216 | 6 | .6328 | .6358 | .6387 | .6416 | .6446 |
| 2 | .2237 | .2258 | .2279 | .2300 | .2321 | 7 | .6475 | .6505 | .6535 | .6565 | .6595 |
| 3 | .2342 | .2363 | .2384 | .2405 | .2427 | 8 | .6625 | .6655 | .6685 | .6716 | .6746 |
| 4 | .2448 | .2469 | .2490 | .2512 | .2533 | 9 | .6777 | .6807 | .6838 | .6869 | .6900 |
| .25 | .2554 | .2575 | .2597 | .2618 | .2640 | .60 | .6931 | .6963 | .6994 | .7026 | .7057 |
| 6 | .2661 | .2683 | .2704 | .2726 | .2747 | 1 | .7089 | .7121 | .7153 | .7185 | .7218 |
| 7 | .2769 | .2790 | .2812 | .2833 | .2855 | 2 | .7250 | .7283 | .7315 | .7348 | .7381 |
| 8 | .2877 | .2899 | .2920 | .2942 | .2964 | 3 | .7414 | .7447 | .7481 | .7514 | .7548 |
| 9 | .2986 | .3008 | .3029 | .3051 | .3073 | 4 | .7582 | .7616 | .7650 | .7684 | .7718 |
| .30 | .3095 | .3117 | .3139 | .3161 | .3183 | .65 | .7753 | .7788 | .7823 | .7858 | .7893 |
| 1 | .3205 | .3228 | .3250 | .3272 | .3294 | 6 | .7928 | .7964 | .7999 | .8035 | .8071 |
| 2 | .3316 | .3339 | .3361 | .3383 | .3406 | 7 | .8107 | .8144 | .8180 | .8217 | .8254 |
| 3 | .3428 | .3451 | .3473 | .3496 | .3518 | 8 | .8291 | .8328 | .8366 | .8404 | .8441 |
| 4 | .3541 | .3564 | .3586 | .3609 | .3632 | 9 | .8480 | .8518 | .8556 | .8595 | .8634 |

*Table V* | *681*

**Table V (continued)**

| *r* | *r* (3rd decimal) | | | | | *r* | *r* (3rd decimal) | | | | |
|---|---|---|---|---|---|---|---|---|---|---|---|
| | .000 | .002 | .004 | .006 | .008 | | .000 | .002 | .004 | .006 | .008 |
| .70 | .8673 | .8712 | .8752 | .8792 | .8832 | .85 | 1.256 | 1.263 | 1.271 | 1.278 | 1.286 |
| 1 | .8872 | .8912 | .8953 | .8994 | .9035 | 6 | 1.293 | 1.301 | 1.309 | 1.317 | 1.325 |
| 2 | .9076 | .9118 | .9160 | .9202 | .9245 | 7 | 1.333 | 1.341 | 1.350 | 1.358 | 1.367 |
| 3 | .9287 | .9330 | .9373 | .9417 | .9461 | 8 | 1.376 | 1.385 | 1.394 | 1.403 | 1.412 |
| 4 | .9505 | .9549 | .9594 | .9639 | .9684 | 9 | 1.422 | 1.432 | 1.442 | 1.452 | 1.462 |
| .75 | 0.973 | 0.978 | 0.982 | 0.987 | 0.991 | .90 | 1.472 | 1.483 | 1.494 | 1.505 | 1.516 |
| 6 | 0.996 | 1.001 | 1.006 | 1.011 | 1.015 | 1 | 1.528 | 1.539 | 1.551 | 1.564 | 1.576 |
| 7 | 1.020 | 1.025 | 1.030 | 1.035 | 1.040 | 2 | 1.589 | 1.602 | 1.616 | 1.630 | 1.644 |
| 8 | 1.045 | 1.050 | 1.056 | 1.061 | 1.066 | 3 | 1.658 | 1.673 | 1.689 | 1.705 | 1.721 |
| 9 | 1.071 | 1.077 | 1.082 | 1.088 | 1.093 | 4 | 1.738 | 1.756 | 1.774 | 1.792 | 1.812 |
| .80 | 1.099 | 1.104 | 1.110 | 1.116 | 1.121 | .95 | 1.832 | 1.853 | 1.874 | 1.897 | 1.921 |
| 1 | 1.127 | 1.133 | 1.139 | 1.145 | 1.151 | 6 | 1.946 | 1.972 | 2.000 | 2.029 | 2.060 |
| 2 | 1.157 | 1.163 | 1.169 | 1.175 | 1.182 | 7 | 2.092 | 2.127 | 2.165 | 2.205 | 2.249 |
| 3 | 1.188 | 1.195 | 1.201 | 1.208 | 1.214 | 8 | 2.298 | 2.351 | 2.410 | 2.477 | 2.555 |
| 4 | 1.221 | 1.228 | 1.235 | 1.242 | 1.249 | 9 | 2.647 | 2.759 | 2.903 | 3.106 | 3.453 |

This table is abridged from Table 14 of the *Biometrika Tables for Statisticians*, Vol. 1 (ed. 1), edited by E. S. Pearson and H. O. Hartley. Used with the kind permission of E. S. Pearson and the trustees of *Biometrika*.

## Table VI
COEFFICIENTS OF ORTHOGONAL POLYNOMIALS

|  | $J = 3$ | | $J = 4$ | | | $J = 5$ | | | |
|---|---|---|---|---|---|---|---|---|---|
|  | 1 | 2 | 1 | 2 | 3 | 1 | 2 | 3 | 4 |
| $X_1$ | −1 | 1 | −3 | 1 | −1 | −2 | 2 | −1 | 1 |
| $X_2$ | 0 | −2 | −1 | −1 | 3 | −1 | −1 | 2 | −4 |
| $X_3$ | 1 | 1 | 1 | −1 | −3 | 0 | −2 | 0 | 6 |
| $X_4$ |  |  | 3 | 1 | 1 | 1 | −1 | −2 | −4 |
| $X_5$ |  |  |  |  |  | 2 | 2 | 1 | 1 |
| $\Sigma c_j^2$ | 2 | 6 | 20 | 4 | 20 | 10 | 14 | 10 | 70 |

|  | $J = 6$ | | | | | $J = 7$ | | | | | |
|---|---|---|---|---|---|---|---|---|---|---|---|
|  | 1 | 2 | 3 | 4 | 5 | 1 | 2 | 3 | 4 | 5 | 6 |
| $X_1$ | −5 | 5 | −5 | 1 | −1 | −3 | 5 | −1 | 3 | −1 | 1 |
| $X_2$ | −3 | −1 | 7 | −3 | 5 | −2 | 0 | 1 | −7 | 4 | −6 |
| $X_3$ | −1 | −4 | 4 | 2 | −10 | −1 | −3 | 1 | 1 | −5 | 15 |
| $X_4$ | 1 | −4 | −4 | 2 | 10 | 0 | −4 | 0 | 6 | 0 | −20 |
| $X_5$ | 3 | −1 | −7 | −3 | −5 | 1 | −3 | −1 | 1 | 5 | 15 |
| $X_6$ | 5 | 5 | 5 | 1 | 1 | 2 | 0 | −1 | −7 | −4 | −6 |
| $X_7$ |  |  |  |  |  | 3 | 5 | 1 | 3 | 1 | 1 |
| $\Sigma c_j^2$ | 70 | 84 | 180 | 28 | 252 | 28 | 84 | 6 | 154 | 84 | 924 |

|  | $J = 8$ | | | | | | $J = 9$ | | | | | |
|---|---|---|---|---|---|---|---|---|---|---|---|---|
|  | 1 | 2 | 3 | 4 | 5 | 6 | 1 | 2 | 3 | 4 | 5 | 6 |
| $X_1$ | −7 | 7 | −7 | 7 | −7 | 1 | −4 | 28 | −14 | 14 | −4 | 4 |
| $X_2$ | −5 | 1 | 5 | −13 | 23 | −5 | −3 | 7 | 7 | −21 | 11 | −17 |
| $X_3$ | −3 | −3 | 7 | −3 | −17 | 9 | −2 | −8 | 13 | −11 | −4 | 22 |
| $X_4$ | −1 | −5 | 3 | 9 | −15 | −5 | −1 | −17 | 9 | 9 | −9 | 1 |
| $X_5$ | 1 | −5 | −3 | 9 | 15 | −5 | 0 | −20 | 0 | 18 | 0 | −20 |
| $X_6$ | 3 | −3 | −7 | −3 | 17 | 9 | 1 | −17 | −9 | 9 | 9 | 1 |
| $X_7$ | 5 | 1 | −5 | −13 | −23 | −5 | 2 | −8 | −13 | −11 | 4 | 22 |
| $X_8$ | 7 | 7 | 7 | 7 | 7 | 1 | 3 | 7 | −7 | −21 | −11 | −17 |
| $X_9$ |  |  |  |  |  |  | 4 | 28 | 14 | 14 | 4 | 4 |
| $\Sigma c_j^2$ | 168 | 168 | 264 | 616 | 2184 | 264 | 60 | 2772 | 990 | 2002 | 468 | 1980 |

*Table VI* | *683*

**Table VI (continued)**

| | $J = 10$ | | | | | | $J = 11$ | | | | | |
|---|---|---|---|---|---|---|---|---|---|---|---|---|
| | 1 | 2 | 3 | 4 | 5 | 6 | 1 | 2 | 3 | 4 | 5 | 6 |
| $X_1$ | $-9$ | 6 | $-42$ | 18 | $-6$ | 3 | $-5$ | 15 | $-30$ | 6 | $-3$ | 15 |
| $X_2$ | $-7$ | 2 | 14 | $-22$ | 14 | $-11$ | $-4$ | 6 | 6 | $-6$ | 6 | $-48$ |
| $X_3$ | $-5$ | $-1$ | 35 | $-17$ | $-1$ | 10 | $-3$ | $-1$ | 22 | $-6$ | 1 | 29 |
| $X_4$ | $-3$ | $-3$ | 31 | 3 | $-11$ | 6 | $-2$ | $-6$ | 23 | $-1$ | $-4$ | 36 |
| $X_5$ | $-1$ | $-4$ | 12 | 18 | $-6$ | $-8$ | $-1$ | $-9$ | 14 | 4 | $-4$ | $-12$ |
| $X_6$ | 1 | $-4$ | $-12$ | 18 | 6 | $-8$ | 0 | $-10$ | 0 | 6 | 0 | $-40$ |
| $X_7$ | 3 | $-3$ | $-31$ | 3 | 11 | 6 | 1 | $-9$ | $-14$ | 4 | 4 | $-12$ |
| $X_8$ | 5 | $-1$ | $-35$ | $-17$ | 1 | 10 | 2 | $-6$ | $-23$ | $-1$ | 4 | 36 |
| $X_9$ | 7 | 2 | $-14$ | $-22$ | $-14$ | $-11$ | 3 | $-1$ | $-22$ | $-6$ | $-1$ | 29 |
| $X_{10}$ | 9 | 6 | 42 | 18 | 6 | 3 | 4 | 6 | $-6$ | $-6$ | $-6$ | $-48$ |
| $X_{11}$ | | | | | | | 5 | 15 | 30 | 6 | 3 | 15 |
| $\Sigma c_j^2$ | 330 | 132 | 8580 | 2860 | 780 | 660 | 110 | 858 | 4290 | 286 | 156 | 11220 |

| | $J = 12$ | | | | | | $J = 13$ | | | | | |
|---|---|---|---|---|---|---|---|---|---|---|---|---|
| | 1 | 2 | 3 | 4 | 5 | 6 | 1 | 2 | 3 | 4 | 5 | 6 |
| $X_1$ | $-11$ | 55 | $-33$ | 33 | $-33$ | 11 | $-6$ | 22 | $-11$ | 99 | $-22$ | 22 |
| $X_2$ | $-9$ | 25 | 3 | $-27$ | 57 | $-31$ | $-5$ | 11 | 0 | $-66$ | 33 | $-55$ |
| $X_3$ | $-7$ | 1 | 21 | $-33$ | 21 | 11 | $-4$ | 2 | 6 | $-96$ | 18 | 8 |
| $X_4$ | $-5$ | $-17$ | 25 | $-13$ | $-29$ | 25 | $-3$ | $-5$ | 8 | $-54$ | $-11$ | 43 |
| $X_5$ | $-3$ | $-29$ | 19 | 12 | $-44$ | 4 | $-2$ | $-10$ | 7 | 11 | $-26$ | 22 |
| $X_6$ | $-1$ | $-35$ | 7 | 28 | $-20$ | $-20$ | $-1$ | $-13$ | 4 | 64 | $-20$ | $-20$ |
| $X_7$ | 1 | $-35$ | $-7$ | 28 | 20 | $-20$ | 0 | $-14$ | 0 | 84 | 0 | $-40$ |
| $X_8$ | 3 | $-29$ | $-19$ | 12 | 44 | 4 | 1 | $-13$ | $-4$ | 64 | 20 | $-20$ |
| $X_9$ | 5 | $-17$ | $-25$ | $-13$ | 29 | 25 | 2 | $-10$ | $-7$ | 11 | 26 | 22 |
| $X_{10}$ | 7 | 1 | $-21$ | $-33$ | $-21$ | 11 | 3 | $-5$ | $-8$ | $-54$ | 11 | 43 |
| $X_{11}$ | 9 | 25 | $-3$ | $-27$ | $-57$ | $-31$ | 4 | 2 | $-6$ | $-96$ | $-18$ | 8 |
| $X_{12}$ | 11 | 55 | 33 | 33 | 33 | 11 | 5 | 11 | 0 | $-66$ | $-33$ | $-55$ |
| $X_{13}$ | | | | | | | 6 | 22 | 11 | 99 | 22 | 22 |
| $\Sigma c_j^2$ | 572 | 12012 | 5148 | 8008 | 15912 | 4488 | 182 | 2002 | 572 | 68068 | 6188 | 14212 |

## Table VI (continued)

| | | | $J = 14$ | | | | | | | $J = 15$ | | |
|---|---|---|---|---|---|---|---|---|---|---|---|---|
| | 1 | 2 | 3 | 4 | 5 | 6 | 1 | 2 | 3 | 4 | 5 | 6 |
| $X_1$ | −13 | 13 | −143 | 143 | −143 | 143 | −7 | 91 | −91 | 1001 | −1001 | 143 |
| $X_2$ | −11 | 7 | −11 | −77 | 187 | −319 | −6 | 52 | −13 | −429 | 1144 | −286 |
| $X_3$ | −9 | 2 | 66 | −132 | 132 | −11 | −5 | 19 | 35 | −869 | 979 | −55 |
| $X_4$ | −7 | −2 | 98 | −92 | −28 | 227 | −4 | −8 | 58 | −704 | 44 | 176 |
| $X_5$ | −5 | −5 | 95 | −13 | −139 | 185 | −3 | −29 | 61 | −249 | −751 | 197 |
| $X_6$ | −3 | −7 | 67 | 63 | −145 | −25 | −2 | −44 | 49 | 251 | −1000 | 50 |
| $X_7$ | −1 | −8 | 24 | 108 | −60 | −200 | −1 | −53 | 27 | 621 | −675 | −125 |
| $X_8$ | 1 | −8 | −24 | 108 | 60 | −200 | 0 | −56 | 0 | 756 | 0 | −200 |
| $X_9$ | 3 | −7 | −67 | 63 | 145 | −25 | 1 | −53 | −27 | 621 | 675 | −125 |
| $X_{10}$ | 5 | −5 | −95 | −13 | 139 | 185 | 2 | −44 | −49 | 251 | 1000 | 50 |
| $X_{11}$ | 7 | −2 | −98 | −92 | 28 | 227 | 3 | −29 | −61 | −249 | 751 | 197 |
| $X_{12}$ | 9 | 2 | −66 | −132 | −132 | −11 | 4 | −8 | −58 | −704 | −44 | 176 |
| $X_{13}$ | 11 | 7 | 11 | −77 | −187 | −319 | 5 | 19 | −35 | −869 | −979 | −55 |
| $X_{14}$ | 13 | 13 | 143 | 143 | 143 | 143 | 6 | 52 | 13 | −429 | −1144 | −286 |
| $X_{15}$ | | | | | | | 7 | 91 | 91 | 1001 | 1001 | 143 |
| $\Sigma c_j^2$ | 910 | 728 | 97240 | 136136 | 235144 | 497420 | 280 | 37128 | 39780 | 6446460 | 10581480 | 426360 |

*Table VII* | *685*

**Table VII**

FACTORIALS OF INTEGERS

| $n$ | $n!$ | $n$ | $n!$ |
|---|---|---|---|
| 1 | 1 | 26 | $4.03291 \times 10^{26}$ |
| 2 | 2 | 27 | $1.08889 \times 10^{28}$ |
| 3 | 6 | 28 | $3.04888 \times 10^{29}$ |
| 4 | 24 | 29 | $8.84176 \times 10^{30}$ |
| 5 | 120 | 30 | $2.65253 \times 10^{32}$ |
| 6 | 720 | 31 | $8.22284 \times 10^{33}$ |
| 7 | 5040 | 32 | $2.63131 \times 10^{35}$ |
| 8 | 40320 | 33 | $8.68332 \times 10^{36}$ |
| 9 | 362880 | 34 | $2.95233 \times 10^{38}$ |
| 10 | $3.62880 \times 10^{6}$ | 35 | $1.03331 \times 10^{40}$ |
| 11 | $3.99168 \times 10^{7}$ | 36 | $3.71993 \times 10^{41}$ |
| 12 | $4.79002 \times 10^{8}$ | 37 | $1.37638 \times 10^{43}$ |
| 13 | $6.22702 \times 10^{9}$ | 38 | $5.23023 \times 10^{44}$ |
| 14 | $8.71783 \times 10^{10}$ | 39 | $2.03979 \times 10^{46}$ |
| 15 | $1.30767 \times 10^{12}$ | 40 | $8.15915 \times 10^{47}$ |
| 16 | $2.09228 \times 10^{13}$ | 41 | $3.34525 \times 10^{49}$ |
| 17 | $3.55687 \times 10^{14}$ | 42 | $1.40501 \times 10^{51}$ |
| 18 | $6.40327 \times 10^{15}$ | 43 | $6.04153 \times 10^{52}$ |
| 19 | $1.21645 \times 10^{17}$ | 44 | $2.65827 \times 10^{54}$ |
| 20 | $2.43290 \times 10^{18}$ | 45 | $1.19622 \times 10^{56}$ |
| 21 | $5.10909 \times 10^{19}$ | 46 | $5.50262 \times 10^{57}$ |
| 22 | $1.12400 \times 10^{21}$ | 47 | $2.58623 \times 10^{59}$ |
| 23 | $2.58520 \times 10^{22}$ | 48 | $1.24139 \times 10^{61}$ |
| 24 | $6.20448 \times 10^{23}$ | 49 | $6.08282 \times 10^{62}$ |
| 25 | $1.55112 \times 10^{25}$ | 50 | $3.04141 \times 10^{64}$ |

## Table VIII

BINOMIAL COEFFICIENTS, $\dbinom{N}{r}$

| $N$ \ $r$ | 0 | 1 | 2 | 3 | 4 | 5 | 6 | 7 | 8 | 9 | 10 |
|---|---|---|---|---|---|---|---|---|---|---|---|
| 1 | 1 | 1 | | | | | | | | | |
| 2 | 1 | 2 | 1 | | | | | | | | |
| 3 | 1 | 3 | 3 | 1 | | | | | | | |
| 4 | 1 | 4 | 6 | 4 | 1 | | | | | | |
| 5 | 1 | 5 | 10 | 10 | 5 | 1 | | | | | |
| 6 | 1 | 6 | 15 | 20 | 15 | 6 | 1 | | | | |
| 7 | 1 | 7 | 21 | 35 | 35 | 21 | 7 | 1 | | | |
| 8 | 1 | 8 | 28 | 56 | 70 | 56 | 28 | 8 | 1 | | |
| 9 | 1 | 9 | 36 | 84 | 126 | 126 | 84 | 36 | 9 | 1 | |
| 10 | 1 | 10 | 45 | 120 | 210 | 252 | 210 | 120 | 45 | 10 | 1 |
| 11 | 1 | 11 | 55 | 165 | 330 | 462 | 462 | 330 | 165 | 55 | 11 |
| 12 | 1 | 12 | 66 | 220 | 495 | 792 | 924 | 792 | 495 | 220 | 66 |
| 13 | 1 | 13 | 78 | 286 | 715 | 1287 | 1716 | 1716 | 1287 | 715 | 286 |
| 14 | 1 | 14 | 91 | 364 | 1001 | 2002 | 3003 | 3432 | 3003 | 2002 | 1001 |
| 15 | 1 | 15 | 105 | 455 | 1365 | 3003 | 5005 | 6435 | 6435 | 5005 | 3003 |
| 16 | 1 | 16 | 120 | 560 | 1820 | 4368 | 8008 | 11440 | 12870 | 11440 | 8008 |
| 17 | 1 | 17 | 136 | 680 | 2380 | 6188 | 12376 | 19448 | 24310 | 24310 | 19448 |
| 18 | 1 | 18 | 153 | 816 | 3060 | 8568 | 18564 | 31824 | 43758 | 48620 | 43758 |
| 19 | 1 | 19 | 171 | 969 | 3876 | 11628 | 27132 | 50388 | 75582 | 92378 | 92378 |
| 20 | 1 | 20 | 190 | 1140 | 4845 | 15504 | 38760 | 77520 | 125970 | 167960 | 184756 |

*Table IX* | 687

## Table IX

POWERS AND ROOTS

| N | $N^2$ | $\sqrt{N}$ | $\sqrt{10N}$ | | N | $N^2$ | $\sqrt{N}$ | $\sqrt{10N}$ |
|---|-------|-----------|-------------|---|---|-------|-----------|-------------|
| **1** | 1 | 1.00 000 | 3.16 228 | | **50** | 2 500 | 7.07 107 | 22.36 07 |
| 2 | 4 | 1.41 421 | 4.47 214 | | 51 | 2 601 | 7.14 143 | 22.58 32 |
| 3 | 9 | 1.73 205 | 5.47 723 | | 52 | 2 704 | 7.21 110 | 22.80 35 |
| 4 | 16 | 2.00 000 | 6.32 456 | | 53 | 2 809 | 7.28 011 | 23.02 17 |
| 5 | 25 | 2.23 607 | 7.07 107 | | 54 | 2 916 | 7.34 847 | 23.23 79 |
| | | | | | 55 | 3 025 | 7.41 620 | 23.45 21 |
| **6** | 36 | 2.44 949 | 7.74 597 | | **56** | 3 136 | 7.48 331 | 23.66 43 |
| 7 | 49 | 2.64 575 | 8.36 660 | | 57 | 3 249 | 7.54 983 | 23.87 47 |
| 8 | 64 | 2.82 843 | 8.94 427 | | 58 | 3 364 | 7.61 577 | 24.08 32 |
| 9 | 81 | 3.00 000 | 9.48 683 | | 59 | 3 481 | 7.68 115 | 24.28 99 |
| 10 | 100 | 3.16 228 | 10.00 00 | | 60 | 3 600 | 7.74 597 | 24.49 49 |
| **11** | 121 | 3.31 662 | 10.48 81 | | **61** | 3 721 | 7.81 025 | 24.69 82 |
| 12 | 144 | 3.46 410 | 10.95 45 | | 62 | 3 844 | 7.87 401 | 24.89 98 |
| 13 | 169 | 3.60 555 | 11.40 18 | | 63 | 3 969 | 7.93 725 | 25.09 98 |
| 14 | 196 | 3.74 166 | 11.83 22 | | 64 | 4 096 | 8.00 000 | 25.29 82 |
| 15 | 225 | 3.87 298 | 12.24 74 | | 65 | 4 225 | 8.06 226 | 25.49 51 |
| **16** | 256 | 4.00 000 | 12.64 91 | | **66** | 4 356 | 8.12 404 | 25.69 05 |
| 17 | 289 | 4.12 311 | 13.03 84 | | 67 | 4 489 | 8.18 535 | 25.88 44 |
| 18 | 324 | 4.24 264 | 13.41 64 | | 68 | 4 624 | 8.24 621 | 26.07 68 |
| 19 | 361 | 4.35 890 | 13.78 40 | | 69 | 4 761 | 8.30 662 | 26.26 79 |
| 20 | 400 | 4.47 214 | 14.14 21 | | 70 | 4 900 | 8.36 660 | 26.45 75 |
| **21** | 441 | 4.58 258 | 14.49 14 | | **71** | 5 041 | 8.42 615 | 26.64 58 |
| 22 | 484 | 4.69 042 | 14.83 24 | | 72 | 5 184 | 8.48 528 | 26.83 28 |
| 23 | ·529 | 4.79 583 | 15.16 58 | | 73 | 5 329 | 8.54 400 | 27.01 85 |
| 24 | 576 | 4.89 898 | 15.49 19 | | 74 | 5 476 | 8.60 233 | 27.20 29 |
| 25 | 625 | 5.00 000 | 15.81 14 | | 75 | 5 625 | 8.66 025 | 27.38 61 |
| **26** | 676 | 5.09 902 | 16.12 45 | | **76** | 5 776 | 8.71 780 | 27.56 81 |
| 27 | 729 | 5.19 615 | 16.43 17 | | 77 | 5 929 | 8.77 496 | 27.74 89 |
| 28 | 784 | 5.29 150 | 16.73 32 | | 78 | 6 084 | 8.83 176 | 27.92 85 |
| 29 | 841 | 5.38 516 | 17.02 94 | | 79 | 6 241 | 8.88 819 | 28.10 69 |
| 30 | 900 | 5.47 723 | 17.32 05 | | 80 | 6 400 | 8.94 427 | 28.28 43 |
| **31** | 961 | 5.56 776 | 17.60 68 | | **81** | 6 561 | 9.00 000 | 28.46 05 |
| 32 | 1 024 | 5.65 685 | 17.88 85 | | 82 | 6 724 | 9.05 539 | 28.63 56 |
| 33 | 1 089 | 5.74 456 | 18.16 59 | | 83 | 6 889 | 9.11 043 | 28.80 97 |
| 34 | 1 156 | 5.83 095 | 18.43 91 | | 84 | 7 056 | 9.16 515 | 28.98 28 |
| 35 | 1 225 | 5.91 608 | 18.70 83 | | 85 | 7 225 | 9.21 954 | 29.15 48 |
| **36** | 1 296 | 6.00 000 | 18.97 37 | | **86** | 7 396 | 9.27 362 | 29.32 58 |
| 37 | 1 369 | 6.08 276 | 19.23 54 | | 87 | 7 569 | 9.32 738 | 29.49 58 |
| 38 | 1 444 | 6.16 441 | 19.49 36 | | 88 | 7 744 | 9.38 083 | 29.66 48 |
| 39 | 1 521 | 6.24 500 | 19.74 84 | | 89 | 7 921 | 9.43 398 | 29.83 29 |
| 40 | 1 600 | 6.32 456 | 20.00 00 | | 90 | 8 100 | 9.48 683 | 30.00 00 |
| **41** | 1 681 | 6.40 312 | 20.24 85 | | **91** | 8 281 | 9.53 939 | 30.16 62 |
| 42 | 1 764 | 6.48 074 | 20.49 39 | | 92 | 8 464 | 9.59 166 | 30.33 15 |
| 43 | 1 849 | 6.55 744 | 20.73 64 | | 93 | 8 649 | 9.64 365 | 30.49 59 |
| 44 | 1 936 | 6.63 325 | 20.97 62 | | 94 | 8 836 | 9.69 536 | 30.65 94 |
| 45 | 2 025 | 6.70 820 | 21.21 32 | | 95 | 9 025 | 9.74 679 | 30.82 21 |
| **46** | 2 116 | 6.78 233 | 21.44 76 | | **96** | 9 216 | 9.79 796 | 30.98 39 |
| 47 | 2 209 | 6.85 565 | 21.67 95 | | 97 | 9 409 | 9.84 886 | 31.14 48 |
| 48 | 2 304 | 6.92 820 | 21.90 89 | | 98 | 9 604 | 9.89 949 | 31.30 50 |
| 49 | 2 401 | 7.00 000 | 22.13 59 | | 99 | 9 801 | 9.94 987 | 31.46 43 |
| 50 | 2 500 | 7.07 107 | 22.36 07 | | 100 | 10 000 | 10.00 000 | 31.62 28 |
| N | $N^2$ | $\sqrt{N}$ | $\sqrt{10N}$ | | N | $N^2$ | $\sqrt{N}$ | $\sqrt{10N}$ |

## Table IX (continued)

| N | N² | √N̄ | √10N̄ |
|---|---|---|---|
| **300** | 90 000 | 17.32 05 | 54.77 23 |
| 301 | 90 601 | 17.34 94 | 54.86 35 |
| 302 | 91 204 | 17.37 81 | 54.95 45 |
| 303 | 91 809 | 17.40 69 | 55.04 54 |
| 304 | 92 416 | 17.43 56 | 55.13 62 |
| 305 | 93 025 | 17.46 42 | 55.22 68 |
| **306** | 93 636 | 17.49 29 | 55.31 73 |
| 307 | 94 249 | 17.52 14 | 55.40 76 |
| 308 | 94 864 | 17.54 99 | 55.49 77 |
| 309 | 95 481 | 17.57 84 | 55.58 78 |
| 310 | 96 100 | 17.60 68 | 55.67 76 |
| **311** | 96 721 | 17.63 52 | 55.76 74 |
| 312 | 97 344 | 17.66 35 | 55.85 70 |
| 313 | 97 969 | 17.69 18 | 55.94 64 |
| 314 | 98 596 | 17.72 00 | 56.03 57 |
| 315 | 99 225 | 17.74 82 | 56.12 49 |
| **316** | 99 856 | 17.77 64 | 56.21 39 |
| 317 | 100 489 | 17.80 45 | 56.30 28 |
| 318 | 101 124 | 17.83 26 | 56.39 15 |
| 319 | 101 761 | 17.86 06 | 56.48 01 |
| 320 | 102 400 | 17.88 85 | 56.56 85 |
| **321** | 103 041 | 17.91 65 | 56.65 69 |
| 322 | 103 684 | 17.94 44 | 56.74 50 |
| 323 | 104 329 | 17.97 22 | 56.83 31 |
| 324 | 104 976 | 18.00 00 | 55.92 10 |
| 325 | 105 625 | 18.02 78 | 57.00 88 |
| **326** | 106 276 | 18.05 55 | 57.09 64 |
| 327 | 106 929 | 18.08 31 | 57.18 39 |
| 328 | 107 584 | 18.11 08 | 57.27 13 |
| 329 | 108 241 | 18.13 84 | 57.35 85 |
| 330 | 108 900 | 18.16 59 | 57.44 56 |
| **331** | 109 561 | 18.19 34 | 57.53 26 |
| 332 | 110 224 | 18.22 09 | 57.61 94 |
| 333 | 110 889 | 18.24 83 | 57.70 62 |
| 334 | 111 556 | 18.27 57 | 57.79 27 |
| 335 | 112 225 | 18.30 30 | 57.87 92 |
| **336** | 112 896 | 18.33 03 | 57.96 55 |
| 337 | 113 569 | 18.35 76 | 58.05 17 |
| 338 | 114 244 | 18.38 48 | 58.13 78 |
| 339 | 114 921 | 18.41 20 | 58.22 37 |
| 340 | 115 600 | 18 43 91 | 58.30 95 |
| **341** | 116 281 | 18.46 62 | 58.39 52 |
| 342 | 116 964 | 18.49 32 | 58.48 08 |
| 343 | 117 649 | 18.52 03 | 58.56 62 |
| 344 | 118 336 | 18.54 72 | 58.65 15 |
| 345 | 119 025 | 18.57 42 | 58.73 67 |
| **346** | 119 716 | 18.60 11 | 58.82 18 |
| 347 | 120 409 | 18.62 79 | 58.90 67 |
| 348 | 121 104 | 18.65 48 | 58.99 15 |
| 349 | 121 801 | 18.68 15 | 59.07 62 |
| 350 | 122 500 | 18.70 83 | 59.16 08 |
| N | N² | √N̄ | √10N̄ |

| N | N² | √N̄ | √10N̄ |
|---|---|---|---|
| **350** | 122 500 | 18.70 83 | 59.16 08 |
| 351 | 123 201 | 18.73 50 | 59.24 53 |
| 352 | 123 904 | 18.76 17 | 59.32 96 |
| 353 | 124 609 | 18.78 83 | 59.41 38 |
| 354 | 125 316 | 18.81 49 | 59.49 79 |
| 355 | 126 025 | 18.84 14 | 59.58 19 |
| **356** | 126 736 | 18.86 80 | 59.66 57 |
| 357 | 127 449 | 18.89 44 | 59.74 95 |
| 358 | 128 164 | 18.92 09 | 59.83 31 |
| 359 | 128 881 | 18.94 73 | 59.91 66 |
| 360 | 129 600 | 18.97 37 | 60.00 00 |
| **361** | 130 321 | 19.00 00 | 60.08 33 |
| 362 | 131 044 | 19.02 63 | 60.16 64 |
| 363 | 131 769 | 19.05 26 | 60.24 95 |
| 364 | 132 496 | 19.07 88 | 60.33 24 |
| 365 | 133 225 | 19.10 50 | 60.41 52 |
| **366** | 133 956 | 19.13 11 | 60.49 79 |
| 367 | 134 689 | 19.15 72 | 60.58 05 |
| 368 | 135 424 | 19.18 33 | 60.66 30 |
| 369 | 136 161 | 19.20 94 | 60.74 54 |
| 370 | 136 900 | 19.23 54 | 60.82 76 |
| **371** | 137 641 | 19.26 14 | 60.90 98 |
| 372 | 138 384 | 19.28 73 | 60.99 18 |
| 373 | 139 129 | 19.31 32 | 61.07 37 |
| 374 | 139 876 | 19.33 91 | 61.15 55 |
| 375 | 140 625 | 19.36 49 | 61.23 72 |
| **376** | 141 376 | 19.39 07 | 61.31 88 |
| 377 | 142 129 | 19.41 65 | 61.40 03 |
| 378 | 142 884 | 19.44 22 | 61.48 17 |
| 379 | 143 641 | 19.46 79 | 61.56 30 |
| 380 | 144 400 | 19.49 36 | 61.64 41 |
| **381** | 145 161 | 19.51 92 | 61.72 52 |
| 382 | 145 924 | 19.54 48 | 61.80 61 |
| 383 | 146 689 | 19.57 04 | 61.88 70 |
| 384 | 147 456 | 19.59 59 | 61.96 77 |
| 385 | 148 225 | 19.62 14 | 62.04 84 |
| **386** | 148 996 | 19.64 69 | 62.12 89 |
| 387 | 149 769 | 19.67 23 | 62.20 93 |
| 388 | 150 544 | 19.69 77 | 62.28 96 |
| 389 | 151 321 | 19.72 31 | 62.36 99 |
| 390 | 152 100 | 19.74 84 | 62.45 00 |
| **391** | 152 881 | 19.77 37 | 62.53 00 |
| 392 | 153 664 | 19.79 90 | 62.60 99 |
| 393 | 154 449 | 19.82 42 | 62.68 97 |
| 394 | 155 236 | 19.84 94 | 62.76 94 |
| 395 | 156 025 | 19.87 46 | 62.84 90 |
| **396** | 156 816 | 19.89 97 | 62.92 85 |
| 397 | 157 609 | 19.92 49 | 63.00 79 |
| 398 | 158 404 | 19.94 99 | 63.08 72 |
| 399 | 159 201 | 19.97 50 | 63.16 64 |
| 400 | 160 000 | 20.00 00 | 63.24 56 |
| N | N² | √N̄ | √10N̄ |

*Table IX* | *691*

Table IX (continued)

| N | N² | √N | √10N |
|---|---|---|---|
| **400** | 160 000 | 20.00 00 | 63.24 56 |
| 401 | 160 801 | 20.02 50 | 63.32 46 |
| 402 | 161 604 | 20.04 99 | 63.40 35 |
| 403 | 162 409 | 20.07 49 | 63.48 23 |
| 404 | 163 216 | 20.09 98 | 63.56 10 |
| 405 | 164 025 | 20.12 46 | 63.63 96 |
| **406** | 164 836 | 20.14 94 | 63.71 81 |
| 407 | 165 649 | 20.17 42 | 63.79 66 |
| 408 | 166 464 | 20.19 90 | 63.87 49 |
| 409 | 167 281 | 20.22 37 | 63.95 31 |
| 410 | 168 100 | 20.24 85 | 64.03 12 |
| **411** | 168 921 | 20.27 31 | 64.10 93 |
| 412 | 169 744 | 20.29 78 | 64.18 72 |
| 413 | 170 569 | 20.32 24 | 64.26 51 |
| 414 | 171 396 | 20.34 70 | 64.34 28 |
| 415 | 172 225 | 20.37 15 | 64.42 05 |
| **416** | 173 056 | 20.39 61 | 64.49 81 |
| 417 | 173 889 | 20.42 06 | 64.57 55 |
| 418 | 174 724 | 20.44 50 | 64.65 29 |
| 419 | 175 561 | 20.46 95 | 64.73 02 |
| 420 | 176 400 | 20.49 39 | 64.80 74 |
| **421** | 177 241 | 20.51 83 | 64.88 45 |
| 422 | 178 084 | 20.54 26 | 64.96 15 |
| 423 | 178 929 | 20.56 70 | 65.03 85 |
| 424 | 179 776 | 20.59 13 | 65.11 53 |
| 425 | 180 625 | 20.61 55 | 65.19 20 |
| **426** | 181 476 | 20.63 98 | 65.26 87 |
| 427 | 182 329 | 20.66 40 | 65.34 52 |
| 428 | 183 184 | 20.68 82 | 65.42 17 |
| 429 | 184 041 | 20.71 23 | 65.49 81 |
| 430 | 184 900 | 20.73 64 | 65.57 44 |
| **431** | 185 761 | 20.76 05 | 65.65 06 |
| 432 | 186 624 | 20.78 46 | 65.72 67 |
| 433 | 187 489 | 20.80 87 | 65.80 27 |
| 434 | 188 356 | 20.83 27 | 65.87 87 |
| 435 | 189 225 | 20.85 67 | 65.95 45 |
| **436** | 190 096 | 20.88 06 | 66.03 03 |
| 437 | 190 969 | 20.90 45 | 66.10 60 |
| 438 | 191 844 | 20.92 84 | 66.18 16 |
| 439 | 192 721 | 20.95 23 | 66.25 71 |
| 440 | 193 600 | 20.97 62 | 66.33 25 |
| **441** | 194 481 | 21.00 00 | 66.40 78 |
| 442 | 195 364 | 21.02 38 | 66.48 31 |
| 443 | 196 249 | 21.04 76 | 66.55 82 |
| 444 | 197 136 | 21.07 13 | 66.63 33 |
| 445 | 198 025 | 21.09 50 | 66.70 83 |
| **446** | 198 916 | 21.11 87 | 66.78 32 |
| 447 | 199 809 | 21.14 24 | 66.85 81 |
| 448 | 200 704 | 21.16 60 | 66.93 28 |
| 449 | 201 601 | 21.18 96 | 67.00 75 |
| 450 | 202 500 | 21.21 32 | 67.08 20 |
| N | N² | √N | √10N |

| N | N² | √N | √10N |
|---|---|---|---|
| **450** | 202 500 | 21.21 32 | 67.08 20 |
| 451 | 203 401 | 21.23 68 | 67.15 65 |
| 452 | 204 304 | 21.26 03 | 67.23 09 |
| 453 | 205 209 | 21.28 38 | 67.30 53 |
| 454 | 206 116 | 21.30 73 | 67.37 95 |
| 455 | 207 025 | 21.33 07 | 67.45 37 |
| **456** | 207 936 | 21.35 42 | 67.52 78 |
| 457 | 208 849 | 21.37 76 | 67.60 18 |
| 458 | 209 764 | 21.40 09 | 67.67 57 |
| 459 | 210 681 | 21.42 43 | 67.74 95 |
| 460 | 211 600 | 21.44 76 | 67.82 33 |
| **461** | 212 521 | 21.47 09 | 67.89 70 |
| 462 | 213 444 | 21.49 42 | 67.97 06 |
| 463 | 214 369 | 21.51 74 | 68.04 41 |
| 464 | 215 296 | 21.54 07 | 68.11 75 |
| 465 | 216 225 | 21.56 39 | 68.19 09 |
| **466** | 217 156 | 21.58 70 | 68.26 42 |
| 467 | 218 089 | 21.61 02 | 68.33 74 |
| 468 | 219 024 | 21.63 33 | 68.41 05 |
| 469 | 219 961 | 21.65 64 | 68.48 36 |
| 470 | 220 900 | 21.67 95 | 68.55 65 |
| **471** | 221 841 | 21.70 25 | 68.62 94 |
| 472 | 222 784 | 21.72 56 | 68.70 23 |
| 473 | 223 729 | 21.74 86 | 68.77 50 |
| 474 | 224 676 | 21.77 15 | 68.84 77 |
| 475 | 225 625 | 21.79 45 | 68.92 02 |
| **476** | 226 576 | 21.81 74 | 68.99 28 |
| 477 | 227 529 | 21.84 03 | 69.06 52 |
| 478 | 228 484 | 21.86 32 | 69.13 75 |
| 479 | 229 441 | 21.88 61 | 69.20 98 |
| 480 | 230 400 | 21.90 89 | 69.28 20 |
| **481** | 231 361 | 21.93 17 | 69.35 42 |
| 482 | 232 324 | 21.95 45 | 69.42 62 |
| 483 | 233 289 | 21.97 73 | 69.49 82 |
| 484 | 234 256 | 22.00 00 | 69.57 01 |
| 485 | 235 225 | 22.02 27 | 69.64 19 |
| **486** | 236 196 | 22.04 54 | 69.71 37 |
| 487 | 237 169 | 22.06 81 | 69.78 54 |
| 488 | 238 144 | 22.09 07 | 69.85 70 |
| 489 | 239 121 | 22.11 33 | 69.92 85 |
| 490 | 240 100 | 22.13 59 | 70.00 00 |
| **491** | 241 081 | 22.15 85 | 70.07 14 |
| 492 | 242 064 | 22.18 11 | 70.14 27 |
| 493 | 243 049 | 22.20 36 | 70.21 40 |
| 494 | 244 036 | 22.22 61 | 70.28 51 |
| 495 | 245 025 | 22.24 86 | 70.35 62 |
| **496** | 246 016 | 22.27 11 | 70.42 73 |
| 497 | 247 009 | 22.29 35 | 70.49 82 |
| 498 | 248 004 | 22.31 59 | 70.56 91 |
| 499 | 249 001 | 22.33 83 | 70.63 99 |
| 500 | 250 000 | 22.36 07 | 70.71 07 |
| N | N² | √N | √10N |

## Table IX (continued)

| $N$ | $N^2$ | $\sqrt{N}$ | $\sqrt{10N}$ |
|---|---|---|---|
| **500** | 250 000 | 22.36 07 | 70.71 07 |
| 501 | 251 001 | 22.38 30 | 70.78 14 |
| 502 | 252 004 | 22.40 54 | 70.85 20 |
| 503 | 253 009 | 22.42 77 | 70.92 25 |
| 504 | 254 016 | 22.44 99 | 70.99 30 |
| 505 | 255 025 | 22.47 22 | 71.06 34 |
| **506** | 256 036 | 22.49 44 | 71.13 37 |
| 507 | 257 049 | 22.51 67 | 71.20 39 |
| 508 | 258 064 | 22.53 89 | 71.27 41 |
| 509 | 259 081 | 22.56 10 | 71.34 42 |
| 510 | 260 100 | 22.58 32 | 71.41 43 |
| **511** | 261 121 | 22.60 53 | 71.48 43 |
| 512 | 262 144 | 22.62 74 | 71.55 42 |
| 513 | 263 169 | 22.64 95 | 71.62 40 |
| 514 | 264 196 | 22.67 16 | 71.69 38 |
| 515 | 265 225 | 22.69 36 | 71.76 35 |
| **516** | 266 256 | 22.71 56 | 71.83 31 |
| 517 | 267 289 | 22.73 76 | 71.90 27 |
| 518 | 268 324 | 22.75 96 | 71.97 22 |
| 519 | 269 361 | 22.78 16 | 72.04 17 |
| 520 | 270 400 | 22.80 35 | 72.11 10 |
| **521** | 271 441 | 22.82 54 | 72.18 03 |
| 522 | 272 484 | 22.84 73 | 72.24 96 |
| 523 | 273 529 | 22.86 92 | 72.31 87 |
| 524 | 274 576 | 22.89 10 | 72.38 78 |
| 525 | 275 625 | 22.91 29 | 72.45 69 |
| **526** | 276 676 | 22.93 47 | 72.52 59 |
| 527 | 277 729 | 22.95 65 | 72.59 48 |
| 528 | 278 784 | 22.97 83 | 72.66 36 |
| 529 | 279 841 | 23.00 00 | 72.73 24 |
| 530 | 280 900 | 23.02 17 | 72.80 11 |
| **531** | 281 961 | 23.04 34 | 72.86 97 |
| 532 | 283 024 | 23.06 51 | 72.93 83 |
| 533 | 284 089 | 23.08 68 | 73.00 68 |
| 534 | 285 156 | 23.10 84 | 73.07 53 |
| 535 | 286 225 | 23.13 01 | 73.14 37 |
| **536** | 287 296 | 23.15 17 | 73.21 20 |
| 537 | 288 369 | 23.17 33 | 73.28 03 |
| 538 | 289 444 | 23.19 48 | 73.34 85 |
| 539 | 290 521 | 23.21 64 | 73.41 66 |
| 540 | 291 600 | 23.23 79 | 73.48 47 |
| **541** | 292 681 | 23.25 94 | 73.55 27 |
| 542 | 293 764 | 23.28 09 | 73.62 06 |
| 543 | 294 849 | 23.30 24 | 73.68 85 |
| 544 | 295 936 | 23.32 38 | 73.75 64 |
| 545 | 297 025 | 23.34 52 | 73.82 41 |
| **546** | 298 116 | 23.36 66 | 73.89 18 |
| 547 | 299 209 | 23.38 80 | 73.95 94 |
| 548 | 300 304 | 23.40 94 | 74.02 70 |
| 549 | 301 401 | 23.43 07 | 74.09 45 |
| 550 | 302 500 | 23.45 21 | 74.16 20 |
| $N$ | $N^2$ | $\sqrt{N}$ | $\sqrt{10N}$ |

| $N$ | $N^2$ | $\sqrt{N}$ | $\sqrt{10N}$ |
|---|---|---|---|
| **550** | 302 500 | 23.45 21 | 74.16 20 |
| 551 | 303 601 | 23.47 34 | 74.22 94 |
| 552 | 304 704 | 23.49 47 | 74.29 67 |
| 553 | 305 809 | 23.51 60 | 74.36 40 |
| 554 | 306 916 | 23.53 72 | 74.43 12 |
| 555 | 308 025 | 23.55 84 | 74.49 83 |
| **556** | 309 136 | 23.57 97 | 74.56 54 |
| 557 | 310 249 | 23.60 08 | 74.63 24 |
| 558 | 311 364 | 23.62 20 | 74.69 94 |
| 559 | 312 481 | 23.64 32 | 74.76 63 |
| 560 | 313 600 | 23.66 43 | 74.83 31 |
| **561** | 314 721 | 23.68 54 | 74.89 99 |
| 562 | 315 844 | 23.70 65 | 74.96 67 |
| 563 | 316 969 | 23.72 76 | 75.03 33 |
| 564 | 318 096 | 23.74 87 | 75.09 99 |
| 565 | 319 225 | 23.76 97 | 75.16 65 |
| **566** | 320 356 | 23.79 08 | 75.23 30 |
| 567 | 321 489 | 23.81 18 | 75.29 94 |
| 568 | 322 624 | 23.83 28 | 75.36 58 |
| 569 | 323 761 | 23.85 37 | 75.43 21 |
| 570 | 324 900 | 23.87 47 | 75.49 83 |
| **571** | 326 041 | 23.89 56 | 75.56 45 |
| 572 | 327 184 | 23.91 65 | 75.63 07 |
| 573 | 328 329 | 23.93 74 | 75.69 68 |
| 574 | 329 476 | 23.95 83 | 75.76 28 |
| 575 | 330 625 | 23.97 92 | 75.82 88 |
| **576** | 331 776 | 24.00 00 | 75.89 47 |
| 577 | 332 929 | 24.02 08 | 75.96 05 |
| 578 | 334 084 | 24.04 16 | 76.02 63 |
| 579 | 335 241 | 24.06 24 | 76.09 20 |
| 580 | 336 400 | 24.08 32 | 76.15 77 |
| **581** | 337 561 | 24.10 39 | 76.22 34 |
| 582 | 338 724 | 24.12 47 | 76.28 89 |
| 583 | 339 889 | 24.14 54 | 76.35 44 |
| 584 | 341 056 | 24.16 61 | 76.41 99 |
| 585 | 342 225 | 24.18 68 | 76.48 53 |
| **586** | 343 396 | 24.20 74 | 76.55 06 |
| 587 | 344 569 | 24.22 81 | 76.61 59 |
| 588 | 345 744 | 24.24 87 | 76.68 12 |
| 589 | 346 921 | 24.26 93 | 76.74 63 |
| 590 | 348 100 | 24.28 99 | 76.81 15 |
| **591** | 349 281 | 24.31 05 | 76.87 65 |
| 592 | 350 464 | 24.33 11 | 76.94 15 |
| 593 | 351 649 | 24.35 16 | 77.00 65 |
| 594 | 352 836 | 24.37 21 | 77.07 14 |
| 595 | 354 025 | 24.39 26 | 77.13 62 |
| **596** | 355 216 | 24.41 31 | 77.20 10 |
| 597 | 356 409 | 24.43 36 | 77.26 58 |
| 598 | 357 604 | 24.45 40 | 77.33 05 |
| 599 | 358 801 | 24.47 45 | 77.39 51 |
| 600 | 360 000 | 24.49 49 | 77.45 97 |
| $N$ | $N^2$ | $\sqrt{N}$ | $\sqrt{10N}$ |

*Table IX* | *693*

**Table IX** (continued)

| N | N² | √N | √10N |
|---|-----|-----|------|
| **600** | 360 000 | 24.49 49 | 77.45 97 |
| 601 | 361 201 | 24.51 53 | 77.52 42 |
| 602 | 362 404 | 24.53 57 | 77.58 87 |
| 603 | 363 609 | 24.55 61 | 77.65 31 |
| 604 | 364 816 | 24.57 64 | 77.71 74 |
| 605 | 366 025 | 24.59 67 | 77.78 17 |
| **606** | 367 236 | 24.61 71 | 77.84 60 |
| 607 | 368 449 | 24.63 74 | 77.91 02 |
| 608 | 369 664 | 24.65 77 | 77.97 44 |
| 609 | 370 881 | 24.67 79 | 78.03 85 |
| 610 | 372 100 | 24.69 82 | 78.10 25 |
| **611** | 373 321 | 24.71 84 | 78.16 65 |
| 612 | 374 544 | 24.73 86 | 78.23 04 |
| 613 | 375 769 | 24.75 88 | 78.29 43 |
| 614 | 376 996 | 24.77 90 | 78.35 82 |
| 615 | 378 225 | 24.79 92 | 78.42 19 |
| **616** | 379 456 | 24.81 93 | 78.48 57 |
| 617 | 380 689 | 24.83 95 | 78.54 93 |
| 618 | 381 924 | 24.85 96 | 78.61 30 |
| 619 | 383 161 | 24.87 97 | 78.67 66 |
| 620 | 384 400 | 24.89 98 | 78.74 01 |
| **621** | 385 641 | 24.91 99 | 78.80 36 |
| 622 | 386 884 | 24.93 99 | 78.86 70 |
| 623 | 388 129 | 24.96 00 | 78.93 03 |
| 624 | 389 376 | 24.98 00 | 78.99 37 |
| 625 | 390 625 | 25.00 00 | 79.05 69 |
| **626** | 391 876 | 25.02 00 | 79.12 02 |
| 627 | 393 129 | 25.04 00 | 79.18 33 |
| 628 | 394 384 | 25.05 99 | 79.24 65 |
| 629 | 395 641 | 25.07 99 | 79.30 95 |
| 630 | 396 900 | 25.09 98 | 79.37 25 |
| **631** | 398 161 | 25.11 97 | 79.43 55 |
| 632 | 399 424 | 25.13 96 | 79.49 84 |
| 633 | 400 689 | 25.15 95 | 79.56 13 |
| 634 | 401 956 | 25.17 94 | 79.62 41 |
| 635 | 403 225 | 25.19 92 | 79.68 69 |
| **636** | 404 496 | 25.21 90 | 79.74 96 |
| 637 | 405 769 | 25.23 89 | 79.81 23 |
| 638 | 407 044 | 25.25 87 | 79.87 49 |
| 639 | 408 321 | 25.27 84 | 79.93 75 |
| 640 | 409 600 | 25.29 82 | 80.00 00 |
| **641** | 410 881 | 25.31 80 | 80.06 25 |
| 642 | 412 164 | 25.33 77 | 80.12 49 |
| 643 | 413 449 | 25.35 74 | 80.18 73 |
| 644 | 414 736 | 25.37 72 | 80.24 96 |
| 645 | 416 025 | 25.39 69 | 80.31 19 |
| **646** | 417 316 | 25.41 65 | 80.37 41 |
| 647 | 418 609 | 25.43 62 | 80.43 63 |
| 648 | 419 904 | 25.45 58 | 80.49 84 |
| 649 | 421 201 | 25.47 55 | 80.56 05 |
| 650 | 422 500 | 25.49 51 | 80.62 26 |
| N | N² | √N | √10N |

| N | N² | √N | √10N |
|---|-----|-----|------|
| **650** | 422 500 | 25.49 51 | 80.62 26 |
| 651 | 423 801 | 25.51 47 | 80.68 46 |
| 652 | 425 104 | 25.53 43 | 80.74 65 |
| 653 | 426 409 | 25.55 39 | 80.80 84 |
| 654 | 427 716 | 25.57 34 | 80.87 03 |
| 655 | 429 025 | 25.59 30 | 80.93 21 |
| **656** | 430 336 | 25.61 25 | 80.99 38 |
| 657 | 431 649 | 25.63 20 | 81.05 55 |
| 658 | 432 964 | 25.65 15 | 81.11 72 |
| 659 | 434 281 | 25.67 10 | 81.17 88 |
| 660 | 435 600 | 25.69 05 | 81.24 04 |
| **661** | 436 921 | 25.70 99 | 81.30 19 |
| 662 | 438 244 | 25.72 94 | 81.36 34 |
| 663 | 439 569 | 25.74 88 | 81.42 48 |
| 664 | 440 896 | 25.76 82 | 81.48 62 |
| 665 | 442 225 | 25.78 76 | 81.54 75 |
| **666** | 443 556 | 25.80 70 | 81.60 88 |
| 667 | 444 889 | 25.82 63 | 81.67 01 |
| 668 | 446 224 | 25.84 57 | 81.73 13 |
| 669 | 447 561 | 25.86 50 | 81.79 24 |
| 670 | 448 900 | 25.88 44 | 81.85 35 |
| **671** | 450 241 | 25.90 37 | 81.91 46 |
| 672 | 451 584 | 25.92 30 | 81.97 56 |
| 673 | 452 929 | 25.94 22 | 82.03 66 |
| 674 | 454 276 | 25.96 15 | 82.09 75 |
| 675 | 455 625 | 25.98 08 | 82.15 84 |
| **676** | 456 976 | 26.00 00 | 82.21 92 |
| 677 | 458 329 | 26.01 92 | 82.28 00 |
| 678 | 459 684 | 26.03 84 | 82.34 08 |
| 679 | 461 041 | 26.05 76 | 82.40 15 |
| 680 | 462 400 | 26.07 68 | 82.46 21 |
| **681** | 463 761 | 26.09 60 | 82.52 27 |
| 682 | 465 124 | 26.11 51 | 82.58 33 |
| 683 | 466 489 | 26.13 43 | 82.64 38 |
| 684 | 467 856 | 26.15 34 | 82.70 43 |
| 685 | 469 225 | 26.17 25 | 82.76 47 |
| **686** | 470 596 | 26.19 16 | 82.82 51 |
| 687 | 471 969 | 26.21 07 | 82.88 55 |
| 688 | 473 344 | 26.22 98 | 82.94 58 |
| 689 | 474 721 | 26.24 88 | 83.00 60 |
| 690 | 476 100 | 26.26 79 | 83.06 62 |
| **691** | 477 481 | 26.28 69 | 83.12 64 |
| 692 | 478 864 | 26.30 59 | 83.18 65 |
| 693 | 480 249 | 26.32 49 | 83.24 66 |
| 694 | 481 636 | 26.34 39 | 83.30 67 |
| 695 | 483 025 | 26.36 29 | 83.36 67 |
| **696** | 484 416 | 26.38 18 | 83.42 66 |
| 697 | 485 809 | 26.40 08 | 83.48 65 |
| 698 | 487 204 | 26.41 97 | 83.54 64 |
| 699 | 488 601 | 26.43 86 | 83.60 62 |
| 700 | 490 000 | 26.45 75 | 83.66 60 |
| N | N² | √N | √10N |

Table IX (continued)

| N | N² | √N̄ | √10N̄ |
|---|-----|------|-------|
| **700** | 490 000 | 26.45 75 | 83.66 60 |
| 701 | 491 401 | 26.47 64 | 83.72 57 |
| 702 | 492 804 | 26.49 53 | 83.78 54 |
| 703 | 494 209 | 26.51 41 | 83.84 51 |
| 704 | 495 616 | 26.53 30 | 83.90 47 |
| 705 | 497 025 | 26.55 18 | 83.96 43 |
| **706** | 498 436 | 26.57 07 | 84.02 38 |
| 707 | 499 849 | 26.58 95 | 84.08 33 |
| 708 | 501 264 | 26.60 83 | 84.14 27 |
| 709 | 502 681 | 26.62 71 | 84.20 21 |
| 710 | 504 100 | 26.64 58 | 84.26 15 |
| **711** | 505 521 | 26.66 46 | 84.32 08 |
| 712 | 506 944 | 26.68 33 | 84.38 01 |
| 713 | 508 369 | 26.70 21 | 84.43 93 |
| 714 | 509 796 | 26.72 08 | 84.49 85 |
| 715 | 511 225 | 26.73 95 | 84.55 77 |
| **716** | 512 656 | 26.75 82 | 84.61 68 |
| 717 | 514 089 | 26.77 69 | 84.67 59 |
| 718 | 515 524 | 26.79 55 | 84.73 49 |
| 719 | 516 961 | 26.81 42 | 84.79 39 |
| 720 | 518 400 | 26.83 28 | 84.85 28 |
| **721** | 519 841 | 26.85 14 | 84.91 17 |
| 722 | 521 284 | 26.87 01 | 84.97 06 |
| 723 | 522 729 | 26.88 87 | 85.02 94 |
| 724 | 524 176 | 26.90 72 | 85.08 82 |
| 725 | 525 625 | 26.92 58 | 85.14 69 |
| **726** | 527 076 | 26.94 44 | 85.20 56 |
| 727 | 528 529 | 26.96 29 | 85.26 43 |
| 728 | 529 984 | 26.98 15 | 85.32 29 |
| 729 | 531 441 | 27.00 00 | 85.38 15 |
| 730 | 532 900 | 27.01 85 | 85.44 00 |
| **731** | 534 361 | 27.03 70 | 85.49 85 |
| 732 | 535 824 | 27.05 55 | 85.55 70 |
| 733 | 537 289 | 27.07 40 | 85.61 54 |
| 734 | 538 756 | 27.09 24 | 85.67 38 |
| 735 | 540 225 | 27.11 09 | 85.73 21 |
| **736** | 541 696 | 27.12 93 | 85.79 04 |
| 737 | 543 169 | 27.14 77 | 85.84 87 |
| 738 | 544 644 | 27.16 62 | 85.90 69 |
| 739 | 546 121 | 27.18 46 | 85.96 51 |
| 740 | 547 600 | 27.20 29 | 86.02 33 |
| **741** | 549 081 | 27.22 13 | 86.08 14 |
| 742 | 550 564 | 27.23 97 | 86.13 94 |
| 743 | 552 049 | 27.25 80 | 86.19 74 |
| 744 | 553 536 | 27.27 64 | 86.25 54 |
| 745 | 555 025 | 27.29 47 | 86.31 34 |
| **746** | 556 516 | 27.31 30 | 86.37 13 |
| 747 | 558 009 | 27.33 13 | 86.42 92 |
| 748 | 559 504 | 27.34 96 | 86.48 70 |
| 749 | 561 001 | 27.36 79 | 86.54 48 |
| 750 | 562 500 | 27.38 61 | 86.60 25 |
| N | N² | √N̄ | √10N̄ |

| N | N² | √N̄ | √10N̄ |
|---|-----|------|-------|
| **750** | 562 500 | 27.38 61 | 86.60 25 |
| 751 | 564 001 | 27.40 44 | 86.66 03 |
| 752 | 565 504 | 27.42 26 | 86.71 79 |
| 753 | 567 009 | 27.44 08 | 86.77 56 |
| 754 | 568 516 | 27.45 91 | 86.83 32 |
| 755 | 570 025 | 27.47 73 | 86.89 07 |
| **756** | 571 536 | 27.49 55 | 86.94 83 |
| 757 | 573 049 | 27.51 36 | 87.00 57 |
| 758 | 574 564 | 27.53 18 | 87.06 32 |
| 759 | 576 081 | 27.55 00 | 87.12 06 |
| 760 | 577 600 | 27.56 81 | 87.17 80 |
| **761** | 579 121 | 27.58 62 | 87.23 53 |
| 762 | 580 644 | 27.60 43 | 87.29 26 |
| 763 | 582 169 | 27.62 25 | 87.34 99 |
| 764 | 583 696 | 27.64 05 | 87.40 71 |
| 765 | 585 225 | 27.65 86 | 87.46 43 |
| **766** | 586 756 | 27.67 67 | 87.52 14 |
| 767 | 588 289 | 27.69 48 | 87.57 85 |
| 768 | 589 824 | 27.71 28 | 87.63 56 |
| 769 | 591 361 | 27.73 08 | 87.69 26 |
| 770 | 592 900 | 27.74 89 | 87.74 96 |
| **771** | 594 441 | 27.76 69 | 87.80 66 |
| 772 | 595 984 | 27.78 49 | 87.86 35 |
| 773 | 597 529 | 27.80 29 | 87.92 04 |
| 774 | 599 076 | 27.82 09 | 87.97 73 |
| 775 | 600 625 | 27.83 88 | 88.03 41 |
| **776** | 602 176 | 27.85 68 | 88.09 09 |
| 777 | 603 729 | 27.87 47 | 88.14 76 |
| 778 | 605 284 | 27.89 27 | 88.20 43 |
| 779 | 606 841 | 27.91 06 | 88.26 10 |
| 780 | 608 400 | 27.92 85 | 88.31 76 |
| **781** | 609 961 | 27.94 64 | 88.37 42 |
| 782 | 611 524 | 27.96 43 | 88.43 08 |
| 783 | 613 089 | 27.98 21 | 88.48 73 |
| 784 | 614 656 | 28.00 00 | 88.54 38 |
| 785 | 616 225 | 28.01 79 | 88.60 02 |
| **786** | 617 796 | 28.03 57 | 88.65 66 |
| 787 | 619 369 | 28.05 35 | 88.71 30 |
| 788 | 620 944 | 28.07 13 | 88.76 94 |
| 789 | 622 521 | 28.08 91 | 88.82 57 |
| 790 | 624 100 | 28.10 69 | 88.88 19 |
| **791** | 625 681 | 28.12 47 | 88.93 82 |
| 792 | 627 264 | 28.14 25 | 88.99 44 |
| 793 | 628 849 | 28.16 03 | 89.05 05 |
| 794 | 630 436 | 28.17 80 | 89.10 67 |
| 795 | 632 025 | 28.19 57 | 89.16 28 |
| **796** | 633 616 | 28.21 35 | 89.21 88 |
| 797 | 635 209 | 28.23 12 | 89.27 49 |
| 798 | 636 804 | 28.24 89 | 89.33 08 |
| 799 | 638 401 | 28.26 66 | 89.38 68 |
| 800 | 640 000 | 28.28 43 | 89.44 27 |
| N | N² | √N̄ | √10N̄ |

*Table IX* | *695*

**Table IX** (continued)

| N | N² | √N | √10N |
|---|---|---|---|
| **800** | 640 000 | 28.28 43 | 89.44 27 |
| 801 | 641 601 | 28.30 19 | 89.49 86 |
| 802 | 643 204 | 28.31 96 | 89.55 45 |
| 803 | 644 809 | 28.33 73 | 89.61 03 |
| 804 | 646 416 | 28.35 49 | 89.66 60 |
| 805 | 648 025 | 28.37 25 | 89.72 18 |
| **806** | 649 636 | 28.39 01 | 89.77 75 |
| 807 | 651 249 | 28.40 77 | 89.83 32 |
| 808 | 652 864 | 28.42 53 | 89.88 88 |
| 809 | 654 481 | 28.44 29 | 89.94 44 |
| 810 | 656 100 | 28.46 05 | 90.00 00 |
| **811** | 657 721 | 28.47 81 | 90.05 55 |
| 812 | 659 344 | 28.49 56 | 90.11 10 |
| 813 | 660 969 | 28.51 32 | 90.16 65 |
| 814 | 662 596 | 28.53 07 | 90.22 19 |
| 815 | 664 225 | 28.54 82 | 90.27 74 |
| **816** | 665 856 | 28.56 57 | 90.33 27 |
| 817 | 667 489 | 28.58 32 | 90.38 81 |
| 818 | 669 124 | 28.60 07 | 90.44 34 |
| 819 | 670 761 | 28.61 82 | 90.49 86 |
| 820 | 672 400 | 28.63 56 | 90.55 39 |
| **821** | 674 041 | 28.65 31 | 90.60 91 |
| 822 | 675 684 | 28.67 05 | 90.66 42 |
| 823 | 677 329 | 28.68 80 | 90.71 93 |
| 824 | 678 976 | 28.70 54 | 90.77 44 |
| 825 | 680 625 | 28.72 28 | 90.82 95 |
| **826** | 682 276 | 28.74 02 | 90.88 45 |
| 827 | 683 929 | 28.75 76 | 90.93 95 |
| 828 | 685 584 | 28.77 50 | 90.99 45 |
| 829 | 687 241 | 28.79 24 | 91.04 94 |
| 830 | 688 900 | 28.80 97 | 91.10 43 |
| **831** | 690 561 | 28.82 71 | 91.15 92 |
| 832 | 692 224 | 28.84 44 | 91.21 40 |
| 833 | 693 889 | 28.86 17 | 91.26 88 |
| 834 | 695 556 | 28.87 91 | 91.32 36 |
| 835 | 697 225 | 28.89 64 | 91.37 83 |
| **836** | 698 896 | 28.91 57 | 91.43 30 |
| 837 | 700 569 | 28.93 10 | 91.48 77 |
| 838 | 702 244 | 28.94 82 | 91.54 23 |
| 839 | 703 921 | 28.96 55 | 91.59 69 |
| 840 | 705 600 | 28.98 28 | 91.65 15 |
| **841** | 707 281 | 29.00 00 | 91.70 61 |
| 842 | 708 964 | 29.01 72 | 91.76 06 |
| 843 | 710 649 | 29.03 45 | 91.81 50 |
| 844 | 712 336 | 29.05 17 | 91.86 95 |
| 845 | 714 025 | 29.06 89 | 91.92 39 |
| **846** | 715 716 | 29.08 61 | 91.97 83 |
| 847 | 717 409 | 29.10 33 | 92.03 26 |
| 848 | 719 104 | 29.12 04 | 92.08 69 |
| 849 | 720 801 | 29.13 76 | 92.14 12 |
| 850 | 722 500 | 29.15 48 | 92.19 54 |
| N | N² | √N | √10N |

| N | N² | √N | √10N |
|---|---|---|---|
| **850** | 722 500 | 29.15 48 | 92.19 54 |
| 851 | 724 201 | 29.17 19 | 92.24 97 |
| 852 | 725 904 | 29.18 90 | 92.30 38 |
| 853 | 727 609 | 29.20 62 | 92.35 80 |
| 854 | 729 316 | 29.22 33 | 92.41 21 |
| 855 | 731 025 | 29.24 04 | 92.46 62 |
| **856** | 732 736 | 29.25 75 | 92.52 03 |
| 857 | 734 449 | 29.27 46 | 92.57 43 |
| 858 | 736 164 | 29.29 16 | 92.62 83 |
| 859 | 737 881 | 29.30 87 | 92.68 23 |
| 860 | 739 600 | 29.32 58 | 92.73 62 |
| **861** | 741 321 | 29.34 28 | 92.79 01 |
| 862 | 743 044 | 29.35 98 | 92.84 40 |
| 863 | 744 769 | 29.37 69 | 92.89 78 |
| 864 | 746 496 | 29.39 39 | 92.95 16 |
| 865 | 748 225 | 29.41 09 | 93.00 54 |
| **866** | 749 956 | 29.42 79 | 93.05 91 |
| 867 | 751 689 | 29.44 49 | 93.11 28 |
| 868 | 753 424 | 29.46 18 | 93.16 65 |
| 869 | 755 161 | 29.47 88 | 93.22 02 |
| 870 | 756 900 | 29.49 58 | 93.27 38 |
| **871** | 758 641 | 29.51 27 | 93.32 74 |
| 872 | 760 384 | 29.52 96 | 93.38 09 |
| 873 | 762 129 | 29.54 66 | 93.43 45 |
| 874 | 763 876 | 29.56 35 | 93.48 80 |
| 875 | 765 625 | 29.58 04 | 93.54 14 |
| **876** | 767 376 | 29.59 73 | 93.59 49 |
| 877 | 769 129 | 29.61 42 | 93.64 83 |
| 878 | 770 884 | 29.63 11 | 93.70 17 |
| 879 | 772 641 | 29.64 79 | 93.75 50 |
| 880 | 774 400 | 29.66 48 | 93.80 83 |
| **881** | 776 161 | 29.68 16 | 93.86 16 |
| 882 | 777 924 | 29.69 85 | 93.91 49 |
| 883 | 779 689 | 29.71 53 | 93.96 81 |
| 884 | 781 456 | 29.73 21 | 94.02 13 |
| 885 | 783 225 | 29.74 89 | 94.07 44 |
| **886** | 784 996 | 29.76 58 | 94.12 76 |
| 887 | 786 769 | 29.78 25 | 94.18 07 |
| 888 | 788 544 | 29.79 93 | 94.23 38 |
| 889 | 790 321 | 29.81 61 | 94.28 68 |
| 890 | 792 100 | 29.83 29 | 94.33 98 |
| **891** | 793 881 | 29.84 96 | 94.39 28 |
| 892 | 795 664 | 29.86 64 | 94.44 58 |
| 893 | 797 449 | 29.88 31 | 94.49 87 |
| 894 | 799 236 | 29.89 98 | 94.55 16 |
| 895 | 801 025 | 29.91 66 | 94.60 44 |
| **896** | 802 816 | 29.93 33 | 94.65 73 |
| 897 | 804 609 | 29.95 00 | 94.71 01 |
| 898 | 806 404 | 29.96 66 | 94.76 29 |
| 899 | 808 201 | 29.98 33 | 94.81 56 |
| 900 | 810 000 | 30.00 00 | 94.86 83 |
| N | N² | √N | √10N |

## Statistics

Alexander, H. W. *Elements of mathematical statistics.* New York: Wiley, 1961.

Anderson, R. L., and Bancroft, T. A. *Statistical theory in research.* New York: McGraw-Hill, 1952.

Bennett, C. A., and Franklin, N. L. *Statistical analysis in chemistry and the chemical industry.* New York: Wiley, 1954.

Box, G. E. P. Non-normality and tests on variances. *Biometrika 40,* 1953, 318–335.

Box, G. E. P. Some theorems on quadratic forms applied in the study of analysis of variance problems: I. Effect of inequality of variance in the one-way classification. *Annals Math. Stat. 25,* 1954, 290–302.

Box, G. E. P. Some theorems on quadratic forms applied in the study of analysis of variance problems: II. Effect of inequality of variance and of correlation of errors in the two-way classification. *Annals Math. Stat. 25,* 1954, 484–498.

Brunk, H. D. *An introduction to mathematical statistics.* Boston: Ginn, 1960.

Carroll, J. B. The nature of the data, or how to choose a correlation coefficient. *Psychometrika 26,* 1961, 347–372.

Cramér, H. *Mathematical methods of statistics.* Princeton: Princeton University Press, 1945.

Dixon, W., and Massey, F. *Introduction to statistical analysis* (ed. 2). New York: McGraw-Hill, 1957.

Edwards, W., Lindman, H., and Savage, L. Bayesian statistical inference in psychological research. *Psych. Rev. 70,* 1963, 193–242.

Grant, D. A. Testing the null hypothesis and the strategy and tactics of investigating theoretical models. *Psych. Rev. 69,* 1962, 54–61.

Graybill, F. A. *An introduction to linear statistical models* (Vol. I). New York: McGraw-Hill, 1961.

Green, B. F., and Tukey, J. W. Complex analyses of variance: General problems. *Psychometrika 25,* 1960, 127–152.

Kempthorne, O. The randomization theory of experimental inference. *J. Amer. Stat. Ass. 50,* 1955, 946–967.

Lehmann, E. L. *Testing statistical hypotheses.* New York: Wiley, 1959.

Lewis, D. *Quantitative methods in psychology.* New York: McGraw-Hill, 1960.

McNemar, Q. *Psychological statistics* (ed. 2). New York: Wiley, 1955.

Mood, A. *Introduction to the theory of statistics.* New York: McGraw-Hill, 1950.

Paull, A. E. On a preliminary test for pooling mean squares in the analysis of variance. *Annals Math. Stat. 21,* 1950, 539–556.

Pearson, E. S., and Hartley, H. O. (Eds.). *Biometrika tables for statisticians, Vol. 1* (ed. 1). Cambridge: Cambridge University Press, 1954.

The RAND Corporation *A million random digits with 100,000 normal deviates.* New York: Free Press, 1955.

Scheffé, H. *The analysis of variance.* New York: Wiley, 1959.

Schlaifer, R. *Introduction to statistics for business decisions.* New York: McGraw-Hill, 1961.

Tate, R. F., and Klett, G. W.  Optimal confidence intervals for the variance of a normal distribution.  *J. Amer. Stat. Ass. 54,* 1959, 674–682.

Tukey, J. W.  One degree of freedom for non-additivity.  *Biometrics 5,* 1949, 232–242.

Wallis, W. A., and Roberts, H. V.  *Statistics: A new approach.*  New York: Free Press, 1957.


## Experimental design

Cochran, W. G., and Cox, G.  *Experimental designs* (ed. 2).  New York: Wiley, 1957.

Cox, D. R.  *Planning experiments.*  New York: Wiley, 1958.

Edwards, A.  *Experimental design in psychological research* (rev. ed.).  New York: Holt, 1960.

Fisher, R. A.  *The design of experiments* (ed. 3).  Edinburgh: Oliver & Boyd, 1942.

Lindquist, E. F.  *Design and analysis of experiments in psychology and education.*  Boston: Houghton Mifflin, 1953.

Snedecor, G. W.  *Statistical methods* (ed. 5).  Ames, Iowa: Iowa State College Press, 1956.

Winer, B. J.  *Statistical principles in experimental design.*  New York: McGraw-Hill, 1962.


## Methods for categorical and order data

Attneave, F.  *Applications of information theory to psychology.*  New York: Holt, 1959.

Cochran, W. G.  The comparison of percentages in matched samples.  *Biometrika 37,* 1950, 256–266.

Garner, W. R.  *Uncertainty and structure as psychological concepts.*  New York: Wiley, 1962.

Goodman, L. A., and Kruskal, W. H.  Measures of association for cross-classifications.  *J. Amer. Stat. Ass. 49,* 1954, 732–764.

Kendall, M. G.  *The advanced theory of statistics* (Vol. I).  London: Griffin, 1947.

Kendall, M. G.  *Rank correlation methods* (ed. 2).  London: Griffin, 1955.

Kruskal, W. H.  Ordinal measures of association.  *J. Amer. Stat. Ass. 53,* 1958, 814–861.

Kruskal, W. H., and Wallis, W. A.  Use of ranks in one-criterion variance analysis.  *J. Amer. Stat. Ass. 47,* 1952, 583–621.

Maxwell, A. E.  *Analysing qualitative data.*  London: Methuen, 1961.

Siegel, S.  *Nonparametric methods for the behavioral sciences.*  New York: McGraw-Hill, 1956.

# GLOSSARY

## Conventional mathematical symbols

| | |
|---|---|
| $A$ . . . . . . . . . . . . . . . . | a set (14) |
| $A = \{a,b,c,d\}$ . . . . . . | set $A$ includes the following members; a set specified by listing (14) |
| $a \in A$ . . . . . . . . . . . . . | $a$ is a member of the set $A$ (14) |
| $a \leqq b$ . . . . . . . . . . . . | $a$ is less than or equal to $b$ (15) |
| $a \geqq b$ . . . . . . . . . . . . | $a$ is greater than or equal to $b$ (15) |
| $a < b$ . . . . . . . . . . . . | $a$ is less than (but not equal to) $b$ (97) |
| $a > b$ . . . . . . . . . . . . | $a$ is greater than (but not equal to) $b$ (38) |
| $\{a|B\}$ . . . . . . . . . . . . | set of all $a$ such that the statement $B$ is true (15) |
| $W$ . . . . . . . . . . . . . . . | symbol for the universal set in some discussion of sets (15) |
| $A \subseteq B$ . . . . . . . . . . . | $A$ is a subset of $B$ (16) |
| $A \subset B$ . . . . . . . . . . . | $A$ is a proper subset of $B$ ($A \subseteq B$, but $A$ does not equal $B$) (16) |
| $\emptyset$ . . . . . . . . . . . . . . . | the empty set (18) |
| $A \cup B$ . . . . . . . . . . | union of sets $A$ and $B$ (19) |
| $A \cap B$ . . . . . . . . . . | intersection of sets $A$ and $B$ (20) |
| $\bar{A}$ . . . . . . . . . . . . . . . | complement of set $A$ (21) |
| $x \notin A$ . . . . . . . . . . . . | element $x$ is not a member of set $A$ (21) |
| $A - B$ . . . . . . . . . . . | difference between sets $A$ and $B$ (22) |
| $A = B$ . . . . . . . . . . . | sets $A$ and $B$ are equal or equivalent (17) |
| $A \times B$ . . . . . . . . . . . | set product or Cartesian product (26) |
| $(a,b)$ . . . . . . . . . . . . . | ordered pair of elements, $a$ from set $A$ and $b$ from set $B$; a member of $A \times B$ (26) |
| $y = f(x),\ y = G(x),$ etc. . . . . . . . . . . . . . | $y$ is functionally related to $x$ (38) |
| $y = f(x,z)$ . . . . . . . . . | $y$ is a function of the two variables $x$ and $z$ (40) |
| $a \rightarrow b$ . . . . . . . . . . . . . | $a$ approaches the value $b$ (59) |

$\infty$ ............... an infinite value (59)

$\Sigma$ ............... sum of (see Appendix A)

$\int_a^b f(x)\, dx$ ......... area under the curve generated by the function $y = f(x)$, as cut off by the $x$ interval with limits $a$ and $b$ (103)

$N!$ ............... factorial of the integer $N$ (134)

$\binom{N}{r}$ ............ number of unordered combinations of $N$ things taken $r$ at a time, $0 \leq r \leq N$; a binomial coefficient (137)

$e$ ................ mathematical constant equal approximately to 2.7182818; base of the natural system of logarithms (219)

$\exp [x]$ ............ alternate form of $e^x$ (38)

$\log_e m$ ............ logarithm to the base $e$ for the value $m$ (563)

$\pi$ ................ mathematical constant, equal approximately to 3.14159265; ratio of the circumference of a circle to its diameter (38)

### Statistical Symbols Used in This Text

$\mathcal{A}$ ............... family of events defined by some sample space (51)

$a_j$ ........ ........ effect of the randomly selected treatment appearing as the $j$th such treatment in the experiment (417)

$\boldsymbol{a}(v)$ ............. effect associated with the randomly selected treatment $v$ (416)

$(A_j, B_k)$ ........... joint event of an observation in category $A_j$ on attribute $A$, and in category $B_k$ on attribute $B$ (589)

$A_h = \dfrac{\psi_h}{nw_h}$ ......... weight given to the orthogonal polynomial coefficient representing a trend of degree $h$ in estimation of a curvilinear prediction function (559)

$\alpha$ ............... (small Greek alpha) probability of rejecting $H_0$ when it is true; probability of Type I error (267)

$\alpha_j = \mu_j - \mu$ ....... effect associated with the $j$th treatment applied; a fixed effect (359)

est. $\alpha_j$ ............ estimated effect for treatment $j$ (381)

$b_k$ ................ random effect associated with treatment $k$ (430)

$b_{Y \cdot X}$ .............. sample coefficient of linear regression of $Y$ on $X$ (504)

$b_{1 \cdot 2}$ ............... linear regression coefficient for prediction of $z_1$ from $z_2$ (567)

$b_{12 \cdot 3}$ ............. multiple regression coefficient applied to variable $z_2$ in predictions of $z_1$ from $z_2$ and $z_3$ (567)

$b_{13 \cdot 2}$ ............. multiple regression coefficient applied to variable $z_3$ in predictions of $z_1$ from $z_2$ and $z_3$ (567)

$b_{12 \cdot 3 \ldots K}$ .......... multiple regression coefficient for weighting $z_2$ in the prediction of $z_1$ from $z_2, \cdots, z_K$ (570)

$\beta$ ............... (small Greek beta) probability of failing to reject $H_0$ when it is false; probability of Type II error (267)

$1 - \beta$ ............ power of a statistical test against some given true alternative to the null hypothesis (267)

$\beta_k$ ............... fixed effect associated with the treatment or factor level $k$ (387)

$\beta_{Y \cdot X}$ ............. regression coefficient for prediction of $Y$ from $X$ in the population (512)

$\beta_1, \beta_2, \cdots, \beta_{J-1} \ldots$    population regression coefficients for linear and curvilinear trends between $Y$ and $X$ (540)

$C$................    number of columns in the data table for a two-factor experiment (393)

$C_{AB}$............    coefficient of contingency (606)

$c_j$...............    constant applied to a sample or population mean corresponding to treatment $j$ in a comparison (462)

$c_{jk}$...............    random interaction effect associated with the combination of treatment $j$ with treatment $k$ (430)

$(c_1, \cdots, c_n)$......    set of $n$ constant weights figuring in some linear combustion of $n$ random variables (234)

$\chi^2$...............    (small Greek chi, squared) random variable chi-square; also the Pearson chi-square statistic (336, 582)

$\chi^2_{(\nu)}$...............    chi-square variable with $\nu$ degrees of freedom (339)

$\chi^2_{(N-1;\alpha/2)}; \chi^2_{(N-1;1-\alpha/2)}$    values in the distribution of $\chi^2$ with $N-1$ degrees of freedom, cutting off the upper $\alpha/2$ and $1-\alpha/2$ proportion of cases, respectively (345)

$$\chi^2 = \sum_j \frac{(f_{oj} - f_{ej})^2}{f_{ej}}$$    Pearson $\chi^2$ statistic in a test of goodness of fit (582)

$\text{cov.}(X,Y)$........    covariance of the two random variables $X$ and $Y$ (670)

$\text{cov.}(M_1,M_2)$.......    covariance of pairs of sample means (334)

$D_i = (Y_{i1} - Y_{i2})\ldots$    difference between the scores for members of matched pair $i$ from among $N$ such pairs (334)

$d_i$...............    deviation of the score for observation $i$ from the grand mean

$\delta$.................    (small Greek delta) noncentrality parameter for noncentral $t$ or noncentral $F$ (323, 384)

$$\Delta = \frac{|\mu_1 - \mu_2|}{\sigma_{Y|X}}$$......    (capital Greek delta) absolute difference between two population means, relative to the standard deviation for either population (329)

$\Delta X$...............    width of an arbitrarily small interval of values for random variable $X$ (100)

$E(X)$.............    expectation of random variable $X$ (see Appendix B)

$E(u;D_1,H_0)$........    expected loss, given decision-rule 1 and truth of hypothesis $H_0$ (259)

$e_{ij}$...............    random error associated with the $i$th observation made under treatment $j$ (360)

$e_{ijk}$...............    random error associated with the $i$th observation in the treatment-combination $j, k$ (387)

$e_i(v)$...............    error associated with observation $i$ made under treatment $v$ (414)

$\eta^2_{Y \cdot X}$...............    (small Greek eta, squared) correlation ratio, for the relation of $Y$ to $X$ (547)

$\epsilon$.................    (small Greek epsilon) an arbitrarily small positive number (59)

$F$................    $F$ ratio computed from a sample; the random variable "$F$" (348)

$F_\alpha$................    value of $F$ required for significance at the $\alpha$ level, one-tailed, for a given number of degrees of freedom (484)

$F_{(\nu_1; \nu_2)}$ . . . . . . . . . . . . random variable distributed as $F$ with $\nu_1$ and $\nu_2$ degrees of freedom (350)

$F_{(\alpha; \nu_1, \nu_2)}$ . . . . . . . . . . value cutting off the upper $\alpha$ proportion of cases in an $F$ distribution with $\nu_1$ and $\nu_2$ degrees of freedom (350)

$f(a) = f(X = a)$ . . . . probability density for random variable $X$ at the value $X = a$ (102)

$F(a) = p(X \leq a)$ . . . cumulative probability of random variable $X$ at the value $a$ (103)

$f$ . . . . . . . . . . . . . . . . frequency of a given measurement or event class (78)

$f_{ej}$ . . . . . . . . . . . . . . . expected frequency in event-category $j$ (581)

$f_{ejk}$ . . . . . . . . . . . . . . expected frequency in the cell $j, k$ of a contingency table (591)

$f_{oj}$ . . . . . . . . . . . . . . . observed frequency in event-category $j$ (581)

$f_{ojk}$ . . . . . . . . . . . . . . observed frequency in the cell $j, k$ of a contingency table (591)

$\gamma$ . . . . . . . . . . . . . . . . (small Greek gamma) coefficient of predictive association between sets of ordered classes (655)

$\gamma_{jk}$ . . . . . . . . . . . . . . fixed interaction effect associated with the combination of treatments $j$ and $k$ (387)

$H:$ . . . . . . . . . . . . . . . indicator of a statistical hypothesis (249)

$H_0:$ . . . . . . . . . . . . . . hypothesis actually being tested; the "null" hypothesis (250)

$H_1:$ . . . . . . . . . . . . . . hypothesis to be entertained if $H_0$ is rejected; the alternative hypothesis (250)

$H(A)$ . . . . . . . . . . . . average uncertainty associated with the attribute $A$ (611)

$H(B|A)$ . . . . . . . . . . average uncertainty associated with the attribute $B$, given the status of an observation on attribute $A$ (612)

$i$ . . . . . . . . . . . . . . . . class interval size in some frequency distribution (81)

$i$ . . . . . . . . . . . . . . . . running subscript, ordinarily indicating the $i$th observation among some $N$ distinct observations (659)

$J$ . . . . . . . . . . . . . . . . number of different experimental treatments or groups in an experiment (312, 660)

$j$ . . . . . . . . . . . . . . . . running subscript indicating the $j$th treatment group or factor level (359, 660)

$K$ . . . . . . . . . . . . . . . in a two-factor experiment, number of treatment groups or levels of the second factor; number of "blocks" of observations in an experiment (452, 661)

$k$ . . . . . . . . . . . . . . . . an arbitrarily small positive number (188)

$k$ . . . . . . . . . . . . . . . . a running subscript, ordinarily indicating the $k$th treatment group or "block" of observations (661)

$L(X_1, \cdots, X_N|\theta)$ . . likelihood of a particular set of $N$ sample values, given the value of the parameter (or set of parameters) $\theta$ (213)

$\lambda_B$ . . . . . . . . . . . . . . (small Greek lambda) assymetric measure of predictive association for a contingency table (608)

$\lambda_{AB}$ . . . . . . . . . . . . . . symmetric measure of predictive association in a contingency table (610)

$M$ . . . . . . . . . . . . . . . the sample mean (161)

$M_D$ . . . . . . . . . . . . . mean difference between $N$ matched pairs (335)

$Md$ . . . . . . . . . . . . . . the median (159)

$M_e$ . . . . . . . . . . . . . . . mean error in a set of $N$ experimental observations (365)

$M_{ej}$ . . . . . . . . . . . . . . mean error for the $n_j$ observations in group $j$ (365)

$m(o)$ . . . . . . . . . . . . measured amount of some property possessed by object $o$ (70)

MS . . . . . . . . . . . . . . mean square in the analysis of variance (368)

$\mu = E(X)$ . . . . . . . . (small Greek mu) mean of the probability distribution of the random variable $X$ (172)

$\mu_0$ . . . . . . . . . . . . . . value of the population mean specified by $H_0$ (270)

$\mu_1$ . . . . . . . . . . . . . . true value of the mean of the population; a value of the mean covered by the alternative hypothesis $H_1$ (270)

$\mu_G = E(G)$ . . . . . . . . mean of the sampling distribution for some statistic $G$ (195)

$\mu_j$ . . . . . . . . . . . . . . true mean of the potential population of observation made under treatment $j$ (359)

$\mu_{jk}$ . . . . . . . . . . . . . . mean of the potential population of observations made under the treatment combination $j$, $k$ (388)

$\mathbf{\mu}(v)$ . . . . . . . . . . . . . . mean of all potential observations made under treatment $v$ (414)

$N$ . . . . . . . . . . . . . . . total number of trials in a simple experiment or of observations in a given sample (59, 76)

$n$ . . . . . . . . . . . . . . . size of any one of several samples containing the same number of observations (329)

$n_j$ . . . . . . . . . . . . . . number of sample observations in treatment group $j$ (360)

$n_{jk}$ . . . . . . . . . . . . . . number of sample observations in treatment combination $j$, $k$ (393)

$\nu$ . . . . . . . . . . . . . . . (small Greek nu) degrees of freedom parameter for a $t$ or chi-square variable (305, 339)

$\nu_1$, $\nu_2$ . . . . . . . . . . . . . number of degrees of freedom for numerator and denominator, respectively, for an $F$ ratio; the parameters of the $F$ distribution (348)

$\omega^2$ . . . . . . . . . . . . . . (small Greek omega, squared) population index showing the relative or proportional reduction in the variance of $Y$ given the $X$ status or value for an observation (325)

est. $\omega^2$ . . . . . . . . . . . sample estimate of the proportional reduction in variance of $Y$ given $X$ (327)

$P$ . . . . . . . . . . . . . . . sample proportion of "successes" in sampling from a Bernoulli distribution (148)

$p$ . . . . . . . . . . . . . . . probability of a given event class; probability of a "success" in a single Bernoulli trial (93)

$p(A)$ . . . . . . . . . . . . . probability associated with a particular event $A$ in a probability function (94)

$p(B|A) = \dfrac{p(A \cap B)}{p(A)}$ conditional probability of event $B$ given the event $A$ (111)

$p(X = r|N,p)$ . . . . . . binomial probability for $X = r$, given the parameters $N$ and $p$ (148)

$\mathscr{P}(H)$ . . . . . . . . . . . . . personal probability associated by the experimenter with the hypothesis $H$ (261)

$\psi$ . . . . . . . . . . . . . . . (small Greek psi) value of a particular comparison among population means (462)

$\hat{\psi}$ . . . . . . . . . . . . . . . . value of a particular comparison among sample means (462)

$\hat{\psi}_g$ . . . . . . . . . . . . . . value of a particular comparison $g$ on a set of sample means (474)

$\varphi$ . . . . . . . . . . . . . . . (small Greek phi) index of mean square contingency for a population or a sample contingency table (604)

$\varphi'$ . . . . . . . . . . . . . . Cramér's statistic for association in a contingency table (606)

$Q$ . . . . . . . . . . . . . . . proportion of cases cut off by a given value on the upper tail of a sampling distribution (309)

$Q = 1 - P$ . . . . . . . proportion of sample "failures" in sampling from a Bernoulli distribution (291)

$q = 1 - p$ . . . . . . . . probability of a "failure" on a single Bernoulli trial (140)

$R$ . . . . . . . . . . . . . . . . number of rows in the data table for a two-factor experiment (393)

$R_{1 \cdot 23}$ . . . . . . . . . . . . . multiple correlation of variable 1 with variables 2 and 3 (570)

$R_{1 \cdot 2 \ldots K}$ . . . . . . . . . . multiple correlation of variable 1 with variables 2 through $K$ (571)

$r_{XY}$ . . . . . . . . . . . . . sample correlation coefficient between $X$ and $Y$ (497)

$r_{12 \cdot 3}$ . . . . . . . . . . . . . partial correlation between variables 1 and 2 with 3 held constant (574)

$r_{(Y', Y)}$ . . . . . . . . . . . correlation between the predicted and actual values of $Y$ (570)

$r_S$ . . . . . . . . . . . . . . . Spearman rank-correlation coefficient (644)

$\rho_I$ . . . . . . . . . . . . . . (small Greek rho, sub $I$) intraclass correlation coefficient for a population (424)

$\rho_{XY}$ . . . . . . . . . . . . . population correlation coefficient between variables $X$ and $Y$ (512)

$\rho_0$ . . . . . . . . . . . . . . value of the population correlation specified by $H_0$ (531)

$\mathcal{S}$ . . . . . . . . . . . . . . . sample space for a particular simple experiment (49)

$S = \sqrt{(J-1)F_\alpha}$ . . constant determining the width of confidence intervals for post-hoc comparisons, Scheffé method (484)

$SE(u; D)$ . . . . . . . . . . subjective expected loss associated with a particular decision-rule $D$ by the experimeter (262)

$S_+, S_-$ . . . . . . . . . . . . number of agreements and disagreements, respectively, about the ordering of pairs of objects in two rank orders (650)

$S_j$ . . . . . . . . . . . . . . . constant value determining the width of a confidence interval for $Y_{ij}$ given $X_j$, for a problem in regression (523)

SS . . . . . . . . . . . . . . sum of squares in the analysis of variance (364)

$s$ . . . . . . . . . . . . . . . . standard deviation computed for a sample of data (177)

$s^2$ . . . . . . . . . . . . . . . sample variance (177)

$\hat{s} = \sqrt{\hat{s}^2}$ . . . . . . . . . corrected standard deviation for a sample (207)

$\hat{s}^2 = \dfrac{N}{N-1} s^2$ . . . . . corrected variance; the unbiased estimator of the population variance from a sample (207)

$s_D^2$ . . . . . . . . . . . . . . . sample variance based on the difference for each of $N$ matched pairs of observations (335)

$s_{Y \cdot X}$ . . . . . . . . . . . . . sample standard error of estimate for predictions of $Y$ from $X$ (505)

$s_z^2$ . . . . . . . . . . . . . . . variance of $z$ or standardized scores calculated from a sample of data (187)

$s_{z_Y \cdot z_X}$ . . . . . . . . . . . . . . sample standard error of estimate for predictions of $z_Y$ from $z_X$ (498)

$s_{z_1 \cdot z_2}$ . . . . . . . . . . . . standard error of estimate for predictions of $z_1$ from $z_2$ (571)

$s^2_{z_1 \cdot z_2 \dots z_K}$ . . . . . . . . . . . sample variance of estimate for $z_1$ values predicted from $z_2, \cdots,$ $z_K$ via a multiple regression equation (571)

$s^2_{1 \cdot 2 \dots K}$ . . . . . . . . . . . sample variance of estimate in the prediction of $X_1$ from $X_2$, $\cdots, X_K$ (572)

$\sigma$ . . . . . . . . . . . . . . . (small Greek sigma) standard deviation of a random variable (183)

$\sigma^2$ . . . . . . . . . . . . . . . variance of a random variable (183)

$\sigma^2_0$ . . . . . . . . . . . . . . value of the population variance specified by the hypothesis $H_0$ (344)

$\sigma^2_A$ . . . . . . . . . . . . . variance of the distribution of random effects $\mathbf{a}(v)$, representing factor $A$ (418)

$\sigma^2_B$ . . . . . . . . . . . . . variance of the random effects representing factor $B$ (433)

$\sigma^2_{AB}$ . . . . . . . . . . . . . variance of the random interaction effects for the factors $A$ and $B$ (434)

$\sigma^2_e$ . . . . . . . . . . . . . . variance of random errors, $e$ (364)

$\sigma_{\text{diff.}}$ . . . . . . . . . . . . . standard error of the difference between two means (315)

est. $\sigma_{\text{diff.}}$ . . . . . . . . . . estimated standard error of the difference between two means (317)

$\sigma^2_G$ . . . . . . . . . . . . . variance of the sampling distribution of some statistic $G$ (196)

$\sigma^2_M$ . . . . . . . . . . . . . variance of the sampling distribution of the mean (198)

$\sigma_M$ . . . . . . . . . . . . . true standard error of the mean, given samples of size $N$ from some population (203)

est. $\sigma_M$ . . . . . . . . . . . sample estimate of the standard error of the mean (302)

est. $\sigma_{M_D}$ . . . . . . . . . . estimated standard error of the mean difference between $N$ matched pairs (335)

$\sigma^2_P$ . . . . . . . . . . . . . variance of a sampling distribution of sample proportions, $P$ (184)

$\sigma_S$ . . . . . . . . . . . . . standard error of measurement for a score (294)

$\sigma^2_Y$ . . . . . . . . . . . . . variance of the random variable $Y$; "marginal" variance of $Y$ in a joint distribution of $(X,Y)$ events (236)

$\sigma^2_Y - \sigma^2_{Y|X}$ . . . . . . . . reduction in the variance of $Y$ afforded by specification of $X$ (325)

$\sigma^2_{Y|X}$ . . . . . . . . . . . . variance of the conditional distribution of $Y$, given the value of $X$ (325)

$\sigma_{Y \cdot X}$ . . . . . . . . . . . . . true standard error of estimate for predictions of $Y$ from $X$ in some population (512)

$\sigma^2_z$ . . . . . . . . . . . . . . variance of a random variable transformed to $z$ or standardized values (188)

$\sigma_{(Z_1 - Z_2)}$ . . . . . . . . . . variance of the difference between $Z$ values for pairs of independent samples (532)

$t = \dfrac{M - E(M)}{\text{est. } \sigma_M}$ . . . . . $t$ ratio based on the mean of a single sample (304)

$t = \dfrac{M_1 - M_2 - E(M_1 - M_2)}{\text{est. } \sigma_{\text{diff.}}}$ $t$ ratio based on the difference between means of two samples (317)

| | |
|---|---|
| $t$ ................. | a random variable following the distribution of $t$ with $\nu$ degrees of freedom (305) |
| $t_{(\alpha/2;\nu)}$ ............ | value of $t$ in a distribution with $\nu$ degrees of freedom, cutting off the upper $\alpha/2$ proportion of cases (312) |
| $t(o)$ ............. | true amount of some property possessed by object $o$ (70) |
| $T_s$ ............. | true score on some test for an individual subject (294) |
| $\tau$ ................. | (small Greek tau) Kendall's coefficient of rank-order agreement (647) |
| $\theta$ ................. | (small Greek theta) general symbol for a population parameter (197) |
| $\theta_0$ ................. | value of $\theta$ specified by the null hypothesis $H_0$ (427) |
| $\theta = \sigma_A^2/\sigma_e^2$ ........ | ratio of the variance of effects due to factor $A$ to the error variance (425) |
| $u(H_0;H_1)$ ......... | loss associated with the decision to accept $H_0$ when $H_1$ is in fact true (258) |
| $u(H_1;H_0)$ ......... | loss associated with the decision to accept $H_1$ when $H_0$ is in fact true (259) |
| var.$(X)$ ........... | variance of the random variable $X$ (671) |
| var.$(M_1 - M_2)$ .... | variance of the difference between means (315) |
| var.$(\hat{\psi})$ .......... | variance of a comparison among sample means (463) |
| $w(b|a)$ ........... | conditional density for $Y = b$ given that $X = a$ (123) |
| $w_g$ .............. | weighting factor used in obtaining the sum of squares for comparison $\hat{\psi}_g$ (474) |
| $X$ ................. | a random variable; the independent variable in an experiment (96) |
| $(X,Y)$ ............ | a joint event, consisting of a value for variable $X$ paired with a value for variable $Y$ (124, 493) |
| $|X - \mu|$ .......... | absolute deviation (disregarding sign) of the value of $X$ from the value of $\mu$ (188) |
| $x$ ................. | midpoint of a class interval (162) |
| $\xi_j$ ................. | (small Greek xi) effect associated with treatment $j$, in the general regression model (543) |
| $Y$ ................. | a random variable; ordinarily, the dependent variable in an experiment (233) |
| $Y'$ ............... | raw score on $Y$ predicted from the value of $X$ (503) |
| $Y_{ij}$ ............... | score associated with the observation $i$ in experimental group $j$ (360) |
| $Y_{ijk}$ .............. | score associated with the $i$th observation in the treatment combination $j, k$ (387) |
| $Z$ ................. | value corresponding to $r_{XY}$ in the Fisher $r$ to $Z$ transformation (530) |
| $z = \dfrac{X - M}{s}$ ....... | standardized score or value corresponding to a sample value $X$, relative to a sample distribution (186) |
| $z = \dfrac{X - E(X)}{\sigma}$ .... | standardized score or value corresponding to a particular value of $X$, relative to a population distribution (187) |
| $|z|$ ............... | absolute value of a standardized score (189) |

$z_1'$ . . . . . . . . . . . . . . . . predicted standardized value on variable $X_1$ (567)

$z_X, z_Y$ . . . . . . . . . . . . standardized scores corresponding to particular values of $X$ and $Y$, respectively (494)

$z_{(1-\alpha/2)}$ . . . . . . . . . . . . standardized value cutting off the lower $1 - \alpha/2$ proportion of cases in a normal distribution (330)

$z_M = \dfrac{M - E(M)}{\sigma_M}$ . . . standardized value corresponding to a particular value of sample $M$ in a sampling distribution of means (203)

$z_Y'$ . . . . . . . . . . . . . . . . predicted standardized value on variable $Y$ (494)

$\zeta$ . . . . . . . . . . . . . . . . (small Greek zeta) value in the Fisher $r$ to $Z$ transformation corresponding to the population correlation $\rho$ (530)

# INDEX

Analysis of covariance, 564
Analysis of variance, 356–458,
    474–478
  computations for, 371–372,
      400–401
  connections among models for, 447
  linear model for, 360
  Model I, 357–408
    assumptions in, 364
    assumptions in two-way, 396
    $F$ tests in, 368–369, 397–398
    fixed effects, 356–408, 515, 543
    importance of assumptions in,
        378
    two-way, 385, 387
  Model II, 358, 414–438
    assumptions in, 417
    assumptions in two-way, 430
    $F$ tests in, 421, 433–435
    importance of assumptions in,
        427
    random effects, 358, 414–458
    two-factor, 429
  Model III, 414, 439–456
    $F$ tests in, 443–444
    mixed model, 439, 440, 453
Analysis of variance, planned
    comparisons in, 474–478
  summary table, 372, 402
Anderson, R. L., 564
Areas, 99–101, 105–106
  as probabilities for discrete
      variables, 99
  as probabilities for continuous
      variables, 103
Association, 118, 127–130
  measures, 325–327, 381–384
    in contingency tables, 603
    linear, 523
    in ordered classes, 655
    predictive, 603, 606
  Pearson $\chi^2$ test for, 589
  statistical, 127–130, 579
  see also Statistical association
Attneave, F., 612
Attribute, 119, 579
Average absolute deviation, 182

Bancroft, T. A., 564
Bayes' theorem, 113–116
  general form, 116
  with personal probabilities, 298

Bayes' theorem, use of, 114–115
Bennett, C. A., 564
Bernoulli, J., 59
Bernoulli distributions, *see* Dis-
    tribution, Bernoulli
Bernoulli trials, 140
Bernoulli's theorem, 58, 189, 203
Binomial coefficients, 137, 686
Binomial distribution, 143–156,
    169–170, 183–185, 227–231
  and binomial expansion, 145–146
  form of, 148–149
  intervals in, 146–147
  for proportions, 148
  use of, 150–154
Bivariate normal distribution,
    assumption of, 527
  and independence of variables,
    528
  rule for, 528
Boole, G., 23
Boolean algebra, 23
Box, G. E. P., 381

Carroll, J. B., 510
Cartesian coordinates, 28
Cartesian product, 26
Central limit theorem, 205, 238–242
  applied to linear combinations,
    241–242
Central tendency, 157–176
  in discrete probability distributions,
    166
  measures of, 157–167, 172–176
Chi-square ($\chi^2$), 336–348, 352–355,
    583
  additive property of, 341, 343
  density function of, 339
  distribution of, 336
  mean and variance of, 340
  with $N$ degrees of freedom, 338
  with one degree of freedom, 337
  Pearson statistic, *see* Pearson $\chi^2$
    statistic
  tables of distribution, 340, 625–
    626

Chi-square statistic, *see* Pearson $\chi^2$
    statistic
Class interval size, 80
Class intervals, 80–87, 89, 91
  apparent limits, 81
  midpoints, 84
  real limits, 81
Cochran, W., 457, 603, 628
Cochran's test, 628
Coefficient of determination, 502
Combinations, 136–138
  irrespective of order, 137
  ordered, 136
Comparisons among means, planned,
    459–483, 517–518, 551–558
  choice of, 482
  confidence intervals for, 464
  independence of grand mean, 472
  number of independent, 473
  orthogonal, 466
  pooling sums of squares for, 478
  for populations, 462
  in regression problems, 517
  sample values for, 463
  sets of weights for, 462
  for trend, 551
Comparisons among means, post-hoc,
    483–489
  interpretation of, 484
  prior $F$ test, 483
  in trend analysis, 562
  versus planned, 487
Concordance, coefficient of, 656
Conditional probability, 111–119,
    247
Confidence intervals, 212, 287–293
  several simultaneous, 312–314,
    484–485
  shortest, 290, 346
  *see also* Confidence limits
Confidence limits, 288–293
  for planned comparison value, 464
  for proportions, 291
  for proportion of variance
    accounted for, 425
  for regression problems, 522

Confidence limits, large sample for
mean, 288–290, 303–304
for single mean, small sample,
311–312
small sample for a difference, 321
using *r* to *Z* transformation, 533
for a variance, 345
Contingency table, 127, 589, 603
Coombs, C. H., 73
Correlation, 493–538
coefficient, 496
assumptions underlying, 509
computation of, 505–506
confidence intervals for, 533
interpretation of, 499–500
descriptive statistics of, 494–505
fourfold point, 605
intraclass, 325, 424
multiple, 570–572
test for, 573
partial, 574–576
test for, 575
in population, 511
problems of, 493
rank order, 641–656
-ratio, 325, 547
significance test for, 529
tests based on Fisher's *Z*, 531
Covariance, 511, 670
as a comparison among means,
517
and independence, 511, 670
of means, 334
population, 511, 670
sample, 511, 517
Cox, D. R., 457
Cox, G., 457
Cramér, H., 606
Cramér's statistic, 606
Critical value, 251
Crossing of experimental factors, 386
Cumulative distribution functions,
103

Darwin, C., 10
Davis, R., 73

Decision-rules, 247–266
choice among, 254–262
conventional, 263, 269
criteria for, 258–262
Deduction, 10
Degrees of freedom, 310, 339–340,
473–477
in analysis of variance, 474
in one-way analysis of variance,
365–368, 372
as parameter of chi-square
distribution, 339
as parameter of *t* distribution, 306
in Pearson $\chi^2$ tests, 583, 588, 591
for variance estimate, 476
Density function, *see* Function,
density *and* Probability
distributions
Dependent variable, 39
qualitative, 595, 616
quantitative, 356
Descartes, R., 27
Differences between means, 314–335
large sample confidence limits for,
319
large sample tests of, 317
sampling distribution of, 315–316
small sample confidence limits for,
321
and statistical association, 324–333
*t* tests for, 320, 322, 335
Distribution, 76, 93, 94
Bernoulli, 140
bivariate, 124–127, 528
hypergeometric, 155, 599
multinomial, 154, 579, 582
*see also F* ratio, Normal distribution, Random variables,
*and t* distribution
Distributions, 76–107
bimodal, 173
comparison of, 578–614
conditional, 325
frequency, *see* Frequency
distributions
moments of, 185

Distributions, probability, *see*
  Probability distributions
  relations among theoretical, 352
  sampling, 193, 194
  "shapes" of, 172
  skewed, 173, 239, 337, 349
  symmetric, 173
  unimodal, 173
Dixon, W., 208

Edwards, A., 457
Effects, 357, 358
  additive, 389
  estimation of fixed, 361
  random, 416
  sum of, 394
  of treatments, 359
Error, 45, 164–166, 360, 496
Errors, 165, 231
  in decision-making, 256
  probabilities of, 254, 267–269
  Type I, 280
    conventions about, 269, 280–281
  Type II, 280, 281
Estimation, 196–215
  accuracy of, 204, 292–296
  interval, 212, 287–293
  point, 196
  sample size determined by,
    204–206, 292
Estimators, 196–202, 206–210
  consistent, 199
  maximum likelihood, 214
  pooled, 209
  relative efficiency of, 199
  sample statistics as, 196–202
  sufficiency of, 200
  unbiased, 197–199, 201, 206–208
Euler, L., 17
Euler diagrams, 17
Event, 9, 49
  -class, 49
  elementary, 49
  impossible, 50
  occurrence of, 49
  sure, 50

Events, 48–63
  associated or dependent, 118–119
  equally probable, 55–58, 64–65
  exhaustive, 50, 93
  family of, 51
  joint, 108–130
    representation in tables, 119
  mutually exclusive, 50, 51, 93
  sequences of, 133
Expectation, 167–171
  algebra of, 170, 667–671
  of binomial variable, 169–170
  of continuous random variable, 171
  in games of chance, 167–169
Expected value, *see* Expectation
Experiment, 5, 335, 409, 412
  simple, 48
Experimental control, 42, 449
Experimental design, 4, 11, 457–458,
    476
  balanced, 387
  factorial, 411
  fully randomized, 450
  matched groups, 451–452
  randomized blocks, 452–455

$F$ ratio, 336, 348
  distribution of, 336, 348–355
  expectation of, 349
  as $t^2$, 354, 375, 465
  tests in analysis of variance, *see*
    Analysis of variance
  use of tables of, 349
  use to test equality of variances,
    351
$F$ test, 348, 351, 368
  for curvilinear regression, 545
  for equal variances, 351
  for linear regression, 521
  for multiple correlation, 573
  as "omnibus" test for comparisons,
    478
  for a planned comparison, 465
  for a trend, 556–557
Factor, 359, 385, 387
  experimental, 356, 385, 386

Factor, level, 387
 nuisance, 449
 sampled, 415, 442
Factorials, 134
Fisher, R. A. (Sir Ronald), 287, 336,
 530
Fisher's exact test, 598–601
Fisher's *r* to *Z* transformation,
 530–533, 576, 680
Fourfold point correlation, *see*
 Correlation, fourfold point
Fourfold table, 589, 595, 599
 measure of association in, 605
 test for association in, 595
Franklin, N. L., 564
Frequencies, 76
 expected, 94, 128, 581, 591
 obtained, 581
 relative, 56, 58, 59, 94
Frequency distributions, 76–92
 cumulative, 91–92
 grouped, 78–80
 with open or unequal intervals,
 87
Frequency polygons, 90–91
Freud, S., 10
Friedman test, 640–641
Function, 13, 34
 argument of, 39
 continuous, 39
 density, 102
 *see also* Probability distributions
 probability, 51, 93
 rule, 38–39
 set, 35
 with several independent variables, 40

Galileo, 42
Galton, F. (Sir Francis), 501
Garner, W., 612
Goodman, L. A., 608, 655
Goodness of fit, 579, 580–588
 test for normal distributions,
 586–588
Graybill, F. A., 564

Histograms, 88–89, 99–101
Homogeneity of variance, 322, 408,
 428, 520
 testing for, 380
Homoscedasticity, 520
Hypergeometric distribution, 155
 *see also* Distribution, hypergeometric
Hypotheses, 151 ff., 214, 248
 alternative, 250, 266, 269,
 270
 directional, 282, 285
 composite, 249
 exact, 249
 simple, 248
 tests of inexact, 275
Hypothesis, null, 266, 269, 280
Hypothesis testing, 245–287
 in analysis of variance, Model I,
 368–370, 397–399
 in analysis of variance, Model II,
 421, 433–435
 in analysis of variance, Model III,
 443–444
 assumptions in, 249
 and common sense, 299
 general theory of, 286
 relative merits of one- and two-
 tailed, 285
 steps in, 250

Independence, 116–124
 of events, 59, 64, 117
 of linear combinations, 467
 of sample mean and variance,
 232–233, 369
Independent variable, 39
 in an experiment, 39
 qualitative, 356, 491
 quantitative, 356, 491
Induction, 10
Inertia, moment of, 181
Inference, 60, 150–153, 215–217
 deductive, 9
 inductive, 9
 statistical, 61, 150

Information theory, 603, 610
  and analysis of contingency tables,
    610
Interaction, 386, 388, 390, 433–435,
    442, 454
  importance of, 390–392, 454–455
  in mixed model, 442
  as nonadditivity, 389
  in random effects model, 432
Intercorrelations, 576
Intraclass correlation coefficient, 424
  confidence intervals for, 425
  significance test for, 427

Kendall, M. G., 646, 647, 653, 655,
    656
Kendall's tau coefficient, 642, 647
  with ties, 652
Klett, G. W., 346
Kolmogorov-Smirnoff test, 614
Kruskal, W. H., 608, 637, 655
Kurtosis, 186

Law of averages, 59
Law of large numbers, 203
Least squares, 496, 568
Lewis, D., 564
Likelihood ratio tests, 287
  for categorical data, 597, 612
Lindquist, E. F., 455
Linear combinations, 233–238
  comparisons as, 462
  sampling distributions of, 234–238
Linear model, 360
Linear regression, *see* Regression,
    linear
Losses, 256
  expected, 258
  subjective expected, 260

McNemar, Q., 602
Mann-Whitney test, 633
Massey, F., 208
Mathematical models, 8
Mathematical relation, 26, 28
  the all-relation, 31

Mathematical relation, domain of, 33
  empty, 31
  functional, 34
  range of, 33
  specification of, 29
Mathematical systems, 7
Maximum likelihood, 212–215
  estimators, 214
Mean, 158, 161–176, 181–183
  as "center of gravity," 163
  deviations about, 164
  of discrete probability distribution,
    167
  as estimator, 201
  as expectation of a random vari-
    able, 167
  of grouped frequency distribution,
    162
  of linear combination, 235
  as a parameter, 171
  pooled estimate of a, 209
  of raw scores, 161
  of sampling distribution, 195
  test for single population, 302
  *see also* Expectation
Mean square, 366 ff.
  between columns in Model I, 397
  between columns in Model II, 433
  for deviations from linear regres-
    sion, 519
  for error, 401, 433, 519
  for error pooled, 437
  between groups, 365
    expectation in Model I, 366
    expectation in Model II, 419
  within groups, 366, 367, 420
  interaction
    in Model I, 398
    in Model II, 433
  for linear regression, 518
  between rows
    in Model I, 398
    in Model II, 431
Mean square contingency, 604
Measurement, 69
  categorical, 69

Measurement, interval scaling, 69, 71, 74, 615
  nominal scaling, 69, 76
  ordinal scaling, 69, 70, 616
  ratio scaling, 69, 73
  and statistics, 73
Measurement scales, 68
Median, 159
  computations for, 160
  interpretation of, 165
  test for independent groups, 620
  test for matched groups, 623
Minimax criterion, 260
Modal class, 158
Mode, 158
  "best guess" interpretation of, 165
Model I, *see* Analysis of variance, Model I
Model II, *see* Analysis of variance, Model II
Model III, *see* Analysis of variance, Model III
Model for linear regression, *see* Regression, linear
Model for linear and curvilinear regression, *see* Regression, curvilinear
Moments, *see* Distributions, moments of
Monotonicity, 643
Mood, A., 287, 598, 624, 625
Multinomial probabilities, 154
  and chi-square approximation, 582

*n*-tuples, 32
Nesting of experimental factors, 386
Neyman, J., 287
Nonparametric statistics, *see* Order statistics
Normal approximation, 226
  to the binomial distribution, 227, 626
  to the chi-square distribution, 347
  to distributions of order statistics, 626, 632, 634, 636, 646, 651

Normal approximation, to sampling distribution of the mean, 239
  to the *t* distribution, 307
Normal distribution, 218–244
  areas under curve for, 221
  assumption in *F* tests, 352
  assumption in test of a variance, 347
  density function for, 219
  goodness of fit test for, 586
  importance of, 225
  multivariate, 529, 573, 576
  parameters of, 220
  properties of, 232, 235
  tables based on, 222
  and theory of error, 231
  use in inferences, 242, 244, 250, 253, 266, 280

Ogive, 92
Ohm's law, 32
Order statistics, 615–658
Ordered pairs, 26
Orthogonal comparisons, 467–471
Orthogonal designs, 393
Orthogonal polynomials, 551–562
  method of, 552
  tables of, 555, 682

Paired observations, test for, 333–335
Parameters, 145, 169–170, 171, 192–193
  of binomial distribution, 145
  of bivariate normal distribution, 528
  of multivariate normal distribution, 529
  of normal distribution, 220
  of population, 192–193
Parameter estimation, 245
  and degrees of freedom, 588, 591
  *see also* Point estimation
Partition of sum of squares, 362–364
  for linear and curvilinear regression, 543
  in regression problems, 516
  two-way analysis of variance, 394

Paull, A. E., 434
Paull's criterion, 434, 444
Pearson, E. S., 287
Pearson, K., 582, 604
Pearson $\chi^2$ statistic, 582–597
  distribution of, 583
  in goodness-of-fit tests, 582–589
  mean and variance of, 584
  in tests for association, 589–597
Pearson product moment correlation
  coefficient, *see* Correlation
  coefficient
Permutations, 134
Phi-coefficient, 604
Physical laws, 32
Planned comparisons, *see* Comparisons among means, planned
Point estimation, 196–215
Populations, 192–193, 215–217, 536–
  538
  defined by sampling methods, 215
  finite, 210
Post-hoc comparisons, *see* Comparisons among means, post-hoc
Power, 269–280
  efficiency, 619
  and error variance, 274
  of $F$ in analysis of variance, 384
  functions, 271
  of order methods, 619
  and sample size, 273
  and size of $\alpha$, 272
  of a statistical test, 269–286
  of $t$ tests, 323
  against various true alternatives,
  270
Precise experiments, 275
Prediction, rules, 491
Probability, 11, 45, 47–67, 92–107
  axioms of, 51
  computations, 131 ff.
  conditional, 111–116, 247
  of an event, 56
  of intersection of events, 50, 53, 108
  marginal, 119
  notation for, 51

Probability, personal, 63, 261, 297
  of poker hands, 138–140
  relative frequency interpretation
  of, 58
  theorems, 52
  theory of, 9, 13, 47, 67
  of union of events, 50, 53
Probability density, 102–104
Probability distributions, 68, 92–107,
  124–130
  cumulative, 103
  groups of, 99, 105
Proportions, 148
  test for, 585
  test for correlated, 601, 628

RAND Corporation, 65
Random effects, 414–455
Random number tables, 65
Random sample, *see* Sample *and*
  Sampling
Random variables, 96
  continuous, 101, 104
  discrete, 96
  independence of continuous, 123
  independence of discrete, 122
  independence of functions of, 124
  representation of joint, 124–127
Randomization, 449, 452
  tests based on, 456, 599, 633
Randomness, 66
Range, 83
  of a function, 33
  of a variable, 36–37
Ratio scales, 73
Real numbers, 28
Regions of rejection, 250
  one-tailed, 282, 344, 369
  two-tailed, 251, 283, 345, 350, 352
Regression, 490–538, 539–573
  coefficient, 504
    computation of, 506
    confidence limits for, 522, 529
    and correlation coefficient, 497
    estimate of, 514
    population, 512

Regression, coefficient, sample, 504
  curvilinear, 539–566
    cubic, 542
    estimation of equation for, 558
    model for, 540
    second-degree, 541
    tests for, 544–546, 548–550,
       555–558
  deviations from, 540
  equation, 496, 503
    estimate of population, 513
  linear, 490–538
    assumptions underlying test for,
       520
    descriptive statistics of, 494–510
    equation for standard scores,
       494–498
    toward the mean, 500–501
    model for, 514–515
    sum of squares for, 515–519
    tests for, 521
    of $z_X$ on $z_Y$, 502
    of $z_Y$ on $z_X$, 496
  multiple, 567–576
    equations for raw scores, 572
    equations for standard scores,
       567–570
  problems of, 492, 539, 564
Relations, 44–46
  monotone, 642
  statistical, 129
  *see also* Mathematical relations
Relative frequency, 56, 94
  in the long run, 58–63
Repeated observations, 455–456, 596
Replication, 392

Sample, 64–67, 215–217
Sample mean, *see* Mean
Sample point, 49
Sample proportion, 148
  as unbiased estimator, 211
  standard error of, *see* Standard
     error
Sample size, 210–211, 331, 332, 384
  finding required, 204

Sample space, 49, 108, 131, 192
Sample standard deviation, *see*
     Standard deviation, sample
Sample variance, *see* Variance,
     sample
Sampling, 62, 64–67, 140–143, 210–
     211, 215
  probability, 215
  with replacement, 64, 67, 154
  without replacement, 64, 67, 155,
     210
  simple random, 64, 215
  stratified, 215
Sampling distributions
  binomial as example of, 149
  uses of, 212
  *see also* Distributions, sampling
Sampling fraction, 211
Scales of measurement, *see* Measure-
     ment, interval, nominal, ordinal,
     ratio scaling
Scatter plot, 127, 506
Scheffé, H., 438, 441, 456, 484
Scheffé method for post-hoc com-
     parisons, 484, 562
Set, 13
  the empty, 18
  operations, 19–26
    complement, 21
    difference, 22
    intersection, 20
    union, 19
  universal, 15
Sets, 13–31, 48–51
  abstract, 23
  algebra of, 23–26
  events as, 49–51
  finite, 17
  infinite, 17
  mutually exclusive, 21
  postulates for theory of, 24
  product of, 26
  specified by listing, 14
  specified by rule, 15
  subsets of, 16
  theorems about, 24

Siegel, S., 601, 614, 632, 635, 637, 646
Sign test, 625
Significance test, *see* Hypothesis
 testing
Skewness, 186
 *see also* Distributions, skewed
Spearman rank correlation, 642–647,
 651–652
Standard deviation, 177–191
 interpretation of, 181
 as measure of variability, 177
 population, 183, 187
  confidence intervals for, 246
  and standard error of mean, 208
  as unit of deviation between
   means, 205, 293
 and radius of gyration, 181
 sample, 178
 as estimator, 208
Standard error, 196, 199
 of a difference, 315
 of estimate, 512
  estimated, 514
  multiple regression, 571
  raw scores, 505
  standard scores, 498
 of the mean, 203, 208
  estimated, 302
 of measurement, 294
Standardized scores, 186–187, 189–
 191, 203–204, 221
 mean of, 187
 representing sample means, 203
 variance of, 187
Statistical association, 118, 128, 129,
 589
 estimates of strength of, 327, 381
 measures of, 603
 sample size and strength of, 329
 *see also* Relations, statistical
Statistical decision theory, 11
 *see also* Decision-rules
Statistical tests, 245–248
 consistency of, 287
 nonparametric, 617
  *see also* Order statistics

Statistical tests, unbiased, 287
 uniformly most powerful, 287
 *see also* Hypothesis testing
Statistics, 6–7
 descriptive, 2
 inferential, 2
 mathematical, 2–4, 7
 sample, 193
Stevens, S. S., 44, 73
Strength of relationship, 324
 curvilinear regression, 544
 estimation of, 546
 linear regression, 511, 544
 *see also* Statistical association,
  measures of
"Student" (Gosset, W. S.), 306
Student's *t*, *see* *t* distribution
Subscripts, 659
Sum of squares, 362–368, 370–371,
 394–402
 between columns, 395
 for error, 395
 between groups, 364
 within groups, 364
 for interaction, 395
 for linear regression, 516
 partition of the, 362–364
 between rows, 395
 for a trend, 556
Summation, 157–158
 rules for, 659–666
Suspending judgment, 263–266

*t* distribution, 304–312, 352–355
 approximated by normal, 307
 density function for, 305
 mean and variance of, 306
 noncentral, 323
 normal assumption underlying, 308
 tables of, 308
*t* ratio, 304, 317, 335, 353
*t* test, 311, 317, 321
 assumptions underlying, 321
 for correlation, 529
 for a difference between means, 320
 for linear regression, 521

*t* test, for matched pairs, 335
  multiple on same data, 471
  for a planned comparison, 465
  power, *see* Power, of *t* tests
  relation to *F* in analysis of vari-
    ance, 375
  for single mean, 311
Tate, R. F., 346
Taylor series, 542
Tchebycheff's inequality, 188
Test statistics, 246, 286
Testing hypotheses, 250–256
  directional, 282
  exact, 253–256, 266–269
  inexact, 275–280
  about a single variance, 344–345
  *see also F* test, Hypothesis testing,
    *and t* test
"Testmanship," 323–327
Thrall, R., 73
Torricelli, 10, 42
Transformations, 380, 392, 563
  linear, 72, 506, 671
Trends, 551–562, 565
  cubic, 542, 555, 556
  higher order, 543, 556
  linear, 540, 553, 556
  quadratic, 540, 554, 556
Tukey, J., 454, 484
Tukey method for post-hoc com-
    parisons, 484

Uncertainty, 6
  measures of, 611–612
  reduction of, 325–327, 611–612

Variable, 36–40
  continuous, 39
  dependent, 39
  independent, 39
Variance, 177–185, 671
  analysis of, *see* Analysis of vari-
    ance

Variance, of binomial distribution,
    184
  confidence intervals for, 345
  of continuous random variable, 185
  of discrete random variable, 183
  of effects, 447–449
  error, 366–369, 396–399, 421, 443
  of estimate, 498
  estimating components of, 422,
    438, 446
  hypotheses about, 344
  interpretation of, 180
  of linear combination, 236
  of the mean, 202, 237
  minimum about the mean, 181–182
  as moment of inertia, 181
  of planned comparisons, 463
  pooled estimate of, 210, 320
  proportion accounted for, 325
    by linear regression, 501, 512
  sample, 177
    as biased estimator, 198
    computing forms for, 178
    corrected, 206
  of sampling distribution, 195
  sampling distribution of the, 341
  as second moment about the mean,
    185
  test for equality of, 351
Variation, 42
Venn, J., 17
Venn diagrams, 17

Wald-Wolfowitz "runs" test, 630
Wallis, W. A., 637
Wilcoxen test, 635
Winer, B., 424, 441, 457

Yates' correction, 586

*z* scores, *see* Standardized scores
*Z* transformation, *see* Fisher's *r* to *Z*
  transformation